Introduction

Construction site safety covers all aspects of current health, safety and environment issues in the building and construction industry. It is designed to help managers, supervisors and small businesses understand how they should comply with, and put into practice, their legal, moral and social responsibilities.

Construction site safety (GE 700)   iv
About the construction industry   iv
Lessons for industry from London 2012 Olympic Games   vi
Further supporting information from
CITB-ConstructionSkills   vii
Acknowledgements   viii

CW00796686

Construction site safety (GE 700)

Construction site safety is a leading publication within the construction industry, based on current construction health, safety and environment legislation, guidance and best practice. It will assist in the crucial areas of:

- ☑ accident prevention
- ☑ the avoidance of occupational ill health
- ☑ environmental good practice.

The content has been written with the site manager in mind, with a balance between outlining the requirements of relevant legislation and providing practical guidance on how to comply.

It is divided into the standard structure, which is used across all core CITB-ConstructionSkills publications:

Section A	**Legal and management**
Section B	**Health and welfare**
Section C	General safety
Section D	**High risk activities**
Section E	**Environment**
Section F	**Specialist activities**

Each section within *Construction site safety* is contained within a separate book.

There is also a new additional supporting book:

Section G	**Checklists and forms**

Section G is a collection of information (such as forms and checklists) that can be used on a day-to-day basis when running a site.

The content of *Construction site safety*, which is developed with construction industry experts, is revised annually to take into account the latest changes in legislation and new or updated health, safety and environment industry guidance and best practice.

There is a companion website that will keep users informed of legislation changes, content updates and links to further guidance.

Construction site safety is also available to purchase online or on CD-ROM.

Construction site safety is the official supporting publication for the CITB-ConstructionSkills Site Management Safety Training Scheme (SMSTS), a five-day course for construction site managers.

About the construction industry

Approximately 2.1 million people are employed in the UK construction industry. It includes housing, utilities, repair and maintenance, refurbishment, shop fitting, demolition, roofing, mechanical and electrical, plumbing and highways maintenance.

It is made up of 175,000 construction firms and 90% of companies employ less than 10 workers.

Construction workers (just like you) will die due to work-related ill health. Work-related respiratory disease covers a range of illnesses that are caused or made worse by breathing in hazardous substances (such as construction dust) that damage the lungs.

4,000 people die each year from asbestos-related lung diseases.

500 people (and more each year) are dying from silica-related lung diseases (dust from cutting blocks, kerbs, and so on). Many more suffer from occupational asthma or are forced to leave the industry due to work-related ill health.

Each year there are an estimated 36,000 new cases of work-related ill health with rates of musculoskeletal disorder significantly higher than average.

On average 50 workers are killed each year due to accidents. The biggest killer (around half) is due to falls from height.

Each year approximately 2,500 are seriously injured (broken bones, fractured skull, amputations) and 5,700 have reportable injuries.

The most common cause of injuries is due to manual handling and slips, trips and falls. 60% of all work at height injuries are due to falls from below head height.

Contents

Introduction   iii

How to use GE 700   ix

01 Health and safety law   **1**

02 The Health and Safety at Work Act   **11**

03 Construction (Design and Management) Regulations   **23**

04 Health and safety policies   **47**

05 Risk assessments and method statements   **57**

06 Induction training   **73**

07 Safety critical communication   **89**

08 Behavioural safety   **113**

09 Leadership and worker engagement   **129**

10 Inspections and audits   **141**

11 Statutory forms, notices and registers   **149**

12 Accident prevention and control   **159**

13 Accident reporting and investigation   **169**

Index   **181**

Why so many accidents?

Many reports of present day construction accidents and ill health make depressing reading because simple actions were not taken to prevent them. In many cases, those planning the jobs totally failed to consider the health or safety of the people carrying out the work (and possibly others who were affected) and to actively manage the situation.

Common examples of such events include:

☑ the increasing number of workers who suffer from cancers and life changing illnesses from breathing and skin complaints. Some of these force the sufferer to give up work, because exposure to dangerous substances such as dust, are not even considered, let alone prevented or controlled

☑ the deaths and serious injuries that occur because people fall from height. Often basic actions (like using temporary work platforms on fragile roofs, installing edge protection or using a safety harness and lanyard clipped to a strong-point) were simply not taken

☑ workers being buried in collapsed excavations because the sides were unstable or not supported

☑ workers being killed or injured by construction plant because pedestrians were not kept out of the plant operating area.

Achieving a reasonable standard of on-site health and safety need not be difficult. Where the work to be carried out is relatively uncomplicated and familiar, the precautions that need to be taken are in many cases simple and common sense or may require just a little investigation or reading. The crucial decision for anyone with responsibility for on-site health and safety is to know when they have reached the limits of their knowledge and capabilities and therefore need the assistance of someone with specialist knowledge.

Caution should also be exercised when a job is not going to plan and there is the temptation to resort to improvised methods of working. If the person in control is not at ease with the way that things are going they should stop the job, step back and think things through carefully before deciding upon a course of action.

Health and Safety Executive (HSE) research has shown that workers are most vulnerable during their first few days on site.

Setting out

Construction is an exciting industry. It is constantly changing as projects move on and jobs get done. As a result of this a building site is one of the most dangerous environments to work in.

But many accidents that occur on sites can be avoided if everyone on site works together. So a free film *Setting out* explains what the site must do and what you must do to stay healthy and safe at work.

 For further information or to view *Setting out* refer to the CITB-ConstructionSkills website.

This film is essential viewing for everyone involved in construction, and should be watched before sitting the CITB-ConstructionSkills' Health, safety and environment test. The content of the film is captured in summary here, and these principles form the basis for the behavioural case study questions, which are a new element of the test from Spring 2012.

Part 1: What you should expect from the construction industry

Your site and your employer should be doing all they can to keep you and their workforce safe.

Before any work begins the site management team will have been planning and preparing the site for your arrival. It is their job to ensure that you can do your job safely and efficiently.

Five things **the site** you are working on **must do**:

☑ know when you are on site (signing in and out)

☑ give you a site induction

☑ give you site-specific information

☑ encourage communication

☑ keep you up-to-date and informed.

Part 2: What the industry expects of you

Once the work begins, it is up to every individual to take responsibility for carrying out the plan safely. This means you should follow the rules and guidelines as well as being alert to the continuing changes on site.

Five things you **must do**:

☑ respect and follow the site rules

☑ safely prepare each task

☑ do each task responsibly

☑ know when to stop (if you think anything is unsafe)

☑ keep learning.

Every day the work we do improves the world around us. It is time for us to work together to build an industry that puts its people first. By working together we can build a better industry that respects those who work in it.

Working Well Together

The Working Well Together (WWT) campaign is an industry-led initiative that helps support micro and small businesses improve their health and safety performance. The campaign undertakes a variety of activities, including health and safety awareness days, designer awareness days, breakfast and evening events, roadshows and regional WWT groups.

 To find out how the WWT campaign can help you and your company refer to its website.

Lessons for industry from London 2012 Olympic Games

The main construction project for London 2012 was completed on time, within budget and with an exemplary health and safety record. It has demonstrated that building projects on time and within budget does not mean compromising on the health and safety of workers.

 HSE shared with the Olympic Delivery Authority an aim to ensure a strong health and safety legacy from the Olympic construction project, and co-operated with them on a series of **research projects** to capture the good practice and lessons learned. Many initiatives adopted on the project were not costly or complicated, and are potentially transferable both to other construction projects and to industry more widely.

HSE believes the experience of London 2012 can be used as a catalyst to effect positive change across the construction industry and beyond, driving up standards of health and safety.

Five key action points

☑ **Lead from the top.** The Olympic Delivery Authority set standards and also visibly engaged with the workforce to direct, motivate and change behaviour.

☑ **Develop competent supervisors.** The positive impact of technically knowledgeable supervisors upon health and safety was understood, as well as how softer communication skills influence understanding and behaviour.

☑ **Foster an open, positive safety culture.** If workers are engaged and feel managers care for their wellbeing, they're more likely to get involved with the health and safety process.

☑ **Reward good behaviour.** Incentives and rewards helped to promote and encourage safe behaviour.

☑ **Review and learn.** Any problems were constantly reviewed and communicated across the organisation.

Learning legacy website

In addition to the research reports, HSE has developed a series of good practice **case studies** demonstrating some of the practical solutions used to manage health and safety during the big build.

 Further case studies, micro reports and summaries of the research reports are available on the London 2012 Learning legacy website.

Further supporting information from CITB-ConstructionSkills

CITB-ConstructionSkills has a wide range of products, publications and courses that could help to improve your health, safety and environment knowledge.

 To discover more about CITB-ConstructionSkills and the services, publications and courses offered visit the CITB-ConstructionSkills website.

Health, safety and environment publications

Site managers
GE 700 *Construction site safety* (printed, CD and online)

RACD *Risk assessment and method statement manager*

SA 03 CD *Health, safety and environmental auditing system*

DVDs Range of topics including scaffold inspection, worker engagement and sustainability

Supervisors
GE 706 *Site supervision simplified* (printed, CD, online)

GT 700 *Toolbox talks* (printed, CD, online)

GT 701 *Safety critical communication toolbox talks* (printed)

Operatives
GE 707 *Safe start*

Health safety and environment test
GT 100 *Health, safety and environment test for operatives and specialists* (printed, DVD, online)

GT 200 *Health, safety and environment test for managers and professionals* (printed, DVD, online)

Introduction

Site Safety Plus courses

Directors	Directors role for health and safety course – one day
Site management	Site Management Safety Training Scheme (SMSTS) – five days
Plant managers	Plant Management Safety Training Scheme (SMSTS) – five days
Supervisors	Site Supervisors' Safety Training Scheme (SSSTS) – two days
Operatives	Health safety and environment awareness – one day
Environment	Site Environmental Awareness Training Scheme (SEATS) – one day
Behavioural safety	Achieving Behavioural Change (ABC) – one day
Shopfitting	Site safety for shopfitters and interior contractors – three days

National Construction College

The National Construction College is focused on creating a highly skilled, safe and professional UK construction workforce.
To achieve this, it has more first-class instructors in more locations than any other construction training provider in Europe and offers free professional advice on finding the right training for individuals and companies.

Acknowledgements

CITB-ConstructionSkills wishes to acknowledge the assistance offered by the following organisations in the preparation of this edition of GE 700:

- ☑ Access Industry Forum
- ☑ Arco
- ☑ Balfour Beatty
- ☑ Britannia Safety and Training
- ☑ Civil Engineering Contractors Association
- ☑ Combisafe
- ☑ Construction Plant Association
- ☑ Drilling and Sawing Association
- ☑ eBrit Services Ltd
- ☑ Environment Agency
- ☑ Environmental and Waste Consulting
- ☑ Federation of Master Builders
- ☑ Health and Safety Executive
- ☑ Henry Boot
- ☑ Highways Term Maintenance Association
- ☑ Home Builders Federation
- ☑ J Breheny Contractors Ltd
- ☑ Lead Paint Safety Association
- ☑ MJ Fuller and Associates
- ☑ Makers Construction Ltd
- ☑ May Gurney
- ☑ Montpellier International Consulting
- ☑ National Access and Scaffolding Confederation
- ☑ National Association of Shopfitters
- ☑ National Construction College
- ☑ National Federation of Demolition Contractors
- ☑ Persimmon Homes
- ☑ Prospect – The Union for Professionals
- ☑ Scafftag
- ☑ Temporary Works Forum
- ☑ Union of Construction, Allied Trades and Technicians (UCATT)
- ☑ Unite
- ☑ Wates
- ☑ Willmott Dixon

And a special thank you to:

- ☑ Carillion
- ☑ Costain
- ☑ Morgan Sindall
- ☑ Skanska

How to use GE 700

The following information sets out how to use *Construction site safety*. Each section is contained within a separate book, which has been designed to provide simple navigation for the end user. It also explains the companion website, which is a significant addition for keeping users informed of legislation changes, content updates and links to further guidance.

Construction site safety structure   x
How to navigate   x
Use of icons   x
Companion website   xi

Construction site safety structure

Construction site safety is divided into the standard structure that is used across all core CITB-ConstructionSkills publications:

Section A   **Legal and management**

Section B   **Health and welfare**

Section C   General safety

Section D   **High risk activities**

Section E   **Environment**

Section F   **Specialist activities**

Within *Construction site safety* each section is contained within a separate book.

There is also a new additional supporting book:

Section G   **Checklists and forms**

This new section is a collection of information that can be used on a day-to-day basis when running a site. The forms, checklists and guidance within Section G follow the same structure as in Sections A to F.

How to navigate

Each section contains a main contents page at the start of the section, followed by the introduction, a detailed chapter contents list at the start of each chapter and an index at the back (but there is no index within Section G).

Chapters have been numbered according to the section you are in. Therefore, chapter one of Section A is numbered 01, chapter two of Section B is numbered 02 and so on. However, references to chapters within other sections will be referred to as A01, B02, and so on.

At the start of each chapter there is a short overview of what the chapter is about.

This is followed by the chapter contents list.

Use of icons

A set of icons emphasises key points within the text and also directs readers to further information. The icons are explained below:

www. Website/further info	**!** Important	**"** Quote
e.g. Example	👍 Best practice	**Aa** Definition
? Question	👎 Poor practice	☑ Checklist
💡 Ideas	✋ Caution	▶ Video
Notes	Consultation	
★ Favourite	🔍 Guidance/case study	

Companion website

A companion website has been created to support *Construction site safety* and it contains up-to-date information on:

- ☑ the current edition of each section (book)

- ☑ news (such as legislation changes, industry guidance and best practice)

- ☑ any minor amendments or updates to the current editions

- ☑ web links/phone numbers/addresses

- ☑ details of CITB-ConstructionSkills' publications and courses.

 This icon indicates that further information (such as useful websites and links) can be found on the companion website at www.citb-constructionskills.co.uk/GE700companion

Rather than printing individual weblinks in each section, which can become out of date, the relevant website will be stated alongside the icon (for example, for more information refer to the CITB-ConstructionSkills website). The actual weblink can then be found on the companion website, referenced to the relevant section and chapter.

The companion website will be regularly updated, to ensure that relevant information (such as weblinks) are current.

 Save the companion website address to your favourites, so it is always available when you need it.

01

Health and safety law

The Construction (Design and Management) Regulations (CDM) apply to all construction activities, regardless of size, duration and cost. The regulations lay down legal requirements for ensuring that health, safety and welfare is an integral part of project design, planning and construction.

This chapter outlines what the regulations are about, what they require, what needs to be done and by whom.

Introduction   2
The progress of health and safety law   2
The Health and Safety at Work Act 1974   3
Health and safety regulations   3
Approved Codes of Practice   4
Standards of compliance   4
Legal duties   5
Summary of health and safety law   6
Corporate Manslaughter and Corporate Homicide Act   7
Health and Safety (Offences) Act   8
Enforcement   9
Fees for intervention   9
Supporting information   10

01

1.1　Introduction

The purpose of health and safety legislation is to protect the wellbeing of people at work and others, such as the general public, by ensuring that work is carried out in a manner that is safe and free of risks to health for everyone who may be affected.

There have always been accidents and ill health resulting from people carrying out work activities. Fortunately, we have come a long way from earlier days when such events were simply accepted as part of having a job – many people went to work and took their chances. Even so, workplace accidents and work-related ill health still occur, with the building and construction industry having a disproportionately high rate of both.

Everyone who goes to work has a right to return home uninjured and in a good state of health. Similarly, visitors to sites and passers-by have the same right to the protection of their health and safety.

When health and safety law is broken, a criminal offence is committed. If the results are sufficiently serious the offence can be punishable by a fine or even imprisonment. The Health and Safety Executive (HSE) usually deals with less serious breaches of health and safety law by issuing enforcement notices or simply offering advice.

Whilst health and safety legislation is embedded in criminal law, in some circumstances legislation gives a person who has been injured or made ill through work the right to take legal action against the employer for compensation, through the civil courts.

 You can insure against civil liabilities but you cannot insure against criminal liabilities.

The primary focus of health and safety legislation is to put legal duties on employers (and the self-employed, who in many cases have the same legal duties as employers) to ensure that work is carried out safely and without risks to health.

It should be noted that some legislation places legal duties upon employees. In specific situations, legal duties are also placed upon 'duty holders', as defined in the relevant legislation. The actions that must be taken to fulfil these duties are explained in the appropriate chapters of this book.

In many situations, site-based staff (such as supervisors, site managers or project managers) will be nominated by the employer to ensure that the employer's legal duties are complied with at site level. However, legal duties still lie with the employer who must be confident in the ability and competence of their supervisors, managers and others who manage health and safety on their behalf.

1.2　The progress of health and safety law

☑ The first Act of Parliament directly concerned with safety was the Factories Act, passed in 1802, which dealt with the morals of apprentices.

☑ From 1812 onwards, a succession of Acts regulated working conditions in factories, with particular reference to women and children.

☑ In 1833, the first four factory inspectors were appointed. Children aged nine were being sent up chimneys as chimney sweeps, where they could work a 48-hour week. They were supposed to spend two hours a day at school. People as young as 13 sometimes worked a 69-hour week.

☑ The first two female factory inspectors were appointed in 1893, the first medical inspector in 1898.

☑ In 1901, a comprehensive Factories and Workshops Act was passed. It lasted until the Factories Act of 1937 replaced it, then this, in turn, was repealed by the Factories Act of 1961.

☑ The Health and Safety at Work Act, the basis for modern legislation, came into force in 1974, bringing with it protection for virtually everyone at work and consolidating much of the earlier industry-specific legislation under a single Act.

☑ The Construction (Design and Management) Regulations 1994 were drafted to address the continuing unacceptably high rate of accidents and ill health befalling construction workers. However, they brought about a culture of bureaucracy and form-filling rather than a focus on risk management.

☑ The revised Construction (Design and Management) Regulations (CDM) are the cornerstone legislation for the construction industry and clearly reinforce the requirements for competence, co-operation and co-ordination, with a focus on 'the right information, to the right people at the right time'.

☑ The coming into force of the Corporate Manslaughter and Corporate Homicide Act and the Health and Safety (Offences) Act, demonstrate a hardening of Government's attitude towards serious breaches of health and safety legislation.

1.3   The Health and Safety at Work Act 1974

The Health and Safety at Work Act 1974 is the primary piece of health and safety legislation in the United Kingdom. The Act is termed as an enabling Act, which allows the Government to make health and safety regulations that become part of the law. The requirements of the Act are very general and wide-ranging, such as:

> It shall be the duty of every employer to ensure, so far as is reasonably practicable, the health, safety and welfare at work of all their employees.

This typical requirement does not specify any technical requirements or set any minimum standards of behaviour that can be measured, but it does clearly outline the requirement for safe places of work.

Health and safety regulations expand upon the legal requirements of the Act with regard to specific occupational activities and include specific and technical requirements. Health and safety regulations are often supported by guidance notes or Approved Codes of Practice (ACoPs), which explain in plain language how compliance with the law can be achieved.

For further information on the Act refer to Chapter A02 The Health and Safety at Work Act.

1.4   Health and safety regulations

Many sets of regulations have been developed and introduced as a means of incorporating European Community legislation into our domestic legal framework. There are many sets of health and safety regulations in existence that are relevant to the work activities carried out by the construction industry. Some sets of regulations apply to construction activities only.

Health and safety regulations are a part of UK law that place duties on employers and employees. It is a criminal offence to contravene them. Some examples of legislation that affect the building and construction industry are shown below.

The Management of Health and Safety at Work Regulations

The main requirement is for employers to carry out a risk assessment. Employers with five or more employees need to record significant findings of the risk assessment.

The Construction (Design and Management) Regulations

There is a strong focus on the idea of competence, which is emphasised in the Approved Code of Practice (ACoP).

To be competent, an organisation or individual must:

☑ have knowledge of the specific tasks to be undertaken and the risks that the work will entail

☑ have sufficient experience and ability to carry out their duties in relation to the project

☑ recognise their limitations

☑ take appropriate action in order to prevent harm to those carrying out construction work, or those affected by the work.

The Work at Height Regulations

Duty holders are required to ensure that:

☑ all work at height is properly planned and organised

☑ all work at height takes account of weather conditions that could endanger health and safety

☑ those involved in work at height are trained and competent

☑ the place where work at height is carried out is safe

☑ equipment for work at height is appropriately inspected

☑ the risks from fragile surfaces are properly controlled, as are the risks from falling objects.

The Provision and Use of Work Equipment Regulations

Correct equipment must be provided, inspected, tested and properly maintained.

The Electricity at Work Regulations

People in control of electrical systems must ensure that they are safe to use and they are maintained in a safe condition.

The Control of Asbestos Regulations

Requires the identification of asbestos-containing materials (ACMs) that may be present before any work is carried out.

Reporting of Injuries, Diseases and Dangerous Occurrences Regulations (RIDDOR)

A legal duty is placed on employers, the self-employed and those in control of premises to report:

- ☑ work-related deaths or major injuries
- ☑ injuries resulting in an absence of more than seven days
- ☑ work-related diseases
- ☑ dangerous occurrences.

1.5 Approved Codes of Practice

The Health and Safety at Work Act 1974 makes provision for the production of Approved Codes of Practice (ACoP), where appropriate, in support of some health and safety regulations.

1.6 Standards of compliance

Within health and safety legislation specific words or phrases are used to qualify or describe the standard of compliance that must be achieved with regard to some legal duties. The meanings of these are explained below.

It shall be the duty of an employer to...

This means that the employer must comply with the legal duty being described. The word 'shall' (if not qualified by the phrase 'so far as reasonably practicable' or the word 'practicable') leaves no scope for not complying with the duty.

It shall be the duty of an employer to... as far as is reasonably practicable

Where a requirement to carry out a specific legal duty is qualified by the phrase 'as far as is reasonably practicable', employers are allowed to exercise their judgement on the extent of the measures that need to be taken to ensure the health and safety of the person(s) carrying out the job and anyone else who may be affected by it.

Deciding what are reasonably practicable measures to take should be based upon the findings of a risk assessment.

 Reasonably practicable means that the risks involved in carrying out the work may be balanced against the cost in terms of money, inconvenience and time.

Where the risks to health and safety in carrying out a job are found to be low in comparison to what would be disproportionately high costs to totally overcome the risks, the employer need only take the measures that are considered to be reasonably practicable.

---

e.g. Reasonably practicable

It was necessary to provide access to working platforms of a scaffold at four different levels for a 12-week period, the higher level being a narrow lift between two structures. A decision had to be made on the best means of access.

Legislation on working at height requires 'every employer to ensure that work at height is carried out in a manner which is, so far as reasonably practicable, safe'.

In planning the job, the risk assessment showed:

- ☑ it would be necessary for tools and materials for various trades to be carried up to and down from the main working platform but not from the higher level lift. The ground was firm and level and there was plenty of space at the bottom of the scaffold
- ☑ if a ladder was used, it could be securely tied to the scaffold and suitable hand-holds could be provided at the stepping-off point. The tools and materials would have to be hoisted up using a small electric hoist fixed to the scaffold
- ☑ various trades could be working together and at the same time only a means of access was required, not a place of work, to the higher level lift. There were no weather considerations that would make the use of a ladder unduly unsafe.

Given the circumstances, it was decided that a ladder was not a reasonably practicable measure to prevent a fall with regard to access to the main working platform where tools and materials were required and therefore a stair tower was used. For access to the higher level lift a ladder was considered to be suitable, complete with a ladder safety gate. The stair tower also offered quicker, safer and easier access.

It shall be the duty of an employer to...as far as is practicable

Practicable means that there is no scope for taking cost and convenience into account; the duty must be complied with if it is possible to carry it out within the current state of knowledge and technology (if it is technically possible, then the duty must be complied with).

 Practicable

It was necessary for someone to use a disc-cutter to cut paving slabs to the required size.

The legal duty requires that the rotating blade of the machine be guarded to the extent that it is practicable to do so. This acknowledges that total guarding of the blade is not possible because the machine could not then be used for the job for which it was designed.

The law requires that the guard be adjusted to expose enough blade to enable the job to be carried out safely whilst providing the maximum degree of protection for the operator.

Not to use a guard at all is not an option, even if it causes cost or inconvenience.

Burden of proof

Many of the duties on employers are qualified with the phrases 'so far as is reasonably practicable' or 'so far as is practicable'.

Generally, in a court of law a defendant is innocent until proven guilty. However, with regard to these phrases, the burden of proof is reversed and so the defendant must prove that it was not reasonably practicable, or practicable, as the case may be, to do more than was done to mitigate the risks. In effect, the defendant is guilty until they prove their innocence.

1.7   Legal duties

The broad legal duties of employers and employees, as specified in the Health and Safety at Work Act 1974 are shown below.

Employers' responsibilities

An employer must, so far as is reasonably practicable:

☑ protect the health, safety and welfare at work of all their employees

☑ provide and maintain plant and systems of work that are safe and without risk to health

☑ have arrangements for ensuring safety and absence of risk to health in connection with the use, handling, storage and transport of articles and substances

☑ provide such information, instruction, training and supervision as is necessary to ensure the health and safety at work of employees

☑ maintain any place of work under their control in a condition that is safe and without risks to health, and with access to and egress from it, that are safe and without such risks

☑ provide and maintain a working environment that is safe, without risks to health and adequate as regards the welfare of employees.

Employees' duties

It is the duty of every employee to:

☑ take reasonable care for the health and safety of themselves or others who may be affected by their acts or omissions

☑ co-operate with their employer in all matters relating to health and safety

☑ not intentionally or recklessly interfere with or misuse anything provided in the interests of health, safety and welfare

☑ use anything provided by the employer in accordance with instructions

☑ report anything that is thought to be dangerous.

The requirement, on the employer, to do what is reasonably practicable to ensure the health, safety and welfare of employees at work is balanced by a requirement, on the employees, to comply with any necessary rules or instructions and to take reasonable care of themselves and others.

1.8   Summary of health and safety law

Health and safety law

Common law
(Duty of care)

Statute law
(Written)

Types of statutory duty		
Absolute duty	Practicable	Reasonably practicable

Health and Safety at Work Act 1974

The Act consists of four parts
Part 1 - Health and safety of people at work and protection of others who may be affected
Part 2 – Employment Medical Advisory Service
Part 3 – Amends to previous law
Part 4 – General and miscellaneous provisions

General duties for employers and employees

Regulations

Regulations require additional specific actions
They can be concerning:
• health and safety management
• workplaces and dangerous substances
• machinery, handling and equipment
• specific areas of work or situations

ACoPs
Approved Codes of Practice

ACoPs explain what measures must be taken to comply with relevant regulations
Following an ACoP (or an equivalent standard) is generally accepted as being legally compliant

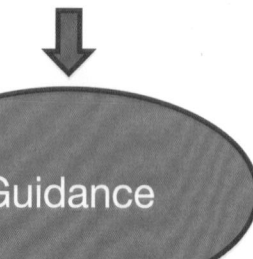

Guidance

Guidance notes
Issued by the HSE and give practical guidance on how regulations may be complied with

Guidance
Practical guidance produced by industry associations, federations and training bodies

1.9   Corporate Manslaughter and Corporate Homicide Act

Since 6 April 2008, companies whose gross negligence leads to the death of individuals can face prosecution for manslaughter (homicide in Scotland) under the Corporate Manslaughter and Corporate Homicide Act.

Under this legislation companies, organisations and, for the first time, Government bodies face an unlimited fine if they are found to have caused death due to their gross corporate health and safety failures. The legislation primarily came about as a result of the failure to identify 'the controlling mind' in companies with complex management structures during court cases, which followed several high profile disasters.

However, presentations by authoritative legal professionals have indicated that the legislation might have much wider ranging implications (such as prosecutions following at-work-related road deaths and fatalities).

The Act offers employees of companies, consumers and other individuals greater protection against corporate negligence. It will also focus the minds of those in companies and other organisations by ensuring that they take their health and safety obligations seriously.

The Corporate Manslaughter Act

During July 2007 the Corporate Manslaughter and Corporate Homicide Act received Royal Assent, bringing it to law on 6 April 2008. The Act applies to the whole of the United Kingdom, with the term 'corporate homicide' applying to Scotland only.

This legislation offers employees of companies, consumers and other individuals greater protection against corporate negligence. The new law will focus the minds of those in companies and other organisations by ensuring that they take health and safety obligations seriously.

The Corporate Manslaughter and Corporate Homicide Act:

- ✓ makes it easier to prosecute companies and other large organisations when gross failures in the management of health and safety lead to death by delivering a new, more effective basis for corporate liability

- ✓ has reformed the law so that a key obstacle to successful prosecutions has now been removed. It means that both small and large companies can be held liable for manslaughter where gross failures in the management of health and safety cause death, not just health and safety violations

- ✓ complements the current law under which individuals can be prosecuted for gross negligence manslaughter and health and safety offences, where there is direct evidence of their culpability. The Act builds on existing health and safety legislation – so the new offence does not impose new regulations on business

- ✓ lifts Crown immunity to prosecution. Crown bodies – such as Government departments – will be liable to prosecution for the first time. So the Act will apply to companies and other corporate bodies, in the public and private sector, government departments, police forces and certain unincorporated bodies, such as partnerships, where these are employers.

The above text is an extract reproduced from a Ministry of Justice press release under licence from Her Majesty's Stationery Office.

An organisation will be guilty of the offence if someone has been killed as a result of the gross failure of an organisation's senior managers, for example, failure to:

- ✓ ensure safe working practices for their employees (for example, staff are properly trained and equipment is in a safe condition)

- ✓ maintain the safety of their premises (for example, ensuring that lifts are properly maintained and fire precautions taken).

The Act covers organisations providing goods and services to members of the public, the construction, use or maintenance of infrastructure or vehicles, or when operating commercially. Crown bodies and other public sector organisations, including police forces, will be on an equal footing with the private sector when carrying out similar activities.

The offence is clearly linked to the standards required under other health and safety laws. It does not apply to circumstances where an organisation does not owe a duty of care or to certain public and government functions whose management involves wider questions of public policy and are already subject to other forms of accountability. For example, it does not apply to strategic decisions about the spending of public money or activities like statutory inspection, holding prisoners in detention, the response of the emergency services, policing or child protection.

If a company is found guilty of corporate manslaughter the penalty will be an unlimited fine. The Act also gives the courts power to impose a remedial order, which can already be imposed for health and safety offences, and requires the company to address the cause of the fatality.

Sentencing

In February 2010 the Sentencing Guidelines Council issued guidance to the courts regarding sentencing options under the Corporate Manslaughter and Corporate Homicide Act. Pertinent points in the guidelines are:

- ✓ fines for companies and organisations found guilty of corporate manslaughter may be millions of pounds and should seldom be below £500,000

- ✓ fines for other health and safety offences causing death should range from £100,000 to several hundreds of thousands of pounds

- ✓ in deciding the level of fine, account must be taken of the financial circumstances of the offending organisation

- ✓ when fixing a fine, a court should not be influenced by the impact on shareholders and directors, nor consider the costs of complying with other sanctions

- ✓ account may be taken of the effect on the employment of the innocent (employees), as may the effect on the delivery of services to the public.

Circumstances that courts should regard as aggravating factors include:

- ☑ the number of deaths
- ☑ injury to vulnerable persons
- ☑ a failure to heed previous warnings or respond to near-misses of a similar nature
- ☑ cost-cutting (profits take priority over safety)
- ☑ failure to obtain or comply with relevant licences.

1.10 Health and Safety (Offences) Act

The HSE has made it clear that its enforcement policy will be to target those who cut corners to gain a financial advantage over competitors, by failing to comply with health and safety law and therefore putting workers and others at risk.

This legislation, which came into force in January 2009, amends Section 33 of the Health and Safety at Work Act 1974, and in doing so it:

- ☑ increased the maximum fine that can be awarded by the courts for breaches of health and safety regulations, from £5,000 to £20,000
- ☑ increased the number of health and safety offences for which a guilty person can be imprisoned
- ☑ enables certain offences, which could previously only be tried in Magistrates' Courts, to be tried in either Magistrates' Courts or Crown Courts.

The table below summarises a new Schedule 3A to the Health and Safety at Work Act 1974; it sets out the offences and maximum penalties under health and safety legislation. The table lists those offences which are likely to be most relevant to employers and site management.

Offence	Court	Maximum penalty
A breach of Sections 2–6, which set out the general duties of employers, self-employed persons, persons who have control of premises, employees, manufacturers and suppliers to safeguard the health and safety of employees and members of the public who may be affected by work activities.	Lower court maximum	£20,000 fine and/or 12 months' imprisonment*
	Higher court maximum	Unlimited fine and/or two years' imprisonment
A breach of Section 7, which is the failure of an individual to take reasonable care of their own health and safety or that of someone else who is affected by their acts or omissions, or to co-operate with the employer in matters of health and safety.	Lower court maximum	£5,000 fine and/or 12 months' imprisonment*
	Higher court maximum	Unlimited fine and/or two years' imprisonment
A breach of Section 8, which imposes a duty on all persons not to intentionally or recklessly interfere with anything provided in the interests of health, safety or welfare.	Lower court maximum	£20,000 fine and/or 12 months' imprisonment*
	Higher court maximum	Unlimited fine and/or two years' imprisonment
A breach of Section 9, which imposes a duty on employers not to make a charge for anything provided in the interests of health or safety.	Lower court maximum	£20,000 fine and/or 12 months' imprisonment*
	Higher court maximum	Unlimited fine
A breach of Section 33(1)(c), which is to contravene any health and safety regulation.	Lower court maximum	£20,000 fine and/or 12 months' imprisonment
	Higher court maximum	Unlimited fine and/or two years' imprisonment
A breach of Sections 33(1) (e), (f) or (g), which are concerned with: ■ contravening any requirement of an inspector when exercising their enforcement powers ■ preventing anyone appearing before an inspector, or ■ contravening any requirement imposed by an improvement or prohibition notice.	Lower court maximum	£20,000 fine and/or 12 months' imprisonment*
	Higher court maximum	Unlimited fine and/or two years' imprisonment

Offence	Court	Maximum penalty
A breach of Section 33(1)(h), which is to intentionally obstruct an inspector in exercising their powers or duties.	Lower court maximum	£5,000 fine and/or 51 weeks' imprisonment** (12 months in Scotland)
	Higher court maximum	Not applicable
A breach of Sections 33(1)(k), (l) or (m), which are concerned with making false statements, false entries in a register or book or forging or using a document to deceive an inspector.	Lower court maximum	£20,000 fine and/or 12 months' imprisonment*
	Higher court maximum	Unlimited fine and/or two years' imprisonment
A breach of Section 33(1)(o), which is to fail to comply with a court remedy order under Section 42.	Lower court maximum	£20,000 fine and/or 12 months' imprisonment*
	Higher court maximum	Unlimited fine and/or two years' imprisonment
A breach of Sections 36 or 37 of HSW Act, which relate to offences committed by corporate bodies due to the personal failings of directors, senior managers, company secretaries, and so on. *See also Note 4 below.*	Lower court maximum	Five years' disqualification
	Higher court maximum	15 years' disqualification

Notes:

1. A lower court is a Magistrate's Court (or Sheriff's Court in Scotland).

2. A higher court is a Crown Court (or High Court of Judiciary in Scotland).

3. *The powers of Magistrates' Courts to award prison sentences of 12 months will not come into force until Section 154(1) of the Criminal Justice Act comes into force and should be read as six months' imprisonment until that time.
   **Similarly, the reference to a 51-week prison sentence will not come into force until Section 281(5) of the Criminal Justice Act comes into force and should be read as six months' imprisonment until that time.

4. On conviction of directors for indictable offences in connection with the management of a company, the courts may also make a disqualification order (Company Directors Disqualification Act 1986, Sections 1 and 2). The courts have exercised this power following health and safety convictions and health and safety inspectors draw this power to the court's attention whenever appropriate.

1.11 Enforcement

Health and safety law

The enforcement of all health and safety law is carried out under the provisions of The Health and Safety at Work Act 1974. This means that methods of enforcement are the same throughout the country.

The Health and Safety Executive (HSE) is responsible for maintaining a force of health and safety inspectors, some of whom specialise in construction industry activities.

Environmental law

Environmental law is enforced by the Environment Agency (EA) and Scottish Environment Protection Agency (SEPA) in Scotland.

 For further information on environmental law refer to Section E *Environment*.

1.12 Fees for intervention

The HSE introduced a fee for intervention (FFI) cost recovery scheme with effect from 1 October 2012, under the Health and Safety (Fees) Regulations.

These regulations put a duty on the HSE to recover its costs for carrying out its regulatory functions from those found to be in material breach of health and safety law.

A material breach is when, in the opinion of the HSE inspector, there has been a contravention of health and safety law that is serious enough to require them to notify the person in material breach of that opinion in writing.

HSE and the Government believe it is right that businesses and organisations that break health and safety laws should pay for HSE's time in putting matters right, investigating and taking enforcement action. Without FFI, this is paid for from the public purse.

 The FFI hourly rate for 2012/13 is £124.

01

FFI will also encourage businesses and organisations to comply in the first place or put matters right quickly when they don't. It will also discourage those who undercut their competitors by not complying with the law and putting people at risk.

 The following information can be found on the HSE's website:

☑ Guidance on the application of fee for intervention (FFI)

☑ Fee for intervention: What you need to know – draft leaflet

☑ Enforcement management model.

1.13 Supporting information

 The HSE offers a range of services to assist employers and employees. Many publications are produced each year – with some at no charge or downloadable from its website.

02

The Health and Safety at Work Act

The Health and Safety at Work Act 1974 (the Act) is the primary legislation covering health and safety in England, Scotland and Wales.

The Act mainly places legal duties on employers, the self-employed and, to a lesser extent, employees.

The aim is to promote health and safety awareness and effective standards of health and safety management by every employer.

This chapter outlines what the Act is about and what is required.

Introduction	12
Aims and scope of the Act	12
Relevant statutory provisions	12
Standards of compliance	12
Main parts of the Act	13
Duty holders under the Act	14
Health and Safety Executive	15
Supporting legislation	17
Health and Safety Commission	17
Employment Medical Advisory Service	18
The Health and Safety (Enforcing Authority) Regulations	18
Examples of health and safety court cases	18
Further information	19
Appendix A – Example of an improvement notice	20
Appendix B – Example of a prohibition notice	21

The Health and Safety at Work Act

2.1   Introduction

The basis of British health and safety law is the Health and Safety at Work Act 1974.

The Act sets out the general duties that employers have towards employees and members of the public, as well as the duties that employees have to themselves and to each other.

These duties are qualified in the Act by the principle of 'so far as is reasonably practicable'. In other words, an employer does not have to take measures to avoid or reduce the risk if they are technically impossible or if the time, trouble or cost of the measures would be grossly disproportionate to the risk.

What the law requires is what good management and common sense would lead employers to do anyway: that is, to look at what the risks are and take sensible measures to tackle them.

It shall be the duty of every employer to ensure, so far as is reasonably practicable, the health, safety and welfare at work of all their employees.

2.2   Aims and scope of the Act

The Health and Safety at Work Act 1974 provides for a comprehensive, legislative framework to promote, stimulate and encourage high standards of health and safety in the workplace.

Its ultimate aim is to promote health and safety awareness and effective standards of health and safety management by every employer.

One of the main aims of the Act is to **involve everyone** in matters of health and safety:

☑ management   ☑ employees' representatives

☑ employees   ☑ controllers of premises

☑ self-employed   ☑ manufacturers of plant, equipment and materials.

The Act also requires that adequate measures are taken to protect the public where otherwise their health or safety would be at risk.

All persons at work are covered by the Act, with the exception of domestic servants in private households and some Crown employees.

The Act is an **enabling Act** that allows the Secretary of State to make further laws (regulations) without the need to pass another Act of Parliament. Regulations are laws, approved by Parliament. These are usually made under the Act following proposals from the Health and Safety Executive (HSE).

2.3   Relevant statutory provisions

The Act requires compliance with the relevant statutory provisions, which are:

☑ the Act itself

☑ other health and safety legislation, as listed in Schedule 1 of the Act

☑ all the legislation made under Section 15 of the Act. (This covers all health and safety regulations made since 1974.)

2.4   Standards of compliance

In many instances in the Act, and in health and safety regulations, a legal duty is qualified by the words **practicable** (or best practicable means) or **reasonably practicable**.

Where a legal duty is qualified by the word **practicable** the duty must be complied with if it is 'capable of being carried out' or 'feasible within the current state of knowledge and technology', at whatever expense, taking note of published information, guidance notes or Approved Codes of Practice. In practical terms, a legal duty qualified by the word practicable cannot be disregarded on the grounds that to comply with it would slow up production, be expensive, difficult or otherwise inconvenient.

Where a legal duty is qualified by the term **reasonably practicable** employers are allowed to exercise their judgement on the extent of the measures that need to be taken to ensure the health and safety of whoever is carrying out the job and others who may be affected by it. This judgement should be based upon the findings of a risk assessment.

Where the risks to health and safety in carrying out a job are found to be low in comparison to what would be disproportionately high costs to overcome the risks totally, the employer need only take the measures that are considered to be reasonably practicable.

Should there be a legal dispute as to a decision of what was or was not reasonably practicable, the onus of proving in court that all reasonably practicable measures were taken lies with the employer.

2.5   Main parts of the Act

The Act consists of four parts:

Part 1	Health, safety and welfare in the workplace.
Part 2	Employment Medical Advisory Service – functions and responsibilities.
Part 3	Building Regulations and relating amendments to the law.
Part 4	Miscellaneous and general provisions.

Managers, supervisors, safety supervisors, safety representatives and others with a responsibility for ensuring legal compliance will be mainly concerned with Part 1 of the Act.

Part 1 – Health, safety and welfare in the workplace

The main provisions of Part 1 of the Act are:

☑ securing the health, safety and welfare of persons at work

☑ protecting persons, other than persons at work, against risks to health and safety, arising out of, or in connection with, the activities of persons at work

☑ duties of employees

☑ establishing the Health and Safety Commission and the Health and Safety Executive, which are to be generally responsible for enforcing and administering the Act, or any of the regulations made under it

☑ the power of the Secretary of State to make regulations, the provision of regulations and repeal and modification of existing statutory provisions

☑ approval by the Health and Safety Commission of Approved Codes of Practice

☑ using Approved Codes of Practice in criminal proceedings

☑ the powers of the Health and Safety Executive to make adequate arrangements for the enforcement of relevant statutory provisions, both in relation to this and other health and safety legislation, whether by appointing its own inspectors or transferring its powers to other Local Authorities

☑ the appointment of Inspectors in writing, specifying their powers and means for the enforcement of the Act and any other legislation pursuant to Section 15

☑ improvement notices

☑ prohibition notices

☑ appeals procedures against improvement or prohibition notices

☑ the provision for criminal offences and punishments.

Part 2 – Employment Medical Advisory Service

The main provision of Part 2 of the Act is the continuation of the Employment Medical Advisory Service (EMAS). The responsibility for maintaining this service has been delegated by the Secretary of State to the Health and Safety Commission.

Part 3 – Building Regulations

The main provision of Part 3 of the Act is the extension of the scope and coverage of the Building Regulations.

Part 4 – General provisions

The main provision of Part 4 of the Act concerns amendments, repeals and modifications to other Acts or instruments.

These amendments affect (among other matters) general fire precautions, including means of escape in most factories, offices and shops. These can now be dealt with by the fire authorities. The Health and Safety Executive remains responsible for control over 'process risks', that is, risk of outbreak of fire associated with particular processes or particular substances.

In future, regulations may be made so that company reports will have to include information on health, safety and welfare arrangements.

The Health and Safety at Work Act

2.6 Duty holders under the Act

The Act **mainly** places legal duties on employers, the self-employed and employees. However:

- ☑ Section 4 places duties on the persons who control premises with regard to the health and safety of other persons who are not their employees

- ☑ Section 6 places duties on the manufacturers, designers, importers and suppliers of equipment

- ☑ Section 8 places a duty on all people, indicating that the duty also extends to members of the public.

Duties of employers

Part 1 of the Act places a general duty on every employer to ensure, so far as is reasonably practicable, the health, safety and welfare at work of all their employees.

The Act goes on to state that, so far as is reasonably practicable, the employer must:

- ☑ protect the health, safety and welfare at work of all their employees

- ☑ provide and maintain plant and systems of work that are safe and without risk to health

- ☑ ensure safety and absence of risks in the use, handling, storage and transport of articles and substances

- ☑ provide any necessary information, including information on legal requirements, to ensure the health and safety of their employees

- ☑ provide adequate supervision and training, as is necessary, to ensure the health and safety of their employees

- ☑ provide and maintain a safe and healthy place of work, with safe access and egress

- ☑ provide and maintain a working environment that is safe and without risks to health and is adequate with regard to welfare facilities and arrangements for welfare at work.

Certain additional duties have been placed on the employer including:

- ☑ where five or more persons are employed, to prepare, publicise and revise as often as may be appropriate, a written statement of the employer's health and safety policy and the organisation and arrangements in force for carrying out the policy

- ☑ to ensure, as far as is reasonably practicable, that the conduct of their activities does not endanger persons not in their employment who may be affected by operations under their control, for example, sub-contractors or the public.

 The Health and Safety Executive recommends that, as best practice, companies give information about health and safety performance in their shareholders' or annual report.

 In certain circumstances employers must provide information to others about those aspects of their undertaking that might affect health and safety. This duty is explicit in the Construction (Design and Management) Regulations.

Trade unions recognised by the management at the workplace have the right to appoint safety representatives from within the workforce.

Employers must:

- ☑ consult union-appointed safety representatives

- ☑ establish safety committees when requested by two safety representatives.

Employers must **not** levy a charge, or permit any employee to be charged, for anything required to be provided in pursuance of any of the relevant statutory provisions.

Duties of employees

The Act places two general duties on employees:

- ☑ to exercise reasonable care for the health and safety of themselves or others who may be affected by their acts or omissions at work

- ☑ to co-operate with the employer, as far as may be necessary, to enable them (the employer) to carry out their legal duties in health and safety matters.

Employees also have duties under various other regulations that expand on these general duties.

Duties of the self-employed

A general duty is placed on the self-employed to conduct their undertaking in such a way as to ensure, so far as is reasonably practicable, that they and other persons are not exposed to risks to health and safety. In many ways, the self-employed person has similar duties to an employer, including giving information to persons other than their employees about those aspects of their undertaking that might affect their health and safety.

Duties of all people

This section of the Act places a duty on all persons to not intentionally or recklessly interfere with anything provided in the interests of health, safety and welfare.

This suggests that not only does it apply to employers and employees but that it also applies to members of the public.

Duties of manufacturers, designers, importers and suppliers

A general duty is placed on any person who manufactures, designs, imports or supplies any article, material or substance for use at work to ensure, so far as is reasonably practicable, that articles and substances are, by design and construction, safe and without risks to health when being used, set, cleaned or maintained by persons at work.

 Information on design noise levels under normal working conditions should be supplied if noise levels may be a risk to health, or exceed the lower exposure action value specified in the Control of Noise at Work Regulations. Similarly, manufacturers of tools that may be a source of hand-arm vibration must provide details of the levels of vibration generated.

More specifically, a duty exists to ensure that arrangements are made to carry out the necessary testing, examination and research, and that steps are taken to provide adequate information about any conditions necessary to ensure that it will be safe when used.

A general duty is placed on installers or erectors of any article for use at work to ensure, so far as is reasonably practicable, that it is safe and without risk to health when used by persons at work.

Duties of those in control of premises

Duties are imposed on anyone who is in control of non-domestic premises to ensure the health and safety of anyone, who is not an employee, who enters those premises to carry out work.

The duties also:

☑ apply to premises where machinery, equipment or substances are provided for the use of others

☑ include a requirement to control noxious or offensive emissions into the atmosphere.

The person in control of non-domestic premises is generally the owner, occupier or other person who has specific obligations for maintenance or repair of those premises by virtue of a contract or tenancy agreement.

2.7   Health and Safety Executive

The Health and Safety Executive has been given certain powers and duties under the Act. The powers may also be exercised by Local Authority environmental health officers on certain smaller sites and in offices.

 For further information on HSE powers refer to Chapter A01 Health and safety law.

Investigation

Inspectors are given a general right to examine and investigate as necessary. They may:

☑ enter premises (accompanied by a police officer or other authorised person if necessary), taking with them any equipment or material required by them for the purposes of the examination

☑ direct that anything shall be left undisturbed if required for examination or investigation

☑ take measurements, samples, photographs and such recordings as may be necessary

☑ have dismantled or tested any article or substance considered dangerous, or take possession of any article for examination and evidence.

Inspectors may inspect or take copies of books or documents. They may demand from an employee any information they think necessary and can ask the employee to sign a declaration of the truth of their answers. In general, they can demand the full co-operation of any person to provide them with such facilities and assistance as they may deem necessary.

The Health and Safety at Work Act

Advisory

Inspectors also act as a source of information and advice. It is their duty to tell employee representatives (safety representatives or trade union-appointed safety representatives) or the employees about anything that may affect their health and safety at work. This information should be similar to that given to the employer.

Enforcement options

Inspectors can use any of the powers listed below against any person taking part in, or in control of, any work activity or piece of equipment. 'Any person' means an employer, self-employed person, a supplier, or the employee.

1. Informal	Inspectors may give advice on compliance in the case of minor breaches.
2. Formal letter	A formal letter may contain details of breaches and the action needed to comply with the legislation. It may also contain more detailed and formalised advice. Whilst visiting a site, an inspector can prepare an instant visit report with a date agreed for work to be completed.
3. Improvement notice	Where a breach is more serious, the inspector may issue an improvement notice, which will outline the work required and the date for completion. This will be at least 21 days from the date of receipt. *Refer to Appendix A for an example of an improvement notice.*
4. Prohibition notice	If an activity involves, or is likely to involve, a serious risk of personal injury, the inspector may serve a prohibition notice to stop that activity either immediately or after a specified time. *Refer to Appendix B for an example of a prohibition notice.*
5. Prosecution	In addition to the enforcement outlined above, the inspector may consider that it is also necessary to prosecute. This can be either in a Magistrate's Court or Crown Court.

 For fees for intervention refer to Chapter A01 Health and safety law.

Fines and imprisonment

Contravention of certain requirements of the Act can lead to summary prosecution in a Magistrate's Court (or Sheriff's Court in Scotland). In October 1992, under the provisions of the Criminal Justice Act, the current maximum fine that may be imposed by a Magistrate's Court or Sheriff's Court was raised from £2,000 to £5,000. This was subsequently raised to £20,000 by the Health and Safety (Offences) Act.

Contravention of other provisions can result in either summary prosecution, or an indictment in the Crown Court. The maximum penalty, on summary conviction, in a Magistrate's Court is £20,000 per offence, or six months' imprisonment, or both. For certain serious offences, which are dealt with at a Crown Court, there is no limit to the fine, and prison sentences of up to two years can be imposed.

 For further information on the provisions as to offences refer to Chapter A01 Health and safety law.

 Magistrate's Court – up to £20,000 fine and up to six months' imprisonment. Crown Court – unlimited fine and up to two years' imprisonment.

Appeals

Anyone served with an improvement or prohibition notice has the right to appeal to an industrial tribunal. This must be done within 21 days of the issue of the notice. The tribunal may cancel, confirm or modify the notice on appeal, following the issue of:

☑ an improvement notice – the notice will be suspended until the tribunal meets and decides the issue

☑ a prohibition notice – the notice will stand until the appeal has been decided, or the tribunal orders it to be suspended.

Offences under the Act can be committed by individuals as well as by corporate bodies, such as limited companies. When an offence has been committed with the help or knowledge of a director, manager, company secretary or other company official, that individual person may be prosecuted as well as the company.

The same duty is placed on the Crown (i.e. Government departments and the Armed Forces) except that the employer cannot be prosecuted. However, individual members of that organisation can be prosecuted for offences they commit, but not for those committed by their employer.

Where a person has been prosecuted for failing to comply with a duty or requirement of the Act, and is claiming that it was not reasonably practicable for them to carry out that duty or requirement, it is the responsibility of that person to prove that it was not reasonably practicable to comply, and that there was no reasonably practicable alternative way in which they could have carried out that duty or requirement.

2.8   Supporting legislation

The requirements of the Act, as outlined above, are very broad in their nature, for example Section 2(2)(b) requires employers to:

> ...ensure, so far as is reasonably practicable, arrangements for the safety and absence of risk in connection with the use, handling, storage and transportation of articles and substances.

Whilst being a legal requirement, this offers no practical guidance to employers upon how the duty should be fulfilled, particularly how to effectively manage hazardous substances used at work. To address such situations the Secretary of State is empowered by the Act to introduce health and safety regulations that:

☑ become a part of health and safety law

☑ clarify and expand upon the legal duties contained in the Act.

For example, to expand upon and explain the 'substances' part of the Section 2(2)(b) quote above, the Control of Substances Hazardous to Health Regulations came into force and have been amended several times since.

Health and safety regulations

In the main, regulations made under the Act place legal duties on employers and the self-employed, although some regulations place legal duties on employees.

Examples of regulations which are relevant to construction industry activities are:

☑ the Construction (Design and Management) Regulations

☑ the Work at Height Regulations

☑ the Control of Vibration at Work Regulations.

In some cases health and safety regulations are supported by additional guidance on how to comply with the law. This is achieved by the issue of Approved Codes of Practice and/or guidance notes.

Approved Codes of Practice

Approved Codes of Practice are prepared and issued by the Health and Safety Executive and are often referred to as ACoPs.

Whilst not strictly a part of the law, ACoPs have special legal status in that failure to comply with the guidance contained in an ACoP may be cited in court as a failure to comply with the law. ACoPs explain in detail what measures must be taken to comply with the regulations to which the ACoP relates.

Where an employer is accused of failing to comply with the requirements of an ACoP it is a valid defence for the employer if it can be shown that alternative measures, which were equally or more effective, were implemented.

ACoPs are generally issued after wide public consultation with stakeholders, the involvement of other Government bodies and with the consent of the Secretary of State.

Guidance notes

These are issued by the HSE and give practical advice on how regulations may be complied with.

While they are not legally enforceable, they do provide practical guidance on how employers and employees may comply with health and safety legislation.

2.9   Health and Safety Commission

The Health and Safety Commission (HSC) was established under the provisions of The Health and Safety at Work Act 1974 and, until its merger with the Health and Safety Executive on 1 April 2008, had an overall role in advising the Government on all health and safety matters.

The merger of the HSC and the HSE to form a single regulatory body took place after extensive consultation, with the aim of strengthening the links between the strategy and delivery of improving workplace health and safety. The single regulatory body is called the Health and Safety Executive which, in addition to incorporating the former Health and Safety Commission as the Board, retains all of its original function and powers.

Health and Safety Executive

The Health and Safety Executive (HSE) is now the single regulatory statutory body, working in accordance with directions and guidance from the Board. It enforces legal requirements, as well as providing an advisory service to both sides of industry.

The board of the HSE comprises representatives of both sides of industry and Local Authorities. It has responsibility for developing policies in the health and safety field. The chairperson of the board is appointed by the Government.

2.10 Employment Medical Advisory Service

The Employment Medical Advisory Service (EMAS) acts as the medical arm of the commission. It is the main channel of medical advice to the inspectorates within the executive, as well as giving advice to employers. EMAS also publishes leaflets under four subject headings:

- ☑ general information
- ☑ specific health hazards
- ☑ research and guidance notes
- ☑ medical series.

These are normally available from EMAS headquarters.

2.11 The Health and Safety (Enforcing Authority) Regulations

The responsibility for enforcing health and safety is broadly split between the HSE and the Local Authority. These regulations provide for the transfer of the responsibility for the enforcement of health and safety legislation between the HSE and the Local Authority (and vice versa) in certain circumstances. Within the Local Authority, environmental health officers are usually the enforcing officers.

Local Authority enforcement

Schedule 1 of the regulations lists the premises for which the Local Authority will be responsible. These include offices, shops, catering establishments, hotels, residential homes, places of sport, most places of entertainment and places of religion.

HSE enforcement

If a category of workplace is not specified in Schedule 1, the HSE will be the enforcing authority. Some examples of workplaces for which the HSE is the enforcing authority are:

- ☑ building and construction sites
- ☑ mines and quarries
- ☑ manufacturing industry
- ☑ fairgrounds
- ☑ hospitals
- ☑ educational establishments
- ☑ agriculture.

Transfer of responsibility for enforcement

Where construction work is carried out on premises for which the Local Authority is normally the enforcing authority, and the work is to be carried out by persons who do not normally work at those premises, the HSE will become the enforcing authority for the duration of the work if that work:

- ☑ is notifiable to the HSE by virtue of the Construction (Design and Management) Regulations
- ☑ in whole or in part involves work to the external fabric or other external parts of the structure
- ☑ is carried out in a physically segregated area of the premises and work activities normally carried out in that area are suspended
- ☑ involves the installation, maintenance or repair of gas or electrical systems
- ☑ involves the use of ionising radiation (in some cases only).

2.12 Examples of health and safety court cases

Below are brief details of two court cases that arose out of failings in the management of health and safety.

 Regina -v- Swan Hunter Shipbuilders Ltd and Telemeter Installations Ltd

This important Court of Appeal case, resulting from a prosecution under Sections 2 and 3 of The Health and Safety at Work Act 1974, demonstrated that an employer (the main contractor) has a duty to inform, instruct and supervise not only its own employees but also other workers (sub-contractors) who might, by their behaviour, endanger the main contractor's employees.

Regina -v- Associated Octel Company Ltd

This equally important Court of Appeal case demonstrates that under Section 3 of The Health and Safety at Work Act 1974 an employer can be prosecuted for failing to secure the safety of an independent contractor's employees, whether or not it has been involved with that third party's activities. If an employer engages an independent contractor to do work that forms part of the conduct of the employer's undertaking, the employer must stipulate the conditions needed to avoid risks to health and safety and that are reasonably practicable to protect that contractor's workforce.

2.13 Further information

There is an abundance of further information available on the web.

 Copies of all acts and regulations can be downloaded from the Government's legislation website.

The HSE's website breaks down regulations into easy to follow topic areas, industry sectors (such as construction) and different levels of guidance aimed at company owners down to employees. It also contains ACoPs and guidance, which are available as free downloads.

Appendix A – Example of an improvement notice

Health and Safety at Work Act 1974

The Health and Safety at Work Act 1974, Sections 21, 23 and

HSE
Health & Safety
Executive

Improvement notice

Serial Number
I

Name

Address

Trading as*

Inspector's full name	I,
Inspector's official designation	one of Her Majesty's Inspectors of Being an Inspector appointed by an instrument in writing made pursuant to section 19 of the said Act and entitled to issue the notice
Official address	of

Telephone number

hereby give you notice that I am of the opinion
that

Location of premises or place of activity	at

you, as an employer / self-employed person / person wholly or partly in control of the premises / other*

are contravening / have contravened in circumstances that make it likely that the contravention will
continue or
be repeated, the following statutory provisions:

The reasons for my said opinion are:

and I hereby require you to remedy the said contraventions or, as the case may be, the matters occasioning
them by
(and I direct that the measures specified in the
Schedule
which forms part of this notice shall be taken to remedy the said contraventions or matters)*

Signature   Date

*An Improvement Notice is also being served on

of

related to the matters contained in this notice

Environment and Safety Information Act 1988	This is a relevant notice for the purposes of the Environment and Safety Information Act 1988 YES/NO* This page only will form the register entry.*

Signature   Date

LP1 (rev 04.97)   *SEE NOTES OVERLEAF*   * delete as appropriate

Appendix B – Example of a prohibition notice

Health and Safety at Work Act 1974

HSE
Health & Safety
Executive

The Health and Safety at Work Act 1974, Sections 22, 23 and 24

Prohibition notice

Serial Number
P

Name

Address

Trading as*

Inspector' s full name	I,
Inspector's official designation	one of Her Majesty's Inspectors of Being an Inspector appointed by an instrument in writing made pursuant to section 19 of the said Act and entitled to issue the notice
Official address	of

Telephone number

hereby give you notice that I am of the opinion that the following activities namely:

which are being carried on by you / likely to be carried on by you / under your control* at

Location of premises or place of activity	

involve, or will involve, a risk of serious personal injury, and that the matters which give rise / will give rise* to the
said risks are:

and that the said matters involve / will involve* contravention of the following statutory provisions:

because

and I hereby direct that the said activities shall not be carried on by you or under your control
immediately / after*
unless the said contraventions and matters have been remedied.
I further direct that the measures specified in the schedule which forms part of this notice shall be taken to remedy
the said contraventions or matters*

Signature   Date

*A Prohibition Notice is also being served on

of

related to the matters contained in this notice

Environment and Safety Information Act 1988	This is a relevant notice for the purposes of the Environment and Safety Information Act 1988 YES/NO* This page only will form the register entry.*

Signature   Date

LP2 (rev 04.97)   *SEE NOTES OVERLEAF*   * delete as appropriate

03

Construction (Design and Management) Regulations

The Construction (Design and Management) Regulations (CDM) apply to all construction activities, regardless of size, duration and cost. The regulations lay down legal requirements for ensuring that health, safety and welfare is an integral part of project design, planning and construction.

This chapter outlines what the Regulations are about, what they require, what needs to be done and by whom.

Introduction	24
General principles	24
The regulations – an overview	25
General health and safety duties on all construction sites	29
Non-notifiable projects	30
Notifiable projects	31
Client	32
Designers	32
CDM co-ordinator	34
Principal contractor	34
Contractors	35
Project documents	36
Appendix A – Pre-construction information	38
Appendix B – The construction phase plan	40
Appendix C – The health and safety file	42
Appendix D – Competence chart	43

3.1 Introduction

The Construction (Design and Management) Regulations 2007 (CDM) cover all construction activities. The regulations lay down legal requirements for ensuring that health, safety and welfare is an integral part of project design, planning and construction. There are additional requirements for notifiable projects.

It is a common misconception that CDM Regulations only apply to larger projects, which are sometimes miscalled CDM projects rather than notifiable projects.

The CDM Regulations are about focusing attention on effective planning and management of all construction activities, from design concept onwards. The aim is for health and safety considerations to be treated as a normal part of a project's development, not an afterthought or bolt-on extra. The object of CDM is to reduce the risk of harm to those that have to build, use, maintain and demolish structures.

Thus the key aims are to:

☑ encourage everyone to work together to make health and safety an integral part of the design, construction and management of projects

☑ improve planning and management from day one to identify hazards so that they can be eliminated or properly managed

☑ target effort where it can be most effective in terms of health and safety

☑ have the right people, for the right job, at the right time to manage the risks on site

☑ encourage co-operation and co-ordination of the project.

CDM implements the European Temporary or Mobile Construction Sites (TMCS) Directive in Great Britain. Other European countries have implemented it in their domestic legislation in different ways. The regulations are supported by an Approved Code of Practice (ACoP) and guidance notes.

Whilst CDM covers most of the construction-specific risks, it is important to ensure compliance with other relevant regulations, such as the Work at Height Regulations and the Control of Substances Hazardous to Health Regulations.

 'Simple risks need simple controls' must be adopted as a principle to enable the true benefits of an appropriate health and safety management system to be experienced and appreciated.

3.2 General principles

The incorporation of the following principles into all construction projects is a legal requirement under CDM. In any event, they should be integral elements of any efficiently run project.

Competence

Under CDM, the requirement for competence extends to everyone who will work in any capacity on a construction project. This includes construction professionals, anyone in a management or supervisory position, and construction workers. The regulations require that:

☑ any duty holder who appoints a CDM co-ordinator, designer, principal contractor or contractor must take reasonable steps to ensure that whoever they appoint is competent to carry out the task

☑ no duty holder must arrange for or instruct a worker to carry out or manage design or construction work unless the worker is:
– competent to carry out the task, **or**
– under the supervision of a competent person

☑ anyone who accepts an appointment or is engaged under the regulations must be satisfied that they are competent to do what is required of them.

It should be noted that the requirement for competence only extends as far as it is necessary to enable the person to do what is required of them in a safe manner; competence in any trade or professional area that is not relevant to the current project cannot be demanded.

The ACoP contains very detailed guidance on the means of assessing the competence of all parties.

Co-operation

The regulations require that every duty holder involved in a project:

☑ seeks the co-operation of any other person involved in any project, whether on the same or an adjoining site

☑ co-operates with all other persons involved in any project, whether on the same or an adjoining site

so far as it is necessary for all persons involved in the project(s) to comply with their duties or functions under the regulations.

Every person involved in a project, who is working under the control of another person, must inform that person of anything believed to endanger the health or safety of any person.

Common examples of co-operation are:

☑ one contractor allowing the workforce of another company to use their scaffold to enable work at height to be carried out safely

☑ site management on one site allowing oversailing by a tower crane on an adjacent site.

Co-ordination

The regulations require that every duty holder involved in a project co-ordinates their activities with the activities of other duty holders to ensure, so far as is reasonably practicable, the health and safety of persons who are:

☑ carrying out construction work

☑ otherwise affected by the construction work.

There are many examples of where the various contractors involved in a project can co-ordinate their work activities, agreeing who works where and when so that construction work runs smoothly and without the risks created by one set of workers endangering the health and safety of other workers.

Risk management

Anyone involved in the design, planning and preparation of a project **must** take into account the general principles of prevention, based upon the significant findings of a risk assessment. Where any person is involved in the construction of the project, they must, **so far as is reasonably practicable,** take this into account.

Consultation with the workforce

This process is often also described as:

☑ worker engagement, or

☑ involving the workforce.

Whatever description is used, the principle is the same: effective two-way communication between management and those at the coalface.

The principal contractor must:

☑ make and maintain arrangements that will enable the principal contractor and the workers to co-operate effectively in promoting and developing measures to:
   – ensure the health, safety and welfare of the workers
   – check the effectiveness of the measures

☑ consult with workers or their representatives on matters connected with the project that may affect their health, safety or welfare, where such consultation is not carried out by the employer

☑ ensure that workers or their representatives can inspect and take copies of any information (with some exceptions) that these regulations require the principal contractor to keep in relation to the planning and management of the project, with regard to health and safety.

The ACoP goes to great lengths to stress the vital importance of, for example, contractors, managers and other people in supervisory positions engaging and consulting with the workforce as an effective way of identifying hazards and controlling the risks.

It is the workforce who have first-hand experience of actually carrying out the job and who may therefore be more knowledgeable about the risks involved.

Encouragement and ample opportunity must be given for all members of the workforce to feed back to management any concerns that they might have regarding health and safety.

Depending upon the circumstances, consultation might be carried out directly with a single worker, groups of workers or through health and safety representatives, whether trade union-appointed or not.

3.3   The regulations – an overview

Main structure

The regulations are structured to ensure that:

☑ there is a co-ordinated approach to health and safety on site, particularly where there are several contractors on site at any one time

☑ adequate time and resources are committed at a sufficiently early stage to draw health and safety into the design and planning phases

☑ there is adequate co-operation and communication between everyone on site who has responsibility for health and safety

☑ everyone on site is trained, as necessary, and is competent to do their job

Construction (Design and Management) Regulations

☑ health and safety issues are considered at the design and planning stage for the whole life cycle of a new structure, which includes:
  – construction
  – maintenance
  – alteration or extension
  – everyday use
  – cleaning
  – demolition.

The following parts of the regulations apply to **all** projects:

Part 1	Introduction.
Part 2	General management duties.
Part 4	Duties relating to health and safety on construction sites.
Part 5	General.
Schedule 2	Welfare facilities.
Schedule 3	Particulars to be included in a report of inspection.

 Parts 1, 2, 4 and 5 of the CDM Regulations cover **all** construction projects, regardless of cost, size or duration.

The following also apply to those projects that are notifiable to the Health and Safety Executive (HSE):

Part 3	Additional duties where the project is notifiable.
Schedule 1	Particulars to be notified to the HSE (Form F10).

Duty holders under CDM

The following groups have specific legal duties under the regulations:

☑ clients

☑ designers

☑ CDM co-ordinators

☑ the principal contractor

☑ contractors.

Everyone controlling site work has health and safety responsibilities. Checking that working conditions are healthy and safe before work begins, and ensuring that the proposed work is not going to put others at risk, requires planning and organisation. This applies to all construction work, whatever the size of the site.

 Whilst duties are not placed specifically on employees by these regulations, duties are placed on every person, which must be taken to include employees.

Definitions

Design. Includes drawings, design details, specifications, bills of quantities and calculations prepared for the purpose of designing all aspects of a structure or any products or electrical or mechanical systems intended for a particular structure.

Construction work. Any building, civil engineering or engineering construction work, including any of the following:

☑ construction, alteration, conversion, fitting out, commissioning, renovation, repair, upkeep, redecoration or other maintenance, cleaning (using water, abrasives at high pressure, or the use of corrosive or toxic substances), decommissioning, demolition or dismantling of a structure

☑ preparatory works including site clearance, exploration and investigation (but not site survey) and clearance or preparation of the site or structure for use or occupation

☑ assembly of prefabricated structures or their disassembly

☑ demolition or dismantling of any structure and the removal of materials and waste.

Structure. This is defined as any:

☑ building, steel or reinforced concrete structure, road, railway line, dock, harbour, tunnel, shaft, bridge, viaduct, waterworks, sewer, sewage works, earthworks or anything similar

☑ formwork, falsework, scaffold or other structure that provides temporary support or access during construction.

Project. Any building, construction or civil engineering project, or anything else that includes any construction work. All planning, design, management or other work involved is part of the project, including:

☑ installation, commissioning, maintenance, repair or removal of any mechanical, electrical, gas, compressed air, hydraulic, telecommunication, computer or similar service.

Notifiable project. Specific details of the project have to be notified to the HSE by the CDM co-ordinator if the construction phase:

☑ is likely to last longer than 30 working days

☑ will involve more than 500 person days of construction work

☑ is not for a domestic client.

The **construction phase** starts when actual construction work on the project commences, and normally ends on the transfer or handing over of the structure to the client. If there is more than one structure (or building), the construction phase does not end until the work on the last structure is complete.

 A 'person day' is the number of hours worked by an individual and includes any shift work. In any one working day, where shift work takes place, there will be more than one person day in the working day. A person day also includes any other length of time worked, which is less than one full day.

 A notifiable project is more than 30 days in duration or 500 person days.

Clients. A client may be a single person, a company or an organisation. They are the people for whom the work is being carried out. They have duties under CDM when a project is commissioned in connection with a business activity, even if it is commissioned by a not-for-profit organisation.

☑ Whether or not the client's duties apply will be obvious on many occasions, but may require some delicate questioning of the client by the designer, contractor or others.

☑ Domestic clients (private householders) are not classified as clients and have no duties under these regulations if the work they commission is not connected with any business activity of the householder.

Designer. Any person who whilst at work (whether they are paid or not) carries out any design work or arranges for someone under their control to do design work.

The CDM co-ordinator. The person appointed under the regulations for notifiable projects only. The main function of a CDM co-ordinator is to help clients to carry out their duties, to co-ordinate health and safety aspects of the design work and to prepare the health and safety file.

Principal contractor. The contractor appointed by the client for notifiable projects. A principal contractor's key duties are to co-ordinate and manage the construction phase of the project, and ensure the health and safety of everyone involved in the construction work or anyone who may be affected by it.

Contractor. In terms of the regulations a contractor is anyone, including a client, principal contractor or other person referred to in the regulations, who as part of a business (whether for profit or not) carries out or manages construction work.

Project documents

With regard to project documentation, CDM requires, for notifiable projects only, the creation of a:

☑ construction phase plan

☑ health and safety file.

Furthermore, the regulations require that relevant pre-construction information is gathered and compiled to form the basis of the construction phase plan in the case of notifiable projects. This must include all the project-specific information that is relevant to health and safety during the construction.

03

Approved Code of Practice and supporting guidance

The regulations are supported by an Approved Code of Practice (ACoP), entitled *Managing health and safety in construction* which expands upon what is expected of duty holders to comply with the regulations.

 It is free to download from the construction area of the HSE's website.

 In addition, guidance notes for each duty holder, which were written by the construction industry, are available on the CITB-ConstructionSkills website.

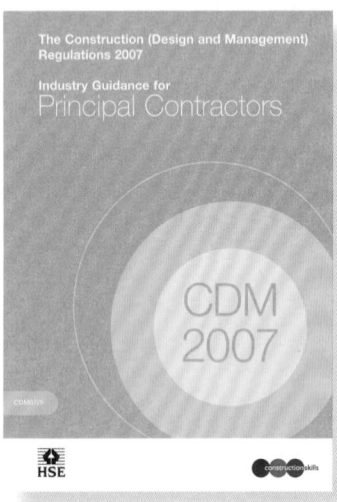

3.4 General health and safety duties on all construction sites

Part 4 of the regulations outlines the requirements for the management of health, safety and welfare on site. It is the duty of every:

 contractor, including the principal contractor

☑ person (other than a contractor) who controls the way in which construction work is carried out

to comply with the duties outlined in the table below, insofar as they apply to the job being carried out.

Every person who is working under the control of another person must report to that person any defect that may endanger the health or safety of any person. The duty to carry out statutory inspections expressly states upon whom that duty is placed.

> **!** The following duties in the table apply to all construction work, regardless of cost, size or duration.

Regulation number and title	Details of duties and requirements
25. Application of Regulations 26 to 44.	This regulation states that everybody carrying out construction work must comply.
26. Safe places of work.	Every place of work must be safe to access, egress and to work at.
27. Good order and site security.	Sites must be tidy, secure (to prevent unauthorised access), have appropriate signs and have no projecting sharp objects.
28. Stability of structures.	Buildings and structures must not be allowed to become unstable during work and any supports provided must be adequate for the job.
29. Demolition or dismantling.	These activities must be carried out so as to prevent any danger and there must be a written plan (for example method statement) in place before work starts.
30. Explosives.	Explosives must be stored, transported and used safely.
31. Excavations.	Work in excavations must be properly planned. They must not be allowed to collapse or have materials falling or slipping into them. No-one should become trapped because of inadequate shoring. Excavations must be inspected and reports written as appropriate. Work in an excavation must not start where an inspection has revealed that it is not safe to do so.
32. Cofferdams and caissons.	Cofferdams and caissons must be suitably designed, constructed, maintained and inspected. Work in cofferdams or caissons must not start where an inspection has revealed that it is not safe to do so.
33. Reports of inspections.	The duty to carry out inspections refers to Regulations 31 and 32 and requires inspections to be made at the start of every shift and after any event likely to affect the safety of the excavation, cofferdam or caisson. A written record of an inspection must be made at intervals not exceeding seven days.
34. Energy distribution installations.	Energy distribution systems (power cables, pressure hoses/pipes, and so on) above, on and below ground must be protected against being damaged or causing injury or damage. Work must not take place where there is a risk of damage to, or accidental disturbance of, energy distribution systems, unless suitable control measures have been taken.
35. Prevention of drowning.	Where there is risk of a person drowning because of falling into water or other liquid, suitable measures must be put in place to prevent falls and, where a risk remains, to have a rescue plan in place. Where workers are transported over water to and from their place of work, suitable steps must be taken to ensure this is carried out safely.
36. Traffic routes.	Traffic routes must be organised to protect people from injury from vehicles, preferably by physical segregation, and be suitable for the vehicles and persons using them. Traffic routes must be properly maintained, suitably signed and regularly inspected. Where it is unsafe for pedestrians to use gates intended for use by vehicles, separate pedestrian gates must be provided and kept free of obstruction.
37. Vehicles.	Arrangements must be made to prevent unintended movement of any vehicle. They must be used safely, not overloaded and prevented from falling into any excavation. No-one must be allowed to ride on any vehicle unless it is designed to carry passenger(s) and it is safe to do so. No-one must remain on any vehicle that is being loaded unless a safe place is provided and maintained on the vehicle.
38 Prevention of risk from fire, and so on.	Steps must be taken to avoid the risk of fire, flooding and asphyxiation.

03

Regulation number and title	Details of duties and requirements
39. Emergency procedures.	A plan must be in place for the safe evacuation of all people on site in situations where there is a foreseeable risk of an emergency. Everyone on site must be made aware of the emergency plan and it must be practised at suitable intervals.
40. Emergency routes and exits.	Adequate means of evacuation (emergency escape routes) to a safe place must be established. Routes must be kept clear of obstruction and be adequately signed.
41. Fire detection and fire-fighting.	Suitable fire-fighting equipment, fire detection equipment and alarms must be provided, examined and tested at suitable intervals and suitably located. Manual fire-fighting equipment (such as hand-held extinguishers), must be easily accessible and indicated by appropriate signs. An appropriate number of on-site staff must be trained in the use of fire-fighting equipment.
42. Fresh air.	Places of work must have adequate fresh or purified air available. Where fresh or purified air is provided by plant, it must be equipped with suitable audible or visible warnings to indicate any inadequacy in the supply or machine failure.
43. Temperature and weather protection.	Steps must be taken to ensure that indoor temperatures are reasonable. Outdoor workplaces must be arranged to provide adequate protection against adverse weather, taking into account usage and any protective clothing or equipment provided.
44. Lighting.	Every place of work, its access and egress routes and any traffic route must be adequately lit, preferably by natural light. Where lighting is by artificial means, a back-up system must be in place where failure of the primary system would result in risks to health or safety. Artificial light must not adversely affect the perception of any health and safety sign.

3.5   Non-notifiable projects

The management of health, safety and welfare duties (Part 2) and general health and safety duties (Part 4) apply to all construction work.

In effect, every construction project or building job, no matter how small, is a CDM job.

Where work is non-notifiable under CDM, the client does not have to:

- [✓] appoint a CDM co-ordinator
- [✓] appoint a principal contractor
- [✓] ensure a written construction phase plan is prepared.

With regard to the last point, even when not part of a notifiable project, some types of construction activity will require a written plan of work (for example a method statement), possibly supported by a permit to work.

The requirement for competence at all levels and the arrangements for the co-ordination of work and co-operation between all those working on the project still apply to non-notifiable projects.

Similarly, CDM requires that for non-notifiable projects demolishing or dismantling a structure or part of a structure must not begin until a written plan of work (such as a method statement) is compiled.

Although a formal health and safety plan is not required for non-notifiable projects, any high risk work must be well planned and managed. It is vital that those doing the work:

- [✓] understand the risks to health and safety that have been identified
- [✓] are aware of and comply with any measures put in place to control the risks
- [✓] know who to speak to if they have concerns about any health and safety issue.

If the risks are low and the precautions well understood by those carrying out the work, there may be no need for a written plan.

Within the ACoP, the Health and Safety Executive (HSE) has provided the following examples of work it considers higher risk where, even though the project is non-notifiable, something closer to a formal construction health and safety plan will be required:

- [✓] significant structural alterations
- [✓] work in deep excavations, particularly in unstable or contaminated ground
- [✓] unusual working methods or unfamiliar safeguards
- [✓] work with ionising radiation or other significant health hazards
- [✓] working near to high voltage power lines

☑ a risk of falling into fast-flowing water

☑ work that involves diving

☑ work that involves the use of explosives

☑ heavy or complicated lifting operations.

On non-notifiable projects, the main responsibility for health and safety will normally rest on the contractors doing the work, but anyone who may control any element of the work will also have duties. For example, a ground worker carrying out excavation work is normally responsible for ensuring that the excavation is safe to work in. If, however, the client specifies that it is dug and supported in a particular way, then the client will have a duty to ensure that the work is carried out in the prescribed safe manner.

3.6   Notifiable projects

03

Notifiable or not?

Any project becomes notifiable when it is likely to last longer than 30 days or involve more than 500 person workdays, providing it is not being carried out for a domestic client.

> The duties of relevant duty holders in respect of notifiable projects are in addition to all their duties for non-notifiable projects.

The process relies on common sense with regard to determining whether a project is notifiable or not. A day is taken as being eight hours' work and a working day is any day where work is planned.

Typical notifiable project under CDM 2007

Consider the following examples.

☑ Demolishing an old warehouse with a planned programme of three weeks, with five people working Monday to Friday, would not be notifiable as the work is planned to last 15 days or 75 person days.

☑ However, if it is evident that the same work would take five weeks with Saturday and Sunday morning working, then it would be notifiable, as the duration of the work would be over 30 days: 25 x whole days and 10 half days (each of which counts as a whole day) = 35 working days.

☑ For a shopfitting project that involved 24-hour working over a six-day period, with split shifts of 40 people all working 12-hour shifts, in CDM terms each 24-hour period is three days for 40 people over six days, therefore 40 x 3 x 6 = 720 person days. As this is greater than 500, the project would be notifiable.

There is no requirement to notify the HSE if a project goes slightly over the length of time estimated at the start of the project; this allows for breakdowns, delivery problems and so on. If, however, there is a major change that will result in a significant delay or change to the project itself, the work would become notifiable, and a CDM co-ordinator and principal contractor must be appointed.

Key to this is the responsibility of the designer and contractors to ensure that the client is aware of their CDM duties. As construction professionals they are in the best place to advise on the planned timescales.

Notification (Form F10)

Project notification should be submitted using the HSE's online Form F10. The online submission system includes the following features:

☑ an automatic email acknowledgement of receipt

☑ the ability to store a copy of the notification, which can be distributed by email

☑ a quick and easy way of sending amendments

☑ an ability to print the completed form for displaying

☑ security features to protect the integrity of the transmitted data.

The online system also allows the retrieval, amendment and re-submission of previously completed F10 forms.

> A blank Form F10 can be downloaded from the CDM section of the HSE's website.

The regulations require either that the client signs the notification or it is signed on their behalf. The online F10 form has a facility for the notifier to show they have made the client aware of their duties and the client has approved submission of the information.

The F10 notification must be sent as soon as possible after the CDM co-ordinator has been appointed. If not all of the details are known at that time, as much detail as possible must be sent and the remaining details forwarded as soon as they become known.

3.7 Client

General duties

The term client excludes domestic clients; people must be having construction work carried out as a part of their business activities (whether for profit or not) to be classified as a client under these regulations. Clients must ensure that arrangements are made for managing the projects and providing relevant information.

Further details of client duties can be found in the ACoP and industry guidance, but are summarised below.

Summary of client duties

Client duties	
All construction work (Part 2 of the regulations)	**Additional duties for notifiable projects** (Part 3 of the regulations)
Check competence and resources of all appointees.	Appoint a CDM co-ordinator.
Ensure there are suitable management arrangements for the project, including welfare facilities.	Appoint a principal contractor.
Allow sufficient time and resources for all stages.	There must be a CDM co-ordinator and principal contractor until the end of the construction phase.
Provide pre-construction information to designers and contractors.	Make sure that the construction phase does not start unless there:
	▪ are suitable welfare facilities
	▪ is a construction phase plan.
	Provide information relating to the health and safety file to the CDM co-ordinator.
	Retain and provide access to the health and safety file.

3.8 Designers

General duties

Designers are in a unique position at an early stage of a project to reduce the potential risks to health and safety that could arise during the construction phase or at a later stage (such as during maintenance of the completed structure).

Further details of designers' duties can be found in the ACoP and industry guidance, but are summarised below.

Summary of designer duties

Designer duties	
All construction work (Part 2 of the regulations)	**Additional duties for notifiable projects** (Part 3 of the regulations)
Eliminate hazards and reduce risks during design.	Check that the client is aware of their duties and that a CDM co-ordinator has been appointed.
Provide information about remaining risks.	Check that the HSE has been notified before starting work.
	Provide any information needed for the health and safety file.

 The HSE have produced CDM red, amber and green lists. These are practical aids for designers on what to eliminate/avoid, and what to encourage.

03

Red lists	
Hazardous procedures, products and processes that should be eliminated from the project where possible.	• Hand scabbling of concrete (such as stop ends).
	• Lack of adequate pre-construction information (such as asbestos surveys and ground contamination).
	• Demolition by hand-held breakers of the top sections of concrete piles (pile cropping techniques are available).
	• The specification of fragile roof lights and roofing assemblies.
	• Processes giving rise to large quantities of dust (such as dry cutting and blasting).
	• On-site spraying of harmful substances.
	• The specification of structural steelwork that is not purposely designed to accommodate safety nets.
	• Designing roof mounted services requiring access (for maintenance), without provision for safe access (such as barriers).
	• Glazing that cannot be accessed safely. All glazing should be anticipated as requiring cleaning and replacement, so a safe system of access is essential.
	• Entrances, floors, ramps, stairs and escalators, not specifically designed to avoid slips and trips during use and maintenance, including effect of rain water and spillages.
	• Design of environments involving adverse lighting, noise, vibration, temperature, wetness, humidity and draughts or chemical and/or biological conditions during use and maintenance operations.
	• Designs of structures that do not allow for fire containment during construction.
Amber lists Products, processes and procedures to be eliminated or reduced as far as possible and only specified/allowed if unavoidable. Including amber items would always lead to the provision of information to the principal contractor.	• Internal manholes/inspection chambers in circulation areas.
	• External manholes in heavily used vehicle access zones.
	• The specification of 'lip' details (such as trip hazards) at the tops of pre-cast concrete staircases.
	• The specification of shallow steps (such as risers) in external paved areas.
	• The specification of heavy building blocks (those weighing > 20 kgs).
	• Large and heavy glass panels.
	• The chasing out of concrete/brick/blockwork walls or floors for the installation of services.
	• The specification of heavy lintels (the use of slim metal or hollow concrete lintels being alternatives).
	• The specification of solvent-based paints and thinners, or isocyanates, particularly for use in confined areas.
	• The specification of curtain wall or panel systems without provision for the tying (or raking) of scaffolds.
	• The specification of blockwork walls > 3.5 metres high using retarded mortar mixes.
Green lists Products, processes and procedures to be positively encouraged.	• Adequate access for construction vehicles to minimise reversing requirements (one-way systems and turning radii).
	• Provision of adequate access and headroom for maintenance in plant rooms, and adequate provision for replacing heavy components.
	• Thoughtful location of mechanical/electrical equipment, light fittings, security devices, and so on to facilitate access, and away from crowded areas.
	• The specification of concrete products with pre-cast fixings to avoid drilling.
	• Specify half board sizes for plasterboard sheets to make handling easier.
	• Early installation of permanent means of access, and prefabricated staircases with hand rails.
	• The provision of edge protection at permanent works where there is a forseeable risk of falls after handover.
	• Practical and safe methods of window cleaning (for example, from the inside).
	• Appointment of a temporary work co-ordinator (BS 5975).
	• Off-site timber treatment if PPA- and CCA-based preservatives are used (boron or copper salts can be used for cut ends on site).
	• Off-site fabrication and prefabricated elements to minimize on-site hazards.
	• Encourage the use of engineering controls to minimise the use of personal protective equipment.

3.9   CDM co-ordinator

General duties

The purpose of the CDM co-ordinator is to provide the client with key project information about construction health and safety risk-management matters. The role of CDM co-ordinator may be filled by an individual, an organisation (such as a company or Local Authority) or by a professional practice (such as an architect's practice or a specialist consultancy).

The more complex the job and hence the more construction disciplines involved, the less likely it is that the role of CDM co-ordinator can be satisfactorily carried out by a single person.

03

Early involvement of the CDM co-ordinator with the client and designers should significantly contribute to the reduction of risk to construction workers and to anyone who has to subsequently work on the completed structure.

Further details of CDM co-ordinators' duties can be found in the ACoP and industry guidance, but are summarised below.

Summary of CDM co-ordinator duties

CDM co-ordinator duties	
All construction work (Part 2 of the regulations)	**Additional duties for notifiable projects** (Part 3 of the regulations)
	Advise and assist the client with their duties. Notify the HSE. Co-ordinate health and safety aspects of design work and co-operate with others involved with the project. Facilitate good communication between the client, designers and contractors. Liaise with the principal contractor about ongoing design. Identify, collect and pass on pre-construction information. Prepare and update the health and safety file.

3.10   Principal contractor

General duties

 A principal contractor is the contractor appointed by the client for notifiable projects.

It should be noted that under the regulations, the definition of contractor includes principal contractor. The practical implication of this is that in addition to carrying out the duties below, each principal contractor must also ensure that they carry out the duties of contractors where they are appropriate.

From the ACoP, the legal duties are interpreted as requiring the principal contractor to ensure that:

☑ they satisfy themselves that the client is aware of their duties, and that a CDM co-ordinator has been appointed and the HSE notified before they start work on site

☑ they are competent to address the health and safety issues that are likely to require managing during the construction phase

☑ the construction phase is properly planned, managed and monitored with adequately resourced, competent site management that is appropriate to the work activities and the risks

☑ all contractors are informed of the minimum time that they will be allowed for planning and preparation

☑ all contractors are provided with the information about the project that they need to enable them to carry out their work safely and without risk to health

☑ they meet requests from contractors for such information promptly

☑ there is safe working, co-ordination and co-operation between all parties involved in the project

☑ a suitable construction phase plan is prepared before construction work starts. The plan should be discussed with any contractors and implemented and kept live throughout the project. This will include arrangements to monitor and review performance

☑ they satisfy themselves that the designers and contractors they engage are competent and adequately resourced

☑ suitable welfare facilities are provided from the start of the construction phase

☑ only authorised persons are allowed onto site or into premises where construction work is being carried out

☑ any necessary site rules are prepared and enforced

☑ (copies of or access to) relevant parts of the plan and other information are provided to contractors, including the self-employed, in time for them to plan their work

☑ they liaise with the CDM co-ordinator on design carried out during the construction phase, including design by specialist contractors, and its implications for the plan

☑ they promptly provide the CDM co-ordinator with any information relevant to the health and safety file

☑ all workers have been provided with suitable health and safety induction, information and training

☑ the workforce is consulted about health and safety matters

☑ a copy of the project notification is displayed in a place (or places) where it is accessible to everyone on site.

While these requirements might seem onerous they are all principles of good management of health, safety and welfare and many companies have been implementing them for a long time.

Summary of principal contractor duties

Principal contractor duties	
All construction work (Part 2 of the regulations)	**Additional duties for notifiable projects** (Part 3 of the regulations)
	Plan, manage and monitor the construction phase in liaison with contractors.
	Prepare, develop and implement a written plan and site rules. (An initial plan must be completed before the construction phase begins.)
	Give contractors the relevant parts of the plan.
	Make sure suitable welfare facilities are provided from the start and are maintained throughout the construction phase.
	Check the competence of all their appointees.
	Ensure that all workers have site inductions and any further information and training needed to carry out the work.
	Consult with the workers.
	Liaise with the CDM co-ordinator regarding ongoing design.
	Secure the site.

3.11 Contractors

General duties

Within CDM the contractor's duties have been extended to emphasise the need for management of health, safety and welfare, even on small projects.

The ACoP clearly states that contractors and those actually doing the work are most at risk of injury and ill health. Consequently, they have a key role to play in controlling risk by co-operating with the principal or main contractor and in planning and managing their work.

All contractors, including, for example, utility companies, specialist contractors and the self-employed, have a part to play in ensuring health and safety on site, via the proper co-ordination of their work, underpinned by effective communication and co-operation.

With regard to **all projects,** the ACoP requires all contractors to:

☑ check clients are aware of their duties

☑ satisfy themselves that they and anyone they employ or engage are competent and adequately resourced

☑ plan, manage and monitor their own work to make sure that workers under their control are safe from the start of their work on site

☑ ensure that any contractor who they appoint or engage to work on the project is informed of the minimum amount of time that will be allowed for them to plan and prepare before starting work on site

☑ provide workers under their control (whether employed or self-employed) with any necessary information, including relevant aspects of other contractors' work, and site induction (where not provided by a principal contractor), which they need to work safely, to report problems, or to respond appropriately in an emergency

☑ ensure that any design work they do complies with the regulations

☑ comply with any requirements listed in Schedule 2 and Part 4 of the regulations that apply to their work

☑ co-operate with others and co-ordinate their work with others working on the project

☑ ensure the workforce is properly consulted on matters affecting their health and safety

☑ obtain specialist advice (for example, from a structural engineer or occupational hygienist) where necessary when planning high-risk work (for example, alterations that could result in structural collapse or construction on contaminated land).

The ACoP outlines the additional duties of contractors on notifiable projects as being to:

☑ not start any work until the CDM co-ordinator has been appointed and they are aware that the HSE has been notified of the project, usually by receiving a copy of the notification form

☑ give information to the principal contractor about the contractor's risk assessments, including any risks to third parties, on how they propose to carry out the work and what steps they will take to control and manage any risks

☑ co-operate with the principal contractor, CDM co-ordinator and others working on the project, or on adjacent sites, so that they each may comply with their duties under these regulations or any of the relevant statutory provisions

☑ comply with site rules and any directions given by the principal contractor

☑ inform the principal contractor of the details of any (sub)contractors that the contractor will engage to work on the project

☑ inform the principal contractor of anything significant that would require the health and safety plan to be changed

☑ provide the principal contractor with material that has been identified as being necessary for the health and safety file

☑ give to the principal contractor details of any accident, illness or dangerous occurrence that is reportable under current legislation.

Summary of contractor duties

Contractor duties	
All construction work (Part 2 of the regulations)	**Additional duties for notifiable projects** (Part 3 of the regulations)
Plan, manage and monitor own work and that of their workers. Check the competence of all their appointees and workers. Train their own employees. Provide information to their workers. Comply with the specific requirements in Part 4 of the regulations. Ensure there are adequate welfare facilities for their workers.	Check that the client is aware of their duties and that a CDM co-ordinator has been appointed and the HSE notified before starting work. Co-operate with the principal contractor in planning and managing work, including reasonable directions and site rules. Provide the principal contractor with details of any contractor(s) engaged. Provide any information needed for the health and safety file. Inform the principal contractor of problems with the plan. Inform the principal contractor of reportable accidents, diseases and dangerous occurrences.

3.12 Project documents

There is a legal duty to compile the project documents described below for notifiable projects only. However, the type of information gained by putting these documents together would be useful in ensuring the effective management of health and safety on some non-notifiable projects.

Pre-construction information

The CDM co-ordinator compiles this information. It contains the site-specific information provided by the client, who may:

☑ already have some or all of the necessary information to hand (for example, by reference to an existing health and safety file), or

☑ have had to approach other organisations (such as utility companies or asbestos surveyors) to gather some of the information required.

The information is issued to all tendering contractors and the successful one develops it as principal contractor into the construction phase plan.

Where the CDM co-ordinator has created a useful pack of information, the tendering contractors' responses to issues raised can be used as part of the assessment of their competence to manage the health and safety issues identified.

Appendix A contains a copy of the HSE's suggested contents list for the pre-construction information.

The information pack should contain site-specific relevant information that forms the basis of the health and safety plan developed by the principal contractor.

The construction phase plan

This may also be referred to as 'the construction phase health and safety plan', the 'health and safety plan' or in some cases simply 'the plan'. It is increasingly common to integrate other related elements such as security and environment. It is the responsibility of the principal contractor to further develop the pre-construction information into the construction phase plan.

As the project develops it is likely that the construction phase plan will be amended and further developed in the light of emerging issues and situations. It is a live working document that is the basis for the effective health and safety management of the project.

The principal contractor must:

☑ prepare a construction phase plan, before the start of the construction phase, which is sufficient to ensure that the construction phase is planned, managed and monitored in such a way that construction work can be carried out without risk to health or safety, so far as is reasonably practicable, paying adequate regard to the pre-construction information provided by the designers

☑ throughout the project, review, revise and refine the plan as often as is appropriate, so that it continues to be sufficient to fulfil the above requirement

☑ arrange for the plan to be implemented in such a way as to ensure, so far as is reasonably practicable, the health and safety of all persons carrying out construction work and other persons who may be affected by it.

Generally, during the construction phase, the construction phase plan will be expanded to outline:

☑ details of the arrangements for protecting the health and safety of all persons who may be affected in any way by the construction work

☑ arrangements for the monitoring of the health and safety performance of persons engaged in construction work to ensure they are complying with relevant statutory provisions and the health and safety plan

☑ information concerning the welfare arrangements that have been made.

> Relevant parts of the information contained in the construction phase plan must be made available to, or be made known to, contractors before construction commences, so that they may be aware of risks to health and safety that may arise for their employees.

With this knowledge they will be able to meet the requirements that are imposed on them under the construction phase plan. They obviously also have to meet the requirements that are imposed on them by the relevant statutory provisions.

The health and safety file

Under CDM the purpose of the health and safety file is to contain the relevant information needed to allow future construction work, maintenance, cleaning, refurbishment and demolition to be carried out safely.

Under CDM, there is an increased emphasis on the CDM co-ordinator to ensure that the health and safety file contains useful information. This means that the role involves selecting relevant information to include and possibly rejecting other material that is submitted. For example, putting the construction phase method statements about groundworks in the file is unlikely to be useful in the future, whereas identifying the position and size of the crane used for lifting in steelwork or air-conditioning units may be of use.

The emphasis is on information that has a relevance to the future.

At the completion of the project, the file is given to the client and, unless further changes to the structure are made, it then remains as a permanent record of how the project was designed and built.

Appendix A – Pre-construction information

Description of project	
1. Project description and programme details including:	
a) key dates (including planned start and finish of the construction phase)	
b) the minimum time to be allowed between appointment of the principal contractor and instruction to commence work on site.	
2. Details of client, designers, co-ordinator and other consultants.	
3. Whether or not the structure will be used as a place of work (in which case the design will need to take account of the relevant requirements of The Workplace (Health, Safety and Welfare) Regulations 1992 (as amended).	
4. Extent and location of existing records and plans.	
Client's considerations and management requirements	
1. Arrangements for:	
a) planning and managing the construction work, including any health and safety goals for the project	
b) communication and liaison between client and others	
c) security of the site	
d) welfare provision.	
2. Requirements relating to the health and safety of the client's employees or customers, or other people involved in the project, such as:	
a) the requirement for site hoardings	
b) site transport arrangements or restriction on vehicle movements	
c) client permit-to-work systems	
d) fire precautions	
e) emergency procedures and means of escape	
f) 'no-go' areas or other authorisation requirements	
g) any areas designated as a confined space by the client	
h) smoking and parking restrictions.	
Environmental restrictions and existing on-site risks	
1. Safety hazards, including:	
a) boundaries and access, including temporary access (for example narrow streets, lack of parking, turning or storage space)	
b) any restrictions on deliveries, waste collection or storage	
c) adjacent land uses (such as schools, railway lines or busy roads)	
d) existing storage of hazardous materials	
e) location of existing services particularly those that are concealed – water, electricity, gas, and so on	
f) ground conditions, underground structures or water courses where this might affect the safe use of plant (such as cranes, or the safety of groundworks)	
g) information on existing structures – stability, structural form, fragile or hazardous materials, anchorage points for fall-arrest systems (particularly where demolition is involved)	
h) previous structural modifications, including weakening or strengthening of the structure (particularly where demolition is involved)	
i) fire damage, ground shrinkage, movement or poor maintenance which may have adversely affected the structure	
j) any difficulties relating to plant and equipment in the premises (such as overhead gantries whose height restricts access)	
k) health and safety information contained in earlier design, construction or 'as-built' drawings (such as details of pre-stressed or post-tensioned structures).	
2. Health hazards, including:	
a) asbestos, including results of surveys (particularly where refurbishment and/or demolition is involved)	
b) existing storage of hazardous materials	
c) existing structures containing hazardous materials	
d) health risks arising from clients' activities.	

Significant design and construction hazards	
1. Significant design assumptions and suggested work methods, sequences or other control measures.	
2. Arrangements for co-ordination of ongoing design work and handling design changes.	
3. Information on significant risks identified during design.	
4. Materials requiring particular precautions.	

03

Appendix B – The construction phase plan

Description of project	
1. Project description and programme details including any key dates.	
2. Details of client, CDM co-ordinator, designers, principal contractor and other consultants.	
3. Extent and location of existing records and plans which are relevant to health and safety on site, including information on existing structures when appropriate.	
Management of the work	
1. Management structure and responsibilities.	
2. Health and safety goals for the project and arrangements for monitoring and review of health and safety performance.	
3. Arrangements for:	
a) regular liaison between parties on site	
b) consultation with the workforce	
c) the exchange of design information between the client, designers, CDM co-ordinator and contractors on site	
d) handling design changes during the project	
e) the selection and control of contractors	
f) the exchange of health and safety information between contractors	
g) site security	
h) site induction	
i) on-site training	
j) welfare facilities and first aid	
k) the reporting and investigation of accidents and incidents including near misses	
l) the production and approval of risk assessments and written systems of work.	
4. Site rules.	
5. Fire and emergency procedures.	

Arrangements for controlling significant site risks	
1. Safety risks, including:	
a) delivery and removal of materials (including waste) and work equipment taking account of any risks to the public (for example during access to or egress from the site)	
b) dealing with services – water, electricity and gas, including overhead powerlines and temporary electrical installations	
c) accommodating adjacent land use	
d) stability of structures whilst carrying out construction work, including temporary structures and existing unstable structures	
e) preventing falls	
f) work with or near fragile materials	
g) control of lifting operations	
h) the maintenance of plant and equipment	
i) work on excavations and work where there are poor ground conditions	
j) work on wells, underground earthworks and tunnels	
k) work on or near water where there is a risk of drowning	
l) work involving diving	
m) work in a caisson or compressed air working	
n) work involving explosives	
o) traffic routes and segregation of vehicles and pedestrians	
p) storage of materials (particularly hazardous materials) and work equipment	
q) any other significant safety risks.	

Arrangements for controlling significant site risks (continued)	
2. Health risks:	
a) the removal of asbestos	
b) dealing with contaminated land	
c) manual handling	
d) use of hazardous substances, particularly where there is a need for health monitoring	
e) reducing noise and/or vibration	
f) work with ionising radiation	
g) exposure to UV radiation (from the sun)	
h) any other significant health risks.	
The health and safety file	
1. Layout and format.	
2. Arrangements for the collection and gathering of information.	
3. Storage of information.	
Significant design and construction hazards	
1. Significant design assumptions and suggested work methods, sequences or other control measures.	
2. Arrangements for co-ordination of ongoing design work and handling design changes.	
3. Information on significant risks identified during design.	
4. Materials requiring particular precautions.	

03

Appendix C – The health and safety file

It is the responsibility of the CDM co-ordinator to ensure that a health and safety file is prepared.
The level of detail should allow the likely risks to be identified and addressed by those carrying out the work.

1. A brief description of the work carried out.	
2. Any residual hazards which remain and how they have been dealt with (for example surveys or other information concerning asbestos, contaminated land, water bearing strata, buried services and so on).	
3. Key structural principles (for example bracing, sources of substantial stored energy, including pre- or post-tensioned members) and safe working loads for floors and roofs, particularly where these may preclude placing scaffolding or heavy machinery there.	
4. Hazardous materials used (for example lead paint, pesticides, special coatings which should not be burnt off and so on).	
5. Information regarding the removal or dismantling of installed plant and equipment (for example any special arrangements for lifting, order or other special instructions for dismantling and so on).	
6. Health and safety information about equipment provided for cleaning or maintaining the structure.	
7. The nature, location and markings of significant services, including underground cables, gas supply equipment, fire-fighting services and so on.	
8. Information and as-built drawings of the structure, its plant and equipment (for example the means of safe access to and from service voids, fire doors and compartmentalisation and so on).	

The file does not need to include things that will be of no help when planning future construction work, maintenance or demolition.

Appendix D – Competence chart

Core criteria for demonstration of competence

Companies, contractors, CDM co-ordinators and designers need to meet the standards set out in the core criteria table below.

Column 1 of the table lists the elements that should be assessed when establishing whether or not a company is competent for the work that they will be expected to do.

Column 2 lists the standards against which the assessment should be made.

Column 3 gives some examples of how a company might demonstrate that it meets those standards.

Companies do not have to produce all of the evidence listed in Column 3 to satisfy the standard – they simply need to produce enough evidence to show that they meet the standard in Column 2, taking account of the nature of the project and the risks that the work entails. This requires judgement as to whether the evidence provided meets the standard to be achieved. **If your judgement is reasonable, and clearly based on the evidence you have asked for and been provided with, you will not be criticised if the company you appoint subsequently proves not to be competent when carrying out the work.**

Remember that assessments should focus on the needs of the particular job and should be proportionate to the risks arising from the work. Unnecessary bureaucracy associated with competency assessment obscures the real issues and diverts effort away from them.

If you employ less than five persons you do not have to write down your policy, organisation or arrangements under Criteria 1 and 2. However, you do need to demonstrate that your policy and arrangements are adequate in relation to the type of work you do. Assessments of competence will be made easier if your procedures are clear and accessible.

Contractor, designer and CDM co-ordinator relate to your function, not to the type of organisation.

Criteria	Standard to be achieved	Examples of the evidence that you could use to demonstrate you meet the required standard
Stage 1 assessment		
Health and safety policy and organisation for health and safety.	You are expected to have and implement an appropriate policy, regularly reviewed, and signed off by the managing director or equivalent. The policy must be relevant to the nature and scale of your work and set out the responsibilities for health and safety management at all levels within the organisation.	A signed, current copy of the company policy (indicating when it was last reviewed and by whose authority it is published). Guidance on writing company policies for health and safety can be found in the HSE's free leaflet INDG 259.
Arrangements.	These should set out the arrangements for health and safety management within the organisation and should be relevant to the nature and scale of your work. They should set out how the company will discharge their duties under CDM (2007). There should be a clear indication of how these arrangements are communicated to the workforce.	A clear explanation of the arrangements that the company has made for putting its policy into effect and for discharging its duties under CDM (2007). Guidance on making arrangements for the management of health and safety can be found in the HSE's free leaflet INDG 259.
Competent advice – corporate and construction related.	Your organisation and your employees must have ready access to competent health and safety advice, preferably from within your own organisation. The adviser must be able to provide general health and safety advice and also (from the same source or elsewhere) advice relating to construction health and safety issues.	Name and competency details of the source of advice (for example a safety group, trade federation, or consultant who provides health and safety information and advice). An example from the last 12 months of advice given and action taken.
Training and information.	You should have in place, and implement, training arrangements to ensure your employees have the skills and understanding necessary to discharge their duties as contractors, designers or CDM co-ordinators. You should also have in place a programme for refresher training (for example, a continuing professional development programme or life-long learning), which will keep your employees updated on new developments and changes to legislation or good health and safety practice. This applies throughout the organisation – from board or equivalent, to trainees.	Headline training records. Evidence of a health and safety training culture, including records, certificates of attendance and adequate health and safety induction training for sitebased workforce. Evidence of an active CPD programme. Sample toolbox talks.

Construction (Design and Management) Regulations – Appendix D

03

Criteria	Standard to be achieved	Examples of the evidence that you could use to demonstrate you meet the required standard
Stage 1 assessment (continued...)		
Individual qualifications and experience.	Employees are expected to have the appropriate qualifications and experience for the assigned tasks, unless they are under controlled and competent supervision.	Details of qualifications and/or experience of specific corporate post holders (for example, board members, health and safety adviser and so on). Other key roles should be named or identified and details of relevant qualifications and experience provided.
		For contractors: Details of number/percentage of people engaged in the project who have passed a construction health and safety assessment (for example the CITB-ConstructionSkills *Health, safety and environment test* or affiliated schemes, or the CCNSG equivalent).
		For site managers: Details of any specific training (such as CITB-ConstructionSkills Site Safety Plus scheme certificate – Site Management Safety Training Scheme (SMSTS) or equivalent).
		For supervisors: Details of any specific training (such as CITB-ConstructionSkills Site Safety Plus scheme certificate – Site Supervisors Safety Training Scheme (SSSTS) or equivalent).
		For professionals: Details of qualifications and/or professional institution membership.
		For site workers: Details of any relevant qualifications or training (such as S/NVQ certificates). Evidence of a company-based training programme suitable for the work to be carried out.
		For design organisations: Details of number/percentage of people engaged in the project who have passed a construction health and safety assessment (for example, the CITB-ConstructionSkills *Health, safety and environment test* or affiliated schemes, or the CCNSG equivalent). Details of any relevant qualifications and/or professional institution membership and any other specific qualifications (such as ICE Health and Safety Register, NEBOSH Construction Certificate, APS Design Register).
		For CDM co-ordinators: Details of number/percentage of people engaged in the project who have passed a construction health and safety assessment (for example, the CITB-ConstructionSkills *Health, safety and environment test* or affiliated schemes, or the CCNSG equivalent). Evidence of health and safety knowledge (such as NEBOSH Construction Certificate).
		Details of professional institution membership and any other specific qualifications (such as APS Design Register, ICE Health and Safety Register or similar).
		Evidence of a clear commitment to training and the continuing professional development of staff.
Monitoring, audit and review.	You should have a system for monitoring your procedures, for auditing them at periodic intervals, and for reviewing them on an on-going basis.	Could be through formal audit or discussions/reports to senior managers. Evidence of recent monitoring and management response. Copies of site inspection reports.
Workforce involvement.	You should have, and implement, an established means of consulting with your workforce on health and safety matters.	Evidence showing how consultation is carried out. Records of health and safety committees. Names of appointed safety representatives. For those employing less than five people, be able to describe how you consult with your employees to achieve the consultation required.

03

Criteria	Standard to be achieved	Examples of the evidence that you could use to demonstrate you meet the required standard
Stage 1 assessment (continued…)		
Accident reporting and enforcement action; follow-up investigation.	You should have records of all RIDDOR reportable events for at least the last three years. You should also have in place a system for reviewing all incidents and recording the action taken as a result. You should record any enforcement action taken against your company over the last five years and the action that you have taken to remedy matters subject to enforcement action.	Evidence showing the way in which you record and investigate accidents and incidents. Records of the last two accidents/incidents and the actions taken to prevent recurrence. Records of any enforcement action taken over the last five years, and what action was taken to put matters right. (Information on enforcement taken by the HSE over the last five years is available on the HSE website.) For larger companies, simple statistics showing incidence rates of major injuries, over three-day injuries, reportable cases of ill health and dangerous occurrences for the last three years. Records should include any incidents that occurred whilst the company traded under a different name, and any incidents that occur to direct employees or labour-only sub-contractors.
Sub-contracting/ consulting procedures (if applicable).	You should have arrangements in place for appointing competent sub-contractors/consultants. You should be able to demonstrate how you ensure that sub-contractors will also have arrangements for appointing competent sub-contractors or consultants. You should have arrangements for monitoring sub-contractor performance.	Evidence showing how you ensure sub-contractors are competent. Examples of sub-contractor assessments you have carried out. Evidence showing how you require similar standards of competence assessment from sub-contractors. Evidence showing how you monitor sub-contractor performance.
Hazard elimination and risk control **(designers only)**.	You should have, and implement, arrangements for meeting your duties under Regulation 11 of CDM (2007).	Evidence showing how you ensure: ■ co-operation and co-ordination of design work within the design team and with other designers/contractors ■ hazards are eliminated and any remaining risks controlled ■ any structure that will be used as a workplace will meet relevant requirements of The Workplace (Health Safety and Welfare) Regulations 1992. Examples showing how risk was reduced through design. A short summary of how changes to designs will be managed. (**Note:** The emphasis here should be on practical measures that reduce particular risks arising from the design, not on lengthy procedural documentation highlighting generic risks.)
Risk assessment leading to a safe method of work **(contractors only)**.	You should have procedures in place for carrying out risk assessments and for developing and implementing safe systems of work/method statements.	Evidence showing how the company will identify significant health and safety risks and how they will be controlled. Sample risk assessments or safe systems of work or method statements. If you employ less than five persons and do not have written arrangements, you should be able to describe how you achieve the above.
	The identification of health issues is expected to feature prominently in this system.	This will depend upon the nature of the work, but must reflect the importance of this risk area.
Co-operating with others and co-ordinating your work with that of other contractors **(contractors)**.	You should be able to illustrate how co-operation and co-ordination of your work is achieved in practice, and how you involve the workforce in drawing up method statements/safe systems of work.	Evidence could include sample risk assessments, procedural arrangements, project team meeting notes. Evidence of how the company co-ordinates its work with other trades.

Criteria	Standard to be achieved	Examples of the evidence that you could use to demonstrate you meet the required standard
Stage 1 assessment (continued...)		
Welfare provision **(contractors)**.	You should be able to demonstrate how you will ensure that appropriate welfare facilities will be in place before people start work on site.	Evidence could include, for example, health and safety policy commitment, contracts with welfare facility providers, or details of types of welfare facilities provided on previous projects.
CDM co-ordinator's duties **(CDM co-ordinators)**.	You should be able to demonstrate how you go about encouraging co-operation, co-ordination and communication between designers.	The evidence should be in the form of actual examples rather than generic procedures.
Stage 2 assessment		
Work experience.	You should give details of relevant experience in the field of work for which you are applying.	A simple record of recent projects or contracts should be kept, with the phone numbers and addresses of contacts who can verify that work was carried out with due regard to health and safety. This should be sufficient to demonstrate your ability to deal with the key health and safety issues arising from the work you are applying for. Where there are significant shortfalls in your previous experience, or there are risks associated with the project that you have not managed before, an explanation of how these shortcomings will be overcome.

Guidance for assessing competence of a CDM co-ordinator for a larger or more complex project, or one with high or unusual risks

Organisations do not have to produce all of the evidence listed in Column 3 to satisfy the standard – they simply need to produce enough evidence to show that they meet the standard in Column 2, taking account of the nature of the project and the risks that the work entails. This requires judgement as to whether the evidence provided meets the standard to be achieved. **If your judgement is reasonable, and clearly based on the evidence provided, you will not be criticised if the company you appoint subsequently proves not to be competent to carry out the work.**

Remember that assessments should focus on the needs of the particular job and should be proportionate to the risks arising from the work. Unnecessary bureaucracy associated with competency assessment obscures the real issues and diverts effort away from them.

Knowledge and experience standard	Field of knowledge and experience	Examples of attainment that should indicate competence
Stage 1		
Task knowledge appropriate for the tasks to be undertaken. May be technical or managerial.	The design and construction process.	Professionally qualified to chartered level (*Note 1*). Membership of a relevant construction institution (for example: CIBSE; ICE; IET; IMechE; IstructE; RIBA; CIAT; CIOB).
Health and safety knowledge sufficient to perform the task safely, by identifying the hazard and evaluating the risk in order to protect yourself and others, and to appreciate general background.	Health and safety in construction.	Validated CPD in this field and typical additional qualification (for example: NEBOSH Construction Certificate). Member of the Health and Safety Register administered by the ICE (*Note 2*). Membership of the Association for Project Safety. Membership of Institution of Construction Safety (formerly the Institution of Planning Supervisors).
Stage 2		
Experience and ability sufficient to perform the task including, where appropriate, an appreciation of constructability, to recognise personal limitations, task-related faults and errors and to identify appropriate actions.	Experience relevant to the task.	Evidence of significant work on similar projects with comparable hazards, complexity and procurement route.

Note 1: Chartered membership of a recognised construction-related institution.
Note 2: Open to any member of a construction-related institution.

04

Health and safety policies

By law if a company employs five or more people it must have a written health and safety policy. This contains a statement of general policy on health and safety at work and the organisation and arrangements in place for putting that policy into practice.

This chapter explains what the benefits of a policy are, what it should contain and how it should be used.

Introduction   48
Key points   48
Competency   49
Policy content   49
Updating safety policies   51
Communication   51
Advice on preparation   52
The business case   52
Third-party contractor assessment   53

Appendix A – Health and safety policy template   55
Appendix B – Example health and safety policy   56

Health and safety policies

4.1   Introduction

A general statement of health and safety policy is the way in which a company sets out its intention to manage health and safety. It will vary from one company to another. There is no such thing as a standard health and safety policy, as a company's policy must be clearly and directly related to its own operations.

It is common for companies to obtain policies via the internet or purchase them from third parties. These are generic, rarely reflect the type of work that is carried out and may lead a company into a false sense of security.

The content of the organisation and arrangements sections of the policy should be specific to each company. If a generic policy is used it is likely that there will be serious omissions in its content and therefore in the way that health and safety is managed.

Each company's policy must be based upon its own work activities, management and organisational structure, and staff competencies.

The act of compiling a health and safety policy will focus the employer, or senior member of staff to whom the job is delegated, on the day-to-day management of health and safety issues. This will help them to become aware of shortcomings, duplications of effort and requirements for certain competences, which can then be rectified.

Evidence shows that companies with a well-structured and properly implemented health and safety policy, together with the organisation and arrangements for putting the policy into effect, have much better overall health and safety performance. Clients and pre-tender documentation now regularly require a company not only to have a health and safety policy, but also to demonstrate its implementation from the most senior management level downwards.

 The Approved Code of Practice for the Construction (Design and Management) Regulations contains a checklist of documents that demonstrate organisational competence. This list includes a health and safety policy.

Health and Safety Executive (HSE) construction accident statistics show that the causes of accidents are substantially the same as they were 10 and 20 years ago. Falls from height and being struck by plant, vehicles and falling objects are still the main types of accident on site. In addition work-related ill health statistics are still alarmingly high (over 4,000 deaths per year) due to lack of awareness and insufficient control measures, but also because symptoms can take years to develop so work-related health issues aren't seen as requiring immediate action. It is through the on-going development of a company's health and safety policy that shortcomings can be identified and procedures put in place to help eliminate common causes of accidents and reverse this unenviable record.

The HSE also states that between 80% and 90% of all accidents (and occupational ill health) could be prevented by the application of proper and effective health and safety management, both within company premises and on site. A comprehensive and accurate health and safety policy is the basis of an effective management system. A small company working on a small site has the same general health and safety responsibilities as a large company on a large site. Being on a small site does not mean that workers are any less likely to fall from height/fragile roofs, breathe in dust, be trapped in collapsed excavations, or be struck by falling material or reversing vehicles. There is no difference in the standard of protection required during a house extension compared to that for a major construction project; what is likely to differ is the complexity of the management system.

Health and safety, and the provision of proper welfare facilities, are crucial to the proper running of any building, construction or civil engineering project. They are not an add-on, an extra or an afterthought, but should be integrated with the normal day-by-day activities of project planning, tendering and management.

4.2   Key points

☑ The Health and Safety at Work Act 1974 requires every employer to have a policy on how health and safety will be managed within the company.

☑ If there are five or more employees, the policy must be written down.

☑ The policy must explain how matters of health and safety will be organised within the company and the arrangements that the company has put in place for implementing the policy.

☑ The policy should be periodically reviewed to ensure that it is still current, and amended when necessary, with the content and changes made available to all employees.

☑ Before letting contracts, main or principal contractors will often make it a contractual requirement to see a written copy of each contractor's health and safety policy so that an assessment of their health and safety competency can be made, even if the contractor has five or fewer employees and there is no legal need to have one.

☑ 'Off the shelf' health and safety policies, obtained from third parties, are unlikely to contain sufficient company-specific content.

04

4.3 Competency

The Health and Safety at Work Act 1974 requires all companies and employers who employ five or more people to have a written statement of their general health and safety policy. This will include details of the necessary organisation and arrangements for implementing the health and safety policy.

People who may be working on a training scheme, trainees on work experience and some self-employed people count as employees for the purpose of this requirement.

> Even if someone is self-employed or employs fewer than five people, the law still requires them to:
>
> ☑ have a health and safety policy, even if it is not written down
>
> ☑ manage their activities in such a way as to protect the health and safety of themselves, those working for them, and anyone else who may be affected by their activities.

04

Clients may, in judging a company's health and safety competence, require that company to have a written policy even if fewer than five people are employed. This is a client's prerogative, which may be reinforced by a contractual requirement. Contractors will have to comply if they want the work.

Whether working as a main or principal contractor or as a contractor, companies must be able to demonstrate how they effectively manage health and safety. If the company cannot demonstrate competence in health and safety issues, it may not be invited to tender in the future. It is no longer acceptable to simply state that the company has been in the industry for many years without experiencing an accident.

Generally, all health and safety legislation requires employers to provide their employees with a place of work that is safe and where risks to health are properly controlled. They are also required to ensure that people who are not their employees are not exposed to risks to their safety and health.

There should be a carefully planned and systematic approach to health and safety issues, where all risks have been assessed and the appropriate control measures put into place.

Irrespective of size, a company must have a general statement of health and safety policy in order to demonstrate to a client or to another contractor that it has committed itself to the principles of health, safety and welfare.

A **health and safety policy** is a statement of how a company will, within its overall business activities, manage health, safety and welfare for the benefit of its employees and all other persons who may be affected by the company's operations.

4.4 Policy content

Section 2(3) of The Health and Safety at Work Act 1974 requires that a safety policy should cover three distinct aspects:

☑ **a general statement of the company's health and safety policy** highlighting the intent of the employer to have high standards of health and safety in the company, including what they intend to achieve and how they will achieve it

☑ **the organisation** within the company for the effective maintenance and implementation of the health and safety management system

☑ **the arrangements** for the effective implementation and on-going monitoring of the health and safety management system.

Section 1 – The statement of policy

The statement of policy should demonstrate a clear commitment to health and safety from senior management by declaring how the company intends to manage health, safety and welfare matters in relation to employees and other persons. It should specifically state the name of, and be signed by, the person responsible for health and safety, who should be the managing director or another director to whom responsibility has been delegated. The policy should be reviewed at least every 12 months and a new copy signed, dated and displayed to demonstrate that it is a live document.

There should be a declaration that the necessary resources will be provided to ensure the health and safety of all employees.

It is usual for the statement of policy to state the importance that the company places upon the health and safety of its employees and what is required of them to achieve the aims of the policy. It should also clearly state that all employees will be informed of the contents of the health and safety policy and that they will be consulted about its application.

An example health and safety policy is shown in Appendix B.

Section 2 – Organisation

This part of the document should:

☑ identify those people within the company who have specific health and safety responsibilities, including the person who has ultimate responsibility for health and safety

☑ outline the methods by which health and safety procedures and other health and safety issues will be communicated

☑ explain the methods by which the effectiveness of the health and safety management system will be measured, reviewed and updated where necessary.

The section must clearly state who has to do what in terms of health and safety. For example, it might say that the contracts manager will receive information from the site manager about accidents, how the results of investigations into those accidents will be managed, and that the health and safety manager will notify the HSE when necessary. It should also detail how health and safety information is to be discussed with and brought to the attention of employees, especially those with specific duties highlighted within the document.

For a sole trader or very small firm, all health and safety duties are likely to be the responsibility of a single person.

It is important to remember that once this information is written down, if there is a serious accident, it will be used in court either by the HSE or lawyers in a civil claim. This means people need to be aware of their responsibilities and have the competence to carry them out.

04

Section 3 – Arrangements

This part of the health and safety policy should clearly show the specific arrangements that a company has put in place for managing health and safety during its normal work activities. It should also detail how emergency situations and any other incidents would be handled both from a management and a site perspective. One area for consideration is for companies to indicate how they compile risk assessments, gather information and develop safe systems of work.

The development of the arrangements section is likely to evolve over a period of time and, to an extent, reflect the findings of the company's risk assessments. It should encompass **who** is responsible, as well as **what** they will do and **when** and **how** they will achieve it. This section should:

☑ explain how the need for (health and safety) competences and training are established and satisfied and, if necessary, what interim measures will be put in place whilst shortcomings exist

☑ outline the means by which health and safety consultation with the workforce will be achieved including, as necessary, reference to management and safety representatives and safety committees

☑ explain the procedures for ensuring that sub-contractors have a satisfactory health and safety management system and exhibit safe working practices on site

☑ list the areas of risk and identify the person who is responsible for managing each risk.

Some of the elements that might need to be addressed are shown below.

Site activities		Administration procedures
■ Hot works.	■ Vehicle movements.	■ Emergency procedures.
■ Production of dust or fumes.	■ Manual handling.	■ First aid.
■ Noise and vibration.	■ Use of access equipment.	■ Fire.
■ Work at height.	■ Scaffolding.	■ Means of escape.
■ Confined space entry.	■ Use of ladders and stepladders.	■ Accident reporting.
■ Protection of the public.		■ Welfare facilities.
■ Authorisation for the use of plant and equipment.	■ Mobile elevating work platforms (MEWPs).	■ Employee consultation.
■ Lone working.	■ Excavations.	■ Monitoring for the effectiveness of health and safety procedures.
■ Machine guarding.	■ Hazardous substances.	
■ Loading and unloading.	■ Working in occupied premises.	

The policy for a company (or sole trader) that carries out a particular trade (such as bricklaying or carpentry and joinery) is likely to be simpler than that for a general builder. This is simply because a jobbing builder may be called upon to carry out a wide range of work activities. An effective way to deal with the health and safety management in these circumstances might be for the jobbing builder to produce a general policy document and then to supplement it with a set of task-specific documents that work at a site level.

Although the majority of work by a small company may be repetitive, the place of work is likely to vary. For example, installing a new toilet system in a new-build house is basically always the same; but to install one in an occupied house while the occupiers are living in the premises gives rise to other potential problems.

This is where so-called generic arrangements need to be site specific. The major weakness of this situation will become apparent if office-based staff develop and issue arrangements that do not reflect actual site conditions.

The arrangements section of the policy must demonstrate clearly how the company plans to carry out its work activities and should identify all the specific site risks associated with them.

Employers are legally required to give their employees all the information, instruction, training and supervision necessary to ensure their health and safety.

The arrangements section of the policy should also cover the situation where a manager is unable to visit a possible work site whilst tendering or preparing a quotation for a job, but instead sends an estimator. In this case the estimator must be trained to assess the health and safety risks of the work, and record the work to be done and the risk control measures necessary.

These notes should indicate all possible hazards, working height, obstructions, and plant and equipment required. Detailed risk assessments can then be carried out and the associated method statements developed. This will allow for employees to be properly instructed on or informed about the work that they are to do.

However, on small works of short duration or emergency repairs, detailed pre-planning may not be possible. Employees may be sent to a client's premises or a customer's house at very short notice. This type of work may create a number of problems for employees, including the need for a short notice or on-site risk assessment, and the arrangements section of the company health and safety policy must cater for this type of eventuality.

Managing health and safety on a large site offers certain challenges, but it is normally far easier than dealing with a large number of minor works. This is purely down to the level of supervision and control that can be put in place.

There is a certain irony that typically it is the smallest and probably least resourced organisations that have the biggest challenges in terms of developing management systems.

4.5   Updating safety policies

The law requires that employers revise their safety policies as often as may be appropriate. This means they should be updated in the light of any new legislation, HSE or industry guidance, British or European Standards, together with taking into account the actual experience in operating with the policy.

Changes in the type of work carried out and changes in staff will also give rise to the need for a review of the policy. In addition, the policy should be regularly reviewed to ensure that it stays meaningful and relevant to the company's overall operations.

Good practice is for an annual review of the policy, with the policy being re-signed, dated and any changes communicated. Even if there are no required changes, it should still be re-signed and dated in order for the company to demonstrate a review has taken place. This is important for companies that have to provide copies of their policy for a third-party assessment scheme or to prospective clients.

4.6   Communication

Employers are legally required to bring their health and safety policy, and any subsequent revisions to it, to the notice of all employees. CDM emphasises the need for consultation with the people who carry out the work. Communicating the health and safety policy is a good way of doing this.

As can be seen from the 'back to the shop floor' programmes on television, often the reality of workplace conditions and the practices that have developed escape the notice of senior management. This may be because pressures, techniques, environments and expectations change over a period of time.

The only way to find out if the requirements of the policy are realistic and workable is to talk to the people who have to comply with them in the workplace.

Under the Information and Consultation of Employees Regulations, employers with more than 50 staff are required to provide information and consultation agreements where over 10% of staff formally request it.

This legislation was not made under The Health and Safety at Work Act 1974 and is not therefore enforceable by the HSE. However, it provides a further opportunity to consult staff over a range of issues, including health and safety.

4.7   Advice on preparation

The HSE has published guidance on the preparation of health and safety policy documents.

 The advice can be downloaded from the HSE's website.

The Construction (Design and Management) Regulations

The client is responsible for ensuring that all contractors are competent, regardless of whether the project is notifiable or not.

On notifiable projects the CDM co-ordinator is likely to assist the client with this task and will formally assess the competence of the likely principal contractor. Part of this assessment process must be a review and critical examination of the contractor's health and safety policy.

The Approved Code of Practice (ACoP) that supports the CDM Regulations suggests that companies bidding for work could compile a competence pack to show how their policies, organisation and arrangements meet the stipulated core criteria for managing health and safety.

However, for low risk, low value jobs, simply providing a copy of the health and safety policy statement and the index page for the arrangements might be deemed sufficient. Obviously, it is much easier to send the whole document if all parts are available electronically.

The appendices to this chapter contain a suggested layout of a health and safety policy for a medium-sized company carrying out small building works. Not all of it will be relevant to some companies and, conversely, it may not contain specific content that some companies require.

- ☑ For most companies, the general statement of health and safety policy should fit onto one side of A4 paper.
- ☑ The organisation and arrangements sections will be longer depending on the size of the company and the type of work that is carried out.
- ☑ Overall, the final document should be a clear indication to clients, employees and other interested parties (such as the HSE) that the company is honestly, openly and totally committed to the proper and effective management of all aspects of health, safety and welfare.

4.8   The business case

In addition to the legal considerations (for example, compliance with the law) there are very strong economic and social drivers for a robust health and safety policy and its proper implementation.

The economic argument is that if there are fewer accidents on site and no occupational ill health, more employees will be at work rather than off sick. This means improved business continuity with a greater prospect of completing projects on time, to budget and to the satisfaction of the client.

The social argument is similar. Clients and customers are far more likely to place business with a company who they see is behaving with integrity, and taking proper care of the health, safety and welfare of their employees and others who might be affected by the activities of the company.

Other business benefits

Clients, in particular Local Authority clients, assessing the competence of small companies that are seeking approval for entry onto approved lists will be looking for evidence of effective health and safety management. Some Local Authorities use a standard questionnaire, which asks companies to provide comprehensive details on:

- ☑ the competent person who provides health and safety advice
- ☑ its general policy on health and safety, its organisation and arrangements for implementing the policy
- ☑ training provision and training providers
- ☑ accident statistics, copies of enforcement notices and details of any prosecution. (These do not mean the automatic exclusion of the company)
- ☑ arrangements for distributing new health and safety information
- ☑ examples of risk assessments
- ☑ arrangements for liaison with clients
- ☑ management arrangements (such as audits and inspection reports)
- ☑ health surveillance (where applicable)
- ☑ arrangements for assessing contractors
- ☑ where applicable, the ability to undertake roles under the Construction (Design and Management) Regulations.

A well-structured health and safety policy will provide a great deal of this information, and any additional information needed can easily be incorporated as an annexe to the policy.

If a company is successful in gaining entry onto an approved list for one Local Authority, it will then be much easier to seek similar approval from other authorities.

4.9   Third-party contractor assessment

Being able to prove your health and safety competence in the construction industry is a crucial element to securing contracts. Clients will always seek highly competent principal contractors who then, in turn, will look for the same in the sub-contractors that they employ.

The Construction (Design and Management) Regulations state that both contractors and sub-contractors must be able to demonstrate Stage 1 competence, which can be approved through an independent assessment scheme.

Assessing health and safety competence can be a complicated and time consuming process. There are two levels that need to be considered.

Stage 1 – The primary level. This is the ability of an organisation to prove that their arrangements for managing health and safety are sufficient to allow them to carry out work safely and without risk to the health of their workers.

Stage 2 – The second level assesses competence in relation to experience and the needs of the particular job. It looks at an individual's track record of working on similar types of project to those being tendered for.

Several schemes have been developed to help clients and contractors alike to meet their obligation to only appoint competent contractors.

The schemes are a pre-qualification assessment designed around the requirements of CDM. Competence is assessed against the criteria set out in Stage 1 including, amongst others, the requirements for contractors to have a health and safety policy, access to competent health and safety advice and to ensure employees are appropriately trained.

By satisfying the scheme assessment, the contractor is able to demonstrate Stage 1 competence to future employers, avoiding the need to repeat the process for every client or contractor worked for. This also helps those buying services from contractors, as they need only worry about Stage 2 type assessments (for example, matching the experience of the contractor to the work being undertaken).

Safety schemes in procurement

The introduction of the Stage 1 competence criteria under CDM provided an opportunity for existing health and safety pre-qualification schemes to build on and formalise mutual recognition already in operation amongst some schemes.

In April 2007, an initial meeting was held at the Health and Safety Executive's headquarters, which included representatives from the **Contractors' Health and Safety Assessment Scheme (CHAS), Constructionline, Exor, and the National House-building Council (NHBC)** to discuss the potential for the Safety schemes in procurement (SSIP) forum.

Following further regular meetings over the next two years, SSIP forum founder members agreed and signed up to an ethos that it would:

- ☑ act as an umbrella organisation to facilitate mutual recognition between health and safety pre-qualification schemes wherever it is practicable to do so

- ☑ actively advise and influence clients about acceptable interpretation and appropriateness of health and safety competence standards in UK schemes

- ☑ embrace the core guidance on competence and training in the Approved Code of Practice (ACoP) of the Construction (Design and Management) Regulations.

SSIP forum members are committed to avoiding duplication within pre-qualification. If contractors have already been assessed by another SSIP member they can apply for registration for another SSIP recognised scheme, usually by downloading and completing the 'Deem to satisfy' application form.

More information about the scheme can be found on the SSIP website.

Constructionline

Constructionline is the Government's national register for contractors, consultants and suppliers. It is run by the Department for Business, Enterprise and Regulatory Reform (formerly the DTI). Like CHAS, Constructionline provides a pre-qualification tool for use in financial standing, technical references and other areas. The CHAS management group supports the principles of a single register and so works jointly with Constructionline.

Health and safety policies

Following agreement between both parties, CHAS and Constructionline formed a mutual working agreement. This sets out how they will work together to provide an improved service for the industry's clients. CHAS and Constructionline are independent bodies but their databases are linked. It is therefore possible that not having an acceptable health and safety policy could be detrimental to company assessment by Constructionline.

 More information about the scheme can be found on the Constructionline website.

Contractors' Health and Safety Assessment Scheme

The Contractors' Health and Safety Assessment Scheme (CHAS) is a pre-qualification scheme, widely used by Local Authorities to identify companies that have demonstrated, through the CHAS assessment process, that they have a robust approach to health and safety management.

The scheme is administered by the London Borough of Merton and concentrates on what it refers to as fundamental health and safety management and compliance issues related to the type of work the applicant has suggested they do. Part of the assessment process will inevitably involve a critical examination of the applicant's written health and safety policy, if there are five or more employees.

 More information about the scheme can be found on the CHAS website.

Safecontractor

Safecontractor is a health and safety pre-qualification assessment accreditation scheme with more than 160 major clients and almost 18,000 contractor members.

Registered members with the Safecontractor scheme include clients and contractors from a wide range of professional disciplines working within a number of industry sectors. The Safecontractor scheme is now used by many large organisations as a way of obtaining competent contractors.

 More information about the scheme can be found on the Safecontractor website.

Safemark

Safemark is the health and safety competence assessment scheme of NHBC. It's the only such scheme designed by house-building specialists for house builders. It is recognised by Safety Schemes in Procurement (SSIP).

 More information about the scheme can be found on the NHBC website.

Appendix A – Health and safety policy template

Health and safety policy

This is the statement of general policy and arrangements for:

Overall and final responsibility for health and safety is that of:

Day-to-day responsibility for ensuring this policy is put into practice is delegated to:

| Name of organisation |
| Name of employer |
| |

Statement of general policy	Responsibility of (Name/Title)	Action/Arrangements (Customise to meet your own situation)
To prevent accidents and cases of work-related ill health and provide adequate control of health and safety risks arising from work activities		
To provide adequate training to ensure employees are competent to do their work		
To engage and consult with employees on day-to-day health and safety conditions and provide advice and supervision on occupational health		
To implement emergency procedures - evacuation in case of fire or other significant incident. You can find help with your fire risk assessment at: (See note 1 below)		
To maintain safe and healthy working conditions, provide and maintain plant, equipment and machinery, and ensure safe storage/use of substances		

Health and safety law poster is displayed:	
First-aid box and accident book are located: Accidents and ill health at work reported under RIDDOR: (Reporting of Injuries, Diseases and Dangerous Occurrences Regulations) (see note 2 below)	

Signed: (Employer)		Date:		
Subject to review, monitoring and revision by:		Every:		months or sooner if work activity changes

Note 1: http://www.communities.gov.uk/fire/firesafety/firesafetylaw/
Note 2: www.hse.gov.uk/riddor

04

Appendix B – Example health and safety policy

 Example health and safety policy

Health and Safety Executive

04

Example policy for an alarm installation company

Setting the scene

Daly Response Alarm Systems supply and install intruder alarms to residential and business premises. Manager and founder John Daly employs a total of 22 staff, consisting of an assistant manager, a receptionist, three customer service support advisers, four sales representatives, two accounts assistants, a head engineer and ten site engineers.

The office is open Monday to Friday 9.00-5.30 and Saturday morning 9.00-12.00 and cleaning is shared by the office-based staff, who have a rota.

John Daly prepared his own health and safety policy statement, using the combined template available on the HSE website at www.hse.gov.uk/risk/risk-assessment-and-policy-template.doc He genuinely cares for his staff and wants to portray this in his health and safety policy.

John downloaded the template and referred to the example policy statement and other guidance available on the HSE website at www.hse.gov.uk/risk. This helped him to think about the things that should be documented and built into his own health and safety policy, such as remote working, personal protective equipment, staff consultation and training etc. He decided that he and his assistant manager would be the most competent (experienced and capable) people to take responsibility for health and safety issues.

John presented the policy statement at the staff meeting and decided to review and update the document every year or straightaway if there are any major changes in the workplace.

Employers with five or more employees must have a written health and safety policy and risk assessment.
For further information and to view our example risk assessments, see www.hse.gov.uk/risk.
Example health and safety policy published by the Health and Safety Executive 09/09

 Example health and safety policy

Health and Safety Executive

This is the statement of general policy and arrangements for: Daly Response Alarm Systems

Overall and final responsibility for health and safety is that of: John Daly – Manager

Day-to-day responsibility for ensuring this policy is put into practice is delegated to: Paul Phillips – Assistant Manager

STATEMENT OF GENERAL POLICY	RESPONSIBILITY OF: Name/Title	ACTION/ARRANGEMENTS (customise to meet your own situation)
To prevent accidents and cases of work-related ill health and provide adequate control of health and safety risks arising from work activities.	John Daly Manager	Relevant risk assessments completed and actions arising out of those assessments implemented. (Risk assessments reviewed every year, or earlier if working habits or conditions change.)
To provide adequate training to ensure employees are competent to do their work.	Paul Phillips Assistant Manager	Staff and subcontractors given necessary health and safety induction and provided with appropriate training (including working at height, asbestos awareness and electrical safety) and personal protective equipment. We will ensure that suitable arrangements are in place to cover employees engaged in work remote from the main company site.
To engage and consult with employees on day-to-day health and safety conditions and provide advice and supervision on occupational health.	John Daly (Manager) Paul Phillips (Assistant Manager) All staff	Staff routinely consulted on health and safety matters as they arise but also formally consulted at regular health and safety performance review meetings or sooner if required.
To implement emergency procedures – evacuation in case of fire or other significant incident.	John Daly Manager	Escape routes well signed and kept clear at all times. Evacuation plans are tested from time to time and updated as necessary. (You can find help with your fire risk assessment at www.communities.gov.uk/firesafety.)
To maintain safe and healthy working conditions, provide and maintain plant, equipment and machinery, and ensure safe storage/use of substances.	Paul Phillips Assistant Manager	Toilets, washing facilities and drinking water provided. System in place for routine inspections and testing of equipment and machinery and for ensuring that action is promptly taken to address any defects. Staff trained in safe handling/use of substances. (See www.coshh-essentials.org.uk.)

Health and safety poster is displayed:	At reception			
First-aid box and accident book are located:	At reception			
Accidents and ill health at work reported under RIDDOR: (Reporting of Injuries, Diseases and Dangerous Occurrences Regs) www.hse.gov.uk/riddor Tel: 0845 300 9923				
Signed: (Employer)	*John Daly*	Date:	01/04/09	
Subject to review, monitoring and revision by:	John Daly	Every:	12	months or sooner if work activity changes

Employers with five or more employees must have a written health and safety policy and risk assessment.
For further information and to view our example risk assessments, see www.hse.gov.uk/risk.
Example health and safety policy published by the Health and Safety Executive 09/09

05

Risk assessments and method statements

The assessment of risk is the fundamental principle behind the drive for a reduction of workplace accidents and work-related ill health.

Risk assessments and method statements need to be suitable and proportionate to the risks, specific to the site and task, and fully understood and appreciated by the workforce.

Assessing risk is not a difficult process, but sadly many companies rely on folders full of generic risk assessments and method statements that bear little resemblance to how their workforce actually carry out the work.

Introduction	58
Key points	58
Some terms used in risk assessment	59
Legislative requirements	59
Understanding control hierarchy	60
The five stages of a risk assessment	61
Types of risk assessment	62
Risk assessment in practice	64
Communication	65
Other considerations	66
Method statements	67
Further information	68
Appendix A – The HSE's example risk assessment for a plastering company	69
Appendix B – Health and safety method statement	71

Risk assessments and method statements

5.1 Introduction

The principle of risk assessment is a fundamental cornerstone of the management of health and safety in the workplace. Legislation places a legal duty on employers to assess the risks, to the health and safety of their employees and others, that arise out of their work activities.

There is also a requirement in other sets of regulations for employers to carry out risk assessments in relation to specific threats to health or safety in the workplace, such as:

- ☑ the use of hazardous substances
- ☑ noise in the workplace
- ☑ manual handling activities
- ☑ the presence of asbestos
- ☑ work at height
- ☑ work with vibrating tools and equipment.

However, this does not put an obligation on employers to carry out two risk assessments for the same hazard. If the general risk assessment covers the specified hazards, that risk assessment alone will be sufficient.

There is no legal definition of a risk assessment but in practice it can be said to be:

a careful and structured examination of a work activity so as to identify:

- ☑ what could cause harm (the hazards) to people (employees or others)
- ☑ how, by the use of appropriate control measures, the risks (the chance that the hazard will cause harm) arising from the hazards may be eliminated or controlled.

The amount of effort that needs to be put into carrying out a risk assessment should be appropriate and proportional to the nature of the hazard on the perceived level of risk.

It is essential that all high risks are assessed and controlled first, before looking at the medium risks. Only look at the low risks once all high and medium risks have been either eliminated or adequately controlled.

Simple work activities with few hazards, which present a low risk, should need only simple assessments.

If a risk assessment is to be effective, it is essential that the person who carries it out is familiar with all aspects of the task being assessed.

Risk assessments do not necessarily need to be carried out by a health and safety professional. When the task being assessed is often repeated or is otherwise familiar, simple or routine, managers and supervisors will often be sufficiently knowledgeable and competent to carry out a risk assessment.

However, where a task presents complex, unusual or technical issues it may be necessary to seek the advice of a competent person, or to seek advice from other sources, such as the Health and Safety Executive (HSE) or the health and safety helpline of a relevant trade organisation.

5.2 Key points

- ☑ The assessment of risk is the fundamental principle behind the drive for a reduction of workplace accidents and work-related ill health.
- ☑ Employers with five or more employees are required by law to record the significant findings of their risk assessments.
- ☑ Main (or principal) contractors may wish to see written risk assessments from any contractor they intend to employ, regardless of the number of employees.
- ☑ Risk assessments must consider the potential risks to the health and/or safety of anyone who may be adversely affected, which may include employees, the employees of other contractors, site visitors, members of the public, and so on.
- ☑ Carrying out risk assessments need not be difficult or unduly time-consuming; the effort should be proportionate to the degree of perceived risk.
- ☑ There is no 'official' content or way of structuring a risk assessment; it is for each employer to decide what works best for their undertaking. Some common conventions have evolved, two of which are included in this chapter.
- ☑ It is vital that written risk assessments and method statements are presented in an easy to understand format for those that are actually doing the work.
- ☑ Method statements are a way of integrating the information gained during the risk assessment process into a structured sequence of work activities for completing a job.

05

5.3 Some terms used in risk assessment

Anyone carrying out risk assessments must be familiar with the meaning of the following terms that are used in process.

☑ **Hazard** – anything that has the potential to cause harm (ill health, injury or damage).

☑ **Risk** – the likelihood of an event occurring from a hazard.

☑ **Likelihood** – the chance that an accident will occur (certain, likely, possible, unlikely or rare).

☑ **Severity** – the severity (consequences) of any incident that arises.

☑ **Danger** – a person is in danger when they are exposed to a risk.

☑ **Accident** – an event that results in injury or ill health.

☑ **Near miss** – (including dangerous occurrence) an event that, while not causing harm, has the potential to cause injury or ill health.

☑ **Competence** – having practical and theoretical knowledge, training and actual experience of the work activities involved.

> **！ Severity**
>
> ☑ At one extreme, someone who is buried in a collapsed excavation could be killed, whereas, at the other end of the scale, the consequences of someone not using a hand tool correctly might only be grazed skin or a cut.
>
> ☑ When assessing risk to health, severity can be misunderstood or underestimated. Someone breathing in silica dust for a day or two will not seemingly be harmed, but continual exposure over many months or years could lead to a fatal lung disease.

05

5.4 Legislative requirements

Principles of risk assessment

All recent health and safety legislation is structured around a goal-setting or risk-based approach to the management of health and safety in the workplace.

Employers are required to establish systems that identify hazards, assess the associated risks, develop and implement suitable control measures, and monitor the adequacy and effectiveness of such risk control systems.

Thus, employers are required to:

☑ **identify the hazards** (things with the potential to cause harm) that arise out of the work activity being assessed

☑ **assess the risks** to the health and safety of any person(s) who is likely to be affected by the hazards

☑ **identify the individuals** or groups of people who are at risk

☑ **eliminate the hazards** (where possible) thereby removing the risk of injury

☑ **identify and implement** appropriate measures to control the remaining risks

☑ **effectively monitor and review** the control measures established for the work activity and amend them if they are no longer valid or become ineffective.

The Management of Health and Safety at Work Regulations

These regulations require employers to carry out a suitable and sufficient assessment of the risks to health and safety for all work activities carried out.

When carrying out risk assessments, employers must consider not only the wellbeing of their own employees, but also anyone else who may be affected by that work activity.

This includes, but is not restricted to:

☑ the employees of other contractors or the self-employed

☑ site visitors (such as delivery drivers)

☑ members of the public, including children

☑ the client, customers or other occupiers of the property.

Particular provision is made in the regulations for the protection of young persons in the workplace.

Although not mentioned in the regulations, it is implicit that any risk assessment must, where appropriate, take into account the requirements of anyone on site who may suffer from a disability (for example, someone who is partially or totally deaf).

Risk assessments and method statements

The duty to undertake risk assessments is placed on all employers irrespective of the number of persons they employ but, where five or more persons are employed, the significant findings of the assessment must be recorded (either in writing or electronically). However, clients may, if they choose, require contractors to produce recorded risk assessments even when fewer than five persons are employed by them. The self-employed have a similar duty to undertake risk assessments for the work that they do, to identify the risks to the health and safety of both themselves and others who may be affected by the work that they carry out.

Once the risk assessment has been carried out, employers must then implement the control measures that are necessary to protect those at risk. It is then very important to ensure that the significant findings of the risk assessment are made known to all persons who are likely to be involved in the work or affected by it.

In order to understand the principles of risk assessment, it is necessary to first understand the meaning of the terms used, as defined by the HSE in its publication *Five steps to risk assessment*.

A **hazard** is anything with the **potential** to cause harm. Examples are electricity, noise, vibration, chemicals, asbestos, working at height, working over water, excavations, confined spaces, manual handling, falling materials, and the use of tools, plant and vehicles.

A **risk** is the likelihood that the hazard will actually cause harm.

 Risks of working at height

If working from a ladder the risk (likelihood) of the person falling could be regarded as high when compared with doing the same job from a scaffold platform fitted with guard-rails. A control measure (the scaffold) has been introduced and the risk of falling is significantly reduced.

Suitable and sufficient

The regulations require that all risk assessments are **suitable** and **sufficient**. For a risk assessment to comply with this requirement it must:

☑ establish the risks arising from the work activity

☑ be appropriate, given the nature of the work, such that it remains valid for a reasonable period of time

☑ be proportionate to the level of risk and the nature of the work

☑ identify and prioritise the control measures required to protect the health and safety of the employees and others who may be affected.

Furthermore, to be suitable and sufficient each risk assessment must take account of any factors that could change during the course of the job, thereby introducing additional hazards or increasing the level of risk arising from existing hazards. Examples of this are variable labour levels, being asked at short notice to do something a different way to accommodate others and work or hired equipment having to be returned if the job overruns.

The law does not expect you to eliminate all risk, but you are required to protect people as far as is reasonably practicable.

5.5 Understanding control hierarchy

Preventative and **protective** (control measures) must be taken to address the hazards and to eliminate or reduce the risks to an acceptable level.

Using a remote controlled trench compactor eliminated the need for a person to be in the excavation

These measures must be based upon the general principles of prevention:

☑ avoiding risks where possible

☑ evaluating risks that cannot be avoided

☑ combating risks at source

☑ adapting the work of an individual, especially regarding the:
  – design of the workplace
  – choice of work equipment
  – choice of working and production methods

☑ adapting to technical progress

☑ replacing the dangerous with the safe or less dangerous

☑ developing a coherent prevention policy that covers:
  – technology
  – organisation of work
  – working conditions
  – social relationships

☑ giving collective measures priority over measures that protect the individual

☑ giving appropriate instructions to employees.

5.6 The five stages of a risk assessment

Step 1. Look for the hazards

Some typical examples of hazards found on construction sites are:

- ☑ an untidy site with lots of slipping and tripping hazards
- ☑ the use of equipment with rotating blades (such as disc-cutters)
- ☑ the use of power tools creating dust
- ☑ the risk of fire from spark-emitting tools (such as angle grinders)
- ☑ work at height with the potential for falls (for example, roofing activities)
- ☑ manual handling activities or working in cramped conditions
- ☑ the operation of construction plant near to people on foot
- ☑ the presence of contaminated ground
- ☑ the use of chemicals, solvents, paints, and so on.

Step 2. Decide who might be harmed and how

Having established the hazards associated with the job you will have to identify the individuals or groups of people who are at risk, for example:

- ☑ yourself
- ☑ other employees (particularly anyone young and inexperienced)
- ☑ employees who need special consideration (for example, someone who is deaf or who is not fluent in English)
- ☑ employees who are pregnant, or nursing mothers
- ☑ employees of other contractors
- ☑ visitors (such as delivery drivers, maintenance staff and clients)
- ☑ members of the public or trespassers (particularly children)
- ☑ anyone else who might be affected by your work (for example, neighbouring businesses).

Step 3. Evaluate the risks and decide upon controls

Having identified the hazards, now consider what risk-control measures are necessary to keep the people who have been identified as being at risk from harm.

Even when precautions have been put in place there will usually be a remaining (residual) risk. You will have to exercise your judgement as to whether, in your opinion, the residual risk is high, medium or low. This part of the assessment is a loop.

If after identifying risk control measures you think that the level of residual risk is still too high, it will be necessary to introduce further control measures, again evaluate the level of residual risk and continue the process until it is considered to be acceptable.

It is a case of you asking yourself 'What have I done to control the risks and what more do I need to do?'

> **! Considerations when establishing controls**
>
> When establishing appropriate control measures, consideration should be given to the following techniques:
>
> - ☑ **combat risks at source** – for example, use a safer method (such as using a block splitter instead of a petrol cut-off saw)
> - ☑ **take advantage of technical progress** and adopt new, safer methods of working. For example, use a modern trestle system, complete with guard-rails and toe-boards, rather than scaffold boards supported on improvised hop-ups
> - ☑ **replace the dangerous with the non-dangerous or less dangerous** – for example, prohibit the use of all 230 V power tools, allowing only 110 V or battery-powered tools
> - ☑ **adopt measures that protect the greatest number of individuals** – for example, safety nets protect everyone working above them, whereas a safety harness only protects the wearer
> - ☑ **give appropriate information**, instructions and training to employees and others – assess the need for training
> - ☑ **provide PPE – always the very last resort**.

Step 4. Record your findings and implement them

Health and safety law requires that all employers carry out risk assessments for their work, although legally only employers with five or more employees need record the significant findings of their risk assessments.

However, in practice, many of the larger contractors will not accept any sub-contractor on site, even those with fewer than five employees, if they do not have written risk assessments. Risk assessments may be recorded electronically providing that they may be easily retrieved for scrutiny if required.

In the interests of clarity, risk assessments may identify where relevant supporting information can be found (such as the company health and safety policy), rather than including masses of information in the risk assessment itself. However, if this approach is taken, the supporting documents may also have to be supplied to whoever wishes to see the risk assessment.

The law does not specify how a risk assessment should be laid out although two common conventions have evolved over time:

- ☑ **quantitive risk assessment** – outlines the hazards present and the risk control measures necessary, and in which residual risk is given a numerical score or categorised as high, medium or low to enable corrective actions to be prioritised

- ☑ **qualitative risk assessment** – in which the process is the same. No attempt is made to quantify the level of residual risk.

Examples of both types of risk assessment are included in this chapter.

Irrespective of how a risk assessment is laid out, it is considered best practice for it to identify the:

- ☑ person who will manage the residual risks

- ☑ date(s) by which any essential actions must be taken, in the interests of health or safety.

Step 5. Review the assessment and revise if necessary

Risk assessments should be reviewed from time to time to ensure the control measures are still appropriate and effective. If there is a change to any aspect of the way the job has to be carried out that might affect health and safety, for example:

- ☑ having to use a different item of equipment part way through the job

- ☑ the arrival of a new operative who is inexperienced

- ☑ unexpected deteriorating weather

- ☑ the late arrival of materials

the assessment must be reviewed and the risks re-evaluated.

5.7 Types of risk assessment

 The risk of something going wrong is considered in terms of **probability** (likelihood) and **consequences** (seriousness).

Generic risk assessments

- ☑ A generic risk assessment is an assessment that may be used more than once because the job to which it relates is being repeated and it can be guaranteed that the hazards and level of risk are the same on each occasion that the job is carried out.

- ☑ When an employer intends to rely on a generic risk assessment, great care must be taken to ensure that there are no factors that could introduce additional hazards or increase the level of risk.

- ☑ In many cases, generic risk assessments are not acceptable within the construction industry because each site is different and conditions change as construction activities progress.

HSE risk assessment

The HSE has produced a simple template that does not use ratings, but instead uses the headings listed below. Some prefer this method as it follows logical risk assessment steps. It can also be easier for the workforce to understand.

What are the hazards?	Who might be harmed and how?	What are you already doing?	What further action is necessary?	Action by who?	Action by when?

The HSE have produced a series of example risk assessments, which can be found on its website.

 The HSE's example risk assessment for a plastering company can be found in Appendix A.

Qualitative assessments

The probability of a hazard actually causing harm or an accident is rated as being high, medium or low in accordance with the following:

☑ **high:** it will happen regularly, or it could be a usual or a common occurrence

☑ medium: it is less regular, but is still recognised as being likely to happen

☑ low: it has not happened for a long time, is known to be infrequent and is not likely to happen.

The consequences of the event, should it happen, can then be categorised as follows:

☑ **high:** the result could be a fatal accident or multiple injuries/major property damage/substantial pollution or environmental impact

☑ medium: it would probably cause serious injuries (or persons would be off work for over three days due to their injuries), substantial property damage or there may be some pollution

☑ low: there would be minor injuries to persons or some slight damage to property.

Probability and consequences can then be shown on a matrix as follows:

Probability	High			
	Medium			
	Low			
		Low	Medium	High
		Consequences		

Probability and consequences can then be assessed and the highest outcome of the two entered in the matrix as follows:

Probability	High	High	High	High
	Medium	Medium	Medium	High
	Low	Low	Medium	High
		Low	Medium	High
		Consequences		

☑ A combined risk of **high** should be totally unacceptable and the work should not be undertaken until the risk has been reduced.

☑ When there is a combined risk of medium, action must be taken and work stopped if necessary to reduce the risk level.

☑ If the combined risk is low, start the work as long as everything reasonably practicable has been done in order to reduce the risk, and review the assessment at regular intervals.

Using this information, decisions can now be made on whether an activity is safe to continue, or whether control measures are necessary, either to completely change the way that the job is done or measures put in place so as to bring the risks down to an acceptable level. In the ideal situation, both probability and consequences should be low.

Quantitative assessments

The principle is the same as for qualitative assessments, but numerical scores rather than a grade are assigned to probability and consequences. The probability or likelihood of the event is rated on a scale of one to five as follows:

5 **Certain** to happen.

4 **Very likely** to happen, and would not be at all unusual.

3 **Likely** to happen, and would not be totally unexpected.

2 **Unlikely** to happen, but not by any means impossible.

1 **Very unlikely** to happen.

The consequences or the severity of the event, should it happen, are also then rated on a scale of one to five as follows:

1 No injury, ill health or damage. It would be a near miss.

2 Minor injury or minor ill health complaint, no time lost. Minor property damage or minor environmental incident.

3 Lost time injury, up to and including reportable injury to the HSE with over seven days' time lost, but not a major injury. Some risk of immediate or long-term health issues. Significant property damage or local environmental damage.

4 Major injury, long-term absence or significant risk that could lead to immediate or long-term health illness, including reportable disease. Substantial property damage, serious environmental impact.

5 Fatal accident or multiple major injuries. Catastrophic event or environmental disaster. Public or others could be involved as well.

Risk assessments and method statements

A matrix can then be constructed using these numbers, as follows:

	5					
	4					
Probability	3					
	2					
	1					
		1	2	3	4	5
		Consequences				

All possible resulting numbers are calculated by multiplying all the probability figures by all the consequence figures. These are included in the matrix, as shown below. This means that once a risk assessment has been made on a particular activity, and the probability factor is multiplied by the consequence factor, the number produced indicates where the assessment places the risk associated with the activity on the matrix.

	5	5	10	15	20	25
	4	4	8	12	16	20
Probability	3	3	6	9	12	15
	2	2	4	6	8	10
	1	1	2	3	4	5
		1	2	3	4	5
		Consequences				

Clearly, the higher the resulting number the less acceptable the level of risk. The matrix shows where actions need to be taken to reduce either the probability or the consequences in order to reduce the risks to an acceptable level.

Employers themselves can use these numbers to set in-house criteria, if desired, along the following lines, and as indicated by the shaded areas in the above matrix.

☑ Risks with a rating **above 15** are totally unacceptable and the work will not be undertaken until the risk has been significantly reduced.

☑ Where the risk rating is between 9 and 14, immediate action must be taken, including a stoppage of work if necessary, to reduce the risk level to acceptable.

☑ If the rating is between five and eight, the risk is acceptable provided that everything reasonably practicable has been done to reduce the risk.

☑ With a rating of **four or less** then the risk is acceptable, provided that the assessment is reviewed at regular intervals and further reduced if possible.

 It is stressed that it is for individual companies or managers to decide where the boundaries between what is and what is not acceptable lie, and the numerical score at which certain actions should be taken. The above matrix is only an indication of what can be done.

If either the qualitative or quantitative methods are used in conjunction with a simple form, then the employer will have a straightforward, basic risk assessment procedure.

5.8 Risk assessment in practice

If the task to be assessed is substantial, difficult or complex then, in all probability, it will not be practical or effective to carry out a single risk assessment to cover the whole of the work. The job will need to be broken down into separate elements or work activities, each of which will have to be assessed separately.

Alternatively, it should be possible to cover the whole of a relatively straightforward job (such as retiling a house) with a single risk assessment.

The process of practical risk assessment has no fixed rules on how it should be undertaken, or how risk assessments should be structured or laid out. Each company will decide upon what suits its needs. The process for developing risk assessments should not be over-complicated. The simpler the process, the less likely that anything will be overlooked. It may need input from both management and employees, and should address the points below.

- ☑ What is going to be done? (This should include plant, equipment, people, materials and the working environment.)

- ☑ How exactly is the activity to be carried out (for example, what plant and competences are required)?

- ☑ Where and when is the work to be done?

- ☑ How could this work affect employees and other people?

- ☑ What risk control measures are already in place?

- ☑ Is the level of risk to health or safety acceptable?

- ☑ What additional risk control measures are necessary?

The above approach to the identification of all relevant hazards associated with the work will address:

- ☑ the likelihood of injury or harm arising to employees and others who may be affected by the work

- ☑ any other specific legal requirements

- ☑ all of the risks

- ☑ the necessary control measure to eliminate or reduce health and safety risks associated with the work hierarchy of preventative and protective measures

- ☑ the information needed for those involved or affected by the work.

What do you do after your risk assessment as an employer?

- ☑ Put into effect the measures that you have decided will adequately control the risks.

- ☑ Communicate the findings of your risk assessments, particularly details of the hazards identified and what control measures are in place, to anyone who needs to know (for example, the main (or principal) contractor, your employees and sub-contractors).

- ☑ It is most important that the findings of risk assessments are communicated to anyone whose health and/or safety is likely to be affected by the job. Do not just store them away!

What should a supervisor do after they receive a risk assessment?

- ☑ They should speak to the site manager on a regular basis.

- ☑ Check that the risk control measures to be put in place are right for the work situation.

- ☑ Seek clarification of uncertainties and make their manager aware of any findings of a point of work risk assessment so that control measures are corrected.

- ☑ Before briefing their work team ensure the risk assessments and method statements are correct for the site specifics.

- ☑ Explain the risk assessments and method statements to their work team, ensure understanding (by asking questions) and record the names of those briefed (and when).

5.9   Communication

Consultation

 Those people physically carrying out the task should be consulted in the assessment process as they can have valuable knowledge and experience. By being involved, they have effectively bought into and better appreciate the risks and the control measures needed, and thus are more likely to follow them.

Documentation

In many cases the person completing the risk assessment is not the person doing or directly supervising the work.

There are many types of documentation with varying levels of complexity and length of content. Whilst a risk assessment or method statement is technically correct, it may be that it is in a format that is too complicated or long for an operative to take in.

Risk assessments and method statements

 Asking the workforce to read pages and pages of text and to obtain a signature to say they have read and understood the content before they start work is not helpful in achieving a safe and healthy workplace. The chances are that they will not read it all, will not appreciate the risk, the consequences and the correct controls needed, and so will continue to work as they always have.

It may therefore be necessary to convert the findings of a risk assessment into a simpler document, both in terms of terminology and layout, which relates to what the workforce must do. Consideration should be given to the use of images or sketches of what is needed (such as a slinging arrangement or pictures of respiratory protective equipment (RPE) being used correctly).

Involving the workforce in the risk assessment process is vital in developing a safe system of work that they feel comfortable with. It may well be that their preferred or alternative method of working is quicker and easier, but it has (or has not got) additional risks. This can then be assessed and any necessary working practices amended and agreed, so the workforce and their supervisors know they are following the risk assessment or method statement.

Language difficulties

The needs of any site workers who have poor, or no, understanding of either written or spoken English must be taken into account when compiling risk assessments.

Effective communication is an essential element of controlling risk; how such communication can be established must be a priority issue where there is the potential for language difficulties on site.

Worker engagement in practice

HSE
Health & Safety Executive

The construction section of the HSE's website contains information on risk assessments and a series of worker engagement case studies. It also has a London 2012 games, Lessons for Industry, section that includes the following case study about the use of photographs in method statements.

 London 2012 Olympic and Paralympic Games case study

Example of one of the photographs used in the method statement

Background – involving your workforce means much more than simply giving instructions. It means sharing information and involving the workforce in finding solutions to reduce health and safety risks.

Issue – ensuring that your workers understand method statements for complex, high-risk work.

Solution – a specialist contractor had to install 12,000 seats in the basketball arena to a tight deadline. The contractor wrote the method statement (MS) for the installation process. A small team tested the MS on a practice run using a model unit in site-specific conditions. Following feedback, the contractor modified the MS and then rolled it out to the entire workforce.

As a result of the early engagement, the MS was modified to include diagrams to explain processes and instructions, a map of the sequence of build, and photographs of work in action. The MS also changed as workers and teams discussed progress at key stages of the project. Changes and modifications were agreed with the workforce before they were put in place.

5.10 Other considerations

Young persons and children

The Management of Health and Safety at Work Regulations contain specific provisions in respect of the health and safety of children and young persons. Employers are required to specifically assess and review the risks to the health and safety of children and young persons due to their lack of maturity, experience, or knowledge of potential risks.

There is a requirement that young persons should not carry out certain types of work, except in circumstances involving training where the young person is no longer a child.

In law, a child is anyone under the minimum school leaving age, and a young person is anyone over the minimum school leaving age but under 18 years of age.

Generally speaking, children under 13 years cannot be employed at all, and those between 13 and the minimum school leaving age cannot be employed in the building or construction industry.

However, children between 13 and the minimum school leaving age may, in accordance with local by-laws and with the permission of the Local Authority, attend a construction site for site visits and organised work experience.

Furthermore, there will be occasions when 14 to 16-year old children are on site under the Young Apprentice Training Scheme, although one of the requirements of the scheme is that they will have had some prior instruction in matters of health and safety on site.

Before a young person is employed, the employer must ensure that any risk assessments pertaining to the job take account of the following factors in relation to the young person:

- ☑ their inexperience
- ☑ their immaturity and lack of awareness of risks
- ☑ the tools and equipment that they may have to use as part of their training
- ☑ the layout of the workplace and the environment in which they may have to work
- ☑ any hazardous substances with which they may come into contact
- ☑ exposure to physical, chemical or biological hazards
- ☑ the organisation of work processes and activities
- ☑ the extent of health and safety training that is to be provided.

Careful consideration must be given to the way in which information is conveyed to young persons to ensure that it is fully and readily understood.

Where children are employed either for work experience or work in offices then the employer must, before commencing the employment of the child, provide that child's parents or guardians with details of any risk assessment that has been carried out. This information must contain details of any risk and a description of any preventative or protective measures, whether the risk arises from the employer's own activity or the activities of others at the workplace.

Employers are further required to consider the special nature of young persons due to their lack of experience, knowledge of risks and the fact that they are not fully mature. To that end, young people must not be employed in any work:

- ☑ with which they cannot physically or psychologically cope
- ☑ that exposes them to a range of hazardous substances, including any carcinogen, toxic substance or radiation
- ☑ where they might not recognise the risk of accidents due to their inexperience or lack of training
- ☑ where their health would be at risk from excessive cold, heat, noise or vibration.

The prohibition above does not apply when a young person is:

- ☑ undergoing recognised training
- ☑ being properly supervised by a competent person or when any risks identified in a risk assessment have been reduced to the lowest level that is reasonably practicable.

For the training provision to apply, the training must be necessary within a trade or occupation, and be part of an identified unit of NVQ, SVQ or other similar work-related qualification.

Expectant and nursing mothers

Special consideration must be given within risk assessments to any employee who is pregnant, has given birth within the past six months or who is breastfeeding, where the nature of the work would put her or her unborn child at risk.

The assessment may identify the need to alter the work environment, work pattern, work activity or working hours and provide additional temporary facilities or support.

Any employee who is pregnant, has given birth within the past six months or who is breastfeeding must notify her employer in writing of her condition within a reasonable length of time.

5.11 Method statements

A **method statement** is a document prepared by an organisation that describes in a logical sequence exactly how a work activity is to be carried out in a manner which is safe and without risk to health.

To a large extent, the way that the job will be undertaken, and therefore detailed in the method statement, will reflect the findings of the risk assessment(s) for the same job. The means selected for controlling risk will influence the method of carrying out the job. In most cases, extensive reference to the risk assessment(s) will be necessary during the drafting of a method statement.

Risk assessments and method statements

Well written method statements provide an ideal means of communicating vital health and safety information to those who will be doing the work and others (such as main contractors) who have an interest in how the job will be carried out.

For routine and repetitive activities (work that is carried out many times where the hazards and risk are the same) a previous method statement may be applied, again provided it has been reviewed at point of work (by the supervisor) to ensure that it is still relevant. This is sometimes called a **generic method statement**.

Where the work is new, more complicated or unusual then a **specific method statement** will need to be produced. This can be a generic method statement updated to take the new situation into account. It should then be used to ensure that the work is carried out safely, properly and in the proper order.

Permit to work

Whilst there is no requirement in law to use a permit to work system, they are often used to regulate how potentially high-risk activities are to be carried out in a healthy and safe manner. As such, they very much support the risk assessment from which they are derived.

Permits to work are often, but not exclusively, required where the work:

- ☑ involves entry into a confined space
- ☑ depends upon the isolation of high-voltage electrical equipment
- ☑ involves the disturbance of any system carrying a fluid or gas under pressure
- ☑ involves hot works.

A permit to work is a formal, dated and time-limited certificate signed by a properly authorised and competent person. Receipt of a permit is acknowledged by the signature of the person in charge of the work, who will retain a copy; another copy will be retained by the person issuing the permit to work.

Other signatures on the permit will certify that any control measures necessary for the job to start have been implemented (for example, locking-out an electrical supply or checking the atmosphere in a confined space). A permit will indicate the time and date at which it expires. If the work is not completed at that time, depending upon the circumstances:

- ☑ it is usually necessary to make everything safe, for everyone to leave the work area before the permit expires and for the permit to be cancelled
- ☑ it may be safe to extend the expiry time and for the work area to be re-occupied.

When the work is completed, or the expiry time has passed, the person in charge of the work must return their copy of the permit to the person who issued it and the permit is cancelled.

5.12   Further information

CITB-ConstructionSkills risk assessment and method statement manager

What is it?

This popular CD-ROM enables users to produce, print and store task-specific risk assessments and method statements as required under the Management of Health and Safety at Work Regulations and other legislation.

- ☑ Save and retrieve previous risk assessments and update them as necessary, either within the programme or as standalone Word documents.
- ☑ Pre-populated common hazards and risk controls in drop-down menus.
- ☑ Facility to add site-specific hazards, methodology and risk controls.
- ☑ Risk assessment and method statement templates, which include:
    - fields for the signing and dating of each document by hand
    - the facility for adding footers to all pages
    - a facility for identifying the owner of each hazard and an action-by date.
- ☑ Option to produce a related or standalone method statement.
- ☑ Includes a *Guide to risk assessment* document, which may be downloaded and printed as a continuing reference.

Who is it for?

Essential for:

- ☑ business owners, managers, supervisors and health and safety professionals.

 For more information on this and other products visit the CITB-ConstructionSkills website.

Appendix A – The HSE's example risk assessment for a plastering company

HSE

Health and Safety
Executive

Example risk assessment for a plastering company

Setting the scene

The manager of a plastering company carried out a general risk assessment that covered their typical work. The deputy manager and the employee safety representative also helped. The risk assessment was used to help manage health and safety at the firm, and when tendering for contracts to demonstrate the firm's approach to health and safety. This meant that in the tender documents it was made clear exactly what was needed from the principal contractor to do the job safely and properly.

The firm won the plastering contract for a development

Important reminder

This example risk assessment shows the kind of approach a small business might take. Use it as a guide to think through some of the hazards in your business and the steps you need to take to control the risks. Please note that it is not a generic risk assessment that you can just put your company name on and adopt wholesale without any thought. This would not satisfy the law – and would not be effective in protecting people.

Every business is different – you need to think through the hazards and controls required in your business for yourself.

Example risk assessment: Plastering company

of a three-storey block of flats. Work was due to start on 1 May 2007. The manager checked the construction phase plan and met the principal contractor's site manager on the site. One of the issues they considered was the sequencing and logistics of the work, alongside that of other fit-out trades, to ensure safe access and working arrangements for all. Another was the issue of fatigue, and the number of work breaks that were needed.

This extra information helped the manager to decide whether the general risk assessment covered all the hazards and risks expected in this job. If it did not, it would need to be amended to make the general risk assessment specific to the work and conditions of this job.

However, the manager decided that for this job his general risk assessment did cover all the expected risks and that therefore no additional paperwork was needed.

How was the risk assessment done?

To produce his general risk assessment, the manager followed the guidance in *Five steps to risk assessment* (www.hse.gov.uk/pubns/indg163.pdf).

1 To identify the hazards the manager:

- used training and experience of similar work;
- took into account the rules of most construction sites; and
- looked at HSE's website for free health and safety

advice and guidance for the construction industry.

2 The manager wrote down who would be harmed by the hazards and how.

3 He considered the risks of each hazard and decided what was needed to control those risks.

4 He discussed the findings with the deputy manager and the safety representative. He then put the risk assessment into practice, writing down who was responsible for doing what, and by when. When each action was completed, it was ticked off and the date recorded.

5 The manager told staff about the risk assessment, explaining that the risks identified were common to most plastering jobs and would be put into practice and the control measures identified would be put into place for all company jobs.

6 However, the manager also said that all sites were different and that extra risk controls might be needed at some jobs. This would be considered during site visits before each job started, and staff are to be made aware of any additional risks and what needs to be done to control those risks.

7 One of the workers did not speak English. The manager had planned for this, having previously arranged with the site manager for another worker, who was bi-lingual in the relevant language, to translate.

05

Health and Safety
Executive

Company name: Smith's Plastering   Date of risk assessment: 1 March 2007

(revised to be specific for internal plastering of three-storey flats job, 23 April 2007)

What are the hazards?	Who might be harmed and how?	What are you already doing?	What further action is necessary?	Action by whom?	Action by when?	Done
Falling from height	Serious or even fatal injury could occur if an operator falls from height. Others working below also at risk.	■ Sufficient Step-Ups available, all in good condition. ■ Platform trellis, with guardrail, used for stairwells and operators are trained in how to put it up, use and dismantle it. ■ Stairs and landings have handrails.	■ Include work at height in toolbox talk before beginning work on day one.	Site Manager Foreman	1/5/07	
Slips and trips	All operators, and tradesmen nearby, may suffer sprains, bruising or fractures if they trip over objects, such as work debris, or slip on spillages.	■ All operators wear safety boots – 'no boots, no job' policy. ■ Good housekeeping, eg debris such as plaster bags put in skip, brush available to use to keep work area clear. ■ All trailing cables in work area hung up or otherwise kept out of harm's way. ■ Safe route to job agreed with site manager based on site health and safety plan.	■ Manager to check on-site housekeeping during visits. ■ Include in toolbox talk before beginning work on day one.	Site Manager Site Manager	From 1/5/07 From 1/5/07	
Workplace transport	Operators risk serious or even fatal injuries from moving vehicles on site – particularly when reversing.	■ Safe route to workplace, and to welfare facilities, agreed with site manager based on site health and safety plan. ■ Staff know that they must never move vehicles on a site unless authorised by site manager. ■ Staff wear high-visibility tabards while on site.	■ Include in toolbox talk before beginning work on day one.	Site Manager Foreman	1/5/07	
Manual handling	Operators risk injury, particularly to the back, from lifting and handling heavy or awkward objects, eg, plasterboard, and from repetitive strain problems from plastering.	■ Dry plaster mix lifted to the work areas using a hoist supplied by the site manager and operated by a competent person. ■ Dry plaster mix supplied in bags weighing less than 25 kg. ■ Plasterboard for ceilings is of smallest size practicable. ■ Operators know and follow safe system of work for fitting plasterboard to ceiling, including knowledge of maximum weight for an individual manual lift. ■ Job rotation between ceiling and walls.	■ Remind operators of plasterboard safe system of work at toolbox talk.	Site Manager Foreman	1/5/07	

Example risk assessment: Plastering company

Risk assessments and method statements – Appendix A

Health and Safety
Executive

What are the hazards?	Who might be harmed and how?	What are you already doing?	What further action is necessary?	Action by whom?	Action by when?	Done
Hazardous substances Dry plaster mix	Operators and nearby tradesmen at risk from dry plaster powder which may irritate eyes or sensitive skin, or cause short-term irritation of respiratory system.	■ Operators know the risks of dry plaster powder and know to avoid skin contact, excessive dust build-up and contact with eyes. ■ Work area suitable to prevent excessive dust build-up. ■ Water supply nearby to wash dust off skin. ■ Operators wear eye protection when plastering ceilings. ■ Operators keep work area clean. ■ Gloves and barrier creams available.	■ At toolbox talk, remind operators of risks of dry plaster powder, and to wear gloves, eye protection and dust masks when emptying sacks and preparing the mix.	Manager	1/5/07	
Electricity	Operators and others risk potentially fatal injuries if they receive a shock from faulty electrical equipment and/or installation.	■ Site manager will arrange for permanent electric supply to be turned off while plastering work ongoing. ■ Site manager to supply 110 v temporary supply. ■ Staff know to check all cables, leads etc of all powered tools/ equipment before use, and to report all faults to their supervisor.	■ At toolbox talk on day one, manager to reinforce rules on electrical safety.	Manager	1/5/07	
Welfare	Good welfare facilities reduce risk of dermatitis, help good hygiene etc.	■ Agreement with site manager that staff may use site welfare facilities – toilets, washing facilities with hot and cold water and mess room/kitchen.	■ Tell staff about facilities at toolbox talk on day one.	Manager	1/5/07	

Assessment review date: **1/7/08**

05

Appendix B – Health and safety method statement

Method statements should be written clearly to enable those doing the work to fully understand the details of the job and its health and safety requirements. The suggested content for a method statement is outlined below.

If the work is of a simple or minor nature, a simplified form of method statement may be more appropriate. Alternatively, it may be preferable to use the format below but to annotate inappropriate fields as 'Not applicable'.

Project/contract details ....

Contractor..

Details of person compiling this method statement

Name .... Position in company ....Tel. no. ....

05

Validity	Insert the issue number of the method statement and brief details of the changes associated with each new issue. Identify the intended start and finish dates.
Hazards	List the known hazards associated with the work, as identified by the risk assessment.
Means of access	Identify: ■ locations of work (for example at height or in excavations) ■ access equipment required ■ specialist contractors involved.
Work details	Outline: ■ the limits of the work covered by this method statement ■ in a logical order, the list of activities that make up the whole job, indicating how health and safety issues will be addressed for identified hazards, including the protection of other trades.
Permits to work	Describe: ■ which tasks will be controlled by a permit to work (for example hot works, access to risers and work in confined spaces) ■ who will issue and co-ordinate the permits.
Supervision	Identify who will supervise the job and, if necessary, who will supervise different parts of the job.
Workforce details	Identify: ■ the specific labour required to carry out the job in a safe and healthy manner ■ any special training or skills required ■ details of competence cards held.
Health and safety monitoring	Specify how day-to-day standards of health and safety will be monitored and controlled.
Plant inspection and operator training	Identify: ■ what items of plant and equipment will be used ■ operators' experience/qualifications ■ thorough examination and maintenance details.
Disconnection/reconnection of services	Identify: ■ which services must be isolated/reconnected ■ who will carry out the work ■ methods of locating buried services ■ who will certify that the services have been isolated/reconnected.
Hazardous substances	Identify: ■ the hazardous substances that will be used or disturbed ■ how those affected will be informed of the health hazards ■ the protective measures to be used ■ details of any sampling that may be required.

Occupational health assessments	Identify: ■ which activities will require health surveillance for the operatives carrying them out ■ which operatives are affected ■ who will arrange for the health surveillance ■ who will carry out the health surveillance.
Personal protective equipment	Identify: ■ which items of PPE/RPE will be used, for which training will be required ■ who is responsible for arranging the training ■ who will carry out the training.
Emergency procedures	Identify: ■ possible causes of emergency or site evacuation ■ how emergency procedures will be communicated ■ who is responsible for calling the emergency services ■ contact details for out-of-hours emergencies.
Environmental controls	Describe: ■ threats to the environment arising from the work ■ which environmental protection measures will be put in place ■ how different types of waste will be stored and disposed of.
Safety of the public and occupiers	Identify who will ensure that the health and safety of the public and other occupiers will be protected. Describe how the health and safety of the public, including, if necessary, the occupiers of the building, will be protected.
Public nuisance	Identify: ■ possible sources of nuisance for neighbouring people/properties ■ who will be responsible for neighbourhood liaison.
Briefing register	List by name those people to whom the method statement has been explained and consider including a signature block to indicate that the content has been understood.

05

06

Induction training

Construction and building sites can be dangerous places to work, even for experienced workers. It is a legal requirement to give everyone on site, whether new to the industry, experienced or even a temporary visitor, basic information about the site so they can remain safe. This is usually done in the form of a site induction and can vary in style, delivery method and length depending upon factors such as company induction procedures, location and size of site, type of work and client requirements.

Whatever the content, it is important that those attending understand it and that it is specific to the site.

This chapter explains why site inductions are important and offers some suggested key content.

Introduction	74
Key points	74
Induction requirements	74
Types of inductees	75
Induction training	75
Induction difficulties	75
Induction content	75
Competency and card schemes	76
Records	78
Appendix A – Site induction topics	79
Appendix B – Employer responsibilities	87
Appendix C – Employee responsibilities	88

6.1   Introduction

It is a requirement of health and safety law that employees are provided with health and safety training whenever they are exposed to new or increased risks.

When employees first arrive in the company or at a new site, this training takes the form of an induction. It is accepted that providing proper and effective health and safety induction training can have a significant impact on the likelihood of accidents and injuries during a person's first few days, weeks or months with a company or on a particular site.

Given that every accident occurring to an employee can be seen as an eventual financial cost to the employer, then anything that can be done to reduce accidents is of direct financial benefit to the employer. The costs of giving proper and effective health and safety induction training are relatively minor when viewed as one of the cost benefits that can accrue from accident avoidance and prevention. This also applies to the prevention of long-term ill health and the avoidance of dangerous occurrences.

6.2   Key points

☑ Everyone arriving on a new site, whether new to the industry, experienced or even a temporary visitor, should be given an induction to the site.

☑ Accident statistics show that chances of accidents happen to people are increased during their first few days on site.

☑ The threats to health and safety will vary from site to site and even on the same site as work progresses and the hazards change.

☑ An effective induction process is an essential part of on-site health and safety management.

☑ The content of the induction presentation must:

– be understandable, comprehensive and relevant to the hazards present on site at that time

– anticipate and inform inductees of forthcoming changes to the hazards on site

– allow for the effective induction of inductees who do not have English as their first language or may otherwise have difficulty in understanding what is being said.

☑ The Construction (Design and Management) Regulations place a specific duty on contractors to provide all of their workers with a site induction.

6.3   Induction requirements

There are two types of induction contained within this chapter: induction training and site inductions.

Induction training

Induction training is for new employees or for training existing employees in new topics or risks.

The Management of Health and Safety at Work Regulations require every employer to ensure that employees are provided with adequate health and safety training when they are being:

☑ recruited into the employer's undertaking

☑ exposed to new or increased risks because:

– they have been transferred or given a change of responsibilities within the employer's undertaking

– of the introduction of new work equipment or a change regarding work equipment already in use within the employer's undertaking

– of the introduction of new technology into the employer's undertaking

– of the introduction of a new system of work or a change regarding a system of work already in use within the employer's undertaking.

Site inductions

The Construction (Design and Management) Regulations specifically require that:

☑ contractors provide all of their workers with the necessary information and training that is necessary for their health and safety, including a suitable site induction, where it is not provided by a principal contractor

☑ the principal contractor takes all reasonable steps to ensure that every worker is provided with a suitable site induction.

The above requirement on contractors to provide site inductions means that inductions must be carried out on any type, size and duration of a project. The requirements of other regulations, which in themselves indicate a need for competence in certain work situations, when viewed against the type of work to be carried out, might indicate additional topics that need to be covered during site induction.

Responsibilities of employers and employees

To assist in preparation and delivery of induction training, an aide-memoire of the responsibilities of employers and employees can be found in Appendices B and C. This could also help training providers with any questions that may arise during or after an induction training programme.

6.4   Types of inductees

Mention of the word *induction* or *inductee* would cause many people to think of a person arriving on site or into the company totally new. Whilst this is the case for some people, there will be a significant number of people who do not fall into this category. In wider terms inductees may be:

- ☑ young people joining the industry for the first time. This will generally be persons joining a company as trainees or apprentices

- ☑ persons arriving at a new site even though they have been in the industry for some time

- ☑ people transferring between companies within the industry

- ☑ persons who have been promoted (for example, from tradesperson to chargehand)

- ☑ employees who have been given different responsibilities (for example, employees who have successfully gained CPCS cards for specific items of plant and will now be driving plant on site as opposed to their former occupation).

It must be appreciated that different types of inductee will probably require different levels or styles of induction training because of their varying levels of knowledge, experience and competence within the industry. It is only if, after induction, they have all the appropriate information as regards company policy and site rules (including the principal contractor's site rules on projects that are notifiable under the CDM Regulations) that they will be able to integrate into the workforce and work without risks to their own health and safety or to others who may be affected.

6.5   Induction training

It will be for the employer to decide when and where the training takes place. However, the sooner the induction training takes place the more opportunity there is to have a significant influence on the people being inducted. It is important that the induction training is seen as a formal company procedure, which the company provides for the benefit of the inductee, so that the employer can be seen to be meeting both the letter and the spirit of the law. If it is seen as 'something that is just necessary, we have to do it anyway' then it will fail to have the desired long-term effects.

The style and content of the presentation will vary between company and site. However, the person giving the presentation needs to have both the necessary skills and knowledge, together with the ability or presence to deliver the programme effectively and in a meaningful manner.

6.6   Induction difficulties

It is essential that the health and safety messages put across during site induction are fully understood. Possible barriers to learning will depend largely upon the training methods used. For example, reliance on written training materials will disadvantage those with dyslexia or other reading difficulties. Similarly, an increasing number of workers do not speak English as their first language, and some may find induction training of limited value if it is not delivered with this in mind. The person organising the training should establish the limitations of those undertaking induction, remembering that some inductees may be embarrassed about their limitations and so reluctant to admit them.

To successfully induct those whose first language is not English, but who have some understanding, it will probably be necessary to modify the presentation in style, speed of delivery and the aids used. Induction aids may need to be more visual, with less reliance upon the written word. Where there are operatives who do not speak English at all, it is likely that specialist help, such as interpreters, will be required. There may also be scope for training someone on the site who speaks both languages to carry out specific induction sessions for specific groups.

Encouragement should be given to those who have reading, writing or language difficulties to seek help from the learning support unit of the local college of higher and further education, or any in-house training arrangements that exist.

Whatever the reason for any inductee experiencing difficulty in understanding what they have been told, all inductees must be given the opportunity to ask for any point to be explained again or in different terms.

6.7   Induction content

Different companies will have different issues to include in the induction training. The requirements will vary as work on the site progresses. In the early days there may be demolition, excavations and other problems at ground level. As the site and above-ground works progress, the hazards will change and it will be necessary for the emphasis in the health and safety training to change.

As the site develops, temporary or permanent traffic routes may be introduced, or the circulation of traffic on site may need to change (for example, due to the repositioning of a crane or the installation of services). All these issues should be reflected in the induction training that will be provided for people arriving on site or as the project progresses. It is quite possible, or even likely, that the induction session delivered on day one of the project will not be valid after three months.

Part of the induction process must be to find out what the audience already knows, to identify key areas that must be covered and use plain language, illustrating with diagrams, drawings and pictures to ensure that inductees can easily take in the information.

06

Induction training

At the end of the induction session, explain to the inductees that they will all be required to add their name and signature to an attendance sheet signifying that they have understood what they have been told.

This chapter (including further detail set out in Appendix A) contains some key issues in a number of areas that should be considered when induction training is to be given. It is not suggested that all are relevant to all sites or that issues relevant to more than one site should be given the same weighting. They are given as an indication of subject areas that need to be covered – the depth to which they are covered will depend upon site conditions. There will undoubtedly be other issues that are specific to a company or site and these will need to be considered and developed by the company concerned.

Site and company rules

Appendix A contains a list of topics that should be considered for site induction content, together with a brief explanation of each. Obviously, users will amend the content in order to reflect the philosophy of their company, site or organisation regarding health, safety and welfare provisions. There may be items covered that you feel are inappropriate and these should be omitted.

Conversely, some additional items not covered may be of particular importance to your company, site or organisation and these should be included. The comments made are of a very general nature and do not attempt to explain the specific requirements of legislation. It is thought that at an induction training session participants do not need to be told specific titles of regulations. However, users can include them if they wish to.

6.8   Competency and card schemes

Competence

In 2011, following consultation with industry, a report was produced for the HSE that looked at the construction industry routes to competence, including all the different competency card schemes.

 The report can be downloaded free from the research section of the HSE's website.

Behavioural competence

The report supported a need for a broader definition of competence to include not just job competence and (above-basic) health and safety awareness, but a third strand of behavioural competence.

This behavioural competence includes:

- ☑ self-awareness
- ☑ risk awareness
- ☑ situational awareness.

 A definition of behavioural competence

Behavioural awareness comprises those individual behaviours, attitudes, self-awareness and limitations that impact upon performance and safety at work. It covers the interaction between people and the environment in which they work, the equipment they use, and the procedures and techniques they use. The objectives of behavioural competence are enhanced effectiveness and safety.

This expanded definition of competence is tripartite and should include:

- ☑ **occupational skills**
- ☑ deep and relevant **knowledge and understanding**
- ☑ on-going evidence of **appropriate behaviours and attitudes**, to be embedded at all levels.

Supervisor and management competency

The report went on to say that qualifications should be enhanced to include mentoring and coaching skills in behavioural competence. In the coming years many of the recommendations from the report will be incorporated into qualifications, training courses and development programmes for supervisors and management, such as:

- ☑ alignment to new definitions of competence, behaviours and attitudes
- ☑ a greater focus on **taught** qualifications whereby the basis of the input of knowledge is on risk, causation, person-management skills and situational awareness
- ☑ continued professional development (CPD) (a necessary aspect and a fundamental component)
- ☑ opportunity to train people in roles to be effective assessors of staff.

For details of courses, training programmes or further information on competency refer to the CITB-ConstructionSkills website.

Other relevant construction organisations where further supporting information can be found include:

- ✓ ConstructionSkills (NI)
- ✓ Construction Employers Federation Limited (CEF NI)
- ✓ Construction Industry Confederation (CIC)
- ✓ Construction Plant-hire Association (CPA)
- ✓ Federation of Master Builders (FMB)
- ✓ Health and Safety Executive (HSE)
- ✓ Heating and Ventilating Contractors' Association (HVCA)
- ✓ Joint Industry Board for Plumbing Mechanical Engineering Services (JIB-PMES)
- ✓ Lift and Escalator Industry Association (LEIA)
- ✓ National Access and Scaffolding Confederation (NASC)
- ✓ National Demolition Training Group (NDTG)
- ✓ Scottish and Northern Ireland Joint Industry Board for the Plumbing Industry (SNIJIB)
- ✓ Strategic Forum for Construction (SFfC)
- ✓ TunnelSkills
- ✓ UK Contractors Group (UKCG)
- ✓ Union of Construction, Allied Trades and Technicians (UCATT)
- ✓ Unison
- ✓ Unite.

Card schemes

Access to construction sites may require a relevant scheme card, which are shown in the table below. Different schemes exist in different professions but all card schemes have similar requirements, such as an NVQ or SVQ and a CITB-ConstructionSkills Health, safety and environment test.

General	CSCS	Construction Skills Certification Scheme.
	CSR	Construction Skills Registration (Northern Ireland).
Plant operatives	CPCS	Construction Plant Competence Scheme.
Demolition operatives	CCDO	Certificate of Competence of Demolition Operatives.
Scaffolders	CISRS	Construction Industry Scaffolders Record Scheme.
HVACR operatives	ESS	Engineering Services SKILLcard.
Plumbers	JIBPMES	Joint Industry Board for Plumbing and Mechanical Services.
	SNIJIB	Scottish and Northern Ireland Joint Industry Board.
Electricians	ECS	Electrotechnical Certification Scheme.

For more information on each of these and other schemes, refer to the CITB-ConstructionSkills website.

Health, safety and environment test

The CITB-ConstructionSkills *Health, safety and environment test* helps raise standards across the industry. It ensures that workers meet a minimum level of health, safety and environmental awareness before going on site.

It should be used as a stepping stone, encouraging employers and their workforce to go on and develop their knowledge even further.

The test has been running for over 10 years and it underwent significant improvements in early 2012. These improvements included an enhanced test and a new delivery infrastructure.

06

A

Induction training

All tests last for 45 minutes and have 50 multiple-choice questions including:

☑ 12 behavioural case study questions about how to behave on a construction site to stay healthy and safe, followed by

☑ 38 knowledge questions to check knowledge of health, safety and environment issues.

Different tests have been developed to meet the demands of different trades and professions. The following tests are available:

☑ operative test

☑ specialist tests

☑ managers' and professionals' test.

 For more information about the test and how to prepare, refer to the CITB-ConstructionSkills website.

6.9 Records

It is extremely important that records are kept showing which workers have attended site induction, together with details of the training they have received and the date it was carried out.

This will enable employers to demonstrate to the Health and Safety Executive, the client, the principal contractor and other interested parties that they have complied with the requirements of legislation and that they are committed to ensuring the health and safety of their employees and any others who may be affected.

Such records could help prove that health and safety induction training was given, should there be a legal challenge.

Site induction register

 Within Section G *Checklists and forms* there is an example of a site induction register that can be copied and used for record purposes on induction training.

Induction training checklist

 Within Section G *Checklists and forms* there is an example of an induction training checklist. This can be:

☑ attached to the induction attendance list as a record of which topics were covered

☑ used by the trainer to ensure that the important basic facts are included in an induction training talk.

06

Appendix A – Site induction topics

Access

Explain the rules regarding access to, and egress from, the workplace. Are there any one-way systems? Are there any prohibited areas? Are there any special rules or conditions applying to the site or workplace?

Accident reporting

The participants should be in no doubt of the requirements for reporting accidents. Explain when, where and to whom accidents must be reported and, in general, how they will be investigated. Your procedures may go beyond those required by legislation as a company policy decision.

Alcohol and drugs

Explain the rules or company policy about arriving or being on site under the influence of alcohol or drugs, or consuming them during the hours of employment, including action that will be taken. There may be a policy of random testing and this should also be explained.

The issue of prescribed drugs should also be covered as some of these can have side effects, such as drowsiness. If the user is authorised to operate plant or drive vehicles, this needs to be addressed and resolved with the supervisor or management.

Asbestos

If the project is a new build on a greenfield site then the probability of finding asbestos is very remote. If, however, the project is on a brownfield site, there may be asbestos in the ground, and if carrying out a refurbishment or renovation then there is significant chance of discovering asbestos within the existing structure. If asbestos or asbestos-containing materials are potentially present, it is essential to provide elementary asbestos awareness training, including details of any prohibited areas, to reflect the site conditions.

You should have a company policy for dealing with any material suspected of being asbestos and employees should be informed of this policy.

06

Assembly points

See also **emergency evacuation**. Explain where the assembly points are for site evacuation in the event of an emergency.

Boundaries

Explain the boundaries of the site if there is no perimeter fence. Include the prevention of trespass.

Buried services

Explain site or company procedures that should be followed if gas, electricity, telecommunications, fibre optics, water, sewerage and other buried services are discovered on site.

CDM Regulations

If the project is notifiable under the Construction (Design and Management) Regulations, explain any appropriate on-site rules, the provisions the principal contractor has made for consultation with the workforce and where the statutory notice F10 (rev) is displayed.

Competence

You may need to advise employees and others of the levels of competence required for operating certain types of plant or carrying out particular pieces of work. See also **registration schemes**.

Confidential issues

Explain the provision for 'whistle blowing'. Also how employees can raise confidential (including medical) issues if the need arises.

Confined spaces

Explain the rules that apply on site. Many employees will fail to recognise that a confined space can be above ground, or be as innocuous as a sub-basement boiler room. Unfortunately, confined spaces have been responsible for a number of deaths in the industry, all of which could have been avoided by compliance with proper health and safety procedures.

Consultation with employees

It is a legal requirement to consult with employees, which should be two way. The questions that you should address during induction include:

- ☑ what the mechanism is for workers to bring any health and safety concerns they have to the attention of site management

- ☑ if there is a health and safety committee on site and, if so, who the members are

- ☑ if there are any trade union-appointed representatives and, if so, who they are.

If there is a suggestion box or scheme, explain how employees can put forward ideas for improvements in health, safety and welfare, waste minimisation and so on, on a day-by-day basis.

Contamination

The raised awareness of environmental matters makes the prevention of ground contamination of growing importance. Explain how employees can prevent spillage of diesel fuel, paint, oil, thinners, cement, concrete or any other substance that could lead to contamination.

Control of Substances Hazardous to Health (COSHH)

Explain the on-site procedures relating to hazardous substances. Are there any substances that are additional to the usual cement, oils, paints, and so on?

Competency card schemes (CSCS cards)

Explain the requirements for CSCS and other cards. See also **registration schemes**.

Dangerous occurrences

Explain the policy in relation to the reporting of dangerous occurrences. It is thought that many go unreported as employees regard them as an accident where nobody was injured. Given that this could lead to a company being prosecuted for failing to report a dangerous occurrence, it is important that the appropriate instructions are given at induction training sessions.

Dermatitis

Explain that contact dermatitis can be caused by some relatively common substances (such as diesel and mould release oil, paints, thinners and cement). Gloves should be worn on appropriate occasions, and barrier creams should be used properly.

These occasions should have been identified by the employer risk assessments.

Discipline

Explain the company policy regarding breaches of health and safety legislation, site or company rules.

Dress code

Explain the effects of sun exposure and the importance of preventing skin cancer. Explain company or site rules on whether shorts or sleeveless vests are permissible on site.

Drying rooms

Explain the location and use of drying rooms. Include who is responsible for maintaining cleanliness, tidiness and disposal of abandoned clothing and equipment.

Edge protection

Explain the standard that is used and the safe system of work for persons working on or near open or leading edges.

Electricity

Explain the site or company rules concerning:

- ☑ temporary or permanent repairs by competent persons on site
- ☑ use of 240 V equipment
- ☑ use of RCD or similar circuit breakers
- ☑ use of transformers and 110 V equipment
- ☑ testing, inspection and maintenance of portable electrical equipment (PAT testing).

Are there any other general rules regarding working with electricity?

Emergency procedure

Explain site or company procedures. What is the siren or alarm? Where are the emergency evacuation assembly points?

Explain the procedures to be followed in the event of an emergency other than fire. This may be civil disturbance, a bomb scare, structural collapse or other eventuality.

Environment

Environmental pollution can include the air, as well as the ground or water. Explain any specific issues of environmental protection and control concerning the company or site.

Escape routes

Explain the recognised escape routes on site and from buildings in the event of a fire or emergency.

Explain that access and egress routes must be well-defined and kept clear. How are they marked? How will they be lit when it is dark or during winter months? How will changes to the escape routes be notified as construction progresses?

Excavations

Explain the policy regarding:

- ☑ permit to dig systems
- ☑ excavation support and inspections
- ☑ proper entry and exit from an excavation, and edge protection around an excavation.

Eye protection

Explain if there are any specific eye protection issues, or rules applicable to the site or any particular work that is taking place. See also **personal protective equipment**.

Fall arrest

You may wish to comment on the use of safety nets, safety decking, air bags and other similar systems. See also **safety harnesses**.

Fall prevention

Explain the hierarchy of control measures that are to be used on site to prevent persons from falling or to catch them safely if they do fall. This will obviously vary depending on the type of site and work undertaken.

06

Fire

In the induction session you should at least cover the following:

- ☑ fire precautions, fire prevention and good housekeeping
- ☑ who will be responsible for summoning the emergency services
- ☑ location of:
  – fire points
  – fire extinguishers
- ☑ training and competence in the use of fire-fighting equipment
- ☑ testing of the fire alarm, fire drills and practice evacuations
- ☑ policy for hot works, including permits.

First aid

Clearly explain the arrangements for first aid provision.

- ☑ Where is the first aid kit?
- ☑ Who are the first aiders, and how can they be contacted or identified?
- ☑ Who are the appointed persons?
- ☑ In the event of an accident requiring more than first aid, who will summon the ambulance or emergency services?

Flammable liquids

If flammable liquids (such as paint thinners, solvents, spirit-based paints and others) are kept and used on site, explain the rules for:

- ☑ storage
- ☑ withdrawal from storage
- ☑ use and return to storage.

Health and safety committee

See also **consultation with employees.** If there is a site health and safety committee, explain the terms of reference for:

- ☑ the committee, membership and how often the committee meets
- ☑ agenda items and how the outcomes of meetings are made known to employees on site.

Hearing protection zones

See also **noise**. Are there any mandatory protection zones on site? How are they marked? Explain the supply and issue of hearing protectors and when they should be worn.

High-visibility clothing

Explain the site or company rules for this clothing to be worn and clearly define the appropriate locations. Also clearly define the standard for high-visibility clothing.

Hoists

Passenger hoists

- ☑ Who is the competent person to operate the hoist?
- ☑ If any person can operate it, do they need training prior to being authorised as competent?
- ☑ If the controls are regarded as so simple that the hoist may almost be regarded as a public lift, is there any danger of controls being overridden?
- ☑ What is the maximum number of persons permitted in the hoist?
- ☑ Which rules apply regarding goods carried in the hoist?

Goods hoists

- ☑ Who is the authorised competent person to drive it or can any other persons be authorised?
- ☑ What are the rules for closing the gates and what is the safe working load?
- ☑ Explain that passengers cannot be carried.

Ladders/stepladders

Explain the company standards for:

- ☑ securing or tying ladders/stepladders
- ☑ use of ladders/stepladders for light work of short duration or gaining access
- ☑ any restrictions imposed on the use of ladders and stepladders (permits).

Lasers

If lasers are to be used on site, explain what class of laser is to be used and what, if any, hazards could be caused. Levelling lasers (used, for example, by suspended ceiling fixers) are not normally regarded as hazardous as long as appropriate health and safety rules are followed.

Legal issues

This is an opportunity to discuss any particular points of law that apply to the company or site where the induction training is being given. Explain that different projects and clients will have different rules and that employees should understand the need for each rule and how it will be enforced. Mention also the statutory health and safety law poster that must be displayed.

Lifting equipment

Explain the following:

- ☑ who has the authority to use lifting equipment of varying sizes and types
- ☑ the duties of slingers and signallers
- ☑ testing and inspection of equipment, and current colour coding, if such a system is used.

Lighting

Explain the site or company rules for provision of work lighting and emergency lighting, including:

- ☑ the placing of luminaires
- ☑ extra lighting during winter months or for work outside normal hours.

Liquefied petroleum gas

Explain the rules for:

- ☑ use, storage and separation of full and empty cylinders
- ☑ separation from oxygen and acetylene, as appropriate
- ☑ use of hose check valves and flashback arresters
- ☑ use of fire extinguishers.

Manual handling

Explain site or company rules regarding:

- ☑ the avoidance of manual handling wherever possible
- ☑ the use of mechanical devices to aid manual handling
- ☑ safe systems of work.

Method statements

Explain the importance of supervisors discussing with employees the method statement to be used for particular tasks, and the benefits to be gained from employee input into method statements.

Method statements must be specific to the site, task and persons carrying out the work.

Mobile elevating work platforms

Explain who has the competence to operate or use mobile elevating work platforms (MEWPs). Give the evidence required to prove competence and training. Where can MEWPs be used and under what ground conditions? Where are they not allowed? Explain the use of safety harnesses when working from platforms. Explain policy on emergency lowering and requirement to use anti-crush protection systems.

Near-miss incidents

Explain the importance of reporting all unsafe conditions and near misses and any site reporting scheme in operation. These can then be investigated and the appropriate remedial measures put into place so that the next near miss does not become an accident.

Needles and syringes

Employees should be warned to be very vigilant, particularly regarding the discovery of used hypodermic syringes (needles and risk of needlestick injury) and other drug-taking equipment.

Explain the action to be taken on finding discarded needles or receiving a needlestick injury.

It should be noted that most gloves in common use on site do not offer very much protection against a needlestick injury.

Noise

See also **hearing protection zones**. Explain the site or company rules concerning the use of equipment that produces excessive noise. Does the Local Authority impose any restrictions? Explain the use of hearing protection and noise control zones.

Occupational health

Stress the importance of employees reporting to supervisors any cases of ill health, as it may be potentially work-related. This is particularly important if employees are working where there may be rats, or if the area has been used for illegal drug taking and related paraphernalia may be found.

In the case of refurbishment and renovation works, there may be residual materials from previous occupants likely to cause ill health.

 Construction dusts are the biggest cause of construction-related ill health, with over 4,000 workers a year dying from respiratory diseases. Risk assessments and method statements must identify dust produced in any activity as a hazard, and control measures must be put in place to minimise exposure.

Overhead electricity cables

Explain the site or company rules on:

- ☑ location and marking
- ☑ allowable proximity for vehicles
- ☑ working nearby and precautions.

Permits to work

Explain company or site procedures regarding issuing, working with and the cancellation of permits to work. Where lock-off systems are used, explain the rules regarding padlock keys.

Personal protective equipment

Explain the site or company rules regarding:

- ☑ minimum personal protective equipment (PPE) (for example, safety helmets, safety footwear, high-visibility clothing, light eye protection and gloves)
- ☑ use of respiratory protection equipment (RPE) and other task specific PPE
- ☑ storage and maintenance of PPE (for example, light eye protection cleaning stations)
- ☑ any other issues (such as dress code).

Remind the inductees that PPE in general, and RPE in particular, should only be used as a means of last resort when all other control measures have been investigated and found to be impracticable. The need for PPE, apart from that which is mandatory, should be covered in the risk assessment and method statement.

 Where task-specific PPE has been identified, the type or grade must be stated. For example, rather than just specifying dust mask the type must be stated, such as FFP3-rated disposable dust mask.

Plant and equipment

Explain the site rules regarding:

- ☑ the authority to operate plant and equipment, including the requirement for competence cards, where necessary
- ☑ any type of plant/equipment that is prohibited (for example mains-powered hand tools)
- ☑ the need for noise control where appropriate
- ☑ the requirement for permits to work where appropriate.

Registration schemes

Explain the site or company rules regarding CSCS, CISRS, CPCS or other registration schemes.

Reporting defects

Explain the importance of reporting all defects in plant and equipment, scaffolding, supports for excavations, and so on. Early reporting will bring about swift remedial measures and help to prevent accidents. The possible consequences of not reporting defects may result in an accident or disciplinary procedures.

Restricted or prohibited areas

Explain whether there are any areas on site that are restricted to all people, or a specific class of people. Include what identifies a restricted area – typical examples are areas where demolition, impact cleaning, water jetting, or asbestos removal are taking place.

Risk assessments

Explain the significant findings of risk assessments, as they will affect staff on site as a whole, or those working on a particular activity. It may be useful to explain the risk assessment process and the health and safety benefits that can be gained by employees. See also **method statements**.

Safe systems of work

The crucial need arising out of risk assessments and method statements is for safe systems of work. Explain that site rules require employees to work in accordance with any safe systems of work that have been developed by the employer.

Safety harnesses

Explain the company or site requirements for inspecting, wearing, using and maintaining safety harnesses and lanyards.
See also **fall arrest**.

Safety policy

Explain any relevant areas of the company's health and safety policy, together with the organisation and arrangements for the implementation of the policy. If relevant, explain where a copy of the policy is displayed on site.

Safety signs and notices

Remind the audience that all employees must comply with all safety signs and notices at all times. Explain the whereabouts of any site notice board, hazard board and how changes and modifications to site rules will be made known to the workforce.

Scaffolding (including mobile scaffolds)

Explain the site rules regarding:

- ☑ who is allowed to erect, alter or dismantle tube and fitting or system-built scaffolds
- ☑ the implications (safety and disciplinary) of unauthorised dismantling or alteration of scaffolds
- ☑ assessing competency to erect proprietary aluminium or tower scaffolds
- ☑ the safe use of mobile tower scaffolds
- ☑ safe access/egress to and from scaffolds.

Explain any other company or site-specific rules about the use of scaffolding as either a working place, or as access to the working place.

Site layout

Explain whether any specific rules apply to pedestrian and traffic movement. This will depend on the size and complexity of the site. You may also include where contractors may lay down materials and which areas they may use for the prefabrication of components.

Site security

Security is very much allied to health and safety in that a breach of security can lead to trespassers on site and possible exposure to a risk of injury. Open a discussion if you have any particular company or on-site rules concerning security. Also consider the issue of health and safety awareness of site security staff, whether they are employees or a sub-contracted security company.

Skin protection

It may be appropriate to discuss the need for skin protection, both in terms of gloves and barrier creams. If barrier creams are used, where are they dispensed? Also explain that the types of gloves used must be the most suitable for the levels of protection needed. If it is likely to be a significant hazard, you should also include details of the risk of skin cancer associated with excessive exposure to the sun.

Smoking

Explain the policy on smoking in the workplace and the canteen, clearly identifying those areas where smoking is not allowed.

Tidiness (housekeeping)

Explain the importance of maintaining a tidy site in order to eliminate many of the slip, trip and fall hazards. Include:

- ☑ materials storage and delivery arrangements
- ☑ how materials are to be distributed and returned
- ☑ how and when to remove rubbish and excess materials
- ☑ who is responsible for organising the delivery of and removal of skips
- ☑ good housekeeping, sweeping up/vacuuming/dust extraction – general tidiness
- ☑ maintaining tidy workplaces, access routes, staircases.

Toilets

See also **welfare facilities**. Explain the site or company rules regarding cleanliness, abuse of facilities and graffiti, and how such behaviour will be dealt with. Include the reporting of defects.

Traffic routes

These are dependent on the size and complexity of the site. Explain:

- ☑ one-way systems and the need to minimise or avoid reversing
- ☑ signallers or bankspersons
- ☑ segregation of pedestrians from vehicles and machines – pedestrian walkways.

Induction training – Appendix A

Training

What training will be given to persons on site? Explain the need for all contractors to ensure that persons working for them on site have been trained and are competent to carry out the work they are required to do.

Vehicles

Explain the site rules for the presence and operation of vehicles on site. Include:

- ☑ the parking of private vehicles
- ☑ delivery vehicles (for example, constraints on access, delivery times, site restrictions, offloading methods (for example, tower crane or telehandler), use of hi-abs and prevention of falls from vehicles)
- ☑ keeping clear of site (working) vehicles
- ☑ who is allowed to operate plant on site, and providing proof of competence to operate plant
- ☑ the security of vehicle keys when not in use
- ☑ security measures to make vehicles unavailable to trespassers and children during non-working hours
- ☑ traffic routes, speed limits and noise (for example, time limitations imposed by the Local Authority).

Vibration

Many people are still unaware of the problems that can be caused by high-speed rotary and percussive equipment. Explain the potential severity of vibration white finger and the company or site policy regarding:

- ☑ the use of vibrating equipment and maximum trigger use times
- ☑ the limitations of PPE
- ☑ design and selection of tools and equipment
- ☑ rest breaks and the rotation of work
- ☑ the symptoms of vibration white finger
- ☑ the need for employees to seek medical advice if they have any symptoms.

Waste disposal

Describe the location of skips and other waste containers. Explain the segregation of waste. Who is responsible for the removal of waste from the workplace? Explain the company or site policy if contractors do not clear away their own waste.

Waste minimisation

Explain that this is a financial issue as well as an environmental matter. It is also closely linked with site tidiness, pollution control, housekeeping and accident prevention. Effective waste minimisation is also an issue within sustainable construction and there are company and national benefits to be gained. There is more likelihood of a project being completed on time and to budget if waste is minimised. See also **environment**.

Welfare facilities

Explain:

- ☑ the location of the welfare facilities and if appropriate, the opening hours of site canteens
- ☑ responsibilities for the cleaning and maintenance of the facilities
- ☑ the provision of barrier creams and rehydrating lotions
- ☑ the need for good personal hygiene.

Working at height

This is allied to fall prevention, safe systems of work and PPE. Explain the company or site rules for:

- ☑ working at height, including safe systems of work
- ☑ competence of employees
- ☑ protection of those below, including the public
- ☑ the prevention of materials falling – use of containment and debris nets.

Working near, on or over water

Explain the site or company rules for working near, on or over water, including:

- ☑ the wearing of life jackets, life preservers or flotation devices
- ☑ prevention of falls into water
- ☑ the rescue of anyone who has fallen into water, plus lookouts and alarms.

Appendix B – Employer responsibilities

The following information is provided as an aide-memoire to training providers, for any questions that may arise during or after an induction training programme.

Set out below, in an abbreviated form, are the principal responsibilities of employers, managers and supervisors. For ease of presentation, the reader is assumed to be an employer.

- ☑ Ensure, so far as is reasonably practicable, the health, safety and welfare of employees.
- ☑ Display an employer's liability compulsory insurance certificate.
- ☑ Have a general statement of health and safety policy.
- ☑ Prepare and display a written health and safety policy, if you employ five or more persons.
- ☑ Make employees aware of your company health and safety policy.
- ☑ Display an approved poster or give each employee a copy of an approved leaflet to comply with the Health and Safety (Information for Employees) Regulations.
- ☑ Carry out risk assessments of your work activities and record the significant findings, if you employ five or more persons.
- ☑ Implement any control measures identified by your risk assessment.
- ☑ Regularly review risk assessments and any associated control measures.
- ☑ Ensure that scaffolding is only erected, altered or dismantled under the supervision of a competent person.
- ☑ Appoint a competent person to assist the company with health and safety requirements, where necessary.
- ☑ Establish a safety committee, if requested by two union-appointed safety representatives.
- ☑ Assess manual handling operations in the workplace and take appropriate steps to reduce the risk of injury to employees.
- ☑ Ensure all accidents that result in injury, however slight, are entered in the accident book and investigated.
- ☑ Report to the HSE all reportable accidents, dangerous occurrences and notifiable diseases.
- ☑ Provide employees with PPE, as necessary.
- ☑ Avoid entry into confined spaces, wherever possible.
- ☑ Protect employees who may be exposed to asbestos at work.
- ☑ Ensure that all excavations are safe and that work in excavations is carried out safely.
- ☑ Provide sufficient and suitable welfare facilities on construction sites, including sanitary conveniences, washing facilities, drinking water and changing facilities.
- ☑ Provide information, instruction, training and supervision to ensure the health and safety of all employees.
- ☑ Appoint trained and competent persons for the purpose of mounting abrasive wheels.
- ☑ Examine, test and properly maintain plant, equipment, cranes, lifting appliances and associated working gear at regular intervals, and record the findings.
- ☑ Provide adequate first-aid facilities with sufficient trained first aiders and appointed persons.
- ☑ Consult with your employees on health and safety matters.
- ☑ Engage only competent persons to carry out work on electrical installations and appliances.
- ☑ Take measures to prevent or adequately control employees' exposure to harmful dusts and fumes.
- ☑ Prepare and maintain a construction phase health and safety plan appropriate to your operations.
- ☑ Ensure that the workplace is safe and without risk to the health of employees.
- ☑ Take the necessary steps to ensure that the health and safety of the public is not put at risk by works being carried out.

Appendix C – Employee responsibilities

Below, in an abbreviated form, are the main responsibilities of employees. The reader is assumed to be an employee.

☑ Co-operate with your employer and follow any information, instructions and training given to you.

☑ Do not interfere with or misuse anything your employer has provided in the interests of health, safety and welfare.

☑ Take reasonable care at all times and make sure that you do not endanger yourself or any other person.

☑ Use all tools and equipment safely and in accordance with instructions given or training received.

☑ Report any defects or potential hazards in equipment to your supervisor as soon as possible.

☑ Make proper use of any safe system of work or mechanical means provided by your employer in connection with manual handling.

☑ Only operate the plant and equipment you have been trained and authorised to use.

☑ Use the PPE supplied by your employer correctly, take care of it and report any loss or defects in the equipment.

☑ Report to your employer any work situation that might present a danger.

☑ Do not erect, alter or dismantle scaffolding unless competent to do so or under the supervision of a competent person.

☑ When operating goods hoists, keep the gates closed except when loading. Do not override any controls. Do not allow any passengers.

☑ Use only the proper safe means provided for entering and leaving an excavation.

☑ Do not block or obstruct any access or means of escape route.

☑ Make full use of any control measures provided to prevent or limit exposure to substances hazardous to health, and wear the PPE provided.

☑ Observe safe use and handling instructions for hazardous substances, and return unused quantities to the designated store.

☑ Do not use a MEWP for any use other than as a work platform.

☑ Co-operate with health and safety inspectors, as required.

☑ Do not remove safety guards or stop any safety device fitted to any plant or equipment from working.

☑ Do not ride on plant or vehicles in unauthorised and insecure places.

☑ Recognise the importance of personal cleanliness, especially when working with substances harmful to the skin.

☑ Never exceed the safe working load of any equipment.

☑ Report to your supervisor all accidents that cause any injury to you.

☑ Understand and comply with all signs that are displayed.

☑ Wear ear protectors in designated areas where mandatory warning signs are displayed.

☑ Follow all company and site health and safety rules.

06

07
Safety critical communication

Good communication is essential for the management of health and safety on construction sites.

Communication problems can occur where workers have limited or no understanding of English, particularly during site induction.

This chapter offers advice to those who may not have company communication policies, and offers some suggested approaches.

One approach is to use images that have been specially created for the construction industry to assist in improving safety critical communication, which are included within this chapter.

Introduction	90
Key points	90
Managing the language situation	90
Critical health, safety and welfare images	91
Delivering a safety critical communication toolbox talk	92
Pre-start assessments	93
Using the images	94
Appendix A – Critical health, safety and welfare images	96
Appendix B – Safety critical communication Toolbox talks (GT 701) – Full content list	111

Safety critical communication

7.1 Introduction

Good communication is essential for the management of health and safety on construction sites. The number of workers on UK sites, where English is not their first language, has increased over recent years.

Some of these workers have excellent skills in spoken and written English, but there are others for whom understanding English is a problem.

This can be a barrier to effective communication of health and safety information.

However, failure to engage non-English speaking workers for this reason will almost certainly be in breach of the provisions of race relations legislation.

7.2 Key points

- ☑ Employers are legally required to provide information that is comprehensible, in other words provided in a format that can be understood by the worker.

- ☑ This requirement can result in problems where the recipients of the information have limited or no understanding of English, particularly during site induction.

- ☑ Communicating using images has the potential to overcome these problems, regardless of the mix of languages spoken on site.

- ☑ A bank of images, each representing a hazard or a simple instruction has been developed.

- ☑ These images have been developed by CITB-ConstructionSkills into a useful, colour-coded resource for use on site: *Safety critical communication toolbox talks* (GT 701).

- ☑ It is likely that it will be necessary to hold separate training sessions to assess the understanding of safety critical words and phrases by those with English language problems.

- ☑ Confirming that the workers being assessed can associate each image with a spoken short phrase in plain English will give supervisors and managers confidence that the workers have an understanding of safety critical words in English.

- ☑ Due to their simplicity, these phrases aid translation into other languages, if needed.

- ☑ Before using any images, workers' competence, training and language skills must be assessed. This will also indicate the level of supervision required generally.

- ☑ The images can be used to support site inductions, toolbox talks or other training, or superimposed on site plans to identify the location of welfare facilities, fire-fighting equipment, and so on.

- ☑ The images also help to fill gaps in translation, as well as improving memory recall of site rules.

- ☑ If appropriate, the images can enhance and complement existing procedures (for example using interpreters), rather than replace them.

- ☑ An understanding of the images should not be solely relied upon to ensure that work of a higher risk nature can be carried out safely.

7.3 Managing the language situation

Contractors who engage workers who cannot speak and/or understand English have a few options when deciding how to manage communications. These include hiring a bilingual supervisor who can give information, instruction and training to workers.

Alternatively, English speaking co-workers are often used on site to communicate with non-English speaking workers. However, their competence (both technically in construction and as a translator) must be assessed first.

Another option is for training materials to be translated or to be represented in a pictorial form (images).

The effectiveness of images to overcome language barriers has been confirmed through research, which resulted in the development of a bank of images, a selection of which is contained in this chapter.

The images:

- ☑ were developed from British Standard safety signs, Health and Safety Executive (HSE) guidance documents and other picture-based guidance

- ☑ have been tested for comprehension on live sites with foreign workers and refined to help contractors to carry out effective health and safety training and, in so doing, discharge their legal duties.

The black and white images were developed for a generic site induction and targeted at the most critical health, safety and welfare issues relevant to construction workers. However, these are only examples of a larger database of images. The coloured images and the text on page 92 demonstrate the principles of using CITB-ConstructionSkills' visual communication resource *Safety critical communication toolbox talks* (GT 701).

7.4 Critical health, safety and welfare images

The images in Appendix A have been designed to enhance induction and other training. Each image is set out in a similar format, as shown below:

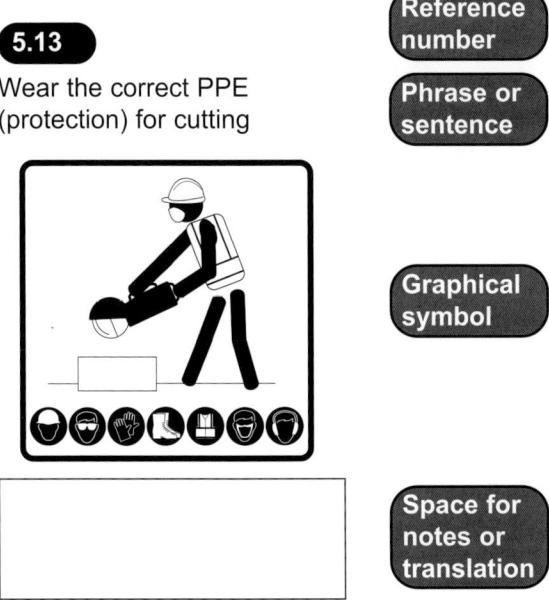

The **reference number** at the top of each image is for ease of identification.

The next element is a **short phrase or sentence**. These have been developed, with help from language experts, to:

☑ communicate, in plain English, the particular health and safety issue depicted by the graphical symbol

☑ aid translation into other languages.

The phrase or sentence will remind the person delivering the training of the response required from the person being assessed. Depending upon the circumstances, a decision will have to be made as to whether it is more beneficial to reveal or hide the phrase or sentence during the assessment. Having sight of the phrase or sentence may have the potential to help workers with a limited understanding of written English to associate the written words with the message of the graphical symbol.

The **graphical symbol** is the main element in each image. Most are self-explanatory. Some enable the person delivering the training to add site-specific information (for example the postal address of the site (image 2.1) or site telephone number (image 2.2)).

As demonstrated in the figures below, it is recommended that some of the images are regarded as linked and are shown sequentially to convey the correct meaning:

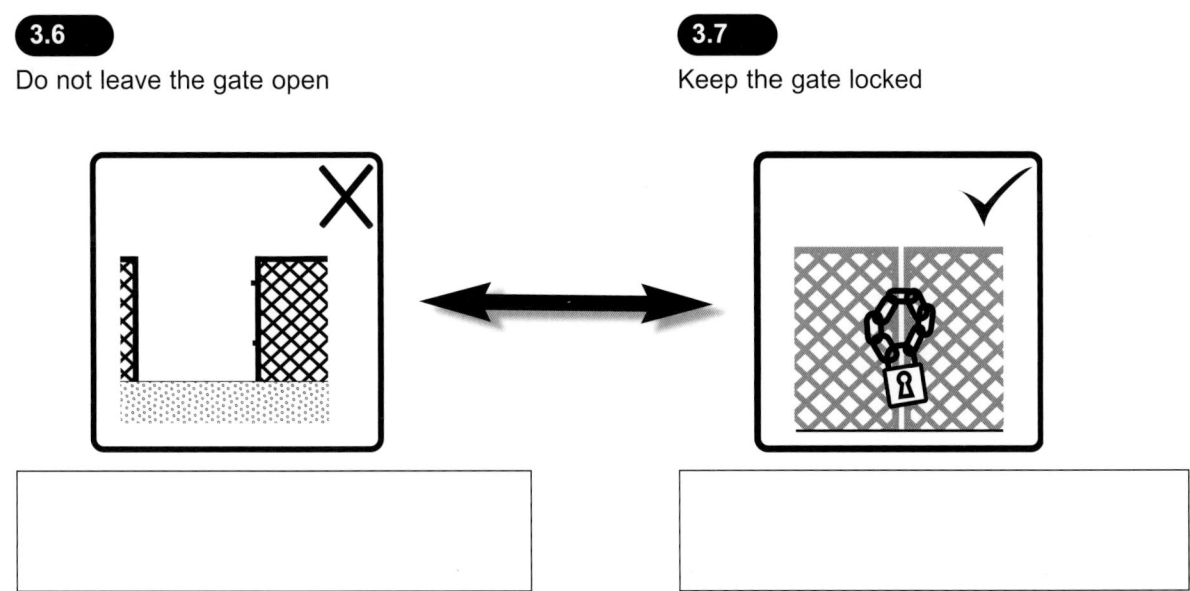

If image 3.7 is shown to a worker who cannot understand the written phrase, it could be misinterpreted as 'the site is closed' or 'keep out'. However, by showing image 3.6 and 3.7 in sequence, a visual link is created and the chance of misinterpretation is reduced.

7.5   Delivering a safety critical communication toolbox talk

1. Find the hazard in the contents list.

2. Turn to the appropriate page
    (yellow image).

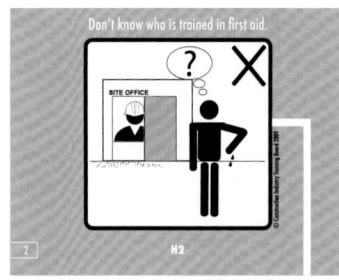

3. View the risk to health or safety on
    the opposing red page.

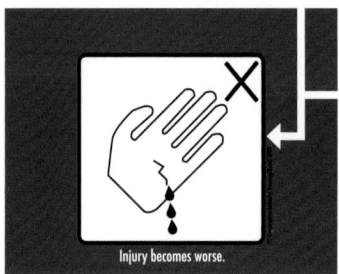

07

4. Fold out the red page to reveal the
    necessary control measures on
    the green page(s).

5. Deliver the toolbox talk.

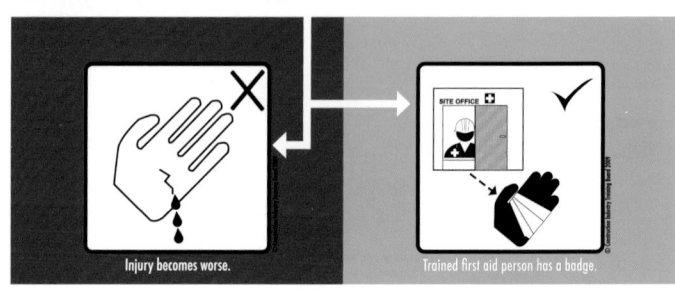

Explanation of the elements on each coloured page

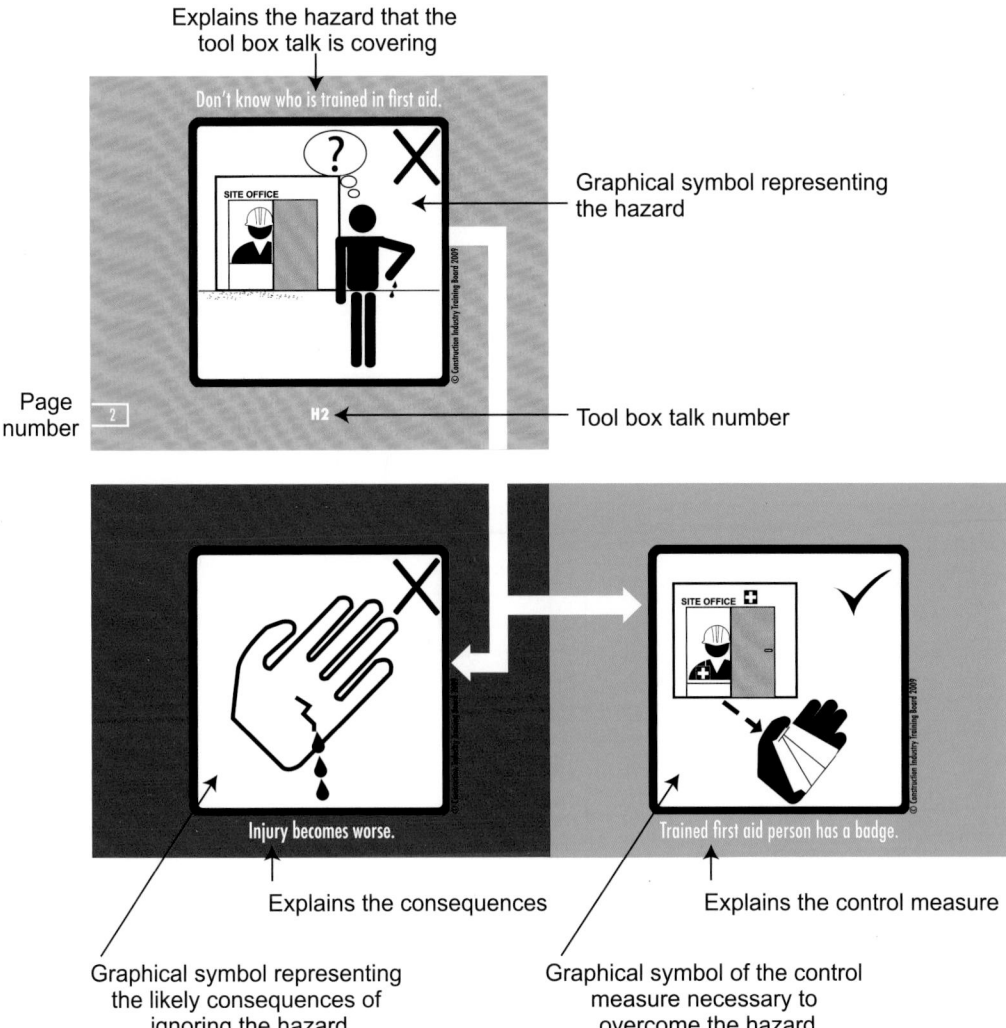

Explains the hazard that the tool box talk is covering

Graphical symbol representing the hazard

Page number

Tool box talk number

Explains the consequences

Explains the control measure

Graphical symbol representing the likely consequences of ignoring the hazard

Graphical symbol of the control measure necessary to overcome the hazard

7.6 Pre-start assessments

Before any worker starts on site certain facts must be established. These are the level of:

☑ the worker's competence and training

☑ the worker's understanding of English

☑ supervision required.

The type of work to be done by the worker will dictate the required level of competence and identify any training needed. Regardless of language issues foreign workers must meet the level of competence and training expected of **any** worker asked to do the task(s). Therefore, contractors should apply the same criteria for non/low-English speaking workers as they do for English speakers, which will require some form of competency assessment.

It is possible that some foreign workers will have trade qualifications gained in their home countries. The National Academic Recognition Information Centre for the UK (NARIC) is a Government-funded agency that offers a service to compare overseas qualifications with UK ones. Although not comprehensive, it is a useful resource.

With regard to training undertaken in the United Kingdom, holding a CSCS, CPCS or similar card will indicate that an acceptable level of training has been undertaken and a minimum level of health and safety knowledge is held.

Failure to prove an acceptable level of competence will indicate that further training is required before considering the other pre-start factors. Such training is beyond the scope of this chapter.

Assuming that the worker meets the contractor's competence criteria, the next thing to consider is the worker's language skills. NARIC can also provide assistance in this respect. There are a number of methods for assessing a worker's English language skills, which use simple self-assessment criteria.

One of these is the Association of Language Testers in Europe (ALTE) 'can do' statements. These can be objectively described and assessed by non-specialists. Therefore, a worker's language skills can be easily determined by site managers and supervisors by following the guidance provided in the ALTE work statements summary (see table on the next page).

Safety critical communication

Workers below ALTE breakthrough level are those with no English language skills whatsoever, who need an interpreter or written translation for all communications. Furthermore, it may be unwise to assume these workers can read in their own language.

To prove their competence these workers will have to demonstrate their understanding of the images without the benefit of reference to the phrases.

Most workers who have lived and worked in the UK for at least one year may have picked up a basic level of understanding of English at listening breakthrough level or Level 1. Workers at this level will find the images and phrases to be useful learning aids.

Co-workers, who can interpret for their colleagues, will need to be at least ALTE Level 3 for listening and speaking. The presence of an interpreter does not make the images redundant as they can still fill gaps that may be lost in translation.

The combination of competence, training and language skills will dictate the level of supervision required. Another factor, as with any worker, will be the result of the employer's risk assessment for the task(s).

However, where there is a language barrier to communication, the level of supervision will also have to consider an appropriate ratio of workers to each bilingual supervisor. This can vary from as much as 1:20 to 1:1 depending on the circumstances.

Where workers are grouped close together in the same area and undertaking low risk work the ratio can be high. But, if the workers are dispersed around the site and/or undertaking higher risk work, the ratio may need to be as low as 1:1.

Lone working for workers with non/low-English language skills is not recommended.

The ALTE work statements summary table

ALTE Level	Listening/speaking	Reading	Writing
ALTE breakthrough level	CAN take and pass on simple messages of a routine kind, such as 'Friday meeting 10 a.m.'.	CAN understand short reports or product descriptions on familiar matters, if these are expressed in simple language and the contents are predictable.	CAN write a simple routine request to a colleague, such as 'Can I have 20X please?'
ALTE Level 1	CAN state simple requirements within own job area, such as 'I want to order 25 of...'.	CAN understand most short reports or manuals of a predictable nature within their own area of expertise, provided enough time is given.	CAN write a short, comprehensible note of request to a colleague or a known contact in another company.
ALTE Level 2	CAN offer advice to clients within own job area on simple matters.	CAN understand the general meaning of non-routine letters and theoretical articles within own work area.	CAN make reasonably accurate notes at a meeting or seminar where the subject matter is familiar and predictable.
ALTE Level 3	CAN take and pass on most messages that are likely to require attention during a normal working day.	CAN understand most correspondence, reports and factual product literature they are likely to come across.	CAN deal with all routine requests for goods or services.
ALTE Level 4	CAN contribute effectively to meetings and seminars within own area of work and argue for or against a case.	CAN understand correspondence expressed in non-standard language.	CAN handle a wide range of routine and non-routine situations in which professional services are requested from colleagues or external contacts.
ALTE Level 5	CAN advise on/handle complex, delicate or contentious issues, such as legal or financial matters, to the extent that they have the necessary specialist knowledge.	CAN understand reports and articles likely to be encountered during their work, including complex ideas expressed in complex language.	CAN make full and accurate notes and continue to participate in a meeting or seminar.

7.7   Using the images

Safety critical communication Toolbox talks

The method of using the colour images contained in the CITB-ConstructionSkills publication *Safety critical communication toolbox talks* (GT 701) is outlined in 7.5.

 For further details and to obtain GT 701 refer to the CITB-ConstructionSkills website.

Site induction

The images in Appendix A are examples of a wider resource for use by site managers or supervisors. It is envisaged that the primary use will be during the induction training of foreign workers.

They can also be used to support other forms of training (such as during the delivery of toolbox talks to foreign workers). However, they have their limitations as described later.

The images are intended to enhance the induction procedures for non/low-English speaking workers. However, in future it may be possible to import the images directly into existing induction presentations.

With careful forethought, this may enable foreign workers to be successfully inducted during the same presentation as other workers. If this approach is taken it is likely that additional effort will be required to confirm the retained level of understanding of the foreign workers, possibly including subsequent follow-up checks.

Existing induction training procedures for foreign workers who do not understand English may involve the use of an interpreter. However, problems can occur during translation and the use of the images may help to fill any gaps in worker understanding.

Site plans

Some of the images (such as those showing the location of welfare facilities, fire-fighting equipment and assembly points) lend themselves to being overlaid (physically or electronically) on site layout plans.

Depending on the size of the plans, it may be feasible in the future for copies of the images to be electronically superimposed directly onto the plans in the appropriate location, or placed in the margin with arrows pointing to the actual location. These can be displayed during site inductions and left in a suitable place for future reference.

Site inspections

The images can be used during site walkabout. For example, a worker not wearing essential personal protective equipment (PPE) can be informed using images starting with the number '5', which show items of PPE required on construction sites.

Furthermore, the images in the CITB-ConstructionSkills database are presented in the sequence Hazard-Risk-Control(s) and can be used to educate the worker by showing them a hazard, which may be an unsafe act or condition, followed by the potential risk (consequences) and the necessary control(s).

Management controls are beyond the worker's direct authority but dealt with using an image containing a 'report to supervisor' message.

Workers can be tested for comprehension by asking them to consider whether an image is good or bad practice; or by showing the first sequence of images (hazard/risk) and asking the worker to identify the correct control image.

In addition, observation of workers after instruction has been given will confirm whether they have implemented the necessary controls/safe system of work.

Limitations of using pictorial images

Whilst pictorial images are very useful aids for communicating health and safety information, they have their limitations. For example, the images in Appendix A contain some activities that need a permit to work. However, the rationale for introducing a particular type of permit or the procedures for obtaining one must be taught through detailed instruction, not easily covered solely by pictorial images.

Images should not be seen as a complete alternative to using interpreters but rather as tools to enhance existing practices; the law requires this should include interpreters where appropriate.

Research outcome

Field testing of the images proved to be very successful with considerable positive feedback. Consequently, CITB-ConstructionSkills embarked upon a project to incorporate the images, in an enhanced colour-coded format, into a communications resource that could be used on site.

The outcome was the development of a handy-sized, ring-bound book entitled *Safety critical communication toolbox talks* (GT 701).

07

Appendix A – Critical health, safety and welfare images

1.1

Manager

1.2

Supervisor

1.3

Safety manager

07

1.4

Safety representative

2.1

Address

2.2

Telephone number

2.3

Fax number

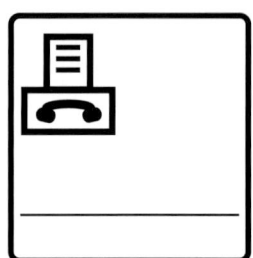

3.1

No unauthorised people are allowed on the site

3.2

Sign the book or swipe the card when you enter the site

3.3

Sign the book or swipe the card when you leave the site

3.4

Drivers sign the book when they enter the site

07

3.5

Drivers sign the book when they leave the site

3.6

Do not leave the gate open

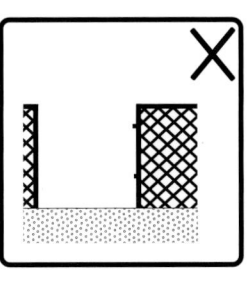

3.7

Keep the gate locked

3.8

Put a guard (board) on the ladder when work is finished

3.9

Remove the key when the machine is not being used

3.10

Lock dangerous things away when they are not being used

4.1

Car park

4.2

Delivery area

4.3

Storage area

4.4

Do not store gas cylinders on their side

4.5

Gas cylinders must be locked away and stored upright

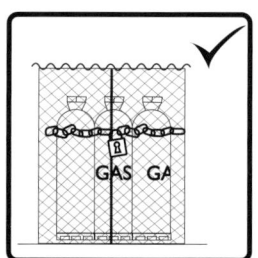

4.6

No smoking

4.7

Beware of flammable material
(things that can burn easily)

4.8

No naked flames

4.9

Pedestrian (walking) route

4.10

Vehicle route

4.11

Do not walk close to the vehicles

4.12

Keep on the pedestrian walkways

4.13

Private vehicles have priority over pedestrians (people walking)

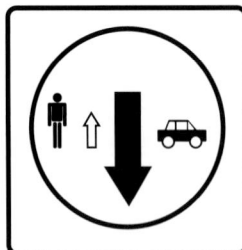

4.14

Site traffic has priority over pedestrians (people walking)

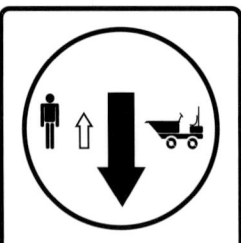

4.15

Pedestrians (people walking) have priority over private vehicles

4.16

Pedestrians (people walking) have priority over site traffic

4.17

Private vehicles have priority over site traffic

4.18

Site traffic has priority over private vehicles

4.19

Speed limit is 5 miles per hour

5.1

Workers need a skill card to work on this site

5.2

Wear a hard hat

07

5.3

Wear eye protection

5.4

Wear gloves

5.5

Wear ear protection

5.6

Wear a respirator (gas mask)

5.7

Wear a mask

5.8

Wear a face shield

5.9

Wear safety boots

5.10

Wear high-visibility clothes

5.11

Wear a welding mask

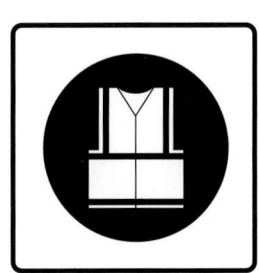

5.12

Wear the correct PPE (protection) for chipping or hammering

5.13

Wear the correct PPE (protection) for cutting

5.14

Wear the correct PPE (protection) for using a grinder (abrasive wheel)

5.15

Wear the correct PPE (protection) for demolition work

6.1

Escape route arrow

6.2

Sound the emergency horn

6.3

Emergency call point

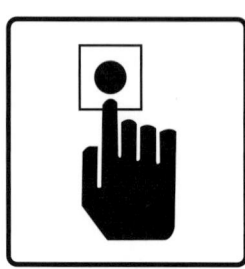

6.4

Assembly point

6.5

Emergency telephone

07

6.6

Fire extinguisher

6.7

Fire alarm call point

6.8

Fire hose reel

6.9

Alert other workers if you see
a fire

6.10

Alert other workers if you see
a flood

6.11

Alert other workers if you smell
gas

07

6.12

Alert other workers of a structural
collapse (building or scaffold)

6.13

Alert other workers if you see an
explosion

6.14

Alert other workers if you see a
bomb

07

6.15

Do not return to the site after an emergency

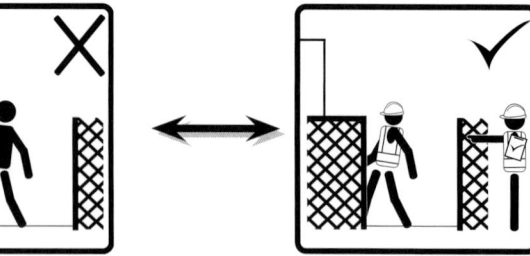

6.16

Only return to the site when a supervisor tells you

6.17

Emergency roll call

7.1

An untrained person should not use a fire extinguisher

7.2

Only a trained person should use a fire extinguisher

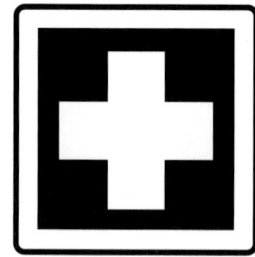

8.1

First aid

8.2

First-aid box

8.3

First-aid person

8.4

Accident book

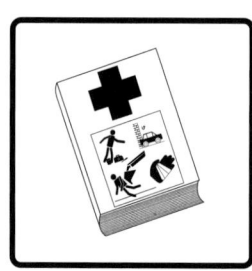

9.1

If you have an accident tell your supervisor to write what happened

10.1

Location of drinking water

10.2

Location of microwave (equipment to heat food)

10.3

Location of kettle or urn (equipment to heat water)

10.4

Location of canteen (eating area)

10.5

Location of restaurant (place to buy and eat food)

07

10.6

Location of toilets

10.7

Wash your hands with soap and water

10.8

Do not make the toilets dirty;
do not make the toilets untidy

10.9

Keep the toilets clean;
keep the toilets tidy

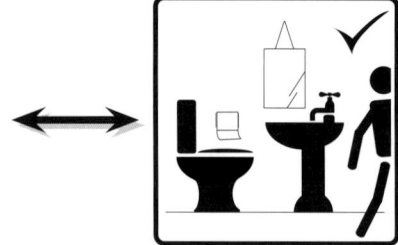

10.10

Use the sun protection cream

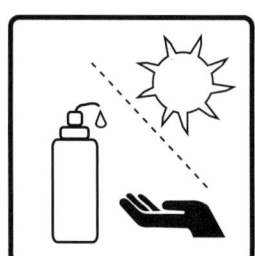

10.11

Use the barrier cream
(protect from chemicals)

10.12

Location of changing room and
drying room

10.13

Location of lockers

10.14

Do not make welfare area dirty.
Do not make welfare area untidy

10.15

Keep welfare area clean. Keep
welfare area tidy

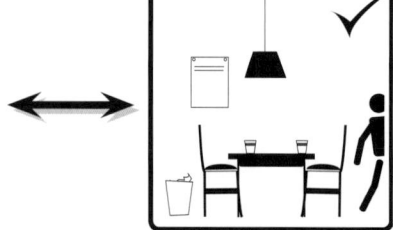

10.16

Location of showers

11.1

Risk assessment or method statement (safety instructions)

11.2

Follow the risk assessment or method statement

07

11.3

Do not leave tools or materials in the work area

11.4

Keep the work area tidy

11.5

Protect other workers if you are doing high risk work (dangerous)

11.6 (Specialist)

Get a permit to work (permission) before you go into an excavation

11.7 (Specialist)

Get a permit to work (permission) before work on electrical circuits

11.8 Specialist

Get a permit to work (permission) before you do any hot work (fire)

11.9 Specialist

Get a permit to work (permission) before you enter a confined space

12.1

Only trained people can use a power tool

12.2

Only trained people can use the machinery

12.3

Keep tools locked away when they are not being used

12.4

Do not use 240 volt electric tools

12.5

Only use 110 volt electric tools

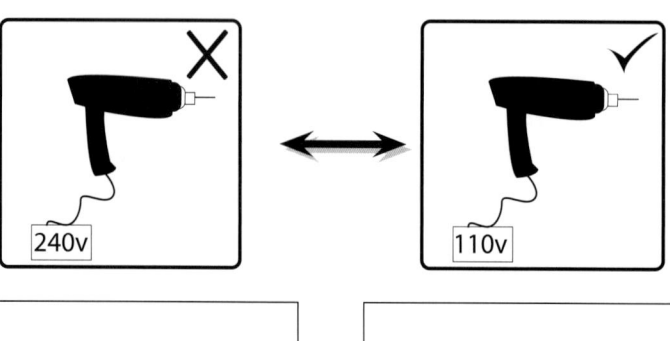

12.6 Specialist

Electrical equipment needs an up to date PAT test (safety test)

07

13.1

Alcohol is not allowed on the site

13.2

Illegal drugs are not allowed on the site

13.3

People with alcohol or drugs will be removed from the site

14.1

Smoking area

15.1

No mobile phones

15.2

No personal music players

07

15.3

No radios

15.4

Mobile phone area

16.1

Tell a supervisor or safety representative about any problems

17.1

Do not remove scaffold or alter scaffold (metal frame)

17.2

Only trained scaffolders can remove scaffold and alter scaffold

17.3

No fooling or fighting

07

Appendix B – Safety critical communication toolbox talks (GT 701) – Full content list

Volume 1

Occupational health and hygiene

First aid

H1 – First-aid equipment

H2 – First-aid person

Health on site

H3 – Dirty toilets

H4 – Dirty skin

H59 – Dust

H68 – Noise

H78 – Hours of work

H79 – Rats and mice

H80 – Alcohol

H81 – Illegal drugs

H82 – Exposure to the sun

H83 – Hand-arm vibration

Manual handling

H5 – Lifting (1)

H8 – Lifting (2)

H9 – Lifting (3)

Working at height

Ladders

H12 – Broken ladder (1)

H13 – Broken ladder (2)

H14 – Ladder positioning (1)

H15 – Ladder positioning (2)

H16 – Ladder positioning (3)

H19 – Ladder positioning (4)

H17 – Ladder use (1)

H18 – Ladder use (2)

H21 – Use of stepladder

H29 – Ladder use (3)

H55 – Ladders not in use

H75 – Ladder use, handholds (4)

H76 – Ladder use, uneven surface (5)

H77 – Ladder use, weak surface (6)

Working platforms/hoists

H20 – Safe working load (platform)

H22 – Safe working load (hoist)

H23 – Competent use

H24 – Guard-rail

Mobile work platforms (MWP)

H25 – Use of MWP (1)

H26 – Use of MWP (2)

H27 – Use of MWP (3)

H28 – Use of MWP (4)

Volume 2

Scaffolding

H30 – Use of scaffolding (1)

H31 – Use of scaffolding (2)

H32 – Use of scaffolding (3)

H33 – Incomplete scaffolding

H74 – Position of people below

Working on a roof

H34 – No edge protection

H35 – Fragile roof

Plant and equipment, safe use

Hand tools

H41 – Use of abrasive (cutting) wheel

H42 – Use of cartridge tool (nail gun)

H43 – Electric tools, condition of (1)

H44 – Electric tools, condition of (2)

H45 – Electric tools, correct voltage

H56 – Use of hand tools near electricity

H67 – Hidden services

Mobile elevating work platforms (MEWP)

H37 – Use of MEWP (1)

H38 – Use of MEWP (2)

H39 – Safe working loads

H40 – MEWP and people

07

Safety critical communication – Appendix B

Mobile cranes/equipment

H46 – Mobile crane, correct use of

H47 – Mobile equipment and passengers

H48 – Mobile equipment and people

H49 – Mobile equipment and untrained personnel

H50 – Mobile equipment, left unattended

H60 – Excavator near electricity

Vehicles

H51 – Vehicle reversing

H52 – Unsafe loads

Excavations

H36 – Excavation unprotected

H57 – Moving equipment into excavation

H58 – Alighting from excavation

H61 – Excavation unprotected

H62 – Incorrect excavation

H63 – Mobile plant near excavation

H64 – Excavation with no support

H65 – Excavation internal supports removed

H66 – Excavation with no support

Fire and flammable substances

H69 – Fire hazards – source of fuel

H70 – Fire hazards – use of flammable substances

H71 – Fire extinguishers

H72 – Smoking

H73 – Correct positioning of gas cylinders

Other hazards at work

H6 – Blocking hazard (1)

H10 – Blocking hazard (2)

H7 – Bad light

H11 – Housekeeping

H53 – Hazardous substances, storage

H54 – Security of site

08

Behavioural safety

The chapter explores what behavioural safety is and the elements of working practice that can have an impact on this, both positively and negatively. It offers information and models that can inform best practice in this significant area of focus for health and safety.

Studies have shown that up to 90% of accidents are attributable in some extent to human failures. Human factors are understandably a key focus for many accident investigations. The importance and relevance of these to preventing incidents, injuries, deaths and ill health within the workplace, as identified through case study research, therefore warrant the attention of all organisations, managers and employees.

Introduction	114
Key points	114
Why use a behavioural safety approach?	115
Preparing to implement a behavioural approach	116
Factors influencing a behavioural approach	117
Key stages in a behavioural safety programme	119
Reducing human error and influencing behaviour	122
Appendix A – Health and Safety Executive Human factors checklist	128

Behavioural safety

8.1 Introduction

Promoting safe behaviour at work is a crucial part of the management of health and safety, because behaviour defines the real experience of systems and procedures. Having good systems in place does not on its own ensure successful health and safety management. The level of success is defined by how organisations 'live' their systems on a day-to-day basis – the behavioural culture of the organisation.

The Health and Safety Executive (HSE) identifies behavioural safety as one key area within the overarching title of human factors that:

> refer to environmental, organisational and job factors, and human and individual characteristics, which influence behaviour at work in a way which can affect health and safety.

Behavioural safety provides a focus for understanding and influencing the way managers and individuals act the way they do in relation to work activities and decision making. It is based on a process of:

Asking workforce for input and ideas

- ☑ identifying and making evident safe and unsafe practice
- ☑ observation and appropriate intervention to encourage safe/amend unsafe practice
- ☑ feedback of vital information to inform decision making
- ☑ training, process, material and environmental change as appropriate.

Behavioural safety represents a proactive rather than a reactive process, engaging all managers and workers within a culture of continuous improvement and safety awareness. For this reason, communication at and across all levels of an organisation is a vital strand to the development of a successful and influential strategy.

Raising the awareness of managers, supervisors and workers to ensure that effective behavioural safety modification is an expected part of the working culture will be a significant factor in helping to reduce these numbers.

 Useful HSE publications are available from the HSE website.

 The HSE has identified human and organisational behaviours to be significant factors in relation to workplace accidents and time lost to work. Studies have shown that up to 90% of accidents are attributable in some extent to human failure.

8.2 Key points

- ☑ Historically improvements in health and safety standards have been achieved through **engineering technology/controls** (plant and equipment) and **safety management systems** (risk assessments, permits to work and so on).
- ☑ These improvements will not fully eradicate incidents and accidents.
- ☑ By understanding how and **why people act** is the vital third element.
- ☑ The biggest gain in improving health and safety performance is integrating and understanding the human element of risk management.
- ☑ Companies that incorporate behavioural safety programmes into the day-to-day running of their business see dramatic drops in accident rates.
- ☑ In order for a behavioural safety approach to work, consistently high standards of engineering technology/controls and safety management systems need to be established.
- ☑ Behavioural safety is not a quick-win initiative – it takes time and commitment from all levels of a company or organisation.
- ☑ Management and workforce support is crucial for the success of any programme.
- ☑ People generally think they are working safely, or that the risk of something happening is minimal due to their knowledge and past experience. Those observing can often see that the risk is greater than first thought and thus intervention techniques play a key role in developing a positive safety culture.

☑ Workers respond more positively to co-worker/peer intervention.

☑ Worker engagement is a fundamental component of any behavioural safety programme.

8.3 Why use a behavioural safety approach?

Over recent years, significant improvements have been achieved in health, safety and environmental performance. This has been gained largely through technological advances and improved focus through the use of management systems.

A levelling-off of this successful downward trend has led to an increased focus on the human elements associated with health and safety practices, awareness, commitment and decision-making.

It is believed that a behavioural safety approach by all associated with the construction and other industries will contribute to more improvements over time.

Evidence and support for this has come from HSE case study investigations and research into major reportable accidents.

The case studies identify actions and strategies that have been implemented within the example organisations in order to improve specific health and safety practice.

Commitment by the team is vital

From this work, the HSE and contributing partners have identified a list of human factor issues. These include separate notes on the following topics:

☑ introducing human factors

☑ competence

☑ humans and risk (integration of human factors into risk assessments and accident investigation)

☑ written procedures

☑ emergency response

☑ maintenance

☑ safety culture

☑ safety-critical communications

☑ alarm handling and control room design

☑ fatigue

☑ organisational change and transition management

☑ human factors and the major accident prevention policy (MAPP).

 The HSE has produced a human factors checklist, which is available on its website.

The checklist offers a series of self-assessment statements that may provide a useful benchmark for areas involved in the human factors approach to behavioural safety.

The HSE also notes other key problems found from inspection and assessment:

☑ too much emphasis being placed on reducing personal accidents (slips, trips, falls), without an equal focus on preventing major accidents

☑ failing to realise that safety culture is about everyone in the company, including managers, not just the frontline staff

☑ not being clear about how the safety management system will prevent or reduce human errors, which may lead to major accidents.

To be effective, a behaviour-based approach to health and safety requires:

☑ clear and unambiguous leadership from the top down

☑ management commitment to the culture of behavioural safety

☑ buy-in at all levels to making the scheme work

☑ an up-front commitment in terms of time, effort and determination

☑ scheme sponsors who believe in the value of making it work, who can be sympathetic to the reasons why some people behave in an unsafe manner and persuasive in convincing those people that they should not behave in that way

08

Behavioural safety

- ☑ effective communication of the scheme objectives
- ☑ a concerted effort to convince those affected that they will not be disadvantaged by the changes that will come about as a result of introducing the approach
- ☑ effective engagement of everyone involved in the approach; not just those working on site but people involved in decision making too.

8.4 Preparing to implement a behavioural approach

The HSE's core guidance defines human factors as the interaction between three main areas affecting human performance at work:

- ☑ the job
- ☑ the individual
- ☑ the organisation.

The job

The job will ideally be well designed to match the skills and strengths of the individual or team undertaking it. In this way, the job is matched to the human.

Job design will have a focus on:

- ☑ areas of work and the environment in which it is carried out
- ☑ materials and tools
- ☑ control and display panels and devices
- ☑ communication and management systems
- ☑ all job-related written guidance and information.

The individual

The organisation and managers will also select individuals who are well matched to meet the needs of the job (fitting the human to the job). Individuals should have:

- ☑ the most suitable physique (size, build and strength)
- ☑ the right personality
- ☑ aptitude
- ☑ competence - the right skills, understanding, experience and training.

The organisation

The organisation will ensure that it supports managers to:

- ☑ take responsibility for all aspects of work and work design
- ☑ devise and maintain a good safety management system
- ☑ encourage a good safety culture by showing genuine commitment
- ☑ consult the workforce on key decisions
- ☑ commit to learning from the latest thinking on best practice in safety
- ☑ openly encourage identification and shared learning from accidents and near misses.

Together, these three areas constitute the solid foundations on which behavioural safety programmes can be addressed and developed.

 Best practice and case studies indicate that prior to commencing any behavioural safety modification programme, intervention, factors relating to the job, the individual and the organisation will all need to be considered.

Before sites embark on a behavioural safety programme, it is recommended that the following preparation has taken place:

- ☑ all hazards have been identified
- ☑ human performance issues have been identified and managed (particularly in relation to safety critical roles and activities)
- ☑ the hierarchy of control has been applied to prevent the occurrence of identified hazards, or minimise their consequences should they occur
- ☑ the site has the required engineering, operating and maintenance capability and experience (including appropriate staffing levels)
- ☑ accurate operating procedures are available for all eventualities, including emergencies
- ☑ individuals (operators) are fully prepared to deal with all conditions. This will include identification of training needs, training, assessment, rehearsal and reassessment

- ☑ training should include underlying knowledge of the process, so that operators can troubleshoot (identify and respond to abnormal situations as they develop). It should not just provide the minimum knowledge required to operate the plant. This will help to manage residual risk arising from hazards that were not identified or effectively addressed

- ☑ lessons have been learnt from site, company and industry experience

- ☑ succession planning ensures that corporate knowledge is retained

- ☑ safety management arrangements and risk control measures have been reviewed to ensure that they remain usable and relevant.

It is recommended that only when these technical and systems issues have been addressed can the timing and appropriateness of a behavioural programme be addressed.

Unsafe working – reasons for implementing a behavioural safety approach

The guidance also goes on to highlight the following for consideration:

- ☑ do not underestimate the resources required – it is not a one-off exercise, but a new way of working that must be maintained for any positive results to be sustained

- ☑ do not be over-optimistic – not all interventions are completely successful in their main aim. High expectations may lead to later disillusionment

- ☑ be clear about what you want to achieve and how you will know that you have achieved it

- ☑ pilot the intervention (for example, to ensure that the approach is workable, that the facilitators or observers understand what is required and that the appropriate data is being recorded)

- ☑ talk to similar companies and trade associations about their interventions and experiences

- ☑ as with all interventions, listen to your employees and use the process to improve dialogue – involve employees early in the choice of programme

- ☑ make the language and style of the package your own, as off-the-shelf packages may not be appropriate for your site's needs

- ☑ use strong site facilitators – the success of such interventions is greatly helped by using a personable, experienced and respected site personnel as facilitators

- ☑ ensure that the focus is on the root causes of behaviours

- ☑ on major hazard sites, don't neglect process safety (beware 'what gets measured gets done').

8.5   Factors influencing a behavioural approach

The practicalities of successfully implementing a behavioural approach to health and safety involve:

- ☑ preparation (see above) – knowing what you are doing and why

- ☑ establishing an effective system of two-way communication to develop mutual trust between management and workforce

- ☑ engaging the right people in the decision making

- ☑ observing people at work

- ☑ assessing their safe and unsafe behaviours (being non-judgemental)

- ☑ making timely and appropriate interventions

- ☑ establishing why unsafe behaviours take place

- ☑ influencing those who behave unsafely not to do so in the future

- ☑ recognising safe behaviours and, if appropriate, rewarding these

- ☑ continuing assessment and research whilst looking for improvements in safe behaviour.

The overall and wider benefits to this implementation can include:

- ☑ more effective communication regarding safety between management and frontline workers

- ☑ greater management visibility

- ☑ increased efficiency

- ☑ greater flexibility and effectiveness of workers

- ☑ a reduction in the number of workplace injuries

- ☑ improvement in the standards of health and safety

- ☑ reduced physical and financial losses for the individual and the employer

- ☑ the extension of safe working practices into home life.

08

Behavioural safety

The following are all factors that are relevant and require consideration when implementing a behavioural safety programme.

The psychology of behaviour

Behavioural safety applies tried and tested psychological principles in order to mediate the way people and organisations do things, particularly how people act or behave in respect of their own health and safety and that of others.

Among many other factors, behavioural approach takes into account:

- ☑ how people think
- ☑ how people act and behave
- ☑ how people respond to certain situations
- ☑ how their immediate surroundings can influence people's thoughts and actions.

Thought processes

Contrary to previous belief, the conscious or alert state of mind can only be actively engaged in one activity or thought process at any one time.

Recent neuroscience research and findings have identified that distractions from a single task can, at best, result in less efficient working and at worst, can contribute to a stress response. This is particularly so if someone tries to finish a task but cannot as time goes on.

The human brain is strongly programmed to avoid a perceived threat and generally (but less strongly) programmed for reward from tasks achieved. This latter results in the small, so-called 'dopamine spike', which drives us to continue with our reward-based behaviour.

In practical terms, if a distraction disturbs a person's thought processes or task, they may, for example, trip over a toolbox they have placed on some steps or fall into a hole they have recently dug. Other thoughts have entered their conscious mind and the hazardous situation is momentarily forgotten.

At the most basic level, good workplace practice (such as avoiding distractions and removing hazards immediately) can support the wider behavioural safety programme.

Often the ability to increase safety awareness by the individual doing a mental risk assessment (that is, asking 'What is going to put me at risk while I do this job?') is not improved or encouraged once relevant training has been undertaken. Practising this type of self-awareness has safety benefits, especially if it is recorded.

People at work benefit from being able to discuss and take responsibility for the day-to-day aspects of their job and from feeling competent to do so. The human side of the working environment is a highly significant factor in determining the success of a behavioural safety environment and this warrants a focus on management training and commitment.

By helping people to understand the implications of how they work and engaging their knowledge, we can identify the process that integrates human factors into the core management system of the business. Effort should be targeted at encouraging positive, open and real communication that resolves issues when they arise, rather than keeping them hidden until an incident occurs.

Habitual behaviours

Habits are subconscious ways of thinking, both positive and negative. They are formed when a task or behaviour is repeated over time.

This enables the thinking part of the brain (the pre-frontal cortex) to conserve energy through reducing its need for active attention and processing. Effectively, the brain is saying 'I have done this before – no need to pay conscious attention to this then!'.

The more repetitions an action has, the stronger the habit, until very little, if any conscious thought is given to the task. This is termed being unconsciously competent, and an example would be driving a car after much experience.

An example of a habit that can have negative consequences is not wearing eye protection when using a disc-cutter because the past is used to justify present actions. The worker has not been injured before so argues that they will not be injured now. Similar arguments are often put forward for many self-protective and safety-focused equipment and practices.

Similarly, a positive habit can be formed by communicating the benefits and consciously ensuring that eye protection is worn. This could be achieved through raising awareness via posters or stickers on the disc-cutter, keeping eye protection with the disc-cutter, or spoken reminders from work colleagues and managers. When encouraged and reinforced through these or similar measures, wearing eye protection becomes a comfortable habit and the expected norm.

Values, beliefs, expectations, attitudes and behaviour

We all have our own values and beliefs (attitudes) that underlie how we think and then drive the way we act and behave.

Being able to influence these areas is a significant management responsibility, which can be achieved through day-to-day working practice, the level and manner of communication and the delivery of any structured programme to address health and safety interventions.

Whilst the commitment of managers can send a powerful positive message regarding behavioural culture, a lack of commitment can be equally but negatively powerful.

Case study material suggests that low expectations and poor leadership from management can create negative attitudes from employees. This in turn can result in poor methods of working resulting in poor health and safety performance.

The challenge

Potential barriers to progress

There are a number of barriers that have been identified from existing behavioural safety programmes. These may include any of the following:

- ☑ management promoting a negative or passive message, making the workforce believe that it is collecting unnecessary data or that the information will never provide solutions

- ☑ middle managers either excluded from communication or not understanding the programme

- ☑ processes not reaching their potential because they are time-consuming and seen as stopping people from getting on with the job without consideration of the huge potential benefits

- ☑ processes that generate committees, create databases and induce an overload that the majority of small and medium businesses find difficult to resource

- ☑ organisations fully understanding that behavioural safety approaches are not short-term solutions but may be 'a change in the way we do things round here' that will need an effective investment of resource and commitment

- ☑ a lack of trust leading workers to feel that they will be blamed in some way

- ☑ an existing environment of poor industrial relationships or grievance procedures.

Enablers to progress

- ☑ Commitment of management to the programme implementation.

- ☑ Middle managers' involvement in, and understanding of, the behavioural safety programme objectives.

- ☑ Sufficient resources at all levels with which to support activities, materials and training.

- ☑ A good level of trust between managers and frontline workers.

- ☑ The absence of industrial relations issues.

- ☑ Existing involvement of the workforce in health and safety practice.

- ☑ Innovative and new practice features to the programme on a regular (for example, annual) basis.

> **!** Recognising the importance of management commitment to a behavioural safety programme is a key determinant in the successful implementation of that programme.

08

Induction for all: enabling progress on a behavioural safety programme

8.6   Key stages in a behavioural safety programme

From research into relevant case studies and literature, The Keil Centre, in its report for the HSE, *Strategies to promote safe behaviour as part of a health and safety management system*, offers the following model of how programmes may be implemented within organisations. Not all elements need to be included in all programmes; this is for guidance and adaptation as appropriate.

> **www.** For further information refer to the HSE's website.

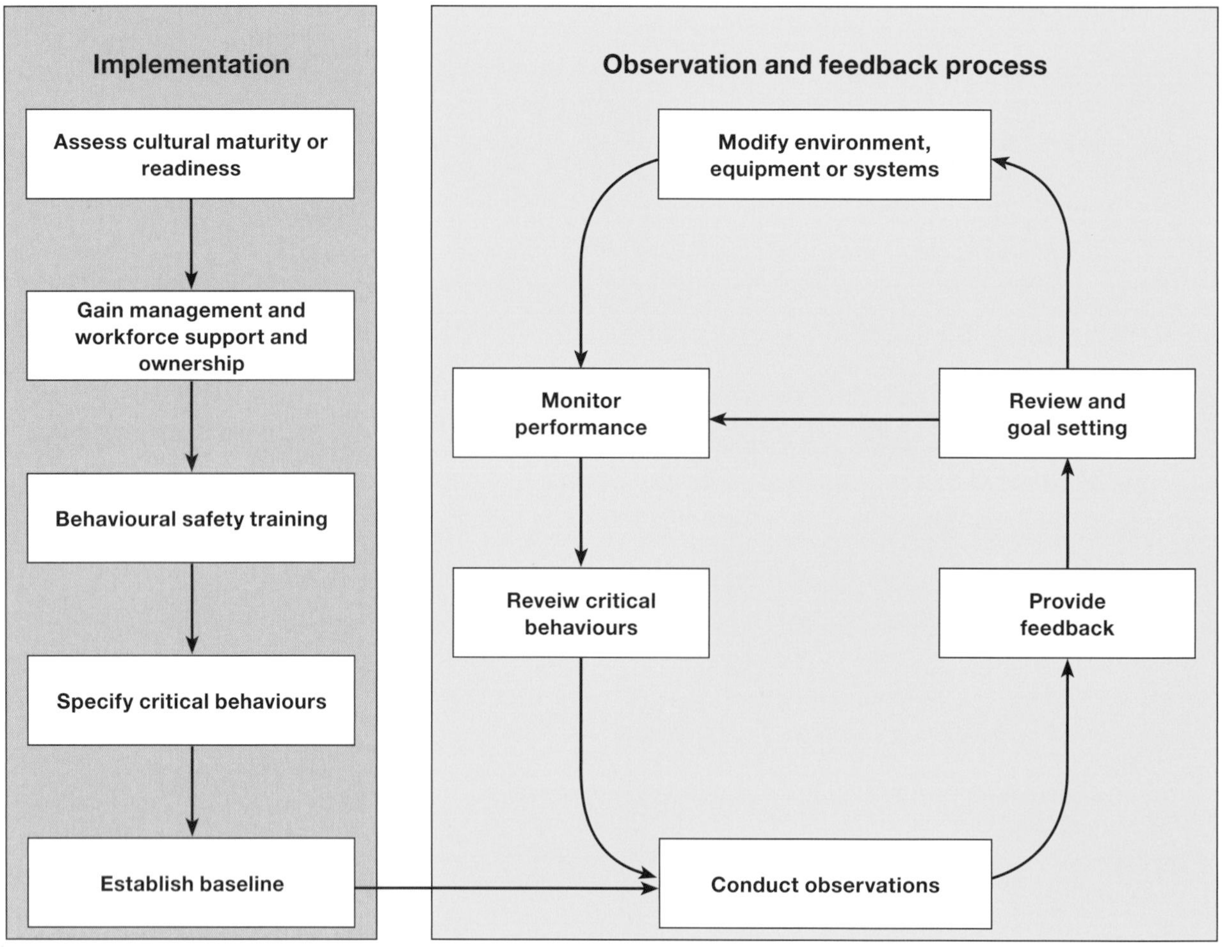

Behavioural safety

Implementation

- Assess cultural maturity or readiness
- Gain management and workforce support and ownership
- Behavioural safety training
- Specify critical behaviours
- Establish baseline

Observation and feedback process

- Modify environment, equipment or systems
- Monitor performance
- Reveiw critical behaviours
- Review and goal setting
- Provide feedback
- Conduct observations

Overview of a behavioural safety programme

Implementation

Assess cultural maturity or readiness

At this first stage, the organisation would assess whether it is ready to commit to the implementation of a behavioural safety programme.

This is the stage where potential challenges to success are identified and addressed. This could include an organisational restructure or relocation. It could also highlight and benchmark management commitment and communication processes, by holding workshops, issuing questionnaires or simply through one-to-one interviews.

Management and workforce support and ownership

Management and workforce support is crucial for the success of the programme. It defines the culture within which the behavioural safety activities occur and can be encouraged through early involvement of all individuals.

Involvement is generally an emotional response and depends both on the commitment of the individual and the organisation's support and appreciation of their input, views and opinions. People will need to see that they carry influence and can impact on the style and content of the programme to be implemented.

Success of the programme will also depend on the opportunities for individuals involved in managing the programme, or in acting as behavioural safety champions. Not everyone can fulfil these roles and so the organisation may create a process for recruiting to a steering group or to co-ordinator roles. Volunteers can be requested and consideration given to representatives from the entire workforce.

 Many programmes require that observations are made of colleagues carrying out tasks. These observations are generally carried out by frontline workers and identify issues relevant to behavioural safety practice and the overall programme. Training is required for these observers to record information, deliver feedback and focus on the objectives that are critical for continuous improvement.

Behavioural safety training

Training managers and workers in the understanding of behavioural safety tools and objectives is crucial to programme success.

At the most basic level, this can be awareness training, whilst co-ordinators, managers and those carrying out key responsibilities will require more in-depth information.

Some programmes train all staff, whereas others train a minority of employees. Decisions regarding this are taken on the basis of internal knowledge and resource (people, financial and material) and the depth of the programme itself.

Specifying critical safety behaviours

Behavioural safety programmes focus on developing a checklist of critical safety behaviours that is completed by the trained observers.

Critical health and safety behaviours are identified through a number of different means. These include, but are not solely based on, the analysis of previous accident and incident reports.

Additional information can also be gained from other sources. These can include reviewing previous risk assessments (such as COSHH) and audits, in addition to formal and informal input from frontline staff and managers. Near-miss or dangerous occurrence reports are equally valid sources of critical safety behaviours.

Preparation that focuses solely on formal reporting is important but limited in scope. This will exclude critical health and safety behaviours that have not yet resulted in serious consequences but which hide latent risk.

It is vital that critical safety behaviours and their measures are sufficiently well defined to enable meaningful observations to be made and recorded.

Formal and informal reporting are significant areas of research when defining the critical safety behaviours to be addressed by the programme. Important contributions to this process can be made from a number of levels within an organisation.

Establishing a benchmark

The final preparatory element involves identifying a baseline, or benchmarking where the organisation is currently, in relation to the selected critical safety behaviours.

This is established through conducting observations of these areas in practice. A benchmark will enable review and evaluation of the programme's effectiveness to be more clearly defined.

08

The continuous process of observation and feedback

After the implementation phase, this next continuous stage of observation, feedback, goal setting and review commences.

Observations

The next stage in the process is conducting observations. This is generally peer-to-peer, but can be done by managers. It is usual for the observer to be provided with a checklist (the critical behaviours identified previously). The observer indicates on the list whether the individual is safe, unsafe or if the behaviour was not observed.

Defining critical safety behaviours clearly at the pre-observation stage and through the benchmarking process will increase quality and meaning clearly during the programme.

Feedback

The provision of feedback is an imperative process within the behavioural safety programme, which can survive or flounder dependent on the skills of observers, their style and credibility. For this reason feedback must be considered to be a critical skill and individuals should be trained accordingly.

Feedback most effectively reinforces safe behaviour when it is positive and delivered by someone perceived as credible and knowledgeable by the individual receiving the feedback. Feedback can have a greater or lesser impact dependent upon:

- ☑ when it is delivered (generally, the closer and more relevant to the observation the more meaningful the feedback)
- ☑ the focus of the feedback (this should be on the observed behaviour, not on the individual practising the behaviour)
- ☑ relevance (the feedback should fit the expectations of the person receiving the feedback and with the behaviour under observation).

There are two main types of feedback:

- ☑ **summative feedback** offers more general comment on an individual's overall performance
- ☑ **formative feedback** provides more detailed information on how they might improve their performance in the future.

Behavioural safety

 The quality of feedback and its style of delivery is critical to the success of a behavioural safety programme. Observers will need to be trained in positive feedback skills in order to contribute as effectively as possible to the behaviour improvement cycle.

Goal setting and review

Goal setting is a participative process involving the observer and either the individual or group concerned.

This process can have an important influence in terms of encouraging supporting behavioural change. People are hard-wired to achieve goals, as this feeds into their brain's internal reward system. The key is to set goals that have the following qualities (SMART):

☑ stated positively (specific)   ☑ realistic

☑ measurable   ☑ time-bound.

☑ achievable

And finally, goals should be within the direct control of the individual. If they do not meet these important criteria, the individual may not be able to achieve the goal set. This can be demoralising, which in turn can have a direct impact on the success of the programme.

Target or goal setting can take place as regularly as is warranted by the critical behaviours themselves; in some instances this might be every week or month. In many instances, it can be undertaken on a pre-scheduled quarterly basis.

Monitor performance

Behavioural safety programmes are monitored over time with a key focus being the impact of the programme on the initially identified critical safety behaviours. A good measure of success is an improved percentage of observations where behaviour is observed as safe.

If there is little or no change in this measure over time for some or all observations, it will be important to review the specific behaviours with regard to barriers to change. These could be people or product/design related that work against safe behavioural practice.

Review list of critical behaviours

A review of critical behaviours can be carried out within a defined timescale in order to ensure that the programme is still addressing areas that are relevant and improving. Once these have become habitual they may be replaced by other significant critical behaviours, which are developed through the same looped cycle as detailed by this general model.

 Once implemented, the success of the programme is highly dependent upon the commitment made, particularly by managers, at each stage of the process. People will value action and communication regarding progress and assume a lack of commitment if these are not carried through as expected.

8.7   Reducing human error and influencing behaviour

People can cause or contribute to accidents, or mitigate the consequences, in a number of ways:

☑ by failing to carry out a job correctly

☑ hearing but not listening or understanding health and safety information that is associated with the task, thereby failing to work to expectations.

People do not generally set out to make errors deliberately but they are often set up to fail by the way the brain processes information. For example, errors may occur as a result of:

☑ stress or fatigue

☑ working long hours without sufficient rest, or with erratic shift patterns

☑ slipping into autopilot mode

☑ a lack of training

☑ poor design of equipment

☑ unclear or lack of effective procedures

☑ shortcomings in the culture of the organisation

☑ poor decision making, even when aware of the risks

☑ misinterpretation of a situation or inappropriate action taken

☑ poor situational assessment leading to incident escalation.

When confident and knowledgeable to do so, other people (such as workmates, supervisors and managers) can intervene to prevent potential accidents or mitigate their possible effects.

The severity of an accident can be reduced by the effectiveness of the immediate or emergency response. This effectiveness can be improved by planning and appropriate training.

The following are some of the topics that can influence human error and behaviour.

Active and latent failures

The consequences of human failure can be immediate or delayed. It is important to have an understanding of active and latent failures and how they impact on health and safety.

☑ **Active failures** have an immediate consequence and are usually made by frontline people (such as drivers, operators or even the public). In a situation where there is no room for error, these active failures have an immediate impact on health and safety.

☑ **Latent failures** are caused by actions generally involving people (such as designers, decision makers and managers) whose tasks are removed in time and space from operational activities. Latent failures are typically failures in the design, implementation or monitoring of health and safety management systems.

Latent failures can provide a significant potential danger to health and safety. These can be highlighted only through positive safety discussions that utilise the experience and knowledge of the workforce.

Latent failures can have serious consequences

Latent failures are generally hidden within an organisation until they are triggered by an event likely to have serious consequences.

Examples of latent failures are:

☑ poor design of workplaces, plant and equipment

☑ gaps in supervision

☑ undetected manufacturing defects

☑ maintenance failures

☑ unworkable procedures

☑ clumsy automation

☑ ineffective competency assurance

☑ ineffective training

☑ ineffective communications

☑ uncertainties of role and responsibility

☑ ageing assets, plant, tools and equipment

☑ poor planning – insufficient people/time

☑ poor information on health and safety incidents.

The impact of change

Change of any type within an organisation can create people and behavioural issues. For example:

☑ an organisation may appoint new leaders and managers

☑ roles can change

☑ the need to develop new skills and capabilities may increase.

Workers may be uncertain and resistant because:

☑ communication and explanation of the change has been limited

☑ people do not see the need for change

☑ they feel that they will be disadvantaged by the change.

Dealing with these issues on a reactive, case-by-case basis puts the progress of the job, workforce morale, and overall performance of the behavioural approach at risk.

Change is unsettling for people at all levels of an organisation. The manager, or management team, will need to focus on working together and understanding that change can lead to:

☑ alterations in typical working practice

☑ stressful responses

☑ a potential need for increased communication and support.

Change affects people personally; this can also be a factor in the implementation of a behavioural safety approach.

08

Behavioural safety

Individuals (or teams of individuals) will require timely information regarding:

- ✓ the changes they will see as a result of a behavioural safety programme
- ✓ what will be expected of them during and after the change programme
- ✓ how they and their behaviours will be measured
- ✓ what success or failure will mean for them and those around them.

Leading by example

The implementation of behavioural safety can pose particular problems with a fragmented and mobile workforce, such as that found in the construction industry.

To be successfully implemented on site, the principles of behavioural safety will need to be embedded within the organisation's culture and understood by the workforce and management from the initiation and planning stages.

The foundations, expectations and compliance processes should be communicated, discussed and agreed from the beginning. If employees and contractors are involved, can influence and are provided with the relevant induction, critical safety behavioural standards will be set for the future.

Managers are a critical element within the success or failure of programmes. Non-compliance and the breaking of basic rules (such as not wearing hard hats or safety goggles) sends a message that a behavioural safety approach is not taken seriously, despite policies and procedures to the contrary.

Similarly, when senior managers visit sites, they should receive the same induction and live by the same rules – body language and example can send a powerful message.

Communication style and content

Communication style and content are important elements that contribute significantly to the building of trust. People feel trust when an individual's behaviour and body language is congruent with what is being said – when 'walking the talk' is evident. Our brains are particularly good at picking up on communication signals from others, whether intended or, as can sometimes be the case, unintended.

Communication is at the heart of all that we do, both at work and in our own time. It takes place in many forms and can be transmitted via various media (for example face-to-face, radio, telephone, email or video conferencing). It is essential, especially within our working environment, that we get it right. Barriers to efficient communication may include background noise, the type of language used and sociocultural issues. The potential for confusion and misinterpretation can be high.

In any communication process, it is vital to give the person receiving information the time and space to be able to think and formulate a response. In communication it is the quality, not the quantity, that matters.

Verbal and non-verbal communication

During a normal conversation, we usually transmit and receive in three ways:

- ✓ what is said (words)
- ✓ how it is said (tonality)
- ✓ body language (conscious or not).

During periods of high workload or stress, our body language goes largely unnoticed. This is when the words we use and the way in which we say them become more important. In addition, our listening capability reduces as our workload or stress increases.

Key points are:

- ✓ communication involves both a communicator and a receiver and is generally the responsibility of the communicator
- ✓ what we say, how we say it and when we say it are perceived differently by different individuals
- ✓ overload of work and stress can be key factors that hinder effective communication. If the receiver is feeling overloaded, communication will need to reflect this. If the message is important then we need to lessen the workload
- ✓ job-critical communication requires undivided attention by both the communicator and the receiver
- ✓ the most effective communicators will always check that the meaning they intend through their communication is the one that has been received.

There is a difference between hearing and listening. Hearing is a mechanical process involving the way sound waves are translated. Listening is the paying attention to what is being said. When we do this, we are able to evaluate the message within the correct context. An appropriate response can then be planned.

Listening is often described as taking place at different levels, from the less attentive Level 1 (conversational listening) to the more engaging Level 4 (deep listening). At this level, the listener is paying as much attention to body language and signals regarding what is not being said as they are to the words that are spoken.

This type of listening takes skill and practice and is the mark of a good communicator. Observers within a behavioural safety programme would find great benefit in becoming listening masters, so they have the potential to pick up on and challenge safety-related information that could otherwise be missed.

08

Questioning skills

How questions are asked can inform the overall effectiveness of a discussion in terms of information shared.

There are several types of question. Those most commonly used are described as:

Type	Response
Closed	A fact or YES/NO.
Open	Invites an extensive reply.
Leading	Indicates the required answer.
Limiting	Restricts options.
Multiple	Many questions in one – confusion.

It is important to recognise that we are always communicating. Silence can imply annoyance or criticism, for example. Take time to consider and understand the effect of your personal communication style on others.

Some good practices in communication are to:

- ☑ control distractions as much as possible
- ☑ where possible, make visual and eye contact
- ☑ clearly identify the communicator and receiver
- ☑ be clear, precise and concise
- ☑ avoid words that could be misinterpreted or that are ambiguous
- ☑ never assume meaning
- ☑ always work to confirm that the intended communication has been appropriately understood
- ☑ encourage inclusive discussion and dialogue
- ☑ use phonetics for alphanumeric information (for example, 'M for mother')
- ☑ acknowledge communication from the listener (closed loop communication).

Facilitation, coaching and mentoring

Managers and team leaders should be as honest and explicit as possible about what impacts on health and safety within their workplace. This is particularly the case when an organisation is undergoing a change programme.

Facilitation, coaching and mentoring are interventions and support mechanisms through which individuals are encouraged to take responsibility and contribute ideas to the benefit and safety of others and the organisation.

Individual commitment, ownership and accountability for safety is vital to making change happen. Everyone must be willing to accept responsibility for change in the areas they influence or control. It is important that the need to support and be supported through change is also recognised throughout the workforce, as a part of the behavioural safety culture.

Ownership of challenges is often encouraged by involving people in identifying problems and crafting solutions. It is reinforced by coaching and facilitation, incentives and, in some instances, rewards. These can be tangible (for example, financial compensation) or psychological (for example, camaraderie and a sense of shared involvement).

The most effective behavioural change programmes reinforce the core messages of safety through regular, timely engagement and communications that are both inspirational and practicable. Facilitated discussions are targeted to provide employees with the right information at the right time and to solicit their input and feedback.

Staffing levels

Some companies operate with the lowest possible number of people required to achieve their commercial objectives. Margins are tight and contracts are won and lost on cost.

Under these circumstances, people can be stretched beyond acceptable limits. Individuals could have a high workload, working long hours and experiencing high levels of stress and fatigue. Operating without sufficient human resource can result in significant risk to the workforce.

Training and competency

It is likely that a workforce is more effective and efficient if it is:

- ☑ motivated and well trained
- ☑ not under unreasonable time pressure
- ☑ given the correct information and training
- ☑ working with the right, well-maintained equipment.

08

Behavioural safety

Conversely, high workloads and tight timescales often result in training and competency assessments falling by the wayside.

This can lead to ineffective decision making, poor working practices, out-of-date certification of plant, equipment and, of course, a negative effect on people's skills and behavioural safety practice.

As part of managing change, it is essential that a training and competency assessment is carried out so that shortcomings are identified and addressed, and consequently people are not put at risk.

Every company is responsible in law to ensure that people are trained and competent to carry out their tasks. Greater production efficiencies are achieved through correct skill levels and further gains are made in completion times and work output.

Intervention

There are many recorded instances of people failing to intervene when they see an unsafe or illegal act.

Unsafe working at height – failure to intervene carries health and safety risks

Whilst it is fully understandable that someone might not want to become involved in a violent confrontation in the street, in the context of work the personal risk to say, a supervisor who intervenes to prevent someone working unsafely, is generally not as great.

However, the behaviour of supervisors and managers can directly affect the behaviour of operatives. The effect of failing to intervene in an unsafe situation is to condone that activity, practice or behaviour.

This in turn, sends a message to the operatives that the activity concerned is permitted, resulting in potential confusion for site teams and their working practices. Intervention by managers and supervisors is therefore crucial in every case in order to show commitment to, and support for, behavioural safety programmes.

From general research and available information, the reasons for a failure to intervene appear to be split between a **lack of knowledge** that anything is wrong and a **conscious decision** not to take any action.

Conscious decision

The conscious decision not to intervene may possibly be based upon financial or time considerations. For example, a supervisor might ignore the unsafe use of a ladder because it saves the time and expense of hiring a mobile elevating work platform (MEWP).

However, there may be other personal factors for not intervening.

- ☑ Overload. The supervisor or manager is suffering from a heavy workload and is simply unable to identify the unsafe situation developing.

- ☑ Actions of others, especially other managers or senior managers, can shape the decisions of the supervisor. Usually the fact that no-one else involved in the operation is concerned about it is excuse enough for not getting involved.

- ☑ Ownership of the situation where the supervisor or manager does not actually believe or understand their duties, or where they are not directly in charge of the operation and believe they have no jurisdiction.

- ☑ Where a supervisor or manager lacks knowledge about the task or the important communication skills, then they are less likely to get involved – having the skills to resolve the issue is important.

- ☑ The risk of possibly entering into a situation where they may be required to make a difficult decision that could have a significant effect on the project. The support of senior managers is critical to allow junior managers and supervisors to become involved in safety issues and empower them to take whatever action they deem necessary if an unsafe situation arises. This could even involve the cessation of work until the safety issue is investigated further.

Risk and safety

Making assessments about risks and reaching an informed decision requires the information held within the safety management system.

The process of obtaining information begins with the recognition that the problem exists, and then raises questions to which answers are required.

Deciding on the level of accuracy and precision of the risk and safety assessment will depend on the sampling and measurement methods used in collating the initial risk information. In behavioural terms, this is done through identifying 'what' is happening during an observation and asking 'why'. The 'whats and whys' are analysed and tabulated to identify trends, often by interpreting the data.

Interpretation is based on the personal perception of what has been observed and so identifying trends can be difficult. Although risk can be quantified as abstract principles, health and safety cannot.

Whilst risk assessment is based on knowledge of the job and past experience, the corresponding judgement on safety is subjective and can be political. It may be possible to obtain group agreement on objective and rational measures of risk for various activities. However, there will often be controversy over what are considered to be safe conditions.

Attempting to define acceptable levels of risk immediately raises the question of 'to whom' or 'on what terms' is the risk acceptable?

The distinction between risk and safety is relevant to many organisations and there are a number of factors to be considered in defining the acceptability of risk.

- ☑ **Cost.** Safety is always compromised by available budget yet it costs far more to investigate and restore safe working conditions after an accident than it does to resolve the issues in the first place.

- ☑ **Controls.** Who has control? Those at the place of work should have control over the safety requirements of the task. Ownership of health and safety controls is critical for a safe working environment.

- ☑ **Customs.** Many risks are taken because certain activities have always been done that way.

- ☑ **Conditions.** Many people are put at risk because conditions have changed, resulting in longer working hours, tight timescales, lack of resources, workload, fatigue, stress or an ageing workforce. This leads to errors, particularly in plant maintenance.

- ☑ **Consequences.** Managers rarely evaluate in advance the consequences of something going wrong. Often the thought process seems to be 'if it hasn't happened yet, it won't happen at all'.

- ☑ **Benefit.** What benefits does the individual get from taking a short cut, such as an early finish when the job is done?

The benefits of health and safety discussions

One method of enhancing any safe system of work is through frequent and open discussions. The heart of any process is communication, with all involved recognising the value of shared ideas and knowledge. This has the potential to impact positively on bottom-line profits, with individuals and teams working more efficiently towards achieving high quality business objectives.

The company's image will also benefit if, by the actions exhibited, it is shown to be committed to a safe and healthy working environment, where no-one is injured or becomes ill as a result of coming to work.

 An example of best practice communication is for site managers to have an informal 10-minute chat with their employees and/or contractors' supervisors at the start of every day. The manager should encourage them to tell each other where they will be working and how their activity could affect other people. This will help supervisors to plan their day, as well as improving co-ordination, consultation, production and, ultimately, safety.

The aim of a behavioural safety discussion is to identify any difficulties in completing tasks safely and to aid the supervisor, manager and individual in identifying problems and achieve a safe system of work. Participants in the discussion should be encouraged to:

- ☑ use open questions

- ☑ smooth the way forward

- ☑ be clear in what they are saying

- ☑ avoid any misunderstanding

- ☑ proactively resolve issues through positive actions rather than reactively observing unsafe actions.

Those with more knowledge and experience can assist newer colleagues in understanding the hazards around them and stop people putting themselves at risk. Learning through a coaching and mentoring approach can be more effective and less onerous than more formal observation activities.

All workers and managers can make valid contributions to discussions on behavioural safety. Above all else, problems or issues should be resolved immediately with someone who has the authority to make the necessary changes.

08

Appendix A – Health and Safety Executive *Human factors checklist*

 The checklist below has been taken from the HSE's
Human factors Briefing Note 1.

This list doesn't cover every aspect of human factors but will give you an idea of what is involved. It includes safety management factors. If you can tick most of the boxes, then your company is probably dealing with human factors and safety culture issues quite well but every company can improve.

Health and Safety Executive *Human factors checklist*

	For all the jobs done on this site, this company usually	Yes	No
1.	Chooses the most skilled people to do the work, either our own people or contractors.		
2.	Gives people interesting and varied work without overloading them.		
3.	Arranges for work to be done in teams if that's the best approach.		
4.	Takes care that the working environment is not too hot or cold or uncomfortable.		
5.	Keeps noise levels down to help communications and concentration.		
6.	Provides good lighting.		
7.	Arranges reasonable working hours, meal and rest breaks.		
8.	Makes sure that there's enough room to work in; that is, not too cramped or confined.		
9.	Issues written instructions and other essential paperwork that work very well.		
10.	Avoids overloading people with information and doesn't give contradictory information.		
11.	Provides the proper tools and equipment to do the work.		
12.	Doesn't apply unreasonable time pressure.		
13.	Minimises interruptions to jobs and doesn't change priorities all the time.		
14.	Makes sure that, if a job is handed over to another shift, key information is handed over with it.		
15.	Provides good supervision of important tasks or of less experienced teams.		
16.	Has practised and realistic emergency plans in place in case there's a problem.		
17.	Encourages a good working culture and good relationships between people.		
18.	Doesn't keep changing the organisation, individual responsibilities or lines of management.		

09

Leadership and worker engagement

This chapter gives a general overview of the principles of leadership and worker engagement. It looks at how these impact on organisations within the construction industry. Additional resource information, tools and techniques are presented, which can inform workplaces and influence leadership and engagement behaviours.

Introduction	130
Key points	131
Understanding worker engagement	131
Worker engagement – Tools and techniques, hints and tips	133
Leadership styles	135
Standards and legislation	137

Leadership and worker engagement

9.1 Introduction

The construction industry is one of the UK's most significant economic sectors, with over 250,000 organisations, 99% of which are small to medium size enterprises (SMEs). It is also consistently one of the most dangerous sectors to work in, according to Health and Safety Executive (HSE) statistics.

The industry is therefore continually seeking to find innovative ways in which it can reduce ill health and accidents by engaging with its workforce. This has a number of identifiable business benefits, including the promotion of sustainable behaviour change to ensure that health and safety is taken seriously on site.

Success is dependent upon the quality of leadership and management practice within organisations. Commitment and responsibility at all levels is a critical step in the development of a successful, innovative business and proactive worker engagement.

Definitions of leadership vary across organisations and leadership experts. These are largely centred around building relationships and interpersonal skills, focusing on individuals who are:

- ☑ visionary
- ☑ motivational
- ☑ inspirational
- ☑ emotionally intelligent
- ☑ trustworthy
- ☑ natural leaders and communicators
- ☑ driven
- ☑ ambitious
- ☑ resilient – able to deal with pressure and failure.

There is a need for a range of skills and knowledge. These fall into three main areas:

- ☑ appropriate technical and professional skills, relevant to the organisation
- ☑ commercial and financial, including a high level of business acumen and experience (both success and failure)
- ☑ skills in people management and development (coaching and feedback, communication and team management).

Good leadership is seen as encompassing a strong mix of all these skills with weaknesses in one area being seen to diminish the overall capability of the leader.

Research has identified various traits, differentiating good from outstanding leadership. These outstanding leaders are described as having the ability to:

- ☑ think and act systematically
- ☑ understand the whole and the connection between internal activities and the external environment
- ☑ see people as the route to performance
- ☑ build relationships and provide an environment in which they can shine
- ☑ be self-confident without being arrogant
- ☑ be professional
- ☑ have personal humility.

A key task facing the leader of tomorrow is that of engaging workers within the day-to-day operation of their own roles in order to support achievement of the wider organisational objectives.

Leaders who are able to bring the full range of worker motivation, creativity, skills and knowledge to their businesses are those whose organisations succeed in an increasingly competitive and fastmoving market place.

Leadership development, worker engagement and business performance are strongly linked. In organisations where management and leadership development are embedded, employee engagement levels are higher.

9.2 Key points

Industry and the HSE have produced a *Leadership and worker involvement toolkit*. It is based on ten key principles.

Don't walk by	It is everyone's responsibility on site to prevent any unsafe acts and conditions that they witness from turning into accidents as soon as they see them. Talk to the person(s) involved and draw their attention to the risks.
STOP	All workers should be encouraged to stop working whenever they feel unsafe, even if their reasons for doing so turn out to be unfounded. Better to STOP than to have an accident.
A safe working environment drives safe behaviour	If you expect your workers to work in a safe way, you need to make sure that you do all you can to make the environment they work in as safe as possible.
Don't blame the worker until you have accounted for all causes	The causes of unsafe ways of working, accidents, incidents and ill health do not always stop with the worker. The problem can often be traced back to less obvious causes such as decisions made by management and the wider organisation. Avoid blaming the worker without having considered the full range of possible causes.
Use your workforce for ideas	Your workers can have a more accurate idea of which efforts to improve health and safety may work than you, your management or other experts. They have to deal with the issues every day. Use and include them.
Change does not usually happen overnight	Do not expect quick wins. Improvements are likely to emerge over time, but only if you stick with it.
Knowledge is not enough	Simply telling workers that something is wrong, or is a risk, is not enough. They also need to know why, and how to avoid harm if they are to act on the information that you provide.
You lead by example	Your behaviour sends strong signals to your workers as to how they should behave. If you carry out your job in a safe way, your workers are more likely to work in safe ways. If you do not then your workers will not.
Encourage co-operation	Treat your sub-contractors in the same way as direct employees. Encourage different sub-contractors and trades to proactively communicate with each other. Getting consistency in standards will then be that much easier.
Don't neglect occupational health	If you look after the health as well as the safety of your workers now, you are less likely to store up problems for either you or your workforce in the future.

9.3 Understanding worker engagement

09

The Work Foundation, a provider of research-based analysis, knowledge exchange and policy advice in the UK, defines employee (worker) engagement in this way:

 Employee engagement describes employees' emotional and intellectual commitment to their organisation and its success. Engaged employees experience a compelling purpose and meaning in their work and give of their discrete effort to advance the organisation's objectives.

 For further information refer to the Work Foundation website.

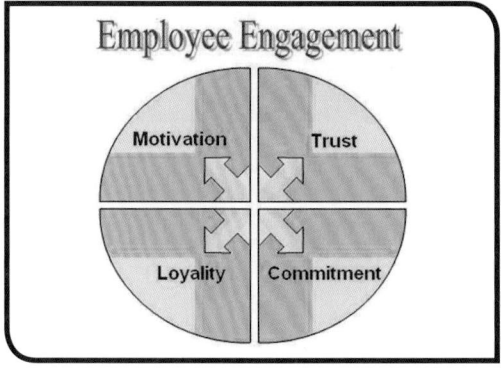

A typical representation of factors influenced by employee (worker) engagement strategies

Effectively, engagement is about how workers behave at work and the impact this has on their own performance and that of the organisation. This is particularly in respect of the discretionary effort that they apply within the workplace.

Within the construction industry, there is a specific focus on health and safety within worker engagement practise.

The HSE's health and safety strategy of the UK talks of 'genuine management workforce partnership based on trust, respect and co-operation' and 'the combined involvement of management and health and safety representatives in inspections, investigations and risk assessments'.

Leadership and worker engagement

The HSE also identifies the growing body of evidence which:

 indicates that effective worker involvement and consultation on health and safety has a positive impact on both individual workers and organisations as a whole. Workers who are involved are also more committed and feel more valued. This is reflected in greater job satisfaction and a lower likelihood of leaving the organisation. For the construction company the result is improved health and safety, which translates into reduced sickness absence, increased productivity and quality, and reduced staff turnover.

 For further information refer to the worker engagement section of the HSE's website.

The Construction Industry Advisory Committee (CONIAC) offers a specific declaration with regard to worker engagement and health and safety, shown below.

Statement of principle

☑ Every construction worker has a right to work in places where risks to their health and safety are properly controlled.

☑ Every worker should have a voice and will be given opportunities to influence health and safety in the places they work.

☑ We commit to actively promoting positive relationships between workers and their representatives, employers, designers clients and those having control of construction work. We recognise the role that unions and safety representatives play in improving worker health and safety consultation.

We will:

☑ expect **all** workers to get involved

☑ encourage clients, employers, designers, project managers and others in control of construction work to ensure workers are listened to and given real opportunities to help improve their working conditions

☑ ensure that sufficient resources, including training, are made available to all sectors of the construction industry to improve worker consultation

☑ develop and share best practice in the industry.

Our aim is to achieve a long-term culture change in the construction industry, in order to improve working conditions for everyone.

 For further information refer to the CONIAC section of the HSE's website.

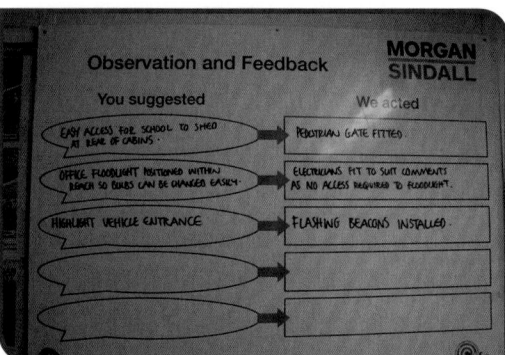

A 'you suggested – we acted' board helps workers see that concerns are being listened to and acted upon

 The HSE's strategy for managing health and safety in the UK includes 'genuine management workforce partnership based on trust, respect and co-operation'

Barriers to workforce engagement

Research by the HSE has identified that barriers to workforce engagement are in many ways similar to behavioural change barriers.

These include:

- ☑ the disparate, transient and multicultural nature of the workforce on site
- ☑ working style associated with a results-focused and target-driven industry
- ☑ disincentives to report health and safety issues, which may result in future loss of projects and income
- ☑ client motivation to adopt worker engagement practices
- ☑ appropriateness of off-the-shelf solutions, given the variance in industry-related organisations
- ☑ lack of management commitment to, or understanding of, the benefits of worker engagement practice.

Overcoming barriers

Potential solutions are:

- ☑ treating each engagement project as a separate strategy
- ☑ training relevant individuals in behavioural change and worker engagement skills
- ☑ focusing on the supply chain as a route for delivery of worker engagement
- ☑ including supply chains and sub-contractors in behavioural change and engagement training
- ☑ running launch events for worker engagement and building in behavioural change and worker engagement standards in to sub-contracts
- ☑ building a preferred supply chain.

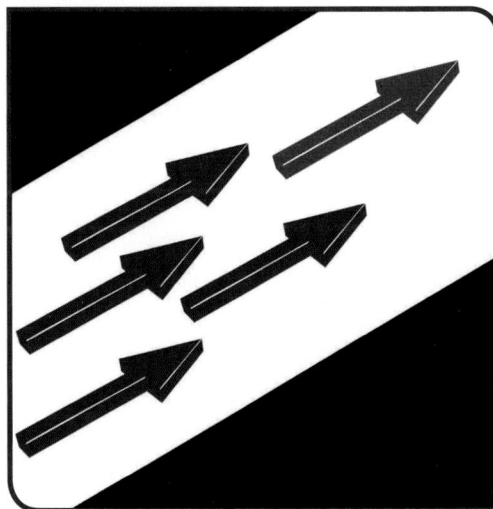

In addition, there is a real focus on worker engagement tools that can be employed to aid implementation of good practice. This is particularly the case for the construction industry, where a lack of worker engagement is directly linked to the potential for health and safety incidents.

Leadership is about vision, motivation and moving towards a common goal

9.4   Worker engagement – Tools and techniques, hints and tips

Leadership and worker engagement toolkit

As a part of its significant focus in this area, the HSE website hosts the leadership and worker engagement toolkit.

This toolkit is designed for the SME business, employing between 11 and 250 workers and contractors. It has been developed by the construction industry's leadership and worker engagement forum to support contractors and managers in making health and safety improvements within their businesses.

 The HSE has provided online access to the leadership and worker engagement toolkit.

The toolkit itself comprises seven steps, each of which is designed to be worked through in order. Each step offers practical tools that can be taken away and used as the individual requires. Guidance from the HSE advises against completing the toolkit in one go; instead, it is recommended that individuals take time to explore each step and to consider how these might support their own worker engagement activities.

Leadership and worker engagement

The seven steps

Step 1	Assess how you're doing.
Step 2	Find the root of the issues.
Step 3	Make it fit with what you do.
Step 4	Lead this in your company.
Step 5	What's in it for your team?
Step 6	How your team can carry it out.
Step 7	Make it last.

 The HSE also offers guidance and materials for workers who as individuals wish to learn more about how they can become proactively engaged within the workplace. Called *Safe and sound at work: Do your bit* this takes the form of links to advisory information with ideas for actions that anyone can take.

Ten key principles

The toolkit is based on 10 key principles, each of which supports best practice leadership and worker engagement in relation to health and safety. These can be found in 9.2 (Key points).

The Best Companies – Engagement survey

'The Best Companies' is a specialist in workplace engagement. Each January it produces a listing, published through a major Sunday newspaper, of the 100 best companies to work for.

It uses a survey methodology to identify workplace performance and best practice according to eight key factors. These are the factors which, through the survey results themselves, have been found to be critical factors in workplace engagement.

☑ **Leadership.** How employees feel about the head of the organisation, senior managers, and the organisation's values and principles.

☑ **My manager.** How employees feel about, and communicate with, their direct manager.

☑ **Personal growth.** What employees feel about training and their future prospects.

☑ **Wellbeing.** How employees feel about stress, pressure at work, and work life balance.

☑ **My team.** Employees' feelings towards their immediate colleagues and how well they work together.

☑ **Giving something back.** The extent to which employees feel their organisation has a positive impact on society.

☑ **My company.** The level of engagement employees have for their job and organisation.

☑ **Fair deal.** How happy employees are with their pay and benefits.

Engaging workers

- ☑ Be patient. The process of engaging workers takes time; those that have done it say that while there were some results within a year, it was nearer five years before they were happy that the process was embedded. Nor is the process **ever** complete.

- ☑ Make sure the directors and senior managers visibly support a worker involvement culture. They can do this by addressing meetings, sending out messages, instructing managers, and 'talking the talk and walking the walk'.

- ☑ Explain why you want to engage workers and what it involves.

- ☑ Run an employee opinion survey and be seen to act rapidly on a couple of suggestions or shortcomings. That way, employees will start to appreciate that the employer is serious about worker engagement.

- ☑ When receiving suggestions, always ensure that the person making the suggestion receives feedback, even if the answer is 'sorry, we can't, and these are the reasons why'. The fact that the employee's views are treated seriously is usually more important than agreeing with them. Linked to this, ensure that you publicise responses to employees' suggestions.

- ☑ You need to engage personnel at all levels of an organisation, using different tactics for different groups and even individuals. For example, email might elicit suggestions from office-based workers, but may be less appropriate in a warehouse. There were, however, fascinating examples (such as steel-encased PC kiosks on the factory floor) that combined processes, holiday forms, emails and worker engagement in health and safety.

- ☑ Be visible. Walk around. Talk to staff. Take small numbers of staff on regular safety walk rounds.

- ☑ An anonymised system of reporting complaints or problems is helpful in the initial stages of embracing worker engagement, but appears to be rarely used once the culture is embedded.

- ☑ Ensure you take the views of shift-workers and part-time staff into account.

- ☑ Take staff to another organisation where worker engagement is working.

- ☑ Worker engagement in health and safety will not happen without a genuine no-blame culture.

- ☑ Ensure representatives have training in how to be a representative (covering eliciting views, presenting a case, feeding back to colleagues) as well as in health and safety. Even in most of the best examples, representatives are often not trained in this role.

- ☑ People are generally reluctant to volunteer as a representative of employee safety, and it may be worth having a quiet word with employees you think would do a good job. Assertive and confident individuals will facilitate better engagement than 'yes' people. Informal leaders (who workers already turn to for advice) may either make good representatives themselves or be important in lending credibility to the notion and practice of engagement. Consider also offering inducements and rewards (financial or otherwise).

- ☑ Make sure that any joint health and safety committees have a workable balance of employee representatives and managers. Managers should consider absenting themselves from part of a meeting in order to ensure that representatives are not intimidated from speaking out. This should not undermine the case for strong leadership from the top, and the need for such temporary absence will diminish as representatives grow in experience and confidence.

- ☑ Ensure your managers and staff are trained in soft skills as well as hard skills.

09

 Worker involvement in health and safety will not happen unless there is a 'no-blame' culture in place.

9.5 Leadership styles

Research has recognised that leadership styles come from the use of emotional intelligence (EI): being acutely aware of the environment, the emotional needs of individuals involved and adjusting leadership style to suit the setting.

These styles can be seen below. They summarise the techniques, scenarios of when they work best and the impact on the organisation and its goals.

Coercive leader

The coercive leader, which is one of the most aggressive of the leadership styles, expects and demands immediate compliance to their orders. This is a style that is designed to accomplish tasks by ordering and dictating, even demeaning their followers at times.

This style is often used in situations where the company requires an urgent and complete turnaround attempt; it is important to note that group discussions are not encouraged or generally permissible under this style. An example could be during disasters, when enforcing health and safety compliance improvements under law.

This style should only be used for short and immediate timeframes, as the medium and longer term impact can be negative.

Authoritative leader

The authoritative leader establishes themselves as being the expert in the company; the person who creates the vision and leads the way.

Authoritative leaders lead the team to the vision and utilise team members to establish how they get there by themselves. This style can be particularly effective in times when a new direction is needed: for someone to come up with the vision and the way forward.

Affiliative leader

The affiliate leader establishes a style of building teams and of putting employees first. This individual offers a significant amount of praise and feedback and there is normally a good sense of team spirit encouraged by this style.

This can be most effective when there are situations of low morale and poor teamwork. Utilising this method will, in the longer term, create good team bonding and heightened team performance.

One negative aspect of this is the potential for poor performance to be accepted, as the leader may avoid difficult conversations in order to avoid conflict.

Democratic leader

The democratic leader will focus on the team as the decision makers to create improvements. Communication is a core skill within this model, whereby all opinions are listened to as a group. The role of the democratic leader is to act as chairperson to encourage effective team decision making.

This style produces a work environment that employees can feel good about, with heightened morale levels. Workers feel that their opinion matters, and because of that feeling they are more committed to achieving the goals and objectives of the organisation.

It will be important to remember that decision making will need to be a focus of attention for this style.

Pacesetting leader

The pacesetting leadership method comes into its own and can be extremely effective when team members are motivated and competent within their roles. These leaders set very high performance standards for themselves and the group and lead by example.

Like the coercive model, this is another of the leadership styles that cannot be sustained for a long time as workers can often burn out due to the energy needed to sustain this approach.

A good example of when to use this style is when a group has been functioning as an effective team for a period of time and is now performing in a strong team culture. At this stage the leader may wish to step things up and move to a new level of performance for a specific project.

Coaching leader

In the coaching leadership style the leader focuses on supporting others in their personal development, and in their job-related activities, towards a goal. The leader helps team members to up-skill and become successful in their development, coaching and mentoring to ensure successful knowledge transfer and independent role development.

This style can be described as a generic management style and works well when the employee is willing to work on both their strengths and areas for development. Whilst this can come across as micromanaging the team, when done well from a trained leader this is an effective style to develop a culture of inclusivity, engagement and learning.

Transformational leadership

This describes a style of leadership that enhances the motivation, morale and performance of followers through a variety of mechanisms. These include connecting the follower's sense of identity and self to the mission and the collective identity of the organisation; being an inspiring role model; challenging followers to take greater ownership for their work, and understanding individual strengths and weaknesses of followers, so the leader can align team members with tasks that optimise their performance.

Transactional leadership

Transactional leadership styles are more concerned with maintaining the normal flow of operations. Transactional leadership can be described as 'keeping the balls in the air'.

Transactional leaders use both disciplinary power and a number of different incentives to motivate employees to perform at their best. The term transactional refers to the fact that this type of leader essentially motivates subordinates by exchanging performance for rewards.

A transactional leader generally tends not to look ahead in strategically guiding an organisation to a position of market leadership; instead, these managers are solely concerned with making sure everything flows smoothly today.

In summary

While coercion and pacesetting do perhaps have their uses, research suggests that these styles can damage the organisation's working atmosphere over time. This will ultimately reduce flexibility and employee commitment. So the key is to use these only when absolutely required (in a case of a health and safety emergency for example) and within a small time frame.

The most effective leader is one who can use different styles in different situations.

The message is clear: from research, employee surveys and case study information, there is no doubt that the quality and effectiveness of management and leadership has a significant impact on the level to which workers are engaged within their jobs. This in turn has direct consequences for health and safety measures within organisations.

9.6 Standards and legislation

National Occupational Standards – Management and leadership

The National Occupational Standards (NOS) for management and leadership are statements of best practice that outline the performance criteria, related skills, knowledge and understanding required to effectively carry out various management and leadership functions.

They are produced by the Management Standards Centre (MSC), the Government recognised standards setting body for the management and leadership areas.

The MSC describes the standards as:

> The activities/functions of management and leadership at various levels of responsibility and complexity. Therefore, they are relevant to anyone for whom management and leadership is, to a greater or lesser extent, part of their work. This applies to managers and leaders in all sizes and types of organisation, and in all industries and sectors.

Accessing this information will provide the opportunity to see the suite of standards most relevant to different levels of management and leadership. These standards are generic and so equally applicable to management and leadership practice within organisations of all sizes and across all sectors.

For further information refer to the standards section of the management standards website.

Legal requirements for communicating with all employees

Employers must inform employees of:

- ☑ the main terms and conditions of employment
- ☑ changes in terms and conditions of employment
- ☑ the reason for dismissing them from their job
- ☑ certain business matters (for example, when there is a significant change in the way the business operates)
- ☑ health and safety issues. There are two principal sets of regulations concerning your duty to consult your workforce on health and safety:
  - – the Health and Safety (Consultation with Employees) Regulations
  - – the Safety Representatives and Safety Committees Regulations

These regulations will apply to most workplaces. The Health and Safety Executive (HSE) has developed easy-to-use guidance that shows the relationship between the two sets of regulations and how they may affect businesses and their workforces.

The business may benefit from consulting employees on a regular basis and making staff aware of ways they can contribute ideas and raise concerns. The business does not need to have complex structures for consultation – often ad hoc groups can work best.

For effective consultation consider:

- ☑ explaining final decisions, particularly when employees' views are rejected
- ☑ giving credit and recognition to those who provide information that improves a decision
- ☑ ensuring that the issues for consultation are relevant to the group of employees discussing them
- ☑ avoiding minor issues and petty grievances
- ☑ making the outcome of the meeting available to everyone.

Good communication processes will make employee engagement much easier and more effective. Key aspects of achieving that include:

- ☑ involving the workforce in building a set of values by which the company will operate
- ☑ building dialogue with the workforce by communicating regularly and openly about matters that affect the business. This will build credibility and create an environment of trust
- ☑ involving the workforce in key employee issues as soon as is possible

09

☑ avoiding leaks of information or rumours spreading

☑ keep living the values.

In the construction industry it is particularly important to ensure that this communication is effective and timely, particularly in relation to health and safety.

All workers, including those in the construction industry, have a right to be consulted on the work they do, to be given adequate information and training to carry out this work in a safe and healthy manner and to have decent site facilities. Being directly involved in the process, employees often see problems as they emerge.

Recent years have seen a large increase in the numbers of foreign workers in all sectors. The increasing size of the European Union has caused an influx of labour for whom English may not be their first language and communication can become more difficult, leading to a greater risk of misunderstanding. These workers must be fully engaged and consulted on matters of health and safety at work: employers must find adequate mechanisms to do this. Similar consideration should be given to other workers who have difficulties in communicating.

The Construction (Design and Management) Regulations place a duty on principal contractors to make and maintain arrangements to enable effective co-operation between all parties on site, and to consult with all workers on site. Consultation means not only giving information to workers, but also listening and taking account of what workers say, before making health and safety decisions. Part of the purpose of consultation is to make sure the measures taken on site to protect workers' health and safety are effective.

Principal contractors are encouraged to develop a variety of methods of communication and consultation with the workforce to develop collaboration and trust. When matters of concern are raised by workers these should be taken seriously and feedback given. Evidence that this is happening provides assurance that effective worker engagement is in place.

Involving the workforce in identifying and controlling risks is crucial in preventing accidents. Whether projects are notifiable or not, contractors have a duty to inform workers of their procedures for stopping work in the event of serious and imminent danger, and to provide training where necessary. This should make sure workers are willing and able to intervene to prevent an accident from happening.

A toolkit has been produced by the construction industry's Leadership and Worker Engagement Forum to help contractors and managers learn how to make health and safety improvements in their businesses.

The Safety Representatives and Safety Committees Regulations

For information on the employer safety representatives' duties refer to the HSE Code of Practice L87.

Role of the safety representative

The role of the safety representative may be summarised as:

☑ representing their members' interests in matters of health, safety and welfare

☑ carrying out the statutory functions outlined in the regulations

☑ representing their members in consultation with the HSE or other enforcing authority.

Functions of the safety representative

☑ Consultation with the employer.

☑ Investigation and reporting of significant hazards and dangerous occurrences.

☑ Investigation of accidents in the workplace.

☑ Representation on general health and safety matters.

☑ Reception of complaints by employees.

☑ Representation in consultation with the HSE or other enforcing authority.

☑ Reception of information from the enforcing authority.

☑ Attendance at meetings of safety committees.

☑ Inspections of the workplace.

The Equality Act

Equality and diversity are issues of rising importance that the construction industry needs to acknowledge and address. This has been brought into sharper focus following the recent changes to legislation, with the introduction of the Equality Act, which became law in October 2010. It replaces previous legislation (such as the Race Relations Act and the Disability Discrimination Act) and ensures consistency in what employers need to do to make the workplace a fair environment and to comply with the law.

The Equality Act covers the same groups that were protected by existing equality legislation – age, disability, gender reassignment, race, religion or belief, sex, sexual orientation, marriage and civil partnership, pregnancy and maternity – but extends some protections to groups not previously covered, and also strengthens particular aspects of equality law.

The Equality Act is a mixture of rights and responsibilities that have:

- ☑ **stayed the same** – for example, direct discrimination still occurs when someone is treated less favourably than another person because of a protected characteristic

- ☑ **changed** – for example, employees can now complain of harassment even if it is not directed at them, if they can demonstrate that it creates an offensive environment for them

- ☑ **been extended** – for example, associative discrimination (direct discrimination against someone because they associate with another person who possesses a protected characteristic) covers age, disability, gender reassignment and sex, as well as race, religion and belief and sexual orientation

- ☑ **been introduced for the first time** – for example, the concept of discrimination arising from disability, which occurs if a person with a disability is treated unfavourably because of something arising as a consequence of their disability.

Whilst construction sites can be hazardous places of work for anyone, employers must accept their legal duties and make reasonable adjustments within the working environment to ensure that fairness is achieved and discrimination does not occur.

There are clear reasons why equality and diversity impacts on the health and safety environment. For example:

- ☑ staff who are bullied or suffer harassment at work may not feel safe or act in a rational manner. Bullying/harassment, including initiation ceremonies and fooling around, can also involve unsafe acts

- ☑ a person may have a visual, hearing or speech impairment that could, for example, make communication of risks difficult

- ☑ a person may have restricted mobility and therefore have difficulty in walking, climbing ladders, lifting or carrying out certain aspects of work activities

- ☑ poorly fitting personal protective equipment (PPE) for employees can be uncomfortable, impede mobility and/or movement necessary for safe working (for example, a person's physique may mean standard issue PPE is too small or large).

A part of making reasonable adjustments is likely to be consultation between the employer and the person(s) on how certain situations will be managed.

Employers have a responsibility to ensure their employees are supported and not discriminated against. Supervisors and managers must be aware of these responsibilities and the way to eliminate or effectively manage situations if they arise.

In addition employers have a responsibility to ensure every employee understands safety information and messages, both in terms of language used and the workplace culture. Ensuring clear messaging can result in better working conditions and practices and a more productive team approach.

09

09

10
Inspections and audits

Measurement is a key step in the management process and forms the basis of continual improvements.

If measures (such as health and safety audits or site inspections) are not carried out correctly, there is no reliable information to show if health and safety risks are being adequately controlled.

This chapter outlines the types of measurement and the benefits of monitoring health and safety.

Introduction   142
Key points   142
Measuring performance   142
Monitoring   143
Inspections   143
Hazard-spotting techniques   144
Inspection reports   145
Audit and review   145
Remedial actions   146
Benchmarking   147
Additional benefits to a company   147
Construction site safety auditing system   147

10.1   Introduction

Employers and employees have a moral, social and legal duty to prevent accidents by every practicable means available to them. The costs of getting it wrong to a firm, its employees and others affected may be great and provide ample motivation to all involved to reduce the risks to health and safety.

Motivation must, however, be translated into effective action, and this can only be achieved by the commitment of management and supervisors at all levels. It is well established and documented that accidents can be prevented by:

☑ **identifying** the hazards that employees face within the workplace

☑ **understanding** how accidents are caused by unsafe acts, unsafe systems of work and unsafe conditions on site

☑ taking steps to **control** the activity of the worker, the work method and the workplace.

Employers, managers, supervisors and safety representatives all have equally important roles to play. By obtaining and providing information through the **inspection, investigation and examination** of the workplace, they can help provide a basis for effective management action to promote safer and healthier workplaces, and induce a greater awareness of health, safety and welfare on the part of all concerned. There are strong links between this topic content and the need to engage with employees on matters of health and safety.

10.2   Key points

☑ Inspections and audits of the workplace, from a health and safety point of view, can form a productive part of the consultation between management and the workforce.

☑ While they are often carried out by a health and safety professional, they do not have to be.

☑ The successful outcome of any inspection or audit is that remedial actions are put in place where shortcomings have been identified.

☑ Workplace inspections are most effective when carried out against a predetermined checklist incorporating some method of recording the findings.

☑ Whereas workplace inspections tend to be a 'snapshot in time', an audit is a thorough examination not only of the site conditions prevailing at any one time but also of the:

– commitment of management to health and safety

– procedures that underpin the health and safety management system.

☑ The emphasis on contractors being able to demonstrate their competence in matters of health and safety management potentially puts a greater importance on them being able to show that inspections and audits are carried out and acted upon.

10.3   Measuring performance

There are several ways in which a company may measure the effectiveness of its health and safety management system. They include:

☑ evaluating the effectiveness of earlier risk assessments

☑ gathering and evaluating information on the number of accidents over a reference period, their causes and effects

☑ the investigation of worker feedback on near misses and dangerous occurrences

☑ gathering information on reportable diseases

☑ the results of health and safety audits

☑ the results of inspections, whether regular, unannounced or specific

☑ the level of health and safety awareness among employees in the form of feedback from training courses and safety committee meetings

☑ benchmarking against previous audits.

The Health and Safety Executive (HSE) has made available a free web-based benchmarking tool, called the health and safety performance indicator, designed to enable smaller companies to assess how they are managing health and safety issues.

 The tool can be accessed through the Business Link website.

10.4 Monitoring

Employers are required to monitor performance. There are two types of monitoring used in auditing and inspecting.

Proactive monitoring

Proactive monitoring measures the current level of compliance with legislation and company procedures. It can take the form of:

 health and safety inspections   hazard-spotting exercises

☑ pre-use checks   ☑ surveys

 safety tours   ☑ audits.

Health and safety inspections tend to be the site manager's snapshot of the health and safety standards on site at any one time. Alternatively, or in addition, a company's health and safety adviser or director may carry out these inspections.

A health and safety inspection or audit may examine the big picture or concentrate on only one feature; irrespective of who carries them out, they must have the knowledge to enable them to detect unsafe situations and the authority to ensure they are rectified.

Reactive monitoring

This type of monitoring investigates anything that has actually happened. Accidents, incidents, near misses and illness resulting in serious injuries and fatalities, including health hazards, are too often a feature of work in the construction industry. The proactive management of health and safety should serve to keep such incidents to a minimum.

> **!** It should not be forgotten that a near miss today could be a potential accident tomorrow. Supervisors have an important role to play in both proactive and reactive monitoring activities.

10.5 Inspections

Formal inspections at reasonably regular intervals should augment the site manager's day-to-day checks, inspections and examinations, which occur as part of any task. These should follow a properly designed checklist for the systematic inspection of the workplace.

> **🔍** A safety, health and environment inspection report can be found in Section G *Checklists and forms*.

The advantages of regular inspections are that they ensure good housekeeping is maintained within the workplace and that awareness is developed, amongst employees at all levels, of the need to promote and maintain safety, health and environmental standards. The disadvantage or danger of regular inspections is that they may become a rather mechanical routine for all concerned, and that their impact might be lessened.

Carrying out joint inspections with safety representatives, other members of the team or even nominated workers from different trades or contractors can help to identify issues that may be overlooked during a routine inspection.

Stopping and engaging a two-way conversation with the workforce during inspections is vital so as to understand why they are doing the work the way they are and what issues they have.

This goes a long way in helping to build a positive safety culture, but it is just as important to follow through or feed back on issues. More often than not, they will be able to help find and agree solutions.

Random inspections carried out without any prior notice to the workforce, on different days of the week, at irregular intervals and at different times of the day, avoid the shortcomings of a predictable inspection and help to encourage a continuous interest in safety by all personnel.

In practice, a combination of both regular and random inspections is probably the best course of action.

> **!** On one project, the site manager carried out his weekly site inspections with a different sub-contract employee. Results of the inspection were jointly presented to the site workforce as a toolbox talk.

10

Safety representatives

Safety representatives are entitled to inspect the workplace and an Approved Code of Practice (ACoP) and guidance notes have been issued by the HSE to support the relevant regulations. These emphasise areas where safety representatives should reach agreement with their employers.

A safety representative may consider the company's safety inspection procedure to be adequate. In such cases, the representative may only need to seek an agreement with the management that they are involved in any future inspections of the workplace.

However, if the company's arrangements for the inspection of the workplace are thought to be inadequate, recommendations should be made in writing in order that action may be taken to remedy the situation.

10.6   Hazard-spotting techniques

Hazard-spotting exercises are a modified version of the safety sampling method, where a particular department, hazard or work activity is singled out for a closer and more thorough examination.

The exercises should be arranged by the health and safety adviser, in conjunction with the company management, or by the training manager through line management, and should involve supervisors, safety representatives and operatives.

Observers may include first line or senior managers, but there should be at least an equal number of operatives. Some managements may prefer a predominant number of operatives up to ganger level in the party, thereby encouraging workers to take an active interest in safety and accident prevention at the workplace.

Hazard-spotting programme

A set and properly structured programme of inspections and sampling will ensure that all of the main activities of a firm are continuously under scrutiny. Hazard-spotting exercises should be used not only where there is seen to be a need to ensure the safety and health of people at work, but also as a preventative and continuing monitoring exercise.

Hazard-spotting party

Members of the proposed hazard-spotting party should have had some training or experience in health and safety matters in relation to the work or hazards to be assessed and be able to:

- ☑ recognise any unsafe acts of people at work
- ☑ recognise unsafe or potentially unsafe conditions of work or methods of work.

One person should be appointed leader of each group, and their functions should include:

- ☑ the collection of the written findings of the members of the party
- ☑ the study of these findings and the summary of unsafe acts and conditions that have been observed during the tour
- ☑ the preparation of a brief report, setting out the unsafe acts and conditions that were observed during the tour and making recommendations for action by the management or their representative to rectify any situation that may have been observed
- ☑ noting and recording the response of the line or senior management, satisfying themselves that action will be taken by management to rectify any situations observed
- ☑ reporting back to members of the party what action will be taken by the line manager concerned.

Sampling

Health and safety sampling of a particular work activity, process or work area may be necessary where:

- ☑ the activity, process or work area presents particular health and safety concerns, where there have been changes to an activity, process or work area that are relevant to health and safety
- ☑ there is a need to improve the health and safety performance in a particular area of operations
- ☑ there are areas of high labour turnover.

Sampling should be carried out by someone familiar with the work activity, process or work area under inspection.

Tours

Directors, senior managers, site managers, engineers, supervisors and operatives should have the opportunity to take note of health and safety conditions prevailing within the workplace during normal construction work.

10

Production, however, will often be their first priority and this need to get the job done may adversely affect their judgement on safety matters. Familiarity with certain activities and hazards may further cause them to overlook, fail to recognise or ignore real or potential dangers that are present at the workplace.

For these reasons, **health and safety tours** (general inspections of the workplace) made by health and safety advisers, supervisors and safety representatives should take place at regular intervals.

10.7 Inspection reports

Details of inspections and their findings should be recorded. Commercially produced versions of inspection report forms are often multi-copy and self-duplicating, with each copy on a different coloured paper to identify the intended recipient.

Whatever the type of checklist or form used, it should provide a record of any action requested to remedy conditions and working practices considered to be unsafe. Space should be provided on the form to record the date and place of the inspection and details of any corrective action identified, subsequent action to be taken or, if no action was required, an explanation of why this was so.

Reports should also contain elements of positive or good practice, such as identifying that safe systems of work for high risk activities were being followed. Best practice should also be captured and shared and opportunities made to offer recognition to individuals that are working safely.

10.8 Audit and review

A health and safety audit is a demonstration of the management's commitment to monitor and improve, where necessary, the effectiveness of the company's safety management system from the top down.

The process of carrying out health and safety audits, evaluating the findings and implementing remedial action, where necessary, results in a continuous cycle of improvement.

Audits tend to be formal, pre-planned, events with the findings documented for later evaluation and review.

 Audit definition: the structured process of collecting independent information on the efficiency, effectiveness and reliability of the total health and safety management system and identifying plans for corrective action.

Therefore, the key requirements of a health and safety audit include:

- ☑ a critical examination of the whole operation
- ☑ an assessment of how the risks to health and safety are being managed
- ☑ the identification of the efficient and safe performance of people
- ☑ the detection and identification of falling standards, ineffective company procedures, and non-compliance with industry standards and legal requirements
- ☑ the use of meaningful standards consistent with the organisation's operations
- ☑ the identification and implementation of a corrective action plan.

Health and safety auditing should also be seen as an integral part of the overall monitoring of health and safety within an organisation.

 The aim of such an audit is to identify problem areas that may exist, so that you can make improvements to your standard of health and safety. The audit should look at the interaction of all the activities of your company, as well as at the activities themselves.

Audits may discover health and safety failings that arise through factors that occur off site (such as design issues), which are therefore outside the direct control of site-based staff. They may also identify good practices that should be shared and incorporated into a process of improvement.

By comparison, health and safety inspections are normally a less formal style of audit; the results are not necessarily recorded and they may be more appropriate for some smaller sites. Remember, however, **no record – no proof!**

10

Inspections and audits

Both health and safety audits and inspections are carried out on a pre-notified or no-notice basis, as suited to the situation at the time. If too many are pre-notified or regularly scheduled, it may tend to create a false impression, as those on site may only improve their behaviour or practices in the short term.

Audits should be carried out by a member of management, often the company health and safety adviser or a director, who may or may not be accompanied by a representative(s) of sub-contractors or the employees. The aim is to identify problem areas, implement improvements and increase the overall standard of safety awareness.

It requires attention to the:

☑ work environment

☑ person carrying out the task

☑ task itself

☑ safety culture

☑ way in which each affects the others.

The important thing is that where shortcomings are found, remedial action is promptly taken and lessons learned to prevent recurrence.

10.9   Remedial actions

A clear understanding of what remedial actions are required to eliminate or lessen the risks to health and safety, and when those actions should be taken, is an essential part of health and safety management.

The following lists suggest how shortcomings that are highlighted during health and safety inspections should be prioritised for remedial action.

Items requiring immediate action

☑ The contravention of any statutory requirements or Approved Codes of Practice.

☑ Any accident or incident that is reportable to the HSE under RIDDOR.

☑ The occurrence of accidents, incidents or near misses that produce situations of possible or immediate danger to the health and safety of employees or other people, including members of the public.

☑ The risk of financial liabilities, as a result of damage to plant and equipment, or compensation to workers or members of the public following litigation, the risks of fire, explosion or other hazards involving electricity, toxic materials or substances.

☑ The existence of unsafe working practices and unsafe places of work.

☑ Any activity or situation that is giving rise to conditions that could affect the short or long-term health of workers (for example, creating dust).

☑ Any shortages of correct and adequate personal protective clothing and equipment.

☑ The risk of serious environmental pollution.

Items requiring prompt action

☑ Any potential hazards that may exist, but which do not cause any imminent or immediate danger of injury, damage or pollution.

☑ Any signs of inadequate information, instruction or supervision, which should have been provided by either the management or others.

☑ Any first-aid facilities and training that fall short of statutory requirements.

☑ Occasions when new plant, new work methods, new equipment or different materials are to be introduced into the workplace.

Items requiring short-term action

☑ Where there is a lack of planning and control affecting safety, occupational health or the environment within the workplace, either directly or indirectly (for example through the inadequate supply of materials and equipment to enable the workforce to carry out their tasks satisfactorily and safely).

☑ Where there are signs of inadequacies in the personal skills, knowledge and experience of the workforce, which may have an adverse effect on safety.

Items requiring long-term planning and action

☑ Where there is a lack of certain categories of safety skills and trained personnel amongst the workforce.

☑ Where there is a need for the training of safety advisers, supervisors and safety representatives, to keep abreast of the future needs of the firm and its employees.

☑ Where there is a need for the improvement of standards of health, welfare and safety within the company.

10.10 Benchmarking

One of the most difficult things about auditing is deciding whether the measured performance is satisfactory. Within health and safety, experienced external auditors will typically audit against two parameters:

☑ performance against internal systems

☑ performance against legal standards.

This is fine as it allows an organisation to self-check, but it does not indicate how a performance rates against others.

As a comparative measure, some companies use accident or injury numbers, or the number of prosecutions and/or enforcement notices.

Various attempts have been made within the industry to produce key performance indicators (KPIs) for health and safety, but difficulties are caused by comparing the relevance of, say, KPIs of a small plastering contractor employing four people to a UK Contractors Group member.

As a result there is no right or wrong answer, and it is a case of selecting areas of measurement most appropriate to a company. Another driver for benchmarking certain elements is that these maybe a requirement of client or pre-qualification questionnaires. Some trade associations, including the National Access and Scaffolding Confederation (NASC), compile accident statistics for their members. The NASC believes that this covers approximately half of the scaffolding industry.

In recent years proactive indicators are measured in addition to the traditionally reactive indicators (such as accident statistics). Proactive indicators can include the number of:

☑ toolbox talks carried out per employee

☑ senior management tours

☑ site inspections and audits

☑ near-miss reports.

Benchmarking can be a very useful exercise but participants need to be aware that the information may need to be interpreted carefully.

10.11 Additional benefits to a company

As legislation increasingly requires risk and other assessments, and main contractors or clients demand sight of health and safety policies and method statements, evidence that you have an auditing programme will help your business.

A good audit will benefit everyone from senior management to the most inexperienced employee, and should be accepted on its merits as the resultant changes bring improvements in health and safety performance.

The health and safety audit should be carried out, as far as possible, by independent auditors. This overcomes the problems faced by line managers when auditing their own area of work, or even a second line manager being critical of their peers. Auditing must be carried out objectively and with a high degree of honesty when identifying non-compliance with management systems and techniques.

The frequency of safety audits should ensure that the health and safety management system of the organisation does not degrade over time or through changes in the company organisation, personnel or the activities it carries out.

Several safety auditing systems are available commercially but, in the main, these are directed towards the larger business, which can afford either to employ its own dedicated auditing team or contract consultants to come in and carry out the audit.

The construction industry identified the need for an auditing system for the smaller and medium-sized company where the site manager or site supervisor could inspect the site and, within a couple of hours, produce an acceptable appreciation of the standard of safety on site.

10

10.12 Construction site safety auditing system

The CITB-ConstructionSkills *Construction site safety auditing system* is closely related to *Construction site safety* (GE 700). It is a CD-ROM containing a number of ready-made auditing forms and is aimed at companies that have not yet addressed the subject or concept of safety audits. It has been designed with simplicity in mind.

The aim is to introduce companies to safety auditing and encourage them to adopt the concept as a part of their overall safety policy. It represents a proactive, cost-effective method of becoming safer, rather than a reactive approach. It shows that the company and its staff are trying to ensure that everything is safe and prevent the conditions that cause accidents to occur, instead of picking up the pieces and changing work practices after accidents have happened.

If, in due course, it is decided that the company has outgrown this auditing system and the move is made to a more complex system, the *Construction site safety auditing system* will have served its purpose.

If, by adopting an effective auditing system, one accident is prevented, then all the work, time and resources that a company has put into its preparation will have been worth it.

 For further information on the Construction site safety auditing system, please contact CITB-ConstructionSkills Publications or visit the website.

10

Inspections and audits

11

Statutory forms, notices and registers

This chapter gives a brief outline of some of the requirements for the completion and use of various statutory and non-statutory forms, notices, signs and registers used within the building and construction industry, and the keeping of some records and other details.

Some guidance on the types of daily and weekly inspection activities that supervisors should carry out and records that must be kept is also included.

Introduction   150
Key points   150
Record keeping   150
Daily user and visual checks   150
List of key requirements   151
Statutory or recommended inspections and examinations 152

Appendix A – Brief explanation of key requirements   153

11.1 Introduction

Record keeping is important as it is the means used to ensure that inspections and examinations are carried out.

Some are required by legislation and others by the employer as they are good practice and vital in preventing accidents.

11.2 Key points

 This chapter gives a brief outline of some of the requirements for the completion, display or use of various statutory and non-statutory forms, notices, signs and registers used within the building and construction industry, and the keeping of some records or other details.

☑ The selection of the forms or notices is appropriate or applicable to the individual site or premises, and the circumstances that exist on that site.

☑ The listings contained in this chapter are not intended to be a full and precise guide to all the statutory requirements that currently exist. All cases of doubt should be resolved by reference to the appropriate enforcing authority or to the legislation.

> **!** A statutory inspection means legally it must be carried out.

11.3 Record keeping

Records are generally split into two categories:

☑ **Proactive** – such as inspecting scaffolding or excavations to ensure they remain safe

☑ **Reactive** – such as an accident investigation to establish the cause.

Records of toolbox talks are also important, as this demonstrates that (usually site-based) training is being provided.

Daily site briefings are often a good way of reviewing what has happened and looking at what has to be done and the associated hazards. These can be extended to point-of-work risk assessments.

11.4 Daily user and visual checks

Daily user and visual checks form a vital part of good site management and reduce the risk of plant and equipment breakdown or failure, for example:

☑ engine/motor seizure due to lack of lubrication

☑ a low-pressure tyre being damaged or causing vehicles to overturn

☑ missing scaffold edge protection causing the potential of falling materials or persons

☑ damaged power plugs, sockets and leads.

Construction plant and equipment are exposed to harsh environments and they require effective maintenance regimes to prevent defects from developing. A programme of daily visual checks, regular inspections and servicing schedules should be established according to the manufacturer's instructions and the risks associated with the use of each vehicle or tool.

Plant hire companies must provide information with all plant and equipment that they supply to enable it to be used and maintained safely. Contractual arrangements between user and hirer should set out who is responsible for maintenance and inspection during the hire period and this should be made clear to all parties.

Plant and vehicles should have a maintenance log to help manage and record maintenance operations. Employers should establish procedures designed to encourage supervisors and operators to report defects or problems, and ensure that problems with plant and vehicles are put right. Planned inspection and maintenance needs to follow manufacturers' instructions.

11.5   List of key requirements

The following is a list of key requirements. For an explanation of these requirements refer to Appendix A.

1.	Accident book BI 510 (rev 2003)	Report of an accident must comply with the Data Protection Act.
2.	F2508	Report of an injury or dangerous occurrence.
3.	F2508A	Report of a case of disease.
4.	F10	Notification of a project.
5.	F2067	Ionising radiation health record.
6.	F2533	Safety representatives' report form.
7.	F2534	Safety representatives' inspection form.
8.	Air receivers	Safe working pressure and record of test.
9.	Asbestos	Licence, notice and records. Where appropriate, maintaining a written asbestos management plan.
10.	Builders' skips	On road, permits and signs.
11.	Consultation with employees	Rights of employees.
12.	COSHH assessments	Maintenance of assessment forms and other records.
13.	Danger areas	Identify with signs.
14.	Dangerous substances and explosive atmospheres	Display of notices.
15.	Diving	Records and registration.
16.	Electrical equipment	Records, certification of new installations.
17.	Electric shock placard	Display in workplaces.
18.	Emergency evacuation	Emergency evacuation route signage as necessary and assembly point sign(s).
19.	Excavations, cofferdams and caissons	Records of inspections of places of work.
20.	Explosives	Certificate and records.
21.	Falsework	Records of design, including calculations, to be kept.
22.	Fire	Notices for extinguishers, fire points and other fire-fighting equipment. Fire exit signs.
23.	First aid	Notice regarding facilities and identity of first aiders.
24.	Food hygiene	Display of notices, and certificates of staff training.
25.	Fragile surfaces	Notice to be displayed.
26.	Hazardous substances	Labels on containers.
27.	Health and safety policy	Display or distribute to all employees .
28.	Holes in floors and similar openings	Cover to be clearly marked.
29.	Information for employees (see also Training)	Display approved poster or distribute approved leaflet to all employees.
30.	Insurance (Employer's liability)	Display of certificate.
31.	Ionising radiation	Advance notification to HSE of work. Licence, records and appropriate signage/barriers at work site.
32.	Lead	Records of inspection and thorough examination of control measures.
33.	Lifting operations	Records of inspection, examination and safe working load (SWL) indication.
34.	Management of health and safety	Risk assessments, appointments, procedures.
35.	Manual handling	Assessment, marking of loads. Training.

11

36.	**Noise**	Marking of hearing protection zones.
37.	**Plant and equipment**	Inspection and records.
38.	**Pressure vessels**	Display of working pressure, and other details.
39.	**Protective clothing and equipment**	Assessments, maintenance, training.
40.	**Safety representatives and safety committees**	Access to documents, minutes, and so on. Information on identity of trade union-appointed safety reps.
41.	**Safety signs**	Signs and notices as appropriate.
42.	**Scaffolding**	Records of inspections, display of 'incomplete' notice.
43.	**Training**	Records.
44.	**Visual display units (VDUs) or display screens**	Records of assessments, training, eyesight tests.
45.	**Waste management**	Completion of duty of care documentation, forms, permits and certificates.
46.	**Work equipment**	Suitability, maintenance, warnings.
47.	**Work in compressed air**	Records of equipment inspection and health surveillance.
48.	**Working time**	Permitted hours of work.
49.	**Working at height**	Records of inspection of equipment.

 Also refer to Section G *Checklists and forms*.

11.6 Statutory or recommended inspections and examinations

The following table sets out the recommended daily user checks, weekly inspections, statutory inspections and examinations.

Work activity plant item	Pre-use daily	Weekly record	Monthly record	3 monthly record	6 monthly record	12 monthly record	Form for statutory examination or report to comply with
	Statutory or recommended						
Excavations, cofferdams and caissons	✓ Inspect	✓ Inspect					Construction (Design and Management) Regulations
Plant and equipment (not electrical or for lifting)	✓ Inspect	✓ Inspect			✓ Examine	✓ Examine	Provision and Use of Work Equipment Regulations
Plant and equipment (electrical) including RCDs	✓ Inspect	✓ Inspect		✓ Examine PAT test			Construction (Design and Management) Regulations, Electricity at Work Regulations
Cranes and plant for lifting people, MEWPs, harness, lifting accessories and safety nets	✓ Inspect	✓ Inspect			✓ Examine	✓ Examine	Provision and Use of Work Equipment Regulations, Lifting Operations and Lifting Equipment Regulations
Cranes and plant used for lifting	✓ Inspect	✓ Inspect				✓ Examine	Lifting Operations and Lifting Equipment Regulations
Work at height, all scaffolds, working platforms, mobile towers, ladders and steps, etc.	✓ Inspect	✓ Inspect					Work at Height Regulations, Provision and Use of Work Equipment Regulations, Construction (Design and Management) Regulations
Fire-fighting appliances		✓ Inspect				✓ Examine	Construction (Design and Management) Regulations, Regulatory Reform Fire Safety Order
Site offices electrical equipment and installation		✓ Inspect				✓ Examine	Construction (Design and Management) Regulations, Electricity at Work Regulations, Workplace Health Safety and Welfare Regulations

Appendix A – Brief explanation of key requirements

1.	**Accident book BI 510** The keeping of an accident book is required by The Social Security (Claims and Payments) Regulations, the Social Security Administration Act and The Reporting of Injuries, Diseases and Dangerous Occurrences Regulations (RIDDOR). While there is no statutory book, the revised BI 510 was produced because the previous version and other similar books did not comply with the Data Protection Act. The design of BI 510 allows for an entry to be made without the personal details of a previous entry being seen. Any business that has its own accident book must ensure their version complies with the Data Protection Act. All accidents that cause any injury to an employee, no matter how slight, must be entered. Entry may be made either by the employee or anyone acting on their behalf. Completed book stubs and records must be kept for three years from the date of the last entry.
2.	**F2508 Report of an injury or dangerous occurrence** Form F2508, report of an accident or dangerous occurrence, is required by The Reporting of Injuries, Diseases and Dangerous Occurrences Regulations (RIDDOR). Notification should now be made online. The form will then be submitted directly to the RIDDOR database and a copy received back for record purposes. All incidents can be reported online but a telephone service remains for reporting fatal and major injuries only.
3.	**F2508A Report of a case of disease** A report on form F2508A is required by The Reporting of Injuries, Diseases and Dangerous Occurrences Regulations (RIDDOR). It must be completed when a registered medical practitioner has diagnosed in writing that an employee is suffering from a scheduled reportable disease **and** the person has been employed in a scheduled work activity by the employer.
4.	**F10 Notification of a project under The Construction (Design and Management) Regulations** This form is required under the above regulations and may be filled out and submitted online or sent to the HSE before the start of any work of building operation or engineering construction, if the project is notifiable. A project is notifiable if the construction phase is likely to: ■ last for more than 30 working days ■ involve more than 500 person days of construction work.
5.	**F2067** Ionising radiation health record.
6.	**F2533 Safety representatives' report forms** The Safety Representatives and Safety Committees Regulations This form is used by trade union-appointed safety representatives to notify the employer of any matter discovered during a workplace inspection, which is considered to be unsafe and/or unhealthy.
7.	**F2534 Safety representatives' inspection forms** This form is used by trade union-appointed safety representatives to record the time, date and location of workplace health and safety inspections carried out.
8.	**Air receivers** The Pressure Systems Safety Regulations Every air receiver must have the safe working pressure clearly displayed on it. It must be examined and tested as laid down in the regulations and records kept.
9.	**Asbestos** The Control of Asbestos Regulations Virtually all work with asbestos requires a licence from the HSE or the giving of 14-days' notice of the intention to work with asbestos to the enforcing authority. The majority of work must only be undertaken by a licensed contractor. This work includes most asbestos removal, all work with sprayed asbestos coatings and asbestos lagging and most work with asbestos insulation and asbestos insulating board (AIB). Brief written records should be kept of non-licensed work, which has to be notified (for example, copy of the notification with a list of workers on the job), plus the level of likely exposure of those workers to asbestos. This does not require air monitoring on every job if an estimate of degree of exposure can be made, based on experience of similar past tasks or published guidance. Persons in charge of premises have a duty to manage the existence of asbestos in those premises, which will entail keeping records of surveys and possibly a register of where asbestos has been found, its condition and how its presence is being managed. If an employee is exposed to asbestos above the control limit, health records of the employee must be maintained and kept for 40 years after the date of the last entry. All products containing asbestos must be properly labelled. All waste must be in properly sealed and labelled containers.

11

10.	**Builders' skips**
	The Highways Act – Section 139
	If a builders' skip is placed on a road, a permit must be obtained from the local highway authority and the requirements of the permit strictly followed. These will include ensuring the skip is properly lit during the hours of darkness. It must not pose a hazard to highway users and pedestrians and be clearly and indelibly marked with the owner's name and telephone number or address.
11.	**Consultation with employees**
	The Health and Safety (Consultation with Employees) Regulations were introduced because The Health and Safety at Work Act 1974 only covered union-appointed safety representatives. They now extend to all employees the right to have consultation with their employers and be provided with information. There are many similarities with The Safety Representative and Safety Committee Regulations and they also implement the consultation provisions of the European Union Framework Directive on health and safety.
12.	**Control of Substances Hazardous to Health and Approved Code of Practice**
	The Control of Substances Hazardous to Health Regulations (COSHH) and the Approved Code of Practice (ACoP) require assessments to be made of substances hazardous to health and, except in the simplest and most obvious of cases, for the assessments to be written and kept accessible for those who need to know the results. If health surveillance is appropriate, the health records of employees under health surveillance must be maintained and kept for 40 years after the date of the last entry. All mechanical control measures (such as dust extraction) must be subject to routine examination in accordance with the regulations and records kept. Substances hazardous to health must be properly labelled.
13.	**Danger areas**
	Identify with signs under The Work at Height Regulations.
14.	**Dangerous substances and explosive atmospheres**
	Under The Dangerous Substances and Explosive Atmospheres Regulations, the following definitions and conditions apply:
	Dangerous substances
	A substance or preparation that is explosive, oxidising, extremely flammable, highly flammable or flammable, or any dust that can form an explosive mixture with air or an explosive atmosphere.
	Explosive atmosphere
	A mixture, under atmospheric conditions, of air and one or more dangerous substance in the form of gases, vapours, mists or dusts in which, after ignition has occurred, combustion spreads to the entire unburned mixture.
	Where an explosive atmosphere may occur, a specific sign is to be erected.
	In accordance with The Health and Safety (Safety Signs and Signals) Regulations, the sign must consist of black letters on a triangular yellow background with black edging.
15.	**Diving**
	The Diving Operations at Work Regulations
	Records have to be kept of the written appointment of all diving supervisors and of the qualifications and medical certificates of divers. All dives have to be recorded in the diver's logbook. Diving rules have to be in writing. Diving is a very specialised area, even in onshore waters. All diving contractors must be registered with the HSE.
16.	**Electrical equipment**
	The Electricity at Work Regulations
	All electrical equipment, including portable equipment, should be inspected on a regular basis by a competent person and records kept. Portable electric tools should be PAT-tested on a three-monthly basis, with a sticker showing the test date and the date the next test is due fixed to each item.
17.	**Electric shock placard**
	The Electricity at Work Regulations
	Guidance notices or placards giving details of emergency resuscitation procedures in the event of an electric shock should be displayed in locations where people are at an enhanced risk of electric shock.
18.	**Emergency evacuation**
	The Construction (Design and Management) Regulations state emergency routes and exits must be established and indicated by suitable signs.
19.	**Excavations, cofferdams and caissons**
	The Construction (Design and Management) Regulations require that excavations, cofferdams and caissons must be inspected and written reports of the inspections made.
20.	**Explosives**
	Virtually all possession of explosives requires an explosives certificate, which is issued by the local chief officer of police. Detailed records have to be kept of all movements or usages of explosives.

21.	**Falsework and temporary works**
	The Construction (Design and Management) Regulations and British Standard BS 5975 Code of Practice for Falsework
	These Regulations include falsework under the definition of construction work and, therefore, the designer's duties apply. Temporary works require designing and can simply be defined as anything that is not part of the permanent works. It is recommended that records should be kept of all design calculations, drawings, estimated loadings and specifications for falsework, together with written permissions to pour concrete or to load falsework, and to dismantle it.
22.	**Fire**
	The Regulatory Reform (Fire Safety) Order
	The requirement for fire certificates is now discontinued. Documentary information relating to fire safety should include:
	■ records of staff training in the use of extinguishers
	■ records of fire extinguisher servicing
	■ records of practice evacuations
	■ written fire risk assessment and a written fire safety plan
	■ display of relevant signs where flammable and highly flammable substances are stored.
23.	**First aid**
	The Health and Safety (First Aid) Regulations states:
	'An employer shall inform his employees of the arrangements that have been made in connection with the provision of first aid, including the location of equipment, facilities and personnel.'
	The guidance notes recommend that first-aid notices are displayed as an effective means of informing the workforce of the employer's arrangement for first aid.
	There is no statutory form but a range of first-aid notices is available from the suppliers of workplace safety signs.
24.	**Food hygiene**
	The Food Safety Act
	Toilets adjacent to food rooms must be separated by a lobby. A notice stating 'Now wash your hands' must be displayed.
	Checks and inspections of equipment and staff training should be recorded.
	Certificates of staff training in food hygiene and handling must be displayed.
25.	**Fragile surfaces**
	A requirement of The Work at Height Regulations is that if people have to work near or pass close by any fragile roofing materials, the appropriate warning notices must be clearly displayed at all approaches to the area.
26.	**Hazardous substances**
	Generally, under The Control of Substances Hazardous to Health Regulations and the European Union Directive for Classification, Packaging and Labelling of Dangerous Goods, all containers containing hazardous substances should be clearly marked with their contents and the appropriate hazard warning symbol.
	Assessments must be made and, with minor exceptions, recorded. (There is no statutory form.) See also entries under **Asbestos** and **Lead**.
27.	**Health and safety policy**
	The Health and Safety at Work Act 1974 requires employers to have a safety policy and arrangements to bring it into force. If more than five persons are employed, that policy must be written down. There is no statutory form but the HSE publication *Writing your health* and *safety policy statement* may be used.
	The policy must be brought to the notice of all employees.
28.	**Holes in floors and similar openings**
	The Work at Height Regulations require that holes in floors and flat roofs, where a person is liable to fall through (referred to as danger areas in the regulations), must be properly protected. If a cover is used over a hole it must be clearly marked to show its purpose.
29.	**Information for employees**
	The Health and Safety (Information for Employees) Regulations requires every employer to display the approved health and safety law poster in a position where it can be easily read by the employees, or to give to each employee a copy of the approved leaflet entitled *Health and safety law. What you should know*, which contains the same information.
30.	**Insurance (employer's liability)**
	The Employer's Liability (Compulsory Insurance) Act requires there to be in force insurance against liability for bodily injury or disease sustained by employees. The Employer's Liability (Compulsory Insurance) Regulations require a certificate of employer's liability insurance to be displayed at the place of business in such a position that it can be easily seen and read by employees, including every construction site. Employers can display an online version of the certificate, providing all employees have access to it. A hard copy may still be displayed.

11

31.	**Ionising radiation**
	Under the provisions of The Ionising Radiation Regulations, any employer intending to use any source of ionising radiation must give 28-days' notice to the HSE. Very detailed records, including health records, have to be kept. Advice should be sought from the HSE or other competent source. The appropriate warning signs and notices for controlled areas must be displayed.
32.	**Lead**
	The Control of Lead at Work Regulations together with the Approved Code of Practice and guidance notes require a number of forms to be completed by employers (and in some cases medical practitioners) if the required risk assessment under the regulations carried out by the employer shows that an employee's exposure to lead is liable to be significant. Some of the types of work likely to lead to significant exposure are: ■ high temperature work (over 500ºC), including welding and cutting ■ abrasion of lead or lead-painted surfaces ■ spray painting with lead paint. Details of all the forms are given in the Approved Code of Practice.
33.	**Lifting operations**
	Under The Lifting Operations and Lifting Equipment Regulations: ■ all machinery and accessories used for lifting are marked to indicate their safe working load (SWL) for each configuration in which they can be used ■ lifting equipment designed to lift persons is clearly marked as such ■ lifting equipment not designed for lifting persons but which could be easily mistaken for such is marked appropriately ■ all lifting equipment and accessories are subjected to a scheme of thorough examination ■ records of thorough examination are made and kept available for inspection.
34.	**Management of health and safety**
	There is no statutory or recommended style of form for risk, or any other assessments. Your own devised form or a commercially obtained form may be completed either manually or on a computer database. Risk assessments must be made of all work activities. **If you employ five or more people, the significant findings must be recorded and, in addition:** ■ health surveillance – if needed, individual health records must be kept ■ emergency procedures – must be written down.
35.	**Manual handling**
	The Manual Handling Operations Regulations Assessment to be made where risks from manual handling cannot be avoided. It is recommended that all but the simplest assessments should be recorded.
36.	**Noise**
	The Control of Noise at Work Regulations requires that all hearing protection zones are identified by means of a sign (see The Health and Safety (Safety Signs and Signals) Regulations). A hearing protection zone is anywhere where an employee is likely to be exposed to a daily personal noise exposure of 85 dB(A) or a peak sound pressure of 137 dB(C).
37.	**Plant and equipment**
	If it is not otherwise provided for, it is strongly recommended that all plant, tools and equipment are subject to inspection and examination, and proper records kept. This will fulfil the employer's obligations under The Health and Safety at Work Act 1974, Section 2 and The Provision and Use of Work Equipment Regulations. A daily inspection and a six-monthly examination may be appropriate. Insurance companies may also require such routine inspections and examinations.
38.	**Pressure vessels**
	The Simple Pressure Vessels (Safety) Regulations apply to all pressure vessels intended to contain air or nitrogen at a greater pressure than 0.5 bar. Any such vessel first used after 1 July 1992 must have (amongst other things) details of the maximum working pressure, maximum and minimum working temperatures, and cubic capacity clearly displayed on it.
39.	**Protective clothing and equipment**
	The Personal Protective Equipment at Work Regulations The following must be recorded: ■ risk assessment of the need for personal protective equipment (PPE) ■ PPE inspection, maintenance or results of any required tests ■ records of PPE issue and use.

11

40.	**Safety representatives and safety committees**
	The Safety Representative and Safety Committees Regulations, and the Approved Code of Practice and guidance notes, give safety representatives the right to inspect and take copies of any document relevant to safety that an employer is required to keep (except health records of identifiable individuals).
	The employer must make available to them any health and safety information that would help safety representatives fulfil their functions. Where a safety committee has been established, proper minutes and records should be kept. Safety representatives may give written reports to management concerning safety in the workplace.
41.	**Safety signs**
	The Health and Safety (Safety Signs and Signals) Regulations
	All signs giving health or safety information or instructions must comply with the relevant British Standard. A safety sign is anything that combines geometrical shape, colour and pictorial symbols to give safety information.
42.	**Scaffolding**
	■ Display of incomplete scaffold notice.
	Under The Work at Height Regulations, designated danger areas must be created where there is a risk of a person falling or being hit by a falling object. In the case of incomplete scaffolding, suitable notices must be displayed to discourage attempted access on to the scaffold.
	■ Handover certificates.
	There are no statutory provisions requiring the use or production of scaffold handover certificates. However, all reputable scaffold contractors will issue them and they can be used to demonstrate that the scaffold was properly erected by competent persons and for the purpose for which the scaffold was designed.
	■ Reports of inspections.
	To be completed and retained to comply with The Work at Height Regulations.
43.	**Training**
	Generally, Section 2 of The Health and Safety at Work Act 1974, together with various other regulations made under the principal Act, require employers to provide information, instruction and training. It is most strongly recommended that all such information, instruction and training are properly and fully recorded so that employers are in a position to prove that duties under the Act or regulations have been met.
44.	**Visual display units (VDUs) or display screens**
	The Health and Safety (Display Screen Equipment) Regulations
	Suitable and sufficient analysis of workstations for the purpose of assessing health and safety risks. All but the simplest and obvious cases must be recorded.
	Entitles employees to eyesight tests. Records of requests and results are recommended.
45.	**Waste management**
	All contractors that carry or collect waste should have a waste carrier's licence and all waste disposal facilities should have a waste management licence or permit unless they are exempt. All waste transfers must be supported by the correct documentation, called a controlled waste transfer note; or in the case of hazardous waste, a consignment note.
46.	**Work equipment**
	The Provision and Use of Work Equipment Regulations
	Records must be kept, including risk assessment for selection and use, regular and statutory inspections, maintenance, training and instructions.
	All work equipment must be marked in a clearly visible manner where necessary, in the interests of health and safety.
	Warnings, audible or visible, to be incorporated into work equipment as necessary.
47.	**Work in compressed air**
	The Work in Compressed Air Regulations
	This is an extremely specialist area where expert knowledge is needed. Detailed records are required to be kept of such areas.
	■ clinical by a doctor
	■ exposure by a compressed air contractor
	■ health by an employer.
	These records need maintaining for 40 years from the date of the last entry.
48.	**Working time**
	The Working Time Regulations give details of permitted work hours and special consideration that should be given to young workers. Records of agreements, which can only last up to five years, must be kept by the employer.

11

49.	**Working at height**
	The Work at Height Regulations
	This regulation specifies the need for competence in all persons involved in any capacity with regard to work at height. Any training carried out to achieve competency should be recorded.
	Where any person at work may pass across or near to a fragile surface, or actually work on it, prominent signs indicating that it is a fragile surface must be fixed at every approach to that place.
	Where any person could be injured by falling or being hit by a falling object, danger areas must be created to prevent such an occurrence. Danger areas must be clearly indicated, usually by signs and/or barriers.
	Where inspections of work equipment are carried out under this regulation, a record of the inspection must be made and retained as specified.

11

12

Accident prevention and control

There are many factors to understand as to why accidents happen in construction, the trends and causes, the impact they can have and the preventative measures that are required. By reading this chapter managers should gain an appreciation of what factors need to be considered when developing construction phase plans, safe systems of work, assessing risk, undertaking site inspections and managing health and safety on site on a day-to-day basis.

Introduction	160
Key points	160
Definitions	161
Accident trends	162
The cost of accidents	162
HSE research into accident costs	163
Causes of accidents	163
Planning for health and safety	164
Factors to consider	164
Hazards	165
The implications of inexperience	166
Contractors and the self-employed	167
Supervision and control	167

Accident prevention and control

12.1 Introduction

Accident statistics are a reliable indicator of the health and safety performance of the construction industry. The Health and Safety Executive (HSE) publishes an annual statistical report of the accidents, fatalities and occupational diseases across all industries.

 This report, which is useful because it highlights accident trends, is freely downloadable from the HSE website.

On average, annual construction industry statistics show:

- ☑ there are 50 construction fatalities
- ☑ there are 2,500 reported major injuries
- ☑ there are 5,600 over seven-day injuries
- ☑ 1,500 workers are injured falling from height and 300 of those injuries involve high falls
- ☑ manual handling accounts for 28% of all reported injuries to workers
- ☑ slips and trips account for 22% of all reported injuries to workers
- ☑ over three million working days are lost within the construction industry due to workplace injury and work-related ill health.

Each year the plan of work for the construction division of the HSE acknowledges that some parts of the industry have made significant steps forward over recent years; this is particularly noticeable on larger projects. However, these improvements are not mirrored to anything like the same extent on smaller sites, where many instances of unacceptable standards can still be found.

Five core issues for focus are:

- ☑ work at height
- ☑ asbestos risks
- ☑ provision of welfare facilities
- ☑ good order/housekeeping, including slips, trips and falls
- ☑ respiratory risks, especially construction dust.

In addition, other issues that require focus are:

- ☑ management of work-related ill health
- ☑ leadership and worker engagement
- ☑ contractor and worker competence
- ☑ temporary works/structural stability
- ☑ mobile elevating work platforms (MEWPs)/mobile plant
- ☑ cranes and lifting operations
- ☑ electricity
- ☑ fire
- ☑ demolition.

Hopefully over the next few years the industry will experience a culture change so that health and safety is not only about the tangible things, like wearing mandatory personal protective equipment (PPE), pedestrian segregation or providing collective fall prevention, but also about the softer issues, such as **worker engagement** and an openness and honesty from both management and the workforce to ensure that work is organised and carried out safely.

12.2 Key points

- ☑ The construction industry consistently accounts for a disproportionately high number of fatalities and major accidents.
- ☑ Accident prevention has to be actively managed; a good safety record will not just happen and everyone on site has their part to play.
- ☑ Reported details of accidents show that in the vast majority of cases the accident could easily have been prevented by taking simple precautions.
- ☑ The HSE has stated that many accidents result from decisions taken before work actually starts (planning and identifying safe systems of work).
- ☑ You may have no influence over these decisions but find that you need to challenge the health and safety implications that arise as a consequence of them.
- ☑ The true cost of an accident goes beyond the financial implications.
- ☑ Statistics show that new starters on site, and those at both ends of the age spectrum, are the most prone to accidents.

12

12.3 Definitions

There are many interpretations of the word 'accident', but it is generally agreed that an **accident** is an unplanned, unscheduled, unwanted event or occurrence, or any undesired circumstance, that may result in injury to persons and damage to property. The injured person may not be an employee and property may not belong to an employer.

Hazard is the potential to cause harm, including ill health and injury; damage to property, plant products or environment; production losses or liabilities.

Risk is the likelihood that a specified, undesired event will occur due to the realisation of a hazard by or during work activities or by products created by work activities.

An alternative word that is sometimes used for an accident is **incident**. The main difference in the use of this word is that an incident is something that happened, which may or may not have resulted in an injury or damage.

This diagram is a modified version of **Bird's Triangle**. Its aim is to simply demonstrate the approximate relationships between the different levels of accident that occur. The triangle shows that for each fatality there are 10 serious injuries, 30 accidents with injury, 600 incidents without injury (near misses or property/equipment/material damage) and thousands of unsafe acts or conditions.

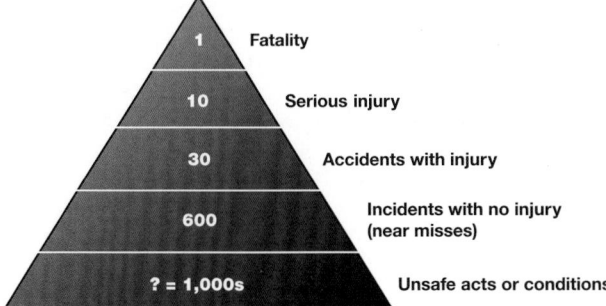

Bird's Accident Triangle

Bird's research illustrates that accident prevention should not be about just concentrating on fatalities and serious injury, but on preventing unsafe acts and conditions. Near misses can be an early indication that unsafe acts or conditions are happening, rather than reacting to actual accident and injury trends. This is why near-miss reporting and proactive hazard-spotting techniques (such as pre-use daily checks, workplace inspections and audits) are so important.

An unsafe act or near miss under a slightly different set of circumstances could be a serious or even fatal accident. This makes accident prevention more difficult, particularly if the incidents go unreported.

Many companies have found that their accident rate has reduced as the number of reported incidents with no injury or near misses has increased through management encouragement for such incidents to be reported.

Near-miss reporting

The importance of learning from experience cannot be overstated. It is an essential element of accident prevention. A near miss is an incident that had the potential to result in personal injury and/or damage to the structure under construction, plant and equipment or the environment. Individual companies will decide on their criteria for categorising an incident as a near miss.

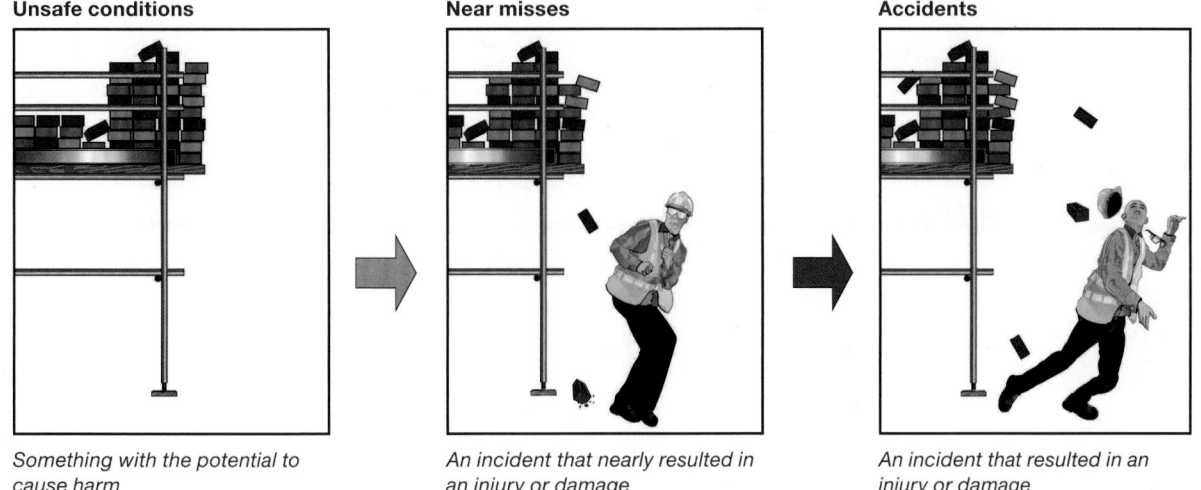

Unsafe conditions
Something with the potential to cause harm

Near misses
An incident that nearly resulted in an injury or damage

Accidents
An incident that resulted in an injury or damage

The details of all near misses must be accurately and honestly reported to enable the circumstances to be investigated and measures put in place to prevent a recurrence. In many cases, the only person able to give a full and accurate account of what happened will be the person who got it wrong.

Accident prevention and control

To achieve an effective reporting system, the workforce must:

☑ trust that management will treat the incident fairly and objectively

☑ be encouraged to report near misses with the assurance that individuals involved will not be disadvantaged by their honesty

☑ have confidence that the issues raised will be addressed, or else 'why bother?'

☑ be provided with the means of promptly recording the details of exactly what happened and offering their opinion as to why it occurred.

Companies may find it is beneficial to provide easily accessible near-miss reporting forms, which can be completed in privacy and anonymously if that is the individual's choice. However, anonymous reporting does not provide the opportunity for follow-up discussions to establish more details, and it may encourage malicious reports to be submitted.

Evidence shows that near-miss reporting linked to recognition or a reward scheme has the best chance of succeeding.

12.4 Accident trends

Broad categories are used to classify all accidents that are reported to the HSE. Each year the HSE publishes the reportable accident statistics for the previous year. This enables year-on-year trends to be established.

> Reportable accident statistics for the construction industry show that the same types of accident figure prominently in the statistics year after year. Falls from height, manual handling injuries, being struck by a moving object (often plant) and slips and trips continue to figure prominently.

Now that the construction industry's output has slowed, further challenges may have been added as the competition for contracts has increased and tendered margins decreased. Commercial pressure may tempt contractors to take increased risks with their employees' health and/or safety.

The stubborn resistance of the accident statistics to significantly reduce is often attributed to the difficult working conditions experienced on construction sites, where the environment of the workplace is continually changing as work progresses. However, in reality it is often due to a lack of training or health and safety awareness among construction workers, or a lack of effective health and safety management. Current accident statistics for the construction industry indicate that about 14 people suffer a major injury every working day and four people are killed every month.

12.5 The cost of accidents

Cost to the victim and their family

☑ Pain and suffering.

☑ Loss of earnings.

☑ Extra expense.

☑ Continuing disability, depression.

☑ Incapacity for the same job.

☑ Incapacity for activities outside the job.

☑ Effect on dependants and friends.

Cost to people directly responsible

☑ Worry and stress.

☑ Recriminations, guilt.

☑ Extra work (reports, training and recruitment).

☑ Loss of credibility.

Cost to the company

☑ Working time lost by victim.

☑ Time lost by other employees out of sympathy, curiosity, discussion.

☑ Time lost by supervisors and others investigating the accident.

☑ Possible damage to machines or materials.

☑ Idle time (replan, repair and reinstate job).

☑ Rise in insurance premiums and cost of prosecution or civil action.

☑ Damage to reputation and possible failure to obtain work.

Cost to the working group

☑ Shock, disbelief, anger and personal grief.

☑ Low morale, effects on production.

Cost to the nation

- [✓] In social and economic terms, accidents are an unwanted expense.
- [✓] Hundreds of thousands of person-days are lost each year.
- [✓] Impact of industrial accidents on NHS resources.
- [✓] Millions of pounds paid in pensions and death benefits.
- [✓] Countless lives changed for the worse.

Whilst there can be no complete end cost figure, the size of the problem can be seen to be huge. Therefore anything that helps to reduce the number of accidents must benefit both the nation and the individuals concerned.

It must be stressed that these are all negative impacts. Good health and safety management prevents accidents, which means less or no victims or affected families, no additional costs to companies, no loss of reputation and no loss of work.

12.6 HSE research into accident costs

HSE Research Report No. 464 contains a number of accident case studies that highlight the cost of accidents to the victims, in the widest terms. Several of the case studies feature accidents to construction workers.

The consequences of each accident are considered from different standpoints:

- [✓] **vocational** – future job prospects
- [✓] **financial** – loss of earnings and future earnings
- [✓] **social** – standard-of-life issue for victim and family
- [✓] **behavioural** – reliance on medication, inability to concentrate, inability to sleep, ill-temper, and so on
- [✓] **psychological** – mood swings, loss of memory, emotional instability and guilt.

Examples of the impact that the accidents had on the victims, as extracted from the construction case studies, are:

- [✓] 'I had no realistic prospect of returning to work in the immediate future'
- [✓] 'I received no support from company or colleagues upon returning to work other than 'light duties' for the first two weeks'
- [✓] 'My family was reliant on state benefits of £66 per week during three and a half months off work'
- [✓] 'I am unable to bathe or dress myself, have problems with walking and no longer visit the gym'
- [✓] 'I am unable to sleep due to discomfort, increased eating and inability to concentrate'
- [✓] 'Years later I still suffer flashbacks and nightmares'.

12.7 Causes of accidents

Examining accident details will help to establish common factors and trends, revealing any weaknesses in a company's health and safety management system. Accidents can be caused by the unsafe acts and attitudes of people at work, which result in unsafe conditions being created. They are also caused by a lack of foresight or planning, which may be a failure to set up a safe system of work, or failure to appreciate the results of risk assessments, COSHH assessments or other similar activities.

 Unsafe acts can create unsafe conditions which can cause **accidents** and these accidents often result in **injury or damage**.

It is impossible to list all the different types of unsafe acts and unsafe conditions that can exist in the construction industry. However, it is worth recording those that have been the most frequent known causes of accidents on construction sites:

- [✓] lack of planning, management control and supervision
- [✓] lack of knowledge of good safety techniques or lack of safety awareness
- [✓] unsafe methods of working at height, including lack of provision for fall prevention
- [✓] incorrect use of machinery and equipment
- [✓] failure to segregate operating plant and pedestrians
- [✓] failure to inspect and maintain all types of machinery and equipment
- [✓] incorrect use of tools and equipment (hand tools and power tools)
- [✓] use of faulty equipment with improvised repairs or modifications
- [✓] unsafe manual handling (lifting, loading, moving, stacking, storing)
- [✓] overloading of working places (scaffolds, false work, hoists, machines, vehicles, roofs)
- [✓] failure to use protective safety equipment (helmets, goggles, gloves, masks, footwear)

12

- ☑ carrying out work on moving parts with guards removed or safety devices inoperative
- ☑ failure to report faulty or unsafe equipment, or dangerous occurrences and incidents
- ☑ creating unstable structures.

12.8 Planning for health and safety

Despite the effort made by the majority to fulfil their legal, moral and social obligations, difficulties are often encountered in human behaviour that require time and tolerance before acceptable safety standards are achieved.

It is essential that careful consideration is given to pre-planning, communication, training, supervision and the dissemination of information, if safe systems and places of work are to be developed and maintained.

All of the following measures can make a significant contribution towards the prevention of accidents through the implementation of safe systems of work and procedures.

- ☑ Allowing enough money and time to do the work safely.
- ☑ Adequate protection and guarding of working places, platforms, machinery, tools, plant and equipment.
- ☑ Implementation of an adequate system for the maintenance and repair of plant, equipment and tools.
- ☑ Provision of appropriate training, instruction and information at all levels, including safety training.
- ☑ Provision of adequate supervision and control.
- ☑ Planning, siting and/or stacking materials and equipment to allow safe access or egress of site plant, vehicles and equipment.
- ☑ Pre-planning and organisation of site layout, which will provide maximum efficiency, safety and progression of the work sequences and operations.
- ☑ The provision of adequate resources and equipment to protect and maintain the health and welfare of all personnel.
- ☑ Producing, declaring, maintaining and supporting a safety policy, and updating it as appropriate to accommodate advancement and development.
- ☑ Bringing about and maintaining an awareness of, and compliance with, all safety legislation and information relating to systems and procedures of work.

The safe separation of construction plant and pedestrians avoids accidents

12.9 Factors to consider

Health and safety at work will be affected by:

- ☑ human and personal factors
- ☑ job factors
- ☑ environmental factors.

Human and personal factors

Attitudes of people at work often play an important part in the prevention of accidents, and conversely, a wrong attitude can cause accidents to happen. Attitudes differ depending on the person, for example their:

- ☑ age and sex
- ☑ general health, natural dexterity, agility, physique and ability
- ☑ disabilities, if any
- ☑ senses of smell, sight, hearing, touch and, sometimes, taste
- ☑ education and qualifications, training and skills
- ☑ home and social life, status at home and work, position in peer group.

 Safe attitudes = safe actions = safe conditions.

Job factors

Every work activity has a degree of inherent hazard. Building and construction sites can be particularly hazardous and demand the co-ordination of a large number of trades, skills and activities at any one time.

Particular attention should be given to:

- ☑ the adequacy of time and resources to plan the job and to do the job
- ☑ provision of tools and equipment that are safe to use and properly maintained
- ☑ implementation of safe systems of work
- ☑ personnel who are unfamiliar with established safe systems of work and practices
- ☑ personnel who are new to a specific worksite or unfamiliar with a new working environment
- ☑ those lacking induction training and/or experience
- ☑ the provision of adequate training, information and supervision
- ☑ balanced workload, fatigue and boredom.

Environmental factors

The majority of people do not work in isolation. The attitudes of others in a working group (for example, managers, supervisors, safety officers, safety representatives and shop stewards) may help to prevent accidents. The following details should also be considered:

- ☑ the accident record of the firm, site and working group
- ☑ the inter-relationship of people within the group
- ☑ information and communication processing methods
- ☑ weather conditions (hot, cold, wet, wind, ice or snow)
- ☑ working at heights, in confined spaces or underground
- ☑ working conditions (noise, dust, light, ventilation)
- ☑ health and welfare facilities.

12.10 Hazards

12

Obvious dangers

Examples of dangerous conditions include:

- ☑ vehicles not being segregated from pedestrians
- ☑ the presence of highly flammable material and other fire hazards
- ☑ work platforms or work places at height with no fall prevention
- ☑ insecurely stacked, slung, lifted and transported loads
- ☑ unsafe machinery, equipment and tools
- ☑ unsafe working areas due to weather conditions
- ☑ confined spaces or unsupported excavations.

Accident prevention and control

Potentially dangerous situations

Examples of circumstances that might result in an accident:

☑ working with machinery or tools with guards or fences removed

☑ using the incorrect type of plant, tools or equipment for the work involved

☑ unauthorised removal of guard-rails, or failure to replace them following removal for access of plant or materials

☑ transport of insecure or unstable loads

☑ dropping tools and materials from a height

☑ failure to wear PPE

☑ working in unstable excavations, without adequate supervision and control

☑ untidy working places or congested walkways and areas – creating a tripping hazard

☑ working at height or over water without edge and/or personal protection

☑ inadequate, incorrect or badly placed lighting

☑ unsafe electrical equipment, buried services and overhead cables.

Operational risks

Examples of work requiring competence, careful monitoring and/or close supervision are listed below.

HIGH RISK activities	Operations creating health hazards or risk of injury
■ Demolition. ■ Working at height. ■ Excavations. ■ Lifting operations. ■ Work in confined spaces. ■ Timber, concrete or steel frame erection. ■ Roof work and cladding. ■ Work associated with live traffic.	■ Work producing dust or fumes. ■ Jobs with continual high exposure to noise or vibration. ■ Jobs with continuous elements of the same type of manual handling (such as block laying and kerb laying). ■ Work with asbestos. ■ Work with hazardous substances (respiratory, eye splash and skin).

Site security

Owners or occupiers of sites have a duty in civil law to protect the health and safety of **anyone** who might enter the site, even if that entry is unlawful. This includes members of the public, particularly young children, who may trespass on the site, either during or outside of normal working hours.

Sadly around four children are killed and many injured every year on construction sites.

These include:

☑ falls into holes, being trapped by earth, or drowning

☑ accidents involving vehicles

☑ accidents involving falls and falling materials.

In all these cases, better site security and management might have prevented the accident. Contractors must take all reasonable and practical steps to ensure that sites are secure.

12.11 The implications of inexperience

Young persons

Before employing a young person, the employer must assess the risks to the young person's health and safety arising from the work they are required to do, in accordance with the regulations. This assessment must take account of a number of factors, such as:

☑ the inexperience and immaturity of young persons, and their lack of awareness of risks

☑ the type of any work equipment involved and the way it is used

☑ the potential for exposure to physical, biological and chemical agents

☑ any health and safety training that is required for young persons.

Having carried out this assessment, employers must then determine whether the level of risk has been reduced to as low as is reasonably practicable. There is particular importance placed on avoiding work that:

- ☑ is beyond the young person's physical or psychological capacity
- ☑ involves harmful exposure to agents that are toxic or carcinogenic, causes heritable genetic damage or harm to an unborn child or which in any way chronically affects human health
- ☑ involves harmful exposure to radiation
- ☑ involves the risk of accident, which it may be reasonably assumed cannot be recognised by young people owing to their insufficient attention to safety or lack of experience or training
- ☑ involves exposure to physical agents (such as extreme cold or heat, noise and vibration).

Consideration to the level of acceptable risk may be given for young persons over the minimum school-leaving age, where the work is necessary for their training, and where they are properly supervised.

New starters

New starters in a company or on a site and inexperienced persons of any age have similar problems to those of young workers.

They are subjected to a new environment, rules, methods and procedures; are under different supervision; and are working with new colleagues using a variety of tools, equipment and manual effort to produce the work required. The start of their health and safety training is usually an induction into the company.

The need for refresher and continuance training should be reviewed at intervals and carried out as necessary.

Older workers

Quite correctly there is legislation in place that makes it illegal to discriminate against older workers. It is also interesting, however, to note that the number of incidents to older workers is higher than average. There are various reasons that have been suggested as to why, such as:

- ☑ overfamiliarity with the job
- ☑ general slowing of reactions
- ☑ general loss of strength and flexibility
- ☑ pre-existing damage to body and systems
- ☑ age-related degeneration of hearing and eyesight.

What is also noteworthy is that when an older person is injured, often the recovery time is longer, because the injury is more severe than it would be for a younger person.

12.12 Contractors and the self-employed

Problems may arise if accident prevention and reporting measures are not communicated to contractors and self-employed persons on site. Arrangements must be made to ensure that contractors and the self-employed are acquainted with, and adhere to, the principal contractor's health and safety standards and procedures, or any other policy or special instructions that may be in force, or relevant to specific operations.

The following recommendations are not exhaustive. Pre-planning at the tender stage may reveal additional requirements.

- ☑ Discussion, as necessary, should take place to ensure complete understanding or clarification of what is required.
- ☑ A listing of site personnel (who's who and details of established channels of communication).
- ☑ The availability, and validity, of certificates and documentation relating to health and safety knowledge and trade competency, including CSCS, CPCS and CISRS cards.
- ☑ Safe systems or methods and sequences of work should be established, particularly where such activities may affect the health and welfare of others.
- ☑ Attention should be given to the requirements for the delivery of plant or equipment, transportation, loading and unloading of materials and provision of means of access; particularly when these activities take place out of normal working hours.

12

12.13 Supervision and control

The accident trend can be strongly influenced by providing adequate training and supervision to control the worker, the machine or the equipment and the working environment.

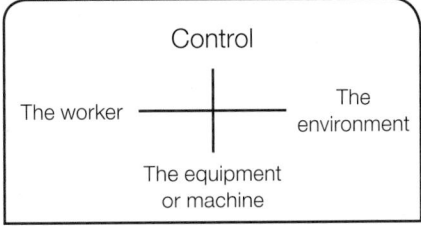

Accident prevention is the control of these factors

The worker

It is essential to ensure that the worker:

☑ is adequately trained and informed of the activities they are expected to do

☑ is aware of all the hazards in any activity they are expected to do

☑ is competent to do the work or is under adequate suitably qualified supervision

☑ adopts a safe system of work and uses the protection provided

☑ is aware of accident and emergency procedures

☑ is aware of the company's health and safety policy, rules and legislation **applicable to the work.**

The working environment

This applies to all areas of the site, including the work area, stores, offices, depot and welfare facilities.

Regular checks are essential to ensure that these areas remain safe and are not a risk to health.

 For further guidance refer to Chapter A10 Inspections and audits.

12

13

Accident reporting and investigation

The recording of incidents and accidents at work is important in establishing what went wrong to help stop them happening again.

This chapter outlines why and how details of incidents and accidents should be captured, what has to be reported to the Health and Safety Executive (HSE) and how to conduct an investigation.

Introduction	170
Key points	170
Accident records	170
The Reporting of Injuries, Diseases and Dangerous Occurrences Regulations	171
Calculating the incidence and frequency rates of accidents	174
Accident investigation	175
Appendix A – Form F2508 Reporting of an injury or dangerous occurrence	179

Accident reporting and investigation

13.1 Introduction

It may be said that there is no such thing as an accident and without people there are no accidents. An accident can always be put down to human error and it is by no means always the fault of the injured person.

In fact, the Health and Safety Executive (HSE) considers that a lack of safety management, or procedures, is a contributory factor in a high percentage of accidents, particularly within construction.

The reporting of certain types of accident is a legal requirement and failure to comply is a criminal offence. The reports that are made allow the HSE to identify accident trends, and to take remedial action by producing additional health and safety guidance and legislation, where it is thought necessary.

If you are an employer, self-employed or are in charge of work operations, you have duties under the law.

You generally have to report deaths, serious injuries and dangerous occurrences immediately, and less serious injuries within 15 days. Certain occupational ill health issues and diseases also have to be reported.

13.2 Key points

☑ It is important that all workplace accidents, no matter how minor, are reported to the injured person's employer, site manager or supervisor as appropriate.

☑ There is a legal requirement for details of all accidents to be recorded.

☑ Once completed, the record of an accident is subject to the Data Protection Act and is confidential.

☑ Certain types of accident, cases of occupational diseases (when connected with specific work activities) and some dangerous occurrences, must be reported to the Health and Safety Executive.

☑ Each company or organisation should have a procedure for investigating workplace accidents.

☑ The investigation of accidents will enable trends to be established and preventative measures put in place.

☑ The level of investigation should be proportionate to the seriousness of the accident.

13.3 Accident records

Employers are legally required to keep records of all accidents. These can be stored in any medium, including electronically, as long as printable copies are readily available if required.

Records must include details of:

☑ date, time and place of accident

☑ name and job of injured or ill person

☑ details of injury/illness and what first aid was given

☑ what happened to the person immediately afterwards (for example, whether they went home, to hospital, back to work)

☑ name and signature of the first aider or person dealing with the incident.

Details of an accident should be recorded by the injured person, but can be completed by any employee. However, some employers insist that records are completed by first aiders, which requires a first aider to be available at all times. This is a company operating procedure and is not strictly necessary.

Completion of an accident record does not meet the employer's obligation to report specific accidents and dangerous occurrences to the HSE or Local Authority.

All accident records have had to comply with the Data Protection Act to ensure the confidentiality of entries. The HSE's accident book BI 510 enables each accident record to be detached and stored separately when complete, thus maintaining the confidentiality of the injured person's details. All personal information must be kept in confidence, and in a secure location, such as a lockable cabinet.

Accident books designed and produced in-house may still be used, provided that:

☑ all details required by BI 510 are recorded

☑ the requirements of the Data Protection Act are met

☑ information recorded electronically can be made readily available in hard copy.

13

13.4 The Reporting of Injuries, Diseases and Dangerous Occurrences Regulations

Key requirements

The Reporting of Injuries, Diseases and Dangerous Occurrences Regulations (RIDDOR) requires the following to be reported directly to the appropriate enforcing authority (either the nearest HSE office or the Local Authority):

- ☑ fatalities and major injuries

- ☑ injuries resulting in incapacity for more than seven days when linked to certain work activities

- ☑ specified diseases

- ☑ dangerous occurrences.

The regulations place a duty on the responsible person to make reports to the enforcing authorities. In the case of injuries to employees, the responsible person will be the employer. In the case of the victim being self-employed or a member of the public, the responsible person will be the person in control of the site where the event occurred.

All sub-contractors must notify both the enforcing authority and the main/principal contractor of any reportable accidents.

Where an accident, occupational disease or dangerous occurrence takes place that requires reporting under RIDDOR, a report should be made online via the HSE website. The online forms are:

- ☑ F2508 Report of an injury

- ☑ F2508 Report of a dangerous occurrence

- ☑ F2508A Report of a case of disease

- ☑ F2508G1 Report of a flammable gas incident

- ☑ F2508G2 Report of a dangerous gas fitting.

The following must be reported immediately to the appropriate authority by the quickest practical method (usually by telephone) and a report submitted on the approved form within 15 days.

- ☑ Death of any person as a result of an accident at work.

- ☑ An accident to any person at work resulting in major injuries or serious conditions specified in the regulations.

- ☑ Any one of the dangerous occurrences listed in the regulations.

Why report and record?

The report informs the enforcing authorities (HSE, Local Authorities and Office of Rail Regulation (ORR), where relevant) about deaths, injuries, occupational diseases and dangerous occurrences, so they can identify where and how risks arise and whether they need to be investigated. This allows HSE, Local Authorities and ORR to target their work and provide advice about how to avoid work-related deaths, injuries, ill health and accidental loss.

Records of incidents covered by RIDDOR are important. They ensure that you collect the minimum amount of information to allow you to check that you are doing enough to ensure safety and prevent occupational diseases. This information is a valuable management tool that can be used as an aid to risk assessment, helping to develop solutions to potential risks. In this way, records also help to prevent injuries and ill health, and control costs from accidental loss.

What must be reported?

Deaths and injuries do not have to be automatically reported, but must be reported if they occur as the result of an accident arising out of or in connection with work.

An accident is a separate event to a death or injury, and is simply more than an event; it is something harmful that happens unexpectedly.

When deciding if the accident that led to the death or injury has arisen out of or in connection to work, the key issues to consider are whether the accident was related to:

- ☑ the way in which the work was carried out

- ☑ any machinery, plant, substances or equipment used for work

- ☑ the condition of the site or premises where the accident happened.

If any of the above factors was related to the cause of the accident, then it is likely that the injury will need to be reported to the enforcing authority. If none of the above factors are satisfied, it is likely that you will not be required to send a report.

13

 Guidance and examples of incidents that do and do not have to be reported are available on the RIDDOR section of the HSE's website.

Deaths

A death must be reported if:

☑ it results from a work accident

☑ a worker sustains an occupational injury before they die

☑ it results from a suicide on a relevant transport system (this is considered to be an accident for the purpose of RIDDOR)

☑ it results from an act of physical violence to a worker.

Injuries to people at work

RIDDOR gives two types of injury that must be reported if the person was at work – major injuries and, from 6 April 2012 over seven-day injuries.

Major injuries

These include:

☑ a fracture, other than to fingers, thumbs and toes

☑ amputation

☑ dislocation of the shoulder, hip, knee or spine

☑ loss of sight (temporary or permanent)

☑ chemical or hot metal burn to the eye or any penetrating injury to the eye

☑ injury resulting from an electric shock or electrical burn leading to unconsciousness, resuscitation or admittance to hospital for more than 24 hours

☑ any other injury leading to hypothermia, heat-induced illness, unconsciousness, resuscitation or admittance to hospital for more than 24 hours

☑ unconsciousness caused by asphyxia or exposure to a harmful substance or biological agent

☑ an acute illness requiring medical treatment

☑ loss of consciousness arising from absorption of any substance by inhalation, ingestion or through the skin

☑ acute illness requiring medical treatment where there is reason to believe that this resulted from exposure to a biological agent, its toxins or infected material.

Over seven-day injuries

On 6 April 2012, the law introduced the over seven-day injury category. This is where **an employee, or self-employed person, is away from work or unable to perform their normal work duties for more than seven consecutive days** (not counting the day of the accident).

Over three-day injuries

From 6 April 2012, **you do not have to report over three-day injuries but you must keep a record of them.** If you are an employer, who has to keep an accident book, the record you make in this will be enough.

Injuries to people not at work

You must report injuries to members of the public or people who are not at work, if they are injured following an accident that arises out of, or in connection with work, and are taken from the scene of an accident to hospital for treatment.

Occupational diseases

Employers and self-employed people must report occupational diseases. This must be done when they receive a written diagnosis from a doctor that they, or an employee, are suffering from one of these conditions and the sufferer has been doing the work activities listed for that illness, for example:

☑ mesothelioma, lung cancer, asbestosis (due to work with or exposure to asbestos)

☑ hand-arm vibration syndrome (due to operating hand-held vibrating tools and equipment)

☑ occupational dermatitis, due to work substances (such as cement, solvents, epoxy resins).

13

Dangerous occurrences

Dangerous occurrences are certain, listed, near-miss events. Not every near-miss event must be reported. There are 21 categories of dangerous occurrences that are relevant to all workplaces, for example:

☑ the collapse, overturning or failure of load-bearing parts of lifts and lifting equipment

☑ plant or equipment coming into contact with overhead power lines

☑ electrical short circuits or overloads causing a fire or explosion, which results in the stoppage of the plant for more than 24 hours or has the potential to cause death

☑ the accidental release of any substance that may damage health.

 A full list of dangerous occurrences applicable to all workplaces, and additional categories of dangerous occurrences, can be found on the RIDDOR section of the HSE's website.

Gas incidents

If you are a distributor, filler, importer or supplier of flammable gas and you learn, either directly or indirectly, that someone has died or suffered a major injury in connection with the gas you distributed, filled, imported or supplied, this can be reported online.

If you are a gas engineer, registered with the Gas Safe Register, you must provide details of any gas appliances or fittings that you consider to be dangerous to the extent that people could die or suffer a major injury. This may be due to the design, construction, installation, modification or servicing, and could result in:

☑ an accidental leakage of gas

☑ inadequate combustion of gas

☑ inadequate removal of products of the combustion of gas.

Keeping records

Records of all reportable deaths, injuries and dangerous occurrences must be kept for a period of three years. No precise method is prescribed, but a photocopy of the approved form is acceptable, as are electronic databanks and computer storage.

Disease reports must be kept in the same manner as accident records and the minimum particulars that must be kept are:

☑ date of diagnosis of the disease

☑ name of the person affected

☑ occupation of the person affected

☑ name or nature of the disease

☑ date on which the disease was reported to the enforcing authority

☑ method by which the disease was reported.

Reportable or not reportable under RIDDOR?

 For simplicity in the following passage of text, the word 'incident' is used to cover any reportable event (such as injury, disease or dangerous occurrence).

The regulations are quite specific about what should be reported, but written in a convoluted way, which can lead to confusion. There is a school of thought that suggests that, if in doubt, report an incident. However, in the construction industry, providing information about the number of past reported incidents is often part of a pre-qualification procedure and, with this in mind, it may not be beneficial to report more than is legally required.

It is considered sensible to only report incidents that should be reported, but to investigate and learn from all incidents.

13

Accident reporting and investigation

The following examples may provide some clarification.

- ☑ A directly employed person breaks their arm at work. This must be reported by the employer, in their capacity as a responsible person, as a major injury.

- ☑ A self-employed sub-contractor breaks their leg at work. The injury must be reported as a major injury by the main/ principal contractor acting in their capacity as the responsible person who was in control of the premises.

- ☑ An employee of a sub-contractor on a notifiable project is informed by their doctor that they are suffering from work-related vibration white finger and subsequently informs their employer. The employer, in their capacity as responsible person, must report the incident to the HSE as a reportable disease.

- ☑ An employee inadvertently hits an underground electric cable whilst operating a road-breaker. There is minor damage to the external sheath, but the conductor is not exposed. This is not reportable as there was not an electrical short circuit with fire and explosion. The incident, however, warrants significant internal investigation.

- ☑ A member of the public is knocked down by a lorry entering the site as it crosses the pavement. They are taken to hospital by ambulance. This would be reportable as it involves a member of the public being taken to hospital.

- ☑ A sub-contracted employee burns their hand and is taken to the Accident and Emergency Department of the local hospital. The employee is back on site later that afternoon and continues to work as normal for the rest of the week. This would not be reportable. However, had the employee been admitted to hospital for 24 hours or more, the incident would be reportable.

- ☑ An employed delivery driver twists their ankle when they step down from their cab. They receive first aid, insist they are fit to drive and later leave the site. They subsequently take the following seven days off because of pain and swelling in their ankle. The incident should have been recorded in the site accident book, but it would seem unreasonable for the site to be aware of the consequence. The delivery driver's employer would have a responsibility to report this as an over seven-day accident.

- ☑ An employee sustains a head injury as a result of falling over debris left on site. The accident occurred on a Friday and because of the injury, the person is unable to return to work until a week later on the following Monday. Although only five actual working days have been lost, the accident must be reported as an over seven-day accident because the Saturday and Sunday also count, as the injured person would have been unfit for work had these been working days.

- ☑ A bricklayer suffers a strained elbow on a Monday and is unable to carry out their normal work until the following Monday. However, they still come to site and carry out less strenuous work during this period. The accident is not reportable, but the bricklayer is unable to perform their primary job for six days. The incident should be recorded in the site accident book, and internally recorded as an over three-day lost time incident.

13.5 Calculating the incidence and frequency rates of accidents

From company accident records and other statistics, it is possible to calculate the incidence and frequency rates for accidents at a particular place of work and for the types of injury, severity or duration.

Accident incidence rate (AIR)

The incidence rate is based on the number of accidents, taken over a fixed period (usually 12 months), per 100,000 employees.

$$\text{Incidence rate} = \frac{\text{Number of reported injuries in a 12-month period x 100,000}}{\text{Average number of employees in a year}}$$

If during a 12-month period there were six reportable accidents and during that year the company employed an average of 120 employees, the calculation would be:

$$\frac{6 \times 100,000}{120} = 5,000$$

The above formula is the one most commonly used by UK Government departments. However, the following formula is also used to calculate the incidence rate, particularly when the number of employees is small.

$$\text{Incidence rate} = \frac{\text{Number of reported injuries in a 12-month period x 1,000}}{\text{Average number of employees in a year}}$$

Accident frequency rate (AFR)

The accident frequency rate allows a calculation to be made that balances the number of reportable accidents that occur against the number of hours worked in a fixed period (usually 12 months).

$$\text{Frequency rate} = \frac{\text{Number of accidents in a 12-month period} \times 100{,}000}{\text{Number of hours worked in that period}}$$

If a company had six reportable injuries in a period during which its 120 workers worked a total of 280,000 hours, the accident frequency rate would be:

$$\frac{6 \times 100{,}000}{280{,}000} = 2.14$$

It should be noted that the HSE uses a multiplier of 1,000,000 rather than 100,000 in its guidance on the calculation of AFR. Generally the industry uses 100,000. 100,000 working hours at 45 hours per week for 49 weeks per year, represents 45 years' work for one person or 90 years' work for two persons, and so on.

All accident rates

Similarly by using the above incident and frequency calculations, all accident rates (minors, lost time and reportable accidents) can be calculated.

Analysis and presentation of data

Computers are ideal for calculating the various incidence and frequency rates, moving averages, and so on. There are many commercially available computer programmes to manage accident statistics or a simple computer programme can be easily devised, using the known labour resources and their total working hours as a basis for calculating the statistics.

To visualise trends more clearly, accident statistics are often displayed as bar charts, histograms and graphs.

The proper and effective reporting of accidents, along with their thorough investigation, can have major benefits for a company. An employer might consider that they could:

- ☑ reduce costs by pro-actively implementing change and preventing accidents
- ☑ identify training needs, which will also improve performance
- ☑ satisfy clients and principal contractors that the workforce is properly trained and totally safety orientated
- ☑ benefit from a possible reduction of insurance premiums following years of hard work to reduce accidents.

13.6 Accident investigation

An effective investigation will:

- ☑ be factual and without bias
- ☑ clearly show the sequence of events leading to the accident or incident
- ☑ identify the immediate cause and the underlying cause (for example unsafe acts or conditions)
- ☑ show the root cause (for example lack of supervision, training or monitoring).

By discovering all causes, especially root causes, you will be able to learn from accidents and incidents and then aim to prevent reoccurrences.

Accident procedure

Many firms have established procedures to be followed in the event of an accident. The procedure below is given as general guidance and outlines the steps that should be taken immediately after an accident.

1.	Attend to the injured person, call for assistance if necessary and arrange for first aid, doctor, ambulance, hospital.
2.	Isolate machine, tools or equipment.
3.	Do not disturb or move anything unless to release an injured person.
4.	Inform the manager, safety adviser, safety representative and other appropriate persons (such as the HSE, fire officers, engineers or insurers).
5.	Ensure any remaining hazard is guarded against.
6.	Take notice of anything significant and make general observations at the scene of the accident.

13

Accident reporting and investigation

Conducting an investigation

It is not usually practical to investigate every minor accident, but those involving major or serious injuries to persons and major damage to plant or equipment should be thoroughly investigated so that immediate action can be taken to prevent a recurrence. The following headings may be useful as a guide to the steps to be taken:

- [✓] investigate promptly and record evidence
- [✓] identify types of evidence (for example factual, corroborative)
- [✓] interview the injured person, if possible
- [✓] question the person in charge and other supervisors'
- [✓] obtain details of the injured person's job and what they usually do
- [✓] interview witnesses
- [✓] inspect plant for signs of misuse or defects
- [✓] establish the full sequence of events
- [✓] ascertain the nature and extent of the injury or damage
- [✓] complete the accident report and the accident book
- [✓] notify the appropriate authorities.

Investigate promptly

The sooner an investigation is started, the better – provided it is safe to do so. Engineers and supervisors will be anxious to find ways and means of repairing any damage to plant, machinery or buildings, but the **first priority** should be to establish the cause of the accident. Safety specialists, managers and safety representatives should concern themselves solely with the safety implications and preventing a recurrence. It is important that the investigation is properly supervised and organised. Where the police or HSE inspectors wish to investigate, any other persons responsible for or involved in investigating the accident must take care not to disturb possible evidence at the scene.

Recording evidence

Statements from witnesses should contain such details as their age and occupation. The time, date and place of interview should be indicated at the end of the statement. Witnesses' statements should always be written in their own words, even if these include slang or expletives.

The completed statement should be read to the witness and, ideally, signed by them and by the person who took the statement.

Identifying the types of evidence

Evidence will usually include:

- [✓] statement of witnesses and others given orally, or in writing. 'Others' may include experts who, for example, might have been called in to examine a machine or the state of a scaffold
- [✓] documentation of all kinds
- [✓] material exhibits of all kinds.

Factual evidence comprises the facts related by persons directly involved, and by witnesses who are able to say what they felt, saw, heard, or give an expert opinion. This type of evidence is primary, direct and positive and should be written in simple language, keeping to the facts and avoiding inferences, opinions and beliefs. The facts should be recorded clearly, accurately and in sequence.

The best witnesses are those persons directly involved who are able to:

- [✓] listen carefully to the questions
- [✓] answer directly, fairly, impartially and truthfully
- [✓] state clearly when they do not know the answer
- [✓] remain calm when they are being asked questions.

Material evidence includes, for example, items of plant, equipment, machines, scaffolds, ladders or hand tools, where the use of, or the state or condition of, the item has a bearing on the accident.

Corroborative evidence tends to support the truthfulness and accuracy of the evidence that has already been given. The confirming evidence may take the form of site records, plant or maintenance records, warning notices, written procedures or reports made by safety officers or safety representatives.

Opinions are not generally acceptable as evidence in a court of law, but people in the vicinity of an accident should be asked to give an opinion. In this way a full picture can be built up of the circumstances of the accident.

Experts, or specialists, who are familiar with the type of accident, or technical and other factors surrounding the accident, may be called upon to express their **expert** opinions. When there is a lack of real or factual evidence, other forms of evidence (such as circumstantial and corroborative evidence) tend to become more valuable.

Photographs taken immediately after an accident record the state of the scene and often highlight conditions that existed at the time. Machines, equipment, tools and obstructions, and factors such as floor conditions, space and dimensions, may show up very well on photographs.

Time, date and place or subject photographed should be written on the back of the pictures.

Too many photographs are far better than too few, and it is a good idea to make drawings of the area where the incident happened. Digital photography may not be accepted as primary evidence but may be suitable as supportive evidence.

Procedures should be in place to ensure that photographs have not been, or cannot be, computer-enhanced, as this would destroy their value as evidence.

Interviewing the injured person

This depends on whether or not the police or the HSE will be involved.

Interviewing the injured person should be an early priority. Even the briefest description of the accident should suffice initially.

The physical and mental state of the injured person will need to be considered, and tact and patience will be required during the interview. The injured person should be fit to answer questions.

The injured person should be encouraged to talk about how the accident happened and it is important they have confidence and trust in the listener. It is important to stress that the purpose of the investigation is to find the cause so that preventive action can be taken. Blame should not be apportioned.

Questioning should not take the form of an interrogation. Someone well known to the injured person is probably the best person to do this. Safety officials are more likely to receive the co-operation of an injured person if they are able to demonstrate a genuine interest in their welfare and recovery. This may involve visiting the injured person, with the doctor's approval, in hospital or at home.

Given the nature of the industry, often with multiple layers of sub-contracting, there may be a number of interested parties. Sharing statements is one way of reducing the stress on witnesses. However, regulators (such as the police and HSE) may be less forthcoming about such arrangements as they may see this as an employer trying to interfere in a criminal investigation.

Questioning the person in charge

Establish from the injured person, manager, supervisor or the person in charge, what the normal job and tasks of the injured person were. Did they include the activity that led up to the accident? Other questions that might be asked are shown below.

- ☑ What task or type of job was being performed?
- ☑ Was it planned or part of a planned activity?
- ☑ At what stage of the work did the accident occur?
- ☑ Was the person involved trained and authorised, and if so, when?
- ☑ Was the person authorised to be where the accident occurred?
- ☑ What instructions had been given?
- ☑ Were safe and correct procedures being observed?
- ☑ Did unsafe acts cause the accident? If so, were they those of the injured person, workmates or others?
- ☑ Did any unsafe conditions contribute to the accident?
- ☑ What safety equipment or personal protection was available and in use?

Interviewing witnesses

Skill is required when interviewing. Witnesses should be interviewed one at a time. If they wish to say anything before notes are taken, they should be allowed to do so. Interviewers should seek answers to the following basic questions.

- ☑ What did the witness actually see or hear?
- ☑ What was the witness doing at the time?
- ☑ What was the proximity of the witness to the accident or occurrence?
- ☑ What actions did the witness take?
- ☑ What actions did others take before and after the accident?
- ☑ What was the condition of the workplace at the time?
- ☑ What hazards or unsafe conditions existed and what unsafe acts were performed?
- ☑ What was the probable cause(s) of the accident or occurrence?

Skilled interviewers allow witnesses to tell things in their own way, intervening only to clear up specific points or answers where necessary. Questions should be impartial and should be recorded together with the answers.

It is quite acceptable to go through an incident with a witness making rough notes and then to take a statement after that. That way, the witness often has more chance to remember and sometimes provides far more detail on the second run through.

13

Accident reporting and investigation

The important witnesses are those persons involved. Their evidence will be more valuable than evidence from witnesses who saw or heard only from a distance, although they, too, should be interviewed. Corroborative evidence and information is often required, particularly when witnesses are few or are not reliable.

As much evidence and information as possible should be collected, since the action taken to prevent a recurrence will be based on what is learned.

Inspection of plant for misuse or defects

Inspection of plant, equipment, tools and machinery immediately after an accident may reveal signs of misuse, or defects, which may or may not have contributed to the accident. The scene should also be carefully examined to see if trip hazards, slippery floors, or some other defect contributed to, or caused, the accident.

Assistance from specialists and persons directly involved or familiar with the type of plant, equipment, or machinery in question can provide valuable information.

Establish a sequence of events

Evidence gained from interviews and from inspection of the scene, plant, equipment or machinery, should give an indication of the sequence of events leading up to the accident.

Ascertain the extent of injury or damage

It is not always possible to ascertain the full extent of injuries and damage resulting from an accident.

There may be complications or delayed effects from injuries. The total time off work will obviously not be known at the time of investigation.

Whilst it may be easy to identify the extent of the damage caused to plant, machinery, equipment, buildings and materials, it is far from easy to measure the overall effects of the accident in terms of lost time, lost production and, of course, the suffering of the injured person or persons.

Completion of the accident investigation report

Accident report details will vary, depending on who produces the report and whom the report is for. To help eliminate or reduce this variation, guidance in making reports and the use of a standard form is recommended.

As far as possible, reports should be concise, based upon fact rather than speculation, be unbiased and should summarise the essential information obtained during the investigation.

It is becoming relatively common for HSE inspectors to simply ask for a copy of an accident investigation report completed by the employer. It could be a criminal offence to manipulate the findings of the report and it is therefore very important to make sure that it is unbiased and, as far as possible, accurate.

13

Appendix A – Form F2508 Reporting of an injury or dangerous occurrence

Health and Safety at Work etc Act 1974 **?**
The Reporting of Injuries, Diseases and Dangerous Occurrences Regulations 1995

Click here for report guidance

Report of an injury or dangerous occurrence

Filling in this form
This form must be filled in by an employer or other responsible person.

Part A

About you
1 What is your full name?

2 What is your job title?

3 What is your telephone number?

About your organisation
4 What is the name of your organisation?

5 What is its address and postcode?

6 What type of work does the organisation do?

Part B

About the incident
1 On what date did the incident happen?

2 At what time did the incident happen?
(Please use the 24-hour clock eg 0600)

3 Did the incident happen at the above address?
Yes ☐ Go to question 4
No ☐ Where did the incident happen?
     ☐ elsewhere in your organisation – give the
        name, address and postcode
     ☐ at someone else's premises – give the
        name, address and postcode
     ☐ in a public place – give details of where it
        happened

If you do not know the postcode, what is
the name of the local authority?

4 In which department, or where on the premises,
   did the incident happen?

F2508 (05.00)

Part C

About the injured person
If you are reporting a dangerous occurrence, go
to Part F. If more than one person was injured in the
same incident, please attach the details asked for in Part
C and Part D for each injured person.

1 What is their full name?

2 What is their home address and postcode?

3 What is their home phone number?

4 How old are they?

5 Are they
   ☐ male?
   ☐ female?

6 What is their job title?

7 Was the injured person (tick only one box)
   ☐ one of your employees?
   ☐ on a training scheme? Give details:

   ☐ on work experience?
   ☐ employed by someone else? Give details of the
      employer:

   ☐ self-employed and at work?
   ☐ a member of the public?

Part D

About the injury
1 What was the injury? (eg fracture, laceration)

2 What part of the body was injured?

Next Page

3 Was the injury (tick the one box that applies)

☐ a fatality?

☐ a major injury or condition? (see accompanying notes)

☐ an injury to an employee or self-employed person which prevented them doing their normal work for more than 3 days?

☐ an injury to a member of the public which meant they had to be taken from the scene of the accident to a hospital for treatment?

4 Did the injured person (tick all the boxes that apply)

☐ become unconscious?

☐ need resuscitation?

☐ remain in hospital for more than 24 hours?

☐ none of the above.

Part E

About the kind of accident

Please tick the one box that best describes what happened, then go to Part G.

☐ Contact with moving machinery or material being machined

☐ Hit by a moving, flying or falling object

☐ Hit by a moving vehicle

☐ Hit something fixed or stationary

☐ Injured while handling, lifting or carrying

☐ Slipped, tripped or fell on the same level

☐ Fell from a height

How high was the fall?

┌─────────────────┐
│   metres │
└─────────────────┘

☐ Trapped by something collapsing

☐ Drowned or asphyxiated

☐ Exposed to, or in contact with, a harmful substance

☐ Exposed to fire

☐ Exposed to an explosion

☐ Contact with electricity or an electrical discharge

☐ Injured by an animal

☐ Physically assaulted by a person

☐ Another kind of accident (describe it in Part G)

Part F

Dangerous occurrences

Enter the number of the dangerous occurrence you are reporting. (The numbers are given in the Regulations and in the notes which accompany this form)

┌─────────────────┐
│   │
└─────────────────┘

Part G

Describing what happened

Give as much detail as you can. For instance

- the name of any substance involved
- the name and type of any machine involved
- the events that led to the incident
- the part played by any people.

If it was a personal injury, give details of what the person was doing. Describe any action that has since been taken to prevent a similar incident. Use a separate piece of paper if you need to.

Part H

Your signature

Signature

Date

If returning by post/fax, please ensure this form is signed, alternatively, if returning by E-Mail, please type your name in the signature box

Where to send the form

Incident Contact Centre, Caerphilly Business Centre, Caerphilly Business Park, Caerphilly, CF83 3GG. or email to riddor@natbrit.com or fax to 0845 300 99 24

[Continue]

For official use			
Client number	Location number	Event number	
			☐ INV REP ☐ Y ☐ N

Index

access 4, 5, 14, 29, 30, 33, 50, 79, 85, 86, 157, 164, 167
    see also confined spaces; emergency routes and exits;
    guards and guarding; hoists/hoist towers; ladders;
    prohibited areas; security; traffic routes
'accident' (definition) 59, 161, 171
accident books 151, 153, 170, 172
accident prevention and control 48, 159–168
accident reporting and investigation 36, 45, 50, 79, 146,
169–180
    see also accident books
accident statistics 48, 114, 147, 160, 162, 166, 174–175
active failures 123
air receivers 151, 153
air supply 29, 30, 165
alcohol 79
ALTE work statements 93–94
appeals 13, 16
Approved Codes of Practice (ACoPs) 3, 4, 6, 12, 13, 17, 19, 28,
35, 36, 146, 154
    see also CDM Regulations ACoP
asbestos 4, 58, 79, 151, 153, 160, 166
assembly points 79, 80, 151
Associated Octel Company 19
audits 44, 142, 143, 145–147
    see also hazard-spotting; inspections

barrier creams 80, 85, 86
behavioural competence 76–77
behavioural safety 113–128, 165
benchmarking 121, 142, 147
'best practicable means' (definition) 12
Bird's accident triangle 161
Building Regulations 13
burden of proof 5, 12, 16
buried services 79, 166

carcinogens 67, 167
CDM co-ordinators 24, 26, 27, 28, 30, 31, 32, 34, 36, 37, 46, 52
CDM projects see notifiable projects
CDM Regulations 2, 3, 14, 17, 18, 24–47, 74, 79, 138
CDM Regulations ACoP 3, 24, 25, 28, 30, 48, 52, 53
CDM Regulations and safety policies 51, 52, 53
CDM Regulations statutory forms etc. 152, 153, 154, 155
charges for equipment 8, 14
children 59, 61, 66–67, 86, 166
CITB-ConstructionSkills 28, 68, 77–78, 90, 94, 95, 111–112, 147
clients 26, 27, 28, 30, 31, 32, 48, 49, 51, 52–53, 59
clothing 30, 80, 82, 84, 146, 152, 156
    see also gloves
co-operation 5, 14, 15, 24–25, 30, 34, 35, 36, 45, 138
    see also worker engagement
co-ordination 25, 27, 30, 34, 35, 36, 45
coaching 76, 125
cofferdams and caissons 29, 151, 152, 154
communication 34, 50, 51, 60, 65–66, 89–112, 117, 124–125,
127, 137–138, 165
    see also consultation; feedback; information provision;
    language problems; worker engagement
competence 24, 30, 50, 59, 76–78, 79, 125–126, 142, 160, 168
competence assessment 32, 34, 35, 36, 43–46, 49, 52–53,
93–94, 126
competency cards 77, 80, 84, 93
compliance standards 4–5, 12
compressed air work 152, 157
    see also pressurised systems
confidential issues 79
    see also Data Protection Act
confined spaces 50, 68, 79, 165, 166
Construction (Design and Management) Regulations see
CDM Regulations
Construction Industry Advisory Committee declaration 132
construction phase 27, 32, 34, 35
construction phase plans 27, 30, 32, 34, 35, 36, 37, 40–41

'construction work' (definition) 26
Constructionline 53
consultation 14, 25, 35, 36, 44, 49, 50, 51, 65, 79–80, 137,
151, 154
    see also worker engagement
contamination see pollution
contractors 19, 24, 27, 34, 35, 49, 52, 60, 142, 167
    see also licensed contractors; principal contractors;
    sub-contractors
contractors' duties 25, 26, 28, 29–30, 31, 35–36, 45–46,
74, 138
    see also employers' duties
Contractors Health and Safety Assessment Scheme (CHAS)
53, 54
Control of Asbestos Regulations 4, 153
Control of Lead at Work Regulations 156
Control of Noise at Work Regulations 15, 156
Control of Substances Hazardous to Health Regulations 17, 24,
80, 151, 154, 155
Control of Vibration at Work Regulations 17
controllers of premises 4, 14, 15, 153, 171
Corporate Manslaughter and Corporate Homicide Act 2, 7–8
Criminal Justice Act 16
criminal proceedings see offences and penalties
critical safety behaviours 121, 122

'danger' (definition) 59
danger areas 151, 154, 155, 157, 158
    see also prohibited areas
dangerous occurrences 4, 36, 80, 121, 142, 146, 151, 153, 170,
171, 173
    see also near misses
dangerous substances 151, 154
    see also hazardous substances
Dangerous Substances and Explosive Atmospheres
Regulations 154
Data Protection Act 153, 170
    see also confidential issues
deaths 4, 7–8, 48, 160, 161, 170, 171, 172, 173
demolition 29, 30, 33, 160, 166
dermatitis 80
design 26, 27, 36
designers 14, 15, 24, 26, 27, 28, 31, 32–33, 34, 35, 45
disabled persons 59, 61, 139
disciplinary procedures 80
discrimination 90, 139, 167
    see also disabled persons
diseases 4, 36, 142, 151, 153, 170, 171, 172, 173
    see also ill health
diving 31, 151, 154
Diving Operations at Work Regulations 154
documentation see health and safety policies; project
documents; records; reports and reporting; statutory forms,
notices and registers
domestic clients 27, 32
dress see clothing
drowning prevention see water safety
drugs 79
    see also needlestick injuries
drying rooms 80
dust and fumes 33, 50, 83, 160, 165, 166
duty holders 2, 3, 14–15, 24–25, 26, 28, 31

ear protection see hearing protection zones
edge protection 33, 80, 81, 166
electrical work and equipment 3, 18, 29, 80, 146, 151, 152, 154,
160, 166
    see also high voltage equipment; overhead electricity cables
Electricity at Work Regulations 3, 152, 154
emergency lighting 82
emergency procedures 30, 50, 80, 116, 154, 155, 156, 168
    see also assembly points
emergency routes and exits 13, 30, 50, 81, 151, 154

employees' duties 2, 5, 12, 13, 14, 17, 26, 28, 88
employers' duties 2, 3–5, 12–13, 14, 17, 18–19, 51, 137–138, 139
    see also contractors' duties
Employment Medical Advisory Service (EMAS) 13, 18
energy distribution installations 29
    see also electrical work and equipment; gases; pressurised
    systems
enforcement 2, 8, 9, 13, 16, 18, 51
    see also fees for intervention (FFI)
Environment Agency (EA) 9
Equality Act 139
    see also discrimination
erectors 15
escape routes see emergency routes and exits
evacuation see emergency procedures; emergency routes
and exits
evidence 176–178
examinations 15, 30, 152, 156
    see also inspections; visual checks
excavations 29, 30, 50, 81, 151, 152, 154, 165, 166
explosive atmospheres 151, 154
explosives 29, 31, 151, 154
eye protection 81, 84

facilitation 125
Factories Act 2
fall prevention 29, 33, 81, 86, 158, 165
    see also safety harnesses; work at height
falling objects 3, 48, 86, 157, 158, 166
falls 48, 157, 158, 162, 166
falsework 151, 155
fatalities see deaths
feedback 25, 121–122, 138, 142, 143
fees for intervention (FFI) 9–10
female employees 61, 67
fines see offences and penalties
Fire Authorities 13
fire detection/alarms 30, 81
fire escapes see emergency routes and exits
fire-fighting equipment 30, 81, 83, 151, 152, 155
fire hazards 146, 165
fire precautions 13, 29, 33, 50, 81, 160
fire safety plans 155
first aid 50, 81, 146, 151, 155
flammable materials/liquids 81, 165
    see also gases
flood prevention 29
floors 33, 151, 155
food 151, 155
Food Safety Act 155
foreign workers see language problems
fragile materials/surfaces 3, 33, 151, 155, 158
free provision of equipment 8, 14

gases 18, 83, 173
general public see members of the public
gloves 80, 83, 84, 85
goal setting and review 122
good housekeeping see tidiness
guards and guarding 5, 50, 164, 166
Guidance Notes 3, 12, 17, 19, 24, 28, 144

'hazard' (definition) 59, 60, 161
hazard-spotting 59, 61, 116, 143, 144–145, 161
hazardous substances 17, 50, 58, 67, 80, 151, 154, 155, 166
    see also asbestos; carcinogens; Control of Substances
    Hazardous to Health Regulations; dangerous substances;
    dust and fumes; toxic materials/substances
hazards 61, 165–166
health see ill health; occupational health
Health and Safety at Work etc. Act 2, 3, 4, 5, 8, 9, 11–21, 49,
155, 156, 157
Health and Safety Commission (HSC) 13, 17

Health and Safety (Consultation with Employees) Regulations
137, 154
Health and Safety (Display Screen Equipment) Regulations 157
Health and Safety (Enforcing Authority) Regulations 18
Health and Safety Executive see HSE
Health and Safety (Fees) Regulations 9–10
health and safety files 27, 32, 34, 35, 36, 37, 42
Health and Safety (First Aid) Regulations 155
Health and Safety (Information for Employees) Regulations 155
health and safety inspectors 8–9, 13, 15–16, 178
Health and Safety (Offences) Act 2, 8–9, 16
health and safety plans see construction phase plans
health and safety policies 14, 43, 47–56, 85, 151, 155, 164, 168
health and safety regulations 3–5, 12, 13, 17, 19
Health and Safety (Safety Signs and Signals) Regulations
154, 157
health, safety and environment test 77–78
health surveillance 152, 154, 156
hearing and listening 124
hearing protection zones 82, 83, 152, 156
high risk work 30–31, 36, 58, 63, 68, 166
high-visibility clothing 82, 84
high voltage equipment 30, 68, 80
Highways Act 154
hired plant and equipment 150
hoists/hoist towers 82
holes in roofs etc. 151, 155
hot works 50, 68, 81
housekeeping see tidiness
HSE 12, 13, 15–16, 17, 36, 170
    see also enforcement; fees for intervention (FFI); notifiable
    projects; RIDDOR
HSE accident statistics 48, 160, 162
HSE benchmarking tool 142
HSE case studies 115, 163
HSE publications 10, 19, 52, 60, 76, 114, 131, 132, 133–134,
137, 155, 163
    see also Approved Codes of Practice (ACoPs); Guidance
    Notes; HSE accident statistics
HSE risk assessment 62, 71–72
HSE strategy 131, 132

ill health 36, 48, 83, 160, 170
    see also diseases
images 90–110
importers 14, 15
Improvement Notices 8, 13, 16, 20
induction training 35, 73–88, 90, 95, 167
Information and Consultation of Employees Regulations 51
information provision 5, 14, 15–16, 51, 137–138, 146, 157, 164,
165, 167
    see also communication; induction training; language
    problems; pre-construction information; reports and
    reporting; worker engagement
information provision by CDM co-ordinators 34, 36
information provision by clients 32
information provision by contractors 35, 36, 74
information provision by designers 32, 33
information provision by plant hire suppliers 150
information provision by principal contractors 34, 35, 37
information provision on health and safety policy 49, 51,
151, 155
information provision to young persons 67
injuries 4, 83, 151, 153, 160, 161, 170, 171, 172, 173
inspections 3, 29, 95, 142–145, 146, 147, 150, 156, 157, 178
    see also audits; examinations; hazard-spotting; health
    and safety inspectors; safety representatives' inspections;
    statutory forms, notices and registers; visual checks
installers 15
instruction see toolbox talks; training
insurance 2, 151, 155
intervention 9–10, 117, 126
ionising radiation 18, 30, 151, 153, 156

Ionising Radiation Regulations 156

ladders 50, 60, 82, 152
    see also steps
language problems 61, 66, 75, 90–95, 138
lasers 82
latent failures 123
lead and lead work 151, 156
leadership 129–139, 160
    see also worker engagement
licensed contractors 153, 157
lifting operations and equipment 31, 82, 151, 152, 156, 160, 165, 166
    see also mobile elevating work platforms (MEWPs)
Lifting Operations and Lifting Equipment Regulations 152, 156
lighting 30, 33, 82, 165, 166
'likelihood' (definition) 59
liquefied petroleum gases 83
listening 124
loading and unloading 50
local authorities 13, 15, 18, 52–53, 171
lone working 50, 94

maintenance 3, 5, 29, 84, 150, 164
Management of Health and Safety at Work Regulations 3, 59–60, 66, 74
manual handling 50, 58, 83, 151, 156, 160, 162, 166
Manual Handling Operations Regulations 156
manufacturers 14, 15
'material breaches' of law 9
medical advice *see* Employment Medical Advisory Service (EMAS)
members of the public 2, 12, 14, 15, 50, 59, 61, 171, 172
    see also children; trespassers
mentoring 76, 125
method statements 29, 30, 36, 45, 51, 65, 67–68, 71–72, 83, 84
mobile elevating work platforms (MEWPs) 50, 83, 152, 160
mobile tower scaffolds 85, 152

near misses 59, 83, 121, 142, 146, 147, 161–162
    see also dangerous occurrences
needlestick injuries 83
new starters 167
    see also induction training
noise 15, 50, 58, 67, 83, 84, 156, 165, 166, 167
    see also hearing protection zones
non-notifiable projects 30–31, 36
non-verbal communication 124
notices *see* signs and notices
notifiable projects 18, 24, 26, 27, 31, 32, 34, 35, 36, 52, 75, 151, 153
nursing mothers 61, 67

observation 95, 117, 120, 121, 122, 126
observers 120, 121, 122, 124, 144
occupational health 83
    see also diseases; ill health
occupiers 15, 59, 166
offences and penalties 2, 3, 7–9, 13, 16, 17, 18–19, 170, 178
    see also burden of proof; 'material breaches' of law
older workers 167
openings 151, 155
overhead electricity cables 84, 166
owners 15, 166

penalties *see* offences and penalties
performance 34, 37, 50, 116, 122, 142, 143
    see also benchmarking
permits 30, 68, 81, 84, 95
person days 27, 31
personal protective equipment 33, 84, 91, 139, 146, 152, 156, 166
    see also eye protection; protective clothing

plant and equipment 5, 14, 15, 50, 84, 150, 152, 156, 164, 165, 166
    see also electrical work and equipment; examination; inspection; lifting operations and equipment; maintenance; personal protective equipment; tools; vehicles
pollution 15, 80, 146
    see also waste management
'practicable' (definition) 4, 5, 12
    see also 'reasonably practicable'
pre-construction information 27, 32, 33, 34, 36, 38–39
pre-qualification assessment 53–54, 147
pre-start assessments 93–94
pregnant women 61, 67
Pressure Systems Safety Regulations 153
pressure vessels 152, 156
pressurised systems 68, 153
    see also compressed air work
prevention principles 25, 60
principal contractors 24, 27, 30, 31, 32, 34, 36, 52
principal contractors' duties 25, 26, 27, 28, 29–30, 34–35, 37, 74, 138, 167
prohibited areas 79, 84
    see also danger areas
Prohibition Notices 8, 13, 16, 21
'project' (definition) 27
project documents 27, 36–42
    see also construction phase plans; health and safety files; pre-construction information; records; statutory forms, notices and registers
proof *see* burden of proof; evidence
prosecution *see* offences and penalties
protective clothing 30, 84, 146, 152, 156
    see also gloves; high-visibility clothing
Provision and Use of Work Equipment Regulations 3, 152, 156, 157
psychology of behaviour 118
public *see* members of the public
publications, EMAS 18
    see also CITB-ConstructionSkills; HSE publications; statutory forms, notices and registers

qualitative/quantitative risk assessments 62, 63–64
questioning skills 125

radiation 18, 30, 67, 151, 153, 156, 167
'reasonably practicable' (definition) 4, 5, 12–13, 16
records 29, 78, 173
    see also accident books; project documents; reports and reporting; risk assessment records; statutory forms, notices and registers
red, amber and green lists 32–33
regulations *see Building Regulations*; health and safety regulations
Regulatory Reform (Fire Safety) Order 152, 155
Reporting of Injuries, Diseases and Dangerous Occurrences Regulations see RIDDOR
reports and reporting 29, 83, 84, 121, 144, 145, 151, 161–162
    see also accident reporting and investigation; employees' duties; information provision; RIDDOR; statutory forms, notices and registers
representatives *see* safety representatives
rescue equipment and procedures 29, 86
restricted areas 84
    see also danger areas; prohibited areas
RIDDOR 4, 36, 146, 153, 171–174
'risk' (definition) 59, 60, 161
risk acceptability 63, 126
    see also severity of risks
risk assessment evaluation 142
risk assessment principles 59
risk assessment records 3, 60, 62, 65–66, 151, 157
risk assessments 3, 25, 36, 45, 58–67, 68–70, 83, 84, 121, 126–127, 150, 155, 156

risk assessments and safety policies 50, 51
risk assessments for young persons 68–69, 166–167
risk rating 63–64
    see also risk acceptability; severity of risks

safe places of work 3, 5, 7, 14, 29, 49, 146
safe systems of work 5, 7, 14, 45, 50, 66, 84, 146, 164, 165, 167, 168
Safecontractor 54
Safemark 54
safety committees 14, 50, 79, 81, 152, 157
safety critical communication *see* communication
safety harnesses 83, 85, 152
safety nets 33, 152
safety representatives 13, 14, 16, 25, 50, 79, 135, 138, 152, 154, 157
Safety Representatives and Safety Committees Regulations 137, 138, 153, 157
safety representatives' inspections 142, 143, 144, 145, 146, 151, 153
safety sampling 144
Safety Schemes in Procurement (SSIP) forum 53, 54
safety tours 143, 144–145, 147
sanitary conveniences 85, 155
scaffolding 4, 33, 50, 60, 85, 147, 152, 157
Scottish Environment Protection Agency (SEPA) 9
security 29, 35, 85, 86, 166
    see also trespassers
self-employed persons 2, 4, 15, 17, 49, 59, 60, 167, 170, 171, 172
severity of risks 59, 63
    see also risk acceptability
signs and notices 29, 30, 85, 151, 152, 155, 157
    see also images; statutory forms, notices and registers
Simple Pressure Vessels (Safety) Regulations 156
site boundaries 79
site layout 85, 95, 164
    see also traffic routes
site managers 2, 76, 127, 144
site rules 35, 36, 75, 76, 80
    see also disciplinary procedures; induction training
skin problems/protection 80, 85
skips 85, 86, 151, 154
SMART goals 122
smoking 85
stability 29, 160
    see also excavations
standards of compliance 4–5, 12
statistics *see* accident statistics; benchmarking
statutory forms, notices and registers 31, 149–158, 171, 179–180
steps 33, 152
    see also ladders
storage 5, 14, 17, 29, 85
'structure' (definition) 26
sub-contractors 14, 36, 45, 50, 53, 133, 171
'suitable and sufficient' (definition) 60
supervision 5, 14, 51, 93, 146, 164, 165, 167–168
supervision of non-English speaking workers 90, 94
supervision of young persons 67, 167
supervisors 2, 13, 58, 65, 76, 126, 144, 145, 146
supervisors' duties 65, 87, 139, 142, 143
suppliers 14, 15, 133, 150
Swan Hunter Shipbuilders 18

Telemeter Installations 18
temperatures 30, 33, 67, 167
Temporary or Mobile Construction Sites (TMCS) Directive 24
temporary structures 155, 160
    see also falsework; scaffolding
testing 3, 15, 30, 77–78, 154
tidiness 29, 80, 85, 160, 166
    see also tripping hazards; waste management

toilets 85, 155
toolbox talks 90–93, 94, 95, 111–112, 147, 150
tools 15, 33, 154, 156, 164
toxic materials/substances 67, 146, 167
trade unions 14
traffic routes 29, 30, 33, 85, 165
    see also site layout; transport; vehicles
training 43, 49, 50, 116–117, 138, 146, 164, 165, 167–168
    see also competence; images; induction training; toolbox talks
training duty 5, 14, 35, 36, 51, 74
training in behavioural safety 120–121, 122, 125–126
training in fire-fighting 30, 155
training in leadership/worker engagement 133, 135
training of non-English speaking workers 90, 91, 93, 95
training of young persons 66, 67, 167
training records 150, 151, 152, 155, 157, 158
transport 5, 14, 17, 29, 165, 166
    see also traffic routes; vehicles
trespassers 61, 79, 86, 166
    see also security
tripping hazards 33, 160, 162, 166
    see also tidiness

vehicles 29, 33, 48, 50, 86, 164, 165, 166
    see also plant and equipment; traffic routes; transport
ventilation 29, 30, 165
verbal communication 124
vibration 15, 33, 50, 58, 67, 86, 166, 167
visitors 2, 59, 61
    see also trespassers
visual checks 150
    see also hazard-spotting; inspections
visual display units 152, 157

warnings and warning devices 30, 157
waste management 80, 85, 152, 153, 157
    see also pollution; tidiness
water safety 29, 31, 86, 166
weather 3, 30, 165
welfare facilities 14, 32, 35, 36, 37, 46, 48, 50, 86, 160, 165
    see also drinking water supplies; rest facilities; toilets; washing facilities
'whistle-blowing' (definition) 79
witness statements 176, 177–178
women employees 61, 67
work at height 50, 58, 60, 86, 152, 158, 160, 165, 166
    see also fall prevention; falling objects; scaffolding
Work at Height Regulations 3, 4, 17, 24, 152, 154, 155, 157, 158
work equipment *see* personal protective equipment; plant and equipment; *Provision and Use of Work Equipment Regulations*
work experience 49, 67
Work in Compressed Air Regulations 157
worker engagement 66, 117, 120, 129–139, 142, 160
    see also audits; consultation; inspections; safety representatives
working hours 152, 157
    see also person days
working platforms 152
    see also mobile elevating work platforms (MEWPs)
Working Time Regulations 157
Workplace (Health, Safety and Welfare) Regulations 152

young persons 59, 61, 66–67, 75, 157, 166–167

Contents

Introduction   iii

How to use GE 700   ix

01 The management of health   1

02 Welfare facilities   15

03 Work-related stress   25

04 Drugs and alcohol   33

05 First aid   51

06 Personal protective equipment   65

07 The Control of Substances Hazardous to Health (COSHH)   83

08 Skin protection   103

09 Asbestos   115

10 Dust and fumes   137

11 Carbon monoxide   149

12 Lead   159

13 Noise   175

14 Vibration   193

15 Manual handling   215

Index   225

Introduction

Construction site safety covers all aspects of current health, safety and environment issues in the building and construction industry. It is designed to help managers, supervisors and small businesses understand how they should comply with, and put into practice, their legal, moral and social responsibilities.

Construction site safety (GE 700)   iv

About the construction industry   iv

Further supporting information from
CITB-ConstructionSkills   vi

Acknowledgements   vii

Construction site safety (GE 700)

Construction site safety is a leading publication within the construction industry, based on current construction health, safety and environment legislation, guidance and best practice. It will assist in the crucial areas of:

- ☑ accident prevention
- ☑ the avoidance of occupational ill health
- ☑ environmental good practice.

The content has been written with the site manager in mind, with a balance between outlining the requirements of relevant legislation and providing practical guidance on how to comply.

It is divided into the standard structure, which is used across all core CITB-ConstructionSkills publications:

Section A	**Legal and management**
Section B	**Health and welfare**
Section C	General safety
Section D	**High risk activities**
Section E	**Environment**
Section F	**Specialist activities**

Each section within *Construction site safety* is contained within a separate book.

There is also a new additional supporting book:

Section G	**Checklists and forms**

Section G is a collection of information (such as forms and checklists) that can be used on a day-to-day basis when running a site.

The content of *Construction site safety*, which is developed with construction industry experts, is revised annually to take into account the latest changes in legislation and new or updated health, safety and environment industry guidance and best practice.

There is a companion website that will keep users informed of legislation changes, content updates and links to further guidance.

Construction site safety is also available to purchase online or on CD-ROM.

Construction site safety is the official supporting publication for the CITB-ConstructionSkills Site Management Safety Training Scheme (SMSTS), a five-day course for construction site managers.

About the construction industry

Approximately 2.1 million people are employed in the UK construction industry. It includes housing, utilities, repair and maintenance, refurbishment, shop fitting, demolition, roofing, mechanical and electrical, plumbing and highways maintenance.

It is made up of 175,000 construction firms and 90% of companies employ less than 10 workers.

Construction workers (just like you) will die due to work-related ill health. Work-related respiratory disease covers a range of illnesses that are caused or made worse by breathing in hazardous substances (such as construction dust) that damage the lungs.

4,000 people die each year from asbestos-related lung diseases.

500 people (and more each year) are dying from silica-related lung diseases (dust from cutting blocks, kerbs, and so on). Many more suffer from occupational asthma or are forced to leave the industry due to work-related ill health.

Each year there are an estimated 36,000 new cases of work-related ill health with rates of musculoskeletal disorder significantly higher than average.

On average 50 workers are killed each year due to accidents. The biggest killer (around half) is due to falls from height.

Each year approximately 2,500 are seriously injured (broken bones, fractured skull, amputations) and 5,700 have reportable injuries.

The most common cause of injuries is due to manual handling and slips, trips and falls. 60% of all work at height injuries are due to falls from below head height.

Why so many accidents?

Many reports of present day construction accidents and ill health make depressing reading because simple actions were not taken to prevent them. In many cases, those planning the jobs totally failed to consider the health or safety of the people carrying out the work (and possibly others who were affected) and to actively manage the situation.

Common examples of such events include:

☑ the increasing number of workers who suffer from cancers and life changing illnesses from breathing and skin complaints. Some of these force the sufferer to give up work, because exposure to dangerous substances such as dust, are not even considered, let alone prevented or controlled

☑ the deaths and serious injuries that occur because people fall from height. Often basic actions (like using temporary work platforms on fragile roofs, installing edge protection or using a safety harness and lanyard clipped to a strong-point) were simply not taken

☑ workers being buried in collapsed excavations because the sides were unstable or not supported

☑ workers being killed or injured by construction plant because pedestrians were not kept out of the plant operating area.

Achieving a reasonable standard of on-site health and safety need not be difficult. Where the work to be carried out is relatively uncomplicated and familiar, the precautions that need to be taken are in many cases simple and common sense or may require just a little investigation or reading. The crucial decision for anyone with responsibility for on-site health and safety is to know when they have reached the limits of their knowledge and capabilities and therefore need the assistance of someone with specialist knowledge.

Caution should also be exercised when a job is not going to plan and there is the temptation to resort to improvised methods of working. If the person in control is not at ease with the way that things are going they should stop the job, step back and think things through carefully before deciding upon a course of action.

Health and Safety Executive (HSE) research has shown that workers are most vulnerable during their first few days on site.

Setting out

Construction is an exciting industry. It is constantly changing as projects move on and jobs get done. As a result of this a building site is one of the most dangerous environments to work in.

But many accidents that occur on sites can be avoided if everyone on site works together. So a free film *Setting out* explains what the site must do and what you must do to stay healthy and safe at work.

 For further information or to view *Setting out* refer to the CITB-ConstructionSkills website.

This film is essential viewing for everyone involved in construction, and should be watched before sitting the CITB-ConstructionSkills' Health, safety and environment test. The content of the film is captured in summary here, and these principles form the basis for the behavioural case study questions, which are a new element of the test from Spring 2012.

Part 1: What you should expect from the construction industry

Your site and your employer should be doing all they can to keep you and their workforce safe.

Before any work begins the site management team will have been planning and preparing the site for your arrival. It is their job to ensure that you can do your job safely and efficiently.

Five things **the site** you are working on **must do**:

☑ know when you are on site (signing in and out)

☑ give you a site induction

☑ give you site-specific information

☑ encourage communication

☑ keep you up-to-date and informed.

Part 2: What the industry expects of you

Once the work begins, it is up to every individual to take responsibility for carrying out the plan safely. This means you should follow the rules and guidelines as well as being alert to the continuing changes on site.

Five things you **must do**:

☑ respect and follow the site rules

☑ safely prepare each task

☑ do each task responsibly

☑ know when to stop (if you think anything is unsafe)

☑ keep learning.

Every day the work we do improves the world around us. It is time for us to work together to build an industry that puts its people first. By working together we can build a better industry that respects those who work in it.

Introduction

Working Well Together

The Working Well Together (WWT) campaign is an industry-led initiative that helps support micro and small businesses improve their health and safety performance. The campaign undertakes a variety of activities, including health and safety awareness days, designer awareness days, breakfast and evening events, roadshows and regional WWT groups.

"EVERY WEEK ONE OF US DIES"

 To find out how the WWT campaign can help you and your company refer to its website.

Further supporting information from CITB-ConstructionSkills

CITB-ConstructionSkills has a wide range of products, publications and courses that could help to improve your health, safety and environment knowledge.

 To discover more about CITB-ConstructionSkills and the services, publications and courses offered visit the CITB-ConstructionSkills website.

Health, safety and environment publications

Site managers	GE 700 *Construction site safety* (printed, CD and online)
	RACD *Risk assessment and method statement manager*
	SA 03 CD *Health, safety and environmental auditing system*
	DVDs Range of topics including scaffold inspection, worker engagement and sustainability
Supervisors	GE 706 *Site supervision simplified* (printed, CD, online)
	GT 700 *Toolbox talks* (printed, CD, online)
	GT 701 *Safety critical communication toolbox talks* (printed)
Operatives	GE 707 *Safe start*
Health safety and environment test	GT 100 *Health, safety and environment test for operatives and specialists* (printed, DVD, online)
	GT 200 *Health, safety and environment test for managers and professionals* (printed, DVD, online)

Site Safety Plus courses

Directors	Directors role for health and safety course – one day
Site management	Site Management Safety Training Scheme (SMSTS) – five days
Plant managers	Plant Management Safety Training Scheme (SMSTS) – five days
Supervisors	Site Supervisors' Safety Training Scheme (SSSTS) – two days
Operatives	Health safety and environment awareness – one day
Environment	Site Environmental Awareness Training Scheme (SEATS) – one day
Behavioural safety	Achieving Behavioural Change (ABC) – one day
Shopfitting	Site safety for shopfitters and interior contractors – three days

National Construction College

The National Construction College is focused on creating a highly skilled, safe and professional UK construction workforce.
To achieve this, it has more first-class instructors in more locations than any other construction training provider in Europe and offers free professional advice on finding the right training for individuals and companies.

Acknowledgements

CITB-ConstructionSkills wishes to acknowledge the assistance offered by the following organisations in the preparation of this edition of GE 700:

- ✓ Access Industry Forum
- ✓ Arco
- ✓ Balfour Beatty
- ✓ Britannia Safety and Training
- ✓ Civil Engineering Contractors Association
- ✓ Combisafe
- ✓ Construction Plant Association
- ✓ Drilling and Sawing Association
- ✓ eBrit Services Ltd
- ✓ Environment Agency
- ✓ Environmental and Waste Consulting
- ✓ Federation of Master Builders
- ✓ Health and Safety Executive
- ✓ Henry Boot
- ✓ Highways Term Maintenance Association
- ✓ Home Builders Federation
- ✓ J Breheny Contractors Ltd

- ✓ Lead Paint Safety Association
- ✓ MJ Fuller and Associates
- ✓ Makers Construction Ltd
- ✓ May Gurney
- ✓ Montpellier International Consulting
- ✓ National Access and Scaffolding Confederation
- ✓ National Association of Shopfitters
- ✓ National Construction College
- ✓ National Federation of Demolition Contractors
- ✓ Persimmon Homes
- ✓ Prospect – The Union for Professionals
- ✓ Scafftag
- ✓ Temporary Works Forum
- ✓ Union of Construction, Allied Trades and Technicians (UCATT)
- ✓ Unite
- ✓ Wates
- ✓ Willmott Dixon

And a special thank you to:

- ✓ Carillion
- ✓ Costain
- ✓ Morgan Sindall
- ✓ Skanska

How to use GE 700

The following information sets out how to use *Construction site safety*. Each section is contained within a separate book, which has been designed to provide simple navigation for the end user. It also explains the companion website, which is a significant addition for keeping users informed of legislation changes, content updates and links to further guidance.

Construction site safety structure   x
How to navigate   x
Use of icons   x
Companion website   xi

Construction site safety structure

Construction site safety is divided into the standard structure that is used across all core CITB-ConstructionSkills publications:

Section A	**Legal and management**
Section B	**Health and welfare**
Section C	General safety
Section D	**High risk activities**
Section E	**Environment**
Section F	**Specialist activities**

Within *Construction site safety* each section is contained within a separate book.

There is also a new additional supporting book:

Section G	**Checklists and forms**

This new section is a collection of information that can be used on a day-to-day basis when running a site. The forms, checklists and guidance within Section G follow the same structure as in Sections A to F.

How to navigate

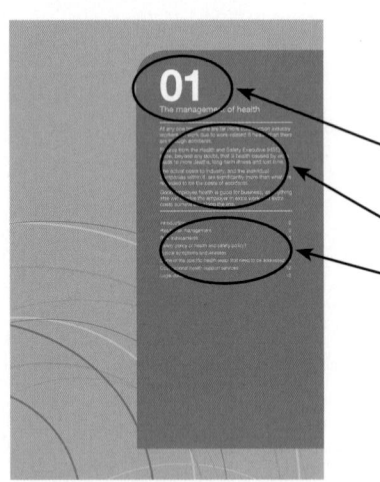

Each section contains a main contents page at the start of the section, followed by the introduction, a detailed chapter contents list at the start of each chapter and an index at the back (but there is no index within Section G).

Chapters have been numbered according to the section you are in. Therefore, chapter one of Section A is numbered 01, chapter two of Section B is numbered 02 and so on. However, references to chapters within other sections will be referred to as A01, B02, and so on.

At the start of each chapter there is a short overview of what the chapter is about.

This is followed by the chapter contents list.

Use of icons

A set of icons emphasises key points within the text and also directs readers to further information. The icons are explained below:

www.	Website/further info	!	Important	"	Quote
e.g.	Example	👍	Best practice	Aa	Definition
?	Question	👎	Poor practice	☑	Checklist
💡	Ideas	✋	Caution	▶	Video
Notes	Notes	👥	Consultation		
★	Favourite	🔍	Guidance/case study		

Companion website

A companion website has been created to support *Construction site safety* and it contains up-to-date information on:

- ☑ the current edition of each section (book)
- ☑ news (such as legislation changes, industry guidance and best practice)
- ☑ any minor amendments or updates to the current editions
- ☑ web links/phone numbers/addresses
- ☑ details of CITB-ConstructionSkills' publications and courses.

 This icon indicates that further information (such as useful websites and links) can be found on the companion website at www.citb-constructionskills.co.uk/GE700companion

Rather than printing individual weblinks in each section, which can become out of date, the relevant website will be stated alongside the icon (for example, for more information refer to the CITB-ConstructionSkills website). The actual weblink can then be found on the companion website, referenced to the relevant section and chapter.

The companion website will be regularly updated, to ensure that relevant information (such as weblinks) are current.

 Save the companion website address to your favourites, so it is always available when you need it.

01

The management of health

At any one time there are far more construction industry workers off work due to work-related ill health than there are through accidents.

Figures from the Health and Safety Executive (HSE) show, beyond any doubt, that ill health caused by work leads to more deaths, long-term illness and lost time.

The actual costs to industry, and the individual companies within it, are significantly more than what are regarded to be the costs of accidents.

Good employee health is good for business, as anything else will involve the employer in extra work and extra costs somewhere along the line.

Introduction	2
Health risk management	3
Risk assessments	3
Safety policy or health and safety policy?	4
Typical symptoms and illnesses	5
Some of the specific health areas that need to be addressed	5
Occupational health support services	12
Legal duties	13

The management of health

1.1 Introduction

One of the reasons why employers have safe systems of work is to avoid accidents and keep employees at work, instead of them being off sick. Exactly the same reasoning should be applied to the prevention of health problems that may arise from work activities.

The prevention of ill health on site can clearly be seen to benefit the employer as well as employees. Employees will be able to work to their full capacity, rather than being off work sick or working under the limitations (physical or physiological) imposed by an illness or other condition (such as stress).

For many years the focus of health and safety legislation has tended to be on the issue of safety on building and construction sites, rather than on the subject of occupational health.

The introduction of The Health and Safety at Work Act 1974 marked a major change in emphasis, acknowledging that ill health arising from work activities was a problem and giving it equal importance to safety.

A number of regulations on subjects such as the control of substances hazardous to health (COSHH), and lead and asbestos regulations have been introduced to further address health issues, as it has become clearly recognised that health is an important subject on building and construction sites.

The legal duties require employers to make provisions to safeguard the health of employees.

- ☑ Construction is an industry with high cancer cases, with 56% of men having cancer as a result of their construction occupation.

- ☑ Over 5,000 occupational cancer cases are estimated to arise each year as a result of past exposures in the construction sector (Cancer Burden Study, 2010).

- ☑ The most significant carcinogen is still past exposure to asbestos (71%), followed by silica (16%) and diesel engine exhaust/ environmental tobacco smoke (6–7% each). Solar radiation, coal tars and pitches are responsible for about 1,300 cancer registrations, mostly causing non-melanoma skin cancers.

- ☑ 4,000 people die each year from asbestos-related diseases.

- ☑ 500 people (and more each year) are dying from silica related cancers (dust from cutting blocks, kerbs, and others).

- ☑ There are an estimated 36,000 new cases of work-related ill health, with rates of musculoskeletal disorder significantly higher than average.

- ☑ 79,000 people whose current or most recent job in the last year was in construction, suffered from an illness (longstanding and new cases), which was caused or made worse by their job.

- ☑ About 2.3 million working days were lost (1.1 days per worker) due to self-reported work-related illness or workplace injury. Just over three quarters of this (1.7 million days/0.87 days per worker) was due to health problems and only one quarter to injuries.

- ☑ Painters and decorators are at high risk, possibly due to solvent exposure.

At any one time there are far more people off work through occupational ill health than there are because of a work-related accident.

Whilst an injury caused by an accident is in most cases instantly obvious, the symptoms of occupational ill health, and therefore knowledge of it, can take months or years to show.

Occupational ill health can result in the sufferer having long periods off work or having to give up work completely, and even short-term sickness absence can have an adverse effect on business activities.

The prevention of occupational ill health is easily achievable if:

- ☑ a suitable assessment of the risks to health is carried out and reviewed as necessary

- ☑ adequate control measures are identified, put in place and adjusted as necessary

- ☑ the persons at risk fully use the control measures provided.

In some circumstances employers have a legal duty to provide health surveillance to employees.

Raising the awareness of managers, supervisors and workers to ensure effective control measures are always put in place and followed is fundamental to help reduce these numbers.

At any one time there are far more people off work through occupational ill health than there are because of a work-related accident.

1.2   Health risk management

The management of health and safety at work principles apply to work-related health risks as well as safety, and require employers to:

- ☑ identify the potential health risks (short, medium and long term) arising from the work activities to be carried out

- ☑ investigate what can be done about them and decide how they are going to be addressed

- ☑ give staff information, instructions and training on the health risks and the control measures to be followed

- ☑ monitor work activities to make sure that the procedures are being implemented and are effective

- ☑ introduce health surveillance where necessary

- ☑ look for benefits and improvements.

One of the most difficult parts of managing health is understanding and assessing the impact an activity can have on an individual. When assessing risk it is therefore important to have an understanding of the short, medium and long-term health impacts.

It is not about assessing the health risk on a given day, but the cumulative effect over time. This difficulty is compounded by the transient nature of the workforce, which can move from employer to employer and from site to site. Regardless of this, the controls on any given day should minimise the risk of work-related ill health.

 Health, safety and the environment must be proactively managed, in the same way that a good supervisor and manager will manage people, quality and productivity.

1.3   Risk assessments

Regulations require that a risk assessment is carried out for every work task to be undertaken. This assessment is intended to identify any risks to health and safety that may be inherent in the task and detail any control measures necessary to reduce the risks to an acceptable level.

Risk assessments must be carried out by someone competent in the work activity being assessed to enable all the risks and hazards to health and/or safety to be identified. Risk assessments must be suitable and sufficient and take into account such factors as the complexity of the task and the competency of the person(s) undertaking the work.

The findings of the assessment must be recorded so that any person with an interest in its content can check that statutory requirements have been met and potential risks and problems identified. They should also be in a format so that the operative understands the risks and the necessary controls required to carry out the task safely. Written risk assessments may be stored in an electronic format, as long as copies can be retrieved and printed as requested.

Ideally, the risk assessment process would identify methods of working that would not put anyone's health or safety at risk. In practice however, this is not always possible, although a good knowledge of the work techniques available to those involved in the installation process can significantly reduce the risks.

The following list, which is not exhaustive, highlights areas that should be considered when carrying out a risk assessment:

- ☑ the competence and experience of the person(s) who will carry out and/or supervise the work

- ☑ the adoption of safe and healthy work procedures and practices, means of access and egress, availability of manufacturers' information and training that has been undertaken or is required

- ☑ the physical environment in which the work is to be carried out (for example, an occupied domestic property)

- ☑ fire precautions and procedures – availability of fire extinguishers, means of escape and alarms

- ☑ the possible need for health surveillance through exposure to hazardous substances, noise or vibration

- ☑ the avoidance of potentially harmful manual handling, but where manual handling is unavoidable, the use of correct lifting procedures

- ☑ the control and suppression of harmful dust/fibres or other materials

- ☑ the adoption of other control measures in preference to using personal protective equipment (PPE)

- ☑ confined spaces (lack of ventilation, fire trap/risk)

- ☑ structural stability of external walls

- ☑ falls from height

- ☑ possible asbestos/disturbed asbestos from fire curtains or lagging

- ☑ competence, knowledge, skills/training and experience.

 Do not rely on generic risk assessments. As a manager or supervisor it is your responsibility to make sure that your workplace is safe.

The following health risks need to be considered:

☑ personal injury caused by inadequate manual handling techniques (such as carrying materials and equipment into the premises)

☑ respiratory problems, the potential for contracting serious respiratory diseases (such as occupational asthma) resulting from the inhalation of existing harmful substances or insulation materials in the course of insulation and cutting operations

☑ noise-induced hearing loss caused by failing to protect the ears when working in noisy environments

☑ dermatitis and other skin complaints, resulting from the failure to protect exposed skin from contact with adhesives, cement mixes, harmful dusts or persistently working with wet hands

☑ asbestos-related illness caused by contact with harmful asbestos materials.

The Reporting of Injuries, Diseases and Dangerous Occurrences Regulations (RIDDOR)

Reporting procedures cover fatalities and major injuries, incapacity to work for more than seven days, specified diseases and dangerous occurrences.

The people covered are employers, employees, self-employed, trainees and other people injured on the premises.

Social Security Act and RIDDOR

☑ Every accident involving personal injury to an employee must be entered in the accident book by the employee or someone acting on behalf of the employee.

☑ The accident book must be kept accessible.

☑ An employer must investigate all accidents reported.

Major injuries include:	Reportable diseases include:
■ fracture of the skull, spine, pelvis, arm, leg, wrist or ankle	■ an employee being absent from work or unable to do their normal duties for more than seven days
■ dislocation of the shoulder, hip, knee or spine	■ some skin diseases (such as occupational dermatitis, skin cancer, chrome ulcer, oil folliculitis/acne)
■ amputation through any bone	■ lung diseases (such as occupational asthma, farmers lung, pneumoconiosis, asbestosis, mesothelioma)
■ loss of sight (temporary or permanent)	■ infections (such as leptospirosis, hepatitis, tuberculosis, anthrax, legionellosis and tetanus)
■ chemical or hot metal burn to the eye or any penetrating injury to the eye	■ other conditions (such as occupational cancer, certain musculoskeletal disorders, decompression illness and hand-arm vibration syndrome).
■ injury resulting from an electric shock or electrical burn leading to unconsciousness or requiring resuscitation or admittance to hospital for more than 24 hours	
■ any other injury leading to hypothermia, heat-induced illness or unconsciousness; or requiring resuscitation; or requiring admittance to hospital for more than 24 hours	
■ unconsciousness caused by asphyxia or exposure to a harmful substance or biological agent	
■ acute illness requiring medical treatment, or loss of consciousness arising from absorption of any substance by inhalation, ingestion or through the skin	
■ acute illness requiring medical treatment where there is reason to believe that this resulted from exposure to a biological agent or its toxins or infected material	
■ hospitalisation for more than 24 hours.	

1.4   Safety policy or health and safety policy?

Under the requirements of the Health and Safety at Work Act 1974, all employers who have five or more employees must:

> prepare, and, as often as may be appropriate, revise a written statement of general policy with respect to the health and safety of employees, and the organisation and arrangements, for the time being in force, for carrying out that policy.

It can be clearly seen that the requirement is for a written policy statement that must set out the employer's aims and objectives for improving work-related health as well as safety at work. It must also set out the organisation and arrangements currently in force for achieving those objectives. *Organisation* can be taken to mean people and their responsibilities; *arrangements* can be taken to mean systems and procedures.

In the past many companies have considered the safety issues within their safety policy document and have carefully devised safe working procedures.

However, it is also important to look at the health hazards involved in the work that is carried out and to devise an equally efficient policy to deal with them.

With an accident on site, the injury or other effects are usually immediate and obvious.

The effects of exposure to most work-related ill health hazards are not immediate or not even felt (unlike an accident that causes injury). Workers may go home from work feeling more or less the same each day and are none the wiser. It can take many weeks, months or even years before symptoms of exposure become a problem to them and irreversible damage may well have occurred.

Work-related ill health can often result in employees being unable to work as hard or as efficiently as before and sometimes they may never work again.

 It should not be forgotten that a near-miss today could be an accident tomorrow. Managers have an important role to play in both proactive and reactive monitoring activities.

1.5　Typical symptoms and illnesses

- ☑ Respiratory diseases:
  - – diffuse pleural thickening
  - – asbestosis
  - – mesothelioma
  - – asthma
  - – silicousus.
- ☑ Vibration white finger/hand-arm vibration syndrome (HAVS).

- ☑ Noise-induced hearing loss/deafness.
- ☑ Skin cancers.
- ☑ Dermatitis.
- ☑ Spine/back disorders.
- ☑ Upper and lower limb disorders.
- ☑ Stress.

Many employees leave the industry due to ill health. Often a person's illness is not traced back to the construction industry, so the actual incidence of ill health caused by work in the industry is probably more than the official figures tell us.

1.6　Some of the specific health areas that need to be addressed

Asbestos

More occupation-related deaths are caused by asbestos than by any other single substance used in the building and construction industry.

Information published by the HSE highlights the problem of asbestos, particularly for tradespeople (such as plumbers, painters, carpenters, electricians, shop fitters, maintenance workers, general operatives and demolition workers) who may come into contact with asbestos while carrying out their work.

It can be said that virtually every building constructed before the 1990s may contain some asbestos in one form or another, ranging from insulation on boilers, pipework or steelwork to gutters and floor tiles.

Even in domestic houses, asbestos can be found as soffits and insulation panels in airing cupboards, and so on. Exposure to asbestos can cause asbestosis or mesothelioma, both of which are crippling and often fatal diseases. There have been a number of successful civil court cases for damages and compensation brought by employees against their employers, and substantial awards have been made against employers.

 For further information refer to Chapter B09 Asbestos.

 Asbestos waste must carry a warning label. The label can also be used to identify and manage known in-situ asbestos.

Manual handling

Nearly a quarter of all accidents reported to the HSE involve manual handling in some form or another. Yet, if the guidance offered in the Manual Handling Operations Regulations had been followed, most if not all of the accidents could have been prevented.

More often than not, manual handling is not adequately assessed or planned, relying instead on the workers making do with the equipment to hand or providing their own solutions, thus increasing the risk of injury and the knock-on effects of this.

Giving employees the appropriate training in the correct manual handling techniques and the use of suitable mechanical lifting aids is highly cost effective.

Adequate supervision is necessary to ensure that employees then use the proper equipment and techniques and do not take shortcuts. This will reduce accidents, the amount of time lost on site, and the disruption to work that is caused when something goes wrong.

The part of the body most vulnerable if bad manual handling techniques are used is the back, particularly the lower back. Once it has been damaged, it is usually weakened for the rest of a person's life.

All the other major joints and muscle groups can also be easily damaged if the correct manual handling techniques are not used.

The consequences of an injury due to bad manual handling, or a musculoskeletal injury or illness as they are often called, can be a long-term or permanent inability to work. The cost to the employer is reduced productivity and having to find others to carry out the work.

For further information refer to Chapter B15 Manual handling.

Noise

Regulations exist on the control of noise at work because of the unacceptable damage that noise can cause to the health of employees. The damage can range from temporary hearing loss to total deafness. As well as hearing problems, excess noise is also known to cause:

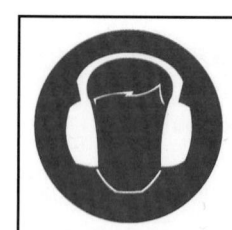

- ☑ annoyance and irritation
- ☑ loss of concentration
- ☑ reduced efficiency
- ☑ fatigue
- ☑ increased accident risk
- ☑ masking of other warning signals.

On site, the failure of an employee to understand instructions that have been given, or to hear a warning signal, can have serious consequences, both for them and for the employer.

For further information refer to Chapter B13 Noise.

Employers have a duty to reduce the risk of damage to employees' hearing to the lowest level that is reasonably practicable.

Vibration

A considerable number of the tools and other equipment that are currently used in the building and construction industry have a rotary or percussive action and so can cause **hand-arm vibration**. This even applies to some widely used small tools (such as hand drills with a hammer action). Other examples of tools that create vibration include pneumatic breakers, vibrating pokers, vibrating rollers, plate compactors and scabbling machines.

The most commonly caused ill health effect is vibration white finger, where the effect of the vibration damages the nerves and blood vessels in the fingers. The fingers become white and there is a loss of feeling that prevents smaller tools from being held or used properly.

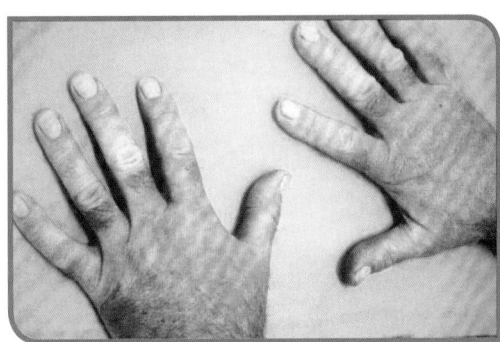

Hand-arm vibration is also known to cause other vascular, neurological and muscular damage in the hands, wrists, elbows and shoulders.

Whole-body vibration, which is caused by the transmission of vibration to the body from sources such as moving plant or vehicles, can bring about long-term back pain.

The effects of both hand-arm vibration and whole-body vibration can be reduced by carrying out risk assessments, appropriate purchasing policies, the correct use of the equipment and the use of the appropriate anti-vibration devices (such as special handles or grips).

 For further information refer to Chapter B14 Vibration.

Stress

In the workplace, stress is a growing problem but one that has not been widely recognised or generally accepted within the building and construction industry.

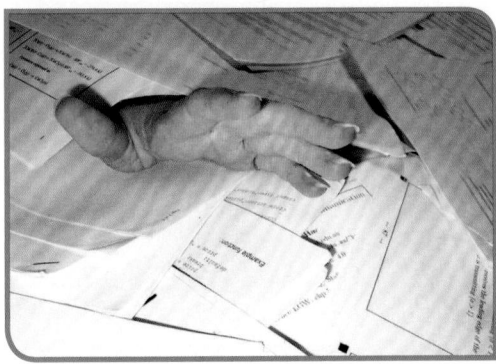

Stress can cause physical problems, such as:

☑ high blood pressure

☑ heart disease

☑ depression.

As well as behavioural problems, such as:

☑ anxiety

☑ irritability

☑ failure to cope as usual

☑ bad time-keeping.

Some of the causes of stress are:

☑ too much work/long working hours

☑ confusion as to what is expected

☑ uncertainty as to responsibilities

☑ conflict of interests.

Work-related factors that lead to stress can be managed but this will require appropriate training for management and operatives. If left unchecked, signs of stress may quickly emerge at the workplace and cause problems.

While a reasonable degree of challenge and stress is acceptable as providing an added incentive to work, excess stress among employees is counterproductive and should be avoided if employees are to work to their best potential.

 For further information refer to Chapter B03 Work-related stress.

Radiation and sunshine

Whenever any work is being carried out that involves the use of ionising radiation, regulations require that competent persons ensure that the detailed requirements of the Ionising Radiation Regulations are properly complied with. This usually means the placing of signs and barriers on site and excluding all but authorised or classified employees from controlled areas. If all the signs and other procedures are obeyed, no-one should be at risk from ionising radiation.

One area of risk that does exist is the radiation from sunshine. The short-term dangers are blisters and sunburn while the well known long term danger is skin cancer.

On site it is tempting for employees to take their shirts off on sunny days to get a suntan, but a suntan does not protect against the risk of skin cancer.

Advice from the HSE and other bodies is that workers on site should 'keep their shirts on'.

People most at risk include those with fair or freckled skin that does not tan easily or that burns before it tans. People with red or fair hair, light-coloured eyes, and those who have a large number of moles (more than 50), are also at a higher level of risk.

As well as protecting against the possibility of sunburn and the long-term risk of skin cancer, a shirt will also provide protection against minor cuts, abrasions and some of the chemicals or dusts that can be found on site.

 For further information refer to Chapter B08 Skin protection.

Contaminated ground

As the drive continues to develop brownfield sites, the magnitude of the health hazard arising from the disturbance of contaminated ground is almost certain to increase.

The disturbance of contaminated ground can release hazardous fibres (such as asbestos), hazardous gases or fumes and even hazardous micro-organisms (such as anthrax spores).

Where ground that has been previously used is to be disturbed, a risk assessment must be carried out to determine whether there will be residual risks to health.

The findings of a thorough assessment of the risks will determine exactly what the hazards are and how the risks can be eliminated or controlled to an acceptable level. Given the wide range of contaminants possible, the potential for ill health may result from inhalation, ingestion or skin contact with the hazardous substance.

 For further information refer to Section E *Environment*.

Bird and bat droppings

The presence of large populations of roosting birds, particularly pigeons, or a bat colony can present significant risks to health if their droppings are disturbed. This has obvious implications for some types of construction work and preliminary work such as surveys.

The main hazard is the inhalation of fungus spores that become airborne as a result of disturbance of the droppings. However, skin contact with pigeon droppings has been known to cause an acne-like skin condition and ulcers.

 For further information refer to Chapter B07
The Control of Substances Hazardous to Health (COSHH).

Dermatitis

Occupational dermatitis causes more time to be lost in the building and construction industry than any other prescribed disease. Yet with proper attention to risk assessments, control measures and good working practices it could be avoided.

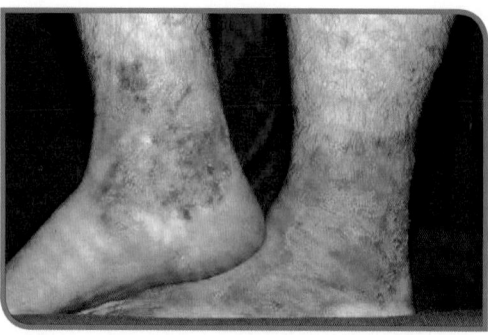

The prevention of dermatitis would save the industry and employers large amounts of money, and also assist in improved productivity on site, as well as improving conditions for the workers.

The agents that cause dermatitis can be divided into five classes, as follows:

- ☑ mechanical factors (such as friction, pressure and trauma)
- ☑ physical factors (including heat, cold, electricity, sunlight and radiation)
- ☑ the use of some chemicals
- ☑ contact with some plants and their products
- ☑ contact with biological agents, organisms, insects and mites.

There are two main types of dermatitis, commonly known as contact dermatitis and allergic dermatitis.

Contact dermatitis

This is sometimes also called irritant dermatitis. It is the commonest form of occupational dermatitis and results from repeated contact with any substance that irritates the skin. Such substances can include cement, lime, plaster, paint, solvents, adhesives, sawdust, oils, pitch, tar, fibreglass, white spirit, thinners and most acids and alkalis.

The effect of the substances is usually to cause the skin to dry out and crack due to the removal of the natural oils. Skin damaged in this way is very vulnerable to other infections.

Allergic dermatitis

This is sometimes also called sensitive dermatitis. It is an allergic reaction by the skin to a specific substance that the skin has been exposed to in the past, and which the skin has become especially sensitive to. Once a person's skin has become sensitised, any future exposure to the substance will cause an immediate skin reaction.

The main sensitising substances on site are cement, resins, glues, hardeners, hardwoods and chrome and nickel compounds. The allergic response is usually specific to an individual as opposed to affecting everyone, and can also appear suddenly after many years' exposure.

The prevention of dermatitis is basically one of good personal hygiene, good housekeeping, safe systems of work that avoid contact with substances that are known to cause dermatitis, and the use of PPE (as a control measure of the last resort), in the appropriate cases.

 For further information refer to Chapter B08 Skin protection.

Smoking

Smoking is now prohibited in all enclosed workplaces (such as site cabins, canteens and company premises). Different legislation applies to England, Wales, Scotland and Northern Ireland.

Although smoking is totally prohibited on many sites, employers or the person in control of a site may make provision for smoking in areas that are not enclosed or substantially enclosed, as long as non-smokers are not exposed to tobacco smoke.

 For further information refer to Chapter B07
The Control of Substances Hazardous to Health (COSHH).

Respiratory problems

Dust

Virtually all types of dust are hazardous to health and there are is no such thing as general dust. The effect dust has depends upon what it is made of, the airborne concentration levels and length of time that it is breathed in. If the amount of dust in the air exceeds 10 milligrams per cubic metre, averaged out over an eight hour working day, then the provisions of the Control of Substances Hazardous to Health Regulations will immediately apply.

A heaped teaspoonful of most dusts would be about 10 milligrams, and if dust can be seen floating freely in the air then the 10 milligrams limit is probably being exceeded. For some dusts that are particularly hazardous to health, much lower limits have been set.

For example, the maximum long-term exposure limits, over an eight-hour working day, for silica dust is 0.4 milligrams per cubic metre and hardwood dusts 5 milligrams per cubic metre.

A number of construction activities can cause respiratory disease, including:

- ☑ cutting kerbs, slabs, bricks, blocks
- ☑ stone-masonry
- ☑ scabbling, surface grinding and grit blasting
- ☑ tunnelling
- ☑ crushing and screening demolition material
- ☑ clearing and removing rubble or sweeping up general dust
- ☑ chasing out mortar before repointing or chasing walls
- ☑ laying epoxy floors
- ☑ carpentry (softwood, hardwood, MDF, glues)
- ☑ painting and decoration (solvents, rubbing down)
- ☑ mixing up and rubbing down plaster.

The inhalation of any dust will eventually cause respiratory problems, including or contributing to such conditions as asthma, bronchitis, pneumoconiosis and certain types of lung cancer. Some dusts cause an allergic reaction causing breathing problems immediately after a dust is breathed in. As well as presenting a health hazard, many airborne dust clouds are also flammable or explosive.

Whenever practicable, the generation of dust should be avoided and, where it cannot be avoided, it should be controlled by ventilation or extraction. The use of PPE by employees must be regarded as the very last resort when all other methods of control have been examined and found not to be practicable.

 For further information refer to Chapter B10 Dust and fumes.

Fumes, including solvent fumes

The vapour given off by many substances has the potential to cause respiratory illness or other symptoms of ill health if not adequately controlled. Other symptoms include headaches, coughing, feeling sick, feeling light-headed, shortness of breath or feverishness.

As well as being inhaled and causing direct problems in the lungs, many fumes can be absorbed into the bloodstream and bring about complications in other parts of the body.

An example of this type of response is cancer of the bladder, which can be caused by inhaling certain aniline fumes (a chemical made for use in textile dyes).

Potential sources of hazardous fumes, which may be inhaled if control measures are not taken, are:

- ☑ solvent-based adhesives, spirit-based or solvent-based paints
- ☑ welding, especially welding galvanised metals
- ☑ oxyacetylene cutting
- ☑ engine exhausts.

If the generation or release of the fumes cannot be avoided, for example by using a water-based solvent or paint instead, then adequate natural or mechanical ventilation should be used. The use of PPE for employees must be regarded as the last resort.

 For further information refer to Chapter B10 Dust and fumes.

Repetitive strain injury

The Chartered Society of Physiotherapy (CSP) has indicated that there has been a sharp rise in the number of cases of repetitive strain injury (RSI) in the workforce in general. The jobs in construction that are most likely to cause RSI are:

- ☑ plumbers
- ☑ carpenters
- ☑ painters
- ☑ plant operators.

Methods by which workers can limit the potential for RSI are:

- ☑ avoiding long periods of repetitive tasks (job rotation)
- ☑ alternating the use of the hands (picking up left then right-handed)
- ☑ taking more short breaks rather than one long break
- ☑ wearing looser clothing to increase ease of movement
- ☑ keeping warm (cold muscles don't expand properly)
- ☑ not overstretching (move closer to the task)
- ☑ reporting pain or other symptoms immediately – RSI is easier to treat in the early stages.

Employers can make a big difference to the health of their workers, which will have business benefits by:

- ☑ assessing each job for the potential for RSI
- ☑ encouraging early reporting
- ☑ allowing workers to organise their work and take breaks as necessary.

Needlestick injuries

A needlestick injury is an accidental puncture of the skin by a hypodermic needle.

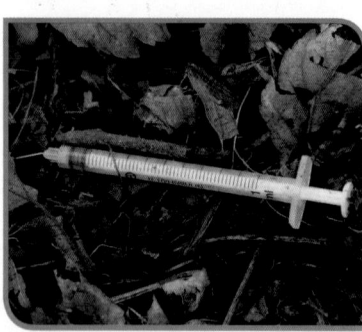

It is a sad fact that the drug culture affects the construction industry as much as other industrial sectors. The abuse of both legal and illegal drugs brings with it the risk of discovering discarded hypodermic syringes or discarded needles.

Employees in the refurbishment sector of the industry are probably at greatest risk, especially if the property is derelict or has been occupied by squatters. However, any work in occupied or previously occupied premises carries with it some risk of finding needles that have been randomly discarded or hidden away in areas where they are difficult to see, until it is too late.

If not handled in a safe manner, discarded needles can pose serious health risks to anyone whose skin is accidentally pricked. Blood on a needle could be infected with a hepatitis or HIV virus.

As part of site induction in the appropriate circumstances, employees should be told to assume that any needle they find has been used by a drug user and is potentially contaminated by infected blood.

Company and site procedures should cover the actions that employees and supervisors should take whenever discarded needles are found. The removal and disposal of such items should be properly covered. Advice may be sought from the site nurse (if there is one) or the Local Authority Environmental Health Department. The local police may also offer guidance.

Generally, employees should be clearly told not to touch or move any needles or hypodermic syringes they find, but to ask a responsible person to guard it whilst reporting the matter to their supervisor.

If a needle or syringe must be moved then suitable instructions to employees might be:

☑ if possible, use a pair of pliers to pick it up

☑ carry it with the needle pointing downwards

☑ do **not** wrap it in paper or put it into a litter bin

☑ if available, place it in a clear glass bottle or jar

☑ place the bottle or jar in a secure location

☑ carefully follow site or company procedures regarding disposal

☑ wash hands thoroughly.

Employees should not panic if a needle punctures their skin. Gently squeeze the area around the wound to encourage bleeding but **do not suck the wound**. Wash the site of the injury thoroughly with soap and water at the first opportunity and obtain medical assistance as soon as possible, from either the site nurse or the nearest hospital with an Accident and Emergency Department. If you can do so safely, take the syringe or needle with you.

If dealt with properly and promptly, the risks of a resulting health problem are small.

For further information refer to Chapter B07
The Control of Substances Hazardous to Health (COSHH).

Leptospirosis (Weil's disease)

When working near to water or on sites that are otherwise wet, consideration must be given to the health implications associated with the presence of rats.

Leptospirosis is an occupational hazard for anyone working near water, damp areas or anywhere else where rats might be present. It is a disease caused by bacteria that is present mainly in the urine of infected rats and is therefore also in the water where they live. The bacteria thrives in damp conditions, of riverbanks or streams, and can enter the body through unprotected cuts and scratches, by swallowing infected water and through the lining of the nose.

If anyone thinks they may have come into contact with the disease, they should be aware that the early symptoms closely resemble the symptoms of influenza, namely:

☑ fever

☑ headache

☑ chill.

Later symptoms include:

☑ tightening of the skin

☑ a yellowing of the skin (similar to jaundice)

☑ internal bleeding.

WARNING!
LEPTOSPIROSIS
HEALTH HAZARD
FRESH WATER STREAMS AND MUD
POSSIBLY POLLUTED WITH BACTERIA
EXERCISE CAUTION

It is essential that anyone who is at risk, and who becomes unwell with flu-like symptoms, should visit their doctor, describe where they have been working and say that they are at risk from leptospirosis. Persons regularly at risk (for example, canal or sewage workers) should carry a card explaining their occupation and the occupational hazard of leptospirosis.

Personal precautions that should be taken include the following:

☑ discourage the presence of rats on site (do not leave food lying around and do not throw away food scraps)

☑ do not handle the carcasses of dead rats

☑ avoid inadvertent entry or immersion in water that could be infected. (If this happens and you think that you may be infected, particularly if you swallowed any water, see a doctor as a matter of urgency.)

☑ wear appropriate PPE

☑ prior to entering the work area, wash any cuts or grazes in clean water. Apply antiseptic to the wound, then cover with gauze, a waterproof dressing and PPE as necessary

☑ upon completion of work, wash hands, forearms and all other exposed areas of skin thoroughly. Remove any wet protective clothing as soon as possible and dry it

☑ avoid rubbing your nose, mouth or eyes with your hands during work

☑ do not smoke, eat or drink without first washing your hands.

Leptospirosis can be fatal, typically within four to six weeks, if the early symptoms are not recognised and treated.

Another form of leptospirosis can be caught from the urine of infected dairy cattle. Anyone engaged in construction work on dairy farms must be aware of this hazard.

Further advice on leptospirosis can be obtained from the Employment Medical Advisory Service of the Health and Safety Executive or by contacting any local office of the Health and Safety Executive.

For further information refer to Chapter B07
The Control of Substances Hazardous to Health (COSHH).

1.7   Occupational health support services

Employment Medical Advisory Service

Employment Medical Advisory Service (EMAS) is an integral part of the HSE that is staffed by specialist occupational health professionals (both doctors and nurses).

In many ways, the functions of EMAS are similar to those of the HSE. EMAS exists to offer advice to employers and employees and take enforcement action where necessary.

EMAS doctors are medical inspectors and EMAS nurses are occupational health inspectors. Both have the same powers as other HSE inspectors under The Health and Safety at Work Act 1974, where HSE is the enforcing authority.

The functions of EMAS staff are to:

- ☑ investigate complaints and concerns of ill health from employers, employees, trade unions, members of the public and other health care professionals

- ☑ investigate ill health reports received from employers under RIDDOR

- ☑ help other HSE inspectors and Local Authorities to make sure that other people comply with health and safety law

- ☑ provide advice in the workplace to employers, employees and trade unions

- ☑ provide expert advice to doctors and nurses in general health care and occupational health

- ☑ provide support for the HSE's occupational health campaigns.

 EMAS staff are based in some but not all HSE offices.
Check the HSE website for their local contact.

Healthy Working Lives

The Healthy Working Lives website, offers employers and workers free confidential advice and operates in Scotland.

 Full details are available on the Healthy Working Lives website.

Constructing Better Health

Constructing Better Health (CBH) is a not for profit, although not free, organisation, with a remit to deliver the construction industry's occupational health scheme. As such, CBH has developed occupational health standards and other resources to assist employers in managing occupational health on site.

 Further details can be obtained on the Constructing Better Health website.

Employees returning from sickness absence

In April 2010 fit notes came into force, replacing the old sick-note system. The new system requires general practitioners to categorise patients as fit for work, or may be fit for work.

The purpose of the new system is to encourage communication between an employee who is categorised as may be fit for work and their doctor and employer, to establish what work the employee might be able to do if returning to work. Fit notes are designed to encourage a controlled return to work, with compromises being made on both sides, as necessary, particularly after prolonged periods of sickness absence. Alternative working hours, adaptations to the workplace and alternative types of work are options available to the employer.

However, ultimately it is the employer's decision regarding what course of action to take in these circumstances. If poor decisions are made and the employee's health deteriorates as a consequence, the employer may be challenged to explain why they took the decisions they did.

Health and well-being practices on a large construction site

- ☑ All operatives issued with a handout, giving details of local accident and emergency facilities, and maps showing routes to them.
- ☑ Advice leaflets on relevant health conditions, as well as a card dealing with abusive and non-abusive behaviour made available at induction.
- ☑ Operatives had envelopes attached to their safety helmets giving details of safety risk medical conditions and next of kin contact details.
- ☑ A sat-nav was provided for the use of first aiders to direct them, in an emergency, to the nearest accident and emergency centre.
- ☑ First aiders were linked to a WiFi pager system activated by push button call points.
- ☑ Trained first aiders carried a small, portable first-aid kit attached to their hi-vis jackets.
- ☑ Occupational health facilities were extended to include talks given by visiting specialists on cancer, stress, lifestyle, diet, relationship and debt-counselling.
- ☑ There were defibrillators and trained operatives on site.
- ☑ The site arranged for an NHS out-reach worker to make regular visits to site to help smokers quit smoking.
- ☑ Healthy meals were provided in the canteen, as well as free fruit.
- ☑ The site also arranged for a reduced membership fee for operatives at the local gym.
- ☑ Random drug and alcohol tests were carried out on site.
- ☑ The contractor offered immunisation injections for flu, tetanus and hepatitis.

1.8   Legal duties

Employers have a duty to assess the risks to health that arise out of their work activities and to introduce measures that control the risks to an acceptable level.

Risk assessments explain:

- ☑ the health hazards of the job (for example, silica dust created when mechanically cutting a block)
- ☑ the risks (such as a person breathing in the silica dust)
- ☑ the control measures needed to minimise the health risk to a safe level (such as wet cut the slab and wear a suitable respirator).

The regulations indicate the general principles of prevention that must be adhered to when making decisions on appropriate risk control measures, for example:

- ☑ avoiding the risk (such as order pre-cut slabs or use a block splitter)
- ☑ combating risks at source (such as suppressing dust by wet techniques rather than relying solely on PPE)
- ☑ adapting to technical progress (such as buying new work equipment that is designed to produce a cleaner cut or which incorporates dust extraction system).

The regulations impose legal duties on employers as follows:

- ☑ providing employees with comprehensive information of the risks identified by the assessment and the measures implemented to control those risks
- ☑ ensuring that employees are capable in all respects of carrying out the work that they are required to do in a safe manner and without risks to health
- ☑ co-operating with other employers, where the employees of more than one employer share a workplace, in the interests of health and safety.

 Specific legislation covering the various health risks is contained within the relevant sections.

02

Welfare facilities

Construction site workers need adequate toilet and washing facilities, a place to warm up and eat their food and somewhere to store clothing.

However, these basic requirements are often neglected. Good facilities can have a positive benefit on health and wellbeing and can help prevent dermatitis.

This chapter describes the minimum welfare facilities that should be provided or made available during all types of construction activity to comply with the Construction (Design and Management) Regulations.

Introduction	16
Key points	16
Welfare at fixed construction sites	17
Facilities at transient construction sites	19
Food safety	21

Welfare facilities

2.1 Introduction

The availability of welfare facilities, their location on site and regular maintenance must be considered at the planning and preparation stages of every construction project, before construction work (including demolition) starts.

Welfare requirements

Welfare facilities in general should be kept clean, adequately lit, ventilated as necessary and kept in a good state of repair.

Washing facilities must include:

- ☑ a supply of hot (or warm) and cold water, ideally from a running supply
- ☑ soap or other cleansers
- ☑ towels or another means of drying
- ☑ separate facilities for men and women except where they:
  - are in a separate room that can be locked from the inside
  - can only be used by one person at a time
  - are only used for washing the hands, forearms and face.

The provision of toilets must include separate facilities for men and women, except where each toilet is in a separate room that can be locked from the inside.

Induction on site

Explain:

- ☑ the location of the welfare facilities
- ☑ if appropriate, the opening hours of site canteens
- ☑ responsibilities for the cleaning and maintenance of the facilities
- ☑ the provision of barrier creams and rehydrating lotions
- ☑ the need for good personal hygiene
- ☑ the company policy regarding damage and graffiti
- ☑ the location of facilities for men and women
- ☑ the arrangements (if any) made for smokers.

Smoking

Smoking in enclosed and substantially enclosed workplaces is now banned by different legislation in England and Wales, Scotland and Northern Ireland.

Broadly, the differing legislation has similar aims in that:

- ☑ the act of smoking in smoke-free premises is an offence
- ☑ the act of **permitting** smoking in smoke-free premises (or a smoke-free vehicle) is an offence
- ☑ generally, vehicles that are used by more than one person must be smoke-free
- ☑ smoke-free premises must have an official no smoking sign, with the approved text, prominently displayed at each entrance
- ☑ smoke-free vehicles must have at least one official no smoking sign prominently displayed.

2.2 Key points

- ☑ Suitable and sufficient sanitary conveniences (toilets) must be provided or made available at readily accessible places.
- ☑ Suitable and sufficient washing facilities, including showers if required, must be provided or made available at readily accessible places.
- ☑ An adequate supply of drinking water, conspicuously marked with the appropriate sign, should be provided or made available at readily accessible places.
- ☑ Suitable facilities must be provided for the accommodation of clothing not worn at work and for clothing worn at work but not taken home. Such facilities shall include provisions for drying clothing when it gets wet.

☑ Facilities must be provided to enable people to change clothing where a person has to wear special clothing for special work and cannot change elsewhere. The facilities shall be separate for men and women, where necessary, for reasons of privacy.

☑ Suitable and sufficient facilities for rest (such as a site canteen) must be made available at readily accessible places, including:
  – sufficient tables and chairs (with backs)
  – suitable arrangements to protect non-smokers from discomfort caused by tobacco smoke
  – where necessary, suitable facilities for pregnant women and nursing mothers
  – a means for boiling water and suitable arrangements to ensure that meals can be prepared and eaten.

2.3   Welfare at fixed construction sites

If you have overall control of the site, you are responsible for making sure that legal requirements for welfare are met for the site. In practice, this means the principal contractor or other person in control of the site will often either provide or arrange for common facilities for everyone.

If work is carried out in occupied premises (for example, offices, factories, and so on) it may be possible to make arrangements with the client to use the permanent facilities at the premises.

Planning

☑ Make sure welfare arrangements are clearly addressed in the health and safety plan, where the Construction (Design and Management) Regulations (CDM) apply.

☑ Consider welfare facilities, their location on site and regular maintenance during the planning and preparation stage of any project, whether or not CDM applies.

☑ Arrange for equipment to be available, provided, sited and connected to services before construction work (including demolition) starts or when additional numbers of workers start on site.

☑ Make sure the facilities reflect the site size, nature of the work, and numbers of people who will use them. If a large number of people are working on site or the work being carried out is particularly dirty or involves a health risk (for example, pouring concrete) you will need more washing facilities, which may include showers, toilets, and so on.

Toilets

☑ Make sure that an adequate number of toilets are provided at all times.

☑ Men and women may use the same toilet, provided it is in a lockable room and partitioned from any urinals that may also have been provided, otherwise separate toilets will be required.

☑ Wherever possible connect toilets to a mains drainage system and ensure they are water flushing. If you cannot do this, use facilities with built in supply and drainage tanks.

☑ Only use chemical toilets as a short-term measure. When they are used, it is important that they are of robust construction, regularly emptied and maintained. Access will need to be provided and kept for emptying and maintaining chemical toilets. Suppliers of portable facilities will be able to advise you.

Drinking water

☑ Ensure that there is a supply of drinking water. Whenever possible it should be supplied direct from the mains; otherwise use bottles or tanks of water. If water is stored, protect it from possible contamination and make sure it is changed often enough to prevent it from becoming stale or contaminated.

☑ Clearly mark the drinking water supply to prevent it being confused with water that is not fit to drink or hazardous liquids.

☑ Provide cups or other drinking vessels at the water tap, unless the water is supplied in an upward jet that can be drunk easily (such as a drinking fountain).

Washing facilities

Washing facilities

☑ Put washing facilities next to both toilets and changing areas and make sure they include:
- basin(s) or sink(s) large enough for people to wash their face, hands and forearms
- a supply of hot water and cold or warm running water
- soap and towels (either cloth or paper) or dryers.

☑ If mains water is not available, use clean water supplied from a tank.

☑ You may need more washing facilities, including showers, where the work is particularly dirty or when workers are exposed to especially hazardous substances (such as development of contaminated land, or demolition of old industrial buildings that are contaminated with toxic substances). These will need to be separate from the main facilities.

☑ Men and women can share basins used for washing hands, face and arms.

☑ A shower may be used by both men and women as long as it is in a separate, lockable room that can be used by one person at a time.

Storing and changing clothing

☑ Every site should have arrangements for storing:
- clothing not worn on site (such as jackets and training shoes)
- protective clothing needed for site work (such as wellington boots, overalls and reflective jackets).

☑ Separate lockers might be needed, although on smaller sites the site office may be a suitable storage area, provided it is kept secure.

☑ Where there is a risk of protective site clothing contaminating everyday clothing, store items separately.

☑ Men and women should be able to change separately.

☑ Make sure that wet site clothing can be dried.

☑ Many fires have been caused by placing too much clothing to dry on electrical heaters, making the heater overheat. If electrical heaters are used, ensure they are properly ventilated and if possible, fitted with a high temperature cut-out device.

Rest facilities

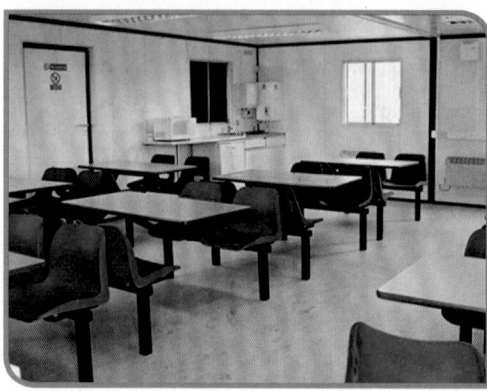

☑ Provide facilities for taking breaks and meal breaks. The facilities should provide shelter the wind and rain, be heated as necessary and contain:
- tables and chairs (with backs)
- a kettle or urn for boiling water
- a means for warming up food (for example, a gas or electrical heating ring, or microwave oven).

☑ On small sites, the site office or hut can make a suitable rest area, especially if it is one of the common portable units.

☑ Do not store plant, equipment or materials in rest areas.

Heating

Rest facilities will normally require heating. Using properly maintained electrical equipment can eliminate the risks associated with LPG heaters. Inadequately ventilated LPG cookers and heaters can produce carbon monoxide, with potentially fatal results. Flammable gas may escape from leaking cylinders that have not been properly turned off. If LPG is used reduce the risks by:

☑ using and storing the cylinders in safe, well-ventilated places outside the accommodation (including overnight) or in purpose-built ventilated storage areas

☑ ensuring that the appliances have been properly installed, checked and maintained by a competent person

☑ providing adequate combustion ventilation (provide fixed grilles at high and low level)

☑ checking that the ventilation provided is not blocked (for example, fixed grilles blocked by newspaper or rags in cold weather to stop draughts)

☑ checking that cylinders are properly turned off when not in use

☑ using wall or ceiling-mounted carbon monoxide detectors.

02

First-aid rooms

On a large building or construction site, a first-aid room, suitably staffed and equipped, should be provided. The need for such a room cannot be decided purely on the numbers of persons employed, but should be assessed on the type of work being carried out and whether a hospital or other emergency facilities are close to hand.

The first-aid room will normally be under the control of the first aider who should be nearby or on call, with access to the room when employees are at work. The name of this person should be displayed, together with the names and locations of all other first aiders and appointed persons. On some larger sites, the first-aid room will be staffed by a qualified nurse.

The room should be clearly identified, available at all times and used only for rendering first aid. It should be of sufficient size to contain a couch with adequate space around it to allow people to work, and provided with an access door to allow the passage of a stretcher or other carrying equipment. Pillows and blankets should be provided and be frequently cleaned.

The room itself should be cleaned each working day, have smooth-topped, impermeable working surfaces and provision for privacy and refuse disposal.

Heating, lighting and ventilation should be effective. In addition to the first-aid materials that should be stored in a suitable cabinet, there should be:

- ☑ a sink with running hot (or warm) and cold water
- ☑ drinking water
- ☑ soap, nail brush and paper towels
- ☑ clean garments for use by first-aid personnel
- ☑ a suitable container for disposal of clinical waste (yellow bags).

In first-aid rooms that are supervised by the site nurse, other items may be provided on their advice.

The room should have a telephone, where possible, and a siren or klaxon to alert personnel on call.

2.4   Facilities at transient construction sites

For the purpose of this chapter, a transient construction site is either where short duration work (up to a week) is carried out at one or many locations, or is of a longer duration carried out while moving over a continuous geographical area (such as major roadworks, cable laying contracts, and so on).

In such cases, it may be appropriate to make arrangements to use facilities provided by the owner of existing premises in which the work is being done, local public facilities or the facilities of local businesses.

Clear agreement should be made with the provider of the facilities; it should not be assumed that local commercial premises can be used without their agreement.

Facilities must be readily accessible to the worksite, open at all relevant times, be at no cost to the workers, be of an acceptable standard in terms of cleanliness and have hand-washing facilities.

Workers need to be made aware of the arrangements to use them and be informed of their location.

When planning welfare provision, consider:

- ☑ the nature of the work to be carried out and the health risks associated with it. For example, consider the provision of showers if the project involves hazardous substances or very dirty work (such as sewer maintenance, dusty demolition activities, work with contaminated land or concrete pouring)
- ☑ the distance workers will have to travel to the welfare facilities
- ☑ the duration of the work and number of different locations
- ☑ the numbers of people who will use them
- ☑ the cleaning and maintenance of the welfare facilities
- ☑ whether they need to be relocated during the construction phase.

Installing and removing from site

You need to plan how welfare units will be moved from delivery vehicles into position. It is preferable to mechanically move these units; if manual handling cannot be avoided then you should manage the risk effectively. Your plans should cover safe lifting practices and ensure proper protection of workers from falls from vehicles or portable units. You should site welfare units and manage traffic effectively to ensure adequate segregation of pedestrians and vehicles.

Use of private and public facilities

Where the construction activity is a long way from central facilities, use of facilities in private premises (such as in cafes) is not considered suitable as permanent alternative arrangements. The use of private facilities may be acceptable in limited circumstances (for example, where there is no alternative and the work is of no more than a week's duration). Permission, preferably in writing, should be obtained from the proprietor in advance of the work starting.

Use of public toilets is acceptable only where it is impractical to return to facilities provided at the main base, or to use a portable installation at the worksite.

Where public or private toilets are used they need to be readily accessible to the worksite, open at all relevant times, be at no cost to the employee, be of an acceptable standard in terms of cleanliness and have hand-washing facilities. Workers need to be made aware of the arrangements to use them and be informed of their location in advance of the work starting.

Drinking water

A supply of wholesome drinking water should be readily available. Where possible, it should be supplied direct from the mains. If water is stored, protect it from possible contamination and make sure it is changed often enough to prevent it from becoming stale or contaminated. Where necessary, clearly mark the drinking water supply to prevent it being confused with hazardous liquids or water that is not fit to drink. Provide cups or other drinking vessels at the outlet, unless the water is supplied in an upward jet that can be drunk easily (such as a drinking fountain).

Toilets

So far as is reasonably practicable you need to provide flushing toilets and running water, connected to mains water and drainage systems. If this is not possible, facilities with a built-in water supply and drainage tanks should be used. Portable chemical toilets are acceptable only if it is not reasonably practicable to make other adequate provision.

Provide an adequate number of toilets. The number needed will depend on the number of workers on site and the type of facilities provided. Portable toilets have a limited capacity and will need emptying. The number of portable toilets needed depends on the number of persons and the frequency of emptying.

Men and women may use the same toilet, if it is in a lockable room and partitioned from any urinals; otherwise provide separate toilets. Adequate supplies of toilet paper should always be available.

Sanitary waste disposal should be provided in facilities used by female workers.

Washing facilities

Provide washing facilities next to both toilets and changing areas. Consider placing them next to rest areas, if these are far from toilets or changing areas. They should include:

- ☑ a supply of clean hot and cold, or warm, water (which should be running water, so far as is reasonably practicable)
- ☑ soap or other suitable means of cleaning
- ☑ towels or other suitable means of drying
- ☑ sufficient ventilation and lighting
- ☑ sinks large enough to wash face, hands and forearms.

Men and women can share sinks used for washing hands, face and arms. Unisex shower facilities can be provided if they are in a separate, lockable room, which can be used by one person at a time.

Showers used for particularly dirty work, or when workers are exposed to especially hazardous substances (for example, development of contaminated land or demolition of old industrial buildings that are contaminated with toxic substances) will need to be separate from the main facilities.

Specialist facilities are needed for certain activities (such as working with lead or asbestos or tunnelling in compressed air).

Heating

Inadequately ventilated LPG cookers and heaters can produce carbon monoxide. Gas may escape from leaking cylinders that have not been properly turned off. You can eliminate these risks by using properly maintained electrical equipment instead.

If this is not possible, reduce the risk by:

- ☑ using and storing the cylinders in safe, well-ventilated places outside the accommodation (including overnight)
- ☑ providing adequate combustion ventilation (provide fixed grills at high and low level)
- ☑ checking that cylinders are properly turned off when not in use. Turn off the tap at the appliance and isolate the cylinder.

2.5   Food safety

☑ This chapter only applies in circumstances where food is prepared, or handled, to be eaten by others.

☑ Getting food hygiene wrong can have severe implications for many other people.

☑ Food hygiene is usually monitored by Local Authority environmental health officers (EHO), who:
- have similar rights of entry to site as HSE inspectors
- can issue hygiene improvement and hygiene emergency prohibition notices and instigate prosecutions
- can close down unsatisfactory catering facilities.

☑ Anyone who handles food for consumption by others:
- must have training in basic food handling techniques
- must report to their supervisor details of any illness that they may be suffering from
- may have to be suspended from work if they contract an infectious illness.

☑ Premises in which food is handled, prepared and served must conform to certain standards of construction and cleanliness.

Food poisoning is caused by bacteria (germs or bugs) that have lain dormant in most uncooked or unprepared foods, whether meat, fish, poultry or some vegetables.

Food poisoning keeps people off work through sickness, just as accidents do.

Complying with food safety legislation, and applying appropriate hygiene standards on site, are essential because of the potential for:

☑ time lost through sickness absence being reduced

☑ avoiding lost production

☑ enforcement action (such as hygiene improvement notices, hygiene emergency prohibition notices and even prosecution by Local Authorities) when your food handling does not come up to the required standard.

The Food Safety Act

The Food Safety Act and regulations apply to all workplaces. This includes building or construction sites where food or drink is supplied, provided or sold by you or anyone else for the benefit of employees and others working on site.

Toilets adjacent to food rooms must be separated by a lobby. A notice stating '**Now wash your hands**' must be displayed.

Employees in food rooms must not smoke. A notice must be displayed to that effect.

Checks and inspections of equipment and staff training should be recorded.

Certificates of staff training in food hygiene and handling must be displayed.

The Food Hygiene (England) Regulations

The regulations do not apply to sites where employees only consume their own food and drink. Nevertheless, in accordance with The Health and Safety at Work Act, and the Construction (Design and Management) Regulations, these areas must be kept in good order and in a reasonable state of cleanliness.

Food safety legislation is enforced by the Environmental Health Department of the Local Authority, and any doubt regarding the application of the regulations should be referred to the Local Authority environmental health officer.

Food inspectors, usually EHOs, may visit the site, with or without prior notice, on either a one-off or regular basis.

Every facility and assistance must be afforded to the inspecting officers. Obstruction in any form is an offence.

Definitions

Food – food or drink of any description, or any of the ingredients used in the preparation of food.

Food room – any room in which a person engages in the handling of food, including a servery or counter.

A building or construction site that has a canteen or mess room where food is stored, sold, supplied or provided (whether for profit or not) is classified as a **business** and the rooms are classified as **premises** for the purposes of the Act.

All food businesses that prepare, cook or sell food for the benefit of others, must be registered with the Local Authority. This involves completing the appropriate form available from the Environmental Health Department of that authority. (Registration is only applicable if food is handled on five days in five consecutive weeks. If in doubt, contact the Local Authority.) There should be no charge for registration.

 These regulations implement European Community Regulations with respect to food hygiene. The relevant Community Regulations are listed in Schedules 1 and 2 of the Hygiene Regulations.

The Community Regulations set out basic hygiene principles. They focus on how to identify and control food safety risks at each stage of the process of preparing and selling food. Controls do not have to be complex; a simple example would be the use of refrigeration to prevent the growth of harmful bacteria on perishable, ready-to-eat foods.

Welfare facilities

The regulations require all food businesses to have a written food safety management system based on the principles of Hazard Analysis and Critical Control Points (HACCP). Such a system should be proportionate to the food safety risks of the business.

The proprietor of the food business must:

- ☑ make sure food is supplied or sold in a hygienic way
- ☑ identify food safety hazards
- ☑ know which steps in the activities are critical for food safety
- ☑ ensure safety controls are in place, maintained and reviewed
- ☑ maintain appropriate documentation.

The premises

The siting, design and construction of the premises must aim to avoid the contamination of food and harbouring of pests. It must be kept clean and in good repair so as to avoid food contamination.

Surfaces in contact with food must be easy to clean and, where necessary, disinfected. This will require the use of smooth, washable, non-toxic materials unless you can prove to the EHO other materials are appropriate.

Adequate provision must be made for cleaning foodstuffs, and the cleaning and (where necessary) disinfection of utensils and equipment. You must take all reasonable, practical steps to avoid the risk of contamination of food or ingredients.

Washbasins must be designated for washing hands, have hot and cold (or appropriately mixed) running water, and be equipped with soap and suitable hand-drying facilities (such as disposable towels). Lavatories must not lead directly into food rooms and they must be kept clean, maintained in good repair and ventilated.

Adequate arrangements and facilities for the hygienic storage and disposal of hazardous and inedible substances and waste (whether liquid or solid) must be available. Food waste must not be allowed to accumulate in food rooms and should be deposited in closable containers.

Adequate facilities and arrangements for maintaining and monitoring suitable food temperature conditions must be available.

The food

Stored raw materials and ingredients must be kept in appropriate conditions that will prevent harmful deterioration and be protected from contamination likely to make them unfit for human consumption.

Water

There must be an adequate supply of potable (clean, drinkable) water that must be used whenever necessary to ensure foodstuffs are not contaminated. This includes the use of ice that must also be made, handled and stored in a way that protects it from contamination.

Temperature control

The Hygiene Regulations state that foods intended for sale or supply, which need temperature control for safety must be held either **hot** (at or above a minimum temperature of 63°C) or **chilled** (at or below a maximum temperature of 8°C). Rather than providing a long list of food items, the regulations apply the requirement for temperature control to all types of food that might support the growth of harmful (pathogenic) bacteria or the formation of poisons (toxins).

 Some of the requirements are different in Scotland; please contact the local Environmental Health Department for details.

Food handlers

Anyone who works in a food handling area must maintain a high degree of personal cleanliness. The way in which they work must also be clean and hygienic. Food handlers must wear clean and, where appropriate, protective over-clothes. Adequate changing facilities must be provided where necessary.

Food handlers must protect food and ingredients against contamination, which is likely to render them unfit for human consumption or create a health hazard. For example, uncooked poultry should not contaminate ready-to-eat foods, either through direct contact or via work surfaces or equipment.

Anyone whose work involves handling food should:

- ☑ observe good personal hygiene
- ☑ routinely wash their hands before handling foods
- ☑ never smoke in food handling areas
- ☑ report any illness (such as infected wounds, skin infections, diarrhoea or vomiting) to their manager or supervisor immediately.

If any employee reports that they are suffering from any condition or illness, the business may have to exclude them from food-handling areas. Such action should be taken urgently. If there is any doubt about the need to exclude, seek urgent medical advice or consult the local Environmental Health Department.

Food handlers must receive adequate supervision, instruction and training in food hygiene. Each food business must decide what training or supervision their food handlers need by identifying the areas of work most likely to affect food hygiene.

Local colleges of higher and further education and private training companies provide food hygiene training courses.

[?] **To determine whether you have complied with all legislative requirements, ask yourself the following questions.**

☑ Have you carried out a hazard analysis of food handling and production techniques?

☑ Are your standards of food hygiene good?

☑ Are your foods stored properly and kept at the correct temperatures?

☑ Have your staff been adequately and properly trained?

☑ Do you understand your food safety responsibilities?

If you can answer **yes** to each of these questions, your standards are probably satisfactory.

03

Work-related stress

Badly managed exposure to pressure caused by work or other demands can result in stress.

Workers who experience stress, anxiety or depression are unlikely to perform effectively in the workplace.

This can be financially costly to employers and, in industries where safety is a core factor (such as construction), stress can create more general health and safety risks.

Introduction   26
Causes of work-related stress   26
Signs of work-related stress   27
Assessing whether stress is a problem at work   28
The management standards for work-related stress   30
Legal duties   31

3.1   Introduction

Stress takes many forms. As well as leading to anxiety and depression it can have a significant impact on an employee's physical health. Research links longer term stress to heart disease, back pain, headaches, gastrointestinal disturbances and alcohol and drug dependency.

This has an impact for organisations in a number of different areas, and notably in terms of managing their health, safety and wellbeing policies.

There is a clear distinction between stress and pressure. Pressure can be a motivating factor and is often a part of every day work.

Figures from the Health and Safety Executive (HSE) show that stress is a factor of significance for UK organisations and workers overall.

- [✓] The total number of cases of stress in 2010-11 was 400,000 out of a total of 1.1 million for all work-related illnesses.
- [✓] Each case of stress-related ill health leads to an average of 30 days off work.
- [✓] A total of 10.5 million working days were lost in Britain in 2004-05 to work-related stress.
- [✓] Up to 5 million people in the UK feel very, or extremely stressed, by work.
- [✓] The cost to society of these figures is between £3.75 million and £3.8 billion every year.

Stress is therefore a serious problem and tackling it can have significantly beneficial effects for organisations and their workers. Stress is a management issue that managers can help to resolve.

Stress is often a symptom of poor employment relations and can seriously affect productivity.

Organisations that talk regularly with their employees and have sound systems and procedures in place for dealing with issues (such as absence and discipline) are much more likely to avoid work-related stress, and to be able to deal with potentially stressful situations when they arise.

Work can have a positive impact on our health and wellbeing. Healthy, well-motivated employees can have an equally positive impact on the productivity and effectiveness of a business.

Stress can cause many challenges within the workplace, including:

- [✓] a fall in a manager's productivity and that of employees
- [✓] risks to health and safety
- [✓] poor decision-making
- [✓] an increase in mistakes that may in turn lead to more customer complaints
- [✓] increased sickness absence
- [✓] high staff turnover
- [✓] poor workplace relations.

Stress often has a cumulative effect. If one member of staff becomes ill through stress, it places added pressure on those covering for them. Equally, a stressed manager may find it difficult to create a positive working environment and monitor stress levels in others.

The work foundation has proposed the following benefits to business in terms of encouraging a healthy workforce:

- [✓] reduced sickness
- [✓] fewer accidents
- [✓] higher commitment
- [✓] improved brand
- [✓] improved retention
- [✓] improved resilience
- [✓] higher productivity.

Organisations must risk assess for the potential of stress at work. This will be covered in more detail later.

3.2   Causes of work-related stress

Work demands – this can include workload and pattern of work, including whether this includes shifts. Adequacy of the management team, the build programme, and the effects of client expectation and contract penalties.

Control over work – how much say someone has about the way that they work.

Support from others – whether employees receive adequate information and support from managers and colleagues, and whether there are accessible systems to respond to individual concerns.

Relationships at work – the nature of work relationships, including mechanisms to deal with unacceptable behaviour (such as bullying).

Your role – whether people understand their jobs and have the skills, experience and support to deliver. Also whether there are conflicts of responsibilities.

The effect of change – how change is managed and communicated within the organisation, and whether work is secure, including when contracting is taking place.

Bullying is a potentially significant factor for workplace relationships. This can take many forms; what appears to be light-hearted banter to one person may be perceived as bullying by another. Personal and work-related bullying behaviours may both be evident within a workplace and can include:

☑ **personal behaviours:**

- ignoring/excluding/silent treatment/isolating
- malicious rumours or gossip
- belittling remarks
- undermining integrity
- lies told about you
- sense of judgement questioned
- opinions marginalised

☑ **work-related behaviours:**

- public humiliation
- being shouted or yelled at
- giving unachievable tasks/impossible deadlines/unmanageable workloads
- giving meaningless tasks/unpleasant jobs/belittling a person's ability
- withholding information deliberately/concealing information/failing to return calls or pass on messages
- undervaluing contribution/no credit where due/taking credit for work that is not their own
- constant criticism.

The construction industry top five causes of work-related stress

More specifically to the construction industry, research has identified the top five causes of work-related stress as:

☑ having too much work to do in the time available

☑ working long hours

☑ travelling or commuting

☑ having a dangerous job.

☑ being responsible for the safety of others at work

Equally, issues external to the workplace can all impact on our ability to cope with pressure at work; these might include personal relationships, financial concerns or domestic issues, including caring responsibilities and bereavement.

3.3   Signs of work-related stress

Anyone can suffer from work-related stress, no matter what work they do or what level they operate at.

In the construction industry the people who tend to report stress more than others are:

☑ managers

☑ designers

☑ road workers

☑ administration staff.

Symptoms

Some of the signs of stress are listed below; this is by no means exhaustive and individuals will vary in terms of how their own symptoms manifest in the workplace.

Behaviour

These are behaviours that may indicate an individual is under stress and can be noticeable in the workplace. People can report that they:

☑ find it hard to sleep

☑ are frequently tearful

☑ have altered eating habits, including food cravings

☑ cannot show their true feelings

☑ smoke or drink more

☑ have a disproportionate response to things

☑ avoid friends and family

☑ deny there is a problem

☑ are generally quiet and withdrawn

☑ avoid difficult situations.

☑ have a lack of assertiveness

Work-related stress

Physical symptoms

Symptoms of stress can vary considerably from one person to another and can include:

- ☑ tiredness
- ☑ indigestion
- ☑ headaches
- ☑ aching muscles
- ☑ palpitations
- ☑ high blood pressure

- ☑ breathlessness
- ☑ chest pains
- ☑ nausea
- ☑ tendency to sweat
- ☑ constipation and diarrhoea
- ☑ restlessness.

Mental symptoms

People can exhibit tendencies to:

- ☑ be more indecisive
- ☑ have poor judgement
- ☑ find it hard to concentrate
- ☑ suffer loss of memory
- ☑ have difficulty in concentrating

- ☑ feel inadequate or have low self esteem
- ☑ dread the future
- ☑ dread failure
- ☑ feel isolated
- ☑ have a lack of interest in others.

Emotional symptoms

Individuals are likely to:

- ☑ get irritable or angry
- ☑ lose their sense of humour
- ☑ be anxious

- ☑ feel numb
- ☑ be hypersensitive
- ☑ feel drained and listless.

Dealing with your own stress

Anyone can suffer from stress, in any role and at any level of an organisation. People who work alone or who may have particular responsibilities that set them apart from their work colleagues, could be particularly vulnerable.

If an individual feels that they may have the symptoms of stress, there are a number of things that they can be advised to do in order to address the challenges that are facing them:

- ☑ identify and tackle the underlying causes
- ☑ talk to someone trusted, with whom they can share issues and challenges
- ☑ seek additional support and guidance where appropriate
- ☑ practise relaxation techniques (these might include meditation or mindfulness, which have been shown through research to benefit individuals suffering from stress and depression)
- ☑ improve diet; avoid foods high in refined sugars and cut down where appropriate on alcohol, smoking and caffeine consumption
- ☑ avoid regularly working long hours if at all possible
- ☑ do regular exercise
- ☑ take time off work for holidays
- ☑ seek additional support and guidance.

 Signs and symptoms of stress can vary for individuals. More guidance on dealing with the symptoms of stress can be found on the MIND website.

3.4   Assessing whether stress is a problem at work

Carrying out a stress audit is one of the best ways to identify whether stress is an issue in your workplace. It will also help you to assess the risks of stress that people in your business may face as part of your health and safety risk assessment.

A stress audit can involve talking informally to staff (either individually or in groups) to find out if they have any concerns. Let employees know why you are carrying out the exercise and what you are trying to achieve (for example, that you hope to prevent future problems or cure any existing ones).

Safety representatives should also be involved in any relevant plans and decision making and ensure that people are confident and assured that the confidentiality of any information gathering will be respected.

A useful starting point for an audit is to ask staff to list the three best and worst things about their job, and whether any of these put them under excessive pressure.

You can also use questionnaires to gather the same information. Although there is a range of commercially available questionnaires, you may be better off developing your own checklist of areas that are particularly relevant to the needs and working conditions of your business.

There are a number of key areas you should consider:

- ☑ work scheduling and the type and design of work
- ☑ working relationships with colleagues
- ☑ the level of communication and reporting
- ☑ the physical working environment
- ☑ employees' expectations of their work.

 The HSE produces a useful checklist, designed to help organisations to clarify whether their own risk assessment approach to stress is appropriate and sufficient. This can be accessed through the HSE website.

Is my risk assessment approach suitable and sufficient?

Answering yes to all of the questions below would indicate that your approach is likely to be considered a suitable and sufficient risk assessment for work-related stress.

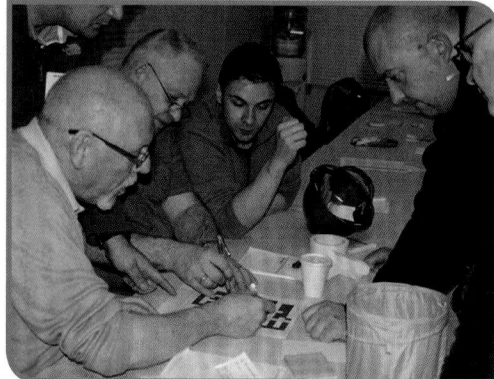
Risk assessment exercise – combined thinking helps

- ☑ Do you include all the steps in the risk assessment process?
- ☑ Do you focus on prevention and organisational level solutions?
- ☑ Do you include provision for dealing with other issues (for example, individual issues)?
- ☑ Do you ensure commitment from all parties (senior management, employees and their representatives)?
- ☑ Do you have arrangements to identify those aspects of the work, work organisation or environment that are known to be risk factors for work-related stress?
- ☑ Does your approach highlight the extent and nature of the gap, if any, between the current situation, and what is seen as good practice (such as the stakes to be achieved in the management standards), for each of the identified stress risk areas?

- ☑ Do you involve the workforce:
  - by asking about their views regarding good and bad features of workplace conditions?
  - by seeking their suggestions, advice and comments on potential solutions to problems (such as improvements to working conditions, changes in the way work is organised, and so on)?
  - by ensuring that people are empowered to contribute and feel that their views are listened to and acted upon?
  - by communicating outcomes (such as action plans)?
- ☑ Do you seek to develop and adopt solutions that are reasonably practicable?
- ☑ Do you provide documentation to show what you have done at each stage of the process and that you are implementing the recommended actions?

The HSE recommends that the process is documented, whatever the approach to carrying out a risk assessment for work-related stress. Documenting the process provides an audit trail to help you demonstrate to any relevant authorities that what has been done represents a suitable and sufficient risk assessment.

The role of the line manager

Managers have a significant impact on the work related stress of people with whom they work, notably their team.

Examples of the impact of managers are:

- ☑ they can both prevent and cause stress simply through their behaviour towards employees
- ☑ the manager's influence or lack of it can protect or expose employees to working conditions that may cause stress. This can be the case for both internal (organisational) factors and for those that are external (perhaps customer related)
- ☑ managers can identify (or miss) the signs of stress at an early stage
- ☑ if an employee is suffering from work-related stress, the manager is likely to be involved in supporting and helping to deliver change that could result in a solution
- ☑ increasingly, managers are responsible for the uptake and delivery of risk assessments for work-related stress in relation to their team and department.

3.5   The management standards for work-related stress

Six main causes of work-related stress have been identified across all organisations and a framework of management behaviours or competencies has been created. The HSE describes the objective behind the standards as follows:

> The management standards define the characteristics, or culture, of an organisation where the risks from work-related stress are being effectively managed and controlled.

03

The management standards for work-related stress, and the underpinning processes that support them, are designed to:

☑ help simplify and carry out stress risk assessments

☑ help all parties to work together to address work-related stress

☑ provide the means by which companies can gauge their performance in tackling the key causes of stress.

In addition management competencies have been developed that describe the behaviours managers need to show in order to prevent and reduce stress in their teams. They map across to the areas identified as being the primary sources of stress at work:

☑ **demands** – issues that should be considered include workload, work patterns and the working environment

☑ **control** – how much control the individual has over the way they do their work

☑ **support** – whether workers feel that adequate encouragement and resources are provided by the company, managers and colleagues

☑ **relationships** – workers at any level must not be subjected to unacceptable behaviours by anyone at work and conflicts must be effectively dealt with

☑ **role** – workers at all levels must understand their role (how they fit into the organisation) and there must not be any conflicting roles

☑ **change** – people can be suspicious of the real motives behind organisational change which, whether large or small, must be well-managed and effectively communicated.

The HSE describes the benefits of implementing these standards as:

☑ being able to demonstrate good practice through a step-by-step risk assessment approach

☑ enabling assessment of the current situation using surveys and other techniques

☑ encouraging active discussion and working in partnership with employees to help decide on practical improvements that can be made

☑ helping to simplify risk assessment for work-related stress by:

– identifying the main risk factors

– helping employers focus on the underlying causes and their prevention

– providing a yardstick by which organisations can gauge their performance in tackling the key causes of stress.

> The management standards themselves revolve around a series of activities and map directly across to the main causes of work-related stress. The process of implementing the management standards is described in full on the HSE website.

There are effectively five discreet processes within the standards, defined below.

☑ **Identify the risk factors.** When assessing the risks to which your employees may be exposed it is important to focus on organisational level issues that have the potential to impact on group and possibly large numbers of employees, rather than individual employees.

☑ **Who can be harmed and how?** The aim of the data gathering and analysis is to get a measure of where an organisation's current performance is against the management standards. To achieve this aim does not require organisations to perform extensive statistical analysis of their data. It is suggested that organisations, where possible, use existing data to identify the underlying causes. Typically, most organisations have access to data relating to sickness absence, staff surveys, turnover data, and so on.

☑ **Evaluate the risks.** The primary aim of this step is to take the output from the previous step, data collection and analysis, discuss the conclusions with a representative sample of employees, and work with them to develop solutions.

☑ **Record your findings.** By now you will have consulted your employees, explored areas of concern and taken some initial steps to develop some proposed solutions. It is important that you record your findings – to do this you could produce and disseminate an action plan. An action plan will:

– help you set **goals** to work towards

– help you **prioritise**

– demonstrate that you are **serious** about addressing employees' concerns

– provide you with something to **evaluate** and review against.

☑ **Monitor and review.** You should review any action you take to tackle the sources of excessive workplace pressure. You need to:

- **monitor** against your action plan to ensure the agreed actions are taking place

- **evaluate** the effectiveness of the solutions you implement

- **decide** what further action or data gathering, if any, is needed.

Line manager competency indicator tool

The line manager competency indicator tool is designed to assess whether the behaviours identified as effective for preventing and reducing stress at work are part of your management repertoire or not. The aim is to help you to reflect upon your own behaviour and management style.

The competencies measured by the tool fall into four main domains, with 12 sub-competencies. These are:

☑ **respectful and responsible**

- integrity

- managing emotions

- considerate approach

☑ **managing and communicating existing and future work**

- proactive work management

- problem solving

- participative/empowering

☑ **reasoning/managing difficult situations**

- managing conflict

- use of organisation resources

- taking responsibility for resolving issues

Risk assessment exercise – combined thinking helps

☑ **managing the individual within the team**

- personally accessible

- sociable

- empathetic engagement.

 The line manager competency indicator tool will enable individuals to compare their own behaviours against the management competencies relevant to the management standards. This can be accessed on the HSE website.

Occupational health support services

Services that are available to support individuals and employers on matters relating to work-related stress include:

☑ **Employment Medical Advisory Service (EMAS)**

☑ **Healthy Working Lives**

☑ **Constructing Better Health (CBH).**

 For further information on these services refer to Chapter B01 The management of health.

3.6   Legal duties

Organisations have a legal responsibility to protect their employees from stress under the following legal principles and general guidance:

☑ Health and Safety at Work Act and Management of Health and Safety at Work Regulations

☑ Protection from harassment

☑ Equality legislation

☑ The Employment Equality Act

☑ Employment Rights Act

☑ Consultation with Employees and Safety Representatives

☑ The Construction (Design and Management) Regulations

☑ Common law negligence.

Work-related stress

Under health and safety legislation, employers have a duty to undertake risk assessments and manage activities to reduce the incidence of stress at work. However, this is a complex area of law and there are also cases brought within civil law where individuals have successfully applied cases against employers.

It is recommended that legal advice is always sought by the individual and the employer should the need arise.

The Health and Safety at Work Act imposes general duties on employers to secure the health, safety and welfare of people at work and protect others against risks arising from the work activity. The act makes it the duty of every employer to ensure, as far as is reasonably practicable, the health, safety and welfare at work of all employees. This includes provision and maintenance of plant and systems of work that are safe and without risks, information, instruction and training.

The Management of Health and Safety at Work Regulations place a legal requirement on employers to assess the risks to health and safety that arise out of their work activities and to introduce measures that control the risks to an acceptable level.

Risk assessments explain:

- ☑ the hazards of the job (for example responsibility for the safety of others)
- ☑ the risks (such as stress)
- ☑ the control measures needed to minimise the risk of stress to a safe level (such as support through other welfare services).

The regulations indicate the general principles of prevention that must be adhered to when making decisions.

The Employment Equality Act – disability discrimination provisions

This act encompasses mental illness. Anxiety, stress and depression may be sufficient to qualify a person as disabled and therefore they will be covered by the act, as long as there is a substantial and long-term effect (for at least a year) on their ability to carry out normal day-to-day duties. Those with clinically recognised mental health diagnoses are very likely to be covered by the act.

If an employee is covered by the act, the organisation has a responsibility to make reasonable adjustments to accommodate the needs of that employee.

Similarly, the **Employment Rights Act** is relevant to issues regarding work-related stress. This may be particularly so for situations where there are challenges made by employees in relation to their rights under this act.

 A full exposition of this act can be found online.

04

Drugs and alcohol

The misuse of drugs and alcohol can have a devastating impact on individuals and employers, which can result in social problems, poor health, absenteeism and therefore loss of productivity, as well as contributing to workplace accidents. It is a growing problem in society and construction sites are no exception, so diligence is required to identify and support those who are affected by it.

This chapter gives a general overview of the misuse of drugs and alcohol; identification, symptoms, impact and management. It also outlines the legal framework that regulates it.

Introduction	34
Key points	34
Definitions	35
Alcohol consumption	35
Driving, alcohol and drugs	36
Work-related drug and alcohol problems	36
Appendix A – Sample template for developing a drug and alcohol abuse policy	42
Appendix B – Common drugs, effects and symptoms	46

4.1   Introduction

Identifying, managing and supporting individuals affected by drugs and alcohol are key challenges facing society and the construction industry. Their effects can have huge negative impact on individuals, employers, their businesses and also any occupants of property where work is being undertaken.

Drug and alcohol misuse poses a threat to individuals in terms of their health, safety and welfare, as well as threatening their existing and future livelihood if not controlled. These substances can cause effects (including drowsiness, trembling, lack of concentration and reduced awareness) that can potentially increase the risk of on-site accident and injury to the individual and others working or living alongside them.

It is easy to associate drug and alcohol misuse with individuals who are addicted to them. However we need to also take into account those who use drugs and alcohol infrequently. In addition, it is important to remember that there can be significant health and safety risks from individuals who have, for example, been heavily drinking the previous evening or those that may have been taking prescription or over-the-counter drugs.

04

☑ Approximately 1,500 to 2,000 deaths per annum are related to drug abuse.

☑ Approximately 6,000 to 7,000 deaths per annum are related to alcohol abuse.

☑ The effects of drug and alcohol misuse causes absenteeism, lack of awareness, focus and productivity, as well as harm to the short and long-term health and wellbeing of individuals.

☑ Approximately 8-10% of adults have used one or more illicit drug within the last year, and around 3% have used Class A drugs.

☑ Approximately 20% of young adults have used one or more illicit drug in the last year, and around 7% of young adults have used Class A drugs.

Successfully identifying, managing and supporting individuals with drug and alcohol problems are beneficial to them, your business and customers. For example, you would save on the cost of recruiting and training new employees to replace those who left work because of untreated misuse.

Offering support to those employees with drug or alcohol-related problems will also help to:

☑ reduce the risk of accidents caused by impaired judgement

☑ create a more productive environment, and improve employee loyalty and morale

☑ enhance public perception of your organisation as a responsible employer

☑ contribute to society's efforts to combat alcohol and drug misuse.

Raising awareness of managers, supervisors and operatives to ensure that effective identification, management and control measures are always put in place and monitored, are key to helping reduce the impact of drugs and alcohol on operatives and, where appropriate, occupants. There is a need to comply with legislation, including the Health and Safety at Work Act, the Management of Health and Safety at Work Regulations, the Road Traffic Act and the Transport and Works Act, and a duty to provide safe systems of work and a safe working environment. In appropriate circumstances, employers may also be held liable for the acts of employees under the Misuse of Drugs Act.

Drug and alcohol misusers are nearly four times more likely to be involved in workplace accidents, three times more likely to be absent from work for seven consecutive days or more and at least 25% less effective overall.

4.2   Key points

☑ Managers and supervisors should be aware of the signs and symptoms of drug and alcohol misuse.

☑ People who misuse drugs and alcohol are likely to be still under the influence when they report for work, so are more likely to endanger themselves and others.

☑ Drinking coffee, eating stodgy food or sucking peppermints does not minimise the effects of alcohol, as individuals' bodies dispose of alcohol at their own rate, which may differ from individual to individual.

☑ There is likely to be a negative impact on productivity, enhanced periods of sickness absence and morale generally.

☑ If people are under the influence of drugs or alcohol at work, decisive action needs to be taken to ensure it does not continue.

☑ Companies should put into place and communicate an approach to dealing with employees who are unfit for work through drug and/or alcohol misuse.

☑ This approach must be reflected in employee handbooks, induction processes and employment contracts. It must cover the right of search and testing, and identify the support in place to assist misusers and the approach to suspension/dismissal from work.

☑ Unless there is related misconduct, substance misuse should be seen as a treatable illness.

☑ Anyone facing up to suffering from a drug or alcohol misuse problem should be offered support and rehabilitation in strict confidence – there are many agencies who can offer professional advice and help.

☑ Drugs testing can be expensive and can introduce more problems than it solves, so the rationale for introducing a testing programme must be thoroughly thought out.

☑ Alcohol and drugs affect co-ordination, perception and reaction times, so driving, using tools or machinery or working in hazardous environments should be avoided.

☑ Driving a motor vehicle on a public road whilst under the influence of alcohol is a criminal offence.

☑ Driving on site under the influence of alcohol is equally, if not more, dangerous than driving on a public road, and employers may consider it appropriate to develop a written policy on the matter. Employers may also need to consider what their policy would be if an employee whose duties included driving (either on or off site) was convicted of drink driving.

4.3   Definitions

Alcohol. A colourless, volatile, flammable liquid that forms the intoxicating element in beer, spirits and wine.

Drug(s) or substance(s). Deemed to refer to all banned substances, pharmaceutical drugs, alcohol and solvents, unless otherwise stated.

04

Substance misuse. The intermittent or continual use of drugs (as defined above) that, when used for non-medical reasons, are detrimental to the employee's health, safety and work performance.

Company premises. All property owned, operated, leased by or otherwise under the control of the company, in whole or in part. This includes building and construction sites as well as company offices on or off site.

Under the influence. When there is a sufficient amount of the substance in a person's system to produce a positive result from a medical test or breathalyser and/or when the person shows behaviour likely to pose a risk to themselves or others or to interfere with their job performance.

 For further information on common drugs, affects and symptoms refer to Appendix B.

 A document detailing drug misuse and statistics can be found on the Information Centre website.

 For information on drug misuse at work refer to the HSE's employers' guide.

4.4   Alcohol consumption

The Department of Health recommends that alcohol intake is limited to 21 units per week (three to four units per day) for men, and 14 units per week (two to three units per day) for women, with at least one day in the week that is alcohol-free.

The usual advice that one glass of wine or one half pint of beer is equal to one unit is misleading and can lead to misunderstanding and accidental over-consumption.

The number of alcohol units is worked out by the formula:

ABV x L

Where: ABV = percentage alcohol content of the drink. L = amount drunk in litres.

If a person drinks one 200 ml glass of wine with 13% alcohol content:

13 x 0.2 = 2.6 units.

Excessive and continued intake of alcohol can result in serious ill health, including scarring of the liver tissue, which then affects its function. Approximately 30% of people diagnosed with the condition of cirrhosis of the liver only survive five years after diagnosis.

Furthermore, 3% of all cancer is directly caused by alcohol consumption.

 The drinkaware alcohol unit calculator, alcohol use disorders identification test and an HSE guide for employers on alcohol at work can all be found online.

4.5   Driving, alcohol and drugs

Driving under the influence of drink

Driving a motor vehicle on a public road whilst under the influence of alcohol is a criminal offence, with penalties that range from a fine, with or without disqualification, to a term of imprisonment. The current legal limit is 80 mg of alcohol per 100 ml of blood.

There is no safe limit of alcohol that you can consume and then drive. Each person's body reacts differently to alcohol. The speed at which alcohol is absorbed into your system (and how quickly your system gets rid of it) depends on a large number of factors, including your sex, weight, metabolism, health and when you last ate.

It is impossible to know how long it will take to sober up after drinking. Drinking coffee, eating, sleeping and showering **do not** help you to sober up any faster.

Too many people are killed or seriously injured on our roads in drink-driving crashes. Current statistics estimate the figure to be about 3,000 people each year, with cyclists having the highest fatality rate of all road users. There is also an increase in young drivers being killed whilst over the limit.

04

Driving under the influence of drugs

It is an offence to drive whilst unfit through drugs. Many people think that if they drive under the influence of drugs a vehicle search and a potential charge of possession is all they have to be worried about. However:

☑ taking drugs will impair driving skills. Driving whilst under the influence of drugs is extremely dangerous and can affect driving in numerous ways

☑ drug drivers can suffer from slower reaction times, erratic and aggressive behaviour, an inability to concentrate properly, nausea, hallucinations, panic attacks, paranoia, tremors (or 'the shakes'), dizziness and fatigue. In such a condition, it is a bad idea to be behind the wheel of a car, for the driver and their passengers

☑ during the phase whilst the effects of drugs are wearing off, the taker may feel fatigued, which will affect their concentration whilst driving.

The law

Under the Road Traffic Act, it is illegal to operate a motor vehicle whilst unfit through drink or drugs, as follows:

☑ a person, who when driving or attempting to drive a mechanically propelled vehicle on a road or other public place is unfit to drive through drink or drugs, is guilty of an offence

☑ a person shall be deemed not to have been in charge of a mechanically propelled vehicle if they prove that at that time the circumstances were such that there was no likelihood of their driving it, so long as they remained unfit to drive through drink or drugs

☑ courts, in determining whether there was such a likelihood of driving, may disregard any injury to individuals and any damage to the vehicle

☑ a person shall be taken to be unfit to drive if their ability to drive properly is, for the time being, impaired.

 This also applies to prescription or over-the counter drugs so you should always read the advice and labelling and, if you're not sure, consult your pharmacist.

4.6   Work-related drug and alcohol problems

Workplace problems can be caused through drug and alcohol consumption, both inside and outside of work, as the effects can be long-lasting. When considering the scale of the drugs or alcohol problem within a company, take into account:

☑ the risk of accidents due to impaired performance through drugs or alcohol

☑ inept and poor decision making

☑ lower standards of work

☑ low productivity caused by employees' inability to cope with workplace situations

☑ disruption and ill discipline by employees under the influence of substances

☑ time lost from the workplace due to absenteeism, lateness or habitual sick leave

☑ long-term health of the workforce

☑ stress factors on employees due to home circumstances

☑ financial stress on employees of feeding any habits or addiction

☑ impact on customers

- ☑ impact on company reputation
- ☑ security concerns
- ☑ potential compensation claims against the employer
- ☑ poor staff retention rates.

Successfully tackling alcohol and drug misuse can benefit both your business and your employees. For example, you would save on the cost of recruiting and training new employees to replace those who left work because of untreated misuse.

Offering support to those employees who declare a drug-related problem will also help to:

- ☑ reduce the risk of accidents
- ☑ create a more productive environment and improve employee loyalty and morale
- ☑ enhance company reputation as a responsible employer
- ☑ contribute to society's efforts to combat alcohol and drug misuse.

Identifying substance misuse

04

Alcohol, drug or solvent misuse by employees may come to light in a variety of ways. The following actions may indicate that a problem exists.

- ☑ Absenteeism without notice.
- ☑ Poor time-keeping.
- ☑ High accident levels and clumsiness.
- ☑ Confusion and disorientation.
- ☑ Poor performance and workmanship.
- ☑ Irritability, aggression and argumentativeness.
- ☑ Misconduct.
- ☑ Failure to remember, or failure to comply with, common instructions.
- ☑ A sudden need for increased supervision.
- ☑ Leaving site either without permission or at lunchtimes to visit licensed premises.
- ☑ Finding empty beer cans, bottles or drug-related paraphernalia.

Physical symptoms of substance misuse may include:

- ☑ rapid loss of weight
- ☑ gaunt appearance
- ☑ tremors or sweating
- ☑ constant tiredness
- ☑ trackmarks, severe bruising or abscesses on arms
- ☑ over-dilated or very small pupils
- ☑ cravings (for example, ice cream, nicotine, sweet foodstuffs).

Behavioural symptoms may include:

- ☑ degenerating personal appearance
- ☑ excessive care about personal appearance
- ☑ hyperactivity
- ☑ severe mood swings
- ☑ avoidance of authority or supervision
- ☑ deteriorating relations with other staff
- ☑ swings in morale
- ☑ minimum involvement with other staff
- ☑ obsessive or compulsive behaviour.

Communicating with and educating employees, supported by an effective workplace policy and community-based treatment, will improve the chances of the early detection of problems.

Employees need to feel secure in asking for help and made aware of the benefits this provides to all parties in supporting them.

Supervisors and managers may require training and supporting information to enable them to identify problems and then manage and support individuals in line with company policy and legal requirements.

Addressing alcohol and drugs misuse at work

Known or suspected misuse should lead to consultation between company, employees and representatives. To agree a way forward is essential if it is to be addressed adequately.

 Employer associations, solicitors and professional bodies (such as Alcohol Concern, Norcas or Drugscope) can advise and help develop a workplace alcohol and drugs policy.

Developing and implementing workplace policies

A substance misuse policy that applies to all staff can be of benefit and may form part of a company's overall health and safety policy.

The substance misuse policy that is adopted will need to take account of the particular needs of the company and the practical situations, including those brought about by working on building and construction sites. However, there are a number of minimum requirements for such a policy, which should:

- ☑ contain a clear statement of the behaviour that is expected of employees

- ☑ apply equally to all employees, including managers and supervisors, in the workplace

- ☑ result from full consultation with employees and, if appropriate, their representatives (such as recognised trades unions) before it is adopted

- ☑ be made known to all employees

- ☑ be an integrated part of an overall health and safety policy

- ☑ include clear statements on the roles and responsibilities of all employees in relation to the policy (for example, site-based operatives, HR Department, Occupational Health Department, site managers)

- ☑ address issues in the work environment that are likely to increase the use of alcohol or drugs

- ☑ encourage those with a problem to come forward under a promise of strict confidentiality and future support

- ☑ to the greatest possible degree, be non-punitive

- ☑ state the conduct likely to result in action being taken under the policy

- ☑ provide for appropriate treatment and rehabilitation for those with problems

- ☑ be evaluated after implementation and amended, if necessary, in line with the outcome of the evaluation.

The potential for the policy to interfere in an employee's private life must be lawful and proportionate. The policy is likely to be lawful and proportionate if:

- ☑ it is instituted to protect and promote employee safety

- ☑ employees are aware of the policy

- ☑ the process of collecting, transporting and testing samples can be proven to be independent and beyond reproach

- ☑ employees will know what the employer will do with the test results

- ☑ the employer has no other reasonable alternative way of obtaining the same result.

Implementing a substance misuse policy

Implementing such a policy has four essential components:

- ☑ the education and information of all levels of management, employees and their representatives

- ☑ the organisational support shown by the company

- ☑ the addressing of issues in the work environment

- ☑ the prevention and rehabilitation support offered by the company to its employees.

Information about a substance misuse policy, covering alcohol and drugs, must be provided to all employees, and be included as part of any induction training for new recruits. The policy must be supported by education about the harmful effects of alcohol and drugs, the rehabilitation services available and the means by which employers will help individuals to access these services.

It is important that management demonstrates its full support for the policy by ensuring observance by all staff, at whatever level, and endorsing changes to the working environment to facilitate the full and proper implementation of the policy.

The provision of treatment and/or referral services is an important component of implementing the policy. If problems are detected early, before serious physical and social effects occur, a brief intervention may be all that is needed.

Confidentiality for employees undergoing treatment and rehabilitation must be guaranteed. Equally, employees should not be disadvantaged in terms of promotion or seniority because they have sought or are accepting help. Treatment and rehabilitation should be covered by adequate leave entitlements.

However, as with all workplace health and safety matters, consultation with employees and the provision of education and information at an early stage, may prevent the onset of alcohol and drug problems at work.

Temporary and sub-contracted staff

The company substance misuse policy should also address the employment of sub-contractors and other temporary staff. Sub-contractors are normally obliged to work within the host or main contractor's policies and this condition could form part of any contract.

Misuse outside of the workplace

Generally, an employee's conduct outside of the workplace is not within the employer's control. However, if drug or alcohol misuse during recreational times creates a risk to their health and safety or to that of others who may be affected by the employee's actions during working hours, consideration must be given to the situation and to what action should or can be taken.

A company's substance misuse policy may also need to consider situations where an employee's behaviour outside the workplace results in a conviction for a criminal offence, and the effect that this would have on the company's image and reputation.

Alcohol or drug screening and testing

Introducing drug testing in the workplace is a difficult and potentially expensive initiative. It is essential to be completely clear on the reasons for doing so, or not. Testing is far from the whole answer and has inherent limitations.

Before any decision is taken by an employer to implement an alcohol or drug testing regime, care must be taken to ensure that an alcohol and drugs policy is fully established, communicated to all employees and, where appropriate, accepted by their representatives.

It is legitimate for employers to take an interest in drug and alcohol use in their workforce. *The independent inquiry into drug testing at work (2004)* concludes that these circumstances are when:

- ☑ employees are engaging in illegal activity in the workplace

- ☑ employees are actually intoxicated during working hours

- ☑ drug or alcohol use is having an impact on work performance that goes beyond a threshold of acceptability

- ☑ the nature of the work is such that the public is entitled to expect a higher than average standard of behaviour from employees and/or there is a risk of corruption.

There remains an open question, as to whether introducing testing for employees constitutes a solution to any of these circumstances. As yet, there is no clear evidence that this is so, but broadly speaking there are valid arguments for and against.

For drug testing

Supporters of drug testing claim that:

- ☑ there are benefits for safety

- ☑ the company is more efficient

- ☑ there is a positive effect on the organisation's external reputation

- ☑ it sends a strong message to employees that drug use is not acceptable.

Against drug testing

Opponents claim that:

- ☒ tests are unreliable for many reasons, chiefly that they do not necessarily prove impairment, dependence or current use

- ☒ there is no clear evidence of any benefit in terms of deterring use, reducing accidents or improving efficiency

- ☒ it is excessively invasive and a potential infringement of human rights

- ☒ it is damaging to work relations, and can hamper recruitment

- ☒ it is very costly, complicated and time-consuming

- ☒ it is possible to cheat drug tests.

The legal position

The extent to which employers can require employees to undertake random drug or alcohol testing is limited, even where there is a right to test the employee in their contract of employment.

An unreasonable request to take a test will result in a breach of the implied duty of mutual trust and confidence. This could lead to an employee successfully claiming unfair constructive dismissal. Obtaining samples without consent could, in addition, constitute the criminal offences of assault or battery.

In the absence of factors indicating that the employee is using, or is affected by, alcohol or drugs at work, the employer will have to ensure it can justify any testing it wishes to carry out.

There is no legal requirement to test employees in any industry and no specific legislation relating to drug testing in the workplace. Consequently, there is a lack of clarity surrounding the legal issues. Case law is also relatively scarce. Important legal decisions hinge on an interpretation of a range of legal implications, the main ones being:

- ☑ health and safety at work
- ☑ data protection
- ☑ human rights
- ☑ disability discrimination.

It is clear, however, that no-one can be tested against their will. It is important to be aware that any attempt to test employees without their express individual consent would constitute a criminal offence.

Why test?

Drug testing might be introduced for a number of reasons. Other than where there is a clear clinical imperative (that is rehabilitation testing), the effectiveness of each approach has not been proven.

Recruitment screening usually refers to testing or assessing the health of potential employees during the recruitment process. Testing of this kind presents far fewer legal and logistical problems than introducing testing for existing employees.

04

Drugs and alcohol

Routine testing is done at specified times, and gives a clear message that it is not acceptable to be affected by alcohol when working. It might be used in situations where employees are in safety critical posts (such as operating or driving construction plant on a public road, or operating machinery).

Random testing or unannounced testing is used as a deterrent to identify previously undetected drug or alcohol misusers. As with routine testing, any use in situations that are not safety critical may cause feelings of resentment amongst the workforce.

Reason or 'with cause' testing might be used if a manager has reason to believe that an employee has been using drugs or drinking. This might be because of their behaviour or by physical signs (such as smelling alcohol). It may also form part of a post-incident or accident investigation.

Rehabilitation testing may be used where an employee has agreed to treatment and the treatment provider is testing to ensure compliance with a prescription (for example, urine testing to ensure that an individual who has been prescribed methadone is not using heroin as well as the prescribed dose). Similarly, testing may be introduced as part of a return to work agreement between employee and employer.

Is testing necessary?

Drug and alcohol testing is a controversial and complex issue that has scientific, ethical, legal, social, industrial and economic ramifications.

It is reasonable to expect employees to be unimpaired by drugs or alcohol whilst at work, but it could be argued that requiring an employee to undergo a test, without cause (randomly or without specific evidence that they are impaired), is unfair and intrusive.

Whether testing is appropriate or necessary should be carefully considered, as the damage to employer-employee relations can potentially outweigh the benefits.

Whilst acknowledging there may be some circumstances where there is a role for testing employees, *The independent inquiry into drug testing in the workplace* concluded:

 There is no justification for drug tests as a way of policing the behaviour of the workforce, nor is it an appropriate tool for dealing with most performance issues.

Whether you decide to introduce testing or not, it must be emphasised that it is not an end in itself. Drug testing is no substitute for good management practice and should never be introduced without:

- ☑ full co-operation from employees
- ☑ a programme of education for managers and employees
- ☑ robust systems for referral to adequately trained health professionals.

Before considering the introduction of a testing programme, employers should be able to fully answer the following questions.

- ☑ Why do we want to test? (What do we hope to achieve by it?)
- ☑ What substances will we test for?
- ☑ Which employees will we test?
- ☑ How will we select them?
- ☑ When will we test them (for example, routinely, randomly, pre-employment)?
- ☑ How often will we test?
- ☑ How will we test (for example, by what method)?
- ☑ Who is best placed to conduct the test (for example, independent company/laboratory, Occupational Health Department)?
- ☑ What will we do with a positive result?
- ☑ What training will be necessary and for whom?
- ☑ What will be the financial costs?
- ☑ What may be the other costs (for example, staff morale)?
- ☑ How will we involve the workforce and gain their consent?
- ☑ What will be our safeguards? (How do we ensure that test results are accurate and legally defensible?)

The conclusions that are drawn from these questions should guide you to a well thought-out and rational decision.

Methods of testing

The variety of methods can be confusing for employers, and each testing company will advocate the advantages of their particular approach. It is vital that those wishing to introduce a testing programme are clear about the requirements of each, and consider logistical issues (such as those listed above) as well as:

- ☑ gaining employee consent
- ☑ clear explanations of the process to employees
- ☑ collection of samples
- ☑ second sampling
- ☑ legal safeguards (chain of custody)
- ☑ employee confidentiality
- ☑ appropriate privacy.

There is a variety in both the methods used for employee testing and in the standards of service offered by drug-testing companies. As yet there is no universally accepted accreditation scheme or quality standard.

It should also be clearly understood that there is a significant difference between testing for alcohol and testing for other drugs.

Alcohol testing indicates whether an individual is under the influence **at that time**. Drug testing shows traces of drugs used in the past, but does not necessarily confirm impairment at the time of testing.

Testing for alcohol use

Alcohol use can be tested by:

- ☑ **breath testing** – a breathalyser measures the level of alcohol in the breath. This is convenient and inexpensive. Employees may be tested prior to commencing a shift, or immediately following an incident

- ☑ **blood testing** – this is the most accurate measure of alcohol in the body, although it is more invasive than a breath test. It is often inappropriate in a workplace setting due to lack of staff suitably trained to take samples.

Testing for drug use

Drug use may involve the use of illegal drugs, or prescribed and over-the-counter medicines. These can be detected by gaining samples from:

- ☑ **oral fluid** – not as invasive as other methods but a relatively new technology so may be expensive or inaccurate

- ☑ **hair** – not accurate for recent use, but depending on hair length the sample may reflect the individual's drug use pattern over a course of months

- ☑ **blood** – very invasive, but can be more accurate than sampling

- ☑ **urine** – potentially invasive, but a well-established science.

Disciplinary procedures

The majority of employers will have a disciplinary procedure in place. It may be appropriate to ensure the procedure covers the consumption of alcohol or drugs in the workplace. You may also wish for the policy to contain a provision that possession, dealing or trafficking in drugs will be reported to the police.

For a drug and alcohol policy to be effective, it is essential that it is consistent with disciplinary procedure.

Taking disciplinary action

Employees with a substance misuse problem or those suspected of misusing drink or drugs should have the same rights to confidentiality and support (or to any other company procedure, including those agreed with the recognised trades unions) as they would if they had any other medical condition, or if any other disciplinary matter were involved.

It can be very difficult for employees to discuss or openly admit to having a drink or drug problem, because of the stigma or fear of reprisals, or the difficulty they have facing up to the issue.

It should also be considered that HSE inspectors may, in appropriate circumstances, issue improvement and prohibition notices (refer to Chapter A02 The Health and Safety at Work Act) and if they were to find an employee under the influence of drink or drugs on site, they would have the option to take appropriate actions against the employer.

Appendix A – Sample template for developing a drug and alcohol abuse policy

<COMPANY>

Drug and alcohol abuse policy

Introduction

<Company> recognises that alcohol and drug abuse related problems are an area of health and social concern. It also recognises that a member of staff with such problems needs help and support from their employer.

The Company also recognises that alcohol and drug abuse problems can have a detrimental effect on work performance and behaviour. The Company has a responsibility to its employees and customers to ensure that this risk is minimised.

Accordingly, Company policy involves two approaches.

Providing reasonable assistance to the member of staff with an alcohol or drug abuse problem, who is willing to co-operate in treatment for that problem.

Disciplinary rules, enforced through disciplinary procedures, where the use of alcohol or drugs (other than on prescription) affects performance or behaviour at work, and where either (1) an alcohol or drug dependency problem does not exist or (2) where treatment is not possible or has not succeeded.

The Company does not have the internal resources to provide or arrange treatment or other forms of specialist assistance. Such services are provided by GPs, hospitals and other agencies. Through this policy the Company will seek both to assist a member of staff in obtaining such specialist help, and to protect their employment.

Assistance for a member of staff

The Company will, where possible, provide the following assistance to a member of staff:

- ☑ help the member of staff to recognise the nature of the problem, through referral to a qualified diagnostic or counselling service

- ☑ support them during a period of treatment. This may include a period of sick leave or approved other leave, continuation in post or transfer to other work, depending upon what is appropriate in terms of the staff member's condition and needs of the Company

- ☑ the opportunity to remain or return to work following the completion of a course of treatment, as far as is practicable, in either the employee's own post or an alternative post.

The Company's assistance will depend upon the following conditions being met:

- ☑ the Occupational Health Service/Company-approved doctor diagnoses an alcohol or drug dependency related problem

- ☑ the member of staff recognises that they are suffering from an alcohol or drug abuse problem and is prepared to co-operate fully in referral and treatment from appropriate sources.

The Company and its employees must recognise the following limits, regarding what assistance the Company can provide.

- ☑ Where a member of staff fails to co-operate in referral or treatment arrangements, no special assistance will be given and any failure in work performance and behaviour will be dealt with through the disciplinary procedure.

- ☑ If the process of referral and treatment is completed but is not successful, and failure in work performance or behaviour occurs, these will be dealt with through the disciplinary procedure.

- ☑ A member of staff's continuation in their post or an alternative post during or after treatment will depend upon the needs of the Company at that time.

Disciplinary action

In line with the Company's disciplinary procedure, the following will be regarded as serious misconduct:

- ☑ attending work and/or carrying our duties under the influence of alcohol or drugs

- ☑ consumption of alcohol or drugs whilst on duty (other than where prescribed or approval has been given).

Breach of these rules will normally result in summary dismissal, and only in exceptional cases will either notice or the reduced disciplinary action of a final written warning be applied.

Where a breach of these rules occurs, but it is established that an alcohol or drug abuse related problem exists, and the member of staff is willing to co-operate in referral to an appropriate service and subsequent treatment, the Company will **suspend** application of the disciplinary procedure and provide assistance as described above.

Staff who do not comply with the treatment suggested or continue to abuse alcohol or drugs will be subjected to the application of the disciplinary policy.

Continued

Procedures

Nature of the procedures

The procedures define management responsibilities and provide guidelines on:

☑ where assistance to a member of staff should be provided and the nature of and limits to such assistance

☑ the application of the Company's disciplinary procedure.

Through the Occupational Health Service/Company-approved doctor, the Company will provide advice and support to managers on:

☑ whether an alcohol or drug related problem exists

☑ progress in treatment

☑ re-establishment or continuation at work of a member of staff or other appropriate arrangements

☑ assistance to members of staff with alcohol or drug abuse related problems.

This does not include directly providing treatment or specialist help, which is the responsibility of GPs, hospitals and other agencies working in the field. The Occupational Health Service/Company-approved doctor, in close liaison with these persons and agencies, will assist staff referred in the following ways:

☑ through counselling, encouraging them to come to a better understanding of their problem and the benefits of seeking treatment or help

☑ providing advice and direction regarding obtaining treatment and specialist help

☑ assisting in continuing at or achieving a return to work.

Alcohol or drug abuse related problems can come to the notice of management through:

☑ failures in work performance or behaviour necessitating use of the disciplinary procedure. In such situations the procedure described above should be followed

☑ other means, whereby a member of staff seeks or agrees to accept assistance on a voluntary basis. In such situations, the procedures described above should be followed.

Situations where use of the disciplinary procedure is appropriate

Recognising the existence of a possible alcohol or drug abuse problem

Abuse of alcohol or drugs can affect performance and behaviour at work. This could be either through serious misconduct at work (where there is a direct and demonstrable breach of the disciplinary rules regarding alcohol or drug abuse at work), or where there is a falling off of standards of work performance or behaviour, and abuse of alcohol or drugs is a possible cause.

The immediate line manager will be responsible for responding to such situations, carrying out either counselling or disciplinary investigations and interviews, supported as appropriate by a more senior manager.

In such interviews the possible existence of an alcohol or drug abuse problem should be explored. The line manager is not required to diagnose the existence of an alcohol or drug abuse problem, merely to assess whether such abuse is a possible factor.

Any requirements of the disciplinary procedure regarding allowing the member of staff representation will be observed.

Diagnosing the existence of an alcohol or drug abuse problem

Should the interviews lead to the conclusion that an alcohol or drug abuse problem might exist and the member of staff accepts referral, the manager should refer the matter to the Occupational Health Service/Company-approved doctor, who will be responsible for establishing whether or not a diagnosis of alcoholism or drug dependence can be made.

Disciplinary action should be suspended until diagnostic advice is obtained. Where appropriate, suspension arrangements in the disciplinary procedure should be followed.

If the interview fails to lead to the conclusion that an alcohol or drug abuse problem exists, or the member of staff rejects or fails to co-operate in referral, disciplinary action should be continued, where and as the situation justifies.

Confirming that an alcohol or drug abuse problem exists and arranging treatment

If a positive diagnosis of an alcohol or drug abuse problem is made, and the member of staff agrees to co-operate in treatment, treatment arrangements should commence.

Where necessary, the Occupational Health Service/Company-approved doctor will advise the member of staff regarding treatment and will be responsible for monitoring progress and advising the manager concerned. This advice should be available at least monthly following commencement of treatment and thereafter as appropriate. (Disciplinary action should be discontinued unless the member of staff fails to co-operate with the treatment arranged.) Should a diagnosis of alcoholism or drug dependence not be confirmed, or should the member of staff refuse to co-operate in treatment, disciplinary action should be continued.

Continued

04

The Occupational Health Service/Company-approved doctor will advise on whether there is a lack of progress with treatment or lack of co-operation by the member of staff. Managers must then review the facts and consider whether or not there should be a return to the use of disciplinary procedures.

Where medical certificates are submitted, sick leave should be given. Should the employee continue to be fit for work during the period of treatment, they should be permitted to continue in their post (or alternative work), unless such an arrangement would have an adverse effect on Company services. In such circumstances, annual or unpaid leave should be approved or, exceptionally, suspension arranged.

If a member of staff has been off work during the period of treatment, before returning to duty, they will be seen by the Occupational Health Service/Company-approved doctor who will advise management regarding capability for continuation in their own post and whether any special supervision or other arrangements are required.

Every effort should be made to comply with the advice provided by the Occupational Health Service/Company-approved doctor. If it is not reasonably practicable to do so, and as a result the member of staff is not able to resume duty, employment may be terminated on the grounds of incapacity (ill health).

If a member of staff is again involved in disciplinary situations resulting from alcohol or drug abuse related problems, a second referral to the Occupational Health Service/Company-approved doctor and suspension of the disciplinary procedure may be appropriate. If they advise positively on the possibilities of further treatment or help and the willingness of the member of staff to co-operate, the disciplinary procedure may be suspended again to permit treatment and help to be undertaken. This second referral will not apply if the further disciplinary problems involve serious misconduct. Third and subsequent referrals are not permissible.

Situations where a disciplinary situation does not exist

There may be situations where the possible existence of alcohol or drug abuse problems affecting a member of staff come to a manager's attention, although there is, or has been, no discernible affect on work performance or behaviour. This could arise if a member of staff confides in their manager about an alcohol or drug abuse problem, or a manager sees a need to approach a member of staff after observing possible indicators of an alcohol or drug abuse problem (such as an absence pattern or information provided by the member of staff's colleagues).

In such situations, the Company would wish staff to feel they could seek help from their employer (in complete confidence) without worry that their job security would be in jeopardy. Accordingly, if managers should be faced with a situation of this type they should:

- ☑ seek the advice of the Occupational Health Service/Company-approved doctor regarding whether and how the matter could be dealt with

- ☑ counsel the member of staff and, if appropriate, arrange for the member of staff to be interviewed by the Occupational Health Service/Company-approved doctor.

As in the procedure described above, the Occupational Health Service/Company-approved doctor will play a facilitating role; seeking to establish whether a problem exists, and advising and directing the member of staff towards appropriate forms of treatment and help.

These steps cannot be taken without the co-operation of the member of staff. If the member of staff does not wish to co-operate, no further action should be taken.

Should a member of staff take up the opportunity of assistance on this voluntary basis there need be no further formal involvement of management in terms of action or the right to learn of progress with treatment. It may be, however, that the member of staff would wish, or agree to, further involvement of management as a means of assisting progress with treatment.

Use of the disciplinary procedures and/or the application of the approach described above would only be appropriate if, subsequently, the member of staff is involved in a breach of disciplinary rules.

Should the problems of the member of staff develop to an extent that their continuation in post or employment became impossible, it may be necessary to identify alternative work or arrange for termination, on the same basis as the Company operates for staff with problems of incapacity due to ill health.

<OPTIONAL SECTION>

Drug/alcohol testing

<Company> will ensure that all its employees work within the laws of the land. The UK laws on use of drugs and alcohol are clear:

- ☑ it is a criminal offence for certain workers (such as drivers or operators of public transport systems) to be unfit for their work due to taking drugs or alcohol

- ☑ it is a criminal offence to be unfit to drive, attempt to drive or be in charge of a motor vehicle when under the influence of drugs or alcohol

- ☑ the possession, supply or production of controlled drugs is unlawful except for in special circumstances (such as when they have been prescribed by a doctor).

Continued

Employees are also legally required to take reasonable care of themselves and to behave in a way that does not pose risks to the health and safety of themselves or others in the workplace. This includes consideration of the effects that intoxication through taking alcohol or drugs may have.

In order to ensure compliance with the law, <Company> will undertake drug/alcohol testing for certain key jobs within the Company. These will be carried out pre-employment, as part of a random testing scheme or as a result of an incident. These jobs are:

- ☑ <Insert jobs in Company that will be subject to testing – usually posts where safety is vital (such as driving or machine operating posts)>. The Company reserves the right to add to or amend this list as appropriate.

Individuals in these posts will be asked to agree to testing as part of their contract of employment.

To ensure the testing is legal and safe the following arrangements will apply:

- ☑ testing will only be carried out as part of this policy, and only by trained staff who will carry out the test in a non-invasive way – usually by urine sample or exhalation

- ☑ samples to be collected under supervised conditions but respecting human dignity. Two identical samples are taken, either on site or split in the test laboratory

- ☑ samples to be kept under chain of custody at all times

- ☑ screening test for alcohol/common drugs to be carried out on one sample with either positive or negative results

- ☑ any positive results from screening to be confirmed by approved scientific techniques

- ☑ results to be reviewed by an expert and reported back

- ☑ second sample to be kept for further analysis as part of any appeal by the employee

- ☑ confidentiality will be maintained at all times.

<Company> believes that effective workplace drug and alcohol policies are a better way of achieving results than drug/alcohol testing and that providing an environment where employees can discuss any drug/alcohol problems they have, with the prospect of gaining help and support, will be more effective than a testing regime. Therefore, the undertaking of drug/alcohol testing in the workplace will be minimal and used only where the Company has a reasonable belief that abuse is taking place.

04

Appendix B – Common drugs, effects and symptoms

With so many different drugs available and so much misinformation, it is difficult to find the right information about and help with drug abuse and drug addiction. As it is important for site managers or supervisors to identify, manage and support individuals with misuse, they should be aware of some of the common drugs, affects and symptoms.

Ecstasy

A Class A drug also known as MDMA, 'e', doves, mitsubishis, apples, rhubarb and custards or callies. It affects individuals with a buzz and intense pleasure, but also causes dizziness, disorientation, breathlessness and sickness. It increases the pulse-rate and can leave you feeling flushed, restless, anxious and maybe paranoid. Your jaw muscles tighten, pupils get bigger, energy increases and you may lose your appetite and desire to sleep. It enhances affection and energy but can make music and light seem even more intense. A penalty for its use or supply can range from a fine to life imprisonment and it is detectable in urine for two to four days.

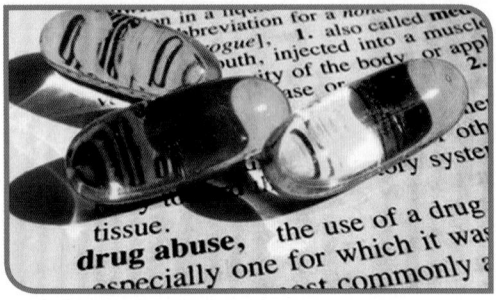

- ☑ A few people are sensitive or allergic to ecstasy, which can cause illness or death.
- ☑ If you have a heart condition, you could have a seizure.
- ☑ It can cause heat stroke, especially if you're in a hot club and dancing a lot, which can cause death as your internal organs stop working.
- ☑ Drinking too much water can also be dangerous as fluid can build up on your brain leading to unconsciousness, coma and even death.
- ☑ If you have an existing condition (such as epilepsy), ecstasy could trigger it.
- ☑ You may develop long-term mental health problems and depression.
- ☑ You could do permanent damage to your internal organs (liver, kidneys, heart and brain).

Cocaine and crack

A Class A drug also known as coke, charlie, gear, banger, snow, crack, rock, bones, stones or freebase. It is a powerful stimulant that speeds up your central nervous system, your heart rate and blood pressure increases and your pupils get bigger. It makes you feel really powerful, as though you can do anything, and it gives you more energy and awareness. The effects of crack are even more intense than coke and you get a much quicker hit, but the effects last for only a short time. A penalty for its use or supply can range from a fine to life imprisonment and it is detectable in urine from 12 hours to four days.

- ☑ You can very easily get hooked – developing a real craving for it, but feeling rough when it wears off.
- ☑ It can cause death, mainly from heart failure or internal bleeding.
- ☑ Regular crack users will almost certainly get breathing problems, because of damage to their lungs.
- ☑ If you snort cocaine regularly you can end up with a perforated septum (the wall between your nostrils).
- ☑ Even if you use cocaine only occasionally you could suffer from disrupted sleep patterns, appetite loss, fatigue, restlessness, anxiety and paranoia.
- ☑ It destroys some of the chemicals in your brain that control your mood, which can make you depressed and even suicidal.
- ☑ It increases adrenaline and this can cause restlessness, extreme paranoia and aggression.
- ☑ Mixing it with alcohol increases the risk of heart and liver damage.

Heroin

A Class A drug also known as smack, brown, H, gear, skag, harry, horse or jack. It is an analgesic, which makes you feel relaxed and acts as a powerful painkiller. It creates a sense of extreme pleasure and feeling good. Heavy use makes you sleepy, sedated and slurry. Many people are sick the first time they use it. A penalty for its use or supply can range from a fine to life imprisonment and it is detectable in urine for one to two days.

☑ There is a high risk of death from overdose, especially if you've been drinking alcohol or taking other depressants (certain types of drugs, like tranquiliser pills prescribed by doctors).

☑ Regular use often means you stop looking after yourself and stop caring about the way you look.

☑ Injecting increases the risk of dangerous infections and abscesses.

☑ Your cough reflex can be reduced for long periods, so you're more likely to get chest infections.

☑ Regular users commonly suffer from constipation.

☑ You can become tolerant quickly, so you need more heroin to get the same hit or stop getting withdrawal symptoms.

☑ If you stop taking heroin for a while your tolerance drops, which means that if you start again and take your normal dose, there is a greater risk of overdosing.

☑ Heroin is very physically addictive and though withdrawal is not fatal it is extremely unpleasant.

Ketamine

A Class C drug also known as K, special K, kettle or kit kat. It can make you feel disoriented, with a sense of numbness and a lack of co-ordination. Low doses can create a sense of extreme pleasure and mild hallucinations (K-holing – a feeling of travelling outside the body towards a tunnel of light). Effects shouldn't last for more than about three hours. A penalty for its use or supply can range from a fine to 14-years' imprisonment and it is detectable in urine for up to 14 days.

☑ Ketamine is an anaesthetic, which numbs pain, so you may injure yourself without realising it until the effects have worn off.

☑ There's a risk of mental health problems from the drug's disorientating experiences.

☑ It can cause sickness, headaches and diarrhoea, and may even paralyse you temporarily.

☑ If you drink alcohol or take other depressants (certain types of drugs, like tranquiliser pills prescribed by doctors), you increase the risk of heart failure, unconsciousness, vomiting and choking.

☑ Serious and permanent bladder problems can develop.

☑ If you inject Ketamine there are the usual risks of dangerous infections through using needles.

LSD

A Class A drug also known as tabs, trips, microdots, strawbs, blotter or acid. It takes between 30-60 minutes to take effect and the effects can last from 8 to 12 hours. Trips are unpredictable and vary hugely from person to person. The drug works on the brain causing changes to thoughts, senses and perceptions. It can cause visual disturbance, hallucinations, anxiety, dizziness or disorientation. A penalty for its use or supply can range from a fine to life imprisonment and it is detectable in urine for two to three days.

☑ The most common health risk is short or long-term psychological damage.

☑ It can trigger a range of mental problems and frequent long-term use can leave you feeling disorientated for quite a long time.

☑ Use of LSD can cause permanent eye damage.

☑ There is a risk that you could injure yourself when you've taken LSD, by doing something dangerous.

☑ You may experience flashbacks (re-living a few seconds or minutes of a trip) weeks, months or even years after taking it.

☑ It doesn't mix well with alcohol and cannabis, increasing the side effects (for example, sickness and anxiety).

Cannabis

A Class B drug also known as marijuana, hash, pot, weed, blow, gear, black, draw, herb, skunk or soap. It is a stimulant, depressant and hallucinogen. It can make you relaxed, giggly, hungry, and appreciate sound and colour more. You may feel anxious and paranoid and the effects can be unpredictable. A penalty for its use or supply can range from a fine to 14 years' imprisonment and it is detectable in urine for two to three days.

☑ Smoking cannabis, especially with tobacco, can cause lung damage, with an increased risk of lung and throat cancers.

☑ Regular use can cause short-term memory loss and make you feel demotivated and listless.

☑ There is an increased risk of mental health problems (such as anxiety and paranoia), which can last into adult life.

☑ It interferes with learning, so you'll find it harder to study and work.

☑ Side effects (such as nausea, palpitations and anxiety) are sometimes made worse by alcohol.

☑ If you become dependent you'll find stopping difficult, due to symptoms (such as sleep disturbance, vivid dreaming, mood swings, irritability and possible aggression, headache and tiredness).

☑ Cannabis can stay in your body for up to 30 days and so can show up positive in drug tests for some time after your last use.

Amphetamines

These are Class B drugs, but are Class A if prepared for injection. They are also known as speed, whizz, billy, crank, meth, pink champagne or amphet. They are stimulants, so they increase your heart rate and blood pressure and you feel more alert, talkative and have more energy. A penalty for its use or supply can range from a fine to seven years' imprisonment and it is detectable in urine for two to four days.

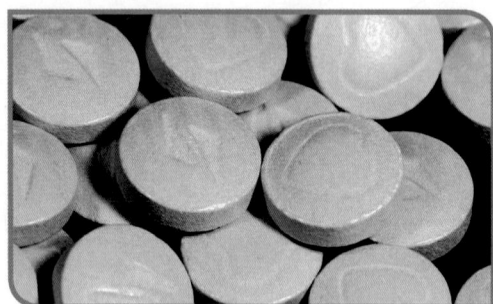

☑ Overuse can cause anxiety, panic attacks, irritability and aggressive behaviour, as well as weight loss and illness, because of eating poorly and generally not looking after yourself.

☑ Regular use can bring on a state of intense paranoia (feeling terrified of things around you).

☑ If you have a heart condition, there is a particular risk of death from heart problems.

☑ Depending on how you take it, an amphetamine can damage your nasal lining, gums or stomach. If you inject it, it can cause permanent damage to your body.

☑ It can also make your jaw feel tight, which can make you grind your teeth and chew constantly.

☑ Amphetamines can reduce your sexual sensitivity and performance.

☑ The comedown can cause aches and pains, hunger, tiredness, depression and loss of self-esteem.

☑ If you snort drugs, the lining of your nose often breaks and bleeds, and you can easily get an infection.

☑ Injecting amphetamines is especially dangerous. It can badly damage your veins and there is the added risk of catching a dangerous disease if you share equipment.

Benzodiazepine

A Class C drug but legal if you have a prescription for them and also known as nitrazepam, mogadon, lorazepam, ativan, flurazepam, clonazepam, rohypnol, roofies, temazepam, temazzies, librium, diazepam and valium. It relaxes you and reduces anxiety, your muscles feel less tense and it can also help you sleep. A penalty for its use or supply can range from a fine to 2-14 years' imprisonment and it is detectable in urine for one to two days.

☑ You may lose co-ordination, become forgetful and vague.

☑ You can become tolerant quickly, so after a few weeks the dose stops being effective.

☑ It can cause sleeplessness and anxiety if you take it for longer than a few weeks.

☑ It can cause vertigo, hypotension, loss of libido, urinary retention and blood disorders.

☑ If you are taking other depressants as well, there's a higher risk of overdose.

☑ If you crush and inject tablets, you're at risk of abscess-blocked veins as well as the usual risks of intravenous drug use.

Methadone

A Class A drug, only legal if it's prescribed, and also known as meth, linctus, green, juice and amps. It has similar effects to heroin, though longer acting (24 hours) and less intense. Some users experience an intense allergy-like itchiness. When prescribed for heroin users it can stop withdrawal symptoms for 24 hours, to allow them to gain control of their lives. A penalty for its use or supply can range from a fine to life imprisonment and it is detectable in urine for three to five days.

- ☑ Methadone is physically addictive and withdrawal can be longer and even more unpleasant than heroin.

- ☑ If you mix methadone with alcohol you are at more risk of passing out and, like heroin, your cough reflex is reduced, which means you could choke if you're sick.

- ☑ Overdose is common in users who are not used to the drug or have lost their tolerance.

- ☑ Injecting it or using undiluted 50 mg ampoules can lead to vein damage, and injecting crushed tablets carries serious risk of vein blocking and abscesses.

- ☑ Methadone is extremely poisonous to children.

Mephedrone

A Class B drug also known as M-Cat, MMCAT, MC, mieow, meow, 4MMC and plant fertiliser. It is a stimulant (increasing alertness and energy) with similar effects to cocaine, amphetamine and ecstasy. The effects can come on in a head rush and be overpowering, which can make you feel sick – more likely if you've been drinking or smoking cannabis. The effects of a single dose can last for at least an hour, although some people report it going on for much longer. A penalty for its use or supply can range from a fine to life imprisonment and it is detectable in urine for up to four days.

- ☑ Taking it carries some serious risks so should be treated with caution. These risks are greater if you use large doses, take it for extended periods of time, or combine it with other drugs.

- ☑ The biggest risk is heart failure, so if you have an existing heart problem or high blood pressure, you should especially avoid using it.

- ☑ Some prescribed medication can react badly with it.

- ☑ Drugs (such as mephedrone and ecstasy) can occasionally cause death because of a direct toxic effect on the body.

- ☑ Like other stimulants, it can cause jaw clenching and teeth grinding, which can damage your teeth.

- ☑ The comedown can make you feel exhausted, depressed, confused and disorientated, with a sore head. You won't be able to sleep properly after taking it.

Over-the-counter drugs

These come in three different types:

- ☑ **stimulants** – such as cough/cold treatments and decongestants, especially non-drowsy, such as Actifed Expectorant, Sinutab and Sudafed

- ☑ **depressants** – such as cough/cold linctuses, painkiller analgesic capsules, and diarrhoea preparations, such as Nurofen Plus, Paracodol, Feminax and Syndol

- ☑ **sedatives** – such as anti-histamines, cough/cold treatments and some night-time sleep aids, such as Piriton, Night Nurse, Benylin and Contac 400.

Stimulants can make you excited, alert, agitated and anxious, increase your heart rate and blood pressure. Depressants can cause mild euphoria, relaxation, detachment, decreased heart rate and blood pressure, increased effects of alcohol, and physical addiction. Sedatives can make you sleepy/drowsy even at normal dosages, and increase the effects of alcohol.

- ☑ Misuse of these products often mimics the classic symptoms of a clinical drug addiction, with physical and psychological effects.

- ☑ Dependence doesn't always mean you're regularly taking large daily quantities of a drug. You can become dependent by having to take a daily amount, under the maximum recommended dosage, over many years.

- ☑ You can become unintentionally addicted to an over-the-counter drug. You may have simply bought it to treat a physical complaint, without being aware that it could be addictive.

05

First aid

In the event of injury or sudden illness, failure to provide first aid could result in a casualty's death. The employer should ensure that an employee who is injured or taken ill at work receives immediate attention.

The Health and Safety (First Aid) Regulations require employers to provide adequate and appropriate equipment, facilities and personnel to ensure their employees receive immediate attention if they are injured or taken ill at work. These regulations apply to all workplaces, including those with less than five employees and to the self-employed.

Introduction	52
Key points	52
Definition of first aid	52
Assessing requirements	53
Equipment and facilities	54
Training and qualifications	56
Training records	58
Legislative requirements	58
Appendix A – Personal accident report	59
Appendix B – Recommended contents of first-aid boxes	61
Appendix C – The Health and Safety (First Aid) Regulations	62
Appendix D – What to do in an emergency	63

5.1   Introduction

The definition of adequate and appropriate will depend on the circumstances in the workplace. This includes whether trained first aiders are needed, what should be included in a first-aid box and if a first-aid room is required. Employers should carry out an assessment of first aid needs to determine what to provide.

First aid at work is covered by the Health and Safety (First Aid) Regulations, together with an Approved Code of Practice (ACoP) and guidance notes that provide further information on such matters as first-aid equipment and training. The regulations provide a flexible framework within which employers can develop effective first-aid arrangements appropriate to their workplace and the size of their workforce.

Under the regulations, duties are placed on employers to:

☑ provide adequate first-aid equipment and facilities appropriate to the type of work or operations undertaken

☑ appoint a sufficient number of suitable and trained people to render first aid to employees who are injured or become ill at work

☑ appoint a sufficient number of suitable people who, in the temporary absence of the first aider, will be capable of dealing with an injured or ill employee needing help from a medical practitioner or nurse, and who are able to take charge of first-aid equipment and facilities

☑ inform employees of the first-aid arrangements, including the location of equipment and personnel. This will require that notices be posted and signs displayed. Provision should be made for employees with language or reading difficulties.

The ACoP sets out the criteria for the provision of trained staff, equipment and facilities, and suggests four factors that will influence decisions:

☑ workplace hazards and risks

☑ the nature of the undertaking and its history of accidents

☑ the size of the establishment and distribution of employees

☑ the location of the establishment and the locations where employees go in the course of their work.

> 66 An employer shall inform his employees of the arrangements that have been made in connection with the provision of first aid including the location of equipment, facilities and personnel.

It is recommended that first-aid notices are displayed as an effective means of informing the workforce of the employer's arrangement for first aid.

There is no statutory form but a range of first-aid notices are available from the suppliers of workplace safety signs.

5.2   Key points

☑ Trained first-aid staff and first-aid equipment must be available on site.

☑ The level of provision of trained staff and first-aid equipment will depend upon several factors.

☑ Everyone working on site should know where the first aiders and the first-aid kits can be found.

☑ All accidents causing injury must be recorded in an accident book.

☑ In an emergency, assess the situation but do not put yourself in danger.

☑ Don't move casualties who are obviously injured unless it is necessary to do so – summon the first aider and dial 999.

☑ Cover severe bleeding with a clean pad and apply direct pressure.

☑ First aiders have the potential to save lives.

5.3   Definition of first aid

First aid is defined in the regulations as:

☑ in cases where a person will need help from a doctor or a nurse, treatment for the purpose of preserving life and minimising the consequences of injury or illness until such help is obtained

☑ treatment of minor injuries, which would otherwise receive no treatment or which do not need treatment by a doctor or nurse.

It should be noted that the definition covers any illness at work and not just accidents. You must, therefore, plan for times when someone has a heart attack or collapses.

Emergency first aiders can give a restricted range of first-aid treatment to someone who is injured or becomes ill at work. Fully trained first aiders can do the above, plus apply first aid to a range of specific injuries and illnesses.

5.4　Assessing requirements

Ambulance

The local ambulance service should be informed about large sites and of any particularly hazardous operations being undertaken. It is helpful to supply a map locating the site and its entrances and, where appropriate, the first-aid room.

Induction

Induction training for employees and other persons joining the site should include details of the location of first-aid boxes, qualified first-aid personnel and actions to be taken in cases of injury or illness.

Responsibility for visitors and other non-employees

The regulations require employers to make first-aid provision for their own employees. However, there is also a general duty upon employers in respect of their premises or activities with regard to people who are not their employees, and first-aid arrangements should extend to cover visitors and other non-employees.

Shared facilities

To avoid the unnecessary duplication of facilities where employees of more than one employer are working together, arrangements may be made to share facilities. Whilst there is no requirement for shared facilities to be formally recorded, industry best practice is that the arrangements are recorded in writing, with each employer retaining a copy.

In such circumstances, it is the responsibility of each employer to ensure that the agreed facilities are actually provided, and that all their employees are aware of these arrangements.

Self-employed persons

Self-employed persons must provide adequate first-aid equipment for themselves. Where the use of potentially dangerous tools and machinery present a hazard, an appropriate first-aid kit should be provided. If a self-employed person is working under an employer or with another self-employed person, it is the responsibility of each to provide first-aid equipment. Shared facilities may be used, subject to the procedures described above.

Trained and suitable personnel

First aiders must have received training and hold a current first-aid certificate issued by an organisation whose training and qualifications are approved by the Health and Safety Executive (HSE).

Where first aiders have received first-aid instruction relating to special or unusual hazards in the workplace, they should undergo refresher training and re-examination as necessary. The employer must keep a written record of such training.

First aid at work certificates, which have been issued by, or in, another country, are not valid in mainland Britain. Certificates are only valid if they have been issued by an HSE-approved training organisation (all of which are in mainland Britain).

Other persons not holding a certificate as described above, but with training and qualifications approved by the HSE for the purposes of the regulations, may be counted as, and act as, first aiders.

Number of first aiders required

The regulations and ACoP do not specify numbers but set out guidelines on the number of first aiders needed, dependent on the size of undertaking, the hazards present and the number of people employed.

The HSE publication *First-aid at work – Your questions answered* contains a table outlining the recommended number of first aid trained staff for various industry sectors and sizes of workplace.

For construction, which the table categorises as higher risk, the recommendation is as follows.

Number of employees/persons on site	Number of first aid trained staff required
Less than five.	At least one appointed person.
Five to 50.	At least one first aider or emergency first aider, depending upon the type of injuries that might occur.
More than 50.	At least one first aider per 50 employees or part thereof.

First aid

In determining the total number of qualified first aiders required, additional factors should be considered. These are:

- ☑ the type of work or operations being carried out
- ☑ whether or not employees work alone or in scattered and isolated locations
- ☑ whether there are special or unusual hazards
- ☑ whether or not there is shift work – first-aid cover will be required at all times that work is being carried out
- ☑ the maximum number of people likely to be on site at any one time
- ☑ the remoteness of emergency medical services
- ☑ cover for first aiders' holidays and sickness absence – first-aid cover will be required at all times that work is being carried out
- ☑ the presence of work-placement trainees.

Unless arrangements have been made for the sharing of first-aid cover and facilities, all contractors on the site must make their own provisions for their own employees.

On sites where special or unusual hazards are present, a proportionately larger number of first aiders, having regard to the factors already mentioned, will be needed. Good practice should encourage all the contractor's site personnel to be trained in basic emergency first aid.

On major construction projects where there is a site nurse and/or a doctor on call, their advice in connection with first aid should be followed.

 Provide 'tear and go' printed map/directions to the nearest Accident and Emergency Department, including phone number and sat-nav postcode.

Appointed persons

An appointed person is someone who has been nominated by the employer to take charge of a situation (for example, to call an ambulance if there is a serious illness or injury).

They will act in the absence of the trained first aider or in situations where it is deemed that a first aider is not required (such as in a small, non-hazardous working area) and where there is easy access to professional medical assistance (such as a hospital Accident and Emergency Department).

Emergency first-aid training should be considered for all appointed persons.

Appointed persons must not be regarded as an alternative to qualified first aiders and they must not be required to render first aid. The appointed person is responsible for first-aid equipment in the absence of the first aider or in the circumstances described above.

5.5 Equipment and facilities

Based upon the findings of an assessment, the employer must:

- ☑ provide and keep stocked suitable first-aid boxes and other appropriate equipment (such as eyewash stations and burns kit), as determined by a risk assessment, in places that can easily be accessed by all employees
- ☑ display notices giving the identity of first aiders and the location of first-aid equipment.

The very minimum that would be expected on any site is a small, basic first-aid kit. On larger sites several kits may be necessary at dispersed locations, and it is wise to consider providing small travelling first-aid kits for those operatives who work alone or in remote locations.

A travelling first-aid kit should be located in each company vehicle.

In situations where specific hazards exist, it will be necessary to consider providing more specialised first-aid equipment (such as rescue equipment and emergency showers).

Location of first-aid facilities

It is essential that all employees should have quick and easy access to first-aid facilities on site. Where employees are working in large numbers and in close proximity, facilities should be centralised in that area. When employees are spread over a wider area, it is necessary to distribute first aiders and equipment accordingly. Sometimes, a combination of these arrangements may be appropriate.

All employees must be aware of the location of first-aid facilities and the arrangements for providing treatment. The location of first-aid facilities should be clearly marked with the appropriate symbol.

First-aid boxes

Every employer must provide one or more first-aid boxes. They should be strategically placed, readily accessible and clearly marked with a white cross on a green background in accordance with the Health and Safety (Safety Signs and Signals) Regulations. The container should hold first-aid equipment and nothing else, and should protect the contents from dust and damp.

The recommended content of first-aid boxes is contained in the HSE publication *First aid at work.* Generally, medicines, pressure bandages and home remedies should **not** be kept in first-aid boxes.

It is essential that the contents of first-aid boxes are replenished after use and checked frequently by the first aider or appointed person. Some of the items are prone to deterioration after a certain period of time. The minimum recommended contents of the first-aid box are listed in Appendix A, which should be adjusted following an assessment of the first aid needs of a specific site.

Travelling first-aid kits

Special or small travelling first-aid kits should be provided to those employees:

☑ who are working alone or in small groups in isolated locations (such as maintenance gangs)

☑ whose work involves travel in remote areas

☑ who use potentially dangerous tools or machinery.

The first-aid kit should only contain the items as recommended in Appendix A.

Supplementary equipment

Where first aiders are employed, stretchers or appropriate carrying equipment (such as a carrying chair or wheelchair) should be provided in an accessible location, clearly identified by a sign. If a site covers a large area, or contains a number of distinct working areas, it will be necessary to provide such equipment at a number of suitable locations.

However, it is recommended that, in most incidents, casualties are moved as little as possible before the emergency services arrive.

First-aid rooms

On a large building or construction site, a first-aid room, suitably staffed and equipped, should be provided. The need for such a room cannot be decided purely on the numbers of persons employed, but should be assessed on the type of work being carried out and whether a hospital or other emergency facilities are close to hand.

The first-aid room will normally be under the control of the first aider who should be nearby or on call, with access to the room when employees are at work. The name of this person should be displayed, together with the names and locations of all other first aiders and appointed persons. On some larger sites, the first-aid room will be staffed by a qualified nurse.

The room should be clearly identified, available at all times and used only for rendering first aid. It should be of sufficient size to contain a couch, with adequate space around it to allow people to work, and have an access door to allow the passage of a stretcher or other carrying equipment. Pillows and blankets should be provided and be frequently cleaned.

The room itself should be cleaned each working day, have smooth-topped, impermeable working surfaces and provision for privacy and refuse disposal.

Heating, lighting and ventilation should be effective. In addition to the first-aid materials (see Appendix A), which should be stored in a suitable cabinet, there should be:

☑ a sink with running hot and cold water

☑ drinking water

☑ soap, nail brush and paper towels

☑ clean garments for use by first-aid personnel

☑ a suitable container for disposal of clinical waste (yellow bags).

In first-aid rooms that are supervised by the site nurse, other items may be provided on their advice.

The room should have a telephone, where possible, and a siren or klaxon to alert personnel on call.

A sufficient number of first aiders should be provided in any work area that is not within easy reach (approximately three minutes) of the first-aid room.

5.6   Training and qualifications

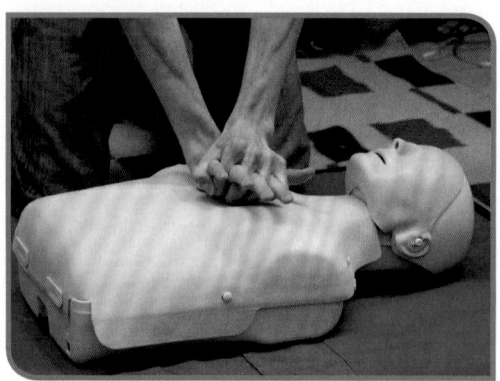

The employer is responsible for ensuring that those people who have been selected as fully qualified first aiders have undergone training and possess qualifications approved by the HSE. Additional training may be necessary to cope with any special hazards in a particular working environment.

The training of emergency first aiders (EFAW) may be carried out either by an HSE approved provider or a provider approved by the Standards and Testing Agency for first aid at work.

Instruction in emergency first aid (such as resuscitation, control of bleeding and treatment of unconsciousness) is desirable for all staff.

Initial selection of first aiders

Whilst it is desirable to appoint staff who have already received first-aid training and utilise their skills, in many instances this may not be an option. On most new sites it is unlikely that a trained first aider will be available, and it will be necessary to arrange training for a suitable member of staff.

In selecting people for this role, consideration should be given as to whether they:

- ☑ have a friendly, reassuring disposition
- ☑ are acceptable to male and female staff
- ☑ can cope with stressful and physically demanding emergency procedures
- ☑ are able to remain calm in an emergency
- ☑ are employed on a task that they can leave immediately in order to go to the scene of an emergency
- ☑ are capable of acquiring the knowledge and qualifications required.

Approval of training organisations

Any organisation or individual employer can seek approval to train first aiders, examine them and award certificates of qualification in first aid. The HSE's criteria for approval include the following:

- ☑ a syllabus that includes both theoretical and practical work, which must conform with HSE guidance
- ☑ suitable arrangements for conducting examinations
- ☑ examinations conducted by qualified, independent examiners not involved in the training of those being examined
- ☑ a programme of examinations that is appropriate
- ☑ qualified instructors conforming to the guidance issued by the HSE.

 More information can be found in the HSE publication *First-aid training and qualifications for the purposes of the Health and Safety (First Aid) Regulations 1981,* which is downloadable from the HSE website.

Fully qualified first aiders

Under the training regime, the full training course, including examination:

- ☑ will normally take three full days (18 classroom hours)
- ☑ need not be completed in a period of three consecutive days – split courses will be permitted.

On completion of the course, students must be able to demonstrate that they are able to:

- ☑ recognise minor and major illnesses
- ☑ act safely, promptly and effectively with emergencies at work
- ☑ use first-aid equipment, including the contents of the first-aid kit
- ☑ understand the duties of employers and the legal framework
- ☑ maintain simple, factual records on the treatment or management of emergencies
- ☑ recognise the importance of personal hygiene in first-aid procedures.

Students must also be able to deal with a casualty who:

- ☑ requires cardiopulmonary resuscitation
- ☑ is bleeding or wounded
- ☑ is suffering from shock
- ☑ is unconscious
- ☑ is suffering from an injury to bones, muscles or joints

- ☑ has an eye injury
- ☑ has been overcome by gas or fumes
- ☑ has been burned or scalded
- ☑ has been poisoned or exposed to a harmful substance.

Students must also be able to manage the transportation of the casualty as required by workplace circumstances.

It may be necessary to provide specialised instruction in the use of protective equipment or rescue techniques, where these are important in the trainee's workplace or if special hazards exist there.

Expiry of certificates

First-aid certificates are valid for three years. Re-qualification training, with re-examination, will be required before re-certification.

First aiders can undertake re-qualification training up to three months before the expiry of their current first-aid certificate. The new certificate will be dated to run on from the expiry date of the previous one. Ideally, employers will take advantage of this period.

However, where this is not possible or practical, re-qualification training can be taken within 28 days after the previous certificate expires.

Where, within the 28 day period, a student passes the re-qualification training, a certificate will be issued and backdated to the expiry of the previous one. If they fail to pass, the full first aid at work course must be taken again, and passed, in order for a certificate to be issued.

In effect, these arrangements provide employers with a four month window in which to get each first aider re-certificated.

Re-qualification training

Re-qualification training for fully qualified first aiders, including re-examination:

- ☑ must last at least 12 hours (two days)
- ☑ can be split over a longer period
- ☑ must be completed within a period of six weeks.

Refresher training

It is recommended that fully qualified first aiders attend a three-hour refresher course each year to brush up on their basic skills and learn about new techniques and developments.

In this context, the term 'refresher training' must not be confused with what is now called 're-qualification training', but which at present is still referred to as 'refresher training' in the ACoP.

First aiders for special or unusual situations

First aiders should have completed training in the subjects described for first aiders, and been given any specialised training related to the particular requirements of their workplace and its hazards.

Some workers carry their own medication (such as inhalers for asthma) or Epipens, which contain injectable adrenaline for the treatment of severe allergic (anaphylactic) reactions (for example, to peanuts). These medications are prescribed by a doctor. If an individual needs to take their own prescribed medication, the first aider's role is limited to helping them do so and contacting the emergency services as appropriate.

Emergency first aiders

Emergency first aiders must undertake a six-hour approved course, with their certificate being valid for three years. As with fully qualified first aiders, the HSE recommends that emergency first aiders undertake an annual three-hour basic skills update and refresher course.

To re-qualify and retain their certification for a further three years, emergency first aiders must retake the six-hour course within their three-year qualification period.

Appointed persons

Training courses normally last four hours and cover the following subjects:

- ☑ what to do in an emergency
- ☑ cardiopulmonary resuscitation

- ☑ first aid for the wounded or bleeding
- ☑ first aid for an unconscious casualty.

HSE approval is not required for this training.

5.7   Training records

In order to be able to demonstrate compliance with the regulations, employers must keep written records of all training that has been given to employees, along with results of that training.

Record of treatment

First-aid treatment should be recorded. The use of an accident book does not normally allow enough detail to be gathered and an additional treatment book may be necessary, particularly in order to keep a record of the use of first-aid materials.

Accident records

Employers are required to keep accident records under the requirements of the Social Security (Claims and Payments) Regulations.

Records can be stored in any medium, including electronic, providing that printable copies are readily available if required.

Records must include details of:

- ☑ date, time and place of accident
- ☑ name and job of injured or ill person
- ☑ details of injury/illness and what first aid was given
- ☑ what happened to the person immediately afterwards (for example, went home, to hospital, back to work)
- ☑ name and signature of the first aider or person dealing with the incident.

Details of an accident should be recorded by the injured person, but can be completed by any employee. However, some employers insist that records are completed by first aiders, which requires a first aider to be available at all times. This is a company operating procedure and is not strictly necessary.

Completion of an accident record does not meet the employer's obligation to report specific accidents and dangerous occurrences to the HSE or Local Authority.

This information can help identify accident trends and possible areas for improvement in the control of health and safety risks.

All accident records have had to comply with the Data Protection Act to ensure the confidentiality of entries. Accident Book BI 510 (available from HSE Books) enables each accident record to be detached and stored separately when complete, thus maintaining the confidentiality of the injured person's details. All personal information must be kept in confidence, and in a secure location (such as a lockable cabinet).

Accident books designed and produced in-house may still be used, provided that:

- ☑ all details required by BI 510 are recorded
- ☑ the requirements of the Data Protection Act are met
- ☑ information recorded electronically can be made readily available in hard copy.

5.8   Legislative requirements

The Reporting of Injuries, Diseases and Dangerous Occurrences Regulations

The RIDDOR Regulations require the following to be reported directly to the appropriate enforcing authority (either the nearest HSE office or the Local Authority):

- ☑ fatalities and major injuries
- ☑ injuries resulting in incapacity for more than seven days when linked to certain work activities
- ☑ specified diseases
- ☑ dangerous occurrences.

People covered by the regulations include:

- ☑ employees
- ☑ self-employed
- ☑ other people who have been injured.

 Trainees are not specifically mentioned within these regulations, but other regulations require that all trainees, including non-employed trainees, must be treated as employees for all health and safety purposes.

Appendix A – Personal accident report

1. Name of employer

2. Site address

    Contact

3. Injured person's surname   Forenames

4. Injured person's address

5. National Insurance no.   Age   Clock no.

6. Normal occupation

7. Occupation at time of accident

8. Exact location of accident

9. Date and time of accident

10. Date and time of ceasing work

11. Precise nature of injury (if eye or limb, state left or right)

12. To who was the accident reported?   Date   Time

13. Entry made in accident book on

14. HSE or Incident Contact Centre informed by telephone, fax or email

    Date   Time

15. F2508 report sent to the HSE on

16. Accident recorded in the official company register (if applicable)

17. Was first aid given on site?

    If treatment was received from a doctor, state name

18. Did the injured person go to hospital?

    Give name of hospital

19. Was the injured person authorised to be at the place of the accident for the purpose of their work?

20. How was the accident caused?

    a) Give a full description of what happened

    b) State what the injured person was doing at the time

    c) If falls of persons from heights or into excavations or holes are involved, state distance of fall in metres

Continued

21. What action has been taken to prevent a recurrence?

22. If machinery was involved

    a) give name and number of machine or part causing the accident

    b) was it working at the time of the accident?

23. Names and addresses of witnesses to the accident. Always obtain witnesses wherever possible.

    a)

    b)

    c)

    Attach signed statements from each witness whenever possible.

24. Use a separate sheet of paper for a sketch plan of the scene.

This form was completed by:

Name   Signed   Date

To be completed by Head Office

Further medical reports on injured person   Date

Injured person ceased employment   Date

New address for injured person

Appendix B – Recommended contents of first-aid boxes

Item	Quantity in first-aid boxes	Quantity in travelling first-aid kits
Guidance card	1	1
Individually wrapped sterile adhesive dressings (assorted sizes)	20	6
Sterile eye pads, with attachment	2	Nil
Individually wrapped triangular bandages	4	2
Safety pins	6	2
Medium-sized, individually wrapped, sterile, unmedicated wound dressings (approximately 12 cm x 12 cm)	6	Nil
Large, sterile, individually wrapped, unmedicated wound dressings (approximately 18 cm x 18 cm)	2	1
Individually wrapped, moist cleaning wipes (suggested minimum number)	Nil	6
Disposable gloves (pair)	1	1

Where tap water is not readily available for eye irrigation, sterile water or sterile normal saline (0.9%) in sealed disposable containers should be provided.

Travelling first-aid kits

Small, travelling first-aid kits are designed for use where the workforce is dispersed widely (possibly with hazardous tools), for self-employed persons, and for employees working away from their employer's establishment.

First-aid kits purchased from major chemists or suppliers will conform to the regulations and vary in size to cater for the numbers of people employed.

05

Appendix C – The Health and Safety (First Aid) Regulations

Checklist

First-aid provision

- ☑ How many employees are involved?
- ☑ How is the workforce distributed/grouped (is it widely dispersed)?
- ☑ Are remote locations involved?
- ☑ Are shifts worked?
- ☑ What is the nature of the work?
- ☑ Does it involve special operations?
- ☑ Can particular hazards be identified (such as falls, electric shock, dangerous substances)?
- ☑ How many first aiders are needed – consider holiday and sickness cover?

Training

- ☑ Which personnel require first-aid training?
- ☑ Does the training offered meet foreseeable needs?
- ☑ Is there a system to trigger a warning to management when a first aider is within three months of their certificate expiring?
- ☑ Are training records kept?
- ☑ Are individuals, who are working in isolated locations, trained to cope with emergencies?
- ☑ Where appointed persons are in charge, do they understand their duties?
- ☑ Does induction training cover first-aid arrangements?

Equipment

- ☑ Is first-aid equipment placed in locations where it is likely to be needed?
- ☑ Does it meet foreseeable needs and special hazards?
- ☑ Are travelling first-aid kits available when required?
- ☑ Is a first-aid room needed, or available, and suitably equipped?
- ☑ Are information signs provided?
- ☑ Are first-aid boxes and kits properly stocked and maintained?

General

- ☑ Has responsibility for first-aid provision and organisation been assigned to an individual?
- ☑ Are there established procedures for reviewing:
  - training and equipment needs
  - new work processes
  - special operations
  - changes in work patterns
  - site locations
  - size of labour force
  - arrangements with contractors?

Appendix D – What to do in an emergency

General first-aid guidance is given in the HSE publication *Basic advice on first aid at work.* The information in this leaflet, which is reproduced below, is not intended as a substitute for effective training.

Priorities

☑ Assess the situation – do not put yourself in danger.

☑ Make the area safe.

☑ Assess all casualties and attend first, to any unconscious casualties.

☑ **Send for help – do not delay.**

Follow the advice given below.

Check for consciousness

If there is no response to gentle shaking of the shoulders and shouting, the casualty may be unconscious. Your priorities are to:

☑ shout for help

☑ open the airway

☑ check for normal breathing

☑ take appropriate action.

The priority is to check the **A**irway, **B**reathing and **C**irculation. This is the **ABC** of resuscitation.

A – Airway

To open the airway:

☑ place one hand on the casualty's forehead and gently tilt the head back

☑ remove any obvious obstruction from the casualty's mouth

☑ lift their chin with two fingertips.

B – Breathing

Look along the chest, and listen and feel at the mouth for signs of normal breathing, for no more than 10 seconds.

If the casualty is breathing:

☑ place in the recovery position and ensure the airway remains open

☑ send for help

☑ monitor that the casualty continues to breathe until help arrives.

If the casualty is not breathing:

☑ send for help

☑ start chest compressions (see CPR below).

C – CPR

To start chest compressions:

☑ lean over the casualty and, with your arms straight, press down (4–5 cm) on the centre of the breastbone, and then release

☑ repeat at a rate of about 100 times a minute (more than one compression per second!)

☑ after 30 compressions, open the airway again

☑ pinch the casualty's nose closed and allow the mouth to open

☑ take a normal breath and place your mouth around the casualty's mouth, making a good seal

☑ blow steadily into the mouth while watching for the chest rising

☑ remove your mouth from the casualty and watch for the chest falling

☑ give a second breath and then start 30 compressions again without delay

☑ continue with chest compressions and rescue breaths in a ratio of 30:2 until qualified help takes over or the casualty starts to breathe normally.

Bleeding

In the case of severe bleeding:

- ☑ apply direct pressure to the wound
- ☑ raise and support the injured part (unless broken)
- ☑ apply a dressing and bandage firmly in place.

Broken bones and spinal injuries

If a broken bone or spinal injury is suspected, **obtain expert help**. **Do not move casualties** unless they are in immediate danger.

Burning clothing

To extinguish the burning clothing of anyone involved in a fire, lay, push or knock the person to the floor to reduce the spread of flames. Cover the burning area with a blanket, coat or other item to smother the flames but do not use synthetic materials (for example, polyester). **Do not remove any of the victim's clothes.**

Apply large amounts of water to the area of the burns as quickly as possible to cool the affected parts, and then keep them wet with more water. Seek medical help urgently (call 999).

Burns

Burns can be serious so, if in doubt, **seek medical help**. Cool the part of the body affected with cold water until pain is relieved. Thorough cooling may take 10 minutes or more, but this must not delay taking the casualty to hospital.

Certain chemicals may seriously irritate or damage the skin. Avoid contaminating yourself with the chemical. Treat in the same way as for other burns but flood the affected area with water for 20 minutes. Continue treatment even on the way to hospital, if necessary. Remove any contaminated clothing that is not stuck to the skin.

Cold burns

The release of liquid propane onto unprotected skin will cause cold burns. This is due to the rapid vaporisation of the liquid, withdrawing heat from the affected area of the body.

The release of liquid, or significant amounts of gas at vessel pressure, can also cause the adjacent fittings to cool. This may be sufficient to cause cold burns if the fittings are subsequently touched by unprotected hands.

Suitable skin and eye protection must be worn whenever there is the possibility of a release of liquefied petroleum gas (LPG).

In the event of a cold burn, treat as for a burn from a hot object. Flush with copious amounts of cold water and seek medical help (call 999).

Electric shock emergencies

On a construction site, a plan should be prepared for potential emergencies, including electric shock. This is a requirement of the Management of Health and Safety at Work Regulations.

The plan should include:

- ☑ posting notices in appropriate and prominent places, publicising the emergency procedures
- ☑ training sufficient workers in the procedures to follow when treating an electric shock casualty, including first aid action
- ☑ instructing workers in the action to take in the event of someone receiving an electric shock (for example, switching off the electrical supply and calling the emergency services).

Eye injuries

All eye injuries are potentially serious. If there is something in the eye, wash it out with clean water or sterile fluid from a sealed container to remove loose material. **Do not attempt to remove anything that is embedded in the eye.**

If chemicals are involved, flush the eye with water or sterile fluid for at least 10 minutes, whilst gently holding the eyelids open. Ask the casualty to hold a pad over the injured eye and send them to hospital.

06

Personal protective equipment

During the course of their work, building and construction workers will have to wear some items of personal protective equipment (PPE), such as safety helmets, high-visibility vests, gloves, light eye protection and safety footwear, as a matter of course.

Other PPE will have to be provided and worn as required, as indicated by the findings of a risk assessment or safe system of work.

Introduction	66
Key points	66
Risk management	66
Using PPE in practice	67
Hearing protection	68
Eye protection	69
Respiratory protection	73
Skin protection	76
Head and foot protection	77
Clothing and other protection	79
Legal duties	80
Appendix A – Laser health risks and control	82

6.1   Introduction

Personal protective equipment (PPE) is any item of equipment or clothing that is used or worn by a person to protect them from any identified risk to their health or safety. A sub-group of that, designed to protect the wearer against respiratory (breathing) hazards (such as the inhalation of dust and fumes), is known as respiratory protective equipment (RPE).

Within the construction industry PPE is commonly thought of as equipment that is used to protect the head, ears, eyes, respiratory (breathing) system, skin, hands and feet.

However it must be appreciated that PPE is also commonly used during construction activities to:

- ☑ prevent or arrest falls (for example, harnesses and lanyards)

- ☑ enable a person in distress to be rescued from a confined space (for example, a rescue harness or escape RPE)

- ☑ enable someone who has fallen into water to stay afloat and be rescued (for example, a life jacket).

If it is found necessary for employees to wear PPE, its selection and use must comply with the Personal Protective Equipment at Work Regulations, to ensure that it will effectively protect the user against the hazard for which it has been selected.

All PPE must bear the CE-mark to show conformity with European Standards. When employers are deciding how best to protect employees from a risk to their health and safety at work, the decision to issue PPE may only be made where it is found that the risk cannot be adequately controlled by other means that are equally or more effective. In effect, the issue and use of PPE is the last resort in terms of risk control.

PPE must be selected by a competent person who, if necessary in conjunction with the suppliers, can identify the PPE that will be effective against the hazards present in the workplace. An example of this is the selection of the correct type of respirator or filter to protect the user against the various types of airborne substances, either particles or gases.

It must be remembered that failure of an item of PPE, or the wrong type of PPE being used, could expose an employee to the possibility of occupational ill health, serious injury or death.

06

6.2   Key points

- ☑ The correct use of PPE is essential in many cases to protect the wearer from harm.

- ☑ Given the nature of most construction sites, the use of some mandatory items of PPE (such as safety helmets and safety footwear) is a daily occurrence.

- ☑ However, it must be remembered that the use of PPE as a means of protecting against risks to health or safety is the last resort; it only protects the wearer and only then if it is:
  - the right PPE for the job
  - in good working order
  - being used properly.

- ☑ Employers have a legal duty to investigate the use of other protective measures before resorting to the issue of PPE.

- ☑ Employees must look after the PPE that has been issued to them and inform their employer if it becomes defective, damaged or is lost.

- ☑ Employees have a legal duty to be supplied the necessary PPE free of charge.

- ☑ RPE is a sub-group of PPE.

6.3   Risk management

After carrying out a risk assessment and establishing the hazards associated with a particular job, the employer must then implement measures to control the risks to health and safety. This may involve the identification and issue of appropriate PPE. However, PPE must only be selected as a means of controlling risks as a last resort.

All other methods of controlling the risks arising from the work activity must have been considered and found not to be reasonably practicable before the decision is taken to rely upon PPE for protection.

It must be remembered that for PPE to be fully effective, the user must have received adequate training and instruction in its use and it must:

- ☑ have been designed to protect the user against the type of hazard that will be present

- ☑ be available at all times that it is needed

- ☑ be adjusted properly where necessary

- ☑ fit the wearer properly and be compatible with other PPE worn at the same time

- ☑ be worn/used during the period(s) of risk

- ☑ be treated with care and returned to its storage after use, where this is necessary

☑ be inspected and maintained as necessary

☑ be replaced if it becomes defective.

Failure of an item of PPE, or using the incorrect type of PPE, could expose an employee to the possibility of serious injury, ill health or even death.

Consultation with employees

Employers are likely to be far more successful in persuading employees to wear the PPE provided if the employees themselves are involved in the process of selecting the PPE purchased.

PPE can be cumbersome and uncomfortable and the cheapest may not be the most suitable for the wearer. In such circumstances the likelihood is that it will not be worn, at least not for long, leaving the worker unprotected against the hazard.

It is much better to purchase PPE that fits comfortably and will be used willingly.

6.4   Using PPE in practice

Construction industry workers will have the need to wear or use PPE on many occasions. They will wear/use it for one of two reasons, because:

☑ they have been told to (site rules)

☑ it makes sense.

The more often that it is done for the second reason, the better. In circumstances when wearing or using PPE is necessary it must become second nature for those workers who are at risk. However, at present this is still often not the case. For example:

☑ cases of occupational asthma and dermatitis show that PPE that protects the skin and respiratory system are not being used where they should. The problem is not being taken seriously either by employers, supervisors or employees

☑ deaths have occurred through falls, either because a harness and lanyard were not being worn or because they were worn but the free end of the lanyard was not clipped onto a suitable anchorage point.

There is the temptation to ignore the need to wear PPE and the protection it gives because 'the job will only take a minute' … and that 'minute' may be all the time that the job needs to kill or injure someone.

The PPE selected must offer the level of protection required for the hazard(s) that have been identified. For example, whether the job involves:

☑ the use of substances that have the potential to create hazardous dust or fumes

☑ the use of substances that could irritate or burn the skin

☑ creating airborne dust through cutting, grinding, and so on

☑ creating fumes from hot-work processes

☑ any process that could result in eye injuries

☑ working at height in circumstances where the wearing of a harness and lanyard is the only practical fall protection measure.

 As well as assessing PPE for the task you must also assess any additional PPE requirements for the surrounding site conditions or from others (such as noise, dust, fumes, falling objects and so on).

Manufacturers and suppliers have a statutory duty to provide information regarding the performance characteristics of the PPE products that they manufacture/sell. If necessary, they should be consulted.

For some basic PPE (such as a pair of general safety spectacles) the exact fit may not be an issue. However, in selecting some PPE, achieving a satisfactory fit is essential, for example:

☑ when a respirator is to be used, the effectiveness of the device is dependent upon the face fit, which in turn will require that the head-harness straps be adjusted to suit the wearer and their facial features

☑ adjusting the head-harness of a safety helmet to suit the wearer will ensure that it is comfortable and secure

☑ gloves should be a close fit to protect from chemical ingress, entanglement and to maximise dexterity. Buying gloves in one size only should be avoided

☑ adjusting the fit of a safety harness, which could at worst have to take the shock loading of an arrested fall, is essential if the harness is to be fully effective.

Where a satisfactory fit is not, or cannot, be achieved, the wearer is likely to suffer discomfort and is much more likely to stop using the PPE and also lose concentration regarding the job in hand.

Co-operation between the employee must be established in the selection of comfortable and acceptable PPE.

06

Personal protective equipment

 Consider the potential wearers' physical needs. If they wear glasses and have to wear a mask, goggles or safety glasses, they may require a special type. If they have a beard and have to wear respiratory equipment, can they obtain an airtight seal? These are crucial considerations.

Supervisors must ensure that employees understand 'why', 'what', 'who', 'how' and 'when' there is a need for PPE.

☑ **Why** is the PPE needed?

☑ **What** will be the implications of not wearing it?

☑ **Who** is going to provide the PPE along with all necessary information, instruction, training and supervision?

☑ **How** is it fitted, worn or adjusted?

☑ **When** must it be worn?

! Protection is available for the hazard that you are about to work with. Find it and use it.

Combinations of personal protective equipment

In many circumstances it will be necessary for operatives to simultaneously wear more than one item of PPE.

Whilst this is entirely acceptable, attention should be given to ensuring that the different types of PPE are compatible with each other, to avoid the possibility of a dangerous situation.

For example, hearing protectors that are fitted directly to a safety helmet will not be effective if the safety helmet is poorly fitted and, by moving around on the head, does not allow the hearing protectors to form an effective seal around the ears.

Counterfeit PPE

The British Safety Industry Federation (BSIF) is a trade body which, amongst other things, represents the interests of the manufacturers of PPE within the United Kingdom.

In recent years the BSIF has become aware of the emergence of counterfeit PPE which, in many cases, looks identical to genuine PPE produced by reputable manufacturers. Much of the counterfeit PPE comes into the UK from abroad.

It is likely that the people within companies who are responsible for purchasing and issuing PPE will be unable to distinguish counterfeit and non-conforming items from the genuine article. Frequently these products are incorrectly (fraudulently) CE marked and do not perform to the required standard. The wearer or user of the PPE will almost certainly be unaware of any problems until it is too late.

It is recommended that PPE is only purchased from reputable suppliers and offers of unduly cheap PPE are resisted.

6.5 Hearing protection

Many types of building and construction activity and equipment generate excessive noise, which can cause permanent hearing damage in those exposed to it, unless appropriate control measures are put into place.

Excessive noise can also cause annoyance, fatigue, loss of concentration and disrupted communication, and may lead directly or indirectly to an increased risk of accidents. Whilst the law requires that the use of PPE as a control measure is only considered as the last resort, the practicalities of working in a construction site environment mean that hearing protection is often the only way of controlling personal exposure to noise.

There are two basic types of hearing protection:

☑ earplugs (either disposable or reusable)

☑ ear defenders.

Hearing protection helps block out hazardous noise. The amount of noise blocked out or reduced is known as attenuation.

To achieve the stated attenuation levels of hearing protection it is vital that it is worn correctly.

Disposable earplugs

These are made of very fine mineral fibre, sometimes ready shaped. They must be inserted correctly and, if taken out, should not be reused. They should only be handled with clean hands.

When it comes to protection from hazardous noise, earplugs are designed to be a safe distance from the sensitive eardrum, even when deeply inserted.

Employees need to be instructed on how to insert disposable earplugs correctly. Disposable earplugs are frequently worn incorrectly, by users not inserting them deeply enough.

A poorly fitted foam earplug actually offers little or no protection from noise.

Reusable earplugs

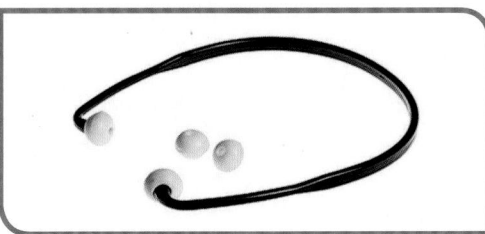

These are made of rubber or plastic, and need regular and careful washing. They must be a good fit. A competent person should be responsible for instructing employees in their correct fitting and use. Different sizes may be required for each ear.

Reusable earplugs, like disposable ones, must be fitted with clean hands, as any contamination by dirt, grease or swarf may cause ear irritation.

Ear defenders

Ear defenders, sometimes referred to as earmuffs, completely cover the ear, and are sealed to the head with a foam or liquid-filled seal. Badly designed or badly produced ear defenders may give little or no protection against the noise.

Ear defenders can be worn over safety glasses but the determining factor is the width of the eyeglass frame where it meets the earmuff cushion. Thin frames (thickness of 2 mm or less) cause very little obstruction to the seal, resulting in no measurable change in attenuation of the earmuff. Thick frames (thickness of 6 mm or more, typically seen on safety glasses with adjustable sidebars) can reduce attenuation by 5-8 decibels. If the workers must wear earmuffs over safety glasses, choose thin frames for best attenuation.

 For further information refer to Chapter B13 Noise.

6.6   Eye protection

Key points

- ☑ Many eye injuries occur to people at work each year because eye protection is not being worn.
- ☑ These accidents are easily preventable simply by wearing the correct type of eye protection.
- ☑ The loss of sight, even in one eye, will have a profound effect on the sufferer and is likely to affect future job prospects and earning power.
- ☑ Given the nature of most construction sites, in many cases protection of the eyes will be achieved by the issue and wearing of appropriate PPE.
- ☑ In common with other types of PPE, employers must:
  - identify the correct type of eye protection necessary
  - provide it at no charge to employees who need it
  - provide adequate information, instruction and training in its use
  - make sure that it is worn.

Personal protective equipment

☑ Users of eye protection must:
  - wear it when there is a risk of eye injury as indicated by a risk assessment
  - look after it, particularly with regard to protecting the lenses or face shield
  - return it to any accommodation allocated to it when not in use
  - report to the employer any defect (such as scratched or crazed lenses) and obtain a replacement
  - report to the employer if it is lost and seek a replacement.

Wear eye protection

The Control of Artificial Optical Radiation at Work Regulations (AOR) came into effect in 2010 and apply to a limited number of construction industry activities.

There are, on average, 1,000 injuries to people's eyes every working day. Some injuries are so severe that they cause partial or even total blindness. A person's eyes are very vulnerable and an accident or injury can completely change that person's way of life.

Analysis of the injuries to people's eyes shows that damage is caused as follows:

☑ 75% by impact

☑ 10% by abrasion following ingress of dust or other foreign body

☑ 15% by burns or chemical contamination.

The majority of these injuries would have been prevented if the correct eye protection had been worn.

The Personal Protective Equipment at Work Regulations, make provision for the protection of the eyes of employees at work, and also persons not employed, who may be at risk.

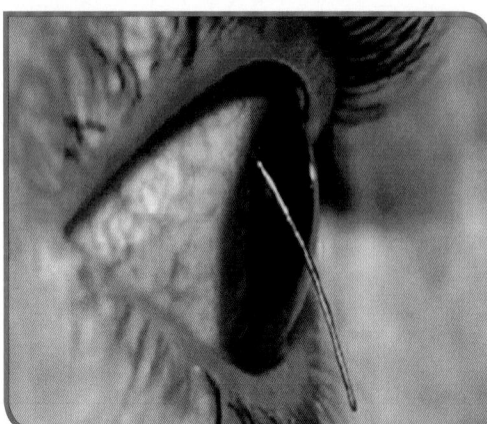

The protection provided must conform to the approved specifications and includes goggles, visors, spectacles, face screens and fixed shields, either free standing or attached to machinery or plant.

Construction personnel engaged in a wide range of activities (for example, grinding, welding, cutting, hammering, and handling chemicals) run the risk of eye injury. The risks include:

☑ impact of solids

☑ ingress of liquid, dust or gas

☑ splashes of hot metal

☑ exposure to glare.

All types of eye protection must:

☑ comply with European Standard specifications

☑ suit the type of work or risk involved – including resistance to impact, heat, dust and chemical penetration

☑ suit the user to ensure minimum discomfort and ease of movement whilst working

☑ be marked to identify their type and suitability

☑ be kept clean and disinfected.

Eye protectors and shields

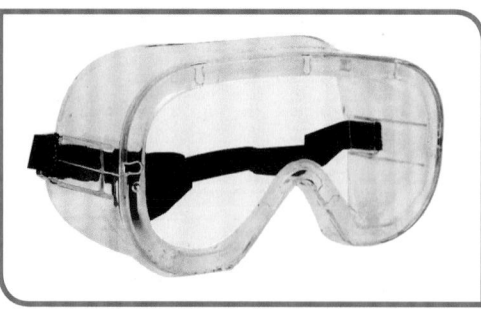

Issue and availability

Eye protectors should be:

☑ issued on a personal basis to the person at risk

☑ maintained and readily available in sufficient numbers for persons occasionally employed.

Replacement of eye protectors

Eye protectors should be kept available in sufficient numbers so if any become lost, destroyed or defective they can be replaced.

Construction and marking

All eye protectors and shields provided must comply with British and European Standard specifications and be:

☑ suitable for the type of work or risk involved

☑ suitable for the user to give them minimum discomfort and ease of movement whilst working

☑ marked to identify their type and suitability

☑ maintained, kept clean and disinfected.

Fixed shields

Fixed shields provided must:

- ☑ conform to the relevant European Standard specification
- ☑ be cleaned regularly, disinfected and properly maintained
- ☑ be so constructed and kept in position as to protect the eyes.

Identifying the type of hazard

Only when the employer has carried out a risk assessment to determine the hazards can the correct type of eye protector be supplied.

Some of the types of hazard detailed require eye protectors to have sufficiently strong lenses or shield to withstand the impact of particles or fragments striking them.

The effectiveness of the seal made between the eye protectors and the operator's skin is very important in affording protection against the type of hazard where irritant or corrosive materials are involved.

The ability to withstand high temperatures or reduce strong light and glare is a main requirement for the other types of eye protector.

 For further information concerning specific requirements or combinations of different kinds of protection, manufacturers' literature should be consulted.

Types of eye protector

There are several types of eye protector and it is important to select and issue the correct type to give the required protection. The types and their markings are listed in Section G *Checklists and forms*.

General purpose safety spectacle

Face shield

☑ **Eye protection safety**

- ☑ Have operations requiring eye protection been identified?
- ☑ Has the work activity been assessed to determine what, if any, hazards exist?
- ☑ Are appropriate types of eye protection available for the various work activities to be carried out?
- ☑ Does all eye protection comply with the relevant standard?
- ☑ Is the eye protection supplied on a personal basis to employees?
- ☑ Are there sufficient quantities of eye protectors available for occasional users?
- ☑ Is the use of eye protection satisfactorily monitored?
- ☑ Have employees been informed of work activities requiring eye protection?
- ☑ Have employees been trained in the correct use and maintenance of eye protection?
- ☑ Are employees aware of their responsibilities with regard to the care and reporting of loss or defective eye protectors?
- ☑ Are appropriate safety signs displayed?

Lasers

Items of equipment producing light amplification by the stimulated emission of radiation, more normally known as lasers, are widely used on construction sites, mainly for alignment and levelling in civil engineering. Most are of the helium or neon continuous wave type and emit visible light, but some lasers emit in the invisible infrared region of the electromagnetic spectrum, and these require extra caution.

The HSE says that it receives few reports of ill health or injury arising from the use of lasers. However, those that are reported arise from misuse of the equipment. The optical radiation produced by a laser is absorbed by the first few centimetres of the body and so the skin and eyes are the tissues most at risk of damage.

All lasers should comply with BS EN 60825. This standard groups laser products into five classes (with some sub-classes), based on acceptable emission levels, and is intended to ensure that the manufacturer and user of laser products comply with current requirements. It should be noted that if users modify instruments (for example, by adding lenses) they take on the responsibilities of a manufacturer for the class of laser.

The use of Class 1 and 2 products is preferred on construction sites because these represent the lowest risk of eye injury. However, even these lower power lasers can cause eye damage if they are misused (for example, staring directly into the beam or viewing the beam through any magnifying device).

Class 3R and 3B lasers, which may sometimes be in use, can involve hazards to both the user and other personnel. Those who maintain, operate and supervise the use of these products must be fully trained, competent and capable of implementing the necessary safety and hazard control procedures.

Where lower power lasers are used, the human blink reflex will offer some protection. However, this should not be relied upon and is unlikely to offer any protection from higher power laser.

Laser beam

General procedures

- ☑ Full training and information must be given to persons using lasers.
- ☑ There should be no unauthorised access to any laser equipment.
- ☑ All personnel must be aware of the hazards when working with lasers, the safe working procedures and accident reporting procedures.
- ☑ Any necessary eye protection equipment, hazard signs or barriers, for example, must be available and in use as necessary.
- ☑ Any eye protectors used in conjunction with lasers must be suited to the wavelength of the laser in use. General purpose safety glasses offer no protection whatsoever against lasers and should not be used.
- ☑ All hazard areas must be clearly defined with signs and barriers.
- ☑ The laser beam should only be directed at non-reflecting surfaces. Any adjacent reflective surfaces must be covered; otherwise the beam will diverge and could affect other areas and people not directly involved in the job.
- ☑ Extra care must be taken when working near reflective surfaces (for example water, dust, spray) that cannot be marked or covered.
- ☑ Special precautions must be taken when working near roads, airfields and other public areas, where a stray beam could cause a hazard.
- ☑ When work activities require the use of high-powered lasers, the work should, when possible, be undertaken when the site is vacated (such as evenings or weekends). If this is not possible, special precautions will be necessary to ensure that unauthorised persons do not enter the work area or any designated area.

In the event of an eye injury caused by a laser:

- ☑ no medication is to be applied to the eye
- ☑ the eye involved should be covered with a clean, dry material
- ☑ immediate medical attention should be sought.

A thorough ophthalmic examination should be carried out within 24 hours, with a full biophysical investigation.

☑️ **Laser safety**

☑ Has a risk assessment been carried out?

☑ Only competent and trained people must be allowed to operate laser equipment.

☑ The hazard area should be defined and clearly marked.

☑ Create an exclusion zone when the more powerful classes of laser are being used.

☑ When work with lasers is taking place, only authorised people should be allowed in the area.

☑ The correct eye protection must be in use during all laser operations.

☑ There should be no danger to any other person(s) resulting from stray reflections or from any activity involving the use of lasers.

☑ Where necessary, the source and direction of the laser beam should be clearly identified.

☑ The laser beam should only be directed at a non-reflecting surface.

☑ Any other reflective surfaces should be covered.

☑ All laser equipment should comply with BS EN 60825.

☑ Beam attenuators and any other safety devices must be in use when using Class 3R and 3B products.

6.7　Respiratory protection

The hazards

Dust has long been known as hazardous to the health of construction workers, especially when inhaled for long periods. While the health issues associated with asbestos are well recognised, the greater part of the dust problem in the industry currently relates to more common substances (for example, cement, plaster, wood, MDF, stone, silica, fillers and plastics). High-speed cutting of most materials can produce sufficient dust to cause a health hazard.

Dust that is visible in the air is generally accepted as being hazardous. However, dust that is too fine to be seen by the naked eye also causes many health problems, the symptoms of which may take many years to manifest themselves. Small dust particles of any material entering the lungs can be absorbed into the body and can cause scarring and sometimes cancer within the lungs.

Skin irritation, dermatitis and ulceration can be caused by contact with some dusts, and eating food with dirty or dust-covered hands can cause stomach disorders.

Fumes from certain substances (such as solvents, paints and adhesives) can have serious health implications. When used in poorly ventilated or confined spaces, it is not uncommon for fatalities to occur.

Such problems are unlikely to arise if occupational exposure limits and the Control of Substances Hazardous to Health Regulations (COSHH) are observed and safe systems of work maintained.

Whenever RPE is to be used for work in circumstances where the COSHH, lead or asbestos regulations apply, then, in line with the supporting Approved Codes of Practice, face-fit testing for employees should be carried out. This test checks that a facepiece (the respirator) matches the person's facial features and seals adequately to the wearer's face. It will also ensure that incorrectly fitting face pieces are not selected for use. This test must be carried out by a competent person.

It is also recommended that face-fit testing takes place whenever RPE is being used in any other work situation.

The training of employees in the correct use of RPE is essential before first use and should be repeated at suitable intervals. It is essential that training is carried out by a competent person and covers:

☑ why the RPE is necessary

☑ the hazards, the risks and the effects of exposure

☑ what RPE is to be provided

☑ how the RPE works

☑ why face-fit testing might be necessary

☑ how to wear and check the RPE correctly

☑ what maintenance is required and when

☑ where and how to clean the RPE and store it

☑ how to report defects in the RPE or any other problem with it

☑ the employer's responsibilities and those of employees

☑ use and misuse of RPE.

Selecting RPE

When selecting suitable RPE it may be necessary to seek expert advice from manufacturers or suppliers. Training in the types and use of respiratory equipment must be given.

Guidance and recommendations are provided in the HSE publication *Respiratory protective equipment at work – A practical guide*.

Personal protective equipment

The provision and use of RPE must only be considered when equally or more effective protective control measures cannot be used. The failure of RPE could have serious consequences.

The importance of the correct type of RPE being provided and used cannot be overstated as it must be assumed that the user will be working in a hostile environment. However, there are several potential problems arising from the selection and/or use of RPE:

- ☑ the **failure** of an item of RPE where, for whatever reason (such as lack of routine maintenance), it fails to provide the necessary level of protection

- ☑ the **misuse** of RPE (such as it being mistreated or not used in accordance with the manufacturer's instructions or the training given)

- ☑ it being the **wrong type** of RPE (for example there would be no protection from a filtering respirator designed solely to capture airborne dust if being used where the workplace hazard is in fact a toxic gas)

- ☑ the effectiveness of the **face fit**. Many types of RPE depend upon a good seal between the facepiece and the skin of the user at all times, including where physical activity and exertion are required. Factors such as facial hair or the shape of the face can interfere with a good fit.

Where the wearing of RPE is inevitable, European Standard BS EN 529 recommends that employers and the self-employed define and document a policy covering the selection, use and maintenance of RPE, which is communicated to, and understood by, all levels of the organisation.

Each type of RPE is assigned a filter protection factor, which gives the user some idea of the level of protection that the device will provide. For example, a filtering half-mask marked:

FFP1   is a low efficiency device offering a protection factor of four

FFP2   is a medium efficiency device offering a protection factor of 10

FFP3   is a high efficiency device offering a protection factor of 20.

A protection factor of 10 means that in controlled conditions, for every 10 units of contaminant outside the mask, only one unit will get inside the mask, or for every 20 units outside the mask there will be two units inside, and so on. It is important, therefore, that the correct filter is selected for the type and level of contaminant in the air.

> It is recognised good practice to use RPE with an FFP3 rating to protect against dust (such as silica) that is created when mechanically cutting concrete, bricks, slabs and so on – even when wet cutting, which only removes about 75% of airborne particles.

There are many types of RPE, including:

- ☑ disposable face mask respirators
- ☑ half-mask dust respirators
- ☑ high-efficiency dust respirators
- ☑ positive, pressure-powered respirators
- ☑ ventilator visor or helmet respirators
- ☑ compressed, air-line breathing apparatus
- ☑ self-contained breathing apparatus.

> It should be noted that nuisance dust masks (cup-shaped filters often held in place by a single strap) are not classed as PPE or RPE. They do not meet any current standards or legislative requirements and offer very little or no protection to the wearer.

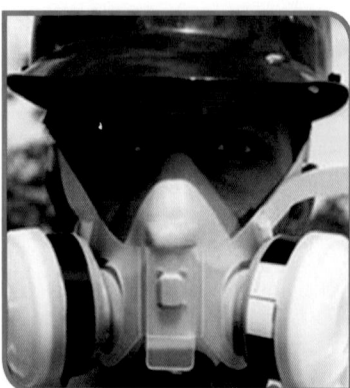

High-efficiency dust respirator

Ventilated visor and ventilated helmet respirator

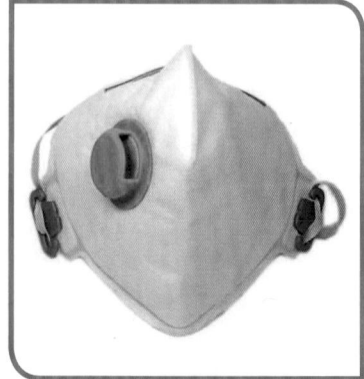

Disposable face-mask respirator

06

Under the Personal Protective Equipment at Work Regulations, the employer must carry out an assessment to determine **when** RPE is required and **what type** is appropriate for controlling exposure to the hazardous material. Selecting RPE that is both suitable for the user and the job must be carried out by a competent person. This is because the choice will depend on a number of interacting factors, such as:

- ☑ the nature of the hazards and materials
- ☑ the measured dust concentrations
- ☑ the period of exposure
- ☑ if working outdoors, the prevailing weather conditions
- ☑ suitability for each user (field of vision, provision for communication and the need to move in cramped or difficult working places, such as confined spaces).

Using and maintaining RPE

Both the employer and the employee have a duty to ensure that all RPE provided is used correctly and that it is stored correctly after use.

Employers must also ensure that non-disposable RPE is thoroughly examined and tested at appropriate intervals. The Approved Code of Practice, which supports the Personal Protective Equipment at Work Regulations, specifies that such examinations and tests are carried out at least every month, and more frequently where conditions are particularly severe. Longer intervals may be more appropriate in the case of certain RPE (for example, half-mask respirators used infrequently for short spells against air contaminants of relatively low toxicity). However, the longest interval between examinations and tests should not exceed three months.

Disposable RPE, provided it is only used for one working day or shift then disposed of, does not require any examination or tests.

 RPE – Common failings

Research undertaken by the HSE targeted workplace RPE inspections and found:

- ☑ a perception that using RPE was simple or obvious
- ☑ managers and supervisors had knowledge gaps on critical aspects of RPE
- ☑ there was limited use of external information sources (for example, manufacturer's literature and websites)
- ☑ there was an assumption that workers know how to put on and use RPE
- ☑ RPE misuse is common – but it is generally blamed on the workers
- ☑ limited management input and involvement
- ☑ little information was provided to the worker
- ☑ poor standards of training, hazard awareness and RPE use
- ☑ little supervision and enforcement
- ☑ deficiencies in provisions for RPE storage and maintenance regimes
- ☑ RPE pre-use checks were unlikely.

In addition other failings include:

- ☑ inadequate face-fit testing
- ☑ wearers having more than one day's stubble growth, which substantially reduces the RPE's seal around the face and thus reduces the protection factor
- ☑ mask straps not being adjusted, tightened or straps in the wrong position on the head.

06

 For further information refer to Chapter B10 Dust and fumes.

 Managers and supervisors must set an example and wear PPE if needed.

6.8   Skin protection

Protective clothing and other PPE provides one of the most practical ways of limiting contact between the skin and other substances. To be effective, all protective clothing must be the right size, fit for the purpose, maintained in good condition, cleaned regularly and stored carefully when not in use.

Protective clothing may include gloves, overalls, eye protectors (such as goggles and face shields), aprons, boots and leggings, depending on the work being undertaken. Legislation requires the provision and wearing of protective clothing for specific processes and operations. The protective equipment provided must be suited to the requirements of the job.

Regular inspections must be made to ensure it remains sound and adequate.

Industrial dermatitis

Industrial dermatitis is caused by contact between the skin (usually the hands) and irritant substances. It is essential that a risk assessment identifies the properties of the hazardous substance so that the correct type of glove can be provided.

Dermatitis, an inflammatory skin disease, accounts for over half of all working days lost through industrial sickness.
There are two general types:

☑ contact or irritant dermatitis – usually where the skin comes into contact with an irritant substance

☑ allergic or sensitive dermatitis – where a person develops an allergic reaction to a substance.

With different people, some substances are known to have the effect as either an irritant or a sensitiser (such as turpentine).

In the course of their work, many construction workers are likely to come into contact with one or more possible skin irritants, such as:

☑ cement, lime and plaster

☑ certain types of wood, resins, fungicides and pesticides

☑ paint

☑ tar, pitch and bitumen

☑ solvents, thinners and degreasers

☑ mineral oils and grease.

 For further information refer to Chapter B08 Skin protection.

Cuts and abrasions

Many people working in the construction industry will carry out manual work that will render them susceptible to cuts and abrasions if the correct type of gloves are not provided and worn.

Again, gloves designed to protect the hands against cuts and abrasions are freely available.

Generally, rigger gloves offer adequate protection for most activities, although for some activities (such as handling sheet glass) specialist Kevlar-impregnated gloves will be necessary.

Hot works

Activities such as welding and grinding will require that the hands, forearms and face are protected against high temperatures and welding fumes or grinding sparks. To achieve this level of protection it may be necessary for those who carry out such activities to wear specialist PPE made for the purpose (for example, welders should wear welding gauntlets that extend up to the elbow and a face shield).

Acid and alkali burns

Some substances that are in common use in the construction industry have sufficiently strong acid or alkali properties that can cause burns to the skin.

Gloves are available to protect the users of such substances from chemical burns.

Vibration

Some retro-fit products are available that are designed to protect operators from vibration. Only those approved by the machine manufacturers should be used.

The wearing of anti-vibration gloves is not recommended. Problems with anti-vibration gloves include:

☑ reduced flexibility at the hands resulting in higher grip and push forces and loss of precise tool control

☑ the possibility of gloves amplifying the tool vibration in some cases (these cases are very difficult to predict)

☑ anti-vibration gloves are only tested in one direction and vibration occurs in three directions

☑ field trials of gloves have shown that the vibration isolation materials are not always durable.

One benefit from gloves is that they keep the hands warm and offer other protection.

If an employer intends to provide items of PPE as part of their strategy to reduce the risks from vibration in the workplace, it is important that the correct PPE is selected.

As with all PPE for use at work, gloves or anti-vibration protection should be selected by a competent person who can ensure, in discussion with the supplier, that they carry the CE-mark and meet the appropriate standards. Most leading manufacturers and suppliers will offer advice on the selection of different types of gloves and other PPE. All PPE produced or imported by reputable companies is manufactured to British and European Standards.

 For further information refer to Chapter B14 Vibration.

Selection of hand protection

British Standards cover many types of protective glove but care is needed in selecting the right type for a particular hazard. For example, a glove suitable for handling abrasive materials may offer no protection against chemicals, while the appropriate glove to protect the skin against contact with diesel oil may offer no protection against some solvents.

All manufacturers offer advice on the most suitable gloves for specific types of hazard, some of which are summarised in the following table.

06

Hazard	Recommended type
Acids, concrete, brickwork, stain removers, solvents, alkalis.	Neoprene, nitrile, PVC, rubber.
Esters, ethers, ketones (mastic, sealers), aldehydes, petroleum-based products.	Medium and heavyweight rubber, neoprene, nitrile, PVC.
High and low temperatures.	Nitrile, PVC, medium and heavyweight rubber.
Abrasion, unloading bricks and blocks, general materials handling.	Rubber, nitrile, PVC, neoprene, chrome-leather with reinforced palm.
Bitumen, hot work.	Asbestos substitute or Nomex gloves.

It should be noted that industrial safety gloves are rated from 1–4 for their resistance to abrasion, tear and puncture, and 1–5 for blade cut. Those specifying and purchasing work gloves must ensure that the correct grade is obtained, if necessary by speaking to the manufacturers or suppliers.

6.9   Head and foot protection

Head protection

It is a requirement to wear suitable head protection on all building and construction sites, unless there is no risk of head injury, either from falling objects or by banging the head.

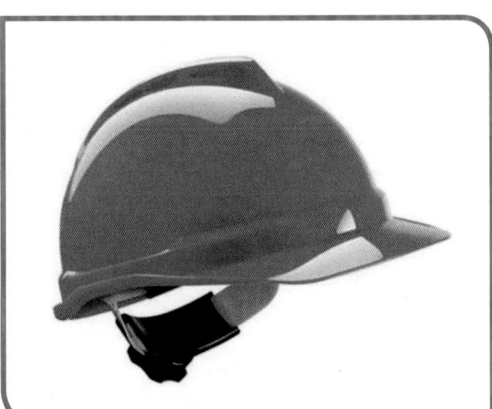

Established best practice is to ensure that head protection is always worn by everyone on site, except when in designated safe areas (such as the site office or canteen).

There are many makes of safety helmet available that are constructed to British Standards, and it is the duty of the employer to provide safety helmets that are suitable for the job and the wearer. Each safety helmet has a kite mark and a date of production. They will need to be changed on a regular basis.

Employees, for their part, must follow their employers' instructions. They must wear the safety helmets at all times, when instructed to do so, and report any damage or loss to their employer.

Safety helmets are designed to offer a pre-determined level of impact resistance if they are correctly worn. **The practice of wearing them back-to-front must not be tolerated.**

It has been established that the solvents in some paint, adhesives and indelible markers can reduce the strength of the plastic from which helmets are manufactured. Employees must be discouraged from marking or decorating their safety helmets, other than applying official stickers (such as first aider) or confirmation of site induction.

A safety helmet that has fallen from height onto a hard surface may have suffered damage that will affect its strength even though no cracks are visible. In most circumstances, a replacement helmet should be obtained.

Where the work involves leaning over exposed edges, or similar, chinstraps must be fitted and worn. Many safety helmets have in-built features that enable compatible ear defenders or a face shield to be securely attached.

Sikhs

Under Regulation 11 of the Employment Act, construction workers who are practising members of the Sikh faith are exempt from wearing a safety helmet whilst wearing a turban. No other workers are covered by this exemption. Sikhs who are not wearing turbans are not exempt from the regulations and, therefore, are required to wear the same head protection as other operatives.

 For more detailed information on the requirements and application, refer to the regulations themselves.

Foot protection

Accidents arising from the manual handling of articles and substances are common causes of injury to feet, as well as to hands.

Foot protection comes in many types and styles, such as safety trainers, safety shoes or boots, safety wellington boots and rigger boots. Properly manufactured and selected foot protection with steel toecaps and mid-soles can protect the feet against dropped objects and penetration of the sole of the foot by upward-pointing nails or glass. They can also be oil and slip resistant.

☑ **Safety trainers** offer good grip on sloping or slippery surfaces and offer more comfort. They are more suitable to trades (such as floor layers) who repeatedly kneel and bend their feet.

☑ **Safety wellington boots** are essential in preventing burns when operatives have to stand in wet concrete. The cement content, when mixed with water, becomes highly corrosive and will cause severe burns to body tissue.

☑ **Safety boots,** as commonly worn by construction workers, provide the required level of protection with steel toecaps and a steel plate moulded into the mid-sole, protecting the wearer against dropped objects and penetration through the sole by sharp objects.

The ankle support provided by some styles of safety boot is important in the prevention of injuries resulting from walking on uneven surfaces and some industries insist on this type (for example, the rail industry).

As with hand protection, manufacturers offer advice on the most suitable footwear for specific types of hazard.

It is essential that protective footwear is worn when people are on site, both from an employer's point of view, in being able to provide a safe place and a safe method of working, and from an employee's position where safety footwear has a benefit in preventing injuries.

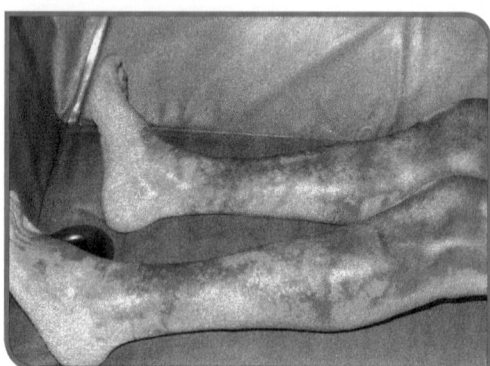

Wellington boots are essential in preventing burns to persons standing in wet cement or concrete. The cement content, when mixed with water, becomes highly corrosive and will cause severe burns to body tissue. It quickly burns and kills nerve endings and can continue to burn deeply without the person feeling much immediate pain.

This picture shows the severely burnt legs of a man who was unaware of the dangers of wet cement, the effect it can have on skin, and the need to wear wellington boots to protect the legs.

06

6.10 Clothing and other protection

Clothing

High-visibility clothing

High-visibility clothing that protects the wearer against any risk to their health or safety is classified as PPE whereas clothing (such as uniforms), when the primary purpose is to promote a corporate image, is not.

There are wide ranges of high-visibility clothing and accessories (including vests, coats, fleeces, polo-shirts, trousers and overalls). Risk assessment or policy will determine the level of visibility required but all high-visibility clothing should comply with BS EN 471.

There are three classes of high-visibility clothing:

☑ **Class 1 – low visibility.**

☑ **Class 2 – medium visibility** required when working on or near A and B class roads or sites with vehicle or plant movements.

☑ **Class 3 – high visibility**, required when working on or near dual carriageways, with a speed of 50 mph or above, or motorways. It can also be a requirement when working in high-risk areas (such as airports, highways maintenance and railways).

06

Cold and wet weather

Clothing that is designed to protect the wearer against cold and/or wet weather is also classified as PPE and must therefore be provided at no charge by the employer.

Such clothing includes:

☑ padded and/or waterproof jackets (either high-visibility or not), equipped with a hood that can accommodate a safety helmet where necessary

☑ padded and/or waterproof leggings

☑ suitable footwear

☑ thermally protective gloves and socks.

Fall protection

Items of equipment that are used by a person to prevent that person falling from height are also classified as PPE.

Examples of this type of equipment are:

☑ safety harness

☑ fall-arrest or restraint lanyard

☑ inertia reel fall-arrest block.

All the employers' and employees' duties that apply to other types of PPE apply to this type of equipment also.

A major additional consideration regarding the use of this type of PPE is the prompt rescue of anyone who has fallen and is suspended in a harness. A medical condition known as suspension trauma, which at worst can result in the death of the suspended person, can occur if rescue is not carried out within 10 minutes.

 For further information refer to Chapter D05 Fall arrest and suspension equipment.

Life jackets

Another category of PPE is that which enables the user to keep afloat should they fall into water or other liquids. These are broadly divided into life jackets and buoyancy aids.

 For further information refer to Chapter F05 Working over or near to water.

6.11   Legal duties

The Personal Protective Equipment at Work Regulations

General principles of the regulations

These regulations require that where a risk has been identified by a risk assessment and it cannot be adequately controlled by other means, which are equally or more effective, then the employer must provide **suitable** PPE and ensure that it is correctly used and cared for by employees.

Detailed requirements of any such risk assessment are specified in the regulations and require the problem to be thought through in a structured manner and the right equipment chosen for the right reasons.

A key factor is the competence of the person carrying out the assessments. If they do not get it right, the consequences for the health and safety of employees could well be very serious.

In essence, PPE may only be used as a last resort after all other means of eliminating or controlling the risk have been considered.

In deciding which type to issue, the employer must take into account the hazard that the PPE is being used to protect against and ensure that the PPE will fit the wearer and allow them to work safely. If more than one item of PPE is being used at any one time, the employer must make sure that individual items of PPE are compatible and do not adversely affect the performance of each other.

This is of particular importance in the building and construction industry since operatives often need to simultaneously wear a combination of PPE (such as safety helmets, eye protection, ear protection or respiratory protection).

One area of the provision of PPE is safety footwear (often safety shoes or boots). A strict interpretation of these regulations requires the employer to provide safety boots free of charge.

However, some employers come to an agreement with their employees whereby safety boots are purchased by the employee and then subsidised by the employer, or provided under other schemes or conditions.

Further complications can arise when deciding how long a pair of safety boots can be expected to last, and whether the employer is responsible for the safety of labour-only employees and some other categories of site-based staff.

Whenever PPE is to be issued, the employer must ensure that employees have been given adequate and appropriate information, instruction and training to enable the employees to understand the risks being protected against, the purpose of the PPE and the manner in which it is to be used.

Whilst the employer must ensure that PPE is supplied and used, the employee has duties to:

☑ properly use the PPE provided, in accordance with the information, instruction and training that they have been given

☑ return PPE to its storage facility, where provided, after use

☑ know the procedures for reporting loss of any PPE or defects in it to their employer.

 The following regulations have alternative requirements.

☑ The Ionising Radiation Regulations.

☑ The Control of Lead at Work Regulations.

☑ The Control of Asbestos Regulations.

☑ The Control of Substances Hazardous to Health Regulations.

☑ The Control of Noise at Work Regulations.

However, this does not mean that PPE need not be provided where it is required when carrying out work under the above regulations.

Where work is carried out under any of the above regulations, any PPE required must be provided to comply with the respective set of regulations. For example, hearing protection **must be** provided to meet the requirements of the Control of Noise at Work Regulations, not the Personal Protective Equipment at Work Regulations.

Supplying suitable PPE

Employers must provide **suitable** PPE to employees and the self-employed must ensure that they are provided with **suitable** PPE.

Where a risk cannot be adequately controlled in some other manner that is equally or more effective, PPE will only be deemed to be **suitable** when:

☑ it is appropriate for the risks involved and the conditions of exposure

☑ it takes account of the ergonomic requirements and state of health of the user

☑ it can fit the wearer properly, if necessary after adjustment

☑ as far as is practicable, it effectively prevents or adequately controls exposure to risk without increasing the overall risk

☑ it complies with any relevant European Community directive.

 The Health and Safety at Work Act requires that employers provide PPE free of charge.

Also supplying one-size-fits-all PPE (such as gloves) or one size of high-visibility vests (for example, XXL) may not offer everyone the same level of protection and could introduce other risks (such as entanglement or snagging).

Employers must ensure the compatibility of PPE when more than one item of PPE must be worn at any one time, so that one item does not reduce the protection offered by another.

Assessing suitability

Employers must carry out assessments of the suitability of PPE regarding the nature of the risk, before selecting it. The assessment must consider:

☑ the risks to health and safety that have not been controlled by other means

☑ the nature of the risks to health and safety, against which the PPE is to protect the user

☑ a comparison of the nature of the risks and the performance capabilities of the PPE

☑ the compatibility of the PPE under consideration and any other PPE that will be worn at the same time.

Reviewing the assessment

Employers must:

☑ review such assessments if it is thought that they are no longer valid or if there has been a significant change in the matters to which it relates

☑ incorporate any changes that are indicated by the review.

Maintenance and storage

Employers must ensure that PPE that has been provided to employees is maintained (which includes replacement or cleaning) in an efficient state, efficient working order and good repair. The same duty is on **self-employed** persons with regard to any PPE provided to them.

Employers and self-employed persons must provide suitable storage facilities for PPE that has been issued, for when it is not in use.

Information, instruction and training

Employers who have provided employees with PPE must also provide **adequate and appropriate** information, instruction and training to enable employees to know:

☑ the risk(s) for which the PPE has been provided

☑ the purpose for which, and the manner in which, the PPE is to be used

☑ any actions that they (the users) must take to keep the PPE in the correct condition

☑ any information that should be available to them.

To be adequate and appropriate, the information must be understandable by the persons receiving it.

Training can be theoretical and/or practical. Where appropriate the employer should, at appropriate intervals, arrange suitable demonstrations in the correct wearing of PPE.

Usage and defects

There is a legal duty on:

☑ employers to take reasonable steps to ensure that the PPE provided to employees is used correctly

☑ employees to use the PPE provided in accordance with any instruction and training provided

☑ self-employed persons to make full and proper use of PPE

☑ employees and the self-employed to take reasonable steps to return PPE to any storage facilities provided

☑ employees to report any defect in the PPE issued, or the loss of it, to the employer as soon as possible.

06

Appendix A – Laser health risks and control

Class of laser	Health risks	Control measures
Class 1M	Potentially harmful to the eye but only if deliberately viewed through an optical magnifying device (such as binoculars).	No-one must be allowed to deliberately look at the beam or to direct the beam into another person's eyes. Magnifying devices (such as binoculars) must not be used by any person who may be exposed to a laser beam whilst using them.
Class 2	May be harmful to the eyes if deliberately misused (for example, if someone stares directly into the beam).	As above.
Class 2M	Harmful to the eyes if viewed through a magnifying optical device.	As above.
Class 3R (formerly Class 3A)	These are higher power lasers that can cause eye injuries; generally exposure is no more hazardous than to a Class 2 device because of the human blink reflex.	BS EN 60825 specifies minimum training requirements for the users of Class 3 and Class 4 lasers. This will include information on the risks from the beam and the advice against misuse.
Class 3B and Class 4	A higher power laser that can cause eye injury, either directly from viewing the beam or from reflections.	Appropriate eye protection (PPE) must be worn whenever Class 3R or more powerful lasers are used. Particular training on these classes of laser is required. The human blink reflex is not likely to offer any protection to anyone accidentally exposed to the beam.

06

07

The Control of Substances Hazardous to Health (COSHH)

Since they were introduced, the Control of Substances Hazardous to Health (COSHH) Regulations have probably been among the most poorly understood pieces of legislation.

However, the regulations are based on very simple principles. The intention of the regulations is to protect human health from exposure to hazardous substances by either totally preventing exposure or, where that is not reasonably practicable, controlling the level of exposure to safe values, by appropriate means.

Two dangerous substances, asbestos and lead, are commonly encountered during construction activities, particularly the refurbishment of older buildings, but are not covered by the COSHH Regulations because they have their own regulations.

Introduction	84
Key points	84
Sources of harm	84
Workplace exposure limits	85
Definitions	86
COSHH Regulations	87
COSHH responsibilities	89
Work on another employer's premises	90
Identifying hazardous substances	90
COSHH assessments	91
Control measures	95
Monitoring exposure at the workplace	96
REACH Regulations	97
Appendix A – Management action plan	98
Appendix B – Health and safety COSHH assessment	99
Appendix C – Self-assessment questionnaire	100

The Control of Substances Hazardous to Health (COSHH)

7.1 Introduction

Much has been written about the poor safety performance of the construction industry in recent years and generally, having put in considerable effort, the industry has raised its game. Sadly, in many cases, exposure to occupational health hazards has not received the same degree of attention.

Whereas the results of accidents are immediately obvious and often dramatic, the onset of occupational health problems are often subtler, slower to develop and therefore easier to miss or ignore.

The COSHH Regulations deal with harmful substances in relation to their health effects. However, the regulations do not cover any flammable or explosive properties that the substances might also possess.

7.2 Key points

☑ Many of the substances **used or created** during work processes have the potential to cause harm to the health of anyone exposed to them.

☑ In construction many COSHH issues relate to substances created (such as dust or fumes), as opposed to chemicals that have been bought in.

☑ Hazardous substances that are already present on site when it is first occupied can also pose hazards to health.

☑ All purchased products that are hazardous to health must carry an appropriate warning symbol on the packaging. However, hazardous substances that are created by the work process or are already present on site will carry no such health warning.

☑ Employers have legal duties to establish the health risks to their employees, and others who may come into contact with hazardous substances, by carrying out an appropriate assessment and putting in place adequate control measures.

☑ The assessment should take into account how the substance is used and should not merely be a copy of the supplier's information.

☑ Ideally, exposure to any hazardous substance would be rendered impossible by eliminating the use of that substance (for example, by changing the way that the job is carried out so that the substance is not necessary). Alternatively, risk can be reduced by:

– the substitution of safer substances (for example, replacing solvent-based paint with water-based paint)

– modifying the method of its use (for example, total enclosure of the process).

☑ In many cases, none of these measures are practical in a construction site environment: If the prevention of exposure is not possible, the level of exposure must be controlled. This can be through engineering controls, safe systems of work and personal protective equipment (PPE).

☑ Using PPE to control exposure must only be considered as a last resort, after other methods have been explored and found not to be reasonably practicable.

☑ In some cases employees exposed to hazardous substances must be offered health surveillance.

7.3 Sources of harm

The regulations cover substances that have chronic or delayed effects, including substances that are carcinogenic (cause cancer), mutagenic (cause mutation of the body) or teratogenic (cause malformation of an embryo).

The purpose is to safeguard the health of people using or coming into contact with any substance that is harmful to health, apart from lead and asbestos.

The regulations apply to those substances that are classified as being very toxic, toxic, harmful, corrosive or irritant under the Classification of Substances and Preparations Dangerous for Supply, in Schedule 1 of the Chemicals (Hazard Information and Packaging for Supply) Regulations, also known as CHIP. The symbols used on the containers of such substances are reproduced in this chapter.

Many of the basic substances (products) bought in and used in the construction industry have the potential to harm the health of people using them.

Additionally, many of the essential construction processes can create potentially hazardous substances, and a third group of substances are harmful substances (including micro-organisms) that may already be on site when a project commences.

Bought-in products

The first, and easiest, stage is to look at the substances that are bought in. This involves identifying what is used, what is not hazardous to health and how much is used. Most construction processes are relatively simple as they rarely use a large number of substances or involve mixing of substances. Mechanical workshops (for example, where plant is serviced) tend to be more challenging simply because of the amount of chemicals present in the substances that they normally use.

Another consideration is the substances that will be brought onto site by other contractors, how those substances might affect other people and the quality of the contractors' COSHH assessments.

Furthermore, the site office and other accommodation must not be overlooked. For example, it is not unreasonable to suppose that strong cleaning materials will be used in catering and other welfare facilities.

Having made a list of all substances, it is then sensible to identify any products that are obviously not hazardous, so that they can be ruled out.

For cleaning chemicals, washing-up liquid does not have any warning symbols on it and therefore, other than noting its presence, no further action is necessary. However, the information on a container of bleach should provide the basis for determining how it can be used safely. Of the two products that have been considered, one requires no control measures to be identified but the second does.

Created by the work process

The situation becomes more complicated when potentially harmful substances (such as many forms of dust or fumes) are created by work processes. The situation is further complicated if the substance created has a workplace exposure limit (WEL) that must not be exceeded. This may require that exposure levels are measured, unless exposure can be eliminated or controlled to a known safe level. Again, it will be necessary to also consider potentially harmful processes that will be carried out by other contractors.

Depending upon the complexity of the project, it may not be possible to complete this part of the exercise prior to the start of the project unless all work processes and substances that will be created are known. In these circumstances, it will be a case of building up the COSHH information as the job progresses, but this must be achieved in such a way that no-one is exposed to a potentially harmful substance until the assessment of it has been carried out and appropriate controls are in place.

Already present on site

A third category of potentially harmful substances are those substances, including micro-organisms, that may already be present on site.

Any number of hazardous substances might be present in the ground when former industrial (brownfield) sites are redeveloped. Examples are:

☑ land, heavily contaminated with fuels, oils and other hazardous liquids that have seeped into the ground over many years

☑ residues of hazardous substances left in pipework, underground tanks and drums

☑ substances (such as asbestos and polychlorinated biphenyls (PCBs)) that were deliberately buried by the past users of the land.

Also in contaminated land there could be sources of micro-organisms. These include:

☑ leptospirosis (Weil's disease) from the presence of infected rats or their carcasses

☑ infected syringes, needles and other items associated with drug taking (for example, where a derelict site is being refurbished)

☑ tetanus from infected ground or other materials

☑ a range of respiratory diseases arising from the disturbance of accumulated pigeon or bat droppings

☑ pipework and sumps containing sewage sludge residue.

Types of exposure

Hazardous substances can enter the body in four ways:

☑ **inhalation** (breathed) into the lungs, when the substance is in the form of a gas, vapour, fume, mist, aerosol or dust

☑ **absorption** through the skin or eyes by contact with a substance that can penetrate unbroken skin, or is absorbed through unprotected cuts or grazes

☑ **injection** by contact with contaminated sharp objects or high-pressure equipment (such as water jetting)

☑ **ingestion** (eating or drinking) by swallowing particles of a hazardous substance resulting from hand-to-mouth transfer.

7.4   Workplace exposure limits

Unsurprisingly, some hazardous substances have legal limits to which people may be exposed. All of these substances have a workplace exposure limit (WEL) that represents a concentration of a substance in the air measured over a specific period of time. The taking of such measurements (workplace monitoring) is a specialist activity that must be carried out by someone who is competent to do so and who possesses the appropriate equipment. Such monitoring must be carried out where a (COSHH) risk assessment indicates that it is necessary.

The Control of Substances Hazardous to Health (COSHH)

The following substances, all of which have a WEL, are commonly used in or produced by construction activities:

- ☑ general dust
- ☑ hardwood dust
- ☑ softwood dust
- ☑ silica
- ☑ white spirit
- ☑ pulverised fuel ash
- ☑ synthetic mineral fibre (rock wool/fibreglass)
- ☑ asphalt
- ☑ welding/cutting fume

- ☑ gypsum
- ☑ portland cement
- ☑ micro-organisms associated with:
  - blood products
  - Weil's disease
  - tetanus
  - sewage
  - certain black mould species
  - anthrax.

This list is not exhaustive. Employers have a legal duty to establish that an in-use substance has a WEL, and to control exposure to it.

 A list of all WELs is published by the HSE in Guidance Note EH40, available in hard copy or for download via the HSE website.

Is there a COSHH problem?

Those who plan and carry out work that could result in exposure to hazardous substances may have difficulty in appreciating that there is a (real or potential) problem. This is particularly true when a hazardous substance is created by the work process.

A hardwood plank should not pose any serious health issues in the form that it is delivered to site. However, cutting or sanding it will produce dust that, unless controlled, has the potential to cause irritation of the nasal passages, sensitisation or, on rare occasions, nasal cancer.

Cutting, sawing, grinding or sanding any substance has the potential to liberate harmful dust. Furthermore, many types of hot works will create harmful fumes or gases that may be inhaled unless the process is closely controlled.

The COSHH Regulations place a duty on the employer to assess whether or not a hazard to the health of the employees, or other persons, will arise from the presence of hazardous substances during work activities. This process is known as carrying out a COSHH assessment.

The decision-making process that must be worked through when carrying out a COSHH assessment will be familiar to anyone who has completed risk assessments.

Establishing the degree of risk can require expertise and experience. For example, if the only way to complete an activity involves using a particularly hazardous substance (such as dry rot treatments) the work will have to be well planned, managed and closely controlled. This would result in a high hazard/low risk situation.

Conversely, it is possible to create very high exposures that may be harmful to health from apparently low risk substances like dust, which is a common COSHH problem in construction.

 Myth: 'Of course it's not a risk to health – we've always done it this way.'
Reality: Some diseases take years to develop. If exposure is high because the task has always been done that way then the task needs re-assessing to protect the workforce.

7.5 Definitions

The meanings of the following words need to be clearly understood:

- ☑ **substance** means any natural or artificial substance, in solid, liquid, gaseous or vapour form, and includes micro-organisms
- ☑ **hazard** is the potential for the substance to cause harm, illness or damage to health
- ☑ **risk** is the likelihood that the hazardous potential of the substance will be realised.

7.6 COSHH Regulations

 The regulations can be downloaded from the HSE or Government legislation websites.

The regulations place duties on both employers and the self-employed. These duties cover:

☑ people actually working with substances

☑ other people (such as the public or other contractors) who might be affected.

If five or more people are employed, the significant findings of the COSHH assessment and the actions that will be taken to control exposures must be written down.

The main requirements of the regulations are as follows:

☑ assess the health risks to employees or other people created by work activities that involve substances hazardous to health

☑ implement suitable control measures to effectively protect employees and others from exposure

☑ review the assessment if there have been any changes that may invalidate it, such as:

  – a change in the way the work is carried out, or

  – the results of monitoring indicating that existing control measures are not effective.

The emphasis under COSHH is to avoid exposure to hazardous substances unless it is not reasonably practicable to do so, in which case adequate control measures must be put in place to control exposure to a safe level.

The regulations require the following thought process in relation to control:

☑ can the work be carried out by a less hazardous method that does not require the use of hazardous substances and, if not,

☑ can the substance be changed (substituted)?

If the answer to both of these questions is 'no' then the introduction of measures to control exposure will be necessary.

Engineering controls should be the first controls to be considered (such as pouring devices to stop splashes, the use of dust extraction, increasing ventilation and so on). PPE should not be considered as a control until engineering control options have been exhausted. PPE:

☑ can be expensive

☑ can be unpleasant to wear

☑ only protects the wearer and then only if it is being used correctly and maintained

☑ often requires considerable management effort to ensure that it is used correctly.

Removing the need to buy and use it makes good occupational health and business sense.

The regulations apply to all industries and while some fixed workplaces (such as factories and warehouses) may find it practical to introduce effective engineering controls, the nature of construction sites and work conditions mean that it will often be difficult to do anything other than use PPE. It is, however, becoming easier to introduce engineering controls as newer equipment is designed to overcome exposure problems (for example, powered hand tools can be fitted with dust extraction and collection attachments). Similarly, a number of UK hire companies stock air movers to enable ventilation to be improved.

The requirements of the regulations are very thorough and one of those requirements is to ensure that the control measures that have been identified as suitable are properly used.

To ensure that the control measures are effective, the regulations require that:

☑ extract ventilation systems must be thoroughly examined periodically

☑ if using substances that are known to damage health, part of the assessment is likely to identify that health surveillance is necessary. Any records must be kept for 40 years and made available to the people who have been exposed to the hazard

☑ there is a duty to communicate the information and provide relevant training to people who may be exposed

☑ emergency arrangements are put in place and, where required, practised.

Summary of the COSHH Regulations

Employers must carry out a risk assessment of health risks created by work involving substances hazardous to health. Each assessment must take account of:

☑ the hazardous properties of the substance

☑ information provided by the supplier on the potential harmful effects

☑ the type, level and duration of exposure

☑ the way in which the job will be carried out, including the amount of the substance used (or present in the case of substances created by a work process)

07

- ☑ activities (such as maintenance) where there is the potential for high levels of exposure
- ☑ any published WEL for the substance
- ☑ the effects of any control measures that are, or will be, in place
- ☑ the results of any health surveillance and/or exposure monitoring that has been undertaken
- ☑ the risks where there is exposure to more than one hazardous substance at any one time
- ☑ other information that the employer may need or have in order to complete the assessment.

Any assessment must be reviewed regularly if there is reason to suspect that the assessment is no longer valid, or if there has been a significant change in the work to which the assessment relates, or exposure monitoring results indicate it is necessary.

Hierarchy of control

The preferable method of prevention or control is to replace the substance or process with a non-hazardous or less hazardous substance or process.

Controls shall be, in order of priority:

- ☑ engineering controls
- ☑ organisational controls
- ☑ providing suitable PPE (as a last resort).

The control measures must:

- ☑ ensure the safe handling, storage, transportation and disposal of hazardous substances
- ☑ ensure maintenance procedures, which involve exposure to hazardous substances, are suitable
- ☑ reduce to a minimum the number of people exposed, the level and duration of exposure and the quantity of hazardous substances present in the workplace
- ☑ include control of the working environment, including the provision of adequate ventilation
- ☑ include adequate hygiene and washing facilities.

This regulation contains further details of measures that must be taken to control exposure to carcinogens, mutagens and biological agents.

With regard to this regulation, it is considered that control of exposure will be generally adequate if:

- ☑ work activities are organised to minimise the release and spread of hazardous substances
- ☑ account is taken of the routes of exposure – inhalation, skin absorption and ingestion
- ☑ the control measures selected:
    - are proportionate to the degree of health risk
    - are effective in minimising the escape and spread of the substance
    - may, where necessary, include a combination of control measures, including PPE
- ☑ the control measures selected are periodically reviewed for their effectiveness
- ☑ users of hazardous substances are informed of the hazards and risks and trained in the use of the control measures provided
- ☑ it does not increase the overall risks to health or safety from other sources.

Employers who provide any control measure are required to ensure that they are properly used or applied. All employees must:

- ☑ make proper use of any control measure (including PPE) provided
- ☑ take all steps to return it to its place of storage after use
- ☑ report any defects in the control measure to their employer.

Monitoring controls

Where control measures are provided in accordance with Regulation 7, adequate maintenance, examination and testing of control measures, including any PPE provided, must be undertaken to ensure they are in efficient working order and remain clean.

Where engineering controls are undertaken, the employer must ensure thorough examinations and testing are carried out on a regular basis.

Where indicated as necessary by the COSHH assessment, monitoring of the exposure to hazardous substances must be undertaken using suitable procedures, unless it can be demonstrated by another method of evaluation that exposure is adequately controlled.

Suitable records of any monitoring should be kept for five years, or 40 years if personal exposures occur.

Health surveillance

Where it is appropriate for protecting employees' health, health surveillance must be carried out and recorded.

Where an employee requires medical surveillance following exposure, and it has been decided that the employee cannot continue in that work, the employer must take steps to ensure the employee adheres to the medical decision unless it has been cancelled.

Upon reasonable notice, an employer must allow the employee to access any medical records applying to them.

Information, instruction and training

Information, instruction and training must be provided for persons who may be exposed to substances hazardous to health so that they are aware of the danger of exposure and the precautions that should be taken.

Incidents and emergencies

Procedures to deal with accidents, incidents and emergencies involving hazardous substances must be provided. These procedures should include:

- ☑ first-aid provisions
- ☑ the use of safety drills and their regular testing
- ☑ identification and details of hazards
- ☑ specific hazards that are likely to occur during any accident, incident or emergency, together with warning and communication systems and emergency actions.

These procedures must be made available to accident and emergency services, and be displayed on site.

7.7   COSHH responsibilities

Designers

The chain of responsibilities starts at the design stage of a project. Under the Construction (Design and Management) Regulations (CDM), designers have a duty to consider the risks created for the construction, maintenance, cleaning and use of a structure that could arise out of their designs. This must include consideration of COSHH issues.

It is important to be aware that this may not eliminate all COSHH risks. Consider, for example, the periodic painting of a high level structure. It may be considered preferable to continue to use a solvent-based paint, as opposed to a water-based paint (a less hazardous product) on the grounds that the periods between painting will be longer, thereby reducing the frequency of working at height.

Furthermore, designers must take all reasonable steps to provide sufficient COSHH information about aspects of the design or its construction or maintenance, to adequately assist the client, other designers and contractors to comply with their duties under the regulations.

Clients

CDM places a duty on the client to provide pre-construction information to other parties involved in a project to protect the health and safety of anyone carrying out construction work, anyone affected by it or those who will use the structure as a place of work.

This will obviously include providing information on any known existing hazardous substances (such as the presence of hazardous residues in pipework or the existence of contaminated ground). Where necessary, this may involve commissioning surveys or taking samples to enable accurate information to be available for a risk-based control. It is no longer acceptable for the client to say: 'there may be the presence of x'.

In accordance with the requirement of the CDM Regulations to identify and collect information about hazardous materials likely to affect a project, the HSE advises lead surveys, where paintwork preparation (disturbance) is involved. This requirement is not date delimited and applies to all buildings.

Contractors and the self-employed

On most construction sites, several contractors may be involved as principal contractors, contractors and self-employed persons.

On projects that are notifiable to the HSE, the principal contractor not only has legal obligations to their own employees but also has duties towards contractors under their control, including self-employed people, and others (for example, visitors and members of the public) who may be affected by the work.

Under CDM and other regulations, organisations that share a workplace must:

- ☑ co-operate with the principal contractor on notifiable projects and help them ensure the work is carried out safely
- ☑ have undertaken their own COSHH assessments in relation to the work they are to undertake
- ☑ have effective arrangements to ensure that control measures are put in place and are monitored.

On projects that are notifiable under CDM, taking account of the above points should assist in compiling the health and safety plan. Some risks are likely to have been highlighted in the information provided by the client and designers. Often designers may simply not be aware of what the job entails, or they may believe the risks are commonplace and therefore any competent contractor should be aware of them.

Employees

Under various sets of health and safety regulations, employees have duties to:

- ☑ work with their employer to enable them to comply with the law
- ☑ make proper use of any control measures provided (including PPE)
- ☑ return any control measure, where provided (mainly PPE), to its accommodation after use
- ☑ report any defects in the control measures to their employer
- ☑ attend health surveillance medicals where required (the employer must pay for the medical and it must be in paid work time).

7.8   Work on another employer's premises

Under CDM the client has a duty to provide pre-construction information to the main or principal contractor, including the information necessary for maintenance or other work to be carried out, where this work is being done in an occupied premises.

Examples of such information are:

- ☑ details of the substances contained in pipework or tanks, if for example a pipefitter is to break into a pipe to replace a valve
- ☑ what gases, vapours or fumes may be discharged through a rooftop ventilation duct during the time a roofer has to work next to it.

There is also a requirement for the client to make sure that contractors are aware of emergency procedures that might arise out of the use of any particular substance(s) on the site.

Obviously, this duty is reciprocal. The contractor has a duty to inform the client or the site occupier if the contractor's work poses risks to the client's staff and visitors and to outline how the risks will be controlled.

This is particularly important where the client has out-of-hours security staff. Often, arrangements that are effective during the working day, to ensure that the contractor and client liaise, can become non-effective after normal working hours (for example, by the security staff entering an agreed exclusion zone due to ignorance of the hazards present).

7.9   Identifying hazardous substances

Packaging or labels

New globally harmonised symbols		Existing European hazard (CHIP) symbols	
☠	Fatal if inhaled, swallowed or in contact with skin.	☠	**Very toxic or toxic** Substances that, in very low quantities or low quantities, cause death or acute or chronic damage to health when inhaled, swallowed or absorbed via the skin.
❗	Warning – harmful if inhaled, swallowed or in contact with skin. Can also cause serious eye irritation.	✗	**Harmful** Substances that may cause death or acute or chronic damage to health when inhaled, swallowed or absorbed via the skin.
❗	Warning – harmful if inhaled, swallowed or in contact with skin. Can also cause serious eye irritation.	✗	**Irritant** Non-corrosive substances that may cause inflammation through immediate, prolonged or repeated contact with the skin or mucous membrane.
🧪	Danger – causes severe skin burns and eye damage.	🧪	**Corrosive** Substances that may, on contact with living tissues, destroy them.
☣	Danger (Category 1) – may cause allergy or asthma symptoms or breathing difficulties if inhaled. Danger (Category 1a and 1b) – may cause cancer.	None	

Material safety data sheets

Before a COSHH assessment is undertaken, it is important to collate information about the substance. Material safety data sheets (MSDS) are available for most substances.

 Material safety data sheets (MSDS) are not COSHH assessments.

Manufacturers and suppliers have a legal obligation to provide the information. Many suppliers have MSDS on their websites. Nevertheless, it should be possible to go into any builder's merchant or DIY store and obtain sufficient information about the products that are being purchased.

By law, data sheets must contain certain information:

- ☑ identification of the substance or preparation and the company or undertaking providing the substance
- ☑ composition and information on ingredients
- ☑ hazard identification
- ☑ first-aid measures
- ☑ fire-fighting measures
- ☑ accidental release measures
- ☑ handling and storage
- ☑ exposure controls and personal protection
- ☑ physical and chemical properties
- ☑ stability and reactivity
- ☑ toxicological information
- ☑ ecological information
- ☑ disposal considerations
- ☑ transport information
- ☑ regulatory information.

Other information can be found in HSE guidance material, technical reference sources, through experience, in information gathered from previous use of the substance(s) and from trade associations.

If the substance is a carcinogen or a mutagen (for example, capable of causing cancer or mutation of the body) every possible step should be taken to eliminate the need for its use.

It is considerably harder to find out information about substances created by the work process.

7.10   COSHH assessments

Overview

An assessment is the fundamental requirement of the COSHH regulations, and it is in two parts.

Part 1: An employer must not carry out any work that is liable to expose employees to any substance hazardous to health, unless a suitable and sufficient assessment of the risks created by the work has been made.

Part 2: If the first part indicates that substances hazardous to health will be used or created, employers must identify the actions to be taken to comply with the remainder of the COSHH regulations.

Who can carry out an assessment?

Employers have the duty to make an assessment, but they can arrange for anyone who is competent to do so to assist with the task, whether from within the company or from outside.

It is the responsibility of the employer to ensure that anyone who carries out any duties under the COSHH Regulations is competent to do so, and has received the necessary information, instruction and training, whether or not the assessor is an employee.

The majority of assessments for small building and construction work can be carried out without the need for the assistance of specialist outside consultants, provided the assessor is competent and:

- ☑ has access to the safety data sheets for the products concerned
- ☑ understands, in basic terms, what the COSHH Regulations require to be done
- ☑ is knowledgeable of the work process being assessed

07

☑ has the ability to systematically gather relevant information regarding exposures to hazardous substances and the subsequent risks to staff by:

   – observing working practices

   – obtaining information on substances used

   – asking questions in the workplace

   – making informed 'what if' judgements regarding possible divergences from standard working practices

☑ can specify the steps and control measures to be taken to comply with the COSHH Regulations

☑ can appreciate their own limitations; knowing when to call in specialists with certain skills (such as when there is a need to undertake air sampling)

☑ has the ability to make valid conclusions, to make a report and communicate findings regarding risks and precautions to the employer and employees.

Carrying out an assessment

1. Know what products and substances you are using.

☑ Compile a list of the hazardous substances that are in use.

☑ Add to the list any hazardous substances that are created as a by-product of a work process.

2. Assess the health hazards they can cause.

☑ From manufacturer's information and other relevant sources, determine the level of risk to health, the degree of exposure and what action is needed to eliminate or control exposure.

☑ Carry out a COSHH risk assessment to establish how the hazardous substances might cause harm.

☑ Record the findings of the risk assessment and the control measures to be taken.

☑ Review any assessment regularly or whenever the exposure monitoring results indicate that it is necessary.

3. Eliminate or minimise the risk of exposure by:

☑ designing a work process that prevents exposure to, or the creation of, hazardous substances (for example, using hydraulic croppers to cut brick pavers, rather than disc-cutting them, to reduce exposure to dust, or using hydraulic shears to cut steelwork, rather than burning gear)

☑ substituting or diluting the substance – designers, managers and specifiers should look towards less hazardous options (for example, lead paint removal by a system that does not heat the paint sufficiently to liberate lead fumes)

☑ using dust or fume extraction – this may be a standalone extractor unit or built-in to some hand tools

☑ using engineering controls (such as totally enclosing the process – often not feasible in the construction environment) or wet cutting

☑ issuing suitable PPE, including respiratory protective equipment (RPE) and making sure it is worn (only after the use of all other risk control measures have been explored).

> **e.g.**
>
> Altering the work method so the process that produces the exposure is no longer necessary (for example, using a demolition shear to cut structural steelwork rather than gas cutting and therefore avoiding a process that may produce metal fumes and toxic gases).
>
> Changing the work method to prevent the production of a hazardous waste product (such as purchasing panels of the correct size, rather than cutting oversize panels on site and producing dust). Given the pressure on reducing waste and manual handling, this is another example where good health and safety is good business.
>
> These examples of controlling the COSHH risk may indicate that some companies are already doing COSHH assessments without realising it.

Some control measures are very simple (for example, damping down the dust on a floor slab before sweeping). Other situations may require a little more thought and ingenuity. However, it is not always possible or reasonably practicable to introduce engineering controls and so the implementation of certain organisational controls may be possible.

4. What to establish.

☑ Who is exposed? Is it just the person using the substance or can it affect other people?

☑ What are they going to do with it? The decision to either spray or apply paint by brush may make a significant difference. Spray application will probably mean a much smaller droplet size, creating a more severe respiratory hazard. This assessment needs to be honest and objective. For example, paint removal gels state on the tin that they are only for brush application, although it is physically possible to spray them. However, the controls required to spray without potentially damaging the skin, eyes or lungs are completely different to those required for brush application.

☑ How often and how much of a substance is used and for how long, are also very important factors.

07

5. Personal protective equipment.

Obtaining appropriate PPE for hazardous substances that can affect the skin might be as simple as identifying the correct type of gloves. However, where there is need for respiratory protection, selecting the correct type of RPE is critical. For example, a filtering face mask designed to filter out dust will be useless against gases, fumes or vapours.

The need for employees to work in masks or respirators is always the last resort. If RPE is necessary, it must:

☑ adequately control exposure to the hazardous substance(s) identified

☑ suit the wearer (comfort and fit)

☑ be appropriate for the job and be used correctly.

Before selecting RPE, proper thought must also be given to:

☑ the physical condition of the employee (breathing through some types of RPE for extended periods can require effort) and whether facial hair or glasses would make the equipment ineffective

☑ providing suitable training on the safe use and maintenance of the RPE.

6. Information, instruction and training.

Before work starts, give information, instruction and training to employees relating to:

☑ the nature and degree of known risks

☑ the control measures adopted and how they should be put into operation

☑ reasons for, and the correct use of, PPE

☑ any exposure monitoring arrangements that are in use

☑ the purpose of, and arrangements for, any health surveillance, if appropriate.

Health surveillance

In many cases, health surveillance must be carried out by an occupational health practitioner and recorded. Employees must have access to medical records that apply to them.

Health surveillance has to be undertaken when an employee is exposed to:

☑ one of the substances and is engaged in a process listed in Schedule 6 of the COSHH Regulations, to which reference should be made, although those listed are unlikely to apply to the construction industry

☑ a hazardous substance that is linked to an identifiable disease related to the exposure (for example, exposure is known to cause asthma) and there are valid techniques for detecting indications of the disease.

Monitoring controls

It is important to monitor the effectiveness of any risk controls. Observation of the task and speaking to the people doing the job is one way to measure the effectiveness of controls. It may also require the regular testing of equipment (such as ventilation), which must be kept in efficient working order.

Organisational controls can be introduced. These are concerned with investigating whether the way in which the job is carried out can be changed so that individual exposure is reduced. For example, by carrying out a job out of normal working hours the number of persons exposed, who would otherwise have to wear PPE, will be significantly reduced. Further examples include:

☑ job rotation so that no individual person is exposed to a substance above its WEL

☑ moving a work activity into the open air to prevent the accumulation of vapour or fumes.

In some circumstances the application of control measures will continue after the actual work activity is completed. Some jobs will require the operatives to go through a full decontamination procedure (for example, working with heavily contaminated land). Anyone who has been in the live working area may have to follow a strict procedure about where they take boots and overalls off, or even go through a shower, and it may involve wearing additional gloves to ensure that contaminants are kept off their skin when decontaminating.

Often, simply washing hands with hot soapy water will suffice. Good COSHH practice and the provision of good welfare facilities are very closely linked. This may mean in some circumstances that eating and drinking are not allowed other than in designated clean zones.

In the past, HSE has targeted a lack of adequate site welfare facilities in relation to occupational health issues. In order to serve a prohibition notice the HSE has to consider whether or not there is imminent risk of harm to health and/or safety. Simply by looking at the substances present and their COSHH assessments may be enough. It is easy to determine, for example, whether a lack of hot water and a hand cleanser has the potential to create a health problem. If there is a lack of such facilities, an HSE inspector may consider there to be an imminent risk to health and therefore justify the serving of a prohibition notice.

Records

The COSHH assessment, training, briefings, monitoring arrangements and health surveillance must be recorded. Some records may need to be kept for 40 years. In companies where there are union-appointed safety representatives, or representatives of employee safety, the above information should be available to them.

Emergencies

If significant or dangerous accidental releases or leakages of a hazardous substance are possible, despite the control measures that have been implemented, an emergency plan should be drawn up and instigated for achieving suitable control and for safeguarding the health of anyone who may be affected.

This needs to be kept in context – spilling 500 ml of gloss paint is probably more of an environmental and quality issue than a serious occupational health hazard.

The emergency plan should include first-aid provisions and safety drills, including the testing of drills at regular intervals.
Any particular hazards that are likely to occur as a result of the emergency must be specified.

The emergency plan should be made available to all people potentially affected and be displayed on site. It should also be made available to the accident and emergency services.

Depending on the substance, a spillage may also be a pollution issue.

Emergency plans must be drawn up and consideration should be given to:

- ☑ making appropriate first aid provision
- ☑ developing and practicing safety drills (for example, site evacuations) as appropriate
- ☑ identification and details of hazards
- ☑ making available details of specific hazards that are known to exist
- ☑ developing warning and communication systems
- ☑ displaying emergency plans
- ☑ making relevant information available to the emergency services.

Summary

The assessment is a considered judgement that balances the hazardous properties of the substance, the method by which it will be handled and the environment in which it will be used.

The skill of the COSHH assessor is to:

- ☑ sift through the information contained on the MSDS and other sources (such as on the container)
- ☑ extract the useful information
- ☑ incorporate their knowledge of how, when and where the substance is used
- ☑ from the information available, produce a useful and useable COSHH assessment to guide those who will be doing the work.

> **e.g.**
>
> Insulating roof spaces with synthetic mineral fibre offers a number of challenges. The material has a WEL for the concentration of fibres in air, and is irritating to the skin. The roof space is an unpleasant working environment as it can be extremely hot in summer and the level of natural ventilation may be low.
>
> The obvious way to reduce exposure is to provide a Type 5 coverall and a disposable mask to CE 149 P3. However, whether this is sufficient must be considered under the requirements of the COSHH Regulations. For a company that employs people full time to insulate lofts, the answer is probably not; they should be looking at the use of ventilation equipment to drive exposures and possibly the temperature down. However, a small contractor carrying out this type of work five or six times a year can be more selective about when to carry out the work, so it could be argued that by carrying out the work during the cooler months, the lower level controls are sufficient.
>
> The judgement is based on experience and backed up with paperwork to justify decisions.

www. The HSE has compiled a set of example COSHH risk assessments for some industries, available on its website.

There is also excellent guidance on silica exposure on the HSE's website.

7.11   Control measures

Use of control measures

Employers should have procedures in place to ensure that measures provided to control exposure to hazardous substances, including the provision of PPE, are properly used or applied. These procedures should include regular inspections of working practices and a system to ensure that, where remedial action is found to be necessary, it is promptly taken.

Employees have a duty to:

☑ make full and proper use of any control measures and to properly wear any PPE provided for their use

☑ take all reasonable steps to return the PPE after use to the accommodation provided

☑ notify any defects at once to management.

These are all common sense measures. Working with hazardous substances also dictates that employees make every effort to practise a high standard of personal hygiene, for example, by:

☑ removing any protective clothing (this may be contaminated) and thoroughly washing before eating and drinking

☑ consuming food and drink only in mess rooms or canteens

☑ making full use of shower facilities

☑ using the storage facilities provided and keeping personal protective clothing separate from ordinary clothing, to avoid possible contamination

☑ smoking only in designated areas and thoroughly washing hands before handling cigarettes or tobacco (including rolling cigarettes), otherwise contamination may spread from hands to the mouth and be ingested into the stomach, which can lead, in some circumstances, to serious health problems.

Maintenance, examination and test of control measures

Employers are required to ensure that all measures installed to prevent or control exposure to substances hazardous to health under the COSHH Regulations are maintained in efficient working order and in good repair.

Certain engineering controls require thorough examination and tests, as follows.

Local exhaust ventilation plant

Local exhaust ventilation plant should be examined and tested at least once every 14 months. This would be expected in, for example, a woodworking shop. Technically, using a vacuum cleaner as an extractor on a power tool is creating a local exhaust ventilation system. However, because this is not a fixed system, it is unlikely that this would be considered for formal testing, but obviously it would need to work effectively.

More frequent testing of local exhaust ventilation is required for those processes listed in Schedule 4 of the regulations, although none of those processes are directly related to construction activities.

Any defects in local exhaust ventilation systems must be reported and promptly rectified.

Non-disposable respiratory protective equipment (RPE)

Thorough examinations and tests of non-disposable respiratory protective equipment (RPE) should be carried out, where appropriate, at suitable intervals.

The Approved Code of Practice (ACoP) that supports the COSHH Regulations (L5) specifies that such examinations and tests should be carried out at least every month, and more frequently where the conditions of use are particularly severe. Longer intervals may be more appropriate in the case of certain RPE (such as half-mask respirators used infrequently for short spells against air contaminants of relatively low toxicity). However, the longest interval between examinations and tests should not exceed three months.

Face-fit testing by someone who is competent is required for any tight-fitting masks. For full-face masks this needs to be quantitative testing using a computerised method.

 For further information on RPE refer to Chapter B06 Personal protective equipment.

Disposable RPE

No examinations or tests are required, provided that the disposable RPE is used for only one working day or shift and then disposed of.

Again, face-fit testing by a competent person is required. This can be qualitative testing using a bitter/sweet solution to check the effectiveness of the fit. (If the wearer can taste or smell the solution then the fit is not correct and the test is a fail.)

07

Records

All examinations, tests and repairs carried out on engineering controls and non-disposable RPE should be suitably recorded in any format provided they are easily retrievable. These records should be kept for at least five years.

 Detailed maintenance arrangements for engineering controls and non-disposable RPE are in the Approved Code of Practice (L5).

Review of assessments

An assessment should be reviewed regularly, and at once, if:

☑ there is reason to believe that it is no longer valid (for example, new information on health risks has come to light)

☑ the work to which it relates has changed significantly (for example, new substances have been introduced, or the method of working is to change, such as the use of a spray gun to apply paint instead of a brush or roller)

☑ environment and/or health monitoring results indicate it is necessary.

The definition of regularly will depend on a number of factors (such as the nature of the risk). However, the maximum period between reviews should not exceed five years.

Each review should trigger an opportunity to consider whether exposure can now be prevented (for example, by substituting a less hazardous substance or by process changes). Similarly, control measures should be reappraised to see whether they are still adequate or if further improvements are necessary and possible.

7.12   Monitoring exposure at the workplace

The Approved Code of Practice (L5) defines monitoring as the use of valid and suitable occupational hygiene techniques, by competent people, to measure the exposure of employees to substances hazardous to health.

There are certain situations, outlined below, in which the monitoring of exposure to a hazardous substance is required. Sometimes, however, it is so obvious that there is a problem that the money may be better spent on solving the problem rather than simply confirming what was already suspected.

Monitoring is required in the following circumstances:

☑ where a serious health hazard could arise because of failure or deterioration of the control measures

☑ where it is necessary to ensure that a WEL or employer-imposed working standard is not exceeded. Significant exposure to silica dust may require monitoring

☑ when it is necessary to carry out an additional check on the effectiveness of any control measure

☑ where work involves the use of any carcinogen or mutagen and any work with substances or processes listed in Schedule 4 of the COSHH Regulations (for example, work involving vinyl chloride monomer or chromium plating).

It is unlikely the competency for carrying out monitoring will be available in-house to many companies. A number of health and safety consultancies can carry out the work. If competent advisors are bought in, it is essential to establish that they have the necessary experience and resource to do it.

 The work would often be considered to be occupational hygiene so it is worthwhile contacting the British Occupational Hygiene Society.

In some situations, information about typical exposure values is available from trade bodies or HSE guidance. If the job being carried out is typical in all respects then, as a starting point, it would normally be acceptable to take these levels of exposure as being typical of the exposure levels actually experienced. However, there are obvious dangers in relying heavily on typical exposure values, particularly if the way the job is being carried out starts to diverge from the norm.

An example of monitoring, would be the use of a personal sampler to monitor an airborne contaminant in the breathing zone of an employee.

Monitoring records

Monitoring records must be kept in a suitable format and be available either as individual records or as a suitable summary for five years. If they are representative of the personal exposures of identifiable employees, the records must be kept for at least 40 years.

Health surveillance

The main purpose of health surveillance is to detect problems with the health of employees at the earliest possible stage. The purpose of control measures is to prevent damage to the health of employees; this is something that health surveillance cannot do. However, adverse health surveillance results may indicate that the existing control measures are not working properly.

Health surveillance has to be undertaken when:

☑ an employee is exposed to one of the substances and is engaged in a process listed in Schedule 6 of the COSHH Regulations, to which reference should be made, although those listed are unlikely to apply to the construction industry

☑ an employee is exposed to a substance that is hazardous to health and there is an identifiable disease or adverse health effect related to this exposure (which may occur because of the conditions of the work) and there are valid techniques for detecting indications of the disease or effect. For example, isocyanates used in two-pack paints are respiratory irritants and can result in sensitisation and asthma.

Working on contaminated land often requires some form of health surveillance. This may include lung function testing or direct analysis of blood, urine or hair samples. Normally this would occur before, during and after the work. It allows a personal baseline to be established and then simply acts as a check that the control measures are working.

Suitable health surveillance can range from surveillance under the supervision of an employment medical adviser, an appointed doctor or a registered medical practitioner, to enquiries about symptoms, or an examination by an occupational health nurse. At the other end of the scale, health surveillance could simply involve a trained manager or supervisor inspecting an employee's hands and forearms, looking for the early signs of dermatitis.

Where the hazardous properties of a substance indicate, via the COSHH assessment, that health surveillance may be appropriate, advice on how to proceed can be sought from the Employment Medical Advisory Service (EMAS) of the HSE.

Employers are required to keep health records of employees under health surveillance for at least 40 years from the date of the last entry.

Information, instruction and training for people who may be exposed to hazardous substances

If an employee is likely to be exposed to substances hazardous to health, the employer must provide sufficient information, instruction and training so that the employee is aware of the:

☑ health risks

☑ precautions that should be taken.

It is important that workers do not put themselves at risk due to lack of information, instruction or training.

Therefore, they should be knowledgeable of the health risks, the precautions they should take (including the control measures), and be able to use the supplied PPE effectively.

They should also know what procedures to follow in the event of an emergency.

7.13   REACH Regulations

REACH is a European Community Regulation on chemicals and their safe use (EC 1907/2006). It deals with the registration, evaluation, authorisation and restriction of chemical substances.

The impacts of this system of registration for chemicals will have some impact on the way that information is made available. REACH is a new regulatory regime on suppliers and will come into force over the next 10 years. It requires suppliers to consider the possible effect that chemicals will have in use.

This is very different to the present situation where the user, who may know little about the chemicals, has to undertake the assessment. REACH will put the responsibility onto those who should be in the best position to do this.

REACH will operate alongside COSHH and is designed so that better information on the hazards of chemicals and how to use them safely will be passed down the supply chain by chemical manufacturers and importers through improved safety data sheets.

 Further information can be found on the HSE's website and on the European Chemical Agency's website.

07

Appendix A – Management action plan

1.	Compile an inventory of all hazardous substances to which employees may be exposed, which are either purchased (proprietary products), created by a work process (dust and fumes) or may be already on site (micro-organisms, contaminated land and residues).
2.	Gather relevant technical information about each substance from sources such as labelling, safety data sheets, the HSE website and trade organisations.
	For each substance, evaluate the work task(s) and working practices associated with it.
	If necessary, observe the work activity in which the hazardous substance is used or created.
3.	From information and observations made, decide if there are any risks to health.
4.	Assess what action needs to be taken to prevent exposure (**priority**), or to control it to an acceptable level.
	Record the significant findings of the assessment.
5.	Take the actions necessary to ensure that the appropriate control measures are provided, properly used and maintained as necessary.
	Provide all users of (or those creating) each hazardous substance with the necessary information, instruction and training.
	From the information gained, decide if there is any requirement for exposure monitoring and health surveillance.
6.	Review the assessment regularly and revise it as necessary.

07

Appendix B – Health and safety COSHH assessment

Diesel fuel

Name of hazardous substance	Auto diesel.
Substance hazard classification	Flammable, harmful/irritant.
Trade name(s)	Any auto fuel production company.
Substance used for	Motive power for plant and other diesel powered vehicles.
Likely circumstances of exposure	Refuelling vehicles or filling other containers.

Potential hazards	Risk control measures	Emergency procedures
Inhalation: Can lead to nausea and headaches.	1. Avoid inhaling vapour or mist; dispense directly into tank using nozzle. 2. Refuel vehicles or otherwise decant in the open air.	Remove to fresh air. Seek medical attention if conditions are severe. Remove the victim from exposure.
Skin contact: Can be irritating and have a defatting effect. Can cause contact or irritant dermatitis.	1. Avoid skin contact. Wear PVC gloves. Do not use as a cleaning agent. 2. Only refuel vehicles from a dispensing nozzle directly into fuel tanks. 3. Use funnel if dispensing into container.	Remove contaminated clothing. Wash skin thoroughly with soap and warm water.
Eye contact: Will cause irritation.	1. Wear eye protection if splashing can occur. 2. Ensure refuelling nozzle is fully inserted into fuel tank neck. 3. Dispense at a rate that avoids splashes.	Rinse immediately with water until irritation subsides. Seek medical advice.
Ingestion: Will irritate mouth, throat, and so on.	1. Do not eat, drink or smoke when handling. 2. Do not attempt to siphon using the mouth.	Do not induce vomiting. Wash mouth with water. Seek immediate medical attention.
Fire: Flammable liquid. Products of combustion are toxic. Vapour/air mixture is explosive.	1. Do not smoke when handling. 2. Store bulk diesel away from heat, sources of ignition and flammable materials. 3. Do not allow to come into contact with hot engine parts during refuelling.	Clear the area. Do not inhale vapours or smoke. If trained, use foam or CO2 extinguisher. Call emergency services to large fires.
Spillage: Fumes/vapour likely to collect in low areas.	1. Do not allow to enter drains. Eliminate ignition sources. 2. Ensure good ventilation.	Contain with sand or granules. Remove into a container. Dispose of as hazardous waste.

Additional information: Environmentally damaging.

Are current controls adequate: Yes/No

Assessment date		Next review date	

Approved for use by (print name and position)	
Signature	

Appendix C – Self-assessment questionnaire

Question	Emergency procedures
1. What is the main purpose of the COSHH Regulations?	The main purpose of the COSHH Regulations is to protect the health of employees working with substances hazardous to health.
2. When do you have to start complying with the regulations?	You must start now. The regulations are fully in force. Unless you act promptly, you could be breaking the law.
3. What is a substance hazardous to health?	(a) Substances listed as very toxic, toxic, harmful, corrosive or irritant. (b) Substances listed as having a workplace exposure limit (WEL). (c) Anything else that produces similar effects to any of the things mentioned above.
4. What is said about lead and asbestos?	They are not covered by the COSHH Regulations but, of course, you must comply with the Control of Lead at Work Regulations and the Control of Asbestos Regulations.
5. Are there any other exceptions to the regulations?	Yes, anything that is a hazard because it is radioactive, explosive or flammable is excepted, but only for those reasons: If the substances have other hazardous properties, like giving off a fume (solvents), these are covered by the regulations.
6. What must you make an assessment of?	The risk to employees of working with a substance hazardous to health and the actions needed to comply with the regulations. Substances may be hazardous solely at high or low temperatures or at high or low pressure.
7. If your assessment shows that an employee will be exposed to a substance hazardous to health, what should you do?	Prevent the exposure, if possible. If you cannot, you must adequately control it.
8. What is the main recommendation about control measures?	Control should be exercised without the use of personal protective equipment, if at all possible.
9. Whose responsibility is it to provide or use control measures?	The employer must provide them, and the employee must use them. The employer must also ensure use by properly supervising the workplace and employees.
10. When is monitoring of the workplace necessary?	When it is necessary to check on the effectiveness of control measures or to protect the health of workers.
11. When is health surveillance required?	Only where special circumstances require it (such as processes mentioned in the regulations or where certain diseases can be identified).
12. What can happen if you do not make the assessments?	The enforcing authority (the Health and Safety Executive or Local Authority) can issue an improvement or prohibition notice or even prosecute in the criminal court in certain circumstances.
13. If it is alleged that you have broken the regulations, what, if any, defence have you got?	You must prove that you took all reasonable precautions and exercised due diligence to avoid committing the offence.
14. Who has to make the actual assessments?	It is the responsibility of employers to ensure that assessments are done, although they can employ a competent person to carry out the assessment.
15. If a substance that can be inhaled does not have a control limit, what would be the adequate control standard?	Control would be considered adequate if the majority of the population could be regularly exposed to that substance at that level of exposure without any adverse effects on their health.
16. Where will you find a list of substances that have a workplace exposure limit?	In HSE Guidance Note EH40 Workplace Exposure Limits (regularly updated).
17. Which assessments have to be recorded?	All assessments must be recorded, unless they are very basic, simple and obvious.
18. Can you use other people's assessments?	Yes, provided that they exactly fit your circumstances, or can be modified or adapted to suit your needs.
19. When must you review an assessment?	When it is, or you suspect it may be, no longer valid because of changes in work methods, introduction of new types of control measures, or new information; or when monitoring shows that controls may not be working and, of course, when new substances are introduced.

Question	Emergency procedures
20. Define the terms **hazard** and **risk**.	A **hazard** is the potential of a substance to cause harm.
	A **risk** is the likelihood of that harm occurring in the circumstances that exist.
21. To whom do you have a duty under the COSHH Regulations?	To employees and anyone else who may be affected, such as contractors and people working or passing nearby.
22. What is the first step in the assessment process?	List all of the products and substances that you use, and determine which are substances hazardous to health.
23. Who has the right to ask to see your assessments?	Enforcing authority inspectors (either the Health and Safety Executive inspector or Local Authority environmental health officer).
	If you have safety representatives, they may also have a right to see your assessments. Principal contractors or your customers could also be included here, although they may not have a legal right.
24. What is the best recommended control measure?	Elimination of the substance altogether or substituting a non-hazardous substance.
25. When can the use of personal protective equipment (PPE) or respiratory protective equipment (RPE) be considered?	Only as a last resort, after every other type of control has been considered and PPE or RPE is found to be the only reasonably practicable method of achieving control.
26. What is the general rule about the maintenance and inspection of control measures?	Anything provided as a control measure, except single-use RPE, must be properly maintained, regularly inspected and records kept. The regulations give details of inspections and records.
27. What information, instruction and training do you have to give your employees?	Information, instruction and training on the risks to health of the substances that they work with the precautions they must take and any controls they must use.
28. What is monitoring?	The use of a valid occupational hygiene technique to properly assess the exposure of employees to substances hazardous to health.
29. When is monitoring necessary?	When it is necessary to ensure the adequacy of the control methods in use or it is otherwise needed to protect the health of employees.

How did you do?

Check which questions you could not answer, or got wrong. List the points covered then take a second look at the sections of this chapter that deal with them. Try the test again later.

07

The Control of Substances Hazardous to Health (COSHH)

08

Skin protection

Active concern for the welfare of employees will encourage their co-operation in reporting skin irritations at an early stage.

Workers are more likely to co-operate in preventative measures if they are told positively what dermatitis is and what can be done to prevent it from occurring.

Introduction   104
Key points   105
Harmful substances   106
Effects of contact with some materials   107
Reducing risks   107
Protecting the worker   107
Inspections and examinations   109
Health risks from working in the sun   109
Legislative requirements   111

Appendix A – Some timbers known to produce
            dermatitis and other irritant effects   112
Appendix B – Model sun safety policy   113

8.1   Introduction

Industrial dermatitis is a major cause of absenteeism, not only in the building and construction industry but across the whole spectrum of industry, and it accounts for over half of all working days lost through industrial sickness.

It is an inflammatory skin condition that is neither infectious nor contagious. It is caused by certain irritants contained in many industrial materials. Although dermatitis is not itself an infection, it can lead to infection when the skin's natural barriers break down.

There are two general types of dermatitis.

Contact (irritant) dermatitis

Irritant dermatitis is usually caused by the skin coming into contact with an irritant substance – usually a chemical, but it can be a mineral.

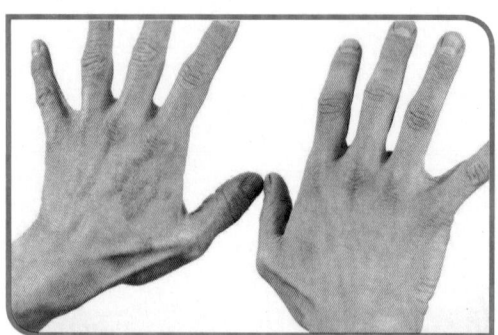

Repeated exposure to extreme heat or cold can lead to physical damage to the skin and make it more likely that irritant dermatitis will occur. Wet work, which involves the hands being wet for long periods (more than two hours a day) or repeatedly getting the hands wet, can also cause dermatitis. Anyone may be affected and the length of exposure, together with the strength of the irritant substance, will affect the seriousness of the complaint. Most cases of dermatitis are of this type.

Allergic (sensitive) dermatitis

Sensitising dermatitis, also known as allergic contact dermatitis, accounts for about 20% of all work-related dermatitis.

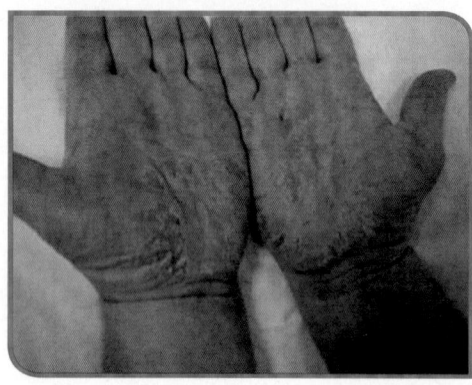

Some people develop a sudden allergic reaction following exposure to a specific substance. The reaction may be after weeks, months or even years of use or exposure to a substance without any ill effects.

However, once that sensitising dermatitis has occurred, any future exposure to the substance will again produce an adverse reaction. The exposure may be to an everyday chemical or mineral, and may be as simple as exposure to nickel in jewellery.

The outer layer of skin forms a natural defence against irritants, providing it is undamaged by cuts and abrasions, or by solvents (such as hydrocarbons, benzene, tetrachloride, spirits and thinners) that remove the skin's natural protective oils. Reaction of the skin to an irritant varies from one individual to another. The reaction may be only a mild redness or it can develop into swelling, blisters and septic ulcers that are both unsightly and painful.

Personal hygiene is particularly important when working with materials that may be irritants, as resistance to an irritant varies with the type of skin. Pores, ducts and hair follicles in the skin may admit irritants to the sensitive inner skin layer and, therefore, washing thoroughly to remove dirt and grime with soap and water is an essential preventative measure.

It is equally important that clothing is kept clean. Oil-stained overalls are a known cause of skin problems around the thighs.

The best course of action is to prevent skin contact with all potentially irritant substances, even if this is achieved by issuing personal protective equipment (PPE). When total avoidance of skin contact cannot be guaranteed, it will be necessary in some cases to implement occupational health screening (depending on the hazardous properties of the substance). Initially this should involve establishing whether the persons involved in the job have had any previous adverse reaction to the substance(s) in use.

Those people who are found to be allergic to one or more substance should be identified and not be allowed to handle or come into contact with them. Any part of the body that comes into contact with a skin irritant may be affected although it is usually the hands, wrists and forearms that are affected initially. Treatment for dermatitis should be sought as soon as possible because, if neglected, symptoms may spread to other parts of the body.

It should be noted that occupational dermatitis diagnosed by a registered medical practitioner is notifiable to the Health and Safety Executive (HSE) under the provisions of the Reporting of Injuries, Diseases and Dangerous Occurrences Regulations (RIDDOR).

 For further information refer to Chapter A13 Accident reporting and investigation.

 Advice on screening can be obtained from the HSE's Employment Medical Advisory Service (EMAS).

Skin burns

Many substances used in the construction industry have corrosive properties that can cause severe burns to the skin. These substances have either strong acid or alkali properties. Hot work processes also have the potential to cause skin burns.

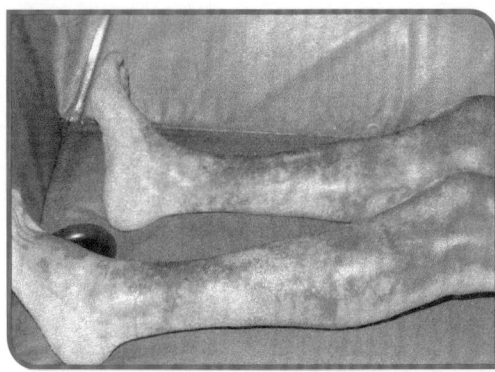

Wellington boots, for example, whether reinforced with protective toecaps, soles or not, are essential in preventing burns from wet cement or concrete. The cement content, when mixed with water, becomes highly corrosive and will cause severe burns to body tissue.

This picture shows the severely burnt legs of a man who was ignorant of the dangers of wet cement, the effect it can have on skin, and the need to wear wellington boots to protect the legs.

Abrasion and cuts

Manually handling objects with rough surfaces and sharp corners can cause damage to the skin of the hands if appropriate gloves (such as rigger gloves) are not worn. Repetitive manual handling may even make the situation worse. Such damage breaks the surface of the skin making it more vulnerable to absorbing other substances that could potentially have severe health effects.

Worn-out gloves must be thrown away and replacements obtained.

Where objects with sharp edges (such as sheet glass and sheet metal components) have to be manually handled, gloves with cut-proof material (such as Kevlar) woven into the fabric must be worn.

Cover all cuts and abrasions
Report sickness immediately

Ideally, work would be organised so that the manual handling of all such objects could be avoided. However, given the nature of construction, total avoidance is usually not possible. For example, a roof tiler may now use an inclined hoist to get the tiles up to roof level, but the hoist must still be loaded and the tiles distributed around the roof by hand.

With the increased emphasis on occupational health issues, tradespeople will often now wear gloves to carry out manual handling, tasks that at one time would have been carried out with bare hands.

08

8.2   Key points

☑ Many of the substances used or created during construction activities have the potential to cause severe skin problems.

☑ The fact that skin complaints (such as sensitising (allergic) dermatitis) are on the increase suggests that the threats to health are not being taken seriously.

☑ The (COSHH) risk assessment and the information on the accompanying data sheet and a substance's container should indicate the degree of risk and the preventative measures necessary.

☑ Ideally, the risk will be eliminated by avoiding the substance altogether, although this will often not be practical.

☑ Hazardous substances created by work processes will carry no health warning but must be identified in a (COSHH) risk assessment.

☑ Skin conditions can be prevented by simple actions (such as wearing the appropriate gloves or PPE).

☑ Barrier creams offer limited protection against some substances but should not be relied upon.

☑ Most substances can enter the body through openings (such as cuts and grazes). Other, more hazardous substances, can penetrate unbroken skin.

☑ Periodic self-checks or hand-checks, carried out by someone trained to recognise the symptoms, are an effective form of initial health surveillance.

☑ Prompt medical advice should be sought if there could be an emerging health problem.

8.3　Harmful substances

Use of harmful substances

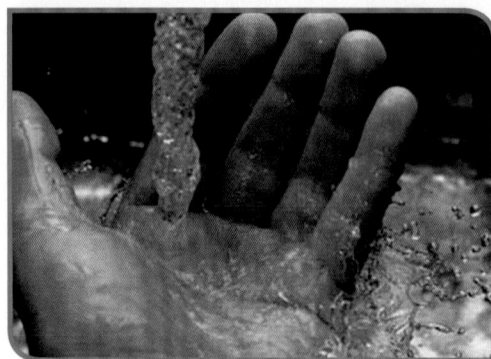 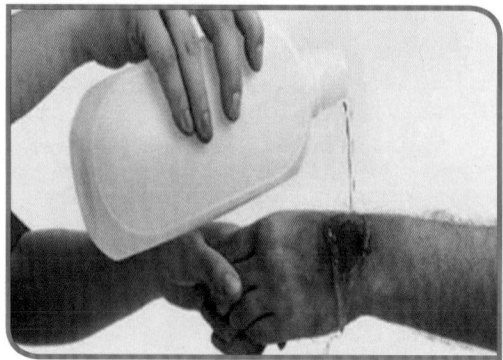

Specifically in relation to skin protection, employers must ensure that the appropriate assessments have been made on any articles and substances used at work, and that they are:

- ☑ safe and free from any risk to health, when properly used
- ☑ used in accordance with the findings of risk assessments, procedures and conditions stipulated
- ☑ properly stored, transported and handled
- ☑ properly marked to indicate any special precautions that need to be taken.

They must ensure that persons using such articles and substances are:

- ☑ suitable and able to carry out the task that is expected of them
- ☑ properly and adequately trained in their use and aware of all necessary precautions that must be taken
- ☑ provided with appropriate personal protective clothing and equipment
- ☑ supplied with all necessary information
- ☑ educated in the dangers of skin conditions, and in methods to be used to prevent those conditions arising
- ☑ able to detect, and be aware of, the need to report any signs of skin infection or dermatitis.

Adequate washing and first-aid facilities must be provided, and barrier and cleansing creams should be available. In addition, the employer is responsible for providing supervision to ensure the above procedures, conditions and correct methods of work are maintained and that the proper facilities and equipment are available.

Potentially harmful substances and agents

Substances and physical agents that can be potentially harmful to the skin include:

- ☑ pitch, tar and bitumen
- ☑ cement or lime
- ☑ brick, stone, tile and plaster dust
- ☑ paints, varnishes, lacquers and stains
- ☑ certain types of timber
- ☑ fibreglass
- ☑ certain epoxy resins
- ☑ acrylic and formaldehyde resins

- ☑ chromates (in primers and cement)
- ☑ organic solvents
- ☑ petrol, diesel and paraffin oils
- ☑ white spirit and thinners
- ☑ acids or alkalis
- ☑ ionising radiation
- ☑ solar radiation
- ☑ other materials (depending on individual reactions).

Identifying hazardous symbols

  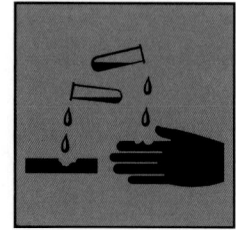

Toxic　　　　　　　　　*Irritant*　　　　　　　　　*Corrosive*

8.4   Effects of contact with some materials

Skin contact with certain materials can cause a variety of reactions and some examples are given below. This list is not exhaustive.

Mineral oils, including fuel oils and mould oils, can lead to inflammatory skin conditions – dermatitis, oil acne or even skin cancer. These may be caused by constant contact with oil or oily clothes and rags (for example, when placed in overall pockets).

Chemicals, including strong alkalis and certain acids, chromates, formaldehyde, are substances that can penetrate the skin causing ulcers (for example, chrome ulceration) and dermatitis.

Cement and lime can also cause chronic dermatitis. Wetted cement and lime become more alkaline, corrosive and therefore potentially very damaging to the skin.

Solvents and de-greasers, including paraffin, turpentine, petroleum products, thinners and similar solvents, affect the skin by dissolving the natural oils (de-fatting), which renders it more vulnerable to attack by other substances and bacteria.

Tar, pitch, bitumen products, including cresols and phenols like mineral oil, cause inflammation, blisters and oil acne.

Radiation, light and heat radiation, including X-rays, beta and gamma radiation, extremes of radiation, temperature and humidity, make the skin more susceptible to dermatitis and other skin problems.

Epoxy resin hardeners, glass fibres, certain woods, fungicides and insecticides may irritate the skin and lead to dermatitis.

8.5   Reducing risks

Substitute products

In line with the requirements of the COSHH Regulations, every effort must be made to ascertain which substances have the potential to cause dermatitis and, where possible, to substitute other materials that either eliminate or reduce the danger. An alternative, where possible, may be to use a more dilute form of the substance.

Reducing contact

If the outcome of an assessment is that there are no alternatives, and substances that cause dermatitis have to be used, methods of work should be implemented that eliminate contact between the skin and the substance.

The use of mechanical handling equipment may be possible but, if this is not available, simple devices and instruments, including splash guards, drip trays, tongs and scrapers will help to reduce the risk.

Healthy working conditions

It may be possible to use localised ventilation and exhaust systems to deal with dust, fumes and oil spray.

Plentiful supplies of clean fresh air and comfortable working temperatures are vitally important, as is the general cleanliness of the working area, the machinery and any other equipment that is in use.

Wherever possible and appropriate, the display of warning and information signs should be prominently made, so that all employees are aware of the hazards existing in that area.

8.6   Protecting the worker

If an employer intends to use any items of PPE (including gloves and barrier creams) as part of their skin protection strategy in the workplace, then it is important that the correct PPE is selected.

All PPE for skin protection that is produced or imported by reputable companies is manufactured to British and European Standards.

As with all PPE for use at work, skin protection should be selected by a competent person who can ensure, in discussion with the supplier, that it meets the appropriate standards.

Most leading manufacturers and suppliers offer an advisory service on the selection of gloves and other items of skin protection.

Protective clothing

Protective clothing and other PPE provides one of the most practical ways of limiting contact between the skin and other substances. To be effective, all protective clothing must be the right size, fit for the purpose, maintained in good condition, cleaned regularly and stored carefully when not in use.

08

Skin protection

Protective clothing may include gloves, overalls, eye protectors (such as goggles and face shields), aprons, boots and leggings, depending on the work being undertaken. Legislation requires the provision and wearing of protective clothing for specific processes and operations. The protective equipment provided must be suited to the requirements of the job.

Regular inspections must be made to ensure it remains sound and adequate.

Gloves

A glove suitable for handling abrasive materials may offer no protection against chemicals. The appropriate glove for sulphuric acid may not be approved for chromic acid.

Much care is needed in selecting the right type of glove to be used for a particular hazard. Manufacturers' charts and recommendations should be followed when selecting gloves to protect the wearer against specific hazards. A properly selected glove can be useful in the prevention of dermatitis if care is taken to avoid getting contaminants inside the gloves when putting them on and taking them off.

The modern materials from which gloves are now made enable them to be effective against hazardous substances whilst generally allowing the necessary amount of feel and dexterity where these factors are an issue.

Industrial gloves – some types and uses

Hazard	Recommended type
Acids, concrete, brickwork, stain removers, solvents, alkalis.	Neoprene, nitrile, PVC, rubber.
Esters, ethers, ketones (mastic, sealers), aldehydes, petroleum-based products.	Medium and heavyweight rubber, neoprene, nitrile, PVC.
High and low temperatures.	Nitrile, PVC, medium and heavyweight rubber.
Abrasion, unloading bricks and blocks, general materials handling.	Rubber, nitrile, PVC, neoprene, chrome-leather with reinforced palm.
Bitumen, hot work, or similar.	Asbestos substitute or Nomex gloves.

 For further information on the selection of work gloves refer to Chapter B06 Personal protective equipment.

Barrier substances

Where exposure of the skin is unavoidable, the use of barrier creams or other preparations may limit the degree of contact.

These substances are applied before starting work and removed by washing after each spell of work. Re-application is necessary before resuming work.

Water-soluble barrier creams are unsuitable where wet work is involved, and some substances are worn off with manual work.

There are many types of barrier substances available and it is essential that the right type is used for the work being done.

Most barrier substances afford only limited protection and should never be relied on as a sole means of protection.

Hygiene

Personal cleanliness is an important factor in the prevention of dermatitis. The necessary washing facilities and an ample supply of clean warm water, soap and clean towels should be made available near to the workplace, and workers should be encouraged to use these facilities.

Facilities for changing out of work-stained or contaminated clothing will also help to promote personal cleanliness.

All facilities should be kept clean and inspected regularly.

Skin cleansers

Soap and water will help restore the skin to its natural state after the use of barrier creams. Skin cleansers may be required where soap and water are not adequate (such as insoluble barrier substances). With some skin cleansers (sanitisers), an additional moisturiser may be needed.

Solvents (such as paraffin, turpentine, thinners and petrol) remove the natural oils from the skin and must not be used for skin cleaning. Conditioning creams, designed to replace the natural oils of the skin, removed through frequent cleansing, should be used when necessary.

First aid

A healthy, intact skin is an effective barrier against some substances and infection, but the slightest cut or other injury may admit infection.

All abrasions to the skin, however minor, should be treated at once. However, be aware that some substances can penetrate unbroken skin.

Treatment of dermatitis

Medical advice should be sought as early as possible when there is concern. Any treatment of dermatitis or its symptoms should be left to a doctor.

8.7 Inspections and examinations

Educating staff in prevention

Regular inspections of the workplace, work methods and precautionary procedures adopted will help ensure that the risk of dermatitis, or other skin complaints, is kept to a minimum. At-risk employees should be encouraged to carry out self-checks for the first signs of dermatitis and, ideally, supervisors should be trained to identify dermatitis. In appropriate circumstances, arrangements should be made for workers to have regular examinations by an occupational health professional to detect early signs of skin complaints, such as dermatitis and skin cancer.

Active concern for the welfare of employees will encourage their co-operation in reporting skin irritations at an early stage. Workers are more likely to co-operate in preventative measures if they are told positively what dermatitis is and what can be done to prevent it from occurring.

The HSE's Skin at Work website contains basic practical advice for employers and employees on the prevention of skin diseases. The site also contains in-depth technical advice for occupational health nurses and health and safety practitioners, plus other resources.

08

CITB-ConstructionSkills publishes a DVD-based occupational health training package entitled *If only I'd known* (DVD 064). This covers many of the points dealt with in this chapter.

8.8 Health risks from working in the sun

A sunny day usually makes most people feel good, but too much sunlight can actually damage the skin. It is not simply sudden exposure while on holiday that is harmful. Even a tan that has been built up gradually can be harmful to health. A tan is a sign that the skin has been potentially damaged.

Skin damage is caused by ultraviolet rays in sunlight. People whose jobs keep them outdoors for a long time (such as building, construction and civil engineering workers) may, if their skin is unprotected, get more sun on their skin than is healthy for them. They will then be at greater risk of developing skin cancer.

The dangers

In the short term, excess exposure of unprotected skin to the sun can cause blistering and peeling. Even mild reddening of the skin is a sign of skin damage. In the long term, too much sun will speed up ageing of the skin, making it leathery, mottled and wrinkled. However, the most serious issue is an increased chance of developing skin cancer; cases of skin cancer have doubled in the last 20 years. Around 40,000 people are diagnosed with skin cancer and 2,000 people die from it each year.

Some medicines, and contact with some chemicals used at work (such as bitumen products), can also make the skin more sensitive to sunlight (photosensitivity).

Skin protection

The risks

Some people are more at risk than others – and the effect that strong sunlight can have on the different types of skin is explained below. People with white skin are most at risk. Workers should take particular care if they have:

☑ fair or freckled skin that does not tan, or goes red or burns before it tans

☑ red or fair hair and light coloured eyes

☑ a large number of moles.

Skin types

Type 1: White skin, never tans, always burns. Often person has red or fair hair, blue eyes, pale skin and freckles.

Type 2: White skin, burns easily, but may tan eventually. Person may have fair hair, blue eyes and freckles.

Workers with skin Types 1 or 2 must take extra care to avoid strong sunshine or cover up with tightly woven clothing and a hat.

Type 3: White skin tans easily and burns rarely. Person has dark hair and eyes and slightly darker skin.

Type 4: White skin, never burns, always tans. Person has dark hair, eyes and skin.

Workers with skin Types 3 or 4 should still take care in strong sunshine.

Type 5: Brown skin.

Type 6: Black skin.

Workers with skin Types 5 or 6 are still at risk from skin cancer. These skin types can still darken and even burn in stronger sunlight.

To protect yourself

Even if their skin is not fair or freckled, workers should be particularly careful whilst working out of doors in summer in the three or four hours around midday when the sun is most intense.

Workers should:

☑ protect themselves with the type of clothing outlined below

☑ try to avoid the mild reddening, which is a sign of skin damage, as well as being a sign of early burning

☑ try to work and take breaks in the shade if they can. This will reduce the danger of harming the skin

☑ not be complacent. The skin's most vulnerable areas are the back of the neck and the head. Where possible, keep these areas covered

☑ try not to get a tan; it might look good but it indicates that the skin has already been damaged.

A suntan does not eliminate the long-term cancer risk, which is associated with prolonged exposure to the sun.

Protective clothing

The main way to avoid the dangers of developing skin cancer is to cover up.

☑ **Work clothing** made from close-woven fabric, such as a long-sleeved shirt and jeans, will stop most of the UV rays.

☑ **Wear a hat.** A wide brimmed hat will shade the face and head. A safety helmet will afford protection and the addition of a hanging flap will protect the back of the neck.

☑ **Keep a shirt or other top on.**

Hats and other clothing are the best form of protection, but sun creams and lotions can add useful protection for parts of the body that are not easy to shade from the sun. A sun protection factor rating of 15 or more is recommended.

Periodic checking of the skin

The first warning sign is often a small scabby spot that does not clear after a few weeks. Workers should be instructed to look for changed or newly formed moles or any skin discoloration. Workers should pay particular attention to any growths that appear on the face, especially around the eyes and nose, or on the backs of hands.

If these signs are noticed, medical assistance should be sought either from the company's medical staff or a local general practitioner, drawing attention to any moles that grow, change or bleed.

Many of these symptoms may prove to be non-cancerous – but they need to be checked to be absolutely sure.

Even if a spot is cancerous, simple modern treatments can usually cure them. This type of cancer very rarely spreads to other parts of the body. The smaller the spot, the easier it is to cure.

 Don't delay If you think something might be wrong, get it checked out.

Employers are strongly encouraged to develop a sun safety policy.

8.9   Legislative requirements

General duties

Employers have a duty to ensure that, as far as is reasonably practicable, safe systems of work are used, that adequate welfare facilities are available and that appropriate information, instruction, training and supervision are provided, as is necessary to ensure safety and the absence of risks to health in the use, handling, storage and transport of articles and substances.

There is a requirement on every employer to make a suitable and sufficient assessment of every work activity in order to identify any hazard to employees (or any other persons) that might be encountered as a result of the work having been carried out. The risk assessment must identify any substance to be used that can cause an adverse skin reaction and the control measures that are necessary to ensure that the substance can be used safely.

Employees are required to take reasonable care for their own health and safety, and that of other persons who may be affected by their work, and to co-operate with the employer so as to enable them to carry out their legal duties and requirements. In addition, employees must not intentionally or recklessly interfere with anything provided in the interests of health and safety.

Manufacturers, importers and suppliers of any articles or substances that are used in the workplace are responsible for ensuring that they have been tested for use, that information on their use is freely available and, so far as is reasonably practicable, that they are safe when properly used. This may include advice on appropriate PPE.

The Control of Substances Hazardous to Health Regulations (COSHH)

These regulations are commonly known at the COSHH Regulations.

The principal points of the regulations place requirements on the employer to protect employees, or any other persons who may be affected by their operations, by:

☑ assessing the health risks created by work involving substances hazardous to health. It should be noted that this is the same assessment as required under the Management of Health and Safety at Work Regulations (as amended). There is no need to carry out two assessments if the requirements of both sets of regulations are satisfied in a single assessment

☑ ensuring that the exposure of employees or others is prevented, or adequately controlled, by putting in place any measures necessary to control the exposure to risks

☑ ensuring that any control methods provided are properly used and maintained by monitoring the work environment, as necessary

☑ carrying out health surveillance in specified circumstances

☑ providing information, instruction and training for employees on the risks to health and precautions to be taken regarding any work with substances hazardous to health

☑ providing procedures for dealing with accidents, incidents and emergencies, including first aid and safety drills.

For further information refer to Chapter B07
The Control of Substances Hazardous to Health (COSHH).

The Personal Protective Equipment at Work Regulations

These regulations require that where a risk has been identified by a risk assessment, and it cannot be adequately controlled by other means, which are equally or more effective, then the employer must provide and ensure that suitable PPE is used by employees.

In essence, PPE may only be used as a last resort after all other means of eliminating or controlling the risk have been considered.

In deciding which type to issue, the employer must take into account the risk that the PPE is being used for, and that the PPE will fit the wearer and allow them to work comfortably.

Whilst the employer must take reasonable steps to ensure that any PPE supplied is worn, employees in turn must ensure that they wear the equipment provided and know the procedures for reporting any loss or defect to their employer.

For further information refer to Chapter B06 Personal protective equipment.

08

Appendix A – Some timbers known to produce dermatitis and other irritant effects

Commercial name	Harmful effects	Severity	Frequency
Afrormosia	Dermatitis and asthma.	Can be severe.	Quite frequent.
African mahogany	Dermatitis.	Severe.	Infrequent at present.
Boxwood	Dermatitis, rhinitis and asthma.	Mild.	Quite frequent.
Chestnut	Dermatitis, conjunctivitis and asthma.	Usually mild.	Infrequent.
Dahoma	Irritation of the chest and dermatitis.	Severe.	Frequent.
East African camphor wood	Asthma and dermatitis.	Fairly severe.	Infrequent.
Ebony	Irritation of nose and throat, and dermatitis.	Fairly severe.	Fairly frequent.
Guarea (also West African cedar)	Nasal irritation, severe vomiting, chest irritation, blisters and dermatitis.	Effects vary from mild to severe depending on sensitivity.	Quite frequent.
Iroko	Skin and eye irritation, asthma and symptoms of the common cold.	Usually mild, occasionally serious.	Very infrequent.
Machaerium	Dermatitis.	Severe.	Infrequent at present.
Mansonia	Irritation of mucous membrane, nasal haemorrhage, sore eyes, dizziness and dermatitis.	Severity varies with individuals.	Frequent.
Satinwood	Dermatitis, headache and coughing.	Quite severe.	Infrequent.
Teak	Dermatitis and eye inflammation.	Can be severe.	Not frequent.
Western red cedar	Asthma, bronchial trouble, dermatitis and septic wounds from splinters.	Severe.	Fairly frequent.
Yew	Bronchial asthma and dermatitis.	Quite severe.	Infrequent.

 A fuller listing may be found in *Health problems associated with wood processing* (published by Building Research Establishment).

Appendix B – Model sun safety policy

1. This company is committed to protecting and educating its workers about the risks to health arising from excessive exposure to strong sunlight. The policy will be implemented as appropriate for all workers who are at risk.

2. Sun protection advice will be provided as part of routine health and safety training for all employees, including supervisors and managers. All new employees will be made aware of the sun safety policy.

3. Wherever possible, working hours and tasks will be scheduled to avoid the midday sunshine. Wherever possible, work that can be carried out indoors or in the shade will be scheduled during periods of strong sunshine.

4. All workers who are liable to be at risk will receive appropriate training on how to protect themselves from prolonged exposure to strong sunlight, regardless of their skin type or hair colour.

5. Workers who are at risk will be encouraged to wear full-length trousers and long-sleeved shirts throughout the year. They will be made aware that, ideally, clothing will be loose fitting and made from a close-weave fabric.

6. In most circumstances, the mandatory wearing of a safety helmet will provide the necessary protection for the head. In the rare circumstances where a safety helmet need not be worn, workers at risk will be advised to wear a hat.

7. Workers at risk will be given information on the appropriate use of sunscreen creams, including advice on the minimum recommended level of protection.

8. Drinking water will be provided in the shade and all workers will be encouraged to drink plenty of water to avoid dehydration.

9. Rest areas in the shade will be provided and workers at risk will be encouraged to use them for their rest breaks.

10. All contractors working on the site will be made aware of the contents of the sun safety policy and will be required to adhere to its guidelines.

11. The effectiveness of this policy will be monitored and it will be reviewed and updated as necessary.

Signed _____ Date _____

Position _____

08

08

09
Asbestos

Asbestos is a risk to health when airborne fibres are breathed in. The greater the number of fibres, and the longer the period over which they are breathed in, the greater the risk of incurable asbestos-related diseases developing. These include cancers in the lungs and chest lining.

Introduction	116
Key points	117
Locating asbestos	117
Types of asbestos	118
The Control of Asbestos Regulations	119
Duty to manage	120
Representative sampling	122
Reoccupation of premises	122
Asbestos surveys	122
Working with asbestos	123
Licensable and non-licensable work	124
Assessment of the hazard	126
Health issues	126
Asbestos waste	127
Training	129
Insurance	130
Sources of further advice	130
Appendix A – Asbestos surveys in accordance with HSG264	131
Appendix B – Checklist for managing asbestos	134
Appendix C – Preventing exposure to asbestos	135

9.1 Introduction

An understanding of this chapter alone is not likely to be deemed sufficient for any person to be considered as a competent person under the Control of Asbestos Regulations. The purpose of this chapter is to give users the following information on the subject of asbestos:

☑ what to look for

☑ the dangers to health that can occur due to exposure to asbestos

☑ the requirements of the current regulations

☑ the duty to manage asbestos.

 You will need at least formal awareness training so you know how to avoid the risks and how to protect yourself.

Asbestos removal work will normally be considered to be construction work as defined in the Construction (Design and Management) Regulations (CDM). This means that the work may be notifiable and a CDM co-ordinator required, in which case the CDM co-ordinator would have to be competent with regard to the hazards associated with the management, disturbance and removal of asbestos.

The Health and Safety Executive (HSE) has previously expressed a number of concerns regarding aspects of health and safety, often associated when working with asbestos but that can be overlooked, such as working at height, the risk of fire, working in confined spaces, the use of machinery, burning, cutting and lifting. It is important not to view asbestos as a hazard in isolation. All associated hazards must be effectively managed.

Not surprisingly, the emphasis of the regulations is on exposure risk management. Work with the most high risk (dangerous) products must be carried out by a licensed contractor. Work with less hazardous products can, in most cases, still be carried out by people providing they are trained and competent and records of non-licensed works are maintained

The key to safe working is a risk assessment, which must be carried out by someone who is competent in terms of:

☑ assessing the likelihood and extent of exposure to asbestos

☑ implementing the requirements of the legislation and supporting guidance

☑ understanding the controls needed.

Damaged asbestos lagging

Generally, work with undamaged asbestos cement products, older textured coatings (such as Artex) and some other materials where the asbestos fibres are tightly bound into a base material is non-licensable. However, records will still need to be maintained if you are intending to work with it.

Some work with asbestos cement products (for example, clearing up fire damaged debris where the cement has been badly damaged and the asbestos fibres are no longer well bound into the base material matrix) is likely to need the services of a licensed contractor.

Asbestos is a risk to health when airborne fibres are breathed in. The greater the number of fibres, and the longer the period over which they are breathed in, the greater the risk of incurable asbestos-related diseases developing. These include cancers in the lungs and chest lining.

 Smokers who are exposed to asbestos have a greatly increased risk of lung cancer.

The use of asbestos materials in construction products was very common from the mid-1940s, reaching its peak in the mid-1970s.

However, asbestos that is in a good condition, which is not damaged and is not likely to be worked on or disturbed, does not pose any immediate problem and may not need to be removed. The HSE advises that it is usually better to leave it in place, and then to manage its presence on an ongoing basis. In the past, asbestos was widely used in the manufacture of building materials and products, and in sprayed coatings in construction work. Current legislation now prohibits the use of asbestos for all of these purposes. As a result, there should be no asbestos issues with any newbuild or refurbishment after 1999.

Although asbestos building materials and products have been largely replaced by safer alternatives, there remains the issue of the ongoing and long-term management of existing asbestos where its removal is not practicable.

Consequently, the regulations place a duty to manage asbestos on the owners or occupiers of non-domestic premises.

 There are many resources available on the HSE website, including video support, which can indicate the likely locations where you may find asbestos.

9.2 Key points

- ☑ All asbestos-containing material (ACM) is hazardous when airborne and dangerous when fibres are inhaled.

- ☑ Asbestos was widely used in the UK until it was banned in 1999; disturbance of the fabric of any building built before this time has the potential to expose asbestos.

- ☑ The requirements for licensed work remain the same: In the majority of cases, work with asbestos needs to be done by a licensed contractor. This work includes most asbestos removal, all work with sprayed asbestos coatings and asbestos lagging and most work with asbestos insulation and asbestos insulating board (AIB).

- ☑ If you are carrying out non-licensed asbestos work, this still requires effective controls.

- ☑ From 6 April 2012, some non-licensed work needs to be notified to the relevant enforcing authority.

- ☑ From 6 April 2012, brief written records should be kept of non-licensed work, which has to be notified (such as copy of the notification with a list of workers on the job), plus the level of likely exposure of those workers to asbestos. This does not require air monitoring on every job, if an estimate of degree of exposure can be made based on experience of similar past tasks or published guidance.

- ☑ Before any work that has the potential to expose anyone to asbestos is carried out, a survey must be carried out and a written risk assessment made.

- ☑ The priority for any employer is to prevent exposure to, and spread of, asbestos.

- ☑ A written, site-specific plan (or register) of work must be kept on site and followed.

- ☑ Anyone who does any work with asbestos must be specifically trained to do it, and this training must be repeated at least annually.

- ☑ Contractors producing hazardous asbestos waste must check that the site receiving your asbestos waste is authorised to receive asbestos. They should have an environmental permit.

- ☑ Be aware of other hazards that may arise from working with or managing asbestos (such as working at height, in a confined space or where the presence of live services must be managed).

- ☑ The Health and Safety Executive (HSE) must be notified:
  - of all work involving the disturbance of asbestos, apart from non-licensable work
  - separately, if the project is notifiable under the Construction (Design and Management) Regulations.

- ☑ The regulations require anyone who issues a site-clearance certificate to be accredited by an appropriate accreditation body as competent to carry out such work.

> **!** Around 4,000 people die in the UK every year due to asbestos-related disease.

09

9.3 Locating asbestos

Asbestos insulation board

This is often a job for an asbestos surveyor and it can be difficult, as the appearance of the asbestos may be changed by surface coatings, heat or ageing. It may also be encapsulated by, or be concealed beneath, other materials, particularly where asbestos removal was carried out to a poor standard in the past. However, original plans or specifications may help to confirm its presence. If a building was constructed between about 1900 and 1999, particularly between 1945 and 1985, there is a probability that it contains asbestos. Generally, industrial and Local Authority buildings, schools, hospitals and system-built buildings are known to contain significant amounts of asbestos. Past uses of asbestos are listed below.

Insulation and sprayed coatings using moulded or pre-formed lagging

- ☑ Boilers, plant and pipework.

- ☑ Fire protection to steel work.

- ☑ Thermal and acoustic insulation of buildings, including loose packing.

Insulation board

- ☑ Fire protection to doors.
- ☑ Claddings on walls and ceilings.
- ☑ Partitioning.

- ☑ Ceiling tiles.
- ☑ Fire breaks in ceiling voids.
- ☑ Electrical equipment and service risers.

Asbestos

Asbestos cement

- ☑ Corrugated roof sheets.
- ☑ Flat sheets for cladding and partitions.
- ☑ Roof and rainwater drainage goods.
- ☑ Underground pipes.
- ☑ Bath panels.
- ☑ Artificial roof slates.

Other uses

- ☑ Vinyl or thermoplastic floor tiles.
- ☑ Insulation of electrical equipment.
- ☑ Some textured coatings.
- ☑ Bakelite sanitary ware, and other products.

Asbestos-based friction materials were widely used in brake and clutch linings in vehicles and plant, including lift equipment, together with gaskets and packing in engines and heating or ventilation systems. Substitute materials have been developed in most cases.

9.4   Types of asbestos

Asbestos is a naturally occurring fibrous silicate mineral material, which does not burn and is resistant to most acids and alkalis. The fire protection and insulating properties of asbestos were the main reason for its use over the years. Three main types of asbestos have been used in the construction industry:

- ☑ chrysotile (white)
- ☑ amosite/grunerite (brown)
- ☑ crocidolite (blue).

Although the colours are often quoted to differentiate between the types of asbestos, the actual colour of a material suspected of being asbestos is not necessarily an accurate indication as to whether or not it is asbestos or an asbestos-containing material, or if it is, of what type.

> **!** It is impossible to rely on colour or appearance to identify different forms of asbestos. This must be undertaken by laboratory analysis.

Changes in colour may occur due to:

- ☑ it ageing or simply becoming dirty
- ☑ the effects of heat
- ☑ surface coatings being applied
- ☑ encapsulation
- ☑ oil or chemical splashes.

The type of asbestos used in the lagging of boilers can be particularly difficult to identify visually. Repairs and modifications can mean that boilers or pipework may be lagged by a mixture of different types of asbestos.

Asbestos fire blanket

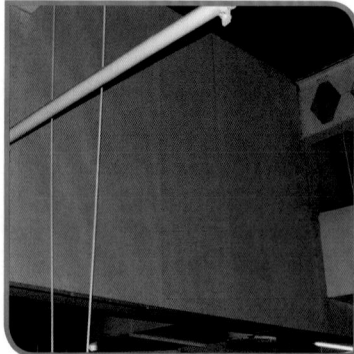
Asbestos (AIB) panels at high level

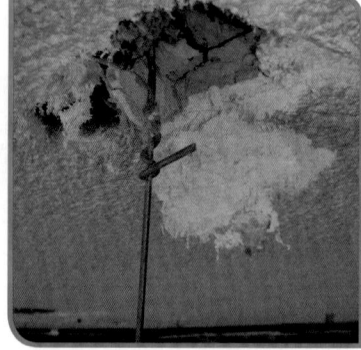
Damaged asbestos spray applied acoustical ceiling material

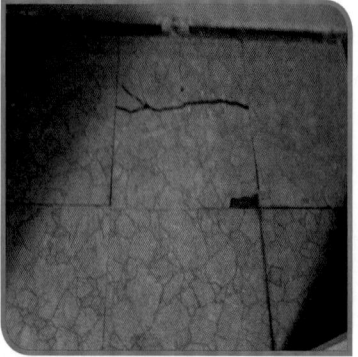
Asbestos floor tiles

Asbestos soffit

Asbestos was widely used as fire protection in building materials, for thermal insulation and also as a sprayed coating to steel structural members. All of these uses now present significant management issues associated with the maintenance of the asbestos over the remaining life span of the building or the removal of the asbestos during renovation, refurbishment or demolition.

Safe working in situations where asbestos might be exposed or damaged demands stringent control, and compliance with recommended precautionary measures and methods of work. These are detailed in the Approved Code of Practice (ACoP) L143 *Work with materials containing asbestos* and the Control of Asbestos Regulations.

 In addition the HSE publication *Asbestos: The licensed contractor's guide* (HSG247) provides specific guidance for high risk (licensable) asbestos work.

9.5 The Control of Asbestos Regulations

Definitions

The Control of Asbestos Regulations defines the following terms.

Licensable work – all high risk work, other than very minor work, with the following products:

- ☑ asbestos insulation
- ☑ coating (excluding textured coatings and paint)
- ☑ asbestos insulation board.

Notifiable non-licensable work – work that will normally fall into this category may involve minor work involving the repair of asbestos insulation, minor work with AIB that meets the short duration criteria, maintenance of and removal of damaged asbestos cement, removal work of decorative coatings that contain ACM.

For work not to require a licensed contractor, an assessment by a competent person must conclude that the:

- ☑ planned exposure is sporadic and low intensity
- ☑ planned exposure will not exceed the control limit.

The work itself must be:

- ☑ short, non-continuous maintenance activities; or removal of materials where the asbestos fibres are firmly linked to the base material matrix
- ☑ encapsulation/sealing of materials that are in good condition
- ☑ subjected to air monitoring, gathering samples or other analytical work.

Work with the following materials will be notifiable and non-licensable providing the risk assessment accurately confirms that the exposure over a four-hour period will not exceed the control limit of 0.1 fibres/cm³, and the maximum exposure will be below a peak of 0.6 fibres/cm³ averaged over ten minutes:

- ☑ asbestos cement
- ☑ textured decorative coatings containing asbestos
- ☑ paints that contain asbestos
- ☑ items of bitumen, plastic, resin or rubber, which do contain asbestos, but the asbestos was not used for its thermal or insulation properties (such as dampproof course, roofing felt, vinyl floor tiles and toilet seats)
- ☑ gaskets, packers and washers
- ☑ items (such as asbestos rope) **where the material is not being used for insulation.** For example, asbestos rope used as a gasket/packer in the joint between two sections of an asbestos cement drainpipe.

It should be noted that asbestos rope wrapped around a pipe, to keep the heat in or stop it from freezing, is acting as insulation.

 Written records should be kept of notifiable, non-licensed work.

Sporadic and low intensity – the concentration of air cannot exceed, or be liable to exceed, 0.6 fibres/cm³ in air measured over a ten-minute period by a United Kingdom Accredited Service (UKAS) laboratory.

Control limit – average exposure measured by a UKAS laboratory for a four-hour period, which is currently set at 0.1 fibres/cm³ for all types of asbestos fibre. This should not take into account any respiratory protective equipment (RPE) worn.

Non-licensable work – work that will normally fall into this category will be:

- ☑ short, non-continuous work with asbestos insulating board (attaching cables, cleaning light fittings and lifting ceiling tiles for inspection)
- ☑ short, non-continuous maintenance and removal work with asbestos cement that is in good condition
- ☑ short, non-continuous work with decorative coatings (drilling, fixing screws).

09

Risk assessment – an assessment of the risk of anyone being harmed through exposure to asbestos, as carried out by someone with both the theoretical and practical experience of the intended work with asbestos-containing materials. This degree of specialism necessary to carry out such a risk assessment may be beyond the competence of many people who would otherwise be considered to be a source of competent health and safety advice under the Management of Health and Safety at Work Regulations.

Prohibitions

These parts of the regulations prohibit the importation, supply, use and reuse of all types of asbestos, as articles or substances for use at work, and also prohibit the supply of products containing them. Further restrictions prevent their use for the manufacture and repair of any product. Any existing products that contain asbestos should be properly disposed of.

If, for example during a refurbishment, asbestos cement sheeting is removed from the roof of a building, it cannot be sold or given away. It must be disposed of properly.

9.6   Duty to manage

This is perhaps the most important part of the Control of Asbestos Regulations for the long-term protection of the health of employees and others. It states that any person who owns, occupies, manages or has responsibility for part or all of non-domestic premises that may contain asbestos has a legal duty to:

☑ manage the risk from asbestos or asbestos-containing materials within those premises, or

☑ co-operate with whoever has the duty to manage the risk.

It should be noted that domestic housing that is owned and/or managed by Local Authorities, housing associations, or similar is not deemed to be non-domestic property and therefore the duty to manage under the regulations will apply to the owner or manager.

Asbestos insulating board (AIB)

Damaged asbestos panels

 HSE publications *Asbestos hidden killer* leaflets and *A short guide to managing asbestos in premises* provides simple precautions to be undertaken and explains this duty to manage in general terms. Both are available to download free from the HSE's website.

If you have any maintenance and/or repair responsibilities for non-domestic premises, either through a contract or a temporary agreement, or because you own or occupy the premises, then you have a duty to manage. This will require you to manage the risk from asbestos by the following means:

☑ finding out if there is any asbestos or suspected ACMs in the premises, how much of it there is, where it is, and what condition it is in (see Note 1)

☑ always presuming that it is asbestos or an ACM unless you know or you have strong evidence proving otherwise (see Note 2)

☑ making, and keeping up to date, a record (an asbestos register) of the location and condition of all the asbestos, ACMs or presumed ACMs in your premises (see Note 3)

☑ assessing the risk that the materials pose to employees and others (see Note 4)

☑ preventing any work on the premises that may disturb asbestos or ACMs until control measures to manage the risk have been put in place (see Note 5)

☑ preparing a plan that sets out in detail how you are going to manage the risk from the material (see Note 6)

☑ taking all of the steps needed to put your plan into action (see Note 7)

☑ reviewing and monitoring your plan and the arrangements that you made to put it in place (see Note 8)

☑ providing information on the location and condition of the material to anyone who is liable to work on or to disturb it (see Note 9)

☑ ensuring that anyone who has information on the whereabouts of asbestos in your premises makes this available to you as a duty holder. Those who are not duty holders, but control access to the premises, have to co-operate with you in managing the asbestos (see Note 10)

- ☑ providing information to the emergency services. In practice this is more important where buildings have large amounts of asbestos products in them. The presence of, for example, one or two rainwater goods products is unlikely to be a major issue

- ☑ if you are a contractor working on someone else's premises where asbestos is likely to be present, you must be given access to the asbestos register, which must outline the location and condition of known asbestos within the building.

 If you are not given access to the asbestos register, you should not start any work that will disturb the fabric of the building.

Note 1. If work will be carried out that will disturb the fabric of pre-2000 non-domestic premises, an asbestos survey must be carried out by a competent person, as outlined in the HSE publication *Asbestos: The survey guide* (HSG264). There are now two types of survey:

- ☑ management survey
- ☑ refurbishment or demolition survey.

 Refer to Appendix A for further details of commissioning a competent asbestos surveyor to carry out a suitable survey.

Prior to any refurbishment or demolition activities it is a client's duty to ensure an invasive refurbishment/demolition asbestos survey is undertaken in accordance with HSG264.

Note 2. If in doubt, presume that the material is asbestos or ACM until you can prove that it is not. It is better to overprotect than to expose employees and others to asbestos.

Note 3. A plan of the premises showing where the materials are will always be extremely useful, and will be essential in larger premises. Such a plan would form an integral part of the ongoing management of the asbestos or ACM. Where applicable, details of asbestos should also be added to the health and safety file.

Note 4. A risk assessment should be undertaken by a competent person who has sufficient knowledge of the subject.

If the materials are in good condition, not liable to be damaged, and will not be disturbed or worked on, then the risk is probably low. If the materials are flaky, crumbling, in a place where they can be damaged by, for example, forklift trucks, then the risk is high. Given the known ill health caused by asbestos, then a high risk of damage calls for urgent action.

Note 5. This could be work by your employees or any contractors or sub-contractors brought in for carpentry, flooring, partitioning, ceiling fixing, plumbing, electrical or other work.

Note 6. If material is not going to be removed by a licensed asbestos removal contractor, consider how you are going to manage the long-term presence of the asbestos. If it is in good condition and not liable to be damaged, then routine inspection and monitoring may be enough if records are kept. A sealing coat may be needed, or other protective works necessary, to lower and to further control the risk.

Note 7. Make it happen by putting your plan into action. What is the organisation, what are the arrangements for the implementation of the plan and who has the responsibility?

Note 8. A regular review of the action plan will ensure that it is working, that the control measures are still effective and that inspection, monitoring and recording are in fact taking place. It may be the case that procedures, notices and policies that have been in place for a length of time tend to be overlooked. A fresh approach may therefore be needed.

Note 9. Part of this information will be the signs that will have been placed to identify the location of asbestos or ACM. In a large workplace or premises, this will also mean keeping a detailed plan of the building or register that describes every individual room or workplace and the asbestos or ACM that is in there. This will inform visiting (non-licensed) contractors of the areas and features of the building that they must not disturb.

 Asbestos will pose a significant risk to health if it is in a condition that allows easy release of fibres that can then be inhaled.

Note 10. Contractors who remove panelling and find what could be asbestos or ACM have a duty to tell you what they have found. However, you may need to remind them about this duty before they start work. Regarding the control of premises, the duty may be with the landlord or management agency.

The regulations also impose duties on employers for the protection of employees who may be exposed to asbestos at work, and other persons affected or who may be at risk of being affected by such work.

Similar duties are placed on self-employed persons.

09

9.7 Representative sampling

If representative samples are needed for laboratory analysis, they must be taken in a prescribed manner to retain their integrity and the safety of anyone who may handle them. It is a legal requirement that any laboratory carrying out analysis has the necessary facilities, expertise and quality control procedures. Laboratories that meet these standards are accredited under the United Kingdom Accreditation Scheme (UKAS).

To confirm or identify the type of asbestos or ACM on the premises, a series of bulk samples may have to be taken for laboratory analysis by a UKAS-accredited laboratory. Methods employed in taking samples of asbestos will vary according to its type and location. Guidance on taking samples is available in HSG264.

Anyone removing samples for analysis must be competent to do so and use appropriate protective clothing and respiratory equipment, particularly if the work involves cutting, boring, drilling or otherwise creating airborne dust or fibres. Precautionary measures to be observed include:

☑ any samples taken should be as small as possible to avoid unnecessary disturbance, but sufficient to be representative

☑ no people, other than those taking the sample, should be in the area

☑ the area from where the sample is to be taken should be dampened using a killer spray

☑ a knife, core borer or hand drill should be used to place the sample in a suitably labelled, double-sealed container (sealed polythene bags). Any tools that will create airborne fibres must not be used

☑ other surfaces on which asbestos dust may fall must be covered with an impervious sheet. The area should be subsequently cleaned by using a dustless method (such as a damp cloth), which should be disposed of in a sealed, polythene bag

☑ any disturbed or damaged surfaces must be sealed after a sample has been taken

☑ consideration should be given to reassurance air-testing during and/or after the survey where the area is sensitive.

The results from the bulk analysis will determine what action should be included in the management plan.

9.8 Reoccupation of premises

The importance of ensuring that a previously contaminated area is totally clear of asbestos before reoccupation cannot be stressed too strongly. The wellbeing of everyone who will occupy the premises is dependent upon it.

The regulations require that anyone who certifies premises as being safe to reoccupy following asbestos work must be accredited by an appropriate body as competent to carry out such work. Organisations accredited under UKAS to ISO/IEC 17020 will have appropriate quality management schemes in place.

Clearance monitoring is carried out as part of the four-stage clearance:

☑ visual inspection of all the paperwork

☑ visual inspection of the enclosure, waste and transit routes (to ensure no visible asbestos remains)

☑ disturbed air tests in the enclosure to ensure the levels are <0.01 fibres/cm^3

☑ subject to satisfactory previous stages, a post enclosure removal inspection.

The above procedures involve the analyst following a set procedure of looking at the site set-up and the cleanliness of the asbestos enclosure and asbestos decontamination unit.

Having completed a detailed visual inspection (which is likely to include a search on hands and knees), the analyst carries out an air monitoring clearance test. This will include vigorously brushing the floor, and surfaces around each air monitoring pump, to disturb any trapped asbestos. The analyst then allows the removal contractor to take down the enclosure before a final visual check of the area is undertaken. A certificate of reoccupation is then issued.

Finally, prior to the decontamination/hygiene unit leaving site, it is inspected and air tested to ensure the asbestos levels are less than 0.01 fibres/cm^3, followed by leaving an air test certificate in the clean end of the unit by a UKAS analyst.

9.9 Asbestos surveys

Two types of survey are defined within the HSE publication HSG264:

☑ **management survey**

☑ **refurbishment and demolition survey.**

To understand the difference between a management and a refurbishment/demolition survey, the simplest explanation is to consider a studwork wall that forms a firebreak. It was originally clad in asbestos insulation board, which was later covered over with plasterboard. In a management survey, the surveyor would correctly identify the outer surface as being plasterboard. However, as there would be no invasive testing, the asbestos would remain undiscovered. An invasive refurbishment and demolition survey would break through the cladding and discover the inner asbestos cladding.

Just because the surveyor did not find any asbestos does not mean that no asbestos is present. In all cases it is important to remember that surveying is as much an art as a science and there will be mistakes.

There are also some asbestos-containing materials that would only be found by luck rather than judgement (for example, asbestos cement shuttering in a slab, or asbestos insulation board used as packers inside a studwork wall). It is important to be wary of unidentified building products and for everyone to have sufficient asbestos awareness training. There should also be management who are in a position to stop work if necessary and question the presence of any 'funny looking plasterboard' found.

 Refer to Appendix A for further details on asbestos surveys.

9.10 Working with asbestos

Requirements of the regulations

The following is a brief overview of the main requirements as they are likely to affect the readers of this chapter, as opposed to the detail of the much more stringent requirements that affect asbestos-removal contractors and others whose business involves working with asbestos.

 The HSE website provides comprehensive and understandable guidance on the types of work methods to be used.

An employer or self-employed person who is required to carry out any work in a building or structure must:

- ☑ make a suitable and sufficient assessment as to whether asbestos is, or is liable to be, present in the premises where work is being carried out. Under CDM, the client has a duty regardless of the size of the project to provide information to the contractor on the known hazards associated with the structure (such as the presence of asbestos)

- ☑ note that:
  - this information should normally be in the form of refurbishment and demolition surveys, as defined in HSG264 for most invasive construction work
  - any existing information on the presence of asbestos, supplied by the client based on a management survey, must be closely scrutinised to ensure that the construction work will not disturb more of the structure than the surveyor checked

- ☑ identify that the material does not contain asbestos or assume it contains brown or blue asbestos if not known (fail-safe system)

- ☑ ensure that a competent person carries out an assessment to decide the likely exposure for the proposed work methods and if the work will, therefore, be licensable or non-licensable

- ☑ prepare a suitable written plan of work

- ☑ provide adequate information, instruction and training for employees and others

- ☑ ensure that training is repeated on an annual basis for any work with asbestos

- ☑ prevent or reduce asbestos exposure to the lowest level reasonably practicable by means other than the use of RPE (for example, use an asbestos H class vacuum cleaner (BS 8520-3:2009) or other fibre suppression techniques (BS 8520-1:2009)

- ☑ ensure the proper use of RPE and that face-fit testing is carried out (minimum P3 filter)

- ☑ maintain respiratory equipment in a clean and efficient state, good order and repair. Regularly examine and test exhaust ventilation equipment (BS 8520-2:2009)

- ☑ provide adequate and suitable protective clothing (minimum Type 5/6 overall) and ensure that it is cleaned or disposed of appropriately

- ☑ prevent the spread of asbestos from the workplace

- ☑ ensure premises and plant involved in work with asbestos are kept clean

- ☑ monitor the air where employees are exposed to asbestos and keep suitable records for a specific period

- ☑ ensure that air monitoring is only carried out by an accredited laboratory

- ☑ provide washing and changing facilities that are adequate and suitable for employees exposed to asbestos, and storage for protective clothing and personal clothing (not worn during working hours)

- ☑ regulate raw asbestos, asbestos waste storage and disposal, ensuring adequate packaging, sealing and marking in accordance with the regulations.

 For further information refer to 9.14 Asbestos waste.

09

9.11 Licensable and non-licensable work

Licensable work

The regulations prohibit the removal or work on all types of asbestos insulation, asbestos coating (except textured coating and paint) and asbestos insulation board, unless it is carried out by a person holding a licence granted by the HSE.

An exception is made in the case of repair or maintenance work of short duration.

 For further guidance on this term refer to the section on notifiable, non-licensable work and non-licensable work.

Following an assessment made by a competent person, work with most other forms of asbestos-containing materials will not require a licence. The following requirements must be complied with:

☑ adequate information and training must be given to employees

☑ adequate information must be given to persons who may be affected by the work, or those in the vicinity

☑ asbestos dust produced by the work, which may affect the above persons, must be reduced to the lowest level reasonably practicable and must not exceed a peak 10-minute exposure of 0.6 fibres/cm³.

A licence is not required for people (usually environmental experts or technicians) engaged in air monitoring or the collection of samples for the purpose of identification.

Licences

There are four types of asbestos licence.

☑ **Full removal licence** – this is normally held by a licensed contractor.

☑ **Supervisory licence** – this is required where a third party actively supervises the work. A client/principal/main contractor does not need one. This type of licence is gradually being phased out as unnecessary.

☑ **Ancillary licence** – this is needed to carry out work associated with the main asbestos removal work, typically by scaffold companies who erect scaffolds to form enclosures for licensed asbestos removal work. A separate notification must be sent to the HSE by the company carrying out the ancillary work.

Companies that service and maintain asbestos removal equipment may also require this type of licence, particularly where there is a high probability of disturbing high-risk asbestos materials.

☑ **Labour supplier** – because the employer of anyone who works with licensable asbestos must be a licensed contractor, labour providers have a special category of licence.

 All licences for work with asbestos insulation, AIB or asbestos coatings are granted by the licensing unit of the HSE.

A new asbestos license will last one year. Upon renewal, it will run for three years unless the HSE is concerned about the health and safety performance of the licence holder, or there has been little activity in this work, thereby preventing an adequate assessment of their performance. In this case, HSE can revoke the licence completely, shorten the term of the licence or impose extra conditions on the licence. It is good practice to look at the licence held by a licensed contractor and question the period of its validity, along with any conditions.

Notification of work with asbestos

Licensed asbestos removal contractors are required to notify the HSE or Local Authority (whichever is the enforcing authority) of all proposed work at least 14 days in advance, using the ASB5 form. Where a scaffold is to be built, that will be used to give access to a workplace where asbestos will be removed or will provide a working platform, then the scaffold contractor may need to be an ancillary licensed contractor.

In an emergency, it is sometimes possible to obtain a dispensation (waiver) from the 14-day period of notification. This should be discussed with the proposed licensed contractor.

All questions on the removal of asbestos should be referred either to the HSE or a competent person. Details of where to find competent advice can be found at the end of this chapter (Appendix A). The unlicensed removal of asbestos, as well as being an offence under the regulations, may also expose employees and others to high levels of airborne asbestos fibres and the subsequent risk of later ill health.

Notifiable non-licensable work

Work that will normally fall into this category may involve minor work involving the repair of asbestos insulation, minor work with AIB that meets the short duration criteria, maintenance of and removal of damaged asbestos cement and removal work of decorative coatings that contain ACM.

A contractor who does not hold an asbestos licence may normally carry out work with certain low-risk asbestos products in situations where the planned exposure:

 is sporadic and low intensity

 will not exceed the control limits (0.1 fibres/cm³ 4 hours or 0.6 fibres/cm³ 10 mins).

Any measurements required to check the exposure limit must be carried out by a UKAS-accredited laboratory and should not take into account the effect on any RPE used.

After April 2015, if a job is notifiable non-licensable work (NNLW) it must be done by persons who have had a medical examination in line with the requirements in the law.

> **www.** Notification of this type of work will be necessary. Once you have confirmed the work is NNLW, you need to notify it to the relevant enforcing authority. Do this online using the online notifications form.

This is the only method of notification – you cannot notify by phone or post.

Notice should be given before the work starts – there is no minimum notice period. You do not need to wait for permission from the enforcing authority – the database will provide a PDF copy of your notification. If you are a licensed asbestos contractor carrying out NNLW work, you will still need to notify.

> **!** Any other work with asbestos-containing materials will normally require an asbestos licence.

> **🔍** Where employers are considering undertaking small works themselves, they should read the relevant HSE publications.

There is an absolute requirement for anyone who undertakes any work with asbestos to have received practical training within the preceding 12 months, and more often if the method or equipment changes.

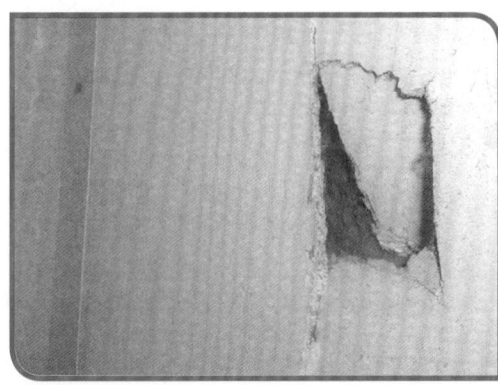
Broken asbestos insulation board (typically contains 40% asbestos)

The following products are likely to fall into non-licensable work:

 short, non-continuous work with asbestos insulating board (attaching cables, cleaning light fittings and lifting ceiling tiles for inspection)

☑ short, non-continuous maintenance and removal work with asbestos cement that is in good condition

☑ short, non-continuous work with decorative coatings (drilling, fixing screws).

The work itself must be:

☑ short, non-continuous maintenance activities, **or**

☑ encapsulation/sealing of materials in good condition, **or**

☑ air monitoring, gathering samples or other analytical work.

Non-licensable work does not need:

☑ notification to the relevant enforcing authority

☑ a licensed contractor to carry it out

☑ asbestos medicals or health records for the workers doing it

☑ specific emergency procedures

☑ the area around the work to be identified as an asbestos area.

While the installation of asbestos insulation and asbestos insulating board is now prohibited, large quantities of these materials still remain in premises throughout the country.

> **🔍** The HSE publication HSG247 provides comprehensive practical guidance on how a licensed asbestos removal contractor should work.

09

9.12 Assessment of the hazard

In the planning phase, and as part of the duty to manage, before carrying out any work involving asbestos or ACMs, including minor repairs, the employer must make an assessment to determine:

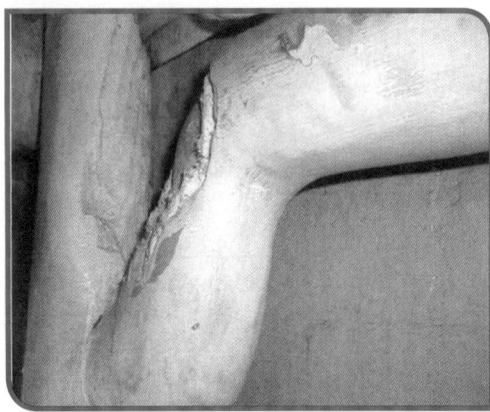

- ☑ the type of work and its possible duration
- ☑ the type and quantity of asbestos involved (using analysis results if available) and if more than one type of asbestos is present
- ☑ if more than one type of asbestos is found, whether stricter controls than usual are required
- ☑ the likely nature and degree of exposure to the asbestos
- ☑ the steps that need to be taken to prevent or reduce such exposure to asbestos (the control measures)
- ☑ the procedures for the removal of any waste from the site
- ☑ the procedures in place for dealing with any emergencies
- ☑ the reasons for the choice of the proposed work method.

Damage to pipework insulation

Much of the information should come from the asbestos management plan for the building. This may be augmented, if necessary, with additional survey work. Under CDM, the client has a duty to provide information on the presence of asbestos, irrespective of whether the project is notifiable or not.

The assessment should be prepared in writing, including where it is for maintenance, repair or small-scale work involving:

- ☑ the handling of existing pre-formed and package bonded asbestos materials in situ
- ☑ small-scale repair or maintenance work not involving the cutting or breaking of asbestos or ACMs.

A competent person with adequate knowledge of the job should carry out the assessment. Where work is of a repetitive nature, covering various locations within a building or site, then a single assessment may be sufficient.

Designated areas

Where licensed asbestos contractors are working, certain designated areas may be created (such as one or more asbestos areas and respirator zones).

In most situations the asbestos area and respirator zone will be the same. However, in certain circumstances there may only be an asbestos area (where the control limits are not exceeded), for example, a transit route/waste route for asbestos. It is advisable to exclude non-essential persons from this asbestos area.

Employers with asbestos removal contractors on their premises should strictly prohibit entry into these areas by their own employees.

Asbestos areas

Where a licensed asbestos removal contractor is undertaking the removal of asbestos, in order to ensure that people other than those involved in asbestos work are not exposed to asbestos by entering asbestos areas, such areas should be designated and clearly identified, using notices that meet the requirements of the Health and Safety (Safety Signs and Signals) Regulations.

Respirator zones

Areas where the removal contractors are working, and where control limits for exposure to airborne fibres are liable to be exceeded, will be designated as respirator zones to ensure that only removal contractors wearing RPE are allowed to enter.

9.13 Health issues

Air monitoring

The HSE prefers that the client of the licensed contractor, rather than the licensed contractor, appoints the UKAS analysts who will carry out any air monitoring. It is felt that this is likely to give a greater degree of independence.

There are various types of monitoring that can be performed. The analysts carrying out the air monitoring must hold the British Occupational Hygiene Society P403 and P404 certificates. When the analysts are counting airborne fibres they have to follow a strict scientific procedure and count any fibres that are of a certain size. This does not allow them to differentiate between fibreglass and asbestos, and may cause problems.

Background monitoring is usually carried out before any asbestos removal work starts to enable the fibre concentration to be measured and any possible problems identified.

Static monitoring can be carried out during work with asbestos. Typically, this will be outside the asbestos enclosure to demonstrate that there are no leaks, or it may be performed on the site boundary during work with asbestos cement to show that there is no offsite fibre emission.

Personal monitoring may be carried out for two reasons:

- ☑ specifically to demonstrate that the RPE being used is effective
- ☑ to measure the fibre levels that whoever is carrying out the work with asbestos is being exposed to.

It would be important to discuss what type of personal monitoring is required with the UKAS analyst, as the monitoring strategy would be different.

Any employer or self-employed person must monitor the exposure during work with asbestos unless they know that the exposure will not exceed the control limit, or they have access to other ways of showing what the level of exposure is. This may be by referring to previous monitoring.

Medical surveillance

Asbestos removal contractors must ensure that their employees, who are liable to be exposed to asbestos above the control limit, are under regular medical surveillance by an HSE-appointed doctor; the local HSE office can supply the names of the appointed doctors who are able to carry out this specialist health surveillance.

Medical examinations should be provided before work with asbestos starts and at prescribed periods thereafter, currently every two years.

Health records containing information on medical examinations have to be maintained and kept for 40 years after the date of the last entry.

 After April 2015, if a job is NNLW, it must be done by persons who have had a medical examination in line with the requirements in the law.

Washing and changing facilities

Asbestos removal contractors must provide adequate and suitable washing and changing facilities for their employees. Where protective clothing and respiratory equipment are in use, storage must be provided for contaminated items. Separate storage must be provided for personal clothing not worn during working hours.

The hygiene facilities (decontamination unit) are usually mobile, single (or more) showers, with three compartments. They should always be accompanied with the appropriate test certificates (electric, gas, dioctyl phthalate, and so on) and have a clean air-test certificate from the previous job (unless it's a new unit).

9.14 Asbestos waste

Asbestos waste is considered to be of two types – combined or fibrous. Combined was previously called bonded and effectively the asbestos is well bound into the material.

Roofing felt, vinyl floor tiles and most asbestos cement is categorised as combined. Asbestos insulation board, pipe lagging and sprayed coating are fibrous. Professional advice may be needed to ensure that the waste is correctly categorised.

Where asbestos waste has been identified for disposal, details of the type, estimated quantities and disposal options should be included in the project site waste management plan in accordance with the Site Waste Management Plan Regulations. These regulations currently apply in England for projects with an estimated value of £300,000 and above with greater detail required when the value exceeds £500,000.

It is good practice to bag or wrap asbestos cement sheets, or other asbestos cement products. If not wrapped they must at least be placed in a suitable skip that has been lined with polythene. The skip should be secured if it is left overnight. It is good practice to bag or wrap waste from internal work to guarantee that when the waste is carried outside there will be no asbestos debris dropped. If a van is being used to carry small volumes of asbestos waste, the waste must be double bagged and the bags secured (for example, by putting them in a lidded bin). The waste must also be physically separated from the driver and any passengers.

Any fibrous asbestos removed should be sealed in proper containers and correctly marked before despatch. Typically, this will be double bagged with the inner bag being red and the outer clear.

The packaging (bagging) and labelling must satisfy the requirements of current legislation and, where asbestos waste is to be transported by road, there is further legislation controlling its safe movement.

Containers should be designed and constructed so as to retain the asbestos without any spillage or loss during normal handling.

Labelling of asbestos waste and used protective clothing

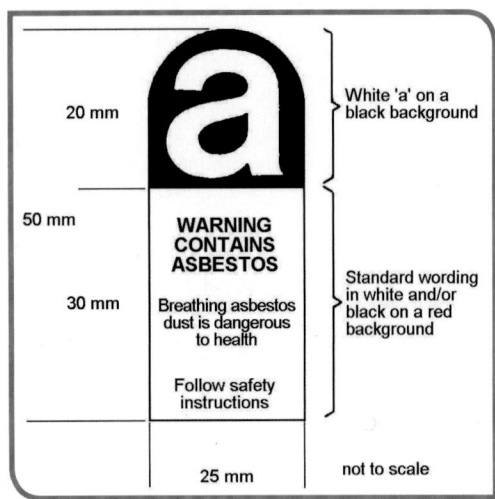

Labelling requirement

Where the asbestos removal contractor uses labels on waste or removed asbestos, the label must be clearly and indelibly printed so that the words in the lower half can be easily read. These words must be printed as specified in the diagram.

The label has to be firmly affixed to the packaging using an adhesive type label, or directly printed onto the packaging (plastic bag).

Disposal of removed asbestos

Any material containing more than 0.1% asbestos on a gravimetric (weight for weight) basis should be disposed of in accordance with the Hazardous Waste Regulations in England and Wales, or the Special Waste (amendment) Regulations in Scotland (as amended).

In practice, this will be most asbestos-containing materials. Sites producing hazardous asbestos waste need to be registered with the Environment Agency (unless exempt). A unique site code will be issued and used on new consignment notes for all future arisings. At present there is no requirement to register sites producing hazardous waste with SEPA in Scotland.

The waste must be carried by a registered carrier and taken to a licensed or permitted site for disposal. There are very few waste disposal sites in the UK that have asbestos cells, and it is becoming common to take the waste to an intermediate waste transfer site. These are licensed facilities, which are allowed to store waste on a temporary basis prior to subsequent disposal to a licensed tip. They normally bulk up the waste to reduce transport costs.

A contractor can have a skip on site for temporary storage during work. Unless their yard was designated as an intermediate waste transfer facility, it is illegal to have an asbestos skip there.

There are slight differences in the respective legislation for England and Wales, Northern Ireland and Scotland. Contractors who work in any of these areas must comply with the relevant national legislation.

In essence, there is a duty of care put on everyone in the waste disposal chain. Clients, whether they are at work or domestic, have a responsibility to ensure that the waste is disposed of correctly. They can be prosecuted if the waste is fly-tipped. Where asbestos has been removed as part of a project, a prudent contractor would ensure that proof of disposal formed part of the information that was given to the client. In England, where a site waste management plan is required under the Site Waste Management Plan Regulations, the plan should be updated to include details of the disposal of the asbestos waste and the waste carrier.

Under CDM, if a project is notifiable, the CDM co-ordinator may require this information to be placed in the health and safety file to confirm that the asbestos is transported and disposed of legally.

Crushed secondary aggregate

Crushed secondary aggregate from construction and demolition activities (C&D waste) may occasionally have small fragments of asbestos, typically as pieces of asbestos cement. The general rule when supplying or receiving this material is that you should not see (by the naked eye) any visible asbestos debris in the product. If you see a fragment of suspected asbestos cement, further investigation should be undertaken to ascertain the extent of contamination, the source material and reasons for this occurring.

It is generally accepted that very small fractions of asbestos will occasionally get missed and end up in these products. However, quantitative analysis should confirm that this level is at least 10 times lower than the threshold of 0.1% w/w for hazardous waste (that is less than 0.01%). As to whether you send or receive this material is a decision that should be carefully considered by a competent person who may require further advice from authoritative organisations (such as The National Federation of Demolition Contractors, The Institute of Demolition Engineers, The Environment Agency or the HSE).

The issue arises where asbestos has been removed so far as is reasonably practicable from a concrete surface. It is foreseeable that there will be some asbestos fibre present. This is most likely to occur where a spray coating or textured coatings have been removed, as it is physically impossible to remove all traces of fibre without removing the top surface of the concrete by grit blasting.

The issues are whether:

☑ the crushed concrete would be considered to be a product to which asbestos had been added

☑ the product would be considered to be hazardous waste.

The health risks are minimal but the potential financial risks associated with incorrect disposal and/or land being deemed contaminated is high. It is suggested that advice is sought regarding this issue if relevant on any projects.

The spraying of asbestos and the installation of asbestos insulation are also prohibited under this legislation.

9.15   Training

All workers who are liable to disturb asbestos during their normal work should be trained so that they can recognise asbestos-containing materials and know what to do if they come across them. The training needs to be appropriate for the work and the roles undertaken by individuals. There are three types of asbestos training:

- ☑ awareness training
- ☑ training for work with asbestos that does not require a licence from the HSE
- ☑ training for asbestos work that does require a licence from the HSE.

Awareness training

This training is for those persons who are liable to disturb asbestos while carrying out their normal everyday work, or who may influence how work is carried out (such as general maintenance staff, electricians, plumbers, gas fitters, painters and decorators, joiners, plasterers, demolition workers, construction workers, roofers, heating and ventilation engineers, telecommunications engineers, fire and burglar alarm installers, computer installers, architects, building surveyors and other such professionals – but note, there are other occupations that are liable to disturb asbestos in addition to those listed).

Training for asbestos work that does not require a licence (non-licensable asbestos work)

This training is for those workers who plan to carry out any work with asbestos that does not require a licence and who may knowingly disturb lower risk asbestos-containing materials. It should be provided in addition to asbestos awareness training and should be job specific. Typically, workers who may need this training include those listed under asbestos awareness training and who carry out such tasks as:

- ☑ drilling holes in asbestos materials (including for sampling and analysis purposes)
- ☑ laying cables in areas containing undamaged asbestos materials
- ☑ removing asbestos-containing floor tiles
- ☑ cleaning or repairing asbestos cement sheet roofing or cladding.

Topics covered by this type of training include:

- ☑ how to make suitable and sufficient assessments about the risk of exposure to asbestos
- ☑ safe working practices and control measures, including an explanation on the correct use of control measures, protective equipment and work methods
- ☑ selection and appropriate use of protective equipment
- ☑ waste handling procedures
- ☑ emergency procedures
- ☑ relevant legal requirements.

Training for asbestos work that does require a licence (licensed asbestos work)

Most work with higher risk asbestos-containing materials must be carried out by licensed contractors. Only suitably trained workers, using appropriate RPE and who are under suitable medical surveillance can undertake licensed asbestos work. This type of training is therefore required for operatives, supervisors and managers working for a licensed contractor.

Refresher training

Refresher training should not be a repeat of the initial training. It should be given at least once a year and be appropriate to the workers' familiarity with the work. Therefore, depending on the individual training need, it could be a structured update training session or a short toolbox talk refreshing experienced workers on the main principles/expectations. The training should be tailored to meet the training needs, for example, if:

- ☑ work methods change
- ☑ the type of equipment used to control exposure changes
- ☑ the type of work being carried out changes significantly.

Taking risks with asbestos

HSE Research Report RR558 outlines the reasons why people still take chances when working with asbestos even though they know the risks. The report highlights the fact that many people deny the importance or relevance of the risk because they think:

- ☑ as most asbestos has been removed, there isn't enough around to worry about
- ☑ exposure only occurs in extreme cases (such as when handling asbestos lagging)
- ☑ some levels of asbestos are actually safe
- ☑ new materials (such as MDF) pose a greater risk

Asbestos

☑ more visible risks (such as working at height) are more important

☑ contact with asbestos is a lottery – there is always some present.

There are also economic factors and pressure from employers (creating a fuss versus keeping your job) and the lack of safety culture (a failure of the employer to promote safe working practices). However, the Working Well Together (WWT) initiative, in conjunction with commercial organisations and local safety groups run Safety and Health Awareness Days (SHADs) around the country for SMEs. These raise awareness of asbestos and other hazards encountered when undertaking maintenance activities.

9.16 Insurance

It is imperative to ensure that anyone who proposes to carry out work with asbestos is insured to do so. In addition to employers' liability insurance, asbestos contractors also usually have public liability insurance for carrying out asbestos work.

With standard public liability insurance there are often explicit exclusions on a contractor carrying out any work with asbestos. Frequently, the contractor has simply not checked the small print on the policy. If people are insured to work with asbestos it normally says openly on the insurance documents.

If in doubt you should check with the broker or underwriter of the insurance policy to confirm the mandatory employers' liability insurance covers them for work with asbestos, noting any specific exclusions (for example, non-licensed work only).

There have been instances of roofing contractors working with asbestos cement who created contamination of occupied premises and simply were not insured for the clean up costs.

9.17 Sources of further advice

Trade associations for licensed removal contractors

 The trade associations listed below can provide information on their members (who can demonstrate having met certain standards of performance) and general advice on work with asbestos:

ACAD – Asbestos Control and Abatement Division

ARCA – Asbestos Removal Contractors Association.

Trade associations for analysts – These provide advice on air monitoring, asbestos surveys and asbestos project management and regarding any of the member laboratories:

ATAC – Asbestos Testing and Consulting.

Asbestos audits

The Asbestos Management Auditing Company

 This provides asbestos-related auditing services to enable asbestos contractors and training providers to comply with ever improving industry standards and requirements.

Organisations relating to competence

British Occupational Hygiene Society (BOHS)

BOHS provides a proficiency scheme for work with asbestos. Subjects covered include:

☑ P401 – Bulk analysis

☑ P402 – Asbestos surveying

☑ P403 – Fibre counting

☑ P404 – Clearance testing

☑ P405 – Management of asbestos in buildings

☑ P406 – Supervisory licence holders

☑ S301 – Certificate of competence in asbestos with oral examination

☑ Asbestos building surveyors ABICS

☑ National Individual Asbestos Certification Scheme (NIACS).

Appendix A – Asbestos surveys in accordance with HSG264

Planning

Good planning is essential to ensure the effectiveness of any survey. The level of planning required will largely depend upon the complexity of the structure to be surveyed and the extent of the survey.

As part of the planning process, the client should be clear as to why the survey is needed and what they want to get out of the survey report. Adequate planning, particularly with regard to:

- ☑ establishing the areas where the surveyor would need access, to carry out the survey, and overcoming potential access problems, and

- ☑ agreeing the amount of intrusive inspection to be carried out

could significantly reduce the number of caveats in the survey report.

Prior to the survey

1. The surveyor will need from the client:

- ☑ the details of the structure or part of it to be surveyed

- ☑ the structure's use, work processes, known hazards and any priority areas

- ☑ plans and prior survey reports on design, structure and construction

- ☑ safety and security information (such as fire alarm testing)

- ☑ access arrangements and any permit systems in operation

- ☑ contact details of relevant staff for operational or health and safety issues

- ☑ the opportunity to carry out a walk-through inspection of the structure in the interests of familiarisation to enable potential problem areas to be identified.

2. The client should expect from the surveyor:

- ☑ details of qualifications and experience

- ☑ the significant findings of their risk assessment

- ☑ references from previous work

- ☑ details of professional indemnity insurance

- ☑ costs

- ☑ proposed scope of work

- ☑ plan of work

- ☑ timetable of work

- ☑ details of any caveats (for example, restrictions or limitations in the survey).

After the survey has been completed, the surveyor must supply the client with a comprehensive survey report, that includes details of any areas not accessed or surveyed.

Competence of surveyors

The duty holder who commissions the asbestos survey must be satisfied that the prospective surveyor, whether an organisation or an individual, is technically competent to carry out the range of work required and will allocate adequate resources to it.

In line with the principles of CDM, it is essential that searching questions are put to each prospective surveyor to ensure their technical competence will be translated into a satisfactory survey that fully meets the duty holder's requirements.

This will entail making reasonable enquires via a two-stage process.

Stage 1. Assess the company's or individual's survey expertise, along with their knowledge of health and safety.

Stage 2. Assess the company's or individual's experience and track record to establish if they are capable of doing the work and that they recognise their limitations.

As a minimum this should entail:

- ☑ seeking evidence of their training and experience in such work

- ☑ confirming that they are qualified and experienced in carrying out the type of work to be done

- ☑ checking that they are going to carry out the survey in accordance with the HSE guidance contained in *Asbestos: The survey guide* (HSG264)

- ☑ ensuring that at least two surveyors will carry out the survey and that in doing so **they will** be working together

- ☑ seeking evidence that they have suitable liability insurance.

09

Asbestos – Appendix A

Personal competence

Individual surveyors can demonstrate their competence in one of two ways.

1. Certification.

Individual surveyors may be able to demonstrate their technical competence to carry out the type of work to be done by virtue of personal certification from a certification body accredited by the United Kingdom Accreditation Service (UKAS). Personal certification provides the client with an assurance that the individual has achieved a defined level of competence to carry out specific activities.

2. Qualifications and experience.

Where personal certification is not held, individuals may be able to demonstrate sufficient competency through a combination of qualifications and experience.

As a minimum, an individual should hold a British Occupational Hygiene Society (BOHS) P402 certificate, plus a minimum of six months' full-time, relevant, field-based experience, working under the supervision of an experienced and suitably qualified surveyor.

Corporate competence

Organisations can demonstrate their technical competence to carry out asbestos surveys through accreditation to ISO/IEC 17020, which is the quality standard against which the performance of inspection bodies (such as asbestos surveying companies and analytical laboratories) can be independently assessed. The standard is awarded by UKAS.

Survey risk assessment

Before a survey is commenced the risks to the surveyor, sampling staff and others, including the building occupants, must be assessed. The risk assessment would normally be conducted by the asbestos surveyor and should cover asbestos risks and non-asbestos risks. Depending upon the type of survey to be carried out and the nature of the premises, the non-asbestos risks could include:

- ☑ working at height
- ☑ working in confined spaces
- ☑ noise, vibration and machinery hazards
- ☑ lone working
- ☑ electrical and chemical hazards.

 The above list is far from exhaustive.

Types of survey

Since the introduction of HSG264 there have been two categories of asbestos survey.

1. Management survey.

The purpose of this type of survey is to locate, so far as is reasonably practicable, the presence and extent of any suspected ACMs, which could be damaged or disturbed by daily activities (such as normal occupancy and building maintenance). Management surveys:

- ☑ will often involve minor intrusive work and some disturbance
- ☑ can involve sampling of materials and/or presumptions that asbestos is present.

2. Refurbishment and demolition survey.

As its name suggests, this type of survey must be carried out before any refurbishment or demolition is commenced. However, this type of survey might also be necessary for other work (such as engineering construction projects).

The survey will locate and describe, as far as is reasonably practicable, all ACMs in the area to be refurbished or the whole structure if it is to be demolished. This type of survey is fully intrusive and involves destructive inspection, as may be necessary, to gain access to all areas, including those that are difficult to reach.

Caveats

Anyone applying the results of a survey should initially check if the surveyor has written any caveats on the survey. In the past it was common for surveyors to exclude access to areas that are over three metres above ground level, as it is not possible for a single surveyor to safely use a ladder higher than this because they cannot foot it. Hence, in such circumstances there should always be a minimum of two surveyors. There may be other areas that have not been accessed; the new HSG264 survey guidance makes these types of caveat unacceptable.

Caveats are restrictions put on the scope of the survey, or the investigative methods to be used. Caveats can be imposed by either party, for example:

☑ they can be imposed by the building owner to reduce the intrusive damage that would otherwise occur to the building as a part of the survey process

☑ conversely, the asbestos surveyor may find it necessary to include caveats in the survey report to cover areas of the building where asbestos could be present but, for whatever reason, access could not be achieved.

Hence, caveats can seriously reduce the usefulness and value of a survey and should only be imposed when absolutely necessary and where they can be fully justified.

Asbestos surveyors are taught to identify the spaces where asbestos is likely to be found and to survey accordingly. The meaning of spaces can be anything from a boiler room to a roof void, an office, an underground duct, a cavity between the two leafs of a wall or anywhere else that asbestos or an asbestos-containing material might have been used. By preventing access to an area or restricting the investigative method necessary, the client could seriously reduce the usefulness of the survey report.

A 'no access' comment on an asbestos report could be simply because:

☑ the door of a room was locked and the surveyor could not gain entry

☑ the space was an underground duct and a mini digger was required to lift the covers

☑ a suspended floor had no access other than by destroying the floor

☑ the electrical system was live during the survey.

Effective planning should help to overcome such obstacles.

Survey report

The outcome of the survey should be a survey report that fulfils the requirements of the client.

A comprehensive report will include a plan of the building with the areas where ACMs have been identified clearly marked. Similarly, areas where access could not be gained, but where asbestos could be present, should also be marked.

HSE guidance recommends that the information is also presented in a tabulated format, room-by-room, for ease of interpretation. This table could then be incorporated into the asbestos register for the building.

The survey report must identify:

☑ the locations where ACMs have been found

☑ the extent of the ACM in each location (area, thickness, and so on)

☑ what type of ACM it is

☑ the level of confidence that it is an ACM (for example, identified through analysis, strongly presumed or presumed)

☑ the asbestos type within the ACM.

For management surveys (and refurbishment and demolition surveys where work will not start for some time), the following information should also be provided:

☑ how accessible the ACMs are

☑ the extent of damage or deterioration

☑ if it has received any surface treatment

☑ an indication of the priority for dealing with each ACM identified

☑ how each ACM should be dealt with.

The client must ensure that the asbestos report fulfils the requirements for which it was commissioned. This will entail checking that the report:

☑ complies with the tender requirements

☑ contains no unagreed caveats or disclaimers

☑ confirms the survey was of the category required

☑ covers all the rooms and areas required

☑ contains clear and accurate diagrams and plans

☑ confirms that an adequate number of samples were taken (usually one or two per room or area)

☑ indicates that sample numbers reflect variations in the same ACM (for example, where two types of suspended ceiling tile have been used in the same room)

☑ does not contain any other obvious omissions, discrepancies or inconsistencies.

09

Appendix B – Checklist for managing asbestos

 Check the HSE webpages for duty to manage asbestos.

Use this checklist to mark your progress.

1. Introduction
Overview of the scheme - checklist.

2. Are you responsible for maintenance or repair?
Does the duty to manage apply to you and your premises?

3. When was it built?
Was it built before 2000, are you on a brownfield site or do you use old equipment?

4. What information do you have already?
Look at building plans, previous asbestos surveys and any other relevant documents.

5. Inspect your building.
Create an asbestos register to list where asbestos may be present.

6. Determining priorities for action.
Use a scoring tool to work out what needs doing first.

7. Decide how to deal with the different types of asbestos.
Use the online tool on how to treat the different types of asbestos (such as sprayed asbestos and asbestos cement).

8. Write your asbestos management plan.
The plan brings together your asbestos register, plans of work and schedule.

9. Testing for asbestos.
If work is required, you need to test for asbestos first.

10. Tell people what you're doing.
You need to tell employees, contractors and maintenance workers about your findings.

11. Getting work done.
Does the work need a licensed contractor?

12. Keep your records up to date.
If any work is done on asbestos, your records need updating, and you need regular checks on the state of the asbestos.

09

Appendix C – Preventing exposure to asbestos

Manager

☑ Avoid disturbing asbestos-containing materials, if possible.

☑ If you are not a licensed contractor, make sure you know what work can be carried out on asbestos-containing materials.

☑ Ensure that anyone going to work on asbestos material has received adequate training.

☑ Use the HSE's *Asbestos essentials* to ensure the job is carried out properly.

☑ Prepare a plan of work, explaining what the job involves, the work procedures and what controls to use.

☑ Ensure that those doing the work understand the plan of work.

☑ Provide the right protective clothing and equipment, including properly fitted respirators and overalls.

☑ Make sure the work area is inspected visually at the end of the job and there is no debris or dust.

☑ Make arrangements for the safe disposal of any asbestos waste.

☑ Consult with others who may be affected by the work.

Worker

☑ Make sure you have been properly trained for work with asbestos and understand what is required of you in the plan of work.

☑ Use HSE's guidance to help you carry out the job properly and ensure that exposure to asbestos is kept as low as possible.

☑ If you have any concerns, stop work and talk to your supervisor.

☑ Don't eat, smoke or drink in the work area.

☑ Use any equipment provided, including that for personal protection; ensure it is clean and in good working order.

☑ Make sure the work area is clean at the end of the job. Don't sweep up dust and debris – use a Type H vacuum cleaner and wet rags.

☑ Ensure asbestos waste is disposed of safely.

Links to HSE guidance

 An HSE *Asbestos essentials* task sheet can be found on their website.

09

Planning – prioritising decisions and managing risk

☑ Identify where there might be asbestos-containing materials.

☑ Consider eliminating the need to work with asbestos. Can you avoid disturbing asbestos by doing the job some other way?

☑ Does the work need to be done by a licensed contractor?

☑ Where it is not possible to eliminate the risk, develop a plan of work that highlights the risks and identifies the controls that must be used. Communicate this so that it is understood by all involved.

☑ Workers must be provided with the appropriate RPE and any other protective equipment identified in the plan of work. This must be properly fitted, clean and in full working order.

☑ Ensure all workers are trained in non-licensable asbestos work and follow the appropriate task guidance sheets.

☑ Use an asbestos waste container and dispose of asbestos waste safely.

Asbestos

10

Dust and fumes

Each year 1,000s of construction workers contract or die from respiratory diseases due to breathing in dust and fumes.

The amount breathed in each day as they work from site to site can seem small or insignificant. In some cases the effects of exposure may be immediate but generally it can take years before the symptoms of ill health become apparent.

Because of this, respiratory risks are often overlooked or underplayed. This chapter explains what dust is, what it can do to the human body, and what must be done to minimise exposure to protect the workforce.

Introduction	138
Key points	138
Respiratory diseases	139
Types of dust and fumes	139
Exposure limits	140
Managing the risk	141
Respiratory protective equipment	142
Monitoring	143
Training and supervision	143
Managing dust hierarchy – summary	143
Appendix A – Silica dust	145

10.1 Introduction

Managing and controlling long-term exposure to dust and fumes is a challenge facing the industry. Many workers are exposed daily, but they only work for short durations on various sites and frequently change employers.

The exposure to airborne dust or fumes can result in skin diseases and severe respiratory illnesses (such as occupational asthma). Asbestos fibres, silica and lead dust are particularly hazardous if inhaled. Such diseases can be totally disabling, causing those affected to give up work or change their employment.

Work-related ill health has devastating consequences for individuals and their families but it is very much misunderstood or underestimated.

- ☑ HSE statistics show that each year up to **7,000** people develop **occupational asthma.**
- ☑ **4,000 people die each year from asbestos-related diseases.**
- ☑ **500** people (and more each year) **are dying from silica-related cancers** (dust from cutting blocks, kerbs, and other items).
- ☑ Many more suffer life-changing illnesses.
- ☑ 2.6 million working days are lost to work-related ill health each year.

Raising the awareness of managers, supervisors and workers, to ensure effective control measures are always put in place and followed, is fundamental in helping reduce these numbers.

 At any one time there are far more people off work through occupational ill health than there are because of a work-related accident.

10.2 Key points

- ☑ The creation of airborne dust or fumes should be prevented or eliminated where reasonably practicable, by:
  - substituting and using a less harmful substance or material
  - using a different process (such as a block splitter instead of mechanical cutting)
  - manufacturing off site.
- ☑ Where the prevention of dust or fumes is not possible, the extent of exposure must be controlled to a level that is safe.
- ☑ Control of dust can be achieved by:
  - extracting dust and fumes through stand-alone extractor units
  - collecting dust in collector bags attached to powered hand tools
  - wet cutting solid materials (such as thermal blocks, bricks or ceramic tiles)
  - where practical, carrying out of work activities in the open air rather than in enclosed spaces.
- ☑ Hazardous fumes usually result from:
  - processes in which materials are heated (such as welding, lead burning or grinding)
  - uncontrolled use of substances (such as solvents and adhesives)
  - the use of equipment and plant powered by internal combustion engines.

 All dusts are hazardous to health. The creation of dust, regardless of amount, must be controlled – all risk assessments and methods statements should state how exposure to dust or fumes will be minimised. It is no longer acceptable to expect workers to work unprotected in dusty conditions.

 For further information on asbestos, lead or carbon monoxide refer to the individual chapters covering those topics.

10.3 Respiratory diseases

With an accident on site, the injury or other effects are usually immediate and obvious. The effects of exposure to most work-related ill health hazards are not immediate or not even felt (unlike an accident that causes injury).

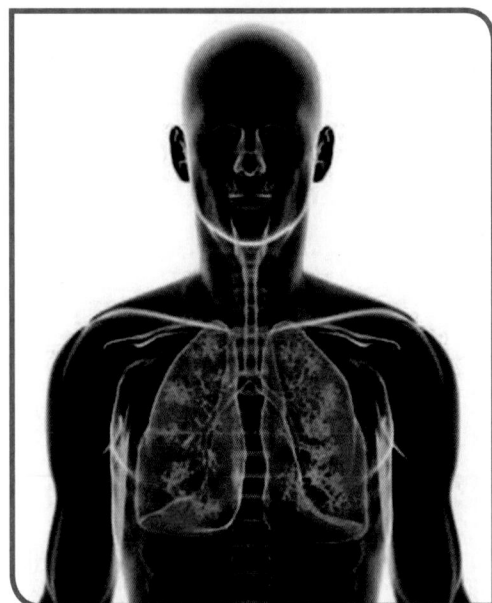

Workers may go home from work feeling more or less the same each day and are none the wiser.

As workers are repeatedly exposed to small doses of dust and fumes, these start to damage their body.

It can take many weeks, months or even years before symptoms of exposure become a problem to them and irreversible damage may well have occurred.

Work-related ill health can often result in employees being unable to work as hard or as efficiently as before, and sometimes they may never work again.

Typical symptoms and illnesses are respiratory diseases, such as:

- ✓ diffuse pleural thickening
- ✓ mesothelioma
- ✓ silicosis
- ✓ asbestosis
- ✓ asthma.

Silicosis

Silicosis is a huge problem within the construction industry. Respirable crystalline silica (RCS) is found in stone, rocks, sands and clays, and so is contained in many construction products (such as concrete, blocks, bricks, ceramics, and so on). Common day-to-day activities produce RCS and many workers are exposed to it knowingly and unknowingly by breathing in silica particles.

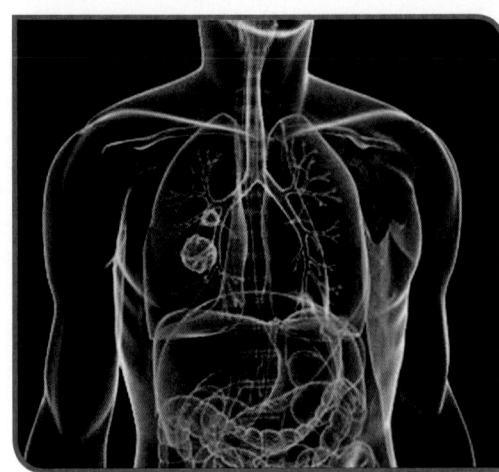

Exposure to RCS over a long period can cause fibrosis (hardening or scarring) of the lung tissue with a consequent loss of lung function. Sufferers are likely to have severe shortness of breath and may find it difficult or impossible to walk even short distances or upstairs. The effect continues to develop after exposure has stopped and is irreversible. Sufferers usually become house- or bed-bound and often die prematurely due to heart failure.

Acute silicosis is a rare complication of short-term exposure to very large amounts of silica. This condition is life-threatening and associated with significant clinical consequences.

Silica may also be linked to lung cancer. Precautions taken to control the risk of fibrosis will serve to control the risk of lung cancer. Workers with silicosis are at an increased risk of tuberculosis, kidney disease and arthritis. Exposure to RCS may also cause chronic obstructive pulmonary disease (COPD).

10

10.4 Types of dust and fumes

The following paragraphs describe the main respiratory hazards that may be encountered on site.

Dust

Dust is produced when solid materials are broken down into finer particles. The longer that the dust stays in the air then the easier it is to breathe in. Airborne dust is usually respirable dust.

Not all harmful dusts are visible. Dusts that are too fine to be seen by the naked eye are the cause of many serious health problems. Like most occupational health problems, it can take several years for symptoms of ill health to manifest themselves.

Skin irritation, dermatitis and ulceration can be caused by contact with some types of dust. Other types of dust, being soluble, may be absorbed through the skin via cuts and abrasions.

The inhalation of dust can cause wheezing, coughing, breathlessness, bronchitis, nasal and other types of cancer. Dust also contains bacteria and viruses and therefore has the potential to cause stomach disorders. These can result from ingesting airborne dust or from eating food with contaminated hands.

Dust and fumes

Mists

Tiny liquid droplets are formed by atomisation of the liquid (for example, when spraying or using an aerosol). Mists may be a combination of several hazardous substances.

Vapours

These are the gaseous state of substances that are liquids or solids at room temperature. They usually form when substances evaporate. One example is the vapour from a tin of glue or solvent that has been left open.

Fumes

Fumes can be produced when some building materials are heated or otherwise worked. A common form of respiratory illness, which has flu-like symptoms, is caused by the inhalation of welding fumes. Other sources of hazardous fumes are uncontrolled exposure to the use of equipment and plant that is powered by internal combustion engines.

Metal fumes

These occur when metal is vaporised at high temperatures (for example, when welding and gas cutting). The physical properties of fumes can be confusing, particularly when identifying suitable respiratory protective equipment (RPE). Usually, metal fumes are actually a solid particle by the time they are inhaled.

When welding is taking place the temperature of the metal at the weld is sufficiently high for the elements in the metal to become gaseous. However, 2–3 mm away from the weld the gases have cooled down sufficiently for the fumes to solidify out as small particles.

Consequently, when purchasing RPE to protect against fumes, a device that protects against solid particles rather than gases is required.

Gases

Gases are airborne at room temperature and normally mix with the air that we breathe. Examples include propane, butane, acetylene, carbon monoxide and hydrogen sulphide. Gases can spread very quickly.

10.5 Exposure limits

It is widely known that almost any excess levels of construction dust can cause health problems. Harmful effects range from simple skin irritation to severe respiratory illness.

Exposure without dust suppression can be massive

Such problems are not likely to arise if occupational exposure limits and the appropriate regulations are observed and safe systems of work are maintained.

Exposure to any unlisted substance or general nuisance dust should be limited by reducing dust levels to the minimum reasonably practicable. These levels should not exceed 10 milligrams of dust per cubic metre of air, when measured over an eight hour period (10 mg/m³ 8H TWA). Within that figure, only 4 mg/m³ should be respirable dust.

Generally speaking, if visible dust can be seen in the air, it is highly possible that the 10 mg limit is being approached (or exceeded).

When dust is inhaled, the body's defence mechanisms can usually deal with the larger particles. However, they struggle to cope with the very small particles. In occupational hygiene terms, dust is divided into two categories:

☑ inhalable dust, sometimes called total dust

☑ much smaller particles, which are called respirable dust.

Because dust is a mix of very small particles, all dusts have been assigned a concentration in air above which they are considered hazardous. It is important to remember that this applies to all dusts, for example those caused by:

☑ sweeping a dusty floor

☑ mechanically cutting concrete products

☑ driving plant on dusty sites

☑ mixing sand and cement to make mortar

☑ sanding down MDF or timber.

The technical descriptions of the two types of dust are:

☑ total inhalable dust approximates to the fraction of airborne material that is inhaled and is available for deposition in the respiratory tract

☑ respirable dust approximates to the fraction of airborne material that is inhaled and penetrates to the gas exchange region of the lung (the alveoli).

Any concentration of **inhalable** dust in excess of:

☑ **10 mg/m³** (10 milligrams of dust per cubic metre of air) averaged out over **eight hours**

or any **respirable** dust in excess of:

☑ **4 mg/m³** averaged over **eight hours**

is deemed to be a substantial concentration of dust and therefore within the definition of a substance hazardous to health.

The official list of exposure limits is updated periodically and published in the HSE Guidance Note EH40. This has been supplemented by a table on the HSE's website under COSHH, which has the up-to-date list of workplace exposure levels.

The lists specify workplace exposure limits (WEL) for a number of dusts, in addition to other substances.

Dusts are therefore classified as substances that are hazardous to health.

10.6 Managing the risk

The Control of Substances Hazardous to Health (COSHH) Regulations requires that every employer shall **not** expose any employees to any hazardous substance, unless a suitable and sufficient assessment of the risks has been carried out, and that adequate precautions are put in place.

Any such assessment should apply the principles of hierarchy of control (see explanation below).

 Hierarchy of control

Follow 'ERIC-PD'

E – Eliminate (Is there a safer substance that can be used? Can the activity involving the hazardous substance be substituted or discontinued? Can the concentration of the substance be reduced?)

R – Reduce (Reduce the frequency and length of exposure to the substance.)

I – Isolate (Isolate the substance away from the user.)

C – Control (Control the use of the substance by enclosing the material, or provide a different method of application, such as extraction or wet cutting.)

P – Personal protective equipment (Should always be seen as the last resort. Wear appropriate gloves, goggles, respiratory masks, and so on.)

D – Discipline (Follow a safe system of work, providing training and information.)

Similarly there are legal duties on every employer to make a suitable and sufficient assessment of every work activity to identify any hazard that employees or any other person might encounter as a result of the work being carried out.

Employers are required to assess the health risks to their employees arising out of exposure to hazardous dusts and fumes, and, if reasonably practicable, put control measures in place to eliminate the work processes and the use of substances that cause exposure. If this is not reasonably practicable, employers must:

☑ control exposure to an acceptable level

☑ inform employees of the hazards involved and the control measures in place

☑ mitigate the effects of any exposure by providing health surveillance where necessary.

Designers have the potential to eliminate or reduce the exposure of operatives, and possibly others, to dust or fumes through their designs.

Examples of how this can be achieved are:

☑ specifying construction methods that avoid hot-works and therefore the creation of fumes, particularly in enclosed areas and confined spaces

☑ stoning up site and haul roads, using vehicle wheel washes and dampening down surfaces will help control dust, both for workers and those near to site (such as neighbouring communities)

☑ specifying that construction materials are cut to size at the point of manufacture, eliminating the need for cutting, planing, sanding and so on

☑ on-site designing of enclosures to contain hazardous dust where its creation is unavoidable.

Principal or main contractors, other contractors and the self-employed have the potential to reduce exposure to dust and/or fumes by co-ordinating work activities, co-operating with each other and adopting work methods explained elsewhere in this chapter.

10

Rubbing down tape and jointing. Traditionally rubbing down creates a lot of dust, which is hazardous to health, has to be cleaned up and is manually intensive. This drywall sander with collection system minimises all these issues to the extent that the operative does not need RPE.

Cement boarding used as part of a vertical cladding system had to be cut to size on site. A circular saw complete with vacuum collection was used in a designated cutting area and the operator also wore FFP3-rated RPE.

 Follow recognised, industry or HSE guidance, which can be downloaded from the construction section of the HSE's website.

10.7 Respiratory protective equipment

Given the nature of some work activities, it is not always practical to completely contain the airborne dust or fumes created. In these circumstances, if no other control measure is reasonably practicable, respiratory protective equipment (RPE) and other personal protective equipment (PPE) as necessary, must be provided for each person working with, or otherwise exposed to, airborne dust or fumes.

Selecting the wrong type of RPE could have serious, even fatal, consequences. Selection must be carried out by a competent person.

The Health and Safety Commission instigated the reduction in the workplace exposure level (WEL) of **crystalline silica to 0.1 mg/m³**, due to concerns about the severe lung disease, silicosis and a form of cancer that can occur as a result of inhaling this substance.

 It is recognised good practice to use RPE with an FFP3 or P3 rating to protect against all construction dust (such as silica), which is created when mechanically cutting concrete, bricks, slabs, and so on – even when wet cutting (which only removes about 75% of airborne particles). FFP3/P3 offers maximum protection compared to FFP1/P1 or FFP2/P2.

For further information on the topics listed below, refer to Chapter B06 Personal protective equipment.

There are various types of RPE approved for use. Details of types and permissible uses are available from the manufacturers.

☑ Disposable face mask respirators.

☑ Nuisance dust masks.

☑ Half-mask dust respirator.

☑ Half masks.

☑ Powered respirators.

☑ Ventilated visor and ventilated helmet respirators.

☑ Self-contained breathing apparatus.

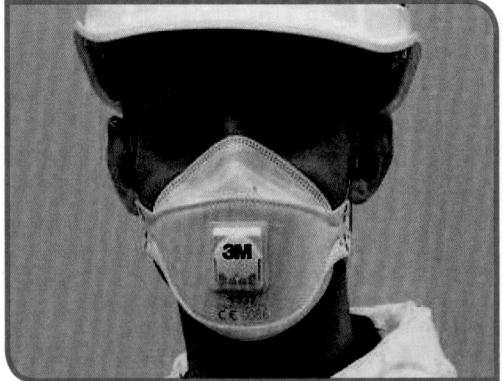

10.8 Monitoring

Sampling is usually carried out by consultants using metered pumps with membrane filters or workers wearing personal dose meters. The dust collected is weighed in relation to the amount of air sampled. Dust samples can also be examined for type.

There are some direct-reading dust sampling monitors available. However, there is some doubt as to the accuracy of these instruments. They are very useful for a long-term project where they can be calibrated regularly by comparing their readings against samples taken from membrane filters. However, they are not recommended as the sole means of measuring a personal exposure to dust. It is also important to be aware that there are a number of different laboratory techniques required for analysis (for example, measuring exposure to silica normally requires x-ray diffraction). This is not a piece of equipment that is commonly available and the best source of advice is the British Occupational Hygiene Society (BOHS).

10.9 Training and supervision

It should be noted that all these sets of regulations place a legal duty on the employer to provide employees with adequate information, instruction, training and supervision to be able to carry out any work task safely and without risks to their health.

Information, instruction, training and supervision, as required by the regulations, must be provided for supervisors and personnel who work in dusty conditions. New employees should receive full instruction before starting work and should be familiarised with the following:

☑ the health risks associated with dust and the preventative measures in operation, as identified by the risk assessment

☑ the correct use and cleaning of protective clothing and equipment

☑ the reasons for air sampling

☑ their duties in respect of the correct use of equipment and of safe systems of work in operation

☑ the procedures for reporting defective or inadequate equipment.

10.10 Managing dust hierarchy – summary

Raise construction dust risk awareness

Construction dust is the most significant risk to workers' health after asbestos. Silica dust alone is thought to accelerate the deaths of around 500 construction workers annually – far greater than those killed by accidents. Many more suffer from a reduced quality of life.

Control through design and different work methods

The first focus should be on reducing the risk at the design stage. Paving can be planned so that the smallest number of cuts is needed. Different sized materials can be chosen so that cutting is minimised. Routes for services can be designed in.

Where a risk remains, this can be reduced by working another way. Cables can be protected and covered with plaster or board instead of chasing. Brackets and cable trays can be directly fixed instead of using drill holes. Block splitters can be used instead of a cut-off saw.

10

Water suppression

Water can be used with some tasks to effectively damp down the dust. Most modern cut-off saws can be attached to a water supply. The water can come directly from the mains or a portable source (such as a hand-pressurised freestanding container). Other devices (such as masonry saw benches) can be selected that come with an in-built water reservoir.

Dust extraction/collection

Water suppression is not suitable for controlling all dust risks. It cannot be used with most electric tools, on wood or where the waste slurry would create a problem (such as in an inhabited building). Extraction is an effective alternative. This sucks the dust away as it is being created and stores it until emptied. The extraction vacuum can also be used for general cleaning instead of dry sweeping.

Correctly working on-tool extraction is made up of a number of different parts. A specially designed hood is needed to collect the dust at the point it is being created. This should be shaped and designed around the cutting/contact point. The hood is attached to an industrial vacuum extraction unit via a hose. For most tasks the industrial vacuum should be either an M or H class.

Respiratory protective equipment

RPE is often used to protect against dust risks. It takes two main forms: a disposable mask or half mask with filters. It should be used as a back-up measure to water suppression or extraction. It should not be used as a replacement for those controls where they can be used.

RPE needs to be to the correct specification if it is to provide the protection needed. For most tasks involving power tools this will be a disposable FFP3 mask or a half mask with a P3 filter.

Other control issues

The right controls still have to be used correctly. A worker may not know what to do or there may be a problem with the control due to poor maintenance. Poor planning might mean no more water is available to refill containers or electricity for extraction. Spare masks may have run out. Supervision may be lacking. Management arrangements are important for tackling this.

The control of dust also needs the user to play their part. The best controls and systems will not work if they are not followed.

One of the reasons for people not following work methods, is that they do not fully appreciate the risks, or have not been involved in any discussions about them.

Appendix A – Silica dust

About silica

Silica occurs as a natural component of many materials used in construction activities. Crystalline silica is present in substantial quantities in sand, sandstone and granite, and often forms a significant proportion of clay, shale and slate. Products (such as concrete and mortar) also contain crystalline silica.

The health hazards of silica come from breathing in the dust. Activities that can expose workers or members of the public to the dust include working with stone, grit blasting, scabbling, cutting or drilling, demolition and tunnelling.

The use of power tools leads to high exposures if exhaust systems/wet cutting processes are not used and maintained.

For some activities, exposure will depend upon how confined the working space is, and the presence or absence of ventilation. For example, tunnelling through dry, silica-bearing rock will always lead to high exposures for workers at or near the cutting face unless precautions are taken.

Breathing fine dust of crystalline silica can lead to the development of silicosis. This involves scarring of the lung tissue and can lead to breathing difficulties.

Exposure to very high concentrations over a relatively short period of time can cause acute silicosis, resulting in rapidly progressive breathlessness and death within a few months of onset.

Silica

Materials	Sand, sandstone, granite, clay, shale and slate.
Common products	Concrete, mortar, bricks, blocks, ceramics, kerbs and paving slabs.
Common operations	Sweeping up, demolition and strip out. Drilling or breaking. Cutting (disc cutter/chasing machine/floor saw). Grinding, polishing, rubbing down, sanding and blasting.
Control measures	Manufacture off site/isolate process. Substitute process (for example, use hand block splitter not disc-cutter). Extraction/vacuum collection/forced extraction. Local exhaust ventilation. Water suppression (typically only 75% of particles are controlled). Dampen down.
Respiratory protective equipment	Half-face respirator or disposal face mask, rated P3 or FFP3.

Good practice methods – silica

Drilling masonry	Control measures
	■ Can material be pre-drilled? ■ Ensure drill bits are sharp. ■ Drilling, especially horizontal at chest or eye level or above head means additional exposure to dust. ■ Where possible use dust collection systems that use a vacuum (not clip on dust bags). ■ Avoid sweeping; instead, vacuum up drill dust, otherwise the dust will disperse around the area and continue to be a hazard. ■ Use RPE (F3 or FFP3 rating).
Cutting slabs/kerbs/concrete	**Control measures**
	■ Can pre-sized material be purchased? ■ Can a block splitter be used? ■ Use a petrol or compressed air cut saw with a constant water feed. ■ Use RPE (F3 or FFP3 rating). *Note: Water feed on its own will only remove approximately 75% of the airborne particles. RPE still needs to be worn.*
Chasing walls	**Control measures**
	■ Check for live services. ■ Ensure eye protection is impact-rated. ■ Use a proprietary system that incorporates a dust extraction system. ■ Regularly empty the vacuum collector. ■ Regularly clean the filter. ■ Consider using additional dust extraction (such as room filter cubes). ■ Use RPE (F3 or FFP3 rating). ■ Check that any escaping dust is not contaminating other areas or affecting others.
Sweeping up – general	**Control measures**
	■ Set up designated cutting areas. ■ Use dust extraction/collection units on equipment. ■ Vacuum the area rather than sweeping. ■ Provide good ventilation. ■ Dampen down area before sweeping. ■ Place dust in bags. ■ Use RPE (F3 or FFP3 rating). ■ Provide a vacuum to clean down equipment and clothing.

10

Silica exposure levels

Examples of typical levels of silica exposure in some common construction activities

Activity	Control measures	Exposure	Improvements required*
Drilling in poorly ventilated undercroft	■ no dust suppression ■ no extraction ■ no forced ventilation ■ inadequate respiratory protective equipment (RPE)	**HIGH – 300 times the MEL**	■ fit water suppression or dust extraction to drilling equipment ■ provide appropriate RPE ■ ensure correct use of RPE
Drilling into brickwork under arch blocked at one end	■ primitive extraction by fan and airbag ■ disposable face masks worn	**HIGH – 5 times the MEL**	■ fit water suppression or dust extraction to drilling equipment ■ provide appropriate RPE ■ ensure correct use of RPE
Using jackhammers to break out concrete in large open indoor area	■ limited ventilation ■ no dust suppression ■ no local exhaust ventilation ■ no RPE in use	**MEDIUM – within the MEL but double the level regarded as reasonably practicable**	■ wet down concrete and rubble
Chasing out cracks in screeded cement floor in large open indoor area	■ RPE provided but not worn properly ■ breathing zone of worker crouching over grinder very close to source of dust	**HIGH – 6 times the MEL**	■ attach dust extraction to grinder ■ wet down ahead of the chasing ■ provide appropriate RPE ■ ensure correct use of RPE
Chasing out mortar between bricks prior to re-pointing	■ ineffective extraction fitted to hand-held electric grinder ■ RPE correctly worn but not to correct standard	**HIGH – 21 times the MEL**	■ attach dust extraction to grinder ■ provide appropriate RPE ■ ensure correct use of RPE
Cutting paving kerb (33% silica) in open area	■ petrol driven saw not fitted with water spray or local exhaust ventilation	**HIGH – 12 times the MEL**	■ provide effective water suppression system to saw
Cutting blue brick (32% silica) in open area	■ petrol driven saw not fitted with water spray or local exhaust ventilation	**HIGH – 5 times the MEL**	■ provide effective water suppression system to saw
Cutting breeze block (3% silica) in open area	■ petrol driven saw not fitted with water spray or local exhaust ventilation	**HIGH – twice the MEL**	■ provide effective water suppression to saw
Cutting window openings in concrete wall with wall saw/ Cutting concrete with floor saw	■ water suppression on saw used	**LOW – well below the MEL and also below the level regarded as significant**	
General clearing and removing rubble	■ hand sweeping with brush	**HIGH – twice the MEL**	■ damp down rubble before clearing ■ use mechanical means to sweep up ■ provide appropriate RPE ■ ensure correct use of RPE
General clearing and removing rubble	■ use of mechanical sweeper with rotating brushes and vacuum extraction	**MEDIUM – within the MEL but double the level regarded as significant**	■ provide appropriate RPE ■ ensure correct use of RPE
Concrete crushing from demolition job for use as hard core	■ machine with enclosed cab ■ water jets fitted	**LOW – well below the MEL and also below the level regarded as significant**	
* To reduce exposure to below the maximum exposure limit (MEL) and so far as is reasonably practicable.			

(Table reproduced from the HSE's Construction Information Sheet no. 36 Silica.)

10

11

Carbon monoxide

Every year, thousands of construction workers and occupants of properties where work is being undertaken suffer lethal and non-lethal illnesses from the effects of carbon monoxide (CO) poisoning.

Although some of the effects can be immediate, they can also manifest over a period of time. The impact can be gradual and difficult to attribute to particular sites, equipment or instances given that many operatives generally work across a number of sites over a period of time.

Carbon monoxide (CO) effects are often overlooked as they can easily be attributable to a number of other illnesses making diagnosis difficult. This chapter gives a general overview of carbon monoxide (CO), its identification, symptoms, impact and management and outlines the legal framework that regulates it.

Introduction	150
Key points	150
Carbon monoxide	151
Health risk management	152
Managing the risk	153
Monitoring and training	155
Appendix A – An example of ventilation requirements for domestic fuel-burning heating appliances when upgrading or installing draught-proofing	156

11.1 Introduction

Managing and controlling exposure to carbon monoxide is a key challenge facing the industry as it can impact, sometimes lethally, both on operatives working on site and also on any occupants of property where work is being undertaken.

Exposure to carbon monoxide (CO) is the most common cause of poisoning in England and Wales today, resulting in long-term illness and even death in extreme circumstances. This poisoning can have devastating effects on workers and families that could lead to long periods of sickness from work and in the case of fatalities, the emotional and financial impact this brings.

One of the main problems is that carbon monoxide is odourless, colourless, non-irritating and therefore difficult to detect or diagnose. As operatives tend to work on multiple sites, exposure may occur over a period of time and symptoms can easily be associated with many other illnesses.

☑ Up to 50 people die in England and Wales every year through accidental CO poisoning and many more suffer ill health from its effects.

☑ Every year, some 4,000 people are diagnosed by the NHS as having been poisoned by CO. This may be just the tip of the iceberg, as under-reporting, lack of awareness and difficult diagnosis means that a greater number may be living with low levels of CO poisoning without their knowledge. This potentially means their condition may deteriorate to the extent where, if not treated, fatalities could occur.

☑ Whilst an injury caused by an accident is in most cases instantly obvious, the symptoms of CO poisoning can take months or years to present.

☑ CO poisoning can lead to workers having long periods of sickness from work, or having to give up work completely.

☑ Even short-term sickness absence can have an adverse effect on business activities.

☑ The prevention of CO poisoning can be achieved through:
  – a suitable assessment of the risks to health being carried out and reviewed as necessary
  – adequate control measures being identified, put in place and adjusted as necessary
  – the persons at risk fully using the control measures provided
  – effective personal protective equipment (PPE).

☑ In some circumstances employers have a legal duty to provide health surveillance to employees.

Raising managers', supervisors' and operatives' awareness to ensure effective identification, management and control measures are always put in place and monitored is key to helping to reduce the impact of CO on operatives and, where appropriate, occupants.

11.2 Key points

☑ The creation of CO fumes should be prevented or eliminated where reasonably practicable by:
  – identifying the potential health risks arising from the work activities to be carried out
  – investigating what can be done about them and deciding how they are going to be addressed
  – giving staff information, instructions and training on the health risks and the control measures to be followed
  – monitoring the work activities to make sure that the procedures are being implemented and are effective
  – introducing health surveillance where necessary.

☑ Control of CO can be achieved by:
  – raising general awareness of the risks associated with CO by communicating the relevant information to friends, family and work colleagues
  – being aware of the sources of CO, especially in domestic properties where a number of appliances could be responsible
  – getting appliances professionally installed and regularly serviced to ensure they work efficiently and safely
  – ensuring adequate ventilation for all fuel-burning appliances
  – installing monitoring devices for the early detection of excess CO
  – recognising the early signs and symptoms of carbon monoxide poisoning, particularly when more than one family or work member is affected, and seeking medical advice promptly.

☑ Hazardous CO fumes usually result from:
  – domestic heating systems
  – blocked flues/chimneys
  – inadequate ventilation in living areas
  – inadequate ventilation in adjoining car garages
  – leakage from faulty appliances and chimneys/flues
  – fumes from generators
  – the use of equipment and plant powered by internal combustion engines.

11.3 Carbon monoxide

Carbon monoxide (CO) is produced by the incomplete combustion of carbon-containing fuels (such as domestic or bottled gas, coal, oil, coke and wood). Gas stoves, fires, heating boilers, gas-powered water heaters, paraffin heaters and solid fuel-powered water heaters are all potential sources of CO. Diesel plant exhaust emissions also contain CO. The problem arises when such appliances are poorly installed, maintained, not serviced, and housed or used in poorly ventilated areas.

When the waste products of combustion are not effectively removed (for example, because of blocked flues and chimneys) then poisonous gas mixtures may re-enter the room. This problem is not just associated with older or poorer homes – it can also affect the occupants of newer homes with gas central heating. Exhaust fumes from cars, vans or generators are other sources of CO.

CO is formed when any fire burns and, if in an enclosed room, the amount of oxygen available gradually decreases whilst the amount of carbon dioxide increases. As the amounts of these two gases change, this causes the combustion process to alter from one of complete combustion to one of incomplete combustion. This results in the release of CO.

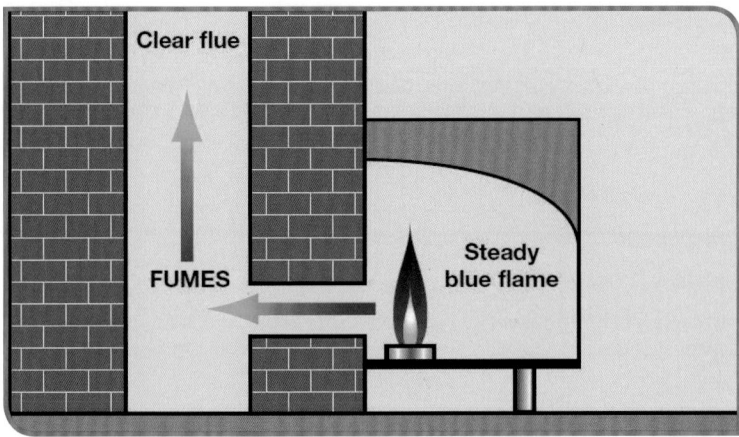

A safe gas appliance

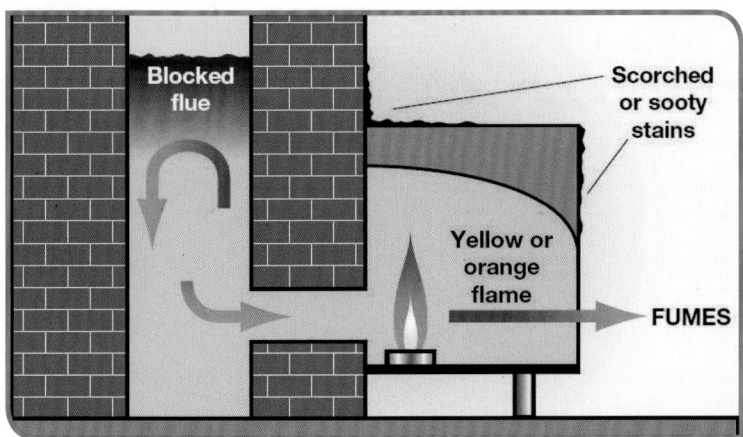

A dangerous gas appliance

Even perfectly designed and maintained heating appliances, or any kind of combustion device, will eventually begin producing dangerous amounts of CO if used in confined and poorly ventilated areas. Having poorly operating appliances only makes the problem worse more quickly. Maintaining appliances and ensuring sufficient fresh air is available are two easy ways of avoiding potentially lethal scenarios.

CO poisoning occurs when you breathe in even small amounts of the fumes. When you breathe in CO, it gets into your bloodstream and prevents your red blood cells from carrying oxygen. Without oxygen, your body tissue and cells die. CO also has direct effects on the blood vessels of the body, causing them to become leaky. This is seen especially in the brain, which swells, leading to unconsciousness and neurological damage.

Levels that do not kill can still cause serious harm to health when breathed in over a long period of time. Long term effects of carbon monoxide poisoning include:

☑ paralysis

☑ brain damage.

Action for suspected CO poisoning

Effectively treating individuals suspected of CO poisoning could make the difference between survival, and short and long-term damage. Move the affected individual(s) away from exposure to the CO source. Their signs and symptoms will then determine what happens next. If the individual is only mildly affected they should seek medical attention, but may not need to be admitted to hospital. All other exposed individuals will require hospital treatment.

Carbon monoxide

Administering 100% oxygen, via a tightly fitting mask with an inflated face-seal, is the first treatment. A high concentration of oxygen in the air being breathed will speed up the formation of oxyhaemoglobin to replace carboxyhaemoglobin. The severity of the CO exposure can be checked by measuring the amount of CO in the air breathed out by the individual or by taking a blood sample and measuring the carboxyhaemoglobin levels, and taking these laboratory tests along with the clinical signs and symptoms present in the affected person.

Symptoms

Carbon monoxide symptoms are similar to flu, food poisoning, viral infections and simply tiredness, so it is quite common for people to mistake this dangerous poisoning for something else.

Other signs that could point to CO poisoning include:

- ☑ symptoms only occur when a person is in one place for a period of time
- ☑ symptoms disappear or get better when the person leaves a location and come back when you return
- ☑ others in the location experience symptoms appearing at a similar time.

One of the difficulties with diagnosing CO poisoning is that many of its symptoms are similar to those of other conditions. Often the onset of symptoms is gradual, occurring without the individual or doctor being fully aware of what is happening. Coupled with this is the fact that the severity of the poisoning depends on:

- ☑ how much CO is actually present in the environment
- ☑ the duration that the person is exposed to CO
- ☑ the age of the individual concerned (elderly, children and foetus are all at greater risk)
- ☑ the person's general state of health
- ☑ the extent of physical activity the person is undertaking (effects are increased with higher activity levels).

Six main symptoms to look out for
1. Headaches
2. Dizziness
3. Nausea
4. Breathlessness
5. Collapse
6. Loss of consciousness

11.4 Health risk management

Employers are required to:

- ☑ identify the potential health risks arising from the work activities to be carried out
- ☑ investigate and decide how they are going to be addressed
- ☑ give staff information, instructions and training on the health risks and the control measures to be followed
- ☑ monitor the work activities to make sure that the procedures are being implemented and are effective
- ☑ introduce health surveillance where necessary
- ☑ look for the benefits and the improvements.

The management of health on site includes areas of confined or enclosed spaces (lack of ventilation, fire trap/risk) and competence, knowledge, skills/training and experience.

Health risks that need to be considered include respiratory problems and the potential for contracting serious respiratory diseases (such as occupational asthma resulting from the inhalation of existing harmful substances).

The Reporting of Injuries, Diseases and Dangerous Occurrences Regulations (RIDDOR)

Reporting procedures cover:

- ☑ fatalities and major injuries
- ☑ incapacity to work for more than seven days
- ☑ specified diseases
- ☑ dangerous occurrences.

They are relevant for employers, employees, self-employed, trainees and other people injured on premises.

Social Security Act and RIDDOR

- ☑ Every accident involving personal injury to an employee must be entered in the accident book by the employee, or someone acting on behalf of the employee
- ☑ the accident book must be kept accessible
- ☑ an employer must investigate all accidents reported.

Major injuries include:

- ☑ unconsciousness through lack of oxygen
- ☑ acute illness due to exposure to certain materials
- ☑ hospitalisation for more than 24 hours.

Reportable occurrences include:

- ☑ release of gases or other dangerous substances
- ☑ failure of breathing apparatus while in use.

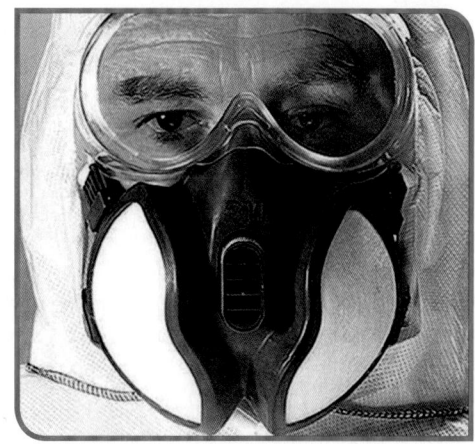

11.5   Managing the risk

The law says you must identify any activities that may expose workers or the public to CO gas, and manage any risk accordingly.

All gas work carried out in the home and in certain commercial premises should be done by a Gas Safe registered engineer.

There are three main ways in which construction work can interface with CO gas issues:

- ☑ site worker and security staff facilities
- ☑ refurbishment work on existing buildings (including use of diesel plant)
- ☑ Gas Safe register for gas engineers.

Site gas-fired appliances, refurbishment work on existing buildings and work on gas systems have all lead to deaths from CO poisoning.

Site worker and security staff facilities

Inadequately ventilated liquefied petroleum gas (LPG) cookers and heaters can produce CO gas. Flammable gas may also escape from leaking cylinders.

Site workers and night security staff have died from CO poisoning on construction projects where such gas-fired appliances have been used in site welfare or rest facilities.

Using properly maintained electrical equipment can eliminate the risks associated with LPG heaters. If LPG is used you can reduce the risks by:

- ☑ using and storing the cylinders in safe, well-ventilated places, outside of the accommodation (including overnight) or in purpose-built ventilated storage areas
- ☑ ensuring that appliances have been properly installed, checked and maintained by a competent person
- ☑ providing adequate combustion ventilation with fixed grilles at high and low level
- ☑ checking that the ventilation provided is not blocked (for example, by newspaper or rags in cold weather to stop draughts)
- ☑ checking that cylinders are properly turned off when not in use
- ☑ using wall or ceiling-mounted CO detectors.

Refurbishment work on existing buildings

Members of the public have died from CO poisoning after refurbishment work (such as roof work) has disrupted gas flues or ventilation systems, causing CO to build up in occupied premises.

The impact of refurbishment work on existing gas-fired systems must be identified during the planning stage and managed throughout the project.

A competent gas engineer should be involved where there is any likelihood that refurbishment work will affect gas-fired systems.

11

Diesel engine exhaust emissions

Diesel engine exhaust emissions (commonly known as diesel fumes) are a mixture of gases, vapours, liquid aerosols and substances made up of particles. They contain the products of combustion, including:

- ☑ carbon monoxide
- ☑ carbon (soot)
- ☑ nitrogen
- ☑ water

- ☑ aldehydes
- ☑ oxides of nitrogen
- ☑ oxides of sulphur
- ☑ polycyclic aromatic hydrocarbons.

 Workers refurbishing a large industrial warehouse became ill and were taken to hospital suffering from the effects of carbon monoxide. They were using diesel-power floats and even though the doors were left open there was insufficient ventilation.

Breathing in diesel fumes can affect workers' health, and exposure to the fumes can cause irritation of the eyes or respiratory tract. These effects are generally short term and should disappear when away from the source of exposure.

However, prolonged exposure to diesel fumes, in particular to any blue or black smoke, could lead to coughing, chestiness and breathlessness.

There is evidence that repeated exposure to diesel fumes over a period of years may increase the risk of lung cancer. Exposure to petrol engine exhaust emissions does not have the same risk.

 The risk assessment and method statement for any diesel plant must address the potential hazard of build up of fumes. Diesel fume extraction fans can be hired and carbon monoxide levels monitored by a suitable gas monitor. It is also important to remember that fumes are heavier than air, and can in effect roll into and build up in an open excavation or trench.

Gas Safe register for gas engineers

Every year, approximately 25 people die from CO poisoning caused by appliances and flues that have not been properly installed or maintained.

All gas work carried out in the home and in certain commercial premises should be done by a Gas Safe registered engineer. Gas work includes installing, repairing or servicing a gas boiler and installing or repairing a gas fire, gas cooker or hob.

The Gas Safe register is the only gas engineer registration scheme approved by the HSE under the Gas Safety (Installation and Use) Regulations.

All gas engineers wanting to undertake domestic and certain other gas work need to be registered with the Gas Safe register.

 For more information visit the Gas Safe register online.

Diagnosing carbon monoxide

Individuals can either be exposed to high levels of CO over a relatively short period of time (acute exposure), or to lower levels of exposure over a longer period of time (chronic exposure).

Acute exposure is easier to diagnose as the symptoms are more pronounced, but it is the common chronic exposure symptoms that are more subtle and difficult to tell apart from other conditions. Where whole families are affected by suspected food poisoning, in some cases this is actually due to CO poisoning. Where such symptoms are reported repeatedly, CO poisoning should be suspected.

Clues that point towards a problem within a specific location include:

- ☑ more than one person is affected
- ☑ symptoms appear or get worse when appliances are in use
- ☑ symptoms are worse in the winter when gas boilers/heaters are in use
- ☑ symptoms improve when operatives or occupants leave a location, but come back on their return.

Important information can also be obtained by inspecting appliances or machinery that run on combustion of carbon-containing fuels. Key problems could include:

- ☑ black soot marks on gas fire burners or on walls near cookers, boilers, gas fires
- ☑ a yellow gas flame colour, rather than the blue colour it should be.

11

> **[?] What should I do if I think an appliance is spilling carbon monoxide?**
>
> - Call the National Gas emergency service on 0800 111 999.
> - Switch off the appliance and shut off the gas supply at the meter control valve.
> - Open all doors and windows to ventilate the room.
> - Visit your GP and explain that you believe you may have been exposed to carbon monoxide.

11.6 Monitoring and training

CO detectors can provide an audible, high-pitched alarm when high levels of CO are detected, or can provide an alarm plus a digital display of the concentration of CO detected in units of 'parts per million' (ppm).

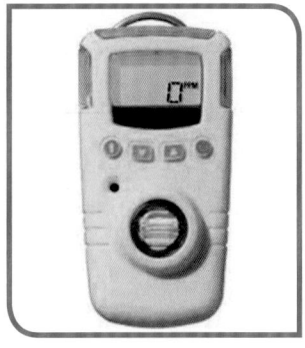

Three types of carbon monoxide detectors are available:

☑ **chem-optical (gel cell or biomimetic) technology** alarms use a type of sensor that simulates haemoglobin in the blood

☑ **electrochemical alarms** work by converting the carbon monoxide electrochemically to carbon dioxide, which generates an electrical current that is taken as a measure of the gas concentration. Electrochemical alarms are usually powered by a battery lasting about five years

☑ **semiconductor technology** alarms use semiconductors or tin dioxide technology to detect carbon monoxide levels. Unlike the alarms above, semiconductor detector alarms do not require any replacement sensors.

Carbon monoxide sensor

It should be noted that all these sets of regulations place a legal duty on the employer to provide employees with adequate information, instruction, training and supervision to be able to carry out any work task safely and without risks to their health.

Information, instruction, training and supervision, as required by the Health and Safety at Work Act and the Management of Health and Safety at Work Regulations must be provided for supervisors and personnel who work in conditions that may expose them to CO. New employees should receive full instruction before starting work and should be familiarised with:

☑ the health risks associated with CO and the preventative measures in operation, as identified by the risk assessment

☑ the correct use and cleaning of protective clothing and equipment

☑ the reasons for monitoring and correct use of monitoring equipment

☑ their duties in respect of the correct use of equipment and of safe systems of work in operation

☑ the procedures for reporting potential CO exposure and defective or inadequate equipment

☑ the procedures for treating individuals suspected of CO poisoning.

Using a Gas Safe registered engineer is the only way to make sure your gas appliances are safe.

A Gas Safe registered engineer has been checked to make sure they are competent and qualified to work safely and legally with gas.

Carbon monoxide alarm

 For information on how to find a gas engineer refer to the Gas Safe website.

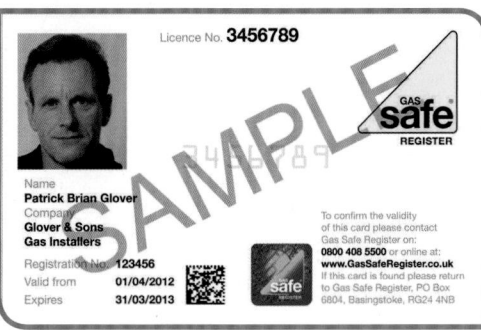

Gas engineers will often have a range of qualifications that allow them to carry out specific types of gas work. It is important to check what work they are qualified to do before you use them. You can find this information using the check an engineer service or by looking on the back of their Gas Safe register ID card.

Every gas engineer carries a Gas Safe register ID card with their own unique licence number, showing the type of gas work they are qualified to do. Before any gas work is carried out, always make sure you ask to see their Gas Safe register ID card.

Appendix A – An example of ventilation requirements for domestic fuel-burning heating appliances when upgrading or installing draught-proofing

Balanced flue (room sealed)

Air supply

☑ No permanent vent required to outside air from room space containing the appliance.

Action

☑ Check flue terminal air inlet and exhaust outlet is not blocked or sealed. If correct proceed with draught-proofing installation.

Open flue gas fire of rated input over 7 kW

Air supply, for appliances of rated input over 7 kW

☑ A permanent vent is required to outside air. This opening shall be 4.5 cm² per kW of rated input over 7 kW.

Action

☑ Verify permanent vent to outside air is present, is not blocked or covered and is of the correct dimensions to produce the free areas required for the appliance rating. If correct proceed with the standard draught-proofing installation.

☑ If a permanent vent to outside air is not present, or is present but blocked, covered or inadequate, leave a minimum of eight metres of window perimeter without draught-proofing or sealants in the appliance.

Where the window perimeter is less than eight metres, both the window and the internal door from the appliance room to the hallway, stairway or passage, which serves the room, shall not be draught-proofed. Where the external door enters the appliance room via a draught lobby that serves no other room, the draught lobby shall not count as a hallway, stairway or passage and another internal door from the appliance room to another room shall not be draught-proofed.

11

A, D, H and I are permanently open vents on the outside. B, C, F and G are permanently open air vents between an appliance compartment and a room or a space.

The area given above is the free area of the vent(s) or the equivalent free area for ventilators of a more complex design. Divide the area given above in mm^2 by 100 to find the corresponding area in cm^2.

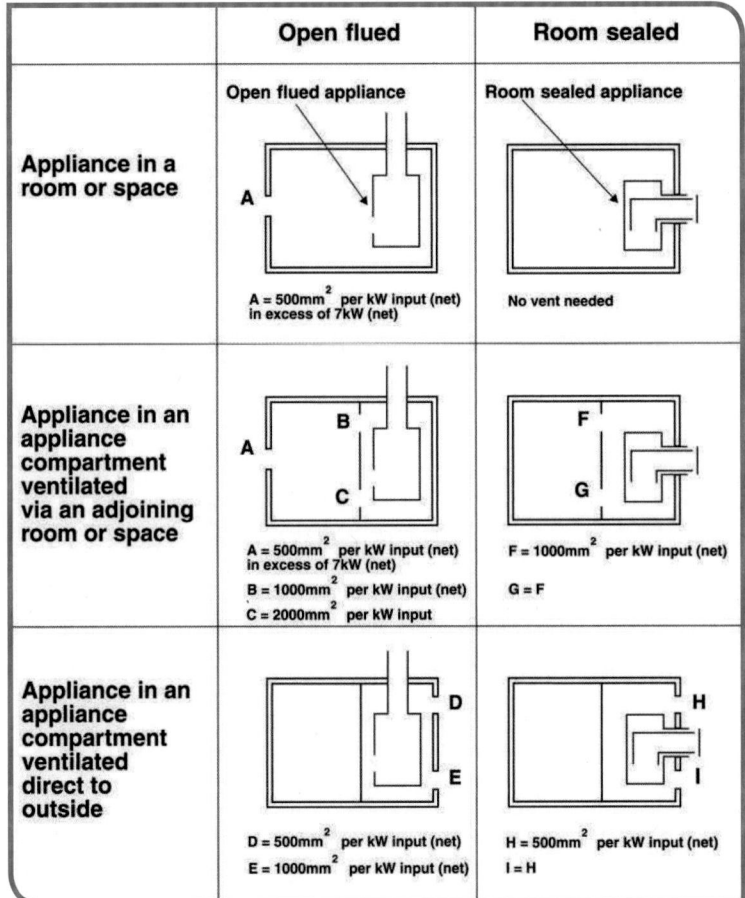

	Open flued	Room sealed
Appliance in a room or space	Open flued appliance A A = 500mm^2 per kW input (net) in excess of 7kW (net)	Room sealed appliance No vent needed
Appliance in an appliance compartment ventilated via an adjoining room or space	A B C A = 500mm^2 per kW input (net) in excess of 7kW (net) B = 1000mm^2 per kW input (net) C = 2000mm^2 per kW input	F G F = 1000mm^2 per kW input (net) G = F
Appliance in an appliance compartment ventilated direct to outside	D E D = 500mm^2 per kW input (net) E = 1000mm^2 per kW input (net)	H I H = 500mm^2 per kW input (net) I = H

Open flue gas appliance including gas fire with back boiler and decorative fuel effect gas fire

Air supply

☑ A permanent vent is required to outside air from the room space containing the appliance to provide free area of:

– 100 cm^2 for decorative fuel effect gas appliance

– 4.5 cm^2 per kW of rated input above 7 kW for any other appliance.

Action

☑ Verify permanent vent to outside air exists and is not blocked or covered and is of correct dimensions. If correct proceed with work.

☑ If a permanent vent to outside air is not present, or is present but blocked, covered or inadequate, leave a minimum of eight metres of window perimeter without draught-proofing or sealants in the appliance.

11

Open solid fuel fire with or without back boiler for central heating

Air supply

☑ A permanent vent required to outside air having a free area of at least 50% of the throat opening.

Note: For a typical domestic open solid fuel fire 50% of the throat opening gives an area of approximately 100 cm². This figure is to be used owing to the practical difficulties of measuring the throat opening.

Action

☑ If a permanent vent to outside air of 100 cm² is present then complete the standard draught-proofing job after verifying that the vent is clear.

☑ If a permanent vent to outside air is not present, or is present but blocked, covered or inadequate, leave a minimum of eight metres of window perimeter without draught-proofing or sealants in the appliance.

Mobile space heating appliance (LPG, paraffin)

Action

☑ Verify permanent vent to outside air of at least 95 cm² exists in the room or hallway where the appliance is used. If the permanent vent is not blocked, covered or inadequate proceed with the standard draught-proofing installation.

☑ Where the appliance is used in a room that does not have a permanent vent to outside air or a permanent vent that is blocked, covered or inadequate, then the room must not be draught-proofed.

☑ Where the appliance is used in a hallway that does not have a vent to outside air or a permanent vent that is blocked, covered or inadequate, then no draught-proofing shall be installed in this property.

Flueless fixed gas convector (space heater)

Air supply

☑ A permanent vent is required to outside air from the space containing the appliance to provide a free area of at least 100 cm², plus 50 cm² for every kW by which the appliance rated input exceeds 3 kW. A window that can be opened for the release of fumes is also required for these units.

Action

☑ Verify permanent vent to outside air exists and is not blocked or covered and is of the correct dimensions to produce the free areas required for the appliance and rating. Verify opening window can be operated without difficulty and maintained open. If correct, proceed with the standard draught-proofing installation.

11

12

Lead

Old, lead-based paint and dust are still likely to affect the majority of UK buildings, although lead paint was completely removed from general sale by 1992. Lead surveys are a mandatory requirement under the Construction (Design and Management) Regulations.

Exposure to lead, lead dust and fumes constitutes a major hazard to the health of those whose work involves lead, lead products and lead-containing materials (LCMs), such as lead-based paint, or leaded exhaust particle contamination in lofts and roof voids, known as ceiling dust.

Lead paint and consequent dust exposure risks are greatest within pre-1970 buildings and structures, especially during repair, maintenance, refurbishment and demolition, if proper precautions are not followed. The build-up of lead 'dust' contamination in lofts and roof voids continued until the general sale of leaded petrol became illegal in 2000.

This chapter sets out to explain the risks and controls that are required.

Introduction	160
Key points	160
How does lead affect your health?	161
The Control of Lead at Work Regulations	162
Approved Code of Practice	164
Training	165
Reporting of diseases	165
Personal protective equipment	165
Welfare arrangements	166
Provision and use of work equipment	167
Control of exposure to lead	167
Significant risk activities	171
Working with lead-based paints	171
Further guidance and advice	173
Appendix A – Specimen health surveillance record	174

Lead

12.1 Introduction

Exposure to lead dust, fumes and vapour constitutes a major hazard to the health of industrial workers, including those in the construction industry, who work with lead, lead products and lead containing materials (LCMs) (such as old lead-painted surfaces).

Construction workers most at risk include:

- ☑ those carrying out blast-removal and burning of old lead paint

- ☑ those stripping old lead paint from doors, windows, and so on

- ☑ those carrying out surface preparation of previously lead-painted surfaces

- ☑ those stripping old wallpaper and disturbing underlying lead-based paint

- ☑ demolition operatives involved in hot-cutting in demolition and dismantling operations

- ☑ plumbers working on lead-flashing, upstands and gutters

- ☑ operatives handling old, architectural lead work

- ☑ anyone involved in structural renovation or refurbishment, including conservation or heritage projects.

Exposure risks from lead paint, dust and fumes are most likely to occur in pre-1970 buildings, especially during repair, maintenance, refurbishment and demolition, if proper precautions are not followed. It should be noted that, wherever paintwork/coatings are likely to be damaged or disturbed, the HSE advises lead (paint) surveys **regardless of the age of the building or the extent of the works.**

 Information on reducing the health risks in construction work can be found on the HSE's website.

The Construction (Design and Management) Regulations (CDM) impose a duty on clients (and their advisers) to identify and collect information about hazardous materials likely to affect a project as part of pre-construction information (PCI) **before** tendering. The lead content of lead-based paint is one such material.

The Control of Lead at Work Regulations (CLAW) and an associated Approved Code of Practice, together with guidance notes and information from the Lead Paint Safety Association (LiPSA) and the Painting and Decorating Association (PDA) have been produced to enable employers to interpret the legal duties placed upon them by the regulations and to take the appropriate actions to protect the health and safety of their employees, who have to work with lead, and other people who may be affected by the way the work is carried out.

Clients have a duty to identify lead hazards before a project commences.

Employers have a legal duty to protect their employees (and any building occupants). For employees this includes monitoring their blood-lead levels, so that individuals whose work involves significant exposure to lead at work (as defined by the CLAW Regulations) can be taken off such work if legal threshold levels are exceeded.

Lead contaminated waste must be disposed of in accordance with the Hazardous Waste Regulations.

12.2 Key points

- ☑ Lead and LCMs (such as lead-based paint) are hazardous. They can become a significant exposure risk if lead dust, fumes or vapour are not prevented or adequately controlled. Any work involving lead must be in accordance with the Control of Lead at Work Regulations, also known as CLAW.

- ☑ Unless adequate precautions are taken, children and pregnant women are particularly at risk when decorators, for example, are disturbing old lead-based paint in homes or schools.

- ☑ Lead is a cumulative poison that is absorbed into the bloodstream. Over time it will also collect in the kidneys and soft tissues, before accumulating in the bones.

- ☑ The ways that lead is likely to get into the body are through the:
  - inhalation of fumes or dust
  - ingestion of lead particles through hand to mouth contact (especially for smokers).

- ☑ All work with lead or LCMs must be subject to a risk assessment, which includes consideration of the amount of lead involved. Hence the legal requirement for lead (paint) surveys.

- ☑ General builders, carpenters and decorators who remove or disturb old lead paint, particularly if involved in window replacement, repairs and general refurbishment or demolition, may be exposed to significant quantities of lead without realising it. Scaffolders are also a significant exposure risk group.

- ☑ Where the risk assessment indicates that employees' exposure to lead is likely to be significant, certain monitoring actions must be taken with regard to the employees affected and the workplace itself. These include sampling to determine blood-lead levels, air-monitoring for airborne lead-dust levels and surface dust contamination checks.

Although there are no legal threshold levels relating to surface dust contamination this is something that HSE inspectors are required to consider during CLAW inspections, as set out in Operational Circular 298/15.

☑ Significant exposure is defined in the regulations as: **Where there is liable to be a substantial ingestion risk.**

 It is the ingestion risk that needs to be substantial, not the amount of lead.

☑ Significant exposure risk also exists where airborne lead-dust levels are greater than 50% of the occupational exposure limit (OEL) for airborne lead.

☑ During health surveillance, employees' exposure to lead is most commonly measured by the concentration of lead in their blood. A saliva check can be used to screen for blood-lead levels.

☑ Above a certain level of exposure, employers have a legal duty to temporarily suspend the affected worker(s) from further work with lead.

In the context of this chapter, the main consideration is identifying where and how much lead could be present. This allows appropriate actions to be taken to protect the health of workers exposed to lead risk and, if necessary, other people who may be affected by the work (such as occupant families at home or children at school, or indeed, workers' families).

Although it is possible for lead exposure risks to be contained and controlled in occupied buildings it is worth noting the advice from the Department for Communities and Local Government with respect to stripping and preparing lead-based paint in older homes. It is contained within their lead worked example risk assessment under the *Housing health and safety rating system, 2004:*

 The occupants should be temporarily rehoused during the stripping and re-painting.

This guidance is consistent with advice in paint manufacturer safety data sheets, which advise:

 …exclusion of other personnel and especially children from the building during actual work and the subsequent clean-up operations.

12.3 How does lead affect your health?

There is no safe level of lead in the body. Harm from lead exposure can go unnoticed because there may be no obvious physical symptoms of an underlying problem.

Blood-lead levels (BLLs) are the best measure of current exposure. If the level of lead in the body gets too high, it can cause headaches, tiredness, irritability, constipation, nausea, stomach pains and loss of weight. Continued uncontrolled exposure could cause far more serious symptoms (such as kidney, nerve and brain damage).

The regulations are specifically intended to protect women of child-bearing age and young persons. A developing unborn child is at particular risk from exposure to lead, particularly in the early weeks before a pregnancy becomes known. Thus, women of child-bearing age who may be exposed to lead should take special care to follow good work practices and observe a high standard of personal hygiene.

Prevention of exposure

The employer has a duty to assess the nature and extent of the exposure to lead and, on the basis of this assessment, to determine the measures necessary to control exposure and comply with the regulations.

Action should be taken to reduce the amount of lead breathed by operatives to below the lead in air standard.

Although inhalation has always been considered to be the major source of absorption, current thinking recognises the much greater contribution of hand-to-mouth contact and a greater risk from ingestion.

Many of the sections of the regulations relate to the prevention of the inhalation/ingestion of lead dust, fumes and vapour. **The basic need is to prevent the liberation of lead dust, fumes or vapour into the workplace.**

If surface finishes are to be disturbed, always check for the presence of lead paint or, if this is not possible, assume the worst (that it is a lead-based paint) and take the appropriate precautions.

12

Lead

Ways of testing for the presence of lead include:

☑ a variety of destructive tests for paint sampling, although these can result in damage to painted surfaces in order for samples to be taken

☑ disposable test kits: Instant, on-site lead/no lead result with 95% accuracy. (These are an indicator only, **not** a laboratory-standard test. Unsuitable and insufficient for risk assessment purposes

☑ paint-sampling kits, which are ready to use (for non-lab professionals) for submission of samples for chemical analysis. (A laboratory-standard test)

☑ dust-wipe sampling kits, which are ready to use (for non-lab professionals) for submission of samples for chemical analysis. (A laboratory-standard test)

☑ professional sampling for accredited laboratory analysis (UKAS approved)

☑ hand-portable devices that use XRF-i (xray fluorescence isotope) technology to obtain laboratory standard readings instantly, on site.

 When taking physical samples for off-site analysis, it is almost impossible to ensure 100% recovery of all of the lead from a given substrate, whether timber, metal, plaster or any other materials – occupationally significant quantities of lead residue tend to be left behind. For this reason laboratory analysis of samples removed from site can significantly understate the severity of the actual on-site hazard – in some cases by up to 500%.

12.4   The Control of Lead at Work Regulations

The regulations aim to give greater health protection to people at work, whether directly or indirectly exposed, by reducing their exposure to lead and thus the concentrations of lead in their blood. Where concentrations are too high, employers are required to remove employees from work with lead. This is known as the **suspension level.** If employers cannot transfer employees to other work not involving exposure to lead, they must pay them suspension pay under the Employment Rights Act.

Concentration levels of lead in blood, which are below the suspension level and known as **action levels,** have been set. If these lower levels are breached, employers have a duty to investigate and remedy the cause. Employers are also required to take steps to reduce the concentrations of lead in air to a level not exceeding the occupational exposure limits stated in the regulations.

Women of child-bearing age and young people are particularly at risk of lead poisoning, and therefore have lower blood-lead action and suspension levels than other workers. The Control of Substances Hazardous to Health (COSHH) Regulations do not apply where the Control of Lead at Work Regulations should be applied.

It should be noted that the Control of Lead at Work Regulations place:

☑ a number of legal duties on employers

☑ limited legal duties on employees.

Duties under the regulations

The main requirements of the Control of Lead at Work Regulations are shown below.

☑ An employer, who is working with lead, or a substance or material containing lead, has to protect from exposure anyone who may be affected by the work as well as their own employees. This includes:

– the workers of other employers, including those not engaged in work with lead (such as maintenance staff and cleaners)

– visitors to the work site

– the families of those who are exposed to lead at work who may become affected by lead carried home unintentionally on the clothing and footwear of the employee

– the occupiers of premises, including private dwellings, irrespective of whether the occupiers are present whilst the work is carried out or they reoccupy the premises later.

☑ Assessment of the risks to health.

☑ Every employer is required to make a suitable and sufficient assessment of the risk to the health and safety of employees while at work. This includes other people who are not employees but who may be exposed as a result of the way the employer carries out the work concerned.

The assessment must be reviewed as often as is necessary and in other certain specified circumstances, and a record made of any significant findings if more than five people are employed. Such an assessment is to allow the employer to make a decision whether the work concerned is likely to result in an employee being significantly exposed to lead, and to identify the measures needed to prevent or adequately control exposure.

Control of exposure

☑ Every employer must ensure that the exposure of employees to lead is either prevented or, where this is not reasonably practicable, adequately controlled by means of appropriate control measures.

- As the preferred control measure, the employer must consider the use of alternative materials or processes as a means of eliminating or reducing the risks to the health of employees.

- Where it is not reasonably practicable to prevent exposure to lead, the employer must introduce protective measures that are appropriate to the work activity and consistent with the findings of the risk assessment. In order of priority, these must be:
  - the design and use of the work process, systems and engineering controls
  - control of exposure at source, including ventilation systems and wet methods
  - where adequate control cannot be achieved by other means, the provision and use of suitable respiratory protective equipment (RPE) and personal protective equipment (PPE).

 Painters and decorators should be aware that most paint manufacturer MSDS sheets advise the use of wet sanding for surface preparation **regardless** of whether the surface contains lead or not. Wet sanding prevents airborne dust generation and provides a superior finish.

- The control measure(s) must include:
  - the safe handling, storage and transportation of lead and waste that contains lead
  - suitable maintenance procedures
  - reducing to the minimum required for the task in hand, the number of employees exposed, the level and duration of exposure and the quantity of lead present in the workplace
  - control of the working environment, including where appropriate, extract ventilation and appropriate daily clean-up using a combination of HEPA vacuuming and wet mopping
  - appropriate hygiene measures, including washing facilities. Decontamination units (DCUs) are an increasingly common choice.

  Irrespective of these control measures, where the exposure to lead is, or is likely to be significant, the employer must provide suitable and sufficient protective clothing.

- Where the inhalation of lead fumes is possible, the control measures will only be regarded as adequate if:
  - the occupational exposure limit is not exceeded, or
  - if it is, the employer identifies the reason and takes immediate steps to rectify the situation.

  Inhaling lead fumes from the uncontrolled use of heat guns or torches is the most likely cause of acute lead exposure and hospitalisation. Up to 90% of the lead content of any lead fumes can be absorbed through the lungs and passed directly into the bloodstream.

- Employers must take reasonable steps to ensure that any control measure provided is properly used or applied.

- Employees must make full and proper use of any control measure provided, and:
  - take all reasonable steps, where appropriate, to return anything provided as a control measure to its accommodation (storage) after use
  - report any defect in any control measure provided to the employer.

- Adequate control of exposure to lead covers all routes of possible exposure (such as inhalation, ingestion and absorption through the skin).

- When eating, drinking and smoking – adequate steps must be taken to control the ingestion of lead. An employer must ensure that, as far as is reasonably practicable, employees do not eat, drink or smoke in any place which is, or is liable to become, contaminated by lead. In practical terms, employees must be warned against doing so. Furthermore, under this regulation employees have a legal duty not to eat, drink or smoke in any place that they have reason to believe is contaminated by lead.

Maintenance, examination and testing of control measures

All control measures provided, including RPE and PPE, must be well maintained, kept in a good state of repair and cleaned as necessary. Any defect in the equipment, or failure to use and apply it properly, which could result in a loss of efficiency or effectiveness, thus reducing the level of protection, should be identified and rectified as soon as possible.

Colorimetric testing of dust contamination can be used to ensure welfare areas are sufficiently lead-free.

Air monitoring

Where employees are liable to receive significant exposure to lead, employers must establish a programme of personal air monitoring, including keeping records of the findings of such monitoring.

Medical surveillance

Where exposure to lead is significant, as defined in Regulation 2, the employer must:

- make sure that employees are under medical surveillance by either a medical inspector (Employment Medical Adviser) or a relevant doctor

- provide suitable facilities for health surveillance to be carried out where the procedures are to be carried out at the employer's premises

- maintain health surveillance records and retain them for 40 years

12

- ☑ allow employees reasonable access to their personal health records

- ☑ provide copies of personal health records to the HSE upon request

- ☑ make all records available to the HSE if ceasing to trade

- ☑ take steps to determine the reasons why any employee's blood sample exceeds the appropriate action level and take appropriate remedial action

- ☑ take the necessary actions, including reviewing the risk assessment, where an employee's blood or urine sample reaches the suspension level.

Employees for whom health surveillance has been arranged must, when required by the employer (and at the cost of the employer), make themselves available for the necessary health surveillance procedures and supply the relevant doctor with such health-related information as the doctor may require.

Information, instruction and training

Employers who undertake work liable to expose employees to lead shall provide such information, instruction and training as is suitable and sufficient to know the risks to health, and the precautions, which should be taken (see *Training* text below).

In addition to this, the Code of Practice requires that an employer should issue a copy of the HSE's free leaflet entitled *Lead and you* to all employees at the start of their first employment on work with lead, and make copies available for issue at the request of any employees or their representatives.

It is thought that this requirement is often not followed with regard to painters and decorators because the information is not sufficiently trade-specific. The Painting and Decorating Association's (PDA) *Health and safety manual* provides a useful source of more relevant information.

Employers must additionally provide employees with written records of concentrations of lead in air to which they have been exposed, the results of the measurements of lead in their blood or urine, and an explanation of the significance of these results.

Note: In construction, blood lead is the most common measure of exposure to inorganic lead (as found in compounds used in old lead paint), with action and suspension levels being expressed in micrograms of lead per decilitre of blood. Urine sampling tends to be used for assessing exposure to organic lead (such as the fumes from tetraethyl lead).

Arrangements for accidents, incidents and emergencies

The employer, in attempting to protect the health of employees (and others) from an accident, incident or emergency, must ensure that procedures, including the provision of first-aid facilities and safety drills, have been prepared and can be put into effect should such an occasion arise. The employer must also ensure that information on such emergency arrangements has been notified to accident and emergency services and that all such information is displayed within the workplace and for occupants in the same premises.

Colorimetric (colour-change) qualitative lead paint and dust-test kits can be kept on site to allow an immediate assessment of likely lead exposure risks when these emerge. Follow-on quantitative analysis should then be used to quantify the severity and extent of the problem.

Exemptions

A certificate of exemption may be granted by the HSE exempting any person or class of persons from all or any of the requirements or prohibitions imposed by the regulations, where they are satisfied that the health and safety of those persons likely to be affected by the exemption will not be prejudiced in consequence of it. Such certificates and any related time limits can, of course, be revoked at any time.

12

12.5 Approved Code of Practice

The Control of Lead at Work Regulations should be read in conjunction with the supporting Approved Code of Practice (ACoP) and guidance, which interprets the regulations and sets out standards relating to controlling any type of work activity liable to expose employees and any other persons to lead. The regulations achieve this by means of risk assessments, control measures, air monitoring, the setting of an occupational exposure limit (OEL), medical surveillance and the setting of an action level and suspension level for lead in the blood.

12.6 Training

With regard to the Control of Lead at Work Regulations (CLAW) (as amended), there is a specific requirement to ensure that the information, instruction and training provided for persons working with lead includes:

- ☑ the type of lead being worked, the potential health hazards and symptoms
- ☑ the relevant occupational exposure limit, action level and suspension level (as explained later in this chapter)
- ☑ any other sources of information (such as a lead survey and/or a lead register)
- ☑ any other legislative provisions relevant to working with lead
- ☑ the significant findings of the risk assessment (such as the amount of lead involved)
- ☑ the control measures that are in place and that must be used to enable work to be carried out safely
- ☑ the results of any personal air monitoring or surface dust contamination checks
- ☑ the results of previous health surveillance, in such a way that the confidentiality of individual cases are not breached.

12.7 Reporting of diseases

The regulations require the responsible person to report to the enforcing authority (normally the HSE) any case of lead poisoning suffered by any person at work that results from exposure to lead whilst at work.

Lead poisoning, when diagnosed by a medical practitioner, is a notifiable disease under RIDDOR and must be reported in accordance with requirements of the regulations.

The regulations contain strict provisions as to medical surveillance and require that employers ensure that basic details of all those who need to be under medical surveillance are recorded. A copy of this form is reproduced in Appendix A. There are additional forms specified by the regulations in respect of:

- ☑ the initial medical assessment, which also contains the past occupational medical and clinical details of the employee, including a smoking history
- ☑ a surveillance record for persons exposed to lead
- ☑ a notification to an employer of biological test results and a record of medical surveillance
- ☑ a certification of unfitness or fitness to return to work
- ☑ an annual return of persons under medical surveillance, to be completed by employers.

 For further information on the Reporting of Injuries, Diseases and Dangerous Occurrences Regulations (RIDDOR) refer to Chapter A13 Accident reporting and investigation.

12.8 Personal protective equipment

In the context of this chapter, the regulations require that where a risk of exposure to lead has been identified by a risk assessment and it cannot be adequately controlled by other means, which are equally or more effective, the employer must provide personal protective equipment (PPE) and ensure it is properly used by employees.

Users of PPE must be trained in its use and care as appropriate.

In essence, PPE may only be used as a last resort after all other means of eliminating or controlling the risk have been considered and are not reasonably practicable.

Respiratory protective equipment

Where control measures do not reduce the lead in air levels to below the control limits, respiratory protective equipment (RPE) of a type suited to the hazard or process involved must be provided and all employees must be properly trained to use it. All such equipment should be serviced, cleaned, maintained and stored correctly, as is appropriate.

Depending upon whether the hazard is lead dust or fumes, adequate protection will be given by the use of compressed air-line breathing apparatus, self-contained breathing apparatus, or a full-face positive pressure-powered respirator fitted with a high efficiency (HEPA) filter.

Because lead is both an ingestion and an inhalation risk, airborne lead levels below the OEL (and even below the significant exposure level) can nevertheless present a substantial ingestion risk. By providing a physical barrier around the nose and mouth, suitable RPE specified to protect against lead dust can also help to minimise ingestion from hand-to-mouth contact.

12

Protective clothing

Wherever exposure is significant, protective clothing must be provided. It must be suited to the hazard or process involved, should resist the permeation of lead dust, and not collect or harbour dust. Laundry facilities should be available so that contaminated clothing is not taken home for laundering. Employees must be instructed to report any damaged or defective ventilation plant or protective equipment, without delay, to their supervisor or safety representative.

All contaminated clothing and footwear should remain on site to prevent the potential of workers' families being exposed to lead – a known problem.

12.9 Welfare arrangements

The regulations require the provision of adequate welfare facilities, particularly in respect of personal hygiene. Contractors must provide or make available:

- ☑ suitable and sufficient washing facilities, including showers if necessary, due to the nature of the work (decontamination units (DCUs) are becoming more commonplace for this)
- ☑ hot and cold (or warm) water, soap or other cleanser and towels or other effective means of drying
- ☑ suitable and sufficient changing rooms
- ☑ lockers or other facilities in which to secure work clothing that is not taken home and personal clothing that is not worn at work
- ☑ suitable rest facilities where meals may be prepared and eaten.

Regular checks (such as dust wipe sampling), should be made to ensure welfare facilities are sufficiently free of lead contamination.

In accordance with HSE *Operational circular* OC 298/15 for inspections under CLAW, inspectors may seek from employers evidence of surface contamination levels.

Changing and washing facilities

This includes accommodation for clothing where necessary. To avoid any risk to health or damage to the clothing concerned, the employer must also provide separate accommodation for an employee's own clothing and any protective clothing the employee may have to wear at work. This requirement will normally apply for protective clothing worn for work with lead.

Adequate and suitable washing facilities are required where operatives are exposed to lead. The ACoP requires that, where employees are exposed to lead, washing and changing facilities provided should allow them to meet a high standard of personal hygiene so as to minimise the risk of them ingesting or otherwise absorbing lead.

The design of the washing facilities should be related to the nature and degree of exposure to lead as indicated by the assessment. Where employees are significantly exposed to lead, and if washbasins alone would not be adequate, the washing facilities should include showers or baths.

An example would be where work is carried out in dusty conditions that could result in the whole body being contaminated by lead. Then the provision of showers or baths would be essential.

Washing facilities should provide at least:

- ☑ one washbasin for every five persons. Basins should be of sufficient size to permit arms to be immersed up to the elbow
- ☑ a constant supply of hot and cold or warm water (running water where reasonably practicable)
- ☑ soap or other cleaning materials
- ☑ nail brushes
- ☑ warm air dryers or roller towels; communal towels should not be used.

For certain types of work (such as lead paint removal work), carried out at premises or sites where such work is not regularly done (for example, certain tank cleaning, lead burning and grit-blasting operations), mobile caravan type washing/showering DCU facilities of suitable design should be provided.

Eating, drinking and smoking

The regulations specifically require employers to reduce the risk of ingestion of lead by ensuring that employees do not eat, drink or smoke* in places that are contaminated, or likely to be contaminated, by lead arising from work activities. Therefore, employers should reduce the risk of employees ingesting lead by ensuring that they are given adequate information on the specific areas that might be contaminated by lead and in which they should not eat (including chewing gum or tobacco), drink or smoke.

The information should be reinforced by displaying a prominent notice to identify those areas in which employees may, or may not, eat, drink or smoke.

The following points should be noted.

- ☑ Clean areas, canteens or mess rooms should be isolated from lead-contaminated work areas and checked regularly for levels of surface lead-dust contamination.
- ☑ Protective clothing should be removed before entering these areas.
- ☑ Washing should take place before eating meals or drinking.

✓ The employer must advise employees where they may not eat, drink or smoke.

✓ A legal duty is placed on employees not to eat, drink or smoke in any place where there is risk of contamination by lead.

* The legal ban on smoking in enclosed places of work may, in many cases, render this legal requirement irrelevant.

Even with a total ban on smoking in enclosed workplaces, those who work with lead but smoke elsewhere (such as at home) must be aware of the need to remove all traces of lead from their hands and clothes at some time between carrying out the two activities.

 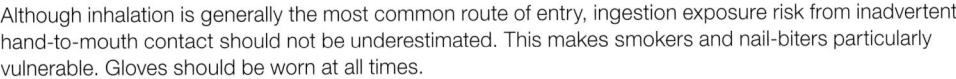 Smokers are likely to ingest between 200-400% more lead than a non-smoker.

Personal hygiene

Anyone who works with lead, lead-containing materials and old lead paint, should take simple personal hygiene measures to prevent the inhalation or ingestion of lead during and after work.

Interestingly, the ACoP that supports the Control of Lead at Work Regulations indicates that nail-biting and roll-your-own cigarettes are often implicated in high levels of lead absorption.

12.10 Provision and use of work equipment

The regulations require that an employer only supplies work equipment that is correct and suitable for the job for which the equipment is going to be used.

The regulations also require that users of work equipment are trained in its use, as appropriate.

12.11 Control of exposure to lead

The hazards

Lead is a cumulative poison that will find its way into the bloodstream, collect in tissue and be stored in bones. Lead poisoning may occur through exposure to lead in its pure form or exposure to products containing lead.

Lead affects the body's ability to produce haemoglobin, which is the protein in blood that carries oxygen to the tissues.

Inorganic lead, the type likely to be encountered during construction activities, can enter the body in one of three ways, by:

✓ inhalation of dust or fumes

✓ ingestion, via the digestive tract from hand-to-mouth transfer of lead particles

✓ absorption, where the presence of sweat can help to dissolve small quantities of lead which, in a liquid state, can be absorbed through the skin.

Although inhalation is generally the most common route of entry, ingestion exposure risk from inadvertent hand-to-mouth contact should not be underestimated. This makes smokers and nail-biters particularly vulnerable. Gloves should be worn at all times.

Whilst the control of exposure through inhalation will be largely controlled by actions taken by the employer, and correct use of lead-safe work methods, the control of exposure through ingestion depends upon the good personal hygiene practices of employees working with lead.

Risk assessment

Employers must not carry out any work that may expose employees to lead unless a suitable and sufficient risk assessment has been carried out. Given the CLAW requirement to **'consider the amount (of lead) involved'**, a suitable and sufficient risk assessment cannot be based on the assumption that lead-based paint is present. A lead register or lead survey, as required under CDM, is the best place to start the risk assessment process.

The purpose of the risk assessment is to enable the employer to:

✓ assess whether the exposure of employees to lead is likely to be significant

✓ identify the measures necessary to prevent or control exposure.

Control measures

Control measures involve substituting lead with less hazardous substances or, if this is not possible, using engineering and organisational methods, similar to those outlined for COSHH, to control exposure.

The control of exposure to lead (by inhalation) will only be regarded as adequate:

✓ if the concentration of lead in the air is kept below the OEL (see below)

✓ if, where the OEL is exceeded, the employer identifies the reasons and takes immediate steps to remedy the situation.

12

Where old, lead-based paint is concerned, removal is not necessarily the best option. Leaving it in situ is often safer, especially if it can be encapsulated with a proprietary coating or rigid covering. Encasement behind plasterboard is also an alternative.

Air monitoring

Where a risk assessment indicates that employees may be liable to significant exposure to lead, the employer must arrange for preliminary personal air monitoring to be carried out to establish the levels of lead in the air at the place of work.

Air monitoring will involve using specialist equipment, fitted to the employee being monitored, to take an air sample from the employee's breathing zone over a set period of time.

Using static air-monitoring equipment to take air samples is not acceptable for preliminary monitoring as the results will not be representative of any employee's personal exposure.

Generally, depending upon the circumstances, monitoring must be carried out for each individual process likely to generate different levels of exposure. The work environment, choice of equipment and the amount of lead in the material being worked on, can all contribute to significant variations. Air monitoring will determine whether the OEL has been breached.

The employer has a duty to retain records of air monitoring results for a period of five years.

Given the temporary nature of construction sites, and the even shorter periods when employees might actually be exposed to lead, this requirement is considered to be largely academic for the construction industry. With tradespeople (such as plumbers and painters) being potentially exposed to lead many times but over relatively short periods, it will be for the employer to decide how frequently air monitoring should be carried out to confirm whether or not existing control measures are adequate.

Occupational exposure limit

The standard for inorganic lead in the air is **0.15 mg** (milligrams) or **150 µg** (micrograms) of **lead per cubic metre** of air determined on an eight-hour time-weighted concentration.

Significant in relation to exposure to airborne lead dust means exposure in the following circumstances:

 where any employee is, or is liable to be, exposed to a concentration of lead in the atmosphere exceeding half the occupational exposure limit for lead.

From the above it can be seen that the significant level would be **0.075 mg** (milligrams) or **75 µg** (micrograms,).

 Units are shown here in micrograms because blood-lead levels are reported in micrograms per decilitre (µg/dL), helping to explain the use and relevance of these numbers and making it easy to relate them to each other.

This quantifies the standard to be met by the control measures for airborne lead under the regulations.

 Even if the significant exposure risk threshold for airborne lead dust is not exceeded, a significant lead exposure risk can still exist because of a substantial ingestion risk.

Medical surveillance

Medical surveillance to detect exposure to lead involves measuring the concentration of lead in the blood or urine and therefore necessitates the involvement of suitable, trained medical staff.

 A saliva check or screening test is now available to determine blood-lead levels from the laboratory analysis of saliva samples. This is highly accurate, non-invasive and easy to do. And, because it is a painless, non-medical procedure, it should encourage compliance. As would be the case with an elevated blood-lead analysis result, a high blood-lead level from a saliva test should be followed up by a (second) blood sample.

Where a risk assessment indicates that employees' exposure to lead is likely to be significant, the employer has a duty to arrange medical surveillance for the affected employees.

 There is a very important difference between everyday use of the word 'significant' and its definition/application under the CLAW Regulations. The amount of lead in an exposure situation can be low or high, but the substantial risk of ingestion can be significant in both cases.

If biological monitoring detects blood-lead concentrations at or above those outlined below, this will trigger continued medical surveillance:

- ☑ women of reproductive capability: **20 micrograms** of lead, or greater, per decilitre of blood

- ☑ all other employees: **35 micrograms** of lead, or greater, per decilitre of blood.

Action levels

The action levels for lead are:

- ☑ women of reproductive capability: **25 micrograms** of lead per decilitre of blood

- ☑ young persons (aged 16–17): **40 micrograms** of lead per decilitre of blood

- ☑ any other employee: **50 micrograms** of lead per decilitre of blood.

If medical surveillance detects blood-lead concentrations at or above these action levels, the employer must:

- ☑ recognise that the employee's blood-lead level is near the suspension level

- ☑ investigate the effectiveness of existing control measures and take the necessary actions to reduce employees' blood-lead levels below the action level

- ☑ prevent the blood-lead level of affected employees from reaching the suspension level.

Suspension levels

If medical surveillance reveals that an employee's blood-lead level has reached or exceeded the levels outlined below, a doctor must decide whether to temporarily suspend them from work that exposes them to lead:

- ☑ women of reproductive capability: **30 micrograms** of lead per decilitre of blood

- ☑ young persons (aged 16–17): **50 micrograms** of lead per decilitre of blood

- ☑ any other employee: **60 micrograms** of lead per decilitre of blood.

In such circumstances, the employer must:

- ☑ ensure that a doctor makes an entry in the health record of affected employee(s) as to whether, in the doctor's professional opinion, they should be suspended from further work liable to expose them to lead

- ☑ review the relevant risk assessment

- ☑ review the actions taken to prevent exposure to lead

- ☑ provide for a review of the health of any other employees who may have been similarly exposed.

If the doctor thinks that there is no need to suspend the affected employee(s) from work, the doctor must note in their health records:

- ☑ the reasons for that decision

- ☑ any conditions under which working with lead may continue.

Doctors practising in this specialist medical field are familiar with the regulations, and if there are some exceptions to the rule, such doctors will be able to explain them. An employer must act on the doctor's decision and an employee will not be able to work with lead again, or be exposed to it, until the doctor considers it safe to do so.

The so-called 'level of concern' for the population as a whole is 10 micrograms of lead per decilitre of blood. In some countries a lower threshold of 5 micrograms has been set for children under six years old. Contractors employing operatives with proper training, supervision and equipment should be able to maintain BLLs below **15 micrograms** of lead per decilitre of blood, even during dry grit-blasting operations.

Refer to Appendix A for an example of a health surveillance record form.

Annexes 1–5 and Appendix 6 of the ACoP record details of an employee under medical surveillance because of exposure to lead.

12

Lead

Understanding lead levels

The illustrations below should help visualise that very small amounts of lead can have a significant effect on a person's health, hence why lead exposure must be carefully assessed and controlled.

1 microgram (µg)= one grain of sugar ÷ 1000

One grain of sugar = 1,000 micrograms (µg)

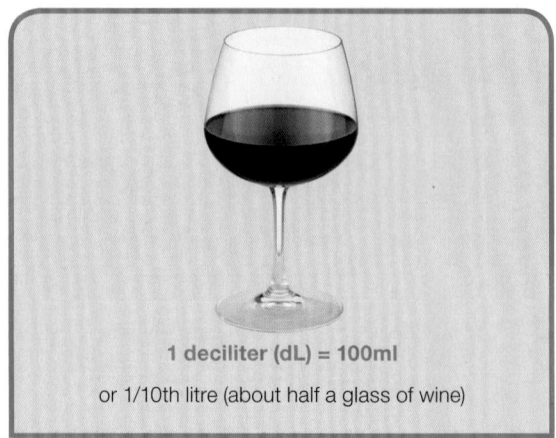

1 deciliter (dL) = 100ml

or 1/10th litre (about half a glass of wine)

For employees the action level is **50 micrograms (µg)** of lead per **decilitre (dL)** of blood.

This is the equivalent of dissolving 1/20th of a grain of sugar into half a glass of wine.

The case study below demonstrates that **36,100 micrograms (µg)** can typically be found in just **1 cm²** of old lead paint.

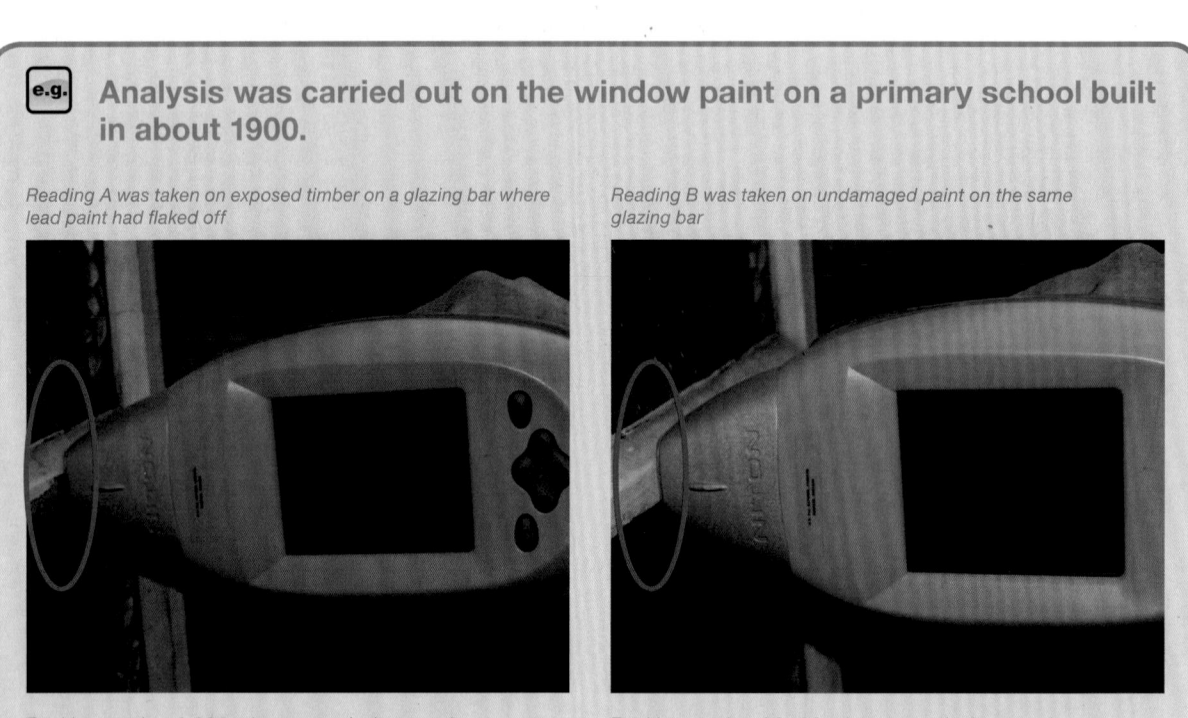

e.g. **Analysis was carried out on the window paint on a primary school built in about 1900.**

Reading A was taken on exposed timber on a glazing bar where lead paint had flaked off

Reading B was taken on undamaged paint on the same glazing bar

Positive result = 8,900 micrograms (µg) per cm²

Positive result = 36,100 micrograms (µg) per cm²

From these readings there is a high risk potential for significant lead levels to be released through removal techniques (such as burning off with a blow torch or dry rubbing down).

Significant levels

Significant exposure to lead can occur where:

☑ any employee is, or is liable to be, exposed to a concentration of lead in the atmosphere exceeding half the occupational exposure limit for lead

☑ there is a substantial risk of an employee ingesting lead

☑ there is a risk of contact between the skin and lead alkyls or other substances containing lead that can be absorbed through the skin.

Employers must provide employees with protective clothing, monitor lead in air-concentrations and place the employees concerned under medical surveillance.

12

The more stringent suspension levels and the action levels introduced by the regulations are intended to tighten controls on exposure to lead and reduce the risk to workers' health. In order to see further improvements in the control of employees' exposure to lead, the Health and Safety Executive has made known its intention to review the suspension levels with a view to reducing the limits further.

In such cases, all the regulations will apply; air monitoring must be carried out regularly to confirm the effectiveness of control measures and the results recorded. Personal protective equipment (PPE) will be required where control measures are not practicable.

12.12 Significant risk activities

Types of work liable to result in significant exposure to lead

Some types of work with lead, carried out as part of construction or decorating activities, have the potential to result in significant exposure to lead unless the employer provides adequate controls and ensures that they are used. For example:

- ☑ burning off old paint
- ☑ dry-sanding old paint
- ☑ high temperature lead-work (such as lead-smelting, burning and welding)
- ☑ working with metallic lead and alloys containing lead (for example, soldering)
- ☑ disc abrasion of lead surfaces and cutting lead with abrasive wheels
- ☑ spray painting with lead-based paints
- ☑ work inside tanks that have contained petrol
- ☑ manufacture of leaded glass
- ☑ hot-cutting, demolition and dismantling operations
- ☑ otherwise removing or disturbing old lead sheet thereby raising contaminated dust
- ☑ recovering lead from scrap and waste
- ☑ perforating top floor ceilings or ceilings below roof voids holding quantities of settled leaded exhaust particles, known as ceiling dust
- ☑ disturbance and/or removal of loft insulation where leaded exhaust particles have settled
- ☑ disturbance of floor voids containing accumulated lead particles
- ☑ welding galvanised metal and flame cutting steelwork that has been painted with lead-based paint.

 The molten metal in a galvanising bath for hot-dipping steelwork typically used to contain 1% lead (approximately) to assist with run-off after the component had been dipped. In the industry it is well known that older dry galvanised coatings typically had a 0.5% lead content. Although this lead content has been reduced over time it has not yet been completely eliminated. So it is not simply leaded paint that can create or contribute to a person's overall exposure risk in this example.

Those operations that do not usually produce significant levels of airborne dust or fumes include low temperature work, ordinary plumbing, soldering, handling clean sheets or pipes of lead and rough painting. In some cases, however, even these activities can present a substantial ingestion risk if not managed properly.

Examples of types of work producing exposures above and below significant levels are given in the ACoP. Frequently, however, these are not sharply divided. For example, if the character of the lead is changed by the work itself, **work with materials containing less than 1% lead can be liable to result in significant exposure.**

12.13 Working with lead-based paints

The residues of lead-based paints are a health hazard. Operatives carrying out work involving the disturbance, preparation or removal of old lead-based paint, and anyone else who might be adversely affected, must be adequately protected when applying or removing paints containing lead.

Similarly, the occupiers of premises (including the residents of private housing) must be protected by not being allowed to return to their premises (or contaminated parts of those premises) until they have been thoroughly and effectively cleaned (see below).

The findings of a risk assessment, carried out before any surface finish is disturbed, will indicate the most appropriate method of removal and the safety precautions that must be taken.

12

For specimen record details refer to Section G *Checklists and forms.*

Sanding

Wet sanding, wet scraping and wet abrasion, regardless of whether or not a coated substrate contains lead, are considered best practice methods for minimising airborne dust and paint chips during surface preparation. Wet residues should be cleaned up before they dry out with the potential to become airborne dust.

Old lead paint should never be dry-sanded by hand as this activity will liberate lead-rich dust into the air. Mechanical or power sanding should only be used if the sander is fitted with a dust extraction/collection unit incorporating a high-efficiency particulate air (HEPA) filter.

 Not all methods of stripping paint remove the residual lead from the grain of the wood. As a result, the subsequent dry sanding of apparently clean wood can liberate a significant amount of lead-containing dust into the air. Whichever of these methods is chosen toxic dust rated RPE (minimum FFP3 or P3) should also be worn.

Burning

Blowlamps or gas torches must not be used to burn off old lead paint as these will heat the paint sufficiently to liberate toxic lead fumes into the air. The use of heat guns, unless very carefully supervised for low-heat use, is likely to generate toxic fumes.

Solvents

Lead paint may be removed by using a solvent or water-rinsable paint remover. If a solvent is used, the work area must be well-ventilated and no smoking or naked flames allowed. Suitable RPE and other appropriate PPE should be used.

Hot-air gun

These must not be confused with blowlamps and gas torches. Used on a low-heat setting **only** (for example, below 360°C) a hot-air gun will not raise the temperature of the paint sufficiently to allow lead fumes to be created. When using a hot-air gun, the old paint must be scraped off as soon as it is sufficiently soft and before it re-hardens. Care must be taken to ensure that the paint does not burn as this indicates that it is reaching too high a temperature where fumes may be given off. The use of RPE to protect against lead-containing dust may be necessary. Care should also be taken to prevent lead dust and paint from being blown everywhere – especially into people's homes or schools during external redecoration works.

Some hot-air gun manufacturers warn against using their products on lead paint surfaces, others advise low-heat working. Hot-air guns should be avoided on commercial projects because of the near impossibility of supervising their correct use. Unless a device has a pre-set operating temperature that cannot be overridden, allowing hot-air gun use on site is asking for trouble.

Infra-red heating

A product is available that safely lifts the old paint from the base material by heating it to a safe temperature using an infra-red heater. Whilst warm, the paint can be safely scraped off. This method is particularly suitable where large surface areas have to be stripped.

The main benefits of using this method, which acts by heating the resins in the wood and breaking the bond between the wood and the first layer of paint, are:

- ☑ all layers of paint are removed in a single hit
- ☑ as a static heat method, the spread of air-blown lead contamination is avoided
- ☑ virtually all residual lead is removed from within the grain of the wood
- ☑ large surface areas can be safely stripped more quickly than by using other methods.

Spraying

Spraying methods should not normally be employed for applying lead-based paints.

Cleaning up the work area

All surfaces that have been stripped of paint should be washed down thoroughly, either with a proprietary lead-specific detergent or with a solution of dishwasher detergent in hot water, and then wiped down again with clean water.

Any residual dust and other debris should be removed using a vacuum cleaner fitted with a HEPA filter. Depending upon the level of contamination, it may be necessary to wear appropriate RPE whilst doing this.

 Normal vacuum cleaners (domestic or industrial) should not be used as their filters are not sufficiently fine to retain the lead-containing dust.

12

For further information refer to Chapter B10 Dust and fumes.

12.14 Further guidance and advice

The Lead Paint Safety Association

The Lead Paint Safety Association (LiPSA) is a not-for-profit organisation. It is at the forefront of efforts to promote awareness and best practice in lead paint safety and compliance. Its overall objective is to prevent, and ultimately eliminate, unnecessary childhood and occupational lead poisoning. Inadequate knowledge and non-compliance with established regulations are widespread.

 For further information visit the LIPSA website.

The Painting and Decorating Association

The Painting and Decorating Association (PDA) represents thousands of painters and decorators across the UK and is the largest trade and employers' association for contractors. The PDA offers health and safety advice to all its members.

 For further information visit the PDA website.

Appendix A – Specimen health surveillance record

Recorded details of an employee under medical surveillance because of exposure to lead (Appendix 6 Approved Code of Practice).

Employee's details

Surname	
Forenames	
Maiden name (if applicable)	
Permanent address	
Place of birth	
Date of birth	
Sex	
N.I. number	
NHS number (if available)	

Doctor's (GP) details

Name	
Address	
Telephone number	
Fax number (if any)	

Employer's details

Name	
Address	
Telephone number	
Fax number (if any)	
Standard Industrial Classification (SIC number)	

Employment details

Years exposed to lead before starting in current employment	
Date of first exposure to lead in current employment (Day Month Year)	
Date of end of exposure to lead in current employment (Day Month Year)	

Additional information

The reason for medical surveillance	
The dates of initial and periodic medical surveillance	
The results of clinical assessments	
The results of measuring blood-lead concentrations and of any other biological tests in enough detail to allow adverse trends to be identified	
Action taken, including periods moved to work not involving exposure to lead, and periods of suspension	

13

Noise

Noise is often taken for granted as an everyday feature of working on construction sites. Many construction activities create levels of noise that have the potential to cause permanent damage to the hearing of those affected if protective measures are not taken.

In addition to the long-term health implications, noise can also affect safety on site by interfering with spoken communications to the point where the risk of accidents is increased.

Introduction	176
Key points	176
The nature of noise	176
Effects of noise at work	177
Establishing noise levels	177
Risk assessment	179
Avoiding exposure to noise	182
Personal hearing protectors	183
The noise at work regulations	186
Appendix A – Exposure levels	188
Appendix B – Sound levels	189
Appendix C – Calculating personal noise exposure	190
Appendix D – Some typical sound levels of construction and piling equipment	191

13.1 Introduction

High levels of noise on construction sites often come from machinery used for demolition, excavation or piling, from compressors and concrete mixers, and so on. Other operations (such as hammering, riveting and the use of cartridge-operated fixing tools) may also be a source of excessive noise.

The degree of nuisance or damage caused by noise is related to the nature of the noise generated as well as its loudness. Intermittent noise is often more disruptive than a continuous noise and high-pitched sounds are more disturbing than low frequency ones. Exposure to high levels of noise can cause permanent damage to hearing in the form of hearing loss, tinnitus and partial or total deafness.

As well as hearing problems, excess noise is also known to cause:

- ☑ annoyance and irritation
- ☑ loss of concentration
- ☑ reduced efficiency
- ☑ fatigue

- ☑ headaches
- ☑ increased accident-proneness
- ☑ masking of warning signals.

13.2 Key points

- ☑ Noise experienced at work, in the home and social environments can cause permanent damage to hearing.
- ☑ There are often early signs that the hearing is being damaged; these should not be ignored.
- ☑ Employers should seek to control noise by other, equally or more effective, ways before resorting to personal protective equipment (PPE).
- ☑ Effective pre-planning of off-site activities and the active management of noise during the construction process can significantly reduce noise exposure on site.
- ☑ In addition to hearing damage, excessive noise can have other health and safety implications (such as not being able to hear alarms or shouted warnings).
- ☑ Establishing the noise levels on-site might not necessarily involve arranging for noise measurements to be taken.

High noise levels

Wear ear protectors

> 66 ... research indicates that only around 60% of workers wearing hearing protection actually get the right amount of protection from it.

13.3 The nature of noise

Sound is the transmission of air vibrations at different frequencies. **Noise** is sometimes defined as unwanted sound. The ear is a pressure-sensitive mechanism, detecting small changes of air pressure over a wide range of frequencies of 20–20,000 cycles per second. The unit of frequency is the hertz (Hz). Those with impaired hearing due to age or other forms of hearing loss are less likely to be able to hear the higher frequency range.

Audiometry is the technique used to determine the capacity of the ear to detect sounds of varying loudness over a range of frequencies. It can be used to measure an individual's hearing capacity against a recognised standard. Successive audiometric checks can confirm whether or not a person is suffering from progressive hearing loss.

When judging the level of noise, the rules of thumb are that if you have to raise your voice to make yourself understood at two metres from the other person, the background noise is around 85 dB(A). If the distance is only one metre, the noise is around 90 dB(A).

A peak sound pressure of 137 dB(C) will be produced by many impact tools (such as cartridge-operated tools).

Two types of noise may damage the hearing of the people who are exposed to it.

- ☑ Continual or periodic noise, which even if varying over the course of time, can be measured and averaged out over an eight-hour (or in some circumstances a weekly) reference period. This is known as the daily (or weekly) personal noise exposure, as referred to in the regulations. This is the common everyday noise that is experienced on many construction sites.
- ☑ Sudden, short bursts of loud impulsive noise (such as that experienced during the driving of piles, the use of explosives or the use of some hand tools). The references in the regulations to peak sound pressure are to this type of noise.

13.4 Effects of noise at work

Noise levels may fluctuate widely or be relatively steady. A reasonably steady sound level is where the level fluctuates through a total of less than 8 dB(A) on a slow response scale.

Exposure to noise can have the following consequences:

☑ it can cause annoyance and irritation

☑ it may affect concentration and efficiency

☑ it may cause fatigue and the likelihood of accident-proneness

☑ it can mask out other sounds, preventing a person's ears from registering instructions and warnings

☑ it can result in temporary hearing loss

☑ regular exposure to loud noise can cause damage to the ear and permanent loss of hearing.

There is also growing evidence that continued exposure to noise has consequential effects on some other illnesses.

Hearing loss

Hearing loss can be temporary or permanent. Temporary deafness is often experienced after leaving a noisy place. It is often accompanied by a ringing in the ears. Although hearing usually recovers within a few hours, this symptom should not be ignored. It should be taken as a sign that further or continued exposure to noise is likely to result in permanent damage. Permanent hearing damage can also be caused immediately by sudden and loud noises (for example from explosives or cartridge-operated tools).

Hearing loss due to prolonged exposure to noise is usually gradual. It may only be when damage caused by exposure to noise over the years combines with normal hearing loss due to ageing that people realise how deaf they have become.

This incurable hearing loss may mean that they cannot hear the television clearly when set at a comfortable volume for the rest of the family, they cannot keep up with conversations in a group or they have trouble using the telephone. Eventually, all sound becomes muffled and people find it difficult to distinguish between 't', 'd' and 's', so they confuse similar words. Social situations become very difficult, as does communication at work.

Prolonged exposure to noise can also cause **tinnitus**, which can be described as a permanent ringing, whistling or buzzing in the ears. This distressing condition can lead to disturbed sleep which, in turn, can lead to fatigue even before an employee arrives at work.

Other adverse effects of noise

At work, noise can also be a safety hazard, interfering with communication, the understanding of instructions and, most serious of all, making warnings harder to hear. Noise can also cause stress. The Control of Noise at Work Regulations do not deal with these problems specifically, but the subject of noise and its attendant problems should be borne in mind when considering the overall subject of occupational health.

13.5 Establishing noise levels

Measurement

The measurement of noise is a specialist activity. An individual's exposure depends not only on the level of noise, which will usually vary as different activities start and stop, but also on the length of time during which they are exposed to noise.

The unit of measurement for sound levels (noise) is called a decibel (dB). This scale is logarithmic and means that 90 dB is ten times the intensity of 80 dB and one hundred times the intensity of 70 dB.

An increase of 3 dB doubles the energy in the sound. This means that, for example, 87 dB is actually twice as damaging as 84 dB, even though the 3 dB difference in sound level is difficult to perceive.

The various action values are meaningless to anyone who does not have a way of accurately calculating the noise levels on site, taking into account the time factor. There are, however, two rules of thumb that should give a rough indication of noise levels:

☑ **one-metre rule** – if two people standing one metre apart (about an arm's length), who are not wearing hearing protection, have to raise their voices to hear each other, the noise level is around or above 90 dB. Hearing protection must be worn to reduce the noise at the ear to below the exposure limit (ELV) or the noise reduced to the ELV by other means. Employers must identify why ELV has been breached and modify organisational and technical measures

☑ **two-metre rule** – if two people standing two metres apart (double arm's length) have to raise their voices to hear each other, the noise level is around 85 dB and hearing protection must be worn.

There is also a third rule that, if there is any doubt, everyone affected by the noise should be wearing hearing protection in the interests of their health.

Where there is likely to be a persistent noise problem, employers should arrange for noise surveys to be carried out across the whole scope of their operations. These surveys must only be carried out by a competent person who has received proper training in noise measurement techniques and has the appropriate noise measuring equipment.

Sound level meters, used for measuring noise levels, have standard filters built into them that attenuate or emphasise signals at different frequencies in order to simulate how the sound affects the ear. This is known as frequency weighting.

13

Noise

An instrument with a frequency weighting known as an 'A' weighted scale is commonly used on construction sites to measure noise from the working environment. Readings are expressed as dB(A).

Sudden impact noises (such as hammer blows) are measured in terms of maximum pressure. In this case measurements are 'C' weighted and therefore expressed as dB(C).

Noise meters vary considerably depending on type, size, complexity and cost, but even the inexpensive range will give a reasonable indication of noise levels being produced and priorities for action. Risk assessments should be based on measurements of the 'Leq', which is an average of the level of noise for the duration of the measurement.

Survey of noise levels

If it is necessary to resort to the measurement of noise, someone who is competent in evaluating the type of workplace, the use of the equipment and the interpretation of the results must be engaged. They must be able to draw valid conclusions from the information obtained and advise management on the actions needed to comply with the requirements of legislation.

The aim of the noise assessment is to:

☑ identify workers who may be at risk of hearing damage to enable an action plan to be prepared to control the noise exposure

☑ determine the daily personal noise exposure (LEP,d) of workers (including times when not actually working (for example, rest areas) and from non-occupational sources, such as personal entertainment systems)

☑ identify additional information to comply with legislation (for example, whether noise control measures or hearing protection are needed and, if so, where and what type).

The employer must:

☑ keep a record of the noise assessments and the employees who are exposed to the noise

☑ regularly review those assessments. This should be done biannually or whenever it is considered that the assessment is no longer valid (for example, whenever there is new equipment or a change to the process that may alter noise levels)

☑ use the assessment to develop an action plan for introducing noise control measures

☑ deal with the immediate risk by providing personal hearing protectors (this should only be until other controls have been investigated and implemented)

☑ identify what steps are reasonably practicable to reduce the noise exposure of employees by engineering or other organisational means

☑ establish priorities for action and consider what changes may need to be phased in over the course of time.

Ideally, one person, with sufficient authority, will be given the responsibility for ensuring that the legislation is complied with and for co-ordinating and monitoring the noise reduction programme where necessary.

A points system has been developed by the HSE, which allows for quick estimates of the noise exposure for a worker. Each process is assigned a number of points per hour. Adding the points from each process carried out (calculated by multiplying the points per hour by the number of hours use) provides an estimate of the total exposure. The upper exposure action value corresponds to 100 points; the lower exposure action value corresponds to 32 points.

! Training should cover the correct use of PPE, including how to communicate clearly whilst wearing it.

	SOUND INTENSITY RATIO	SOUND LEVEL IN dB(A)		SOUND SOURCE
Harmful range	100 000 000 000 000	140		Jet engine
	10 000 000 000 000	130		Riveting hammer
				THRESHOLD OF FEELING
	1 000 000 000 000	120		Propeller aircraft
	100 000 000 000	110		Rock drill
Critical zone	10 000 000 000	100		Plate fabrication shop
	1 000 000 000	90		Heavy vehicle
	100 000 000	80		Very busy traffic
	10 000 000	70		Private car
	1 000 000	60		Ordinary conversation
	100 000	50		Quiet office
Safe range	10 000	40		Soft music from radio
	1 000	30		Quiet whisper
	100	20		Quiet urban dwelling
	10	10		Rustle of a leaf
	1	0		**THRESHOLD OF HEARING**

Typical sound intensities

There is a lot of equipment that produces high levels of noise in the building and construction industry. Sound levels are measured in decibels (dB) and some typical examples include:

☑ electrical hand tool – 95 dB

☑ hammer drill – 102 dB

☑ circular bench saw – 107 dB

☑ bulldozer/grader – 121 dB.

Employers have a duty to reduce the risk of damage to employees' hearing to the lowest level that is reasonably practicable.

13.6   Risk assessment

Risk assessment

Action and limit values

The regulations specify the following three levels of exposure to noise, each of which requires that certain actions are taken:

☑ **lower exposure action value.** This is reached when a daily or weekly personal exposure reaches 80 dB(A) or a peak sound pressure of 135 dB(C) occurs

☑ **upper exposure action value.** This is reached when a daily or weekly personal exposure reaches 85 dB(A) or a peak sound pressure of 137 dB(C) occurs

☑ **exposure limit value.** This is the maximum level of noise to which anyone at work may be exposed. It is set at 87 dB(A) at the ear, measured on a daily or weekly basis as appropriate or when a peak sound pressure of 140 dB(C) occurs.

If any employee is likely to be exposed to noise **at or above the lower exposure action value**, the employer must carry out a risk assessment, which may or may not result in the need for a competent person to measure the actual level of noise exposure.

Other methods of assessing noise levels should be used by employers before resorting to the actual measurement of noise levels. Any new tool or equipment that generates a potentially harmful level of noise should state the actual level of noise generated, either on the tool itself or in the accompanying documents. This can be useful in identifying potentially problematic tools, but it is important to remember that the actual noise experienced by the operator depends on many factors (such as the acoustics of the working environment, tool configuration and material being worked).

The most effective way of controlling exposure is to eliminate the source of noise, thereby removing the risk of damage to hearing. This is often not practical although sometimes a change of work process is possible.

Where noise elimination is not practical, there are several control techniques that might be applied. Which method is chosen will depend upon the nature of the equipment, the way in which it is used and the work environment.

The five stages to assessing risk

Stage 1: Arrangements.

Decide how the company intends to manage the risk of hearing damage. The arrangements can be used as a tool to help monitor and review safety performance, and ensure that it continues to control risks effectively.

The arrangements for dealing with noise risks should link with the overall health and safety policy.

Ask the following questions.

☑ **Purpose/aim.** What will the arrangements achieve? Will they prevent anyone being exposed to loud noise?

☑ **Scope.** Who do the arrangements affect?

☑ **Legal duties.** What are the legal duties specific to noise?

☑ **Objective(s) and targets.** What are the objectives and how can you measure progress? It is important to choose objectives and set sensible targets to measure progress and, where relevant, to specify and measure a baseline to assess how much progress has been made.

☑ **Risk control measures.** How can you engage the workforce to work with you to reduce the risks?

☑ **Information and training.** How can you train and encourage your workforce to reduce the risks? Should you provide some incentives, formal training, toolbox talks, and/or on the job training?

☑ **Monitoring.** How will you check that the arrangements manage risk effectively? Are there any activities that you particularly need to review and monitor? How and when will you monitor the health of those who are still exposed to a risk?

☑ **Audit and review.** When and how will you review the arrangements?

13

Stage 2: Assess health risks.

The risk assessment is to help decide how to ensure the health and safety of workers who are exposed to noise. It should:

☑ identify where there might be a risk from noise

☑ clarify who is likely to be affected

☑ contain a reasonable estimate of your employees' exposures

☑ identify what you need to do to comply with the law (for example, whether additional control measures are needed and, if so, where and what)

☑ identify any workers who need health surveillance.

It should be possible to do a basic risk assessment without the need for measurement. It will show whether exposures are likely to exceed the exposure action values and allow planning and prioritising of control actions effectively.

It is quite common for people to use the one and two metre rules (described previously in 13.5) to indicate whether there is a potential noise problem. Alternatively, use manufacturers' noise data or have actual measurements taken as a basis for estimating exposures. A detailed exposure assessment may help you to:

☑ decide which control actions might be most effective and practicable in reducing noise exposure

☑ be more certain whether exposures are likely to exceed the action or limit values

☑ check whether your controls are effective.

The regulations require that reasonably practicable steps are taken to control noise. In many cases you will not need a detailed assessment to identify which steps to take initially.

Exposure depends on a combination of noise level and exposure time. Be wary about just relying on self-reported estimates of exposure because these are unlikely to be accurate. Observe the work; it is just as easy to over as well as underestimate exposure. Take account of background noise that may add to your workers' exposures (for example, construction work near a high-speed road).

It may be useful to observe work activities, measure the exposure time over part of a day and then use the information to estimate exposure for a full shift. If an employee is exposed to noise from more than one tool or work process during a typical day, you will need to collect information about the likely noise level(s) and exposure time for each source.

Once the relevant noise data and exposure times have been collected it may be helpful to use an exposure calculator to assess each employee's daily exposure.

The Supply of Machinery (Safety) Regulations requires manufacturers and suppliers to design equipment that will minimise noise risks. Equipment should be CE-marked to show that it complies with these requirements, and health and safety information should feature in the instructions that are supplied with a machine. This should include:

☑ information on safe use and, where necessary, training requirements

☑ information on how to maintain the equipment

☑ a statement of the noise emission (where the equipment noise level exceeds 70 dB at the operator position), together with information on the test method.

Manufacturers' information can indicate whether further assessment and action might be required. However, general data is unlikely to fully represent the actual conditions of use.

Stage 3: Eliminate risk.

The purpose of the Control of Noise at Work Regulations is to make sure that people don't suffer damage to their health from noise – so controlling the risks from exposure to noise should be where you concentrate your efforts.

Clients and designers can have a big influence over eliminating noise risks on site (for example, by specifying prefabricated components or work methods that avoid the need for noisy tools and processes).

Where noise exposures are below the lower exposure action value (LEAV) 80 dB, the risk of damage to health is generally lower and so will only be expected to take actions that are simple and inexpensive.

Where the assessment shows that employees are likely to be exposed at or above the exposure action values, a planned programme of noise control must be implemented. It is rarely acceptable just to rely on hearing protection alone, except as a short-term measure.

 See the HSE website for a case study relating to hearing damage.

☑ Look for alternative work methods that eliminate or reduce exposure to noise. Trade associations, industry contacts, equipment suppliers and trade journals may help to identify good practice.

☑ Mechanise or automate work so that the operator is removed from the noisy environment (such as excavator cab).

☑ Make sure that equipment is suitable and can do the work efficiently. Equipment that is unsuitable, too small or not powerful enough is likely to take longer to complete the task and increase exposure to noise.

☑ Select tools that produce the least noise.

☑ Limit the use of high-noise tools wherever possible.

☑ To cut large holes in brickwork, use a diamond-tipped hole-cutter with a rotary action rather than a tungsten-tipped bit, which requires rotary and hammer action. This reduces both vibration and noise exposure.

☑ Use vibration-dampened stone-cutting saw blades. Construction processes that lead to high levels of hand-arm vibration are often high-noise processes too.

When work equipment gets damaged or worn seek replacement kit that is suitable for the work, as well as being quiet and efficient. Ensure that your purchaser specifies low noise and vibration equipment.

 Refer to the HSE website for good practice relating to low noise machines.

Stage 4: Control risk.

Power tools and other work equipment should be serviced and maintained in accordance with manufacturers' instructions and maintenance schedules. This should help to prevent unnecessarily high noise levels and ensure efficient operation. Maintenance includes:

☑ keeping cutting tools sharp

☑ correctly dressing abrasive wheels

☑ replacing worn parts

☑ carrying out balance checks and corrections as necessary

☑ checking and replacement of defective vibration dampers, bearings and gears

☑ sharpening chainsaw teeth and keeping the correct chain tension

☑ tuning and adjustment of engines

Stage 5: Manage remaining risk.

You can manage any remaining health risks by using a range of measures (such as PPE, information, health surveillance and routine monitoring).

For work schedules, job rotation can be used to share a noise exposure between several people, for example:

☑ limit the time that each worker is exposed to noise

☑ where tools require continual or frequent use, introduce rotas to limit individual exposure times

☑ weekly averaging may be used to ensure that exposures are managed; include quiet days in the rotas.

Effective job rotation is more complex if workers use more than one tool or process that involves a noise exposure.

There are generally two types of hearing protection available – ear defenders or muffs, and ear plugs – and there is plenty of choice. Different products may not offer the same level of protection so, when purchasing PPE, check the product information for details.

Workers need to understand the risks of noise exposure. Where workers are exposed above the lower exposure action values the following should be explained:

☑ the likely noise exposure and the risk that this creates

☑ what you are doing to control risks and exposures

☑ where and how people can obtain hearing protection

☑ how to report defective noise control equipment and hearing protection

☑ what their duties are under the Control of Noise at Work Regulations

☑ what they should do to minimise the risk (such as the proper way to use noise control equipment and hearing protection, storage and maintenance)

☑ health checks and surveillance.

 Further information can be found online in the HSE publication *Noise. Don't lose your hearing!*

Working with safety representatives and employees' representatives is a useful way to communicate about health and safety. For example, discuss the risk assessment and action plan, including any proposal to average exposure over a week, selection of hearing protection, any hearing protection zones and the health surveillance programme.

13

Involving employees in decisions can help improve working relationships, make employees more receptive to new ideas and help control exposure to noise.

13.7   Avoiding exposure to noise

Planning against excess noise levels

Attention should be given at the planning stage to developing a noise control strategy that considers the:

- ☑ design of the project and of the processes and equipment that will be involved
- ☑ phasing of differing operations, especially if a number of contractors are working on site
- ☑ requirements of the Local Authority
- ☑ location of the site; or sites if the project involves more than one location
- ☑ noise levels that are likely to be produced by the work being carried out
- ☑ layout of the site, including the siting of access points, batching plants, and so on
- ☑ hours of working that are planned (or perhaps limited by the Local Authority)
- ☑ provisions available for controlling noise on site
- ☑ possibility of disturbance to nearby residents and properties (if this is likely, the situation and measures to be taken to reduce noise should be explained to persons likely to be affected).

Failure to plan the control of noise may lead to delay and increased cost later. Where appropriate, noise levels must be a consideration for designers under the CDM Regulations.

Attention should be given to the Local Authority powers under the Environmental Protection Act, which deal with noise as a statutory nuisance, and the Control of Pollution Act, which relate particularly to activities on construction sites.

[Ear defenders must be worn beyond this point]

Managing noise levels during construction

Exposure to noise can be eliminated or reduced by:

- ☑ controlling noise at source
- ☑ employing engineering controls where possible
- ☑ using a purchasing/hire policy for plant, equipment and tools that takes noise into account
- ☑ introducing alternative methods and processes that eliminate or reduce noise levels
- ☑ giving consideration to the careful siting of noisy plant and equipment
- ☑ where practical, storing bulk materials to form an acoustic screen
- ☑ carrying out job rotation for employees to reduce exposure to noise
- ☑ providing rest rooms or acoustic refuges for staff during breaks from work
- ☑ rearranging work locations for staff, if possible, away from noisy equipment
- ☑ as a last resort, providing personal hearing protectors.

Control of noise at source

Controlling the noise at its source can be achieved by a variety of means:

- ☑ the design and manufacture of the equipment
- ☑ the use of acoustic covers and exhaust silencers for equipment
- ☑ the use of alternative, less noisy equipment or methods of working
- ☑ enclosing noisy equipment within temporary structures
- ☑ regular inspection and maintenance of the equipment being used
- ☑ fitting noise-absorbent mountings to reduce the transmission of noise through adjacent structures.

Engineering controls

Measures that can be taken include ensuring that all equipment, which has the potential to create excessive noise, is:

- ☑ kept well maintained

☑ kept in good order, including ensuring that there are no loose panels or casing and that exhaust mufflers are in good condition

☑ not left running when it is not actually in use.

Siting or location

Effective siting or location includes:

☑ removing the source of the noise to a distance whenever possible

☑ orientating plant to direct the noise away from the work area

☑ placing site buildings, stores, and so on between the noise source and noise sensitive areas

☑ screening the noise source with a barrier, wall, acoustic screen, spoil heap, or by locating the source behind partly completed buildings.

The effectiveness of a noise barrier will depend on its dimensions, its position relative to the source and the listener, and the material used in the construction of the barrier. Care must be taken to ensure that barriers do not, by reflecting sound, transfer the noise nuisance from one sensitive area to another and so create a health problem for someone else.

Demolition

Where demolition operations are carried out in locations likely to affect the general public, the Local Authority may request the principal contractor to submit an application under the Control of Pollution Act (COPA), specifying working methods, working hours and maximum noise levels (called prior consent). A Local Authority can issue an abatement notice for failure to comply with consent conditions, or where noise levels are creating a statutory nuisance.

In accordance with the Control of Noise at Work Regulations, where noise levels are above (or expected to be above) the lower exposure action value, the demolition contractor must ensure that a noise assessment has been carried out and that, where possible, people are kept out of the danger area.

Any machinery that is to be used in the demolition process should, as far as possible, be fitted and used with soundproofing equipment (for example exhaust silencers).

Where it is necessary for people to work within the area of noisy operations, adequate hearing protection must be provided and used as necessary. If the upper exposure action value is exceeded, or likely to be exceeded, hearing protection must be worn and hearing protection zones clearly indicated.

Where the findings of a risk assessment indicate that the hearing of any employee is at risk due to noise exposure at work, health surveillance, including hearing checks, must be provided.

13.8 Personal hearing protectors

All hearing protectors produced or imported by reputable companies are manufactured to British and European Standards. As with all PPE for use at work, ear protectors should be selected by a competent person who can ensure, in discussion with the supplier, that it possesses the necessary performance characteristics. Most leading manufacturers and suppliers will offer their own advisory service.

 PPE cannot be used for long-term noise risk management.

Competence in the selection of this type of PPE is particularly important, as ear protectors that give good protection against noise at a high frequency may not offer very much protection against low frequency noise, and vice versa.

All reasonably practicable methods must be used to reduce noise levels, but where these remain at or above the upper exposure action value, after control measures have been implemented, ear protectors must be made available and worn. Ear protectors are not a substitute for other methods of noise control; they are an absolute last resort.

Employees may initially be reluctant to wear ear protection and those who are at risk must be made aware of the potential for hearing loss that can be caused by exposure to excessive noise levels.

 Comfort, motivation and supervision are the paramount factors that determine the wear rate and therefore the protection that is achieved in practice.

13

Other considerations

☑ Personal hearing protectors must be provided on an individual basis.

☑ A competent person must be responsible for any training that may be necessary in the correct use of personal hearing protectors.

☑ Personal hearing protectors should normally be provided as an interim measure while more effective and permanent methods of control are sought.

☑ Employees must be trained in the use, care and storage of ear protectors.

Noise

☑ Ear protectors must be suited to the user, suitable for the type of noise and provide an effective seal.

☑ They should be stored in a clean place when not in use, unless disposable.

☑ They should be inspected regularly for deterioration or damage and replaced when necessary, unless disposable.

☑ Personal hearing protectors should not over protect, whereby users can become isolated from their work environment and be unable to hear warnings.

 A check should be made to ensure that hazard warning signals are audible to individuals wearing ear protectors, and the volume, tone, or method of signalling changed if necessary.

Types of personal hearing protectors

The two basic types of protector are ear plugs and ear defenders.

Disposable ear plugs are made of very fine mineral fibre or foam, sometimes ready shaped. They must be inserted correctly and, if taken out, should not be reused. They should only be handled with clean hands.

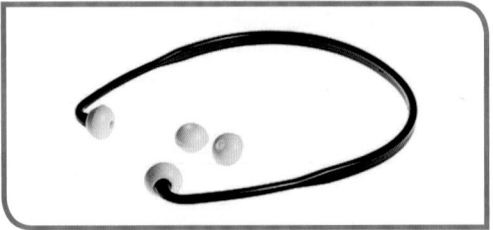

Reusable ear plugs are made of rubber or plastic, and need regular, careful washing. The initial supply and fitting should be carried out by trained persons. Different sizes may be required for each ear and must be a good fit. They must be fitted with clean hands as any contamination by dirt, grease or swarf may cause ear irritation. Ear plugs are therefore unsuitable on site for intermittent use (such as can occur when operating a breaker).

Ear defenders (or muffs) completely cover the ear and are sealed to the head with a foam or liquid-filled seal. Badly designed or badly produced defenders may give little or no protection against noise. Other points are as follows:

☑ pressure from the seal may cause wearers to complain of tightness, but loose defenders lose most of their protective capability and are ineffective

☑ damage and deterioration to seals also results in ineffectiveness and loss of protection

☑ in fitting, account needs to be taken of people with different sized or shaped heads or ears, hair styles and spectacles

☑ facial hair and the arms of spectacles may interfere with the seal on ear defenders

☑ defenders fitted to safety helmets may cause problems by not fitting tightly to the ear, or by moving as the helmet moves

☑ defenders must be chosen to deal with a particular noise problem; ones that offer protection against low frequency sound may be ineffective at high frequency, and vice versa.

Ear defenders that incorporate a sound enhancement system are available. When noise levels are low, sound detected by a microphone is replayed to the wearer enabling them to communicate normally. When noise levels are high, the sound replay system is automatically cut, such that the defenders act as regular ear protectors. Such products are particularly suitable for those exposed to unpredictable, short bursts of noise.

Ear protectors are only effective while they are being used. If protectors are worn for only half the shift, only some 10% protection is gained; if worn for 7¾ out of 8 hours, the protection factor is still only 75%.

13

Selection of hearing protection

In order to select the correct type of hearing protection you first need to know the noise level on site and then be able to select the right type of hearing protection required to reduce the noise exposure to a safe level (which is below 80 dB).

For example, 100 dB would need to be reduced by 20 dB to bring it to 80 dB. This reduction is known as attenuation or single noise reduction (SNR) and this value is shown on manufacturers' products.

The HSE recommends providing hearing protectors that perform 4 dB better than the required minimum, in order to take into account real world factors (such as poor fitting). This means that to protect the worker against 100 dB of noise, you need to select hearing protection with attenuation or SNR of 24 dB.

The optimum value with hearing protection is between 70 dB and 80 dB. Thus, in this example, select hearing protection with an attenuation or SNR of between 24 dB and 34 dB.

Standards for hearing protection. Personal hearing protection must be CE-marked, showing it meets the relevant European Standard, BS EN 352.

EN 352-1 – Hearing protectors – earmuffs

In addition to the standard number, maker and model identification:

■ indication of orientation of the earmuff, where required (for example, 'top' and/or 'left' and 'right').

EN 352-2 – Hearing protectors – earplugs

Markings may only appear on the packaging. In addition to the standard number, maker and model identification:

■ whether disposable or re-useable

■ fitting instructions

■ nominal size of formable plugs, in range 5 to 14 mm

■ left-right differentiation for custom moulded plugs.

EN 352-3 – Hearing protectors – earmuffs attached to a safety helmet

In addition to the standard number, maker and model identification:

■ indication of orientation of the earmuff, where required (for example 'top' and/or 'left' and 'right').

EN 352-4 – Hearing protectors – earmuffs attached to a safety helmet

■ As for EN 352-1.

EN 352-5 – Hearing protectors – active noise reduction earmuffs

■ As for EN 352-1.

EN 352-6 – Hearing protectors – earmuffs with electrical audio input

■ As for EN 352-1.

EN 352-7 – Hearing protectors – level dependent earplugs

■ As for EN 352-2.

EN 352-8 – Hearing protectors – entertainment audio earmuffs

■ As for EN 352-2.

13.9 The noise at work regulations

A summary of legal requirements can be found in the table below.

 For further details of the regulations and guidance refer to the HSE's website.

Employers' duties	Exposure below the lower exposure action value of 80 dB(A)	Exposure at or above the lower exposure action value of 80 dB(A) or peak sound pressure of 135 dB(C)	Exposure at or above the upper exposure action value of 85 dB(A) or peak sound pressure of 137 dB(C)	Exposure at or above the exposure limit value of 87 dB(A) or peak sound pressure of 140 dB(C)
Assessment of noise exposure				
■ Risk assessment to be carried out and reviewed as necessary.		✔	✔	✔
■ Record of significant findings and control measures put in place.		✔	✔	✔
■ Risk assessment to include extra considerations in higher risk situations.			✔	✔
General duty to reduce risk				
■ Risk of hearing damage to be eliminated or reduced to the lowest level reasonably practicable.	✔	✔	✔	✔
■ Implement organisational and technical control measures, excluding issue of personal hearing protection.			✔	✔
■ Reduce exposure below exposure limit value (ELV), if ELV breached, identify why and modify organisational and technical measures.				✔
■ Ensure noise exposure in rest facilities is kept to acceptable level.		✔	✔	✔
■ Adapt control measures as necessary to take account of employee(s) who may be particularly at risk from exposure to noise.		✔	✔	✔
■ Consult with employees or their representatives on protective measures taken.		✔	✔	✔
Provision of hearing protection				
Ensure that personal hearing protectors are:				
■ provided to employees who ask for them		✔	✔	✔
■ provided to all those exposed			✔	✔
■ used by all those exposed.			✔	✔
Create hearing protection zones, designated by appropriate signs and:				
■ restrict access if justified by the level of risk			✔	✔
■ ensure as far as is reasonably practicable that all who go into a marked hearing protection zone use hearing protection.			✔	✔
Maintenance and use of equipment				
Ensure so far as is reasonably practicable that:				
■ all equipment provided under the regulations, except personal hearing protectors, are fully and properly used			✔	✔
■ all equipment is maintained in an efficient state and good working order.	✔	✔	✔	✔

Employers' duties	Exposure below the lower exposure action value of 80 dB(A)	Exposure at or above the lower exposure action value of 80 dB(A) or peak sound pressure of 135 dB(C)	Exposure at or above the upper exposure action value of 85 dB(A) or peak sound pressure of 137 dB(C)	Exposure at or above the exposure limit value of 87 dB(A) or peak sound pressure of 140 dB(C)
Information instruction and training				
Provide adequate information, instruction and training and update it as necessary, on:				
■ the nature of the risks to hearing from noise		✔	✔	✔
■ the organisational and technical measures taken				
■ the action and limit values				
■ the significant findings of the risk assessment				
■ how to obtain a personal hearing protector				
■ how to detect and report signs of hearing damage				
■ the entitlement to health surveillance				
■ the results of any **collective** health surveillance.				
Provide information, instruction and training for anyone who has responsibilities for ensuring the employer's legal duties are carried out.		✔	✔	✔
Health surveillance				
Provide as appropriate if the risk assessment indicates there to be a risk to employees' health resulting from noise at work.		✔	✔	✔
Keep and maintain records of health surveillance and enable employees access to their own health surveillance records and allow the HSE to access records as necessary.		✔	✔	✔
Where employees are found to have hearing damage:		✔	✔	✔
■ ensure the employee is informed by a suitably qualified person				
■ review the risk assessment and control measures				
■ consider assigning the employee to alternative (non-noisy) work				
■ continue with health surveillance				
Employee's duties				
Use of equipment				
Employees must:				
■ make full and proper use of personal hearing protectors			✔	✔
■ use any other control measures provided by the employer		✔	✔	✔
■ report any defects discovered in the protective measures to the employer.	✔	✔	✔	✔
Health surveillance				
Attend health surveillance procedures as required by the employer in working hours and at the employer's expense.		✔	✔	✔

13

Appendix A – Exposure levels

The effect on maximum working times due to exposure without protection

Average noise level dB(A)	Maximum exposure in one working day if 80 dB(A) (LEP,d) is not exceeded
80	8 hours
83	4 hours
86	2 hours
89	1 hour
92	30 minutes
95	15 minutes
98	7.5 minutes
101	3.75 minutes

Increase of protection gained in relation to time if ear protectors are worn

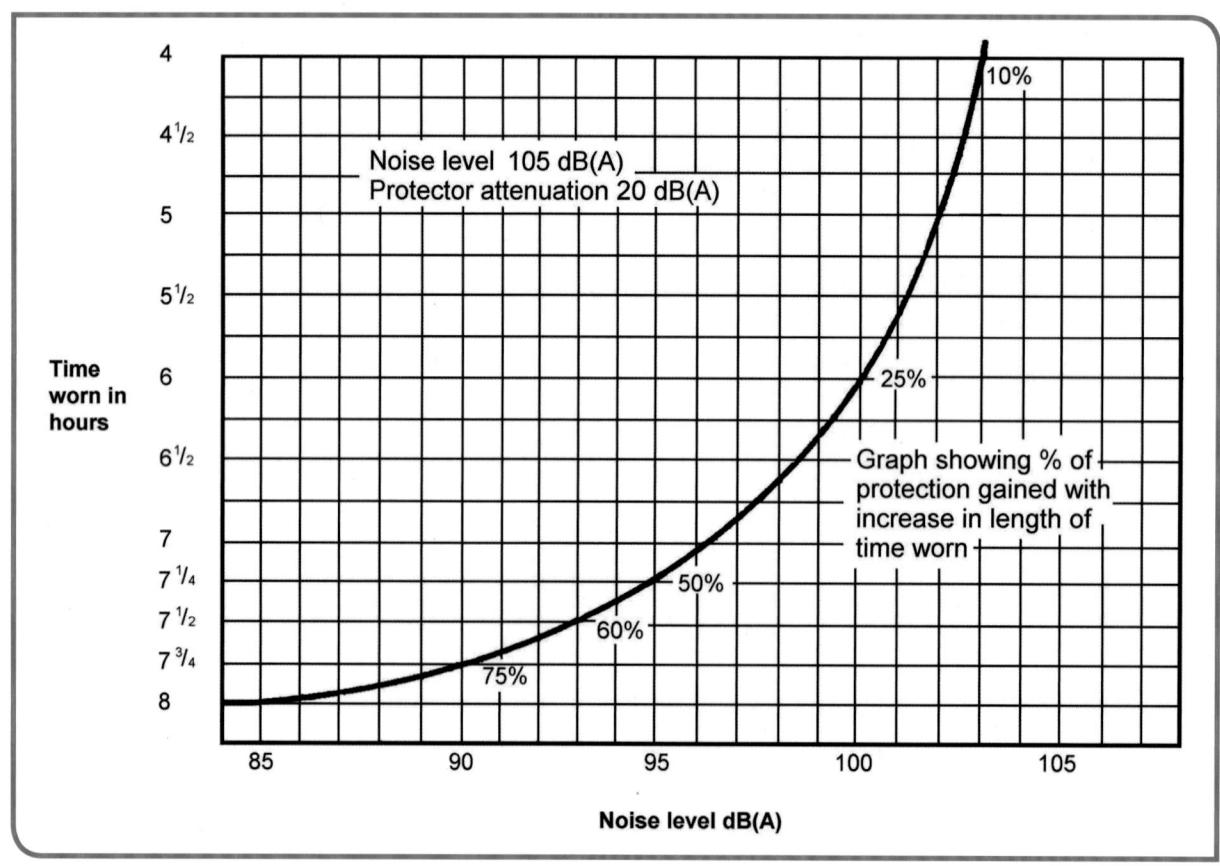

Appendix B – Sound levels

How sound levels vary with distance from source

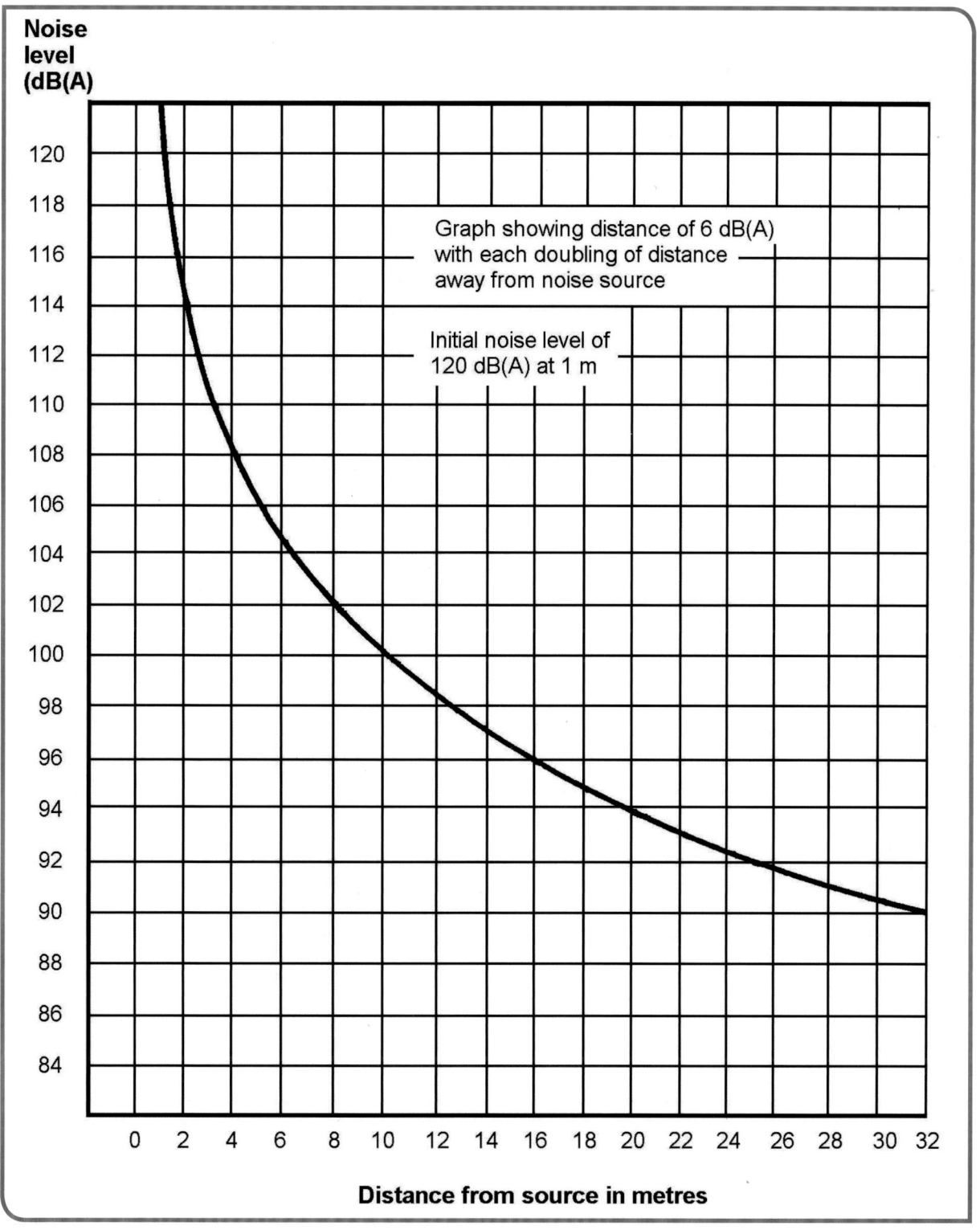

Graph showing distance of 6 dB(A) with each doubling of distance away from noise source

Initial noise level of 120 dB(A) at 1 m

Noise level (dB(A)) (vertical axis)

Distance from source in metres (horizontal axis)

Appendix C – Calculating personal noise exposure

 Two personal exposure calculators are available on the HSE website.

Microsoft Excel is required to use these calculators, which enable users to calculate the daily or weekly exposure of individuals to noise. An on-site measurement of sound pressure (noise) must first be taken, which requires specialist knowledge and equipment. The daily noise exposure calculator enables an individual's exposure to noise to be apportioned across up to eight different tasks carried out within any one day, each with different levels of exposure.

A third calculator on the same webpage enables users to establish the protection factor required in any hearing protection that they provide. In this case, by knowing the noise levels within the workplace and the protection information on the hearing protection, its suitability can be determined.

Two noise exposure ready reckoners (for daily or weekly exposure) can be accessed through the same webpage (Adobe Acrobat required). The noise level on site must again be known.

Exposure calculator

	Noise level (L_{Aeq} dB)	Exposure duration (hours)	Exposure points (job/task)	Exposure points per hour
Job/task 1				
Job/task 2				
Job/task 3				
Job/task 4				
Job/task 5				
Job/task 6				
Job/task 7				
Job/task 8				
Total duration				
Daily noise exposure ($L_{EP,d}$)				

 Exposure points can be used to prioritise noise control. The highest exposure points are given by the jobs and tasks, which make the greatest contributions to daily noise exposure. Therefore, tackling these noise exposures will have the greatest effect on daily noise exposure.

Instructions for exposure calculator

Enter the L_{Aeq} (in dB) and select the daily exposure duration (in hours) in the white areas for up to eight jobs or tasks carried out by a person during their working day.

Rounding noise levels to the nearest decibel and durations to the nearest 15 minutes (0.25 hours) is sufficiently precise.

Exposure points will appear for each entry and the overall daily personal noise exposure ($L_{EP,d}$) will be displayed.

The lower exposure action value (an $L_{EP,d}$ of 80 dB) is represented by 32 exposure points, the upper exposure action value ($L_{EP,d}$ of 85 dB) by 100 points.

Appendix D – Some typical sound levels of construction and piling equipment

(Levels given are average at source)

Sound level dB(A)	Construction equipment	Piling equipment
95	Hand tools – electric	
100	Hand tools – air	
101	Forklifts	
102	Hammer drill	
103	Dumpers	
104	Concrete mixer	
105	Hand tools – petrol	
106	Tower cranes	
107	Circular bench saw	
108	Trucks	
109	Excavators	6 tonne drop hammer (cased piles)
110	Crawler cranes	
111	Heavy lorries	
112	Ready mix	
113	Hoists diesel	
114	Loading shovel	
115	Rock drill	
116	Batching plant	Trench hammer (sheet piles)
117	Generators	Rotary bored piles
118	Loaders	Screen drop hammer (sheet piles)
119	Cranes – lorry mounted	
120	Compressors – compactors	Impact boring (driving case method)
121	Bulldozers – graders	2 tonne drop hammer (pre-cast concrete piles)
125		Vibration system (sheet piles)
126		Resonant system 'h' section
128		Single acting air hammer (pre-cast concrete)
136		Diesel hammer (sheet piles)
138		Double acting air hammer (sheet piles)

These sound levels are for guidance only. Information should be sought from the manufacturer or the plant hire company regarding machines on site.

By virtue of Section 6 of The Health and Safety at Work Act 1974, manufacturers and suppliers are required to provide information about the noise levels generated by the equipment made or supplied if the noise level is at or above the first action level or peak action level.

Noise levels emitted from the machines will be affected by the competence of the operator and the quality of maintenance.

For accurate measurement of site noise, a survey is necessary.

13

14

Vibration

A considerable number of the tools and other pieces of equipment that are currently used in the building and construction industry have a rotary or percussive action and so can cause **hand-arm vibration.**

This even applies to some widely used small tools (such as hand drills) that have a hammer action. Other examples of tools that create vibration include pneumatic breakers, vibrating pokers, vibrating rollers, plate compactors and scabbling.

Introduction	194
Key points	194
Exposure to vibration	194
Tools likely to cause harmful levels of vibration	196
Managing vibration	197
Health issues	201
Legislative requirements	203
Appendix A – Initial hand-arm vibration screening questionnaire	207
Appendix B – Annual hand-arm vibration questionnaire for health surveillance	209
Appendix C – Sample health monitoring questionnaire	211
Appendix D – Estimating exposure to hand-arm vibration	212

14.1   Introduction

A wide range of tools commonly used during construction and demolition activities, particularly those with rotary or percussive action, have the potential to cause serious health problems. The seriousness of the situation will depend largely on how frequently and for how long vibrating tools are used although other factors contribute to the potential for ill health.

The control of vibration at work makes good business sense for employers. Employees who are able to work are of far greater benefit to the employer than those who are off sick as a result of work-related ill health, or those who cannot work to maximum effect due to hand-arm vibration syndrome (HAVS), vibration white finger (VWF) or back pain.

The main points to consider are:

☑ exposure to hand-arm vibration has the potential to cause disabling injuries

☑ exposure to whole-body vibration (WBV) can cause severe back pain but vibration can be controlled by, for example, improved technology in mobile plant (such as improved suspension and driver's seat), operator training, smooth operation of machines and job rotation

☑ employers have a legal duty to reduce the risks to the health of employees by either eliminating exposure to vibration or reducing it to an acceptable level

☑ employers have various means at their disposal of estimating exposure to vibration before resorting to having measurements carried out

☑ if it is necessary to have vibration measurements taken, it is essential that the person doing so is trained and competent.

Some of the things that can be done to control the potentially harmful effects of exposure to hand-arm vibration are:

☑ adopting alternative (non-vibrational) work methods

☑ ensuring that tools are either low-vibration by design and/or well-maintained

☑ adapting work patterns

☑ ensuring that ergonomic factors are taken into account

☑ preventing those person(s) exposed to vibration from becoming cold and/or damp

☑ training workers how to minimise the risks from vibration.

14.2   Key points

In summary, the regulations require that the employer, should:

☑ assess the risks to the health of their employees from vibration, and to effectively plan for its control

☑ properly manage the risks

☑ provide suitable work equipment for their employees, having regard for technical developments in tool design and vibration suppression

☑ maintain equipment fully and correctly

☑ give employees and supervisors information and training on the risks to health caused by vibration, and on the safe use of the work equipment that is provided

☑ provide health surveillance/health monitoring where risks cannot be completely eliminated

☑ report any confirmed cases of HAVS or VWF to the Health and Safety Executive (HSE)

☑ consult employees and their appointed representatives on proposals for dealing with vibration.

14.3   Exposure to vibration

Hand-arm vibration

The most common form of vibration affecting those who work in construction is hand-arm vibration syndrome (HAVS), which has the potential to damage the circulation, nerves, joints and bones in the hands and arms.

HAVS is usually caused by the continued use of rotating or percussive tools (such as disc-cutters, needle guns, hammer-action drills, hand-held sanders, brush-cutters, chainsaws, and so on).

The factors that can influence the degree of severity of HAVS include:

☑ the frequency at which the tool vibrates

☑ the exposure pattern – length and frequency of work and subsequent rest periods

☑ the sharpness and suitability of cutting tool or blade to cut the material being worked on

☑ the grip, push and other forces used to guide and apply the vibrating tools. The tighter the grip, the more vibration energy is transferred to the hands (vibration may increase as a tool becomes blunt and the user pushes harder)

☑ other factors that potentially affect blood circulation (such as workplace temperature, whether the person smokes and individual susceptibility)

☑ the hardness of the material being worked

☑ the posture of the tool user, because tense muscles are more susceptible to hand-arm vibration (for example, using vibrating tools at arm's length increases the effect).

The symptoms

HAVS can develop into a severe and potentially disabling condition known as vibration white finger (VWF). Symptoms of VWF are usually triggered by the cold.

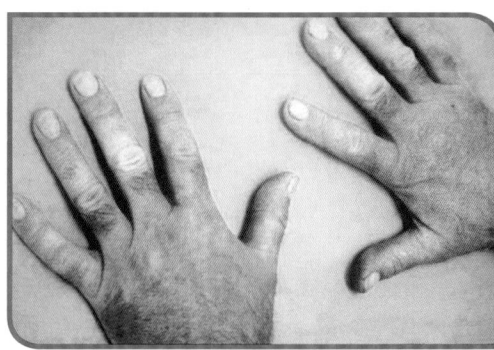

Early signs are:

☑ pale fingertips

☑ loss of sense of touch

☑ severe pain and numbness

☑ pins and needles

☑ loss of grip

☑ loss of dexterity (such as when doing up buttons, and so on).

In the longer-term, VWF can result in disabling conditions, including ulceration and gangrene.

Vibration damage to the fingers, hands or body is very much dose-related. The greater the exposure to vibration, the more likely there is to be damage. Increased exposure could be due to being exposed to greater magnitudes of vibration or being exposed for longer durations.

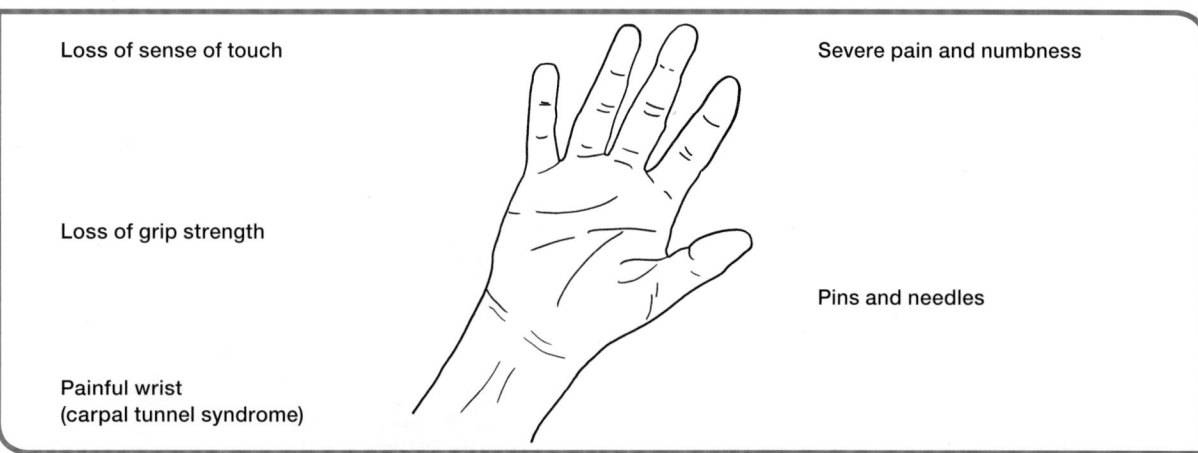

Loss of sense of touch

Severe pain and numbness

Loss of grip strength

Pins and needles

Painful wrist
(carpal tunnel syndrome)

Vibration damage to areas of the hands and wrists

Other factors that can influence the risk of developing HAVS include:

☑ the grip, push and other forces used to guide and apply the vibrating tools or pieces of work equipment. The tighter the grip, the more vibration energy is transferred to the hands

☑ tools with blunt cutting edges usually require more time to complete the task, higher grip and push forces, and often result in greater vibration emission

☑ the exposure pattern, length and frequency of work and rest periods

☑ how much of the hand, and other parts of the body, is exposed to the vibration

☑ factors that potentially affect blood circulation (such as workplace temperature, smoking and individual susceptibility)

☑ the hardness of the material being worked

☑ tool maintenance (important in order to keep it running smoothly and efficiently).

> Use a breaker attachment on an excavating machine to break concrete rather than using a handheld breaker.

Whole-body vibration

Whole-body vibration (WBV), as its name suggests, is vibration or jolting of the whole body through the surface that is supporting the body (such as a machine seat or floor).

WBV, which often results from driving or operating some types of construction plant or vehicles, has the potential to cause back injury or make an existing back condition more painful.

Back pain can be caused by many work and non-work activities. It can lead to time off work, loss of productivity and compensation claims. Mobile machine operators and drivers (especially those who work off-road) are at increased risk from back pain.

There are things that you can do to help your employees avoid the problem, but you cannot prevent all back pain, so early reporting of symptoms, proper treatment and suitable rehabilitation is essential.

Most exposure to WBV at work is unlikely on its own to cause back pain. It may pose a risk when there is unusually high vibration or jolting, or the vibration is uncomfortable for a long time on most working days. In such situations, the risk from vibration is related to the overall time the operator or driver is exposed to the vibration and the number of shocks and jolts they experience each day.

Among those most likely to experience high vibration exposures are regular operators and drivers of off-road machinery, such as:

☑ construction, mining and quarrying machines and vehicles, particularly earthmoving machines (such as scrapers, bulldozers and building site dumpers)

☑ tractors and other agricultural and forestry machinery, particularly when used in transportation, tedding (turning hay), primary cultivation and mowing.

14.4 Tools likely to cause harmful levels of vibration

Many tools are obtained through hire companies who use a traffic light system for vibration risks. Whilst rudimentary, these are a good starting point in selection of equipment and give an appreciation of what type of equipment is low, medium and high risk. Hire companies also hire out vibration monitoring equipment which is attached to the tool and data collected at the end of the day.

Based on manufacturers' data the colour coding implies that 'green' tools do not pose a significant hand-arm vibration risk – whereas many tools would be classified as 'amber' or 'red' if categorised according to field vibration data.

14

Hand-arm vibration

Tools and plant used in the construction industry that could cause exposure to risks from hand-arm vibration include:

- road and concrete breaking drills
- concrete pokers
- plate vibrators/wacker plates
- demolition picks
- compressor guns
- pneumatic drills
- angle grinders
- percussive (hammer) drills
- sanders, and similar reciprocating tools
- cut-off saws/disc-cutters
- power hammers and chisels, including Kango hammers
- needle guns/scabblers
- chainsaws
- strimmers
- woodworking machinery.

This is irrespective of the tools' power source. Other equipment that may occasionally be used and that is a source of vibration includes rotavators, lawnmowers, brush-cutters and leaf blowers.

Whole-body vibration

Tools and plant used in the construction industry that could cause exposure to risks from WBV include:

- rough-terrain forklift trucks and telehandlers
- vibratory rollers
- mobile crushers
- dumper trucks and other forms of earth-moving machinery
- delivery vehicles if required to travel on rough terrain.

14.5 Managing vibration

Vibration risk assessment in practice

A general risk assessment can be briefly defined as a systematic examination of a work process, carried out by a competent person on behalf of an employer.

A vibration risk assessment follows the same principle, but with the emphasis solely on vibration and its potential to cause ill health in employees.

The principle of risk assessment is not new. In fact, it is quite likely that many employers have been carrying out risk assessments, including vibration risk assessments, during the day-to-day course of their business activities, possibly without thinking of the process in terms of a risk assessment.

 To cut large holes in brickwork, use a diamond-tipped hole-cutting drill bit with a rotary action rather than a tungsten-tipped hole bit, which requires rotary and hammer action.

14

Changing the process

Mechanisation removes the risk. Machine-mounted pick replaces hand-operated breakers.

Identify at-risk persons

A survey of what work activities are carried out, using what tools and equipment, and by whom, will establish who is at risk. If there is any doubt as to whether a particular job has the potential to cause vibration-induced health problems or injury, it is better to assume that it has, initially at least.

Having established who could be at risk it is necessary to examine work activities in detail to determine which work activities are of genuine concern. As outlined in the summary of the Control of Vibration at Work Regulations, only when all other investigative methods have been exhausted should it be necessary to carry out vibration measurements.

There are many sources of information available to employers, such as:

 the users of vibrating tools themselves; they are the ones who may have experienced the early symptoms of HAVS

 free online vibration measurement databases, which are based on the actual vibration measurements achieved during the testing of hundreds of tools of different types in different conditions

 the HSE's vibration management publications

 tool manufacturers' published vibration data, although this should be treated with caution as it can be based upon laboratory testing rather than field trials, and usually underestimates exposures under real work conditions.

> **www.** The HSE's web-based vibration calculators are accessible through their website.

In construction, it is likely that those exposed to WBV will exceed the **exposure action value** if they operate machines for several hours per day. The **exposure limit value** should only be exceeded if the machine is operated very aggressively or with non-approved attachments.

For HAV, the guidance from the HSE is that an employee is probably at risk from HAVS if they are using:

 hammer action equipment for more than 15 minutes each day

 rotary equipment for more than one hour each day.

Employees who fall into these categories, as well as other at-risk employees, should be asked to complete a short health surveillance questionnaire (refer to Appendix A).

> ✋ An important factor in establishing who is at risk is the actual time that someone is using a vibrating tool, commonly referred to as the 'trigger time'. This is the actual time the tool is operating, not the time holding the tool. When asked, it is usual for users to overestimate the length of time that they actually use the equipment. Their response may be 'I use the equipment all day' when in fact what they mean is that they use it on-and-off all day with, for example, a total 'trigger time' of less than 60 minutes per day.

The elimination or control of exposure to vibration in the workplace

On the basis of the general principles and hierarchy of control measures, employers must ensure that employees' exposure to vibration is either eliminated or reduced so far as is reasonably practicable.

Where it cannot be eliminated the employer must introduce a programme of organisational and technical measures (control measures) consistent with their risk assessment.

This must include consideration of:

- [x] alternative methods of carrying out the work that eliminate or reduce employees' exposure to vibration (for example, stripping off surface coatings by chemical treatment rather than power-sanding)

- [x] choice of work equipment that, because of its design or features, or the nature of the work to be done, produces the least possible vibration

- [x] the provision of ancillary equipment that reduces the risk of injury being caused by vibration (for example, manufacturer approved vibration absorbent handles for hand-held equipment)

- [x] proper maintenance arrangements for the work equipment, workplace and workplace systems (for example, maintaining ground surfaces over which vehicles regularly travel)

- [x] the design and layout of workplaces, workstations and rest facilities

- [x] suitable and sufficient information and training for employees so that they may use the equipment safely and correctly in order to minimise their exposure to vibration (such as training mobile machine operators how to correctly adjust their seats and the benefits of driving less aggressively)

- [x] limitation of the duration and intensity of the vibration (for example, by job rotation)

- [x] appropriate work schedules with adequate rest periods

- [x] the provision of clothing to protect employees from cold and damp

- [x] arranging for operatives to stay warm by providing heating for the workplace where needed and possible, together with suitable clothing and gloves

- [x] ensuring that any new tools have vibration control measures built in

- [x] by adopting a buy smooth/hire smooth policy, in which a commitment is made to choose tools that incorporate low vibration technology

- [x] the reduction of vibration transmission in the path between the source and the handles or other surfaces gripped by operatives' hands

- [x] the minimisation of the amount of force required to apply and control the tools, and keeping them in good order.

The HSE has developed a points system that allows for quick estimates of the hand-arm vibration exposure for a worker. Each process is assigned a number of points per hour. Adding the points from each process carried out (calculated by multiplying the points per hour by the number of hours' use) provides an estimate of the total exposure.

- [x] For HAV the **exposure action value** corresponds to 100 points and the **exposure limit value** corresponds to 400 points.

- [x] For WBV the **exposure action value** corresponds to 100 points and the **exposure limit value** corresponds to 529 points.

- [x] Points from HAV and WBV should not be combined. Exposure times are actual trigger times, and not the time holding the tool or carrying out the task.

 Further guidance on estimating exposure is contained in Appendix D.

A further benefit gained as a result of controlling vibration can be a reduction in noise levels; in some circumstances reducing noise will also reduce vibration, hence many noise control techniques also involve techniques for controlling vibration.

 HSE's information on practical ways to avoid/reduce use of vibrating equipment can be found on its website.

Information and training for employees

If the risk assessment shows that there is a risk to the health of employees because of vibration, or they are exposed to vibration in excess of the exposure action value, then the employer must give employees and their representatives information, instruction and training on:

- [x] how the employer is managing vibration in the workplace

- [x] the exposure limit values and exposure action values

- [x] the significant findings of the risk assessments, including details of any measurements taken

- [x] what employees should look for in themselves as regards HAVS, VWF and low-back pain and how they should inform their employer

- [x] the entitlement to health surveillance

- [x] the safe working practices in place to minimise employees' exposure to vibration

- [x] the collective (as opposed to individual) results of any health surveillance undertaken.

14

Vibration reduced breaker:

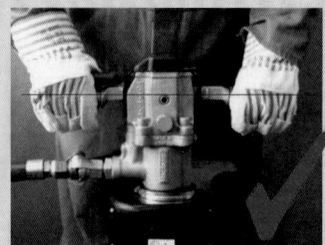

☑ keep the moil point sharp

☑ break a little at a time, don't get jammed

☑ don't force anti-vibration handles

☑ stop breaker before pulling out.

Work equipment

Selection of tools and equipment

All equipment that is liable to vibrate, and that is manufactured for use as work equipment, should be designed to have low vibration operating characteristics.

Manufacturers are required to provide information on all aspects of their equipment, including details of any vibration that may be expected. In particular, suppliers must provide information on vibration levels if the tool or machine is likely to subject workers to levels of vibration exceeding the exposure action value of 2.5 metres per second squared.

The Supply of Machinery (Safety) Regulations require that suppliers provide purchasers with information on the amount of vibration generated by an item of equipment during normal expected use, so that an informed judgement may be made when purchasers are selecting tools and machinery.

However, as some manufacturers may base their vibration figures on laboratory simulation rather than field trials, the figures quoted may be unrealistically low. In many cases information is also available from independent real or simulated work measurements.

Vibration emission is one of many important factors to consider when selecting a tool. For example, a very heavy tool might not emit much vibration but could cause manual handling risk. Similarly, some tools might emit less vibration than others but be relatively inefficient, resulting in increased exposure times, higher grip and push forces. Always select the right tool for the job.

Regular maintenance of tools

Correctly installed and smooth running machines will, in time, vibrate as the machinery parts become worn.

The parts of machinery and vehicles that contribute to vibration are:

☑ worn bearings

☑ dirty fan blades (unbalanced fans)

☑ worn mountings or worn anti-vibration pads

☑ misaligned shafts

☑ unbalanced rotating parts

☑ loose bolts

☑ damaged gear teeth

☑ blunt cutting tools and blades

☑ worn suspension components

☑ incorrect tyre pressures

☑ damaged seats

☑ damaged tyres/tracks.

The lack of correct maintenance and lubrication will produce increased vibration magnitudes. Machines should, therefore, be maintained at regular intervals and any detected faults rectified as soon as possible, thus reducing the risk of vibration problems. Cutting tools or blades should be kept sharp by maintenance or replacement, as appropriate.

Measuring vibration

The measurement of vibration is usually carried out by specialist companies, although some larger construction companies have bought their own vibration measuring equipment and trained their staff to carry out in-house vibration measurements. There is an obligation to physically monitor the use of plant per operative (for example, use the breaker for five minutes then rest for 45 minutes), a chart should be completed and signed by a supervisor to record that monitoring has taken place. The legislation specifies two levels of vibration that require employers to take action:

exposure action value is a level of vibration that if reached, as determined by vibration measurements, requires that employers put in place control measures to manage the exposure of employees

 exposure limit value is a measure of vibration, again determined by measuring vibration, above which employees may not be exposed and therefore the activity must stop.

> Where a heavy grinder is used at a permanent workstation to do repetitive work, suspend it from a counterbalance system to reduce the load on the operator's arms and the tightness of grip needed.

14.6 Health issues

Health surveillance

If the findings of the risk assessment, feedback from employees or other sources of information show that there is a risk to the health of employees because of their use of vibrating tools, or that employees are exposed to vibration in excess of the exposure action value, then the employer must ensure that the employees are under suitable medical surveillance where it is appropriate.

The HSE recommends a five-stage system of health surveillance for HAV.

1. An initial questionnaire to be answered when employees first move into any job that involves exposure to vibration (see Appendix A).

2. A short questionnaire answered annually by employees exposed to vibration (see Appendix B).

3. A formal HAVS health assessment carried out by a qualified person (for example, an occupational health nurse).

4. A formal diagnosis made by a doctor who is qualified in occupational health, and who will assess fitness for work.

5. (Optional) if considered necessary, the doctor refers the employee for certain tests for HAVS to assist the doctor in making the judgements required in Stage 4.

> HSE's five steps to manage health risk can be found on its website.

Employers who consider that their employees are at a potential risk from HAVS should appoint a person to manage the health surveillance programme and be actively involved in the initial stages.

This person:

 does not need to be medically qualified

 should not attempt diagnosis or be judgemental as to the causes of HAVS with regard to individual cases

 should receive training from an occupational health professional

 must be able to describe the symptoms of HAVS.

The person should have experience of the working environment, be able to gain the trust and co-operation of employees, and understand the importance of confidentiality.

The HSE recommends that employees who are known to be at risk of HAVS but report no symptoms for three consecutive years on their annual questionnaire (Stage 2), should be referred to an occupational health nurse for an independent view of symptoms that may have been overlooked by the individual.

For WBV, detailed health surveillance is not possible, as there are many non-vibration causes of back pain. Therefore, the HSE recommends health monitoring, which is a structured system for self-reporting of symptoms. An example of a health monitoring questionnaire is given in Appendix C.

Keeping records

Health surveillance records should be stored in-house, in a way that retains their confidentiality, possibly under the control of the person nominated to manage the health surveillance system.

Employers should create a health record for each individual who is exposed to vibration and keep them for at least as long as they are under health surveillance, and possibly longer.

Health records should be kept up-to-date and should include full details of the employee's exposure to vibration and any questionnaires that have been completed.

The records can be kept in any form providing it is possible to produce a copy if required by the enforcing authority, usually the HSE.

It is considered to be good practice if employees are offered a copy of their health records when they leave their employer.

14

Work patterns

One of the most simple but also one of the most effective ways of minimising risks arising from vibration is by reducing the time when operatives are actually exposed to vibration.

If the use of a vibrating tool is shared between a team of employees, as opposed to it only being used by one person, the tool may be kept in productive use for the day.

Moving any employees not operating the tools at that time onto other areas of work will considerably lessen the effects of vibration on users, by splitting and rotating the work. This will also assist the maintenance of blood circulation, thus lessening the chances of injury or ill health being caused to users by the vibrating tool.

 Organise employees to work in teams where they switch tasks within the team to avoid individuals having unnecessarily high exposure to vibration.

Maintaining blood circulation

Keeping the hands and body warm is essential to help maintain good blood flow to the fingers and reduce the risk of injury due to HAV. Specific measures might include:

- ☑ wearing gloves
- ☑ using proprietary heating pads for the hands
- ☑ using tools with heated handles
- ☑ avoiding tools that have pneumatic exhausts that discharge towards the hands
- ☑ allowing operatives to warm up before starting work, and helping them to stay warm
- ☑ wearing warm, weatherproof clothing in cold, wet areas
- ☑ massaging and exercising fingers during work breaks.

Personal protective equipment

Some retro-fit products are available that are designed to protect operators from vibration. Only those approved by the machine manufacturers should be used.

The wearing of anti-vibration gloves is not recommended. Problems with anti-vibration gloves include:

- ☑ reduced flexibility at the hands resulting in higher grip and push forces and loss of precise tool control
- ☑ the possibility of gloves amplifying the tool vibration in some cases (these cases are very difficult to predict)
- ☑ some anti-vibration gloves only cut out the high frequency levels of vibration, which aren't harmful
- ☑ anti-vibration gloves are only tested in one direction and vibration occurs in three directions
- ☑ field trials of gloves have shown that the vibration isolation materials are not always durable.

However, if anti-vibration gloves are to be tried, it is essential that they carry the CE-mark and are selected by a competent person. One benefit from gloves is that they keep the hands warm and offer other protection.

Therefore, if an employer intends to provide items of PPE as part of their strategy to reduce the risks from vibration, it is important to understand that PPE will not fully protect the worker. The aim of specifying gloves should be to keep the operator's hands warm and not to expect gloves to reduce exposure to vibration.

All PPE produced or imported by reputable companies is manufactured to British and European Standards. As with all PPE for use at work, gloves or anti-vibration protection should be selected by a competent person who can ensure, in discussion with the supplier, that they meet the appropriate standards. Most leading manufacturers and suppliers will offer advice on the selection of different types of gloves and other PPE.

Ear defenders should be worn to lessen the effects of the noise created by vibrating tools, and eye protection should be worn to avoid the risks from dust or flying particles.

Compensation and civil claims

Cases are now regularly reaching the civil courts in which employees are pursuing claims for compensation after having reportedly developed HAVS, VWF or similar conditions from the use of plant and equipment that generated vibration.

Complying with the Control of Vibration at Work Regulations, following the guidance on the regulations and implementing an occupational health programme that monitors and manages employees' exposure to vibration will help to reduce the number of employees suffering from symptoms, and thus help reduce such court cases and their potential costs to an employer, as well as perhaps having some influence on the level of future insurance premiums.

It should be noted that records of compliance need to be kept.

14

14.7 Legislative requirements

The Control of Vibration at Work Regulations

These regulations implement the requirements of the European Directive regarding the exposure of employees to vibration. They impose duties on employers to protect employees (and others) who may be exposed to risk of ill health because of vibration at work.

The main requirements of these regulations reflect earlier HSE guidance and for the most part support existing good practice within the construction industry.

The vibration regulations are, in places, very technical, particularly in relation to the measurement of vibration. It is anticipated that the services of a qualified technician or occupational health professional may be needed in those sectors of the industry where the measurement of vibration is a significant issue.

The regulations place legal duties on employers and employees with regard to the control and management of employees' exposure to vibration.

Definitions

The regulations give a number of definitions, knowledge of which will help readers better understand the requirements of the regulations.

- ☑ **Hand-arm vibration (HAV)** means mechanical vibration that is transmitted into the hands and arms by a work activity.
- ☑ **Whole-body vibration (WBV)** means mechanical vibration that is transmitted into the body through the supporting surface when a person is seated or standing during a work activity.
- ☑ **Mechanical vibration** means vibration occurring in a piece of machinery, equipment or vehicle as a result of its operation.
- ☑ **Daily exposure** means the extent of the mechanical vibration to which a worker is exposed during a working day, which takes account of both the magnitude and duration of the vibration.
- ☑ **Exposure action value (EAV)** means the level of daily exposure that, if exceeded, requires specific action to be taken to reduce the risk.
- ☑ **Exposure limit value (ELV)** means the level of daily exposure for any worker that must not be exceeded.
- ☑ **Working day** means a daily working period, irrespective of the time of day, when it begins or ends, or whether it begins or ends on the same day.
- ☑ **Health surveillance** means an assessment of the state of health of an employee as related to their exposure to vibration.

Exposure limit and action values

For hand-arm vibration:

- ☑ the **daily exposure action value** is 2.5 metres per second squared (2.5 m/s^2 A(8))
- ☑ the **daily exposure limit value** is 5 metres per second squared (5 m/s^2 A(8)).

For whole-body vibration:

- ☑ the **daily exposure action value** is 0.5 metres per second squared (0.5 m/s^2 A(8))
- ☑ the **daily exposure limit value** is 1.15 metres per second squared (1.15 m/s^2 A(8)).

> The 'A (8)' notation after each value indicates that the measurement of exposure to vibration is 'time weighted' over an eight hour period.

Duties of employers

> Further information on duties of employers can be found in the flowchart in Section G *Checklists and forms*.

Employers' duties to non-employees

Where these regulations place a duty on employers with respect to the health and safety of employees, the employer shall, so far as is reasonably practicable, also be under a similar duty to **anyone else, whether at work or not,** who may be affected by the vibration created by the employer's work activities, except for the provision of:

- ☑ health surveillance
- ☑ information, instruction and training (unless the non-employees are at the same place of work as where the noise is being created).

Vibration

Employers' duties to employees

If employees are likely to be exposed to risks from vibration in the course of their work the employer must:

☑ carry out an assessment of the risks to the health and safety of the employees exposed to vibration. The risk assessment must identify the measures that need to be taken to meet the requirements of these regulations

☑ as part of the risk assessment, assess the daily exposure of employees to vibration by:
  – observing work practices
  – referring to information on the probable level of vibration corresponding to the equipment used in those particular conditions
  – if necessary, arranging for vibration levels to be measured

☑ assess whether any employee is likely to be exposed to vibration at or above the **exposure action value** or the **exposure limit value.**

The risk assessment must include consideration of:

☑ the magnitude, type and duration of exposure to vibration, including intermittent vibration and repeated shocks

☑ the effects that the vibration might have on employees whose health is particularly at risk from exposure

☑ any effects that vibration might have with regard to work equipment, such as the:
  – proper handling of controls
  – reading of indicators
  – stability of structures
  – security of joints

☑ any information provided by the manufacturers of the equipment that creates the vibration

☑ the availability of alternative equipment that is designed to reduce exposure to vibration

☑ exposure of employees to WBV when not actually working (such as in rest areas and canteens)

☑ specific working conditions (such as working in low temperatures)

☑ the availability of appropriate information obtained from health surveillance including, where possible, published information (such as various HSE publications).

The employer must regularly review the risk assessment if:

☑ there is reason to believe that it is no longer valid

☑ there has been a significant change in the work to which the assessment applies and immediately implement changes to the risk assessment as identified by the review process.

The employer must record:

☑ the significant findings of the risk assessment as soon as is practicable after the risk assessment has been carried out or changed

☑ the measures taken to eliminate or control exposure to vibration

☑ the measures taken to provide information, instruction and training for at-risk employees.

The employer must:

☑ ensure that exposure to vibration is eliminated at source or reduce it to the lowest level that is reasonably practicable

☑ where exposure is likely to be at or above the exposure action value, reduce exposure to vibration to as low a level as is reasonably practicable, by implementing organisational and technical measures that are appropriate to the work activity being carried out

☑ ensure that the actions taken to comply with the above two requirements are based upon the principles of prevention set out in the Management of Health and Safety at Work Regulations and must include consideration of:
  – alternative work methods that eliminate or reduce exposure to vibration
  – alternative work equipment or an appropriate ergonomic design which, taking account of the work to be done, produces the least vibration
  – the design and layout of the workplace, including any rest facilities
  – the provision of extra equipment that has the effect of reducing injuries caused by exposure to vibration
  – the effective maintenance programmes for equipment that can create vibration, the workplace itself and workplace systems
  – the provision of information and training for at-risk employees, such that they are aware of how to use work equipment correctly and safely in order to minimise exposure
  – limiting the duration and intensity of exposure to vibration
  – adjusting work schedules and ensuring adequate rest periods
  – the provision of work clothing to protect at-risk employees from cold and damp.

The employer must ensure that employees are not exposed to vibration above the exposure limit value or, if they are, immediately:

- ☑ reduce exposure to below the exposure limit value
- ☑ identify the reasons for the exposure limit value being exceeded
- ☑ take appropriate actions to prevent it occurring again.

These points do not apply where the exposure of an employee to vibration is usually below the exposure action value but varies markedly from time to time and may **occasionally** exceed the exposure limit value, provided that:

- ☑ the exposure to vibration averaged over one week is less than the exposure limit value
- ☑ there is evidence to show that the risk from the actual pattern of exposure is less than the corresponding risk from constant exposure to the exposure limit value
- ☑ the risk from exposure is reduced to as low a level as is reasonably practicable
- ☑ the employees concerned are subject to increased health surveillance, where appropriate.

Any measures taken to comply with this regulation must be adapted where necessary to take account of any employee(s) who is particularly at risk from exposure to vibration.

If the risk assessment indicates that:

- ☑ there is a risk to the health of employees who are exposed to vibration
- ☑ those employees are likely to be exposed to vibration at or above the exposure action value

the employer must ensure that those employees are placed under suitable health surveillance, where appropriate.

The health surveillance will be appropriate if:

- ☑ a link can be established between exposure to vibration and an identifiable disease or any other adverse effect on health
- ☑ it is probable that the disease or other effect on health may occur under particular working conditions
- ☑ there are valid ways of detecting the disease or other effect on health.

The employer must:

- ☑ ensure that a record is kept and maintained for each employee who undergoes health surveillance and that records are readily available in a suitable form
- ☑ allow employees to see their health surveillance records upon being given reasonable notice
- ☑ provide copies of the records to the enforcing authority (usually the HSE) upon request.

Where, as a result of health surveillance, an employee is found to have an identifiable disease or other adverse effect on health, which is considered by a doctor or other occupational health professional to be the result of exposure to vibration, the employer must:

- ☑ ensure that the employee is informed by a suitably qualified person, including advice regarding a need for further health surveillance
- ☑ ensure that the employee is informed of any significant findings of the health surveillance, allowing for medical confidentiality
- ☑ review the risk assessment
- ☑ review existing control measures, taking into account any advice given by a doctor, occupational health professional or enforcing authority
- ☑ consider reassigning the employee to other work where there is no risk from further exposure, taking into account any advice given as above
- ☑ ensure that the health of any other employee(s) who has been similarly exposed is reviewed, including the provision of a medical examination where recommended by a doctor, occupational health professional or the enforcing authority.

Where the risk assessment shows a risk to the health of employees who are (or are liable to be) exposed to vibration at or above the exposure action value, the employer must provide the employees and their representatives with suitable and sufficient information, instruction and training, which must include:

- ☑ the organisational and technical measures taken to eliminate or control exposure to vibration
- ☑ the exposure limit value and the action values
- ☑ the significant findings of the risk assessment, including details of any measurements taken, with an explanation of the findings
- ☑ why and how to detect and report signs of injury resulting from exposure to vibration
- ☑ the employees' entitlement to health surveillance
- ☑ how to work safely to minimise exposure to vibration
- ☑ the collective results of any health surveillance carried out. These must be anonymous so as not to reveal the personal health record of any individual.

The information, instruction and training provided as above must be updated by the employer to take account of any significant changes in the type of work carried out or method of working.

The employer must ensure that any person, whether an employee or not, who has been given the responsibility to ensure that the employer's duties are carried out (for example a site manager or project manager) receives suitable and sufficient information, instruction and training to enable compliance with the regulations.

Duties of employees

Under these regulations, employees have a legal duty to make themselves available for health surveillance checks (during working hours) as required by the employer, the health surveillance being at the employer's expense.

Appendix A – Initial hand-arm vibration screening questionnaire

Medical in confidence – when completed

Initial screening questionnaire for workers using hand-held vibrating tools, hand-guided vibrating machines and hand-fed vibrating machines.

Date				
Employee name				
Occupation				
Address				
Date of birth				
National insurance number				
Employer name				
Have you ever used hand-held vibrating tools, machines or hand-fed processes in your job?	Yes		No	
If YES:				
a) list year of first exposure				
b) when was the last time you used them? (detail work history overleaf)				
1 Do you have any tingling of the fingers lasting more than 20 minutes after using vibration equipment?	Yes		No	
2 Do you have tingling of the fingers at any other time?	Yes		No	
3 Do you wake at night with pain, tingling, or numbness in your hand or wrist?	Yes		No	
4 Do one or more of your fingers go numb more than 20 minutes after using vibration equipment?	Yes		No	
5 Have your fingers gone white* on cold exposure?	Yes		No	
6 If YES to 5, do you have difficulty re-warming them when leaving the cold?	Yes		No	
7 Do your fingers go white at any other time?	Yes		No	
8 Are you experiencing any other problems with the muscles or joints of the hands or arms?	Yes		No	
9 Do you have difficulty picking up very small objects (for example screws or buttons) or opening tight jars?	Yes		No	
10 Have you ever had a neck, arm or hand injury or operation?	Yes		No	
If so, give details				
11 Have you ever had any serious diseases of joints, skin, nerves, heart or blood vessels?	Yes		No	
If so, give details				
12 Are you on any long-term medication?	Yes		No	
If so, give details				
* Whiteness means a clear discoloration of the fingers with a sharp edge, usually followed by a red flush.				

14

Occupational history

Dates   Job title

....

....

....

....

....

....

....

....

I certify that all the answers given above are true to the best of my knowledge and belief.

Signed: .... Date: ....

Return in confidence to:

(Reproduced from the Health and Safety Executive publication Hand-arm vibration (L140) under licence from The Controller of Her Majesty's Stationery Office.)

Appendix B – Annual hand-arm vibration questionnaire for health surveillance

Screening questionnaire for workers using hand-held vibrating tools, hand-guided vibrating machines and hand-fed vibrating machines.

Date	
Employee name	
Occupation	
Address	
Date of birth	
National insurance number	
Employer name	
Date of previous screening	

Have you been using hand-held vibrating tools, machines or hand-fed processes in your job, or if this is a review, since your last assessment? (Detail work history overleaf)	Yes		No	

If NO or more than two years since last exposure, please return the form – there is no need to answer any further questions.

If YES:

1	Do you have any numbness or tingling of the fingers lasting more than 20 minutes after using vibrating equipment?	Yes		No	
2	Do you have numbness or tingling of the fingers at any other time?	Yes		No	
3	Do you wake at night with pain, tingling or numbness in your hand or wrist?	Yes		No	
4	Have any of your fingers gone white* on cold exposure?	Yes		No	
5	Have you noticed any change in your response to your tolerance of working outdoors in the cold?	Yes		No	
6	Are you experiencing any other problems in your hands or arms?	Yes		No	
7	Do you have difficulty in picking up very small objects (for example, screws or buttons) or opening tight jars?	Yes		No	
8	Has anything changed about your health since the last assessment?	Yes		No	

* Whiteness means a clear discoloration of the fingers with a sharp edge, usually followed by a red flush.

I certify that all the answers given above are true to the best of my knowledge and belief.

Signed: .... Date: ....

Return to:

Hand-arm vibration syndrome (HAVS):

☑ is a disorder which affects the blood vessels, nerves, muscles and joints of the hand, wrist and arm

☑ can become severely disabling if ignored; and

☑ its best known form is vibration white finger (VWF), which can be triggered by cold or wet weather and can cause severe pain in the affected fingers.

Signs to look out for in hand-arm vibration syndrome:

☑ tingling and numbness in the fingers

☑ in the cold and wet, fingers go white, then blue, then red and are painful

☑ you can't feel things with your fingers

☑ pain, tingling or numbness in your hands, wrists and arms

☑ loss of strength in hands.

Occupational history

Dates	Job title

(Reproduced from the Health and Safety Executive publication Hand-arm vibration (L140) under licence from The Controller of Her Majesty's Stationery Office.)

Appendix C – Sample health monitoring questionnaire

Date of assessment				
Employee number/Payroll number				
Name				
Date of birth				
Job title				
Any change in duties since last questionnaire?	Yes		No	

Recent experience

Is there **currently** any movement or activity that causes you pain in your back?	Yes		No	
Have you suffered any back/neck/shoulder pain **in the last 12 months?**	Yes		No	

Please describe the severity of the pain experienced:

No pain										Pain as bad as it could be
0	1	2	3	4	5	6	7	8	9	10

Note: If severity above 5 is indicated, refer on for further advice. However if rank less than 5, but for three consecutive assessments, then refer for further advice.*

Have you had to take any medication to deal with the pain experienced?	Yes		No	
Have you had to seek medical advice regarding this pain?	Yes		No	
Has this back/neck/shoulder pain resulted in time off work?	Yes		No	
Have you had any accidents or injury to your back in the last two years?	Yes		No	

Action/advice

Referral for further advice?	
Other advice provided?	

* Further advice should be sought from an occupational health professional or GP in these cases.

(Reproduced from the Health and Safety Executive publication Whole-body vibration (L141) under licence from The Controller of Her Majesty's Stationery Office.)

Appendix D – Estimating exposure to hand-arm vibration

You may be able to get suitable vibration data from the equipment handbook, or from the equipment supplier. See Table 1 for examples of vibration levels HSE has measured on equipment in use. There are also some databases on the internet that may have suitable vibration data.

If you plan to use the manufacturer's vibration data you should check that it represents the way you use the equipment (see 'Duties of manufacturers and suppliers') since some data may underestimate workplace vibration levels substantially. Ask the manufacturer for an indication of the likely vibration emission of the tool when your employees are using it. If you are able to get vibration data from the manufacturer that is reasonably representative of the way you use the equipment, it should be suitable for you to use in estimating your employees' exposure. **However, if the only information available to you is the vibration emission declared in the equipment's handbook, it may be safer to double this figure before using it for estimating daily exposures.****

You also need to check, by observing them, how long employees are actually exposed to the vibration (that is the total daily trigger time with the equipment operating and in contact with the employee's hand(s)). Employees are unlikely to be able to provide this information very accurately themselves. You could observe and measure the trigger time over, for example, half an hour and then use the result to estimate the trigger time for the full shift. Alternatively, where the work task is repetitive, for example drilling large numbers of holes in masonry, you could measure the trigger time when drilling several holes and multiply the average by the number of holes typically drilled in a shift.

** This sentence does not apply to new machinery manufactured after December 2009 due to the introduction of new standard tests as required by the Supply of Machinery (Safety) Regulations.

Table 1 Some typical vibration levels for common tools

Tool type	Lowest	Typical	Highest
Road breakers.	5 m/s^2	12 m/s^2	20 m/s^2
Demolition hammers.	8 m/s^2	15 m/s^2	25 m/s^2
Hammer drills/combi hammers.	6 m/s^2	9 m/s^2	25 m/s^2
Needle scalers.	5 m/s^2	–	18 m/s^2
Scabblers (hammer type).	–	–	40 m/s^2
Angle grinders.	4 m/s^2	–	8 m/s^2
Clay spades/jigger picks.	–	16 m/s^2	–
Chipping hammers (metal).	–	18 m/s^2	–
Stone-working hammers.	10 m/s^2	–	30 m/s^2
Chainsaws.	–	6 m/s^2	–
Brushcutters.	2 m/s^2	4 m/s^2	–
Sanders (random orbital).	–	7–10 m/s^2	–

If the employee is exposed to vibration from more than one tool or work process during a typical day, you will need to collect information on likely vibration level and trigger time for each one.

 Once you have collected relevant vibration data and exposure times you will need to use an exposure calculator to assess each employee's daily exposure (see the HSE's vibration web pages).

Alternatively, you can use the simple exposure points system in Table 2 to estimate the daily exposure.

Workplace vibration measurements

If you want to obtain vibration measurements for your own tools you will need to arrange for a competent person to carry out measurements for you using specialised equipment. Measurement results can be highly variable, depending on many factors, including the operator's technique, the condition of the work equipment, the material being processed and the measurement method. The competence and experience of the person who makes the measurements is important so that they can recognise and take account of these uncertainties in producing representative vibration data.

Table 2 Simple exposure point system

Tool vibration (m/s²)	3	4	5	6	7	10	12	15
Points per hour (approximate)	20	30	50	70	100	200	300	450

Multiply the points assigned to the tool vibration by the number of hours of daily trigger time for the tool(s) and then compare the total with the exposure action value (EAV) and exposure limit value (ELV) points.

100 points per day = exposure action value (EAV)

400 points per day = exposure limit value (ELV).

(The above text is an extract from the HSE's free leaflet Control the risks from hand-arm vibration (INDG175 rev2), which is reproduced under licence from the Controller of Her Majesty's Stationery Office.)

 Further advice on estimating and managing exposure to hand-arm vibration can be found on the HSE's website.

15

Manual handling

All construction and building work involves lifting and handling to some extent. Although mechanical equipment should be used whenever practicable, much of the work will inevitably continue to be done manually.

The risk of injury can be greatly reduced by a knowledge and application of correct lifting and handling techniques and by taking a few elementary precautions.

Introduction	216
Key points	216
Common injuries	216
The manual handling assessment	217
Lifting and handling	218
Legal duties	222

15.1 Introduction

More than a quarter of all reported accidents each year result from poor manual handling techniques. Many cause absence from work, and in the worst cases, permanent disability and physical impairment.

Giving employees the appropriate training in the correct manual handling techniques and the use of mechanical lifting aids is highly cost effective.

Adequate supervision is necessary to ensure that employees then use the proper equipment and techniques and do not take shortcuts. This will reduce accidents, the amount of time lost on site, and the disruption to work that is caused when something goes wrong.

The part of the body most vulnerable if bad manual handling techniques are used is the back, particularly the lower back. Once it has been damaged, it is usually weakened for the rest of a person's life.

All the other major joints and muscle groups can also be easily damaged if the correct manual handling techniques are not used.

The consequences of an injury due to bad manual handling, or a musculoskeletal injury or illness as they are often called, can be a long-term or permanent inability to work. The cost to the employer is reduced productivity and having to find others to carry out the work.

15.2 Key points

- ☑ Poorly thought out or badly performed manual handling activities are the cause of many injuries to construction workers.
- ☑ Manual handling includes lifting, lowering, pulling, pushing or carrying a load by physical effort.
- ☑ Several factors will determine whether it is safe for an individual to manually handle a load.
- ☑ Employers must:
  - avoid, so far as reasonably practicable, their employees having to carry out manual handling activities likely to result in an injury
  - where that is not reasonably practicable, assess the risks to the employee
  - put in place control measures to prevent such an injury occurring.
- ☑ Employees must:
  - make full and proper use of the employer's safe system of work
  - use (lifting) equipment and machinery in accordance with instruction and training given
  - report to the employer any situation where it is considered the system of working is not safe.
- ☑ Where sustaining an injury is a possibility and handling a load cannot be avoided, using a mechanical means of carrying out the activity is the best solution.
- ☑ The HSE has developed two online assessment tools to assist employers:
  - a manual handling assessment chart (MAC), to help assessors carry out general manual handing assessments
  - an assessment of repetitive tasks tool (ART) to assist where employees have to carry out rapid repetitive tasks.

15.3 Common injuries

Injuries resulting from unsafe or incorrect manual handling can affect the:

- ☑ whole body
- ☑ back
- ☑ shoulders
- ☑ arms
- ☑ hands
- ☑ feet and toes.

Back injuries are the most common, but hernias, ruptures, sprains and strains are all conditions that can result from poor manual handling techniques.

Legislation requires that adequate and appropriate protective clothing and equipment be provided by the employer and worn by the employee. Gloves, footwear, hard hats and overalls all play an important part in reducing the type and severity of accidents arising from manual handling.

There are conflicting views on the benefits of wearing a back-support belt. Some authoritative bodies believe that wearing one may render some people more likely to suffer an injury. There is no evidence to support the theory that they reduce manual handling injury rates. There may be some benefit derived from the fact that wearing a back support will keep the lower-back muscles warm.

The cost of physical injury can be very high for the employer through:

- ☑ lost production and raised costs
- ☑ legal liabilities leading to possible prosecution.

And, for the employee, through:

- ☑ pain and suffering permanent disability, leading to lost wages.

Anyone who believes that they have suffered a manual handling injury, particularly a back injury, should be encouraged to seek prompt medical advice.

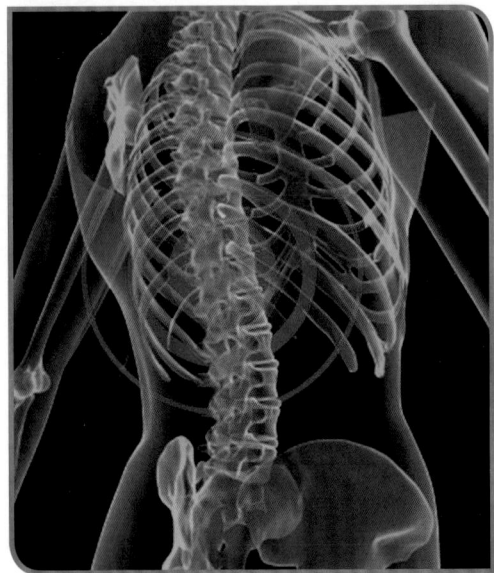

Musculoskeletal disorders (MSD) covers any injury, damage or disorder of the joints or other tissues in the upper limbs or the back, neck and shoulders; less often they affect the lower limbs. Health problems range from discomfort, minor aches and pains, to more serious medical conditions.

Strains and sprains to muscles and joints, torn ligaments and tendons, disc trouble and hernias. These are often caused by sudden and awkward movements (for example, twisting or jerking while lifting, or handling heavy loads). They are also caused by persons attempting to lift loads beyond their physical capabilities. The muscles of the abdominal wall are particularly vulnerable, and excessive strain may lead to ruptures.

Cuts and abrasions from rough surfaces, sharp or jagged edges, splinters, projections, and so on. Personal protective equipment (PPE) and clothing should be worn as necessary (such as leather gloves to protect the hands).

Back injuries are most frequently sustained while lifting and handling manually. They may be the cumulative effect of repeated minor injuries, or the result of an abrupt strain. Stoop lifting (see below) should be avoided; it greatly increases the chances of sustaining back injuries. Laboratory tests show that the stresses imposed on a rounded back during stoop lifting is six times that experienced if the trunk is kept straight while bending at the knees.

The risk of injury is reduced by knowledge of correct lifting techniques and, by not attempting to lift excessively heavy loads without assistance.

Crushing of limbs, and so on by falling loads, or by fingers, hands or feet becoming trapped by loads. Correct positioning of hands and feet in relation to the movement of the load is essential. Timber wedges or other blocks should be used when beginning to raise or lower heavy loads.

 Manual handling and lifting injuries are often for life.

15.4 The manual handling assessment

An ergonomic approach to the problems of manual handling and lifting can help to overcome many of the problems.

Ergonomics have been described as 'fitting the job to the person, rather than fitting the person to the job'. This requires attention to the following.

☑ **The task.** What has to be achieved and by when?

☑ **The load.** Is it too heavy to lift and, if so, can it be broken down into smaller loads? Can two people lift it?

☑ **The individual.** Male or female, large or small frame, age, stature, state of health/previous injuries?

☑ **The work environment.** Consider hazards en-route (such as uneven floor surfaces, slopes, steps and narrow passages).

Where the assessment indicates potential risks to the health of employees from the manual handling of loads, the employer must develop a safe system of work that avoids the risks.

The employer must consider:

☑ **the task:**
 – can manual handling be avoided completely?
 – can the distance a load has to be moved be reduced by better on-site planning?
 – can lifting aids be used?
 – does the load have to be raised to, or lowered from, above head height?
 – does the task involve repetitive lifting?
 – is it possible to avoid lifting from the floor?
 – can the centre of gravity move (fluid loads)?
 – can it be carried close to the body?
 – does it have sharp edges?
 – should it be carried by two (or more) people?

☑ **the individual:**
 – do they need manual handling training?
 – do they need additional PPE?
 – is there any known reason why they might not be suitable for the job?

15

Manual handling

☑ **the load:**

    – can it be broken down into smaller loads?

    – is the weight known and, if not, can it be found out?

    – are there adequate handholds?

    – can lifting accessories be built or cast in, or fixed into position

    – is it evenly balanced (centre of gravity)?

    – are there any manufacturers' recommendations or constraints for methods of lifting?

☑ **the environment:**

    – is the floor surface sufficiently level?

    – are there any space constraints or trip hazards that should be removed?

    – is the level of lighting adequate?

    – is the workplace temperature satisfactory?

    – is the surface slippery? (Consider varying weather, such as frost, ice and dew in the mornings.)

Employees must co-operate by:

☑ using the appropriate equipment supplied in accordance with their training and instructions

☑ following the systems of work laid down by their employer.

Online assistance

The HSE has developed two online tools to assist employers to carry out manual handling assessments. These are shown below.

1. Manual handling assessment chart (MAC)

This tool helps users identify high-risk manual handling activities by helping them to understand, interpret and categorise the level of risk of the various known risk factors associated with manual handling.

 The MAC, which can be accessed online, incorporates a numerical and colour-coded scoring system to enable priorities to be identified.

2. Assessment of repetitive tasks (ART)

As its name suggests this tool, which uses a numerical score and a traffic light system, assists employers to assess the risks of musculoskeletal disorders arising out of repetitive tasks.

 The tool can be downloaded from the HSE's website.

15.5 Lifting and handling

Lifting capacities

The weight that can be lifted by any individual will vary according to personal physique, age, condition and practice, and the techniques employed. Lifting capacity declines with age and an older person may not be capable of lifting the same load as a younger person; this, however, can be offset to some extent by employing a better technique.

The general rule is that the load should not be lifted if it causes a feeling of strain. Assistance should be available if required, and employees must not be required to lift loads beyond their capacity.

Youthful exuberance and bravado often tempt younger employees to try to lift loads that are too heavy. While they may succeed in the short term, long-term damage may be done to the ligaments, muscles and back.

After taking account of expert opinion and the long history of complaints over handling heavy blocks, the Construction Industry Advisory Council has concluded that there is a high risk of injury in the single-handed, repetitive manual handling of building blocks or other loads heavier than 20 kg.

If single person handling is needed, either blocks or other materials of 20 kg or lighter should be specified and used, or other precautions should be implemented to reduce the risk by, for example, the provision of mechanical handling.

With blocks or other materials weighing less than 20 kg, manual handling risks are still significant and suitable precautions should be taken to minimise these risks as much as possible.

Some of the solutions listed below will require a degree of training and expertise; indeed some will require a driving licence.

Avoiding manual handling – some solutions

Reducing the risk of injury can be helped by using mechanical aids such as:

- ☑ genie lifts
- ☑ kerb lifters
- ☑ sack trolleys
- ☑ pallet trucks
- ☑ skids
- ☑ telehandlers
- ☑ correct delivery locations
- ☑ built-in lifting attachments

- ☑ wheelbarrows
- ☑ stillages
- ☑ conveyor belts
- ☑ suction pads
- ☑ temporary handles/grips
- ☑ material hoists
- ☑ excavators/dumpers.

 Bricklaying – stacking bricks and mortar on a platform at waist height allows more of the work to be done between waist and shoulder height, thus avoiding stooping.

Preparing to lift

Before lifting and handling any load, the following points should be established.

- ☑ What has to be moved?
- ☑ Does it really have to be moved?
- ☑ What does it weigh?
- ☑ Can it be broken down into smaller loads?
- ☑ Can the process that requires it to be moved be changed?
- ☑ Where is the load's centre of gravity?
- ☑ Can it be safely handled by one person?
- ☑ Will assistance be required?
- ☑ Can the move be carried out more safely with mechanical assistance?
- ☑ How far does it have to be moved and from where to where?
- ☑ Is the route clear of obstructions?
- ☑ Can it be put down safely?

Suitable protective clothing should be worn. This may include gloves, safety footwear, safety helmets, and special overalls if hot or corrosive substances are to be carried.

Ensure that the lifting and lowering areas are clear of tripping hazards, and likewise check the route over which the load is to be carried.

The load

Large, heavy loads should, if possible, be broken down into smaller, lighter and more manageable sizes. It is obviously easier to lift 10 kg five times than to try to lift 50 kg once.

Where the load has to be moved by a woman, the weight should be reduced by approximately 30%.

15

As a rough guide, where lifting is repetitive, weights should be reduced as follows.

Special factors in operation	Rough guide
Operation repeated once or twice a minute.	Reduce weight by 30%
Operation repeated five to eight times a minute.	Reduce weight by 50%
Operation repeated more than 12 times per minute.	Reduce weight by 80%
'Average' female.	Reduce weight by 30%
Handler twists through 45 degrees.	Reduce weight by 10%
Handler seated and twisting.	Less than 5 kg.
Handler seated.	About 5 kg.
Pushing or pulling a load (assuming that force is applied).	About 25 kg for starting or stopping a load.
With hands between knuckle and shoulder height.	About 10 kg for keeping a load in motion.

The size and shape of a load may be as significant as its weight in determining whether assistance is required. Large awkward loads, which require the arms to be extended in front of the body, place more strain on the back and abdomen than compact objects carried close to the body.

The absence of natural or designed handling points can also make it difficult to raise and carry objects without strain and may require barrows or other lifting and handling aids.

Not all loads need to be carried, of course. It may be easier to roll or push them, depending on the contents. Even so, assistance might still be required to avoid the risk of injury.

Manual handling – a few techniques

Plan the task

☑ What has to be moved?

☑ Where to, where from, how far, is the route clear of obstructions?

☑ Is it safe for one person to do it alone?

☑ Will help be required? If so, how much and for what purpose?

Use your body wisely

☑ Let the leg and thigh muscles do the work. They cope better than the back muscles.

☑ Try to keep your spine straight – not necessarily vertical, but straight. However, slight bending of the back, knees and hips is permitted if necessary and is certainly preferable to fully flexing the back (stooping) or fully flexing the hips and knees (deep squatting).

☑ Once you have started to lift (taken the full weight) don't flex your back any further, which can happen if you begin to straighten before you have raised the load.

☑ Avoid twisting the back or leaning sideways, especially whilst the back is bent.

☑ Use the movement of your own body weight to get things moving. Do not snatch the load.

Bend your knees

Feet slightly apart; one foot slightly forward; balance; keep the back straight. Avoid tight clothing that prevents you from bending your knees.

Get a good grip

Use your hands – not fingers. Tilt the load slightly to get a secure grip as close to the body as possible. Keep your elbows tucked in.

Lift with your legs

Do not jerk or snatch. Let the thigh muscles do the bulk of the work. Lift in stages, if necessary from the ground onto a low platform.

Putting the load down – plan before you start

☑ To floor level: It will probably be a reversal of the lifting process. Attention must be given to the positioning of the feet and back.

☑ To a higher level: Depending upon the height of the surface to which the load is to be positioned, it may be less of a stress on the body to lower the load and assistance may be required.

Team lifting

If the load is large, heavy or awkward – get assistance, preferably from someone of about the same size and build as yourself to help maintain the balance of the load during lifting. Always plan the lift with your helper and agree who will give directions as to when and how you will lift.

Using simple mechanical aids

Hoist being used for loading out roof materials

Steel pipes and round timbers make effective rollers or mechanical aids, and should be used when necessary, but great care must be taken to:

☑ co-ordinate the movement of the load with the positioning of the rollers

☑ keep the hands of the person who positions the rollers well out of the way of the moving load.

The use of a wheelbarrow or sack truck will make the manual handling of suitable loads that much easier. Using lifting straps or handheld suction devices will assist in moving some sheet materials.

The use of simple mechanical aids lowers the level of risk, can prevent accidents and avoids unnecessary fatigue and strain.

Whenever practical, mechanical handling and lifting should replace manual techniques. This will reduce the risk of fatigue, improve efficiency and reduce the risk of accidents.

15

Handling building blocks

☑ Specify/order blocks that weigh less than 20 kg.

☑ Store blocks where they will not get wet (and increase their weight).

☑ Arrange work so that lifting over shoulder height is not carried out.

☑ Deliver blocks as close to the point of laying as possible.

Scaffold

Manual handling will be an activity linked to the erection, alteration and dismantling of scaffolds. It is also likely that those who work from scaffolds will be involved in manual handling activities during the course of their work.

Employers carrying out scaffolding activities must assess the risks arising out of manual handling. This is usually undertaken as part of the general risk assessment and method statement/scaffold plan.

Specific manual handling techniques and skills are required for scaffolding. These enabling skills are comprehensively covered by the CISRS training courses. Labourers, trainee scaffolders and scaffolders who have not been trained through CISRS scheme should receive specific manual handling training.

15.6   Legal duties

The Manual Handling Operations Regulations

These regulations specify how employers have to deal with risks to the safety and health of employees who have to carry out manual handling in the course of their employment, as follows.

☑ Assess the manual handling task to identify any risk that may be inherent in the operation.

☑ Avoid the need to carry out manual handling as far as possible.

☑ Where a risk is identified, implement control measures to reduce that risk.

The requirements relevant to lifting and handling are described below.

WHAT YOU NEED TO KNOW
Manual Handling Operations Regulations 1992

These regulations (revised in 1998 and updated in 2004) place duties upon the employer to ensure that employees avoid hazardous manual handling operations so far as reasonably practicable. Employers should assess unavoidable manual handling operations and take steps to reduce the risk of injury from such operations as is reasonable practicable.

Establish if the lift be avoided or if you can you use a mechanical aid to lift or move the load. If not:

1. Assess the load
Ensure you know what you are lifting, where it is to go and its weight. Be aware of awkward shapes or unbalanced loads.

2. Personal limitations
Know the limit of your own ability. Ask for help if needed.

3. Stance
If lifting alone face the direction of travel. Stand over the load, feet shoulder width apart and one slightly in front of the other. Bend your knees whilst keeping your back straight.

4. Proper Grip
Ensure you have a firm grip of the load, using the palms of your hands and the roots of the fingers. Never lift with the finger tips!

5. Body Position
Keep your arms close to your body, ensuring your legs take the weight of the load and not your arms. Tuck your chin to your chest, this helps keep the back straight.

6. Lifting
Use your legs to lift both your upper body and the load, ensuring you keep your back straight and the load close to your body.

7. Moving
Keep the load close to your body. Without twisting the trunk, use your legs to move the load.

8. Co-ordinated Lifting
If the load is unsafe to be lifted by one person, co-ordinate the lift with a colleague, ensuring the above techniques are followed.

Employer's duties

Each employer shall, so far as is reasonably practicable, avoid the need for employees to undertake any manual handling operations at work, that involve a risk of their being injured; or where this is not reasonably practicable, each employer shall:

☑ make a suitable and sufficient assessment of all such manual handling operations to be undertaken by their employees, having regard to those points contained in the manual handling of loads checklist in Section G *Checklists and forms*

☑ take appropriate steps to implement control measures, thereby reducing the risk of injury to those employees undertaking any manual handling operations, to the lowest level which is reasonably practicable

☑ take appropriate steps to provide any of those employees who are undertaking any manual handling operations with general indications and, where it is reasonably practicable to do so, precise information on:
  – the weight of each load
  – the heaviest side of the load whose centre of gravity is not positioned centrally.

Any assessment that an employer has made must be reviewed where:

☑ there is reason to suspect that it is no longer valid, or

☑ there has been a significant change to the manual handling operations to which that assessment relates.

Where changes to an assessment are required, as a result of any review, an employer shall make them.

When determining for the purposes of this regulation whether manual handling operations at work involve a risk of injury, and to determine the appropriate steps needed to reduce that risk, particular care shall be taken to check:

☑ the physical suitability of the employee to carry out the operation

☑ the clothing, footwear and other personal effects worn by the employee

☑ the employee's knowledge and training

☑ the results of any relevant risk assessment carried out under the Management of Health and Safety at Work Regulations

☑ whether the employee is within a group of employees identified by that assessment as being especially at risk

☑ the results of any health surveillance provided under the Management of Health and Safety at Work Regulations.

Employers must additionally:

☑ provide safe systems and places of work

☑ ensure the safety of their employees and, where possible, the absence of risks in the handling, storage and transport of all types of articles and substances

☑ provide the information, instruction, training and supervision necessary to ensure the health and safety of their employees.

Employee's duties

It is the duty of each employee, while at work, to:

☑ make full and proper use of any system of work provided for use by the employer in connection with manual handling

☑ use any machinery or equipment provided by the employer in accordance with any training or instruction received

☑ inform the employer, or anyone else responsible for safety, of any dangerous work practice or shortcomings in the employer's arrangements for safety.

Index

Index

ABC of resuscitation 63
accident books 4, 58, 153
accident reporting and investigation 4, 58–60
    see also RIDDOR
acids 76, 105, 106, 107
action levels, lead 162, 165, 169, 170, 171
action values *see* exposure action/limit values
air monitoring 123, 124, 126–127, 163, 165, 168, 170, 171
alcohol and drugs 33–49
alkalis 76, 105, 106, 107
allergic dermatitis 8, 76, 104
ambulance services 53
amphetamines 48
anti-vibration gloves 76–77, 202
appointed persons 54, 55, 57
asbestos 2, 3, 4, 5, 8, 21, 73, 115–136
asbestos areas 125, 126
asbestos registers 120, 121
asbestos surveys 117, 121, 122–123, 131–133
asbestos waste 5, 123, 127–128
Assessment of repetitive tasks (ART) tool 218

back injuries 6, 7, 64, 196, 216, 217
barrier creams 16, 106, 107, 108, 109
bat droppings 8, 85
benzodiazepine 48
bird droppings 8, 85
bitumen products 76, 106, 107
bleeding 64
blood circulation 202
broken bones 64
bullying 27
    see also harassment
burning clothing 64
burning of lead-based paints 172
burns 64, 76, 105

cancer 2, 35, 73, 116, 139, 142, 154
    see also carcinogens; skin cancers
cannabis 48
carbon monoxide 18, 20, 149–158
carcinogens 2, 9, 84, 91, 96, 139, 142, 154
cement 76, 78, 86, 105, 106, 107
charges for equipment 69, 79, 80, 81
chemicals 107
    see also acids; alkalis; chromates; fungicides
Chemicals (Hazard Information and Packaging for Supply) Regulations 84
chromates 106, 107
cleaning and cleanliness 8, 11, 16, 95, 104, 107, 108–109
    see also clothes care and changing facilities; food safety;
    washing facilities
cleaning and cleanliness in asbestos work 123
cleaning and cleanliness in lead work 163, 167, 172
cleaning and cleanliness of first aid rooms 55
clients 89, 121, 123, 128, 160, 180
clothes care and changing facilities 18, 22, 95, 108, 123, 127, 166
cocaine 46
cold burns 64
'company premises' (definition) 35
compatibility of PPE 66, 68, 80, 81
Constructing better health (CBH) 12, 31
Construction (Design and Management) Regulations 17, 21, 31, 89–90, 116, 123, 126, 128, 160, 167, 182
consultation 29, 31, 38, 67, 181
contact dermatitis 8, 76, 104
contaminated ground 8, 85, 97
contractors 89–90, 121, 141
    see also licensed contractors; principal contractors;
    sub-contractors
'control limit' (definition) 119
Control of Artificial Optical Radiation at Work Regulations 70
Control of Asbestos Regulations 80, 116, 119–125

Control of Lead at Work Regulations 80, 160, 162–164, 167, 168
Control of Noise at Work Regulations 80, 177, 180, 183, 186–187
Control of Pollution Act 182, 183
Control of Substances Hazardous to Health Regulations 9, 73, 80, 83–101, 107, 111, 141, 162
Control of Vibration at Work Regulations 198, 203–206
COSHH assessments 85, 86, 87–88, 89, 91–94, 96, 99, 106, 111, 141
counterfeit PPE 68
crack (drug) 46
crush injuries 217
crushed secondary aggregate 128
cuts and abrasions 11, 76, 105, 109, 139, 217

daily exposure to vibration 203
    see also exposure action/limit values
Data Protection Act 58
de-greasers 76, 107
deafness 4, 5, 6, 177
    see also hearing protection
demolition 183
dermatitis 4, 5, 8, 67, 73, 76, 104, 107, 109, 112, 139
designated areas 126
designers 89, 141, 180
diesel engine exhaust emissions 2, 154
disabled persons 32
disciplinary procedures 41, 42, 43–44
discrimination 31, 32, 38, 162
    see also bullying
diseases 4, 5, 21, 22, 138
    see also cancer; dermatitis; respiratory problems;
    RIDDOR; stress
disposable RPE 74, 95
drinking alcohol 34–45
drinking during lead work 163, 166–167
drinking water supplies 17, 19, 20, 55
driving 36
droppings 8, 85
drugs and alcohol 33–49
    see also needlestick injuries
dust and fumes 3, 9–10, 67, 73, 74, 86, 106, 107, 137–149
    see also asbestos; carbon monoxide; exhaust emissions;
    gases; lead-based paints; respiratory protective equipment

ear protection *see* hearing protection
eating *see* food safety
ecstasy 46
electric shock 64
emergency first aid 63–64
emergency procedures for carbon monoxide poisoning 151–152
emergency procedures for hazardous substances 87, 89, 90, 94, 97, 111
emergency procedures for lead 164
emergency services 53, 54, 89, 121, 164
employees' duties for hazardous substances 88, 90, 95, 106
employees' duties for health surveillance 164, 206
employees' duties for lead work 163, 164, 167
employees' duties for manual handling 218, 223
employees' duties for noise and hearing protection 187
employees' duties for PPE 70, 75, 77, 80, 81, 111
Employment Medical Advisory Service 11, 12, 31, 97, 104
Employment Rights Act 31, 32, 162
Environmental Protection Act 182
Equality Act 31, 32
examination 75, 87, 88, 95–96, 109, 110, 123, 163
exemption certificates for lead work 164
exhaust emissions 2, 154
exhaust ventilation plant 95, 107, 123
exposure action/limit values for lead 162, 163, 165, 169, 170
exposure action/limit values for noise 178, 179, 180, 183
exposure action/limit values for vibration 179, 198, 199, 200, 201, 203, 205

exposure levels *see* daily exposure to vibration; exposure limits; noise levels; silica exposure levels
exposure limits 9, 85–86, 96, 124, 125, 140–141, 142, 169, 177
    see also exposure action/limit values
eye injuries 64, 67, 70, 72
eye protection 64, 69–73, 108, 202

face-fit testing 73, 95, 123
face shields 70–71, 76
fall-arrest and suspension equipment 66, 67, 79
first aid 11, 51–64, 72, 89, 94, 106, 109, 111
    see also emergency procedures
first aid equipment and facilities 19, 52, 53, 54–55, 61, 164
first aid needs assessments 52, 54, 55
first aiders 13, 19, 52, 53–54, 55, 56–58
fit notes 12
fixed sites 17–19
Food Hygiene (England) Regulations 21–22
food safety 11, 21–23, 73, 93, 95, 163, 166–167
    see also rest facilities
Food Safety Act 21
foot protection 78, 79, 80, 105
formaldehyde 107
fractures 64
free provision of equipment 69, 79, 80, 81
fuel oils 106, 107
fumes *see* carbon monoxide; dust and fumes; exhaust emissions; gases; metal fumes
fungicides 76, 107

Gas Safe register 153, 154, 155
gases 8, 140
    see also carbon monoxide; exhaust emissions; LPG
glass fibres 107
gloves 67, 76–77, 79, 105, 107, 108, 167, 202

hand-arm vibration 5, 6–7, 194–196, 197, 198, 199, 201, 202, 203, 207–210, 212–213
harassment 31
    see also bullying
'hazard' (definition) 86
hazardous substances 18, 20, 83–101, 106–107, 111, 141
    see also asbestos; *Control of Substances Hazardous to Health Regulations*; dust and fumes; lead and lead work; skin protection
Hazardous Waste Regulations 128, 160
head protection 77–78
Health and Safety at Work etc. Act 2, 4, 21, 31, 32, 34, 81, 155
Health and Safety (First Aid) Regulations 52, 53, 62
health and safety plans 17, 90
health and safety policies 4–5
    see also substance misuse policies
Health and Safety (Safety Signs and Signals) Regulations 55, 126
health management 1–13
health support services 12–13, 31
health surveillance 2, 3, 87, 89, 90, 93, 97, 141
health surveillance for hearing problems 183, 187
health surveillance for manual handling injuries 223
health surveillance for skin problems 104, 111
health surveillance for vibration injuries 198, 199, 201, 202, 203, 205, 207–211
health surveillance in asbestos work 127, 129
health surveillance in lead work 163–164, 165, 168–169, 170, 174
health surveillance records 89, 93, 97, 127, 163–164, 169, 174, 187, 201, 202, 205
healthy working lives website 12, 31
hearing loss 4, 5, 6, 177
hearing protection 6, 68–69, 177, 178, 181, 182, 183–185, 186, 188, 202
heating 18–19, 20, 156–158
    see also carbon monoxide; LPG heaters and cookers

heroin 47
high-efficiency dust respirators 74
high-visibility clothing 79
hot-air guns 172
hot works 76, 86, 105
    see also temperatures
hygiene *see* cleaning and cleanliness

identification of hazardous substances 90–91, 97, 106
ill health *see* diseases; health management; injuries; sickness absence; stress
importers' duties 111
induction training 10, 16, 38, 53, 143, 155
industrial dermatitis *see* dermatitis
information provision 3, 13
information provision on asbestos 120, 121, 123, 124
information provision on carbon monoxide 155
information provision on first aid arrangements 52
information provision on hazardous substances 87, 88, 89, 93, 97
information provision on laser use 72
information provision on lead 165
information provision on manual handling 223
information provision on noise 187
information provision on PPE 67, 69, 80, 81
information provision on skin protection 111
information provision on substance misuse 38
information provision on vibration 199, 203, 205
infra-red heating 172
injuries 2, 4, 153, 216–217
    see also back injuries; cuts and abrasions; eye injuries; first aid; musculoskeletal problems; needlestick injuries; RIDDOR
insecticides 107
inspections 67, 95, 108, 109, 110
insurance 130
ionising radiation 7, 106
Ionising Radiation Regulations 7, 80
irritant dermatitis 8, 76, 104

ketamine 47

lasers 72–73, 82
    see also radiation
lead and lead work 20, 73, 159–174
lead-based paints 89, 160, 161, 164, 166, 168, 170, 171–173
Lead Paint Safety Association 160, 173
leptospirosis 11–12, 85
licensable asbestos work 119, 124, 129
licensed contractors 116, 124, 125, 126, 127, 128, 129, 130
life jackets 79
lifting *see* manual handling
lifting capacities 218, 219–220
lime 106, 107
limit values *see* exposure action/limit values
line managers 29, 31
local exhaust ventilation plant 95, 107, 123
LPG cold burns 64
LPG heaters and cookers 18–19, 20, 153, 158
LSD 47

Management of Health and Safety at Work Regulations 31, 32, 34, 64, 111, 120, 155, 204, 223
manual handling 3, 4, 6, 19, 215–223
    see also cuts and abrasions
Manual handling assessment chart (MAC) tool 218
manual handling assessments 217–218, 223
Manual Handling Operations Regulations 6, 222–223
manufacturers' duties 67, 91, 111, 200
'mechanical vibration' (definition) 203
medical surveillance *see* health surveillance
mephedrone 49
metal fumes 10, 140
methadone 49

Index

mineral oils 76, 107
mists 140
Misuse of Drugs Act 34
mould oils 107
musculoskeletal problems 2, 5, 6, 216, 217
    see also back injuries; repetitive strain injury

needlestick injuries 10–11, 85
noise 4, 6, 175–191, 199
    see also Control of Noise at Work Regulations; hearing loss;
    hearing protection
noise assessments 178, 179–182, 183, 186
noise exposure action/limit values 178, 179, 180, 183
noise levels 177–179, 182, 188, 190
non-disposable RPE 95
non-licensable asbestos work 116, 119–120, 124–125, 127, 129
notification of asbestos work 119–120, 124–125, 127
nuisance dust masks 74

occupational exposure limits *see* exposure limits
occupational health *see* health management; health surveillance
occupational health support services 12–13, 31
occupied premises 10, 17, 90, 154

Painting and Decorating Association 160, 173
paints and painting 2, 9, 73, 76, 78, 89, 106
    see also lead-based paints
paraffin 107
personal accident report 59–60
personal hygiene *see* cleaning and cleanliness; washing facilities
personal protective equipment 3, 8, 64, 65–82, 87, 92, 93
    see also eye protection; gloves; hearing protection;
    protective clothing; respiratory protective equipment;
    skin protection
Personal Protective Equipment at Work Regulations 66, 70, 75,
80–81, 111
personal protective equipment for lead work 163, 165, 171, 172
personal protective equipment for manual handling 217
personal protective equipment for vibration 202
petroleum products 106, 107
pitch 2, 76, 106, 107
prevention principles 13
principal contractors 17, 89, 90, 141
protective clothing 7, 22, 76, 79, 95
    see also clothes care and changing facilities; eye protection;
    foot protection; gloves; head protection; skin protection
protective clothing for asbestos work 122, 123, 127, 128
protective clothing for lead work 163, 166, 170
protective clothing for manual handling work 216, 217, 219
protective clothing for vibration 76–77, 199, 202, 204

radiation 7, 106, 107
    see also lasers
REACH Regulations 97
records of air monitoring 168
records of asbestos 116, 119, 121, 125, 126
records of first aid arrangements 53, 58
records of food safety 22
records of hazardous substances 88, 93, 96
records of health surveillance 89, 93, 97, 127, 163–164, 169,
174, 187, 201, 202, 205
records of noise 178, 187
records of risk assessments 3, 87, 162, 204
records of RPE 96
records of stress assessments 29, 30
reoccupation of premises 122
repetitive strain injury 10
*Reporting of Injuries, Diseases and Dangerous Occurrences
Regulations see* RIDDOR
representative sampling 122
resins 76, 106, 107
respirator zones 126
respiratory problems 4, 5, 9, 85, 139–140
    see also droppings; dust and fumes

respiratory protective equipment 66, 67, 68, 73–75, 93, 95–96
respiratory protective equipment for asbestos work 122, 123,
127, 129
respiratory protective equipment for dust and fumes 140,
142–143, 144
respiratory protective equipment for lead work 163, 165, 172
rest facilities 18, 20, 166, 182
    see also food safety
resuscitation 63
RIDDOR 4, 58, 104, 153, 165
'risk' (definition) 86
'risk assessment' (definition) 120
risk assessment records 3, 87, 162, 204
risk assessments 2, 3–4, 13, 32
    see also COSHH assessments; first aid needs assessments;
    manual handling assessments; noise assessments; stress
    assessment
risk assessments for asbestos 116, 119, 120, 121, 123, 126, 132
risk assessments for contaminated ground 8
risk assessments for dust and fumes 138, 154
risk assessments for lead 161–162, 163, 165, 167, 168, 171
risk assessments for PPE 66, 80, 81
risk assessments for skin protection 111
risk assessments for vibration 197–198, 204, 205
risk management 66–67, 116, 120–122, 141–142, 143–144,
152–155, 181–186, 197–201
Road Traffic Act 34, 36

safety harnesses *see* fall-arrest and suspension equipment
safety helmets *see* head protection
safety spectacles 68, 71
sanding lead-based paints 172
sanitary conveniences 16, 17, 18, 20, 21, 22
scaffolding 124, 222
screening *see* health surveillance
screening for drugs or alcohol 39–41, 44–45
self-employed persons 53, 80, 81, 87, 89–90, 121, 127, 141
sensitive dermatitis 8, 76, 104
shared first aid facilities 53
shields 70–71, 76
short duration work 19, 20, 124, 125
sickness absence 12
significant levels of lead 170–171
Sikhs 78
silica dust 2, 9, 86, 96, 142, 143, 145–147
silica exposure levels 147
silicosis 139, 142
Site Waste Management Plans (SWMPs) 127, 128
skin cancers 2, 5, 7, 107, 110
    see also sun safety
skin cleansers 109
skin problems 8, 67, 73, 85, 139
    see also burns; dermatitis
skin protection 4, 64, 67, 76–77, 103–113
    see also foot protection; gloves; protective clothing
smoking 9, 16, 172
smoking and asbestos exposure 116
smoking and cancer 2
smoking and health surveillance records 165
smoking in food rooms 21, 22
smoking as ingestion hazard 11, 95, 163, 166–167
solvents 2, 10, 73, 76, 77, 106, 107, 109, 172
'sound' (definition) 176
sound levels 177, 189, 191
Special Waste (Amendment) Regulations 128
spinal injuries *see* back injuries
'sporadic and low-intensity' (definition) 119
storage of PPE 75, 80, 81, 88, 95, 123, 127, 163
strains/sprains *see* musculoskeletal problems
stress 5, 7, 25–32, 36
stress assessment 28–29, 30
sub-contractors 38
'substance' (definitions) 35, 86
    see also drugs and alcohol; hazardous substances

'substance misuse' (definition) 35
substance misuse identification 37
substance misuse policies 38–39, 42–45
sun safety 2, 7, 109–110, 113
supervision 6, 22, 106, 111, 143, 155, 216, 223
suppliers' duties 67, 91, 97, 111, 200
Supply of Machinery (Safety) Regulations 180, 200
suspension levels 162, 163, 165, 169, 171

tar 2, 76, 106, 107
team lifting 221
temperature control of food 22
temperatures 107
     see also cold burns; hot works; weather protection
temporary staff 38
testing 75, 88, 93, 95–96, 123, 162, 163, 164
     see also face-fit testing
testing for drugs or alcohol 39–41, 44–45
thinners 76, 107
timber 9, 76, 86, 106, 107, 112
toilets 16, 17, 18, 20, 21, 22
tools *see* vibration; work equipment
trainees 58
training 3
training for asbestos work 116, 123, 124, 125, 129
training for carbon monoxide 155
training for dust and fumes 143
training for first aid 53, 54, 56–58, 64
training for food safety 21, 22
training for hazardous substances 89, 93, 97
training for hearing protection 183
training for laser use 72
training for lead 165
training for manual handling 6, 223
training for noise 187
training for PPE 66, 69, 80, 81, 165, 178
training for RPE 73, 93
training for skin protection 111
training for stress management 7
training for substance misuse identification 38
training for vibration 199, 203, 205
transient sites 19–21
Transport and Works Act 34
travelling first aid kits 13, 54, 55, 61
trigger time 198
turpentine 107

'under the influence' (definition) 35

vapours 140
     see also dust and fumes; gases
ventilated respirators 74
ventilation for dust and fumes 9, 10, 107
ventilation for hazardous substances 87, 88, 95
ventilation for heating appliances 18, 20, 156–158
ventilation for lead work 163
vibration 6–7, 76–77, 193–213
     see also hand-arm vibration; whole-body vibration
vibration measurement 196, 200–201, 203, 204, 212–213
     see also exposure action/limit values; trigger time
vibration white finger 5, 6, 195
visitors 53, 162

washing facilities 16, 18, 19, 20, 22, 88, 95, 106, 108
washing facilities for asbestos work 123, 127
washing facilities for first aid 54, 55
washing facilities for lead work 163, 166
waste management 19, 55, 160, 163
     see also asbestos waste
water, food safety 22
     see also drinking water supplies; leptospirosis; washing
     facilities
water suppression 144

weather protection 79, 202
Weil's disease (leptospirosis) 11–12, 85
welfare facilities 15–23, 93, 111, 166–167
whole-body vibration 7, 194, 196, 197, 198, 199, 201, 203
women employees 20, 161, 162, 169, 219
work equipment 69, 79, 80, 81, 167, 199, 200–201, 204
     see also personal protective equipment
'working day' (definition) 203
workplace exposure limits (WELs) *see* exposure limits

Contents

Introduction   iii

How to use GE 700   ix

01   Site organisation   1

02   Fire prevention and control   9

03   Electrical safety   41

04   Temporary works   51

05   Plant and work equipment   59

06   Mobile plant and vehicles   81

07   Lifting operations   91

08   Lifting equipment   117

Index   151

Introduction

Construction site safety covers all aspects of current health, safety and environment issues in the building and construction industry. It is designed to help managers, supervisors and small businesses understand how they should comply with, and put into practice, their legal, moral and social responsibilities.

Construction site safety (GE 700)   iv

About the construction industry   iv

Further supporting information from
CITB-ConstructionSkills   vi

Acknowledgements   vii

Construction site safety (GE 700)

Construction site safety is a leading publication within the construction industry, based on current construction health, safety and environment legislation, guidance and best practice. It will assist in the crucial areas of:

- ☑ accident prevention
- ☑ the avoidance of occupational ill health
- ☑ environmental good practice.

The content has been written with the site manager in mind, with a balance between outlining the requirements of relevant legislation and providing practical guidance on how to comply.

It is divided into the standard structure, which is used across all core CITB-ConstructionSkills publications:

Section A	**Legal and management**
Section B	**Health and welfare**
Section C	General safety
Section D	**High risk activities**
Section E	**Environment**
Section F	**Specialist activities**

Each section within *Construction site safety* is contained within a separate book.

There is also a new additional supporting book:

Section G	**Checklists and forms**

Section G is a collection of information (such as forms and checklists) that can be used on a day-to-day basis when running a site.

The content of *Construction site safety*, which is developed with construction industry experts, is revised annually to take into account the latest changes in legislation and new or updated health, safety and environment industry guidance and best practice.

There is a companion website that will keep users informed of legislation changes, content updates and links to further guidance.

Construction site safety is also available to purchase online or on CD-ROM.

Construction site safety is the official supporting publication for the CITB-ConstructionSkills Site Management Safety Training Scheme (SMSTS), a five-day course for construction site managers.

About the construction industry

Approximately 2.1 million people are employed in the UK construction industry. It includes housing, utilities, repair and maintenance, refurbishment, shop fitting, demolition, roofing, mechanical and electrical, plumbing and highways maintenance.

It is made up of 175,000 construction firms and 90% of companies employ less than 10 workers.

Construction workers (just like you) will die due to work-related ill health. Work-related respiratory disease covers a range of illnesses that are caused or made worse by breathing in hazardous substances (such as construction dust) that damage the lungs.

4,000 people die each year from asbestos-related lung diseases.

500 people (and more each year) are dying from silica-related lung diseases (dust from cutting blocks, kerbs, and so on). Many more suffer from occupational asthma or are forced to leave the industry due to work-related ill health.

Each year there are an estimated 36,000 new cases of work-related ill health with rates of musculoskeletal disorder significantly higher than average.

On average 50 workers are killed each year due to accidents. The biggest killer (around half) is due to falls from height.

Each year approximately 2,500 are seriously injured (broken bones, fractured skull, amputations) and 5,700 have reportable injuries.

The most common cause of injuries is due to manual handling and slips, trips and falls. 60% of all work at height injuries are due to falls from below head height.

Why so many accidents?

Many reports of present day construction accidents and ill health make depressing reading because simple actions were not taken to prevent them. In many cases, those planning the jobs totally failed to consider the health or safety of the people carrying out the work (and possibly others who were affected) and to actively manage the situation.

Common examples of such events include:

- [✓] the increasing number of workers who suffer from cancers and life changing illnesses from breathing and skin complaints. Some of these force the sufferer to give up work, because exposure to dangerous substances such as dust, are not even considered, let alone prevented or controlled

- [✓] the deaths and serious injuries that occur because people fall from height. Often basic actions (like using temporary work platforms on fragile roofs, installing edge protection or using a safety harness and lanyard clipped to a strong-point) were simply not taken

- [✓] workers being buried in collapsed excavations because the sides were unstable or not supported

- [✓] workers being killed or injured by construction plant because pedestrians were not kept out of the plant operating area.

Achieving a reasonable standard of on-site health and safety need not be difficult. Where the work to be carried out is relatively uncomplicated and familiar, the precautions that need to be taken are in many cases simple and common sense or may require just a little investigation or reading. The crucial decision for anyone with responsibility for on-site health and safety is to know when they have reached the limits of their knowledge and capabilities and therefore need the assistance of someone with specialist knowledge.

Caution should also be exercised when a job is not going to plan and there is the temptation to resort to improvised methods of working. If the person in control is not at ease with the way that things are going they should stop the job, step back and think things through carefully before deciding upon a course of action.

Health and Safety Executive (HSE) research has shown that workers are most vulnerable during their first few days on site.

Setting out

Construction is an exciting industry. It is constantly changing as projects move on and jobs get done. As a result of this a building site is one of the most dangerous environments to work in.

But many accidents that occur on sites can be avoided if everyone on site works together. So a free film *Setting out* explains what the site must do and what you must do to stay healthy and safe at work.

 For further information or to view *Setting out* refer to the CITB-ConstructionSkills website.

This film is essential viewing for everyone involved in construction, and should be watched before sitting the CITB-ConstructionSkills' Health, safety and environment test. The content of the film is captured in summary here, and these principles form the basis for the behavioural case study questions, which are a new element of the test from Spring 2012.

Part 1: What you should expect from the construction industry

Your site and your employer should be doing all they can to keep you and their workforce safe.

Before any work begins the site management team will have been planning and preparing the site for your arrival. It is their job to ensure that you can do your job safely and efficiently.

Five things the site you are working on must do:

- [✓] know when you are on site (signing in and out)
- [✓] give you a site induction
- [✓] give you site-specific information
- [✓] encourage communication
- [✓] keep you up-to-date and informed.

Part 2: What the industry expects of you

Once the work begins, it is up to every individual to take responsibility for carrying out the plan safely. This means you should follow the rules and guidelines as well as being alert to the continuing changes on site.

Five things you must do:

- [✓] respect and follow the site rules
- [✓] safely prepare each task
- [✓] do each task responsibly
- [✓] know when to stop (if you think anything is unsafe)
- [✓] keep learning.

Every day the work we do improves the world around us. It is time for us to work together to build an industry that puts its people first. By working together we can build a better industry that respects those who work in it.

Working Well Together

The Working Well Together (WWT) campaign is an industry-led initiative that helps support micro and small businesses improve their health and safety performance. The campaign undertakes a variety of activities, including health and safety awareness days, designer awareness days, breakfast and evening events, roadshows and regional WWT groups.

 To find out how the WWT campaign can help you and your company refer to its website.

Further supporting information from CITB-ConstructionSkills

CITB-ConstructionSkills has a wide range of products, publications and courses that could help to improve your health, safety and environment knowledge.

 To discover more about CITB-ConstructionSkills and the services, publications and courses offered visit the CITB-ConstructionSkills website.

Health, safety and environment publications

Site managers	GE 700 *Construction site safety* (printed, CD and online)
	RACD *Risk assessment and method statement manager*
	SA 03 CD *Health, safety and environmental auditing system*
	DVDs Range of topics including scaffold inspection, worker engagement and sustainability
Supervisors	GE 706 *Site supervision simplified* (printed, CD, online)
	GT 700 *Toolbox talks* (printed, CD, online)
	GT 701 *Safety critical communication toolbox talks* (printed)
Operatives	GE 707 *Safe start*
Health safety and environment test	GT 100 *Health, safety and environment test for operatives and specialists* (printed, DVD, online)
	GT 200 *Health, safety and environment test for managers and professionals* (printed, DVD, online)

Site Safety Plus courses

Directors	Directors role for health and safety course – one day
Site management	Site Management Safety Training Scheme (SMSTS) – five days
Plant managers	Plant Management Safety Training Scheme (SMSTS) – five days
Supervisors	Site Supervisors' Safety Training Scheme (SSSTS) – two days
Operatives	Health safety and environment awareness – one day
Environment	Site Environmental Awareness Training Scheme (SEATS) – one day
Behavioural safety	Achieving Behavioural Change (ABC) – one day
Shopfitting	Site safety for shopfitters and interior contractors – three days

National Construction College

The National Construction College is focused on creating a highly skilled, safe and professional UK construction workforce.
To achieve this, it has more first-class instructors in more locations than any other construction training provider in Europe and offers free professional advice on finding the right training for individuals and companies.

Acknowledgements

CITB-ConstructionSkills wishes to acknowledge the assistance offered by the following organisations in the preparation of this edition of GE 700:

- Access Industry Forum
- Arco
- Balfour Beatty
- Britannia Safety and Training
- Civil Engineering Contractors Association
- Combisafe
- Construction Plant Association
- Drilling and Sawing Association
- eBrit Services Ltd
- Environment Agency
- Environmental and Waste Consulting
- Federation of Master Builders
- Health and Safety Executive
- Henry Boot
- Highways Term Maintenance Association
- Home Builders Federation
- J Breheny Contractors Ltd

- Lead Paint Safety Association
- MJ Fuller and Associates
- Makers Construction Ltd
- May Gurney
- Montpellier International Consulting
- National Access and Scaffolding Confederation
- National Association of Shopfitters
- National Construction College
- National Federation of Demolition Contractors
- Persimmon Homes
- Prospect – The Union for Professionals
- Scafftag
- Temporary Works Forum
- Union of Construction, Allied Trades and Technicians (UCATT)
- Unite
- Wates
- Willmott Dixon

And a special thank you to:

- Carillion
- Costain
- Morgan Sindall
- Skanska

How to use
GE 700

The following information sets out how to use
Construction site safety. Each section is contained
within a separate book, which has been designed
to provide simple navigation for the end user. It also
explains the companion website, which is a significant
addition for keeping users informed of legislation
changes, content updates and links to further guidance.

Construction site safety structure   x
How to navigate   x
Use of icons   x
Companion website   xi

Construction site safety structure

Construction site safety is divided into the standard structure that is used across all core CITB-ConstructionSkills publications:

Section A	**Legal and management**
Section B	**Health and welfare**
Section C	General safety
Section D	**High risk activities**
Section E	**Environment**
Section F	**Specialist activities**

Within *Construction site safety* each section is contained within a separate book.

There is also a new additional supporting book:

Section G	**Checklists and forms**

This new section is a collection of information that can be used on a day-to-day basis when running a site. The forms, checklists and guidance within Section G follow the same structure as in Sections A to F.

How to navigate

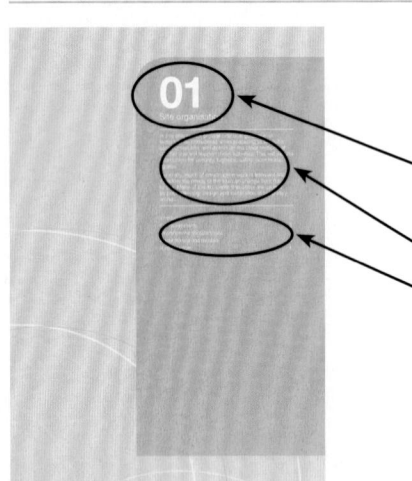

Each section contains a main contents page at the start of the section, followed by the introduction, a detailed chapter contents list at the start of each chapter and an index at the back (but there is no index within Section G).

Chapters have been numbered according to the section you are in. Therefore, chapter one of Section A is numbered 01, chapter two of Section B is numbered 02 and so on. However, references to chapters within other sections will be referred to as A01, B02, and so on.

At the start of each chapter there is a short overview of what the chapter is about.

This is followed by the chapter contents list.

Use of icons

A set of icons emphasises key points within the text and also directs readers to further information. The icons are explained below:

www.	Website/further info	!	Important	"	Quote
e.g.	Example	👍	Best practice	Aa	Definition
?	Question	👎	Poor practice	☑	Checklist
💡	Ideas	✋	Caution	▶	Video
📝	Notes	👥	Consultation		
★	Favourite	🔍	Guidance/case study		

Companion website

A companion website has been created to support *Construction site safety* and it contains up-to-date information on:

☑ the current edition of each section (book)

☑ news (such as legislation changes, industry guidance and best practice)

☑ any minor amendments or updates to the current editions

☑ web links/phone numbers/addresses

☑ details of CITB-ConstructionSkills' publications and courses.

 This icon indicates that further information (such as useful websites and links) can be found on the companion website at www.citb-constructionskills.co.uk/GE700companion

Rather than printing individual weblinks in each section, which can become out of date, the relevant website will be stated alongside the icon (for example, for more information refer to the CITB-ConstructionSkills website). The actual weblink can then be found on the companion website, referenced to the relevant section and chapter.

The companion website will be regularly updated, to ensure that relevant information (such as weblinks) are current.

 Save the companion website address to your favourites, so it is always available when you need it.

01

Site organisation

In this chapter we provide practical guidance on factors to be considered when preparing to set out a construction site, and details on the other sections of GE 700 that will support these activities. This will include information for security, logistics, safety, access and egress.

Generally, much of construction work is transient and therefore the needs of the site can change from day to day. Many of the accidents that occur are caused by poor planning, design and installation of temporary works.

Introduction	2
Key requirements	2
Environmental considerations	7
Waste storage and disposal	8
Human factors	8

01

1.1 Introduction

This chapter aims to give employers and managers general practical guidance on site set-up, the organisation and layout, how it will be run and the effect on people working on it, those living nearby and visitors.

This chapter also covers management preparation information, pre-job briefing, competence, site discipline, welfare requirements, security, materials storage and utilities.

This chapter gives a different slant to some of the topics found in other sections of GE 700. Its content should be read as well as, not instead of, those sections.

 The construction phase health and safety plan provides specific information about hazards that will need to be considered during the setting-up phase of a construction site.

 Draw or use scale cut-outs of site accommodation, plant and plant turning circles, material storage, buildings and temporary works (such as scaffold) and excavation working space on site drawings to plan site set-up and logistics. Remember to take into account the finished building or structure when decommissioning the site.

 One project used a sheet of clear Perspex over a site plan and outlined items such as site accommodation, fencing and temporary roads. Work activities (such as excavations, crane positions and material storage) were colour-coded and plotted daily, which helped identify and plan for potential issues.

1.2 Key requirements

Temporary works

☑ Is the area for the site cabins suitable, and has a foundation assessment been carried out?

☑ Have any temporary roads been assessed for their capability to withstand loads during construction works on the site, especially if they cross existing services?

☑ Undertake checks for ground bearing capabilities for hand standing for craneage and outriggers.

☑ Design the site hoardings and gates to withstand wind loadings, particularly to ensure swing gates are managed during high wind conditions.

☑ Be careful that material storage areas are planned with an awareness of shallow services that can be damaged.

☑ If crane lifts will be required from neighbouring streets, a works engineer must be aware of below ground services (such as basements and subways).

☑ Is a 110 volt distribution system required and, if so, is a live 230/415 volt system available to power it? Who will design and install it, and finally who will test and ensure it meets ECA/NICEIC standards?

 For further information refer to Chapter C04 Temporary works.

Site features and facilities

☑ Consider previous uses of the site, including contaminated ground or unexploded ordnance that may need to be cleared, and previous storage of dangerous goods or hazardous substances in buildings, cellars or tanks, that might result in substantial site transport movements and additional time and cost.

☑ Do watercourses need to be protected from contamination?

☑ Think about isolating buried services, or the use of equipment to create barriers or goalposts for live overhead cables. Cross or go around the site if these are present.

☑ Consider the suitability of any existing buildings for intended use. Involve a structural engineer in these processes.

☑ Is there, or could there be, any asbestos on the site (refer to existing survey information)? Is a refurbishment and demolition survey needed?

☑ Have any protected wildlife or plants been identified?

☑ Are any invasive species (such as Japanese knotweed) present?

☑ Are there any existing health and safety files or historic records available of, for example, asbestos in existing buildings/structures on site?

☑ Is demolition required as part of this project?

 For further information refer to Chapter D08 Underground and overhead services, and Chapter B09 Asbestos.

Site security

☑ Secure the boundary immediately on possession, preferably with lockable gates and suitable hoarding to prevent unauthorised access or fly-tipping.

☑ If the whole site cannot be secured then ensure areas with potentially hazardous operations are appropriately secured.

☑ Make specific security arrangements for particular pieces of plant or equipment, if required.

Pedestrian/traffic routes, movement of plant and people

☑ Provide separate routes for pedestrians and vehicles, with separate entrances if possible.

☑ Ensure these entrances minimise traffic hazards on public roads.

☑ Provide a car park for privately owned vehicles, preferably accessed directly from a public road, with entry to the construction area prevented, if practical.

☑ Ensure that site offices and other facilities are connected to this entrance (for example, for visitors).

The safe separation of construction plant and pedestrian avoids accidents

☑ Traffic routes need to be organised to minimise the risk to pedestrians – physical segregation is always the best way.

☑ Ensure safe, designated pedestrian routes are available to all work locations as work progresses.

☑ Make use of a turning area if space is tight but try to avoid reversing on site – one way systems are ideal.

☑ Ensure availability of competent signaller if reversing is required, if entry onto a site is awkward or pedestrians cannot be completely segregated.

☑ Consider the possible requirement for a wheel wash and/or a road sweeper to keep site and public roads clear of mud and other debris.

Site organisation

Internal access routes and housekeeping

Good housekeeping – cables routed along ceiling and over doors to minimise slips and trips

☑ Internal access routes need to be kept clear to maintain good housekeeping and reduce fire risks.

☑ Careful consideration should be given to location and routing of temporary electric supplies.

Materials storage and lay-down areas

☑ Create and communicate a materials delivery schedule.

☑ Ensure all contractors and suppliers are aware of any delivery restrictions specific to the site or surrounding area (such as schools, low bridges or one way systems).

☑ Make provision for safe storage to ensure site and access roads are kept clear of obstructions.

☑ Consider what access is needed to these materials and what lifting equipment may be required (such as telehandlers, forklift trucks, mobile or tower cranes).

☑ Try to place heavy items (such as heavy goods that need to be moved by hand) near where they will be needed, to avoid double handling.

☑ Ensure stored materials are stacked appropriately, to avoid them falling and breaching the site boundary.

☑ Make sure pallets of materials are stored in stable stacks with a safe limit on the height of each.

☑ Safe provision must be made for the storage of flammable substances (such as bottled gases and fuels).

 For further information refer to:
Chapter C07 Lifting operations,
Chapter C08 Lifting equipment, and
Chapter B07 The Control of Substances Hazardous to Health (COSHH).

Utility services

☑ Give early consideration to the provision of a 230 volt (mains) supply or a 415 volt three-phase supply when there may be heavy electrical loads (for example, a tower crane).

☑ Similarly, early consideration will be required for any provision of telephone and broadband connections.

☑ Ensure there is a supply of clean water, which must be suitable for drinking, and may require installation by the local water company.

☑ Make arrangements for the drainage of surface and foul water. The Local Authority needs to be aware of any new connections, and discharge consents are required if waste will be discharged into rivers.

☑ Gas or oil may be required for heating.

☑ The size of the site will determine what communication links are needed, including in emergencies.

☑ Ensure the provision of a generator and appropriate amounts of fuel, where required.

 For further information refer to Chapter E01
Sustainable construction and the environment.

Work at height

☑ A risk assessment will determine the most appropriate type of equipment required.

☑ Consider methods of fall prevention from unloading, including early deliveries for accommodation works (such as fencing and site accommodation).

☑ Temporary site accommodation, welfare units and containers can be pre-slung or slung using a method that attaches to the bottom of the unit's legs rather than having to access the roof to attach slings to the top of it.

☑ If scaffolding is being used, it must be erected, altered or dismantled by, or under the direct supervision of, a competent person and be inspected periodically by a competent person.

☑ If mobile elevating work platforms (MEWPs) are used they must be suitable, operated by competent persons and have adequate ground conditions.

 For further information refer to Chapter D01 The Work at Height Regulations.

Excavations

☑ Sufficient working space for spoil, earth work support laydown areas, pipes, plant and machinery must be taken into consideration when planning the work.

☑ Suitable equipment (such as guard-rails) will be required to form effective, physical barriers around excavations to prevent falls of persons, machinery or vehicles.

☑ Provide suitably anchored stop blocks or similar devices for the prevention of vehicles, especially tipping dumpers, from falling into excavations.

☑ If the sides of an excavation need to be supported to prevent falls of soil, rock or materials, then a system of support must be designed by a competent person.

☑ Ensure safe means of access and egress for persons who need to enter the excavation; this should be by a secured ladder, but avoid the use of service lines.

☑ Arrangements must be in place for statutory inspections of all excavations.

 For further information refer to Chapter D07 Excavations.

The site office

☑ If the site office has more than one level, particularly where non-construction staff are employed, then temporary planning permission may be required. Also check for any planning restrictions in the contract documents.

☑ Administrative staff and others, who may not have personal protective equipment (PPE), should have safe access from the car park to the site office.

☑ Site offices should offer comfortable accommodation for all types of weather and ranges of temperature.

☑ A suitable, safe form of heating should be provided.

☑ Provide a suitable electrical supply and telecommunications.

☑ Compile registers for portable appliance testing, fire alarms and other emergency planning and ensure the site visitors' log is available.

☑ Consider using temporary accommodation, which often has better environmental performance features than traditional accommodation (such as improved insulation, double glazing, door closers and PIR lighting).

 For further information refer to Chapter B05 First aid.

Welfare facilities

☑ Provide clean and hygienic portable buildings, where workers can change and secure clothing, make a hot drink, heat and eat meals and take shelter in bad weather.

☑ It may be necessary to provide alternative arrangements until the welfare facilities, power or water connections are made. A variety of standalone, self-contained units are available to suit site needs.

☑ Additional welfare facilities may be needed for peak workforce levels and provisions should be made for their delivery and installation.

☑ Where there are both women and men on site, suitable provision must be made for toilet, washing (if necessary, shower) facilities, changing rooms and rest facilities.

 For further information refer to Chapter B02 Welfare facilities.

First aid

In addition to the items covered in 'The site office' on the previous page:

 the appropriate number of qualified first aiders or appointed persons (emergency first aiders) will be needed, depending on the number of people and the risk to their health

☑ details of the first aider(s) and the location(s) of first-aid box(es) must be displayed and given out during induction.

🔍 For further information refer to Chapter B05 First aid.

Fire safety

☑ Think about the level of risk from works to be carried out and flammable substances that may be stored and used.

☑ Any third-party fire arrangements (for example, working in shared or occupied premises) must be maintained and close liaison is vital.

☑ Provide a sufficient number of fire extinguishers, suitable for the types of fire that might occur, and place them in highly visible fire points in appropriate places, including offices and welfare accommodation.

☑ Be aware that these points need to be reviewed on a regular basis, given the changing nature of construction sites.

☑ A suitable number of staff should be trained in the use of the fire extinguishers.

☑ Fire exit and emergency escape route signs must be displayed, and illuminated in periods of darkness.

🔍 For further information refer to Chapter C02 Fire prevention and control.

Emergency plans

☑ From the start of any project, plans must be put in place for the safe evacuation of the site.

☑ On complex or refurbishment projects, it is useful to liaise with local fire authorities to identify fire-fighting strategies for the plan, together with the locations of fire-fighting cores, dry risers and lifts/hoists to be used or not used.

☑ Emergency escape routes must be identified and labelled with appropriate signs and communicated to all on site.

☑ For larger sites, the emergency plan may be part of the health and safety construction plan and fire wardens may be appointed for specific areas of the site.

☑ A suitable assembly point should be identified. This should accommodate the maximum number of people, be a safe distance from potential hazards and not be an obstruction or hazard to the emergency services.

☑ A head count of people on site and who is accounted for must be available in the case of an incident.

☑ Display information about actions to be taken in an emergency, including what the alarm sounds like, days/times when it will be tested and where the assembly point(s) are.

☑ Ensure that suitable equipment is provided for use in the event of an environmental emergency (such as spill kits for use with a fuel spillage).

☑ It is important that workers are trained in the use of spill kits or other equipment provided.

Personal protective equipment

- ☑ Employers have a duty to provide suitable PPE to their employees without charge.

- ☑ A stock of PPE will need to be held in the site office, to cover specific tasks that may be undertaken by employees or, to replace previously issued PPE and for visitors.

- ☑ For specific activities you may need to seek advice when purchasing respiratory protective equipment (RPE), eye protection, hearing protection and gloves.

- ☑ Provide means to clean, maintain and store PPE.

 For further information refer to Chapter B06 Personal protective equipment.

Signs and notices

- ☑ Signs should be displayed at site entrance(s) to inform all persons entering the site about the health and safety requirements for the site. This should include, for example, minimum standards of PPE and state that all visitors must report to the site office.

- ☑ Other signs to be displayed include a selection of appropriate mandatory, warning, prohibition and safe condition signs.

- ☑ Traffic management signs will also be required, as appropriate to the specific site. These may also include directional signage to site and instructions for deliveries.

- ☑ Ensure adequate fire signage (such as showing escape routes, fire assembly points and where the fire points (alarms and extinguishers) are located).

- ☑ Signs will also be required to identify the presence of liquid petroleum gases (LPG) and other flammable substances (such as vehicle and small plant fuels (petrol)).

1.3   Environmental considerations

Construction work can impose a severe impact on the environment. Therefore, measures must be taken to prevent or reduce the potential damage.

- ☑ Consider electing an 'environmental champion' for the site.

- ☑ Clearly identify and explain environmental issues in inductions and briefings.

- ☑ Identify and protect watercourses and drainage systems.

- ☑ Ensure you have licences for discharges of proposed water or effluent discharge and arrange for settlement tanks, if appropriate.

- ☑ Have a plan detailing measures to be taken in the event of a spillage (such as preventing seepage into the ground or contaminating watercourses, including sources of drinking water).

- ☑ Ensure correct handling, storage and disposal of construction and other types of waste.

- ☑ Identify and deal with the existence of protected species of mammals, insects and plants.

- ☑ Show how you propose to reduce noise levels, as far as reasonably practicable. You may need to consider restricting some construction processes to certain times.

- ☑ Demonstrate a caring attitude towards local residents with regard to site lighting and camera use during night hours.

- ☑ By means of risk assessments, reduce the volume of substances used that give off environmentally damaging vapours or fumes.

- ☑ Be aware of not causing nuisance to neighbouring properties and do not leave engines running when not in use.

 For further information refer to Section E Environment.

1.4   Waste storage and disposal

Waste that is created on a site must be disposed of appropriately. Hazardous waste will need to be stored in appropriate containers and removed by licensed contractors using waste transfer notes.

A chute and tipping skip provides the workforce with a quick, safe and easy method to remove waste from a scaffold

Non-hazardous waste generated during works undertaken by mobile groups of workers or lone workers can be transported to their base for sorting and transferring to suitable recycling facilities or landfill sites.

A plan to reduce and manage waste should be created before the project begins. Relevant content should also be communicated to contractors and those carrying out the work.

The following will need to be considered:

☑ if the waste is suitable for transporting – hazardous or non-hazardous, and if it requires special handling

☑ if the person planning to remove it is competent to do so

☑ provide skips or space for the waste to be segregated (such as plasterboard, metal, timber and electrical waste)

☑ if asbestos waste is generated, specialist contractors will need to remove it and then transport it to a licensed facility

☑ all sites producing hazardous waste must be licensed by the Environment Agency (or SEPA in Scotland), disposed of by a licensed contractor and be supported by a consignment note.

 For further information refer to Chapter E03 Waste management.

1.5   Human factors

Competence

☑ A worker must be competent or under the supervision of a competent person.

☑ Site staff should have an appropriate competency card (such as CSCS, CPCS, CISRS, PASMA, IRATA, ATLAS or other approved card).

☑ You will need to check the competence of contractors/persons coming onto site (such as those persons erecting, altering or dismantling scaffolds, operating site plant, digging excavations and installing the supports or installing traffic management systems).

☑ One of the earlier competences to check on site would be that of the cabin installer.

Consultation

☑ Employers must consult with employees or their representatives on issues of health and safety.

☑ Employees must be able to raise issues with you, as an employer, directly or through their representatives.

☑ Where appropriate, and if appointed, trade union safety representatives must be allowed to become actively involved in the consultation process.

☑ As part of site set-up, consideration must be given as to how effective employer/employee consultation can be achieved.

Co-operation

☑ The CDM Regulations require all involved in a construction project to co-operate with each other in the interests of health and safety.

☑ How to achieve this co-operation is best decided at an early stage when the site is being set up.

Contact with emergency services

☑ You should ensure the local emergency services are informed about the site's location, particularly if it is difficult to locate.

☑ It is good practice to display, in the site cabin, a road map showing the quickest route to the nearest hospital.

☑ If you are running a large site, you should nominate an emergency controller to liaise with the emergency services and oversee site emergency actions.

 Whoever you are or whoever you work for, while on a construction site you have a responsibility to ensure you work safely and don't endanger yourself or others by your actions or omissions.

02

Fire prevention and control

This chapter outlines the sources of risk that could lead to a fire on site, the measures that should be taken to prevent a fire and additional measures that are necessary to ensure that everyone on site can escape to a safe place and be accounted for, if a fire occurs.

Several major fires have occurred during maintenance activities and the refurbishment of premises, simply because hot work activities were not adequately controlled.

Implementing and maintaining basic measures can eliminate the risk of fires or reduce the risk to an acceptable level.

Introduction	10
Key requirements	10
The principles of fire risk management	11
Common sources of fire risk	16
Practical fire risk management	17
Hot work	22
Flammable liquids and gases	23
Higher risk projects	25
Fire detection and fire-fighting equipment	26
Site accommodation	29
Training	31
Appendix A – Example of a fire risk assessment	32
Appendix B – Example of a fire risk assessment for temporary accommodation units	35
Appendix C – Example of a fire risk management action plan	36
Appendix D – The enforcement of fire safety law	37
Appendix E – The nature of fire and the selection of extinguishers	38

2.1 Introduction

Fire is an ever-present threat throughout the majority of construction and demolition projects. As construction or demolition progresses the nature of the fire risk is likely to change as different work activities start and are completed. Therefore, not only must the risk of fire be managed continuously, but the management process must allow for the changing nature of the risk.

For all but the smallest of fires, which can be confidently and efficiently dealt with by on-site staff, the simplest fire procedure is as easy as:

A – raise the alarm

B – call the local fire and rescue service

C – evacuate and account for workers, staff, clients and others who may be on site.

Employers, through their site management structure, must be satisfied that the risk of fire is proactively managed, which includes managing:

- [✓] the everyday fire precautions that are a feature of all sites
- [✓] any additional fire risks that arise out of work processes (for example hot work)
- [✓] and maintaining fire detection, fire fighting and fire exit routes.

It is essential that everyone on site knows what to do if the fire alarm sounds, whether it is for real, a practice drill or a false alarm.

Health and safety law places a legal duty on employers to make sure that anyone given a specific role with regard to fire safety is adequately instructed and competent to carry out their responsibilities.

 It is in everyone's interest to make sure that, at any point during the construction or demolition process, the risk of fire is understood and adequate protective measures are in place.

2.2 Key requirements

- [✓] Assess the risk of fire occurring, based upon the chance of a flammable substance and a source of ignition coming together.
- [✓] Take into account any third party fire plans when working in or next to shared premises, especially during refurbishment, repair or maintenance.
- [✓] Put preventative measures in place to ensure fire does not happen.
- [✓] Develop a fire action plan to address any shortcomings in fire risk management, as identified by the fire risk assessment, making sure that higher risks are addressed first.
- [✓] Review and update the fire risk assessment and fire action plan, as necessary, as circumstances change on site.
- [✓] Where circumstances on site demand it, a fire risk manager should be appointed from within the management team to monitor site fire safety and review and update the risk assessment and fire action plan as necessary.
- [✓] Communicate the significant findings of the fire risk assessment, and any significant changes to it, to everyone on site.
- [✓] Inform the fire and rescue services (FRS) of the location of bulk stores of flammable materials, particularly liquefied petroleum gas (LPG) and other explosive gases.
- [✓] Put in place a hot-work permit scheme to control the way in which high-risk activities are carried out.
- [✓] Pay particular attention to the manner in which bulk flammable materials (such as timber, gases, adhesives and highly flammable liquids) are stored.
- [✓] Make sure that fire safety is included as a part of site induction, including what site staff should do in the event of a site evacuation.
- [✓] As far as emergency escape measures are concerned:
  - appoint at least one person to call the emergency services (except where a practice drill is being carried out)
  - make sure that there are always sufficient emergency escape routes to allow safe evacuation, from all parts of the site, by the maximum number of people likely to use each one
  - regularly check that escape routes are kept clear and are not blocked by changes to work activities (such as erecting a mobile tower on a staircase or in a corridor which is an escape route)
  - identify emergency escape routes by installing fire exit signs that direct people to a place of safety via the shortest safe route, and move the signs if necessary should the emergency escape routes have to be altered
  - install a suitable fire alarm system that can be heard in all parts of the site
  - identify with signs one or more assembly points to where site staff should report after a site evacuation.
- [✓] Provide an adequate number of clearly identified fire points that are equipped with appropriate types of fire extinguisher.

☑ Train sufficient people in the selection and use of fire extinguishers to enable small fires to be dealt with before they can become larger, more serious fires.

☑ Pay particular attention to fire safety in site accommodation:
 – a complex of interlinked, and possibly multistorey site cabins is likely to make it necessary to appoint one or more fire wardens to assist in an emergency evacuation
 – such accommodation can quickly become smoke-logged in a fire, increasing the risk of smoke inhalation and possibly creating disorientation and panic in anyone trying to escape
 – it could be argued that the extensive use of mains-powered office equipment and electric heating increases the fire risk.

☑ If cylinders containing LPG, or any other explosive gas, are being heated in a fire:
 – the emergency services must be called immediately
 – there is a risk of a major explosion with the cylinders becoming airborne projectiles
 – attempts to fight the fire must not be made by site staff
 – a prompt site evacuation must be carried out and everyone accounted for
 – upon their arrival the FRS will need to know the location of the cylinders and will organise a 200-metre cordon around the site.

 Fire safety can be a complex issue on large, fast-moving sites with significant numbers of people to evacuate. Where the expertise is not present on site or within the company, it is advisable to seek the advice of a fire safety specialist.

 In this chapter, in most cases, where the word 'construction' appears the point being made will also be applicable to demolition. However, for simplicity's sake only the word 'construction' will be used.

2.3 The principles of fire risk management

The Health and Safety Executive (HSE) regards major construction site fires as low infrequency/high impact events. The effects of a major fire can be devastating for those working on the site and also those living and working nearby. Fires on large, timber-frame projects have resulted in multiple secondary fires, spread over a large area, and the destruction of adjacent businesses and domestic accommodation. The resulting damage and investigations stop all work on the site for a significant length of time with consequences for the people who work there and the employer(s) who may face enforcement action by the HSE or the FRS, potentially putting the future viability of those companies in doubt.

As soon as any item of plant or a site-cabin arrives on site, the risk of fire occurring is increased and the situation must be managed. As the job progresses, various activities will start and be completed and the level of fire risk will vary. It is the dynamic nature of construction sites that makes continual attention to fire risk management so important.

On many projects, as the structure is gradually completed, areas within it become enclosed by rooms, corridors, plant rooms, and so on. At that time, any fire is likely to cause smoke-logging within the areas affected, when toxic smoke will progressively fill the area, displacing breathable oxygen.

It is perhaps at this time that a fire would be most dangerous to those working on site because:

☑ there is likely to be more flammable materials incorporated within the fabric of the structure

☑ the smoke is a toxic hazard

☑ escape routes are likely to be longer as the internal walls and partitions are built

☑ by its dense, black nature, the smoke could make it more difficult to determine the exact path of the escape route (for example, from a multi-room basement, through smoke-logged corridors up to street level)

☑ in an emergency situation, people can panic and may not act in a rational manner.

Whilst any fire on site will create a potentially dangerous situation, it is considered that, in many cases, the threat to personal safety during a fire greatly increases as the structure is nearing completion. By the very nature of the operations carried out (cutting, burning, grinding, welding, and so on), the use of flammable substances and the amount of wood and other combustible materials used or stored on site, the potential for fire is always present and must be effectively managed by:

☑ taking steps to prevent a fire from starting in the first place (managing the process fire risks)

☑ preparing for, effectively reacting to, and limiting the effects of, a fire if it does occur (managing the general fire precautions).

Fire safety law requires that in every workplace a **responsible person** is appointed, whose duty it is to see that the law is complied with, in that effective fire risk management measures are put in place and monitored. In law it would, in most cases, be the employer who would be regarded as the responsible person. However, as with other health and safety legislation, where the employer is not site based, the day-to-day, on-site management of the risks will be delegated to the site manager.

The following text highlights some of the common factors that have to be considered when deciding how best to manage the risk of fire on site.

Assessing fire risks

In presentations to industry stakeholders the FRS has made it clear that if they have to visit a site they will expect to see a site-specific fire risk assessment that addresses current and future fire risk issues. Generic fire risk assessments and those with irrelevant and unsatisfactory details copied and pasted from previous jobs will simply not be acceptable.

If you do not properly assess the risks, there is no way that you can adequately control them.

The principles of carrying out a fire risk assessment are broadly the same as for other risk assessments, although the recommended steps are slightly different to those outlined for more general risk assessments in the Management of Health and Safety at Work Regulations.

The steps in carrying out a fire risk assessment are to:

- identify the fire hazards that will be present on site during the period covered by the risk assessments

- identify the people who will be at risk, which may include people who are not actually on site, evaluate those risks, plan how to remove or reduce them and how to protect people from any risks that remain

- record the significant findings of the risk assessment, develop an emergency plan and inform and instruct those on site regarding the fire risks identified

- periodically review the fire risk assessment to ensure it is still valid, update it as necessary and communicate the changes to those at risk.

The HSE publication *Fire safety in construction* (HSG168) covers this in more detail.

In many cases, carrying out a fire risk assessment will be relatively straightforward, simple and can be carried out by the responsible person or someone nominated by them to do it. In most cases the responsible person on a site will be the main or principal contractor.

On small jobs the initial assessment might be valid all the way through to completion. On larger or complex sites, where perhaps there are a greater number of people to evacuate in an emergency or there are long travel distances to a place of safety, someone with a detailed knowledge of fire risk management (such as a consultant) may be required. In this scenario, it is likely that periodic reviews and updates of the assessment will be required.

Irrespective of the size or complexity of the project, anyone carrying out a fire risk assessment must be competent to do so, in that they can accurately identify the hazards, assess the risks and put effective control measures in place.

For a sample fire risk assessment, in the format recommended by the HSE, refer to Appendix A.

Five stages of a fire risk assessment are described below.

1. Identify potential fire risks on site

Anything that burns is fuel for a fire; in general, fires start in one of three ways:

- accidentally (for example, when an inspection of a work area after hot work has been carried out fails to discover smoldering materials)

- by act or omission (such as in the example above, if the inspection was simply not carried out)

- deliberate arson attack on the structure or, for example, a waste skip.

- Compile an inventory of the flammable materials that are, or will be present, and where they will be stored and used. Consider whether anything can be done to reduce the risk by:
  - altering work processes so that hot work is not necessary
  - using alternative, less-flammable materials
  - reducing the number or quantities of flammable materials on site at any one time.

- Make sure they are stored and used away from sources of ignition, unless unavoidably used as part of a hot-work process.

- Identify the sources of ignition that are, or will be, present, taking account of, for example, hot works that are scheduled in the future.

Examples of the factors that must be considered are:

- [x] the use of any equipment that incorporates a naked flame, hot air stream or hot surface
- [x] preventing the use of faulty electrical equipment
- [x] making sure that electrical equipment is not misused (for example, by overloading circuits)
- [x] the periodic testing and inspection of electrical circuits and equipment, including safety devices
- [x] the safe disposal of discarded smoking materials in the areas where smoking is allowed
- [x] the use of temporary lighting, particularly halogen floodlights
- [x] heat generated by operating plant
- [x] the use of heating and cooking appliances.

2. Identify the people who are at risk

In doing this:

- [x] decide who are the individuals and/or groups of people likely to be at risk if a fire breaks out
- [x] consider whether anyone is at an enhanced level of risk because of what they do, where they work or because of a disability (such as a lack of mobility or reduced hearing)
- [x] consider the impact that a fire would have on neighbouring properties and all forms of traffic passing the site. For example, the FRS will impose a 200-metre cordon and evacuation zone around any fire in which gas cylinders are involved. Experience has shown that such a fire can involve evacuating many people and closing major traffic routes, including railway lines.

3. Evaluate, remove, reduce and protect from risk

Having determined the hazards and who is likely to be harmed, the person who is managing fire safety must take the necessary actions to reduce the risks to an acceptable level.

This is a two-stage process that involves considering how to reduce the risk of:

- [x] a fire occurring, and
- [x] harm to people if a fire does occur.

There are potentially many practical measures that can be taken to reduce the risk of a fire occurring, such as:

- [x] ensuring that electrical office equipment, electrical appliances and portable hand tools are PAT tested at appropriate intervals to detect if any item is starting to break down
- [x] the effective quarantine of defective electrical equipment awaiting repair (or disposal if not repairable)
- [x] the routine testing of electrical distribution systems
- [x] storing flammable and highly flammable liquids in appropriately constructed and sited secure stores that prevent the escape of spillages or impact by traffic or plant
- [x] storing gas cylinders in secure stores that allow any leakage to disperse, with the separation of some gases as is necessary
- [x] prohibiting the refuelling of petrol or diesel-powered equipment and plant whilst it is still hot
- [x] the regular inspection and maintenance as necessary of any system that carries a flammable gas or liquid (such as the supply pipework to oxy-fuel sets, cabin heaters, the canteen cooker or a stand-by generator)
- [x] not allowing oxy-fuel sets to be used unless flash-back arrestors are fitted to the pipework
- [x] preventing arson by putting in place effective security measures, both within and outside of site operating hours
- [x] the introduction and effective implementation of a hot-works permit system for high risk activities
- [x] ceasing hot-work activities at least one hour (two hours for higher risk sites, such as large, timber-frame projects) before site closure, and regularly monitoring the work area and surrounding structure in the intervening time
- [x] maintaining a strict smoking policy; if smoking is permitted in certain areas of the site, provide safe means of disposing of used smoking materials.

Similarly, there are many practical measures that can be taken to reduce the risk to people if a fire should occur, such as:

- [x] making fire safety and evacuation procedures part of site induction
- [x] understanding how fires spread *(see Appendix E)*
- [x] maintaining a strict regime of clearing up solid, flammable waste materials and putting them in skips
- [x] ensuring that any flammable liquid waste is stored safely and disposed of at the first opportunity.

4. Record, plan, instruct and train

Where there are five or more employees, the significant findings of the risk assessment, including details of any actions taken to reduce the fire risk, must be recorded in a manner that can be easily retrieved should it be necessary to do so. Even when there are fewer than five employees, it is considered good practice to record the significant findings of the fire risk assessment as it will assist in developing the emergency plan and will show more clearly where weaknesses in fire risk management lie. If called upon by the enforcing authority to provide evidence of sound fire risk management practices, a written risk assessment is far preferable to a verbal briefing.

The word significant above allows the risk assessor to ignore trivial risks of fire. Producing masses of paper by recording trivial risks is not considered to be good practice. The position of the dividing line between trivial and significant is subjective but it is advisable to err on the side of caution. Asking the question: *Could the physical features of this place, and/or the activities carried out in it, result in personal harm if a fire was to start?* might help in coming to a decision.

Points that require recording include the:

- ☑ significant fire hazards identified

- ☑ hazards that will be eliminated

- ☑ preventative measures that will be taken to reduce the risk of fire from those hazards that cannot be eliminated

- ☑ people who are at risk

- ☑ actions that have been taken to reduce the spread of fire and smoke if a fire should occur

- ☑ details of the general fire precautions (such as the maintenance of escape routes, and the location and maintenance of fire-fighting equipment), plus any fire extinguisher training given

- ☑ details of any instructions given to individuals regarding the actions to take to prevent fires and to escape from the site safely if a fire does occur

- ☑ details of people with particular fire safety responsibilities (such as the fire risk manager and fire marshals).

> Record other fire-related issues, including the delivery of appropriate toolbox talks and other fire-related briefings. These records could be useful at a later date.

The development of the emergency plan and how it must be communicated to all on site has already been covered above.

The fire-related information and training that must be given to those on site includes:

- ☑ the significant findings of the fire risk assessment

- ☑ the measures that have been put in place to reduce the risk

- ☑ what people should do in the event of a fire

- ☑ the identity of people with responsibilities for fire safety (such as fire wardens)

- ☑ any special arrangements that are necessary to protect people on site from serious or imminent danger from fire.

It will also be necessary to provide training on the selection and use of portable fire extinguishers to an appropriate number of staff.

5. Review the fire risk assessment

It could be argued that this stage is more important on construction sites, due to the ever-changing nature of the site, than it is in many other types of workplace. A review provides the opportunity to critically examine the effectiveness of the fire risk assessment with regard to site conditions at that time and to update it as necessary.

For example, consider the changes that might be necessary as a result of:

- ☑ last week's escape route becoming a dead-end today

- ☑ the increasing complexity of escape routes as large structures are built

- ☑ a significant increase in people on site since the last review

- ☑ the start of a hot-work process

- ☑ the start of a process that necessitates the storage of flammable substances (such as LPG and other gases) in bulk

- ☑ the need to extend the fire detection system

- ☑ a poorly carried out practice evacuation

- ☑ the occurrence of a fire-related near miss.

Many local FRS will provide guidance on carrying out fire risk assessments.

The fire action plan

 Through a well-thought-out action plan, you will be better prepared to prevent fire and to cope with one should it occur.

Depending upon the findings of the fire risk assessment, it will normally be necessary to compile a fire action plan to enable the person responsible for fire safety to keep track of fire risks, on a day-by-day basis, throughout the project and to adjust preventative and protective measures as required.

The fire action plan must be compiled and updated as necessary by a person who is competent to:

✓ identify the potential fire and explosion risks

✓ appreciate when these may change, particularly if they significantly increase

✓ implement the measures necessary to minimise the risk of fire and explosion, and mitigate the effects if a fire does occur.

The person(s) selected to do this:

✓ may come from within the existing site management team or,

✓ where particular expertise is required, from a consultancy or specialist fire safety practice

✓ in many cases will not be the same person who is the responsible person in law.

Examples of sites where external expertise might be required include those:

✓ that are large in area with a high number of people to evacuate via multiple escape routes

✓ where the structure being built or refurbished has several floors with limited access between them

✓ that have long or complex escape routes with changes in direction and level.

The nature of the fire action plan will depend upon many factors (such as the size of the site and the fire risks arising out of the type of work being carried out). In many cases it will be a formal document that forms a part of the construction phase plan, compiled in accordance with the Construction (Design and Management) Regulations (CDM). On smaller sites and/or where the fire-related hazards are familiar and simpler to manage, a formal fire action plan may not be required. If this is the case or if only a simple fire action plan is required, it could be within the competence of the site manager to manage fire risks.

The competent person should be responsible for:

✓ compiling the fire action plan, regularly reviewing it and updating it as necessary

✓ making sure that the content (in whole or part) of the fire action plan is communicated to all who need to know (for example, publicising the evacuation procedure to operatives during site induction sessions)

✓ if necessary, establishing a network of fire safety marshals to assist in promoting and updating the plan and in site evacuations (these are usually appointed from the other companies on site)

✓ ensuring that relevant parts of the site fire-safety plan are clearly understood by all on the site, by adequate coverage of fire safety matters during site induction sessions

✓ ensuring fire action notices are displayed on noticeboards and next to fire alarm call-points

✓ implementing a system to locate site visitors, get them to an allocated assembly point and account for them after an evacuation

✓ if necessary, establishing a hot-work permit system and monitoring its effectiveness

✓ ensuring that regular checks of the fire-fighting equipment and facilities are carried out

✓ ensuring that the site fire action plan is clearly understood and complied with by all those on the site

✓ ensuring that all alarms and detection devices are tested at least weekly

✓ arranging for the routine testing and inspection of fire-fighting appliances and for items to be serviced or replaced, as necessary

✓ carrying out weekly inspections of emergency escape routes, and more frequent inspections if deemed necessary due to fast-moving/changes in circumstances

✓ ensuring that access for the emergency services is always maintained

✓ liaising with the emergency services as necessary

✓ liaising on matters of fire safety with site security staff

✓ liaising with any third parties that could be affected (for example, neighbouring properties, highways or railways)

✓ putting in place the arrangements for calling the emergency services

✓ instigating practice evacuation drills and, in conjunction with the fire marshals, monitoring the effectiveness of the procedure in terms of:

   – the time taken to evacuate the site

   – any problems in accounting for everyone on site

   – the need for any improvements to the evacuation procedure that become apparent

✓ monitoring the efficiency of the evacuation procedure during genuine emergency situations and again implementing procedures where necessary.

The fire action plan should include details of:

☑ an organisation chart for fire risk management, where necessary

☑ the names and positions of persons and their responsibilities for the various aspects of fire safety (for example, calling the FRS

☑ general site fire precautions

☑ the location and type of fire-fighting appliances and arrangements for their servicing and inspection

☑ the location of the fire assembly point(s), with details of the persons/companies assigned to each, where there is more than one

☑ process fire risks (for example, hot works)

☑ details of the fire detection and warning alarms installed on site

☑ arrangements for maintaining fire escape routes in an unobstructed state and changing them, as necessary, as work progresses

☑ arrangements for notifying all on site of the emergency escape routes and any changes to them

☑ procedures for implementing a hot-work permit system, if one is in use

☑ details of all site temporary accommodation units, their uses and particular fire hazards (such as a cooking range)

☑ the fire evacuation plan

☑ the access route(s) for the emergency services and making sure they are kept clear

☑ fire drills and training, and the procedure for maintaining written records.

2.4   Common sources of fire risk

Storage and use of flammable materials

Many materials and substances used in the construction process will readily catch fire if exposed to a source of ignition. Additionally, other potentially flammable and explosive substances that are not directly used within the construction process (such as vehicle fuels and gases for cooking and heating within site accommodation) also pose a fire risk if not stored and used correctly.

☑ Where practical, all combustible materials should be stored outside the structure under construction, particularly potentially high risk flammable materials (such as petrol and LPG). Ideally all materials will be stored in a locked compound or storage container, with adequate separation between different types of product. Where internal storage is inevitable, the storage area must:

– not be located so that it poses a threat to people trying to evacuate the site in the event of a fire

– be constructed and arranged so that the spread of fire would be limited

– be separated from the rest of the structure by a partition that provides a minimum of 30 minutes' fire resistance.

☑ Flammable waste materials should not be allowed to accumulate but instead be cleared away promptly to skips located outside the structure; the more waste material there is within the structure, the greater the fire loading.

☑ The HSE has stated in its publications that LPG is the most significant contributor to the risk of fire on construction sites and that it has been implicated in many serious fires and explosions, particularly where leaks have occurred in site accommodation. It must be stored and used in a manner that:

– minimises the amount of LPG stored on site to that needed for immediate and short-term use

– minimises the risk of leaks or damage to cylinders and associated equipment

– allows leaking gas, which is heavier than air, to safely disperse.

☑ The storage of other highly flammable and explosive materials (such as solvents, paints, adhesives, oxygen, acetylene and petrol) must be stored in a manner that:

– minimises the risk of leaks, which will ideally be in a well-ventilated place in the open air

– is protected from direct sunlight

– enables oxygen cylinders to be stored separately from LPG and acetylene cylinders.

Hot work

The failure to adequately control hot work has been the cause of many construction site fires, many of them on refurbishment and maintenance jobs. Hot work is generally:

☑ any task in which heat is deliberately introduced into the work process to achieve a particular aim. Typical examples of this type of hot work include welding, burning, flame-cutting, soldering, heat-stripping of paint, and heat-sealing of roofing membrane. The tools used to create the required level of heat include gas-powered blowlamps and hot-air guns, and various types of welding equipment

☑ other work activities in which the generation of heat is not the prime aim, including the use of halogen spotlights or angle grinders and disc-cutters, which have been the cause of major fires.

A hot-work permit scheme must be introduced to make sure that such work can be carried out in a safe and controlled environment.

Electrical systems and equipment

By its very nature, an electric current will generate heat. In properly designed and maintained circuits and equipment the heating effect will be minimal and a fire hazard will not exist. However, misuse, damage or a lack of maintenance can increase the heat generated and create a potential fire hazard.

Arson

Several major construction site fires, particularly on large timber-frame projects, have been started deliberately. The security of the site should include measures to minimise arson (such as locking up flammable liquids, avoiding build up of waste and rubbish, and locating skips away from buildings).

Smoking

With the introduction of a ban on smoking in enclosed places, this threat has been significantly reduced, although it is possible that some smokers may still be tempted to light up in enclosed, quiet areas of the structure. If smoking areas are provided:

☑ provisions must be made for the safe disposal of spent smoking materials

☑ the designated area must be away from combustible and flammable materials.

Bonfires

Due in no small part to environmental considerations, bonfires are not nearly as common as they were in the past and are now used mainly as a means of disposing of vegetation during site clearance for major road construction. However, if permission for a bonfire is granted, it must be lit and monitored in compliance with a permit system.

Plant and equipment operations

Most engine-driven plant and equipment will generate heat during use; often more heat than necessary if it is poorly maintained or if it is being used beyond its design capacity. Furthermore, plant can easily represent a fire hazard when it is being refuelled or stored away, under cover, whilst still hot.

The lead-acid batteries used in plant and other vehicles give off an explosive gas when the batteries are being recharged, if the batteries are of a type where the filler caps have to be removed or loosened. The same will apply to any type of electrical equipment (for example, temporary traffic light units, which incorporate this type of battery).

Poor housekeeping

The accumulation of flammable waste material:

☑ will increase the fire loading of any structure

☑ has the potential to put people at risk by blocking access to fire alarms, fire-fighting equipment and escape routes.

Advice on good practice in the storage and disposal of waste is included later in this chapter.

Other examples of poor housekeeping that increase fire risk are:

☑ work being carried out in designated escape routes (for example, tower scaffolds erected on staircases)

☑ flammable and highly flammable liquids and gases not being returned to their proper storage areas after use

☑ access routes for the emergency services being blocked and preventing access to all parts of the site.

2.5   Practical fire risk management

The person with responsibility for fire risk management must consider the following areas at all stages of the project and then review, revise and communicate the changes of the fire risk assessment and fire action plan to those who are at risk, as necessary.

You must:

☑ establish when and where flammable materials of any type will be stored, used or incorporated into the structure

☑ establish when and where sources of ignition will be present

☑ ensure that flammable materials and sources of ignition cannot come into contact

☑ ensure that should a fire occur, everyone on site immediately becomes aware of it

☑ ensure that everyone can evacuate the site to a place of safety

☑ be aware of, and guard against, the threat of arson, which can defeat otherwise sound fire risk management precautions

☑ liaise with contractors working on the site to establish what flammable materials or substances, or what hot-work processes, they propose to use on the site.

Emergency escape routes

There must be sufficient escape routes from all parts of the site to a place of safety, in the open air and at ground level.

These will ideally be determined at the design stage to ensure their continued integrity. The escape routes must be:

- ☑ adequate with regard to the number of people likely to use them, bearing in mind that this is likely to change on a regular basis on fast-moving sites
- ☑ always available in case of fire
- ☑ kept free of obstructions and checked that they are unobstructed at least weekly
- ☑ altered as necessary as the project advances
- ☑ equipped with adequate signage and lighting (possibly including emergency lighting) as necessary, all of which must be moved as the escape routes change.

Fire drills

Emergency evacuations should be practised at suitable intervals. The interval will:

- ☑ vary from site to site and even on the same site as work progresses
- ☑ depend upon many factors, not least the complexity of the site and the potential difficulty in accounting for everyone known to be on site.

Such drills will provide evidence of suitability in the effectiveness of the alarm signal, or possibly prove that it cannot be heard in some areas. It will also show any bottlenecks where there could be problems in a real emergency unless action is taken. Everyone should be made aware of what the alarm signal sounds like during site induction and the timing of any regular testing for which no action is necessary.

An accurate system of booking in and out of the site is absolutely essential to enable the person running an evacuation to know who is on site at any time.

No-notice drills provide the most useful information on the effectiveness of the evacuation procedure, but it is recognised that in many cases such drills will be impractical. However, even pre-notified drills will provide information on evacuation time and the problems faced by fire marshals in the event of a fire or emergency.

Fire detection systems

During the early stages of new-build projects it is inevitable that the only way of detecting fires is visually; someone will spot a fire and raise the alarm by word of mouth or whatever other means of raising the alarm has been provided. However, on larger and higher-risk sites, as areas within a structure become enclosed, with increasing amounts of flammable materials present, the benefits of an automatic fire detection become obvious. Where a permanent automatic fire detection system is planned, activation of the system should be programmed in as early as possible.

During refurbishment work, which has been the cause of many serious fires, if an automatic fire detection system already exists, it should remain live throughout the work where it is practical to do so.

Fire alarm systems

In the event of a fire, it is essential that the alarm is raised as quickly as possible so that employees and others (such as visitors) can quickly and safely reach a place of safety.

A means of detecting and warning of fire must be provided in sufficient positions so that no fire goes undetected and everyone on the site is aware that the alarm has sounded. Hand bells, klaxons or manually or electrically operated sounders may be suitable so long as they are clearly audible above background noise in all areas and can be readily identified as being a fire alarm. Flashing lights or vibrating pagers may be required in certain circumstances (for example, where there is continuous or frequent loud noise).

The HSE has made it clear that, with the emergence of low-cost wireless technology, the size or complexity of the site would not be regarded as a valid barrier to having effective fire warning and alarm systems.

Legible, written emergency procedures (fire action notices) must be displayed in prominent locations around the site, and should include:

- ☑ the location of the notice to enable the location of the fire to be pinpointed
- ☑ instructions for raising the alarm
- ☑ instructions for calling the FRS
- ☑ instructions to report to the nearest assembly point
- ☑ clear information as to the whereabouts of the assembly point

- [✓] a clear instruction not to leave the assembly point until a roll-call has been taken

- [✓] an indication of the locations of fire escape routes

- [✓] an instruction not to re-enter the building or site until it has been declared safe to do so by someone in authority.

Fire-fighting equipment

An extensive range of equipment is available for fighting fire. This is covered later in this chapter.

Smoking restrictions

Smoking in enclosed and substantially enclosed workplaces is now banned in England and Wales, Scotland and Northern Ireland. The following advice refers to situations where smoking is allowed in some non-enclosed areas.

Given that smoking in the open air is not prohibited, site rules must be established to ensure safe smoking areas are available and provision is made for the safe disposal of smoking materials, as carelessly discarded smoking materials have the potential to cause fires on site.

Areas where smoking is allowed should be equipped with adequate fire-fighting equipment. Non-combustible containers should be provided to aid safe disposal of discarded smoking materials.

As work progresses and the site develops it will be necessary to monitor the changes in the fire risk areas and review the areas where smoking is allowed accordingly.

Site rules should ensure that smoking is prohibited for an appropriate period, usually one hour at the end of each working day. This will allow any fire to be discovered and dealt with before the site closes.

Heating appliances

The term *heating appliances* covers a range of equipment, ranging from wall-mounted, electric site-cabin heaters, through small, free-standing, infrared or ceramic heaters, to large, forced-air LPG heaters. The precautions that will be necessary depend upon the nature of the hazard presented by the type of heater(s) in use.

The risk of fire arises from the use of heating appliances if they are sited and installed incorrectly, inadequately maintained or are not suitable for the intended use or location.

Fuel supplies for gas-fired appliances, especially propane or butane, should be kept secured outside the building and piped in through fixed pipework. Any flexible pipework should be kept as short as possible, and used only for the final connection to the cylinder. Any room in which a gas fire is used must be fitted with a permanently open vent or louvre to enable the fire appliance to operate properly without producing excess carbon dioxide. (A window that could be closed in cold weather, for example, is not acceptable.)

Gas fires, plus the associated pipework, connections and so on, must be regularly serviced by Gas Safe registered engineers.

Combustible material should be kept well away from heaters and stoves. The practice of drying wet clothing in front of, or on, heaters should be prohibited; if a drying room is needed one should be provided.

Care must be taken to see that combustible materials are not allowed to build up around such heaters. Spare cylinders must not be stored in site cabins or anywhere else where they may be subjected to being heated.

All heaters and stoves, including cookers, must be turned off at the end of the working day with the supply valve on the cylinder closed.

Storage of waste

Most construction sites generate large quantities of rubbish and waste material that present a potential fire risk. Good housekeeping is essential.

A build up of combustible material causing a fire risk

Rubbish and waste should be cleared from site on a regular basis, if the risk of fire is to be controlled. Although not all rubbish and waste can be taken to a centralised point for disposal, sites should be organised so that skips and other waste disposal containers can be safely positioned not less than three metres away from any building or structure.

Skips and other waste disposal containers should not be placed adjacent to the structure under construction or the means of escape from it. However, they must be positioned to:

- [✓] encourage the regular clearing and segregation of waste

- [✓] be readily available to vehicles contracted to collect and deliver skips

- [✓] be away from canopies, overhanging eaves, and so on

- [✓] be more than three metres away from all other structures, unless precautions to prevent the spread of skip fires are taken.

The following points should also be considered.

- [✓] Site rules should state that contractors must clear their rubbish daily, or more often if required due to the nature and volume of the rubbish created.

- [✓] Skips should be emptied or replaced before the flammable waste in them represents a significant fire load.

The protection of finished surfaces

Once a building is nearing completion, it is common practice to use temporary coverings to protect finished surfaces and installed equipment during the remaining fitting-out phase. These coverings often take the form of plastic sheeting, fibreboard or similar materials, some of which may be flammable. They can therefore add to the fire loading of the building, and consequently assist in spreading fire. Ideally, purpose-made, fire-retardant materials should be used.

If non-fire-retardant materials are used the:

- ☑ protective covering should be fitted as late as possible in the project
- ☑ fire protection measures must be suitable to cover the enhanced risk.

Electrical safety

Electrical installations should be professionally designed, installed, inspected and maintained. This will ensure that the installation has the required capacity to cope with the intended loads and that it will remain in a safe condition. On most sites, particularly larger ones, a regime of regular inspection and maintenance of the system will be required.

Unauthorised alterations must not be made to the distribution system. Such a move indicates that the system, as installed, no longer fully satisfies the needs of the site and that it should be upgraded, with both the design and installation carried out by competent persons.

Halogen light fittings can get very hot and cause materials near them to ignite. Historically they have been a common source of ignition for site fires and it is best practice to only use them where other forms of task lighting are not suitable and the fire risk assessment shows that it is safe to do so.

The failure of electrical hand tools and mains-powered office equipment has also been the cause of fires. The regular testing of portable electrical appliances and hand tools (PAT testing) will confirm whether the internal insulation is breaking down or there are other defects rendering the equipment a potential fire hazard. Portable electrical equipment should be switched off and disconnected from the supply when not in use for extended periods, particularly those items that it might be tempting to leave on overnight (such as photocopiers and fax machines).

Possible causes of electrical fires are the:

- ☑ overheating of poorly maintained or damaged equipment and hand tools
- ☑ overloading of electrical circuits
- ☑ overloading of electrical sockets in site accommodation
- ☑ accumulation of combustible rubbish alongside cables (frequently in ceiling voids) or distribution boards
- ☑ by-passing of circuit safety devices, rendering them inoperative
- ☑ fitting of the incorrect rating of fuse or residual current device (RCD)
- ☑ unauthorised modification or tapping into of the site electrical distribution system
- ☑ failure to carry out the periodic testing of electrical circuits and safety devices
- ☑ ignition of explosive airborne particles or fumes by sparking within electrical equipment or tools
- ☑ accidental damage to equipment and conductors that have not been adequately protected.

Bonfires

In most cases environmental factors and/or Local Authority restrictions make the controlled burning of rubbish on site an unacceptable practice. Furthermore, the potential for the reuse or recycling of waste materials should always be considered. Generally bonfires are only acceptable, in limited situations, for the burning of vegetation or rubbish as part of site clearance for road building projects. Furthermore, a bonfire should not be lit where drifting smoke would be a nuisance to others, particularly where it would present a danger to users of nearby roads by reducing visibility.

If, under exceptional circumstances, bonfires are allowed:

- ☑ prior approval and the necessary permits must be obtained from the relevant authorities
- ☑ no fire should be left unattended during working hours, or left smouldering or burning after work has ceased
- ☑ the attendant should have a suitable fire extinguisher and have been trained in its use
- ☑ the volume of material burnt at any time must be limited to what can be fitted into a single incinerator, typically a spent 50 gallon oil-drum that has been cleaned to remove any residue of the original content
- ☑ prior to burning, the waste material should be checked for hazardous items (such as empty aerosol cans and other highly flammable substances)
- ☑ they should be situated away from any buildings, boundaries, roadways, overhead lines, fuel stores or other combustible materials or structures
- ☑ consideration must be given to wind direction and strength.

Never light a bonfire using any flammable liquid. There could be a danger to the person lighting the fire being burnt by the flash as the flammable liquid ignites and also a chance of secondary fires starting as heavier-than-air vapours spread.

Fire marshals

The site fire risk manager or other competent person may, in consultation with the principal or main contractor, need to arrange for the appointment of fire marshals to assist in the evacuation of the site, and the implementation of the site fire action plan, particularly any site evacuation. On large sites it is usual for at least one fire marshal to be appointed from each company of sub-contractors to account for that company's staff in the event of a site evacuation.

Where fire marshals' duties are more extensive, they must be allowed sufficient time to carry out their duties and to undertake any training that may be necessary.

Arson

 Some people take great delight in setting fire to structures under construction; don't let it happen to you. Keep your security tight.

Arson has been the suspected cause of many construction site fires and so, ideally, flammable materials should not be stored where they could be seen and set alight from outside the site boundary. Effective site security is essential to prevent arson. If necessary consider patrols by contracted security guards and/or the use of CCTV.

The only effective way to prevent arson is to make sure that:

- ☑ only authorised people have access to the site during normal working hours
- ☑ effective site security prevents unauthorised access to the site out of normal working hours
- ☑ flammable materials are not left in a place where they can be seen and set on fire from outside the site
- ☑ if necessary, remove flammable liquids, LPG, other gases and combustible material whilst the site is closed.

The positioning of the stores for flammable substances and gas bottles should be such that any fire in the vicinity would not prevent the use of an emergency escape route, thereby forcing people past the hazard.

Specialist advice

The Fire Protection Association (FPA), in conjunction with the Construction Confederation (CC), published the eighth edition of *Fire prevention on construction sites* in July 2012. This joint code of practice (CoP) deals with the protection from fire on construction sites and buildings undergoing renovation.

The CoP does not have any legal status; however, it does outline good practice and many insurance companies now require that the authoritative guidelines (such as those detailed in the CoP) are properly implemented on construction projects before they will give full insurance.

This chapter broadly outlines the requirements of the CoP.

 The FPA also publishes *Construction site fire prevention checklist – a guide for insurers, surveyors and construction industry professionals.*

Liaison with the fire and rescue service

Contact should be made with the FRS at an early stage of the project, if it is envisaged that there will at some time be significant quantities of flammable materials (of any type) on site, to enable them to plan their response to any emergency. It is likely that the FRS will visit the site as a result.

A site layout plan should be made available to the FRS, as should any updated versions of it. The site layout plan should indicate:

- ☑ a FRS access point if there is more than one site access
- ☑ emergency escape routes
- ☑ the location of fire points and other fire-fighting equipment
- ☑ the location of flammable and highly flammable material storage areas (particularly LPG)
- ☑ positions and types of fire alarm sounders
- ☑ location of assembly point(s).

The FRS are likely to be particularly interested in sites where:

- ☑ there is a significant fire risk to the public resulting from a large scale evacuation of a high number of people
- ☑ large or high fire-risk structures (such as multistorey timber frame) are to be built close to other occupied premises
- ☑ highly flammable materials will be stored and used
- ☑ there may be difficult access to the site by the FRS
- ☑ work will take place above 18 metres, in which case specialist access equipment is required
- ☑ work is taking place in a building that is partially occupied by others.

02

2.6   Hot work

Cutting, burning and welding operations, together with the use of blowlamps and other LPG-fuelled tools, have been the cause of many fires on building and construction sites. It is essential that anyone engaged in hot works is:

- ☑ aware of the fire risk in the particular location where work is to be carried out

- ☑ aware of how heat might be transmitted to other areas

- ☑ trained and competent to use the equipment that will produce the source of heat

- ☑ trained and competent to select and use mobile fire extinguishers.

Precautions must be taken where heat from a work process could be transmitted to other combustible materials (for example, where hot works are carried out on steelwork or pipes adjacent to, or passing through, flammable materials, such as studwork walls or timber floors). Where this kind of operation is anticipated, it is essential that all combustible materials, including liquids, are protected before any work is allowed to start. Special care should be taken when cutting or welding is carried out above flammable materials. Precautions must be taken to prevent sparks or hot fragments of metal from dropping onto and igniting the flammable material below (such as removing it or covering it with fire-resisting material).

The following precautions must be observed where using bitumen boilers:

- ☑ the distance between the boiler and LPG cylinder must be at least three metres

- ☑ the boiler must never be left unattended, moved or towed whilst the burner is alight

- ☑ if possible avoid taking boilers onto roofs; if this cannot be avoided, place the boiler on a non-combustible, insulating base

- ☑ appropriate fire-fighting equipment must be located nearby.

Hot work should cease:

- ☑ one hour before the site is vacated at the end of the day with the area actively monitored for signs of fire until the site is vacated, or

- ☑ two hours before the site is vacated on high-risk sites (such as large, timber-frame projects), with the area actively monitored for the first hour and then checked again at the two hour point.

Checks must include an inspection of cavities, around eaves, behind studding, and so on, and into other voids where smouldering material would otherwise go undetected.

The introduction of a permit system should be considered for all hot work, except where the risk of fire is considered to be low. Hot-work permits are formal management documents that should only be issued by someone with official authority to do so. Hot-work permits should normally include:

- ☑ the location where the work will be carried out

- ☑ a description of the hot work to be carried out

- ☑ the proposed start time and duration of the workplaces

- ☑ the time at which the permit expires (the work must be completed or cease at that time).

Other precautions to be taken, which should be reflected in the hot-work permit, include instructions for:

- ☑ clearing all combustible material from the surrounding area

- ☑ checking for combustible material in adjacent hidden locations

- ☑ having a suitable and serviceable fire extinguisher at the place of the work

- ☑ maintaining a careful watch for the early signs of fire during the work

- ☑ protecting combustible material that cannot be cleared (for example, by the use of asbestos matting)

- ☑ carrying out the post-work checks already mentioned.

 For an example of a hot-work permit refer to Section G *Checklists and forms*.

Even where a formal hot-work permit scheme is in operation, because of a perceived low risk of fire, basic fire safety precautions (such as having a serviceable fire extinguisher to hand) are still required.

2.7   Flammable liquids and gases

 You cannot be too careful when LPG is being used on your site; the person doing the job must be competent and you must ensure that they are.

Liquefied petroleum gas should be stored in purpose-designed, fireproof compounds or cages that prevent the accumulation of vapour in the event of a leak. Compounds should have a level base of compacted earth, concrete or paving slabs and be surrounded by a secure chain-link fence at least 1.8 metres high. There should be sufficient shelter to prevent cylinders from being exposed to extremes of weather. Signs must be clearly displayed indicating the presence of LPG, and prohibiting smoking and the use of any naked flame in the area of the store.

Precautions for the use of LPG include:

- ☑ minimising the amount of LPG on site at any one time

- ☑ turning off cylinder valves before connecting or disconnecting any equipment

- ☑ checking cylinders and all associated equipment before use; do not use if there are signs of damage or leaks

- ☑ use soapy water to try to detect the exact location of leaks; the smell should provide the initial indication

- ☑ store LPG cylinders:
   - with their valves uppermost, apart from cylinders used to provide fuel for LPG-powered plant, which are used and stored on their side
   - away from oxygen, highly flammable liquids, oxidisers, toxic or corrosive gases or substances
   - a distance of at least three metres from other substances, although they may be kept in the same compound.

Small, easily portable LPG cylinders and canisters should ideally be removed from site after work.

 LPG cylinders must never be stored in unventilated metal boxes or site accommodation.

Following mechanical failure of LPG equipment, or any other event that causes the release of LPG, the resulting gas will form a flammable mixture with air at gas concentrations between approximately 2% and 10%.

Ignition of released LPG, where the concentration exceeds 2%, can result in fire or, if confined, an explosion. If a leak does not ignite immediately, and the LPG and air mixture drifts from the point of release, it will gradually become more diluted. However, if the concentration still exceeds 2%, ignition could cause a flash or cloud-fire back to the point of release.

A leak of LPG may be noticed either by the smell or the noise of the gas escaping. There may also be condensation or frosting on the outside of the cylinder.

Leaks must not be traced with a lighted match or naked flame as this would almost certainly cause an explosion. Only soapy water or a proprietary leak-finding fluid should be used.

If it is suspected that LPG has leaked inside a building, no attempt should be made to touch any electrical apparatus.

 Never turn on light switches or any other electrical equipment if a leak of LPG is suspected.

Open all doors and windows, if it is safe to do so, and leave immediately. Do not re-enter the building until advice has been sought and you are told it is safe.

All LPG cylinders and regulators for use with fixed heaters, cookers and lighting within site huts must be kept outside and the gas supply piped in using rigid copper piping. The use of flexible hosing is permitted only between the cylinders and changeover valves or manifolds, and for the final connection to appliances, but this must be kept as short as possible.

All pipework should be exposed and easily accessible for inspection, but located to prevent accidental damage. Any work on LPG pipework or other parts of a fixed installation, including testing, must only be carried out by appropriately trained (Gas Safe registered) persons.

Ventilation for heaters and cookers must be permanent and adequate. It should be divided equally between vents at high and low level.

 e.g.

A two-burner cooker in a site hut needs approximately 150 mm x 150 mm ventilation. A 3 kW convector heater needs approximately 225 mm x 225 mm ventilation.

Inspections of all appliances must be carried out before use. If soot forms or smells occur, do not use or allow the appliance to be used. Find out the reasons for the problem and have it put right.

Before using LPG equipment in an enclosed space a risk assessment must be carried out. It is essential to ensure that there is adequate ventilation, which may have to be forced. This is necessary to ensure full combustion and also to make certain that the products of combustion, other fumes and excess oxygen from any cutting apparatus are removed. Enhanced fire safety precautions and the use of atmospheric monitoring should be considered.

Wherever practicable, cylinders used with operations in confined spaces should be located in a safe area, preferably in the open air. The supply pressure should be reduced to the lowest practicable level on leaving the source of supply.

Where cylinders are used below ground level, the number must be kept as small as possible. All cylinders and hoses should be removed as soon as work has finished or if it is interrupted for a substantial period (for example, overnight).

LPG cylinders must not be taken into confined spaces, as defined in the Confined Spaces Regulations, unless exceptional safety precautions are taken.

Highly flammable and explosive substances (such as adhesives, solvents and paint) should be stored in:

☑ an external, secure, purpose-built compound, where site conditions allow

☑ a suitable secure, internal, fireproof storeroom where external storage is not practical, although it will be necessary to install fire detection and suppression systems

☑ a metal, lockable cabinet or bin, for immediate or imminent use at the place of work.

No petrol in timber frames or enclosed buildings – use designated refuelling and cutting points or better still another type of powered equipment

Where it is necessary to store bulk quantities of highly flammable substance, the storage area should:

☑ be located outdoors, apart from in exceptional circumstances, in a position where it cannot be accidentally hit by vehicles or plant

☑ have a gently sloping concrete pad with a sump to catch any leaks or spillage and a bund that is able to contain the contents of the largest can or drum stored + 10%, where bulk liquids are stored

☑ be protected against direct sunlight.

☑ be at least two metres away from nearby buildings or boundaries, except where the boundary of the store forms part of a solid wall, cans or drums may be stacked up against that wall up to one metre from the top

☑ be fitted with appropriate signage to indicate the content (such as 'highly flammable' or 'flashpoint below 32°C')

☑ be fitted with an 'EX' sign when an assessment under the Dangerous Substances and Explosive Atmospheres Regulations (DSEAR) indicates that an explosive atmosphere could be present in the event of a leak

☑ be fitted with 'No smoking' or 'Naked flame' signs

☑ be kept locked when access is not required

☑ be equipped with intrinsically safe electrical circuits and fittings where electrical supplies are necessary

☑ be equipped with dry powder or foam fire extinguishers

☑ be equipped with a quantity of absorbent material, to soak up any spilt liquids, and a suitable container for the collection and safe disposal of the contaminated absorbent

☑ if necessary, be equipped with racking made from a non-ferrous metal or other non-combustible material.

> ❗ The secure storage of dangerous materials in a proper compound or cabinet is as equally important as using them in a safe manner.

If for any reason it is not practical to store highly flammable or other dangerous substances outside (for example, if the footprint of the structure under construction completely fills the land available) conditions for outdoor storage above apply, and the DSEAR assessment must consider whether the risks of storage indoors are acceptable. If not, safe, off-site storage and transportation must be arranged.

In deciding whether or not the risks associated with indoor storage are acceptable, it is likely that expert advice will be required to determine the suitability of the proposed storage area with regard to its fire and explosion resistance.

It is recommended that the maximum quantities that may be stored in cabinets and bins are no more than 50 litres for highly flammable liquids (and flammable liquids with a flashpoint below the maximum ambient temperature of the workroom/working area) and no more than 250 litres for other flammable liquids with a higher flashpoint of up to 55°C.

Under no circumstances should storage areas be located underground as this would prevent the dispersal of heavier-than-air vapours, should a leak occur.

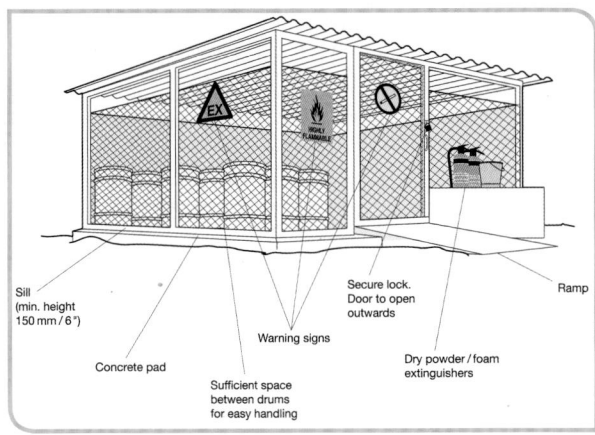

When not in use, containers of flammable liquids needed for current work activities should be kept closed and stored in suitable cabinets or bins of fire-resisting construction, designed to retain spills (110% volume of the largest vessel normally stored in it).

All signs must conform to the Health and Safety (Safety Signs and Signals) Regulations.

Sill (min. height 150 mm / 6")

Concrete pad

Warning signs

Sufficient space between drums for easy handling

Secure lock. Door to open outwards

Dry powder / foam extinguishers

Ramp

A secure dangerous substances storage area

When storing materials at the workplace, ready for use, only store one day's supply, or less, where highly flammable materials are to be used.

On many sites there will be a need to store bulk quantities of vehicle fuels, particularly diesel oil, usually in a bowser or drum. If storage drums are used, the same conditions apply as for the storage of other highly flammable and explosive substances.

Carelessly dispensing fuel into vehicles or plant when the engine is still hot has been the cause of many serious fires and injuries.

Where fuel oil is to be dispensed into containers or vehicles, the outlet must be fitted with a valve or nozzle, which closes automatically when not in use and cannot be fixed in the open position unless an automatic cut-off nozzle is used on the end of the hose.

The hose and nozzle should be housed in an enclosed, secure cabinet with a drip tray when not in use, or have a lockable valve where the feed leaves the tank. Hoses should be kept locked or kept within the bund when not in use.

Any permanent valve or tap that opens directly from the tank must:

- [x] be located within the secondary containment system (bund wall)
- [x] discharge vertically downwards
- [x] be locked off when not in use.

Finally, no vent must discharge outside of the bund in the event of an overfill.

Generally, petrol is only used in relatively low quantities for small generators and some hand tools (such as chainsaws) but, however small the quantity, it must be stored safely. Petrol will usually be stored in 20 litre metal jerry cans or five-litre, purpose-made plastic containers. The jerry cans or containers must be kept closed, except for when the content is being decanted.

The positioning of fire extinguisher points, and the types of extinguisher, must be based in part upon where construction materials, flammable substances and gases will be stored and used.

The positioning of the stores for flammable substances and gas bottles should be such that any fire in the vicinity would not prevent the use of an emergency escape route, thereby forcing people past the hazard.

2.8   Higher risk projects

The HSE has identified two types of construction project that have suffered potentially life-threatening fires that have been particularly difficult to deal with.

Timber-frame structures

The emergence of new construction techniques (such as large, timber-frame developments) has demonstrated how devastating construction site fires can be, not only with regard to the potential loss of life and the total destruction of the structure itself, but also the major fire damage that can be caused to other properties over a wide area.

As such structures are at their most vulnerable when the timber structure is being erected and before any cladding or protective skins are installed each structure should be clad at the earliest practical opportunity. Designers should give consideration to the use of materials that have been given a fire protective/retardant treatment.

Ideally, large timber-frame structures will be compartmentalised at the earliest opportunity to prevent the spread of fire and to ensure a safe travel distance for anyone who has to evacuate the structure in an emergency.

Consideration must be given to using fire-resistant boarding to temporarily fire-stop ducts and shafts until the permanent fire-engineered solution is installed.

Temporary or permanent fire-resisting doors, panels and fire stopping should be installed as early in the construction programme as is practical.

Where there are multiple, timber-frame structures on a site, the fire risk assessment must consider how a fire in one of them could be prevented or slowed from spreading to the others or to adjacent premises. To this end, temporary non-combustible cladding could be used to cover exposed timber and other combustible construction materials prior to the final cladding being installed.

High risk timber-frame buildings require additional fire prevention measures

Multistorey buildings

The FRS should be informed where work will take place above 18 metres, as specialist access equipment may be required.

This type of structure, during either construction or refurbishment, can pose particular problems with regard to the management of fire risk. Incomplete or absent fire-engineered solutions can result in the rapid spread of fire, leaving any workers on the upper floors particularly at risk. Furthermore, it is possible that in some circumstances it will not be practical to supply sufficient water for fire-fighting purposes to the higher levels.

In these circumstances a specific risk assessment must be undertaken to establish how the safety of those working on the upper levels can be assured in the event of a fire.

Designers have a major part to play in maintaining fire safety, not only in the selection of materials and the work methods that are necessary as a result of design decisions, but also in ensuring that:

☑ temporary, fire-resistant compartmentalisation or other fire-engineering solutions are incorporated as necessary until permanent fire stopping is in place, particularly above 18 metres

☑ with new-build or refurbished premises, a working fire alarm system 'follows the building up' so that it can be heard in all parts of the building at all stages of construction

☑ the fire alarm system is electrically operated (hard-wired or wireless) with break-glass call points and sounders at each level

☑ the rising water main(s) are installed and commissioned at an early stage before interior work starts

☑ if some floors are already occupied, the risk assessment and fire emergency plans allow for:
  – the integration of the fire alarm systems for both the construction areas and the occupied floors
  – any restrictions that prevent construction workers accessing the occupied part of the building, particularly escape routes
  – the possibility that construction workers may not be allowed access to occupied parts of the building

☑ access to all staircases, or other protected routes, is maintained at all times, as far as possible, with one staircase designated as a fire-fighting staircase for the sole use of the fire and rescue service during an emergency

☑ fire doors with self-closers are fitted to protect the escape stairways in accordance with the findings of a risk assessment.

2.9　Fire detection and fire-fighting equipment

Fire detection

Details of what should be provided to detect and warn others of the existence of a fire can be found earlier in this chapter (*2.5 Practical fire risk management*).

Portable fire extinguishers

Fire extinguishers do not prevent fires. However, they can be used by trained employees in an attempt to minimise loss and damage after a fire has started. It goes without saying that preventing the fire in the first place is a far better option.

Where there is a realistic possibility that staff will have to use a fire extinguisher, they should be trained in their use. Fire safety law requires that an appropriate number of staff are trained in the selection and use of fire extinguishers, although some companies may take the view that all staff should simply evacuate the structure and leave fire fighting to the professionals.

In line with the risks identified in a fire risk assessment, adequate numbers of suitable types of portable fire extinguisher must be provided and kept available throughout the premises.

Extinguishers must be located in conspicuous positions near exits on each floor. They should be fixed to the wall with their carrying handles approximately one metre above the floor level. Where this is not possible, they should be fixed in position (for example, using base plates or stands) at floor level.

In the open, extinguishers should be situated in red painted boxes, which are either sitting on the floor or raised 500 mm above ground level, with a 'Fire point' sign at a height readily seen above any obstructions. Care must be taken during winter months to ensure that extinguisher contents do not freeze.

To protect electrical distribution panels and items of electrical equipment, appropriate extinguishers (usually carbon dioxide) must be provided near but not dangerously close to the equipment concerned.

For large or costly items of equipment (such as computer suites) the installation of automatic fire detection and extinguishing systems should be considered.

A good fire point on site

Colour-coding of fire extinguishers

It is essential that staff who may be called upon to use a fire extinguisher have been trained in their use and have a clear understanding of the colour-coding system. All fire extinguishers are painted red with a contrasting colour somewhere on the casing (such as a contrasting panel or handle), which indicates what extinguishing agent the extinguisher contains.

Colour-coding by agent or medium enables a trained person to rapidly identify the type of extinguisher needed in an emergency.

Extinguishing medium	Water	Foam	Powder (all types)	Carbon dioxide
Colour of panel	Red	Cream	Blue	Black
	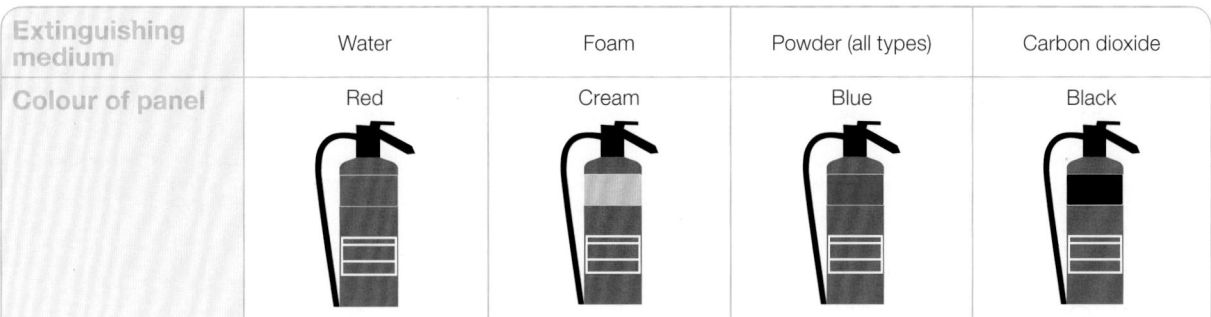			

A few extinguishers may still be in use that complied with a much earlier standard of colour-coding. This standard required that the whole body of each extinguisher was painted in the same contrasting colours that are now used in the later standard.

In addition, a small number of extinguishers are bright silver or self-coloured metal with a designated panel stating the medium they contain. The colour-coding of the panel is the same as that listed above.

Inspection and maintenance

Fire-fighting equipment should be inspected monthly and maintained and tested at least once a year by a competent person. The maintenance and tests should be carried out in accordance with the manufacturer's instructions and recorded in the appropriate register.

In addition to the monthly inspections of fire-fighting equipment it is particularly important to check extinguishers which, within a year, are sent to more than one site. When a site is set up, on receipt of the fire extinguishers, the site manager must inspect them for serviceability and the date that the next check is due.

Extinguishers should be tested by discharge at intervals specified in BS 5306, and always be recharged immediately after any use. The maintenance and inspection of fire-fighting equipment should be recorded in a register.

Hazardous vapours from fire extinguishers

The discharge of a carbon dioxide (CO_2) extinguisher in any small, enclosed or confined space will reduce the percentage of oxygen in the air. The dust cloud from a dry powder extinguisher may, in a confined space, produce local and temporary breathing difficulties and poor visibility.

Once an extinguisher has been discharged in such circumstances, the user should leave the area immediately. When it is safe to do so, the area should be thoroughly ventilated before allowing anyone to re-enter. If there is a need to re-enter before the air has cleared, suitable breathing apparatus will have to be worn.

Staff training in the selection and use of fire extinguishers

 For further information on which extinguisher(s) should be used on different types of fire refer to Appendix E.

There is a legal requirement for employers to ensure that all employees are familiar with fire procedures, and that an appropriate number of employees are trained in the use of fire-fighting equipment. Training in the selection and use of portable extinguishers is essential if they are to be used effectively in fighting small fires. It is also very important that the right type of extinguisher is used on certain types of fire.

Attention should be given to the physical strength of persons who may have to use extinguishers. Some extinguishers weigh 20 kg.

During staff training on the use of extinguishers, the following points also need to be emphasised.

- ☑ Think of evacuation first.
- ☑ Only use an extinguisher if it is safe for you to do so.
- ☑ Do not let the fire come between you and your escape route. You may become trapped if the fire develops.
- ☑ If the extinguisher does not appear to be working or is ineffective on the fire, get out immediately.
- ☑ If the fire starts to increase or gets out of control, get out immediately.

During induction training or ongoing staff training, the following points should be made to all staff.

- ☑ Do not use a fire extinguisher unless you have been trained to do so.
- ☑ Do not misuse fire extinguishers.
- ☑ Do not move fire extinguishers from their allocated positions (for example, do not use fire extinguishers as door stops).
- ☑ Immediately report any fire extinguishers that appear to have been used, misused or damaged.

Hose reels

Hose reels linked to a constant water supply may sometimes be available, and can be an effective means of fire fighting. They are more likely to be found in a live state on projects where premises are being refurbished and, if trained staff are available, they are a very useful aid in fighting some fires.

On new build projects or where the water supply to existing hose reels has been drained, it is good practice to make the supply live as the fire loading of the structure increases, providing trained staff are available.

Training employees in the correct use of hose reels is essential if fire fighting is to be effective. Staff need to be fully aware of how the hose reels work, and what type of fire they would be effective on before they use them in an emergency.

A hose reel must not be used on:

- ☑ live electrical apparatus
- ☑ any fire involving fat, oil, paint or other flammable liquids
- ☑ any fire involving burning metal or metal powder.

To do so could lead to electrocution, or a violent explosion of burning liquid or metal.

Fire blankets

Fire blankets are usually sufficient to deal with small, contained fires involving tea-making facilities, frying pans and so on, and are usually found next to cooking facilities. Training in the use of a fire blanket is desirable, if not entirely necessary, because to fight a small fire using one involves actually approaching the fire and so it is far better that practice is gained during training.

Before attempting to extinguish such fires, the electricity or gas supply must be turned off.

The blanket must be pulled from its container with the corners wrapped around the hands of the person using it, making sure that their hands and forearms are completely covered. The blanket must be held at chest level and gently placed over the burning container to exclude the air from the fire.

The blanket must not be thrown because it may miss the burning container or cause it to spill, spreading the fire.

The blanket must be left in place until the container has cooled down. It is essential that no-one lifts a corner to check if the fire is out as this may allow enough air in to reignite the fire. The container must not be moved before it is cold.

2.10 Site accommodation

 In the drive to get the project built, it is easy to overlook the potential health and safety issues arising out of the occupation of site accommodation.

Temporary accommodation units (TAUs) include site offices, canteens, rest rooms, drying rooms and toilets. They are often of timber construction, with fire-resisting surface materials. From site to site they will range from a single site cabin, combining the functions of office and canteen, to a range of single-storey, interlinked units, or they may form a multi-floor administrative complex. Ideally all TAUs would be easily accessible by the FRS, should the need arise.

Location of temporary accommodation units

TAUs should be located in the open air and separated from the building under construction and storage compounds by a fire break of at least six metres (20 metres on timber frame and other high risk sites). If such separation is not possible, the risk of fire spreading can be reduced if the TAU or the adjacent part of the structure is fire resisting to a minimum of 30 minutes. For TAUs that are located inside the building under construction, their fire resistance needs more careful consideration. Under no circumstances should they be located in timber-frame structures.

TAUs should be designed and constructed:

☑ of materials that would not contribute significantly to the growth of a fire or the propagation of smoke or corrosive fumes

☑ of fire-resisting material to BS 476 with regard to walls, roof, doors and windows, to achieve 30 minutes' fire resistance

☑ where stacked vertically, the floor and roof assembly, and members supporting it, should have at least a 30 minute fire resistance.

Where TAUs do not sit flush on the ground, measures must be taken to prevent the accumulation of rubbish in the space beneath the floor, a gap which will also enhance under-floor ventilation.

Fire action notices

Legible written emergency procedures must be displayed in prominent locations within offices and should include:

☑ the location of the notice to enable the location of the fire to be pinpointed (for example, first-floor photocopier room)

☑ instructions for raising the alarm

☑ instructions for calling the FRS

☑ instructions to report to the nearest assembly point

☑ clear information as to the whereabouts of the assembly point

☑ a clear instruction not to leave the assembly point until a roll-call has been taken

☑ an indication of the locations of fire escape routes

☑ an instruction not to re-enter the building or site until it has been declared safe to do so by someone in authority.

Fire alarm systems

The fire alarm system for TAUs will inevitably vary between sites. For a single or double site cabin set-up, a verbal shout of 'fire' would be acceptable providing it can be heard throughout the site in normal circumstances. Where a fire could remain undetected for a period of time, smoke alarms should be installed.

The more TAUs there are, which will be generally indicative of bigger sites, the more sophisticated the alarm system should be. For small TAU complexes, a hand-operated fire bell might be sufficient providing it is audible throughout the complex. For larger complexes and areas where cooking is carried out, an electrical break-glass system with multiple call points and sounders may be required.

For TAUs that are within the building under construction, the TAU fire alarm should be integrated as for the rest of the building.

Fire alarm systems should be tested weekly to confirm that they are audible throughout the complex. Where multiple call-points are installed, they should be used in rotation for the purpose of testing the system. Test records should be maintained.

Consideration should be given to fitting automatic fire-detection systems and intruder alarms to temporary buildings where flammable substances are stored.

Means of escape

For single and double cabin set-up, the means of escape will generally be obvious and special considerations will not be necessary. Ideally in all TAU complexes, there will be escape routes in at least two different directions from all points within the complex.

If, in places, there is only one escape route:

☑ it must be adequately protected from fire so that it will always be available, if needed

☑ any high-risk equipment or materials must not be located adjacent to it

☑ it is likely that specialist advice will be necessary to assess travel distances and the capacity of the escape route to handle the maximum number of people who would have to use it.

Needless to say, all escape routes must be kept clear of obstructions that are likely to hinder an emergency evacuation.

Employers (or the responsible person) must have regard for the requirements of the Disability Discrimination Act when considering means of escape.

They should also consider the following points:

☑ as part of emergency planning, dedicated escape routes should be decided on, clearly signed and adequately lit

☑ all directional signs should be clearly visible, kept unobstructed and conform to the Health and Safety (Safety Signs and Signals) Regulations

☑ such signs should be positioned where the escape route changes direction or level. The signs must indicate the final exit to a place of safety.

Fire escape routes can be blocked unintentionally

Fire-fighting equipment

All TAUs should be equipped with handheld fire extinguishers as a minimum. The appropriate type of extinguisher will depend upon what the fuel for any fire would be. For example:

☑ water fire extinguishers should be provided where the fuel is likely to be paper, cardboard, timber and so on

☑ carbon dioxide extinguishers will be required where there is a significant amount of electrical equipment (such as computer terminals, server and photocopier rooms)

☑ dry powder extinguishers will be required where there is a significant quantity of flammable liquids

☑ a fire blanket will be required in any TAU where cooking oils are heated (such as kitchens and canteens).

Fire extinguishers should only be used by people who have been trained to do so. Even then, they must always have at least one route of escape available to them in case fire fighting has to be abandoned; they must also be capable of making that decision.

Emergency evacuation

In the event of a fire, the first priority is to get everyone out of the TAUs and account for them. How difficult this will be depends upon the size of the TAU complex, how many people are involved and whether they have full mobility. Visitors must also be accounted for.

Toxic smoke is the main cause of fatalities in premises fires, which makes it a greater hazard in enclosed office-complex fires than for fires that occur in the open air. Prompt evacuation is paramount.

Everyone must know their designated assembly point and what to do when they get there. The appointment of fire wardens will assist in confirming that no-one remains in larger TAU complexes following evacuations.

Periodically practising emergency evacuations (fire drills) will give some idea of how effective the emergency evacuation plan is and whether further work on it must be done.

No-notice practice evacuations are the most accurate way of assessing how effective the evacuation plan is. However, it is accepted that operational reasons may make these impractical.

Where construction site offices are located in a multiple-occupancy building, the safety of other occupiers, as well as their visitors and members of the public, must be a consideration. For example, emergency exit routes from the premises may have to be maintained or provided for other occupiers through the construction area or other provisions made for their safety.

Location of occupants

In larger office complexes, it may be necessary to appoint fire wardens whose job it is to ensure that offices and other accommodation are completely evacuated in the event of the fire alarm sounding (including practice drills) and to conduct a roll-call at the assembly point.

The fire wardens must be trained in their duties and have a clear understanding of the area of the complex for which they are responsible.

The number of fire wardens required will depend on several factors, including the area and layout of the office complex and the number of levels it comprises.

The location and number of staff can be identified by the use of an in/out board, signing in/out book or swipe card system that can be taken to or accessed at the assembly point and used for the roll-call.

Arrangements must be made for visitors to be logged into and out of offices so that, in the case of an emergency, they can be located quickly and escorted to a safe place.

Emergency lighting

Emergency lighting should always be considered when assessing the fire safety requirements for satisfactory means of escape.

If the lighting circuits fail, a standby emergency lighting system must switch on automatically and clearly illuminate:

- ☑ exits and directional signs
- ☑ corridors and associated exits
- ☑ circulation areas
- ☑ changes in levels
- ☑ any projections and protrusions (such as temporary partitioning, office equipment and storage)
- ☑ internal and external staircases.

Emergency lighting, whether by battery, standby generator or a combination of both, should be tested on a regular basis by a competent person.

Records of tests of the emergency lighting equipment should be kept and must be available for inspection when required.

Calling the fire and rescue service

If a fire is discovered, everyone within the TAUs must be aware of it and the FRS must be called. Where there is a switchboard, it is usual for the switchboard operator to be nominated as the person who always makes the call. However, with virtually everyone now carrying a mobile phone, it is common for several calls to be made to the emergency services about the same incident, which is preferable to everyone assuming that someone else has made the call.

Anyone calling the FRS should give the full postal address of the site and any geographical features that will assist them in locating it. It may be necessary to give further instruction if the site has more than one entrance, particularly if one has been nominated for access by the emergency services.

Even if the site has a fire alarm that is automatically connected to the FRS via an alarm company, an emergency telephone call must still be made to confirm that the automatic call has been received.

2.11 Training

 You cannot expect people to react effectively in emergency situations unless they have been told what to do.

The responsible person must ensure that employees are provided with adequate safety training, which includes suitable and sufficient instruction and training on the appropriate precautions and actions to be taken by employees in order to safeguard themselves and other relevant persons on the premises. The training delivered must take account of the significant findings of the fire risk assessment and the emergency procedures, and be easily understandable and repeated periodically. The training should cover:

- ☑ discovering a fire
- ☑ how to raise the alarm
- ☑ what to do on hearing the alarm
- ☑ the procedure for alerting visitors and all staff
- ☑ calling the fire service
- ☑ evacuation procedures, assembly points and fire drills
- ☑ the location and use of fire-fighting equipment
- ☑ the location of escape routes

- ☑ how to open escape doors
- ☑ the importance of fire doors
- ☑ how to stop equipment and isolate power
- ☑ not using lifts
- ☑ the use and risks of highly flammable and explosive substances
- ☑ good housekeeping
- ☑ smoking policy and smoking areas.

Appendix A – Example of a fire risk assessment

There are five steps to fire prevention and control.

1. **Identify hazards.** Consider how a fire could start and what could burn.

2. **People at risk.** Employees, contractors, visitors and anyone who is vulnerable (for example, people nearby or anyone with a disability).

3. **Evaluation and action.** Consider the hazards and people identified in Steps 1 and 2 and act to remove and reduce risk to protect people and premises.

4. **Record, plan and train.** Keep a record of the risks and action taken. Make a clear plan for fire safety and ensure that people understand what they need to do in the event of a fire.

5. **Review** your assessment regularly and check it takes account of any changes on site.

Fire risk assessment			
Company name			
Site address		Assessment by	
		Name	
		Title	
		Signature	
Risk assessment reference		Issue date	
		Review date	
Activity specific details (for example, site locations/activities/zones)			
Other work being carried out in this area		Interfaces with other trades	
Period of validity of this risk assessment			
Start date		Expiry date	
Remember: All hot works must cease at least one hour before the site closes (or more depending upon risk assessment as defined in HSG 168)			

Step 1 – Identify hazards. Consider how a fire could start and what could burn.		
Sources of ignition *(Hot works, faulty electrical equipment, uncontrolled smoking)*	Sources of fuel *(Untidy site, off-cuts, paper, wrappings)*	Areas of particular risk *(Near site boundary, waste skips, hot work areas)*

Step 2 – People at risk. Employees, contractors, visitors and anyone who is vulnerable (for example, people nearby or anyone with a disability).

Step 3 – Evaluation and action. Consider the hazards and people identified in Steps 1 and 2 and act to remove and reduce risk to protect people and premises.

Step 4 – Record, plan and train. Keep a record of the risks and action taken. Make a clear plan for fire safety and ensure that people understand what they need to do in the event of a fire.

Checklist	Tick
Fire plan prepared and made known to all who may be affected.	
Record hazards and risks and kept under constant review.	
Record actions taken to reduce hazards and risks to lowest level.	
Select suitable people and arrange for training and updates for people involved.	
Practise alarm and evacuation procedures.	
Put plan in place to measure and correct defects from lessons learned.	
Plan for rewarding good performance awareness and good housekeeping.	

02

Review dates	Completed by	Signature

Step 5 – Assessment review. You must review and record your assessment regularly and check it takes account of any changes on site.

Review of outcomes – lessons learnt and control measures put in place

Fire action plan status/currency – latest issue date
(Check current issue displayed)

Appendix B – Example of a fire risk assessment for temporary accommodation units

Record of significant findings

Risk assessment for	Assessment undertaken by	
Single storey site accommodation comprising five interlinked cabins Site address: Premier Place, Carrow Road, Anytown	Date:	3rd January 2013
	Completed by:	Chris Hughton (Site manager)
	Signature:	C Hughton

Part of temporary accommodation units (TAUs) covered, if not whole area as identified above: N/A	This area is used for: General office activities Meeting room and inductions Canteen Toilets, changing and drying room

Step 1 – Identify fire hazards

Sources of ignition	Sources of fuel	Sources of oxygen
Electrical appliances and office equipment Electrical heater units Cleaning chemicals if mixed	Overheating/electrical failure Office furniture and equipment Project paperwork and drawings	None above ambient level

Step 2 – People at risk

Office-based and visiting site staff, workers in canteen and toilets and other visitors

It is NOT considered likely that the activities carried out within the office accommodation could pose any risk of harm to anyone outside the site boundary (12 m away)

Step 3 – Evaluate, remove, reduce and protect from risk

(3.1) Evaluate the risk of the fire occurring	Meeting room sometimes used for storing used packaging material prior to disposal Desks too close to electric heaters in project office Chairs/clothes too close to electrical heaters in canteen
(3.2) Evaluate the risk to people from a fire starting in the premises	A fire in the meeting room could be undetected for some time A fire in the canteen on ground floor could prevent access to the rear emergency exit Otherwise, emergency evacuation not considered to be problematic
(3.3) Remove and reduce the hazards that may cause a fire	Improved housekeeping required to prevent accumulation of flammable waste materials Furniture to be re-arranged – requires relocation of telephone connection point Drying room has enclosed oil covered heaters with hooks for drying clothes – emphasise during induction Fit cages around electrical fires in canteen
(3.4) Remove and reduce the risks to people from a fire	When the defects noted above have been rectified, the existing fire precautions will be considered to be adequate It is noted that the fire extinguishers are due inspection in early April 2013

Assessment review

Review due before	Completed by	Signature
3rd August 2013		

Review outcome (where substantial changes have occurred a new record sheet should be used)

Fire action plan

Will this risk assessment result in a fire action plan being drawn up?	YES / ~~NO~~
	Delete as applicable

Appendix C – Example of a fire risk management action plan

Fire risk management action plan

Action plan for	Action plan compiled
	Date
Site address	Compiled by
	Signature

Risk management

Unacceptable fire risk	Corrective action required	Action by (person)	Action by (date)

Review and revision

Current revision number	Date previous review carried out
Date next review due	Carried out by

Appendix D – The enforcement of fire safety law

Should something go wrong with regard to fire safety and an external investigation takes place, one or more of the enforcement agencies will visit the site to conduct an investigation and interviews. This Appendix outlines the circumstances in which the HSE and FRS have responsibilities for carrying these out.

The enforcement of fire safety legislation on construction sites is complex and is dependent upon:

☑ the nature of the site

☑ what work activities are being carried out.

Responsibility for the enforcement of fire safety legislation is split between:

☑ the HSE, or possibly the Local Authority on small non-notifiable sites, either of which would usually take enforcement action under the Construction (Design and Management) Regulations or the Management of Health and Safety at Work Regulations. However, the HSE also has enforcement powers under The Regulatory Reform (Fire Safety) Order (England and Wales)

☑ the local FRS, which would enforce their powers under the Regulatory Reform (Fire Safety) Order (England and Wales) or the Fire (Scotland) Act (Scotland only).

For enforcement purposes, construction sites are divided into three categories:

1. Completely segregated and separate construction sites, with their own perimeter fence or hoarding, upon which the only activity carried out is construction work.

   In this case, both general fire precautions (GFP) and process fire safety issues are enforced by the HSE, although the FRS will be the enforcing body over any temporary accommodation units which are outside the site boundary.

2. Construction sites in shared or occupied premises that have an unbreached and continuous fire-resistant wall to separate the construction activities from the occupier's activities.

   In this situation a fire in the construction part of the premises would not affect the other occupied area(s) and consequently both GFP and process fire safety issues are again enforced by the HSE within the construction site area, with the FRS enforcing them in the other occupied parts of the building.

3. Construction sites in occupied or shared premises where there is a breached (not totally fire or smoke-proof) partition or wall between the construction and the occupier's activities, so that a fire in either section would have implications for the other section.

   In this situation, the HSE is the enforcing body with respect to the GFP in the construction area, whilst the FRS is the enforcing body with respect to process fire safety.

The FRS will also be the enforcing authority for off-site premises (such as a company's head office premises or a storage yard).

02

Appendix E – The nature of fire and the selection of extinguishers

The conditions for a fire to start

In order to take the measures required to prevent fires starting, it is first necessary to understand the conditions that must be present to enable a fire to start.

Three factors are necessary for fires to burn:

☑ **fuel** or combustible material. Any material or substance, whether liquid, solid or gas, which will burn given sufficient amounts of heat and a supporter of combustion, such as air or oxygen

☑ **heat** or ignition source. Every fuel has an ignition temperature. All solids and liquids give off vapour when heated, and it is this vapour that ignites

☑ **air** (or other supporter of combustion, such as oxygen) which is always there to sustain fire, providing the other factors are present.

Once a fire has started, if any one of these factors is isolated or removed, the fire will be extinguished. There are three basic ways of achieving this:

☑ removal of the fuel or combustible material, leaving nothing to burn

☑ removal of the heat by the application of water to cool the burning material

☑ reduction or exclusion of the air/oxygen by smothering the burning material. Foam, dry powder, carbon dioxide (CO_2) and fire blankets are all smothering agents.

How fire can be spread

Fire can be spread in four ways:

☑ conduction ☑ radiation

☑ convection ☑ direct burning.

Conduction is where heat is transmitted from one place to another along or through solid material (such as along a metal pipe or through a door or wall). The conduction of heat therefore has the potential to start a fire in a location that is remote from the original source of heat.

Convection occurs where superheated gases or heat rising from a fire ignites other combustible material or when particles of burning material in the circulating air are deposited in another place, causing another fire.

Radiation is the transfer of radiated heat from the fire, through the air directly to other flammable materials nearby, which will cause those materials to be raised to their ignition temperature and then burn.

Direct burning is a combination of conduction, convection and radiation and is where the fire spreads and reaches other combustible materials and ignites them, adding further fuel to the fire.

The classes of fire

All fires can be placed into one of the following six categories.

1. **Class A** – carbonaceous material (such as paper, cloth, wood and rubber) often referred to as solid fuel fires.

2. **Class B** – flammable liquids or liquefiable solids (such as oil, fat, paint and fuel). These can be subdivided into:

    B1 – fires involving liquids that are soluble in water (such as methanol). They can be extinguished by carbon dioxide, dry powder and water spray

    B2 – fires involving liquids that are not soluble in water (such as petrol and oil). They can be extinguished using foam, carbon dioxide and dry powder.

3. **Class C** – flammable gases or liquefied gases (such as propane, butane, hydrogen or acetylene).

4. **Class D** – combustible metals (such as magnesium, sodium and phosphorus).

5. **Electrical fires** – any fire involving electrical apparatus or equipment.

6. **Class F** – high temperature cooking oils or fats (such as those used in deep fat fryers in large catering establishments or restaurants).

Class A – carbonaceous material

On the majority of building or construction sites, the following carbonaceous items are freely available sources of fuel:

☑ cardboard, paper and cloth ☑ dirty rags, oily rags and clothes

☑ wood ☑ packaging materials.

If a fire occurs involving carbonaceous material, a hose reel or a water extinguisher should be used. The jet of water should be aimed at the base of the fire first, and then moved progressively over the whole of the burning area. Always remove the material from the source of heat if possible, but without endangering the person involved or starting a fire in another location.

Class B – flammable liquids or liquefiable solids

Fires involving flammable liquids, such as:

- petrol or diesel
- oil
- paraffin
- paint
- resin and adhesive.

This type of fire should be dealt with using foam or dry powder extinguishers, depending on whether the fire is contained or flowing.

If the fire is contained, use a foam extinguisher with the jet of foam directed at the back of the container. This allows a blanket of foam to build up and spread across the surface of the burning liquid.

If the fire is flowing, a dry powder extinguisher should be directed at the front edge of the fire, in an attempt to separate the flames from the fuel.

The aim of using extinguishers in such a way is for the fire to be covered with a blanket of either foam or dry powder. This will cut off the supply of air, and thus the oxygen, to the fire.

Once the blanket has been laid, do not disturb it until the liquid has cooled. Any reintroduction of air may cause the fire to re-ignite.

Never use a water extinguisher or a hose reel on a fire involving any flammable liquid. The water will react violently with the burning liquid and cause an explosion.

Class C – flammable and liquefied gases

Extreme caution is necessary when dealing with fires involving liquefied gases as there will always be the danger of an explosion.

LPG expands to a ratio of 274:1 so a leak of just one litre of liquid would produce a cloud of gas, if diluted in air to the right concentration, large enough to fill a room 3 m x 2 m x 2 m. This would cause an explosive atmosphere.

If a fire occurs in which a compressed gas cylinder is directly involved:

- call the FRS and tell them of the location of the cylinders and type of gas involved
- attempt to turn the gas off at the cylinder, if it is safe to do so
- attempt to turn off any gas appliances, if it is safe to do so
- activate the emergency evacuation procedure and clear the site.

Do not try to fight a fire in which a compressed gas cylinder is directly involved; leave it to the FRS as an overheated cylinder can explode.

If a fire involves other combustible materials (for example, timber that might cause the fire to spread to the location of the cylinders) a decision based upon personal safety will have to be taken on whether to attempt to fight the fire to prevent an escalation of the situation.

Class C fires are best dealt with by the use of dry powder extinguishers.

Class D – combustible metals

Fires of this type involve magnesium, sodium, phosphorus and similar metals, and should only be dealt with by trained fire fighters.

Never apply water to any burning metal fire or a fire involving powered metal. It would cause an immediate explosive reaction.

Specially formulated powders are available for use in controlling fire in metals but, as a last resort, if no proprietary powder is available dry sand or earth may be applied to smother the burning area.

The proprietary powder should be carefully placed and not thrown onto the burning metal. Throwing the powder will cause the burning material to spread.

Be sure either to wear darkened safety glasses whilst attempting to cover the fire, or to look away from the extreme brightness. Failure to take these precautions could damage the eyes.

Electrical fires

Fires involving electrical equipment can be dealt with using carbon dioxide (CO_2) or dry powder.

In staff training, the following simple rules for safety should be emphasised.

- Do not use water on any fire involving electrical equipment. You may be electrocuted.
- Switch off the electricity supply, if possible, before fighting the fire. It is then just an ordinary fire.
- Do not approach closer than one metre to any fire where the electrical supply has not been switched off.
- Carbon dioxide (CO_2) is the best extinguishing medium if the concentration of gas can be confined (for example, within an electrical distribution cupboard).
- In extinguishing electrical fires, direct the discharge from the extinguisher to one edge of the fire and, with a sweeping movement, pass to the far edge until the fire has been extinguished.

Electrical equipment used on building and construction sites sometimes incorporates devices to protect against overheating and fire.

Most fires in electrical equipment are due to misuse or neglect where appliances have not been properly maintained or are being used for a purpose, or in a manner, for which they were not designed.

A fuse larger than the appliance rating will negate the purpose of the fuse and render the appliance potentially unsafe.

All staff should be properly trained so that they do not misuse equipment, and ensure that damaged or defective equipment is reported, taken out of use and professionally repaired.

Other types of fire

Flammable adhesives and flammable liquid stores

Use dry powder or foam.

Extreme care must be taken if the adhesive is petroleum or spirit-based as explosive vapours will be given off.

Cooking ranges

Use foam, dry powder, carbon dioxide (CO_2) or a fire blanket. Never move a burning saucepan or chip pan from a cooker. The contents may splash and cause serious burns.

Petrol and diesel in stores

Use foam or dry powder.

Petrol or diesel-powered plant

Use foam or dry powder.

Hot work with cutting or welding equipment and bitumen boilers

Use foam, dry powder or carbon dioxide (CO_2). Turn off the heater.

The correct types of fire extinguisher must be provided and kept close at hand, with a careful watch being maintained for fire breaking out whilst work is in progress.

Types of portable fire extinguisher and the types of fire to use them on

Make yourself aware of the instructions on the fire extinguisher before using it.

Fire class	Substances, materials, and so on	Water (red label)	Foam (cream label)	Carbon dioxide (CO_2) (black label)	Dry powder (blue label)
A	Carbonaceous and organic materials, wood, paper, rag, textile, cardboard, common plastics, laminates, foam.	YES, excellent	YES	Difficult to use outdoors in windy conditions. **For small fires only if no water available**	YES
B	Flammable liquids, petrol, oil, fats, adhesives, paint, varnish.	NO	YES, if liquid is not flowing	YES, but not ideal	YES
C	Flammable gas: LPG, butane, propane, methane, acetylene.	NO, not effective on gas flame but will cool the area and put out secondary fires	YES, if in liquid form	YES	YES
D	Metal, molten metal, reactive metal powder.	NO	NO	NO	YES, trained person – if no explosive risk. Special powders are available, but DRY sand or earth may be used
Electrical	Electrical installations, typewriters, VDUs, computers, photocopiers, televisions, and so on.	NO	NO	YES	YES, but not ideal. Or switch off electricity and deal with as an ordinary fire

Note: Dry powder may not penetrate spaces or behind equipment; Light water foam (AFFF) may be used instead of water or foam.
Extinguishers used to control Class B fires will not work on Class F fires because of the high temperatures generated

03

Electrical safety

This chapter highlights the dangers associated with working on or near to live electrical circuits and the good working practices that must be adopted to ensure that such work can be carried out safely.

Each year the presence of electricity is the cause of deaths and injuries, mainly burns, on construction sites. Furthermore, over the years electricity has been a contributory factor to the starting of several fires on construction sites.

Introduction	42
Key requirements	42
The Electricity at Work Regulations	43
Site electrical supply	43
Site distribution systems	44
Safe working practices with electricity	46
Appendix A – Typical example of a permit to work	50

3.1 Introduction

Electricity can be regarded as a hidden killer. Unlike other hazards, in most cases, it cannot be seen, felt, smelt or heard; it may not become obvious that a cable is live until someone touches it. There may be occasional circumstances where the hum from a transformer or the noise from a motor running, indicate that at least some circuits are live, but relying upon this as a risk control measure is certainly not a safe method of working.

The Health and Safety Executive (HSE) regard the risk of electrocution on construction sites as coming from four sources:

- contact with live parts of the electrical distribution system in the structure under construction being renovated or otherwise worked upon, and associated site accommodation
- contact with overhead power lines
- contact with buried cables
- the use of defective electrical equipment, including hand tools.

This chapter will cover the dangers from electricity and the means of working safely on site and site accommodation.

 The dangers associated with overhead power lines, buried cables and electrical hand tools are covered in other chapters of this book.

The presence of live electrical cables may not be obvious; cables inside partition walls or other hidden voids are just waiting for the unwary to accidentally damage them resulting in serious injury or even death.

The temporary electrical distribution systems found on site tend to operate in a harsh environment and must be treated with care and respect.

The HSE regard refurbishment work in buildings as presenting the highest risk. Many of the accidents resulting from such work arise out of:

- confusion and lack of communication as to what circuits have been made dead
- hitting cables buried underground, hidden by wall coverings, in voids, and so on
- workers, who have not been trained, knowingly working on live equipment.

Electric shock may not be the only consequence of live electrical circuits; a fault within a circuit or equipment can result in heating or sparking, which have the potential to ignite flammable materials, causing a fire or explosion as well as disrupting services to adjacent properties.

 An electrical safety poster should be prominently displayed, in a number of locations if necessary, and there should be someone on site who can treat a casualty who has suffered an electrical shock or burns.

3.2 Key requirements

- No-one other than a qualified electrician must install, maintain or alter the site distribution system.
- Electrical safety must be covered during site induction and refresher training, where it must be emphasised that unauthorised alteration to, or extension of, the site electrical distribution system will not be tolerated.
- Ideally, apart from mains-powered (230/240 volt) equipment in site offices, all other electrically powered equipment (such as electrical hand tools) should be run off a 110 volt supply.
- The power supply for 230/240 volt equipment must be fed through a safety device in addition to a fuse (for example, a residual current device (RCDs)). Fuses only protect equipment; they do not 'blow' quickly enough to prevent an electric shock.
- The reason behind any safety device tripping, apart from deliberate testing, must be investigated, if necessary by bringing in a qualified electrician; attempts to reset a tripped safety device must not be made until this has been carried out.
- Work on or near to live, exposed conductors poses an obvious danger. Competence is required and such work must only be carried out under a formal permit to work.
- Electrical circuits must be tested periodically by a competent person.
- Safety devices (such as RCDs) must be tested frequently by the user.
- A permit to work system must be introduced and enforced for higher risk work (for example, where a danger from exposed live electrical wires or equipment exists).

3.3   The Electricity at Work Regulations

The regulations are concerned with the safety of electrical installations and as such the details, in the main, are technical and not of general interest to site management staff, providing they have employed competent contractors to carry out electrical work. However, there are some requirements within the regulations which, if contravened, should be fairly obvious and would require addressing. Briefly, these are:

- ☑ working on or near to live electrical parts can only be carried out where:
  - it is unreasonable in the circumstances to make the live parts dead (for example, testing could not be carried out if it was not live)
  - it is reasonable in the circumstances to allow live working (there is no other way of doing the job)
  - suitable safety precautions (for example, trained workers, a permit to work and no lone-working) are in place

- ☑ electrical equipment, which may be exposed to hostile environments or mechanical damage, should be constructed or protected and/or positioned to avoid danger

- ☑ all electrical wiring that could result in personal danger must be either insulated, otherwise protected or positioned out of harm's way

- ☑ a suitable means must be provided for:
  - cutting off the supply to any item of electrical equipment
  - enabling it to be securely isolated
  - identifying all electrical circuits.

 Everyone who potentially will come into contact with live electrical wiring or equipment must be fully trained and competent in how to protect themselves and others.

3.4   Site electrical supply

The supply of electricity on construction sites will normally be provided by one or both of the following:

- ☑ public supply from the local electricity company

- ☑ site generator, as a standby supply, if the public supply fails or where connection to the public supply is not practicable or is uneconomic.

Public supply

A public supply of electricity being provided depends on the following:

- ☑ written application being made to the local electricity company, as soon as possible during the planning stage

- ☑ the name, address, and telephone number of the main contractor and developer, giving the full site address and a location plan

- ☑ details of the maximum demand load (in kilowatts) that is likely to be required during construction

- ☑ details of the maximum final demand load (in kilowatts) that will be required when the job is complete

- ☑ dates when the supply is needed

- ☑ a discussion with electricity company staff to determine the necessary precautions to avoid damage or hazards from any existing overhead or underground cables

- ☑ the establishment of supply points (where incoming cables will terminate), switch gear, metering equipment and requirements for earthing.

Generators

Generators, even if for stand-by purposes, may be required, and will be powered by petrol or diesel engines. Attention should be given to the siting of such equipment in order to minimise pollution caused by noise and fumes. Other environmental considerations (such as fuel spillage and leaks) must also be considered (drip trays and bunds).

Site generators range from relatively small portable machines used to power one or two electrical tools to large permanently sited stand-by machines capable of powering an extensive distribution system should the public system fail. It should be noted that some of the smaller machines have dual outputs (230/240 volt and 110 volt) meaning that making separate arrangements for deriving a 110 volt supply is not necessary. Generally, the output of the larger machines is a 415 volt, three-phase supply, mimicking the public supply arrangements.

It is normal for stand-by generating systems to auto-start upon the failure of the public supply. Such an unexpected event could have safety implications if the siting of a standby generator is not given due consideration.

Any permanently sited generating system, including the earthing arrangements, must be designed and installed by competent persons.

Calculating power requirements

The calculation for power requirements should be left to an experienced person or to the electricity supply company.

To enable the total site requirements to be established, an electrical demand table, which itemises all anticipated electrical loads, must be compiled. It is likely that a member of the site management team will become involved in this by advising upon the electrical loads that will be in use.

The person compiling the demand table will allow a diversity factor that acknowledges that not all electrical equipment will be in use at the same time.

3.5   Site distribution systems

With regard to new build, the term site distribution system refers to a temporary and flexible electrical distribution system that enables electrical power to be available around the site for construction purposes. However, with regard to refurbishment work or similar, the distribution system may comprise a combination of the fixed electrical system within the building (providing it is safe to leave it live) and elements of a temporary distribution system to enable hand tools, task lighting, and so on to be used.

Safe voltages

 Site accidents have shown that mains voltage (230/240 volts) can be a killer. Apart from where absolutely necessary 110 volt or battery-powered equipment must be used.

Generally, the site distribution system comprises of a combination of mains (230/240 volts or 415 volts) and low voltage (110 volt) circuits. To ensure that the appropriate supplies are available where they are required, and that there is no overloading of any part of the system, it must be designed and installed by competent persons.

Whilst it is likely that the main incoming supply will be at 230/240 volts or 415 volts, by using a transformer, the voltage present at the workface for hand tools, task lighting, and so on, should be reduced to a maximum of 110 volts. In some high-risk situations, transforms are available to provide extra low voltages of 25 or 50 volts.

 The way in which 110 volt systems are earthed means that the maximum voltage shock that anyone can receive is 55 volts, which is regarded as relatively safe for healthy adults.

Distribution equipment

Electrical distribution equipment must be obtained from a reputable supplier or hire company, to ensure that it has been manufactured to a known standard and tested. This is particularly important where electrical distribution equipment is to be sited outdoors, where the ingress of water and, to a lesser extent, dust could be a problem.

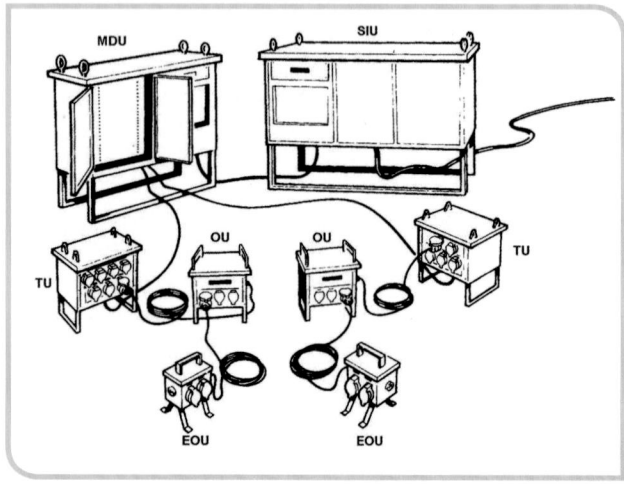

There are many types of distribution equipment available, all of which are suitable for different situations:

☑ **supply incoming unit (SIU)** generally have a rating of up to 300 amps per phase. These units include main switch gear and metering equipment

☑ **mains distribution unit (MDU)** for the control and distribution of electricity on site, either 415 volts three-phase, or 230/240 volts single-phase AC

☑ **transformer units (TU)** are either single-phase (reducing 230/240 volts to 110 volts) or three-phase (reducing 415 volts to 110 volts). Such transformer units can be used for portable tools and plant, and general floor lighting

☑ **outlet units (OU)** 110 volt socket outlet units rated at 16 or 32 amp. Such outlet units can be used for portable tools, floodlighting and extension outlets. They are not usually protected by circuit-breakers

☑ **extension outlet units (EOU)** equipped with one or more 110 volt socket outlet, rated at 16 amp. Such units can be used for portable tools, local lighting and hand lamps. They are not usually protected by circuit-breakers.

In most cases at least part of each piece of distribution equipment will be colour-coded to indicate its output voltage. Furthermore, the arrangement and number of pins within the electrical connecters are different for each voltage, which prevents, for example, a 110 volt power tool being plugged into a 230/240 volt supply unit.

The colour coding is as follows:

	Violet	25 volts
	White	50 volts
	Yellow	110–130 volts
	Blue	220–240 volts
	Red	308–404 volts
	Black	500–750 volts

Case study

On this project the site team planned ahead and installed temporary supplies and general lighting to the soffit of main access routes. The lights in the foreground were fixed drops, each with two 110 volt sockets for equipment, which could be moved into rooms as and when required.

Residual current devices

All attempts should be made to use 110 volts or battery-powered tools where possible. However it is inevitable that some 230/240 volt equipment will be in use, even if only in the site office. In such circumstances the 230/240 volt supply must be supplied through an RCD. Another common situation in which a 230/240 volt supply is used is where work is carried out within an existing building in which the 230/240 volt circuits are still live, using a 110 volt hand tool and a 230/240 volt/110 volt transformer is the preferred option.

Under fault conditions, RCDs detect an imbalance in the current in the circuit and disconnect the supply before the person at risk can receive a potentially fatal electric shock.

There are two types of RCD:

☑ those that are fitted as part of an electrical distribution system and, for example, are found within the supply panel for a site office. This type of RCD can only be installed by a competent electrician

☑ plug-in RCDs (commonly known as power-breakers) that are plugged into a mains supply socket and have an in-built socket into which an individual mains-powered electrical tool or other appliance is plugged.

Both types of RCD have a test button that simulates a fault and operates the device:

☑ RCDs built into supply panels should be tested weekly

☑ power-breaker type devices should be tested before each use.

It should be noted that:

☑ RCDs do not reduce current flow or the voltage, only the time that the current flows (about 30 milliseconds), and thereby the severity of the shock

☑ RCDs are delicate devices and should be treated with care. Advice on suitable RCDs for construction sites should be sought from manufacturers or suppliers

☑ the use of an RCD does not give a 100% guarantee of safety

☑ the device does not have a fail-safe feature and will not give an indication if it is faulty.

Site accommodation

The incoming electrical supply to site accommodation must be properly designed and be installed and commissioned by competent electrical contractors.

Site offices and welfare facilities are the only locations where electrical equipment that runs off a 230/240 volt supply should be in use. The electrical supply panel for such facilities must incorporate an RCD in each circuit. The correct operation of each RCD must be confirmed weekly by operating the test button, which should trip the device and switch off the circuit running through it.

All portable electrical equipment must be electrical safety tested (PAT) at appropriate intervals as decided by a competent person. This includes:

- ☑ common types of office equipment (such as fax machines and photocopiers)

- ☑ kitchen-type equipment (such as kettles, microwave ovens, and so on)

- ☑ small items (such as chargers for site radios and battery-powered tools).

3.6   Safe working practices with electricity

The HSE have shown concern at the number of people killed and injured each year through accidents whereby the presence of electricity was a contributory factor. These accidents occur equally to electricians and to members of other trades. In many cases:

- ☑ the risks of doing the job had not been adequately assessed

- ☑ shortcuts in working practices were being taken

- ☑ pre-work investigation had failed to identify live electrical circuits (particularly in renovation projects)

- ☑ circuits that had been made dead were re-energised by someone who did not realise that the system was being worked on by others.

 HSE publications: *Electrical safety and you. A brief guide* (INDG 231) and *Electricity at work, safe working practices* (HSG85).

Assessing the risks

Working near to live electrical circuits and equipment can only be carried out safely once the significant risks of injury or death have been identified and effective control measures put in place to eliminate the risks or reduce them to an acceptable level. The people doing the work and anyone else who might be adversely affected by it must be informed of the:

- ☑ significant risks arising out of the work

- ☑ part they must play in ensuring the work can be carried out safely.

The biggest risks arise out of:

- ☑ deliberately working on live circuits or equipment

- ☑ being unaware that nearby electrical equipment or wiring existed and/or were live.

The person carrying out the risk assessment, and reviewing and updating it at a later stage, must be sufficiently competent to identify the significant risks and to devise effective control measures.

Managing the risk during refurbishment work

Refurbishment projects pose particular electrical risks if the whole electrical system to the building is not made dead. A number of electrocutions have involved workers who were not electricians but who were carrying out other works (such as plumbers and joiners). These incidents could have been reduced or eliminated by:

- ☑ **understanding the system** – those responsible for planning and managing refurbishment work must understand the electrical system of the building in which the work takes place and liaise with the building occupier. This will enable building work to be planned and managed so that the integrity of the electrical system is not compromised and the workforce remains safe

- ☑ **working dead** – relevant parts of the electrical system should be isolated if the refurbishment work (such as labouring, joinery or plumbing) is liable to disturb or damage the existing electrical system and expose people to electrical danger

- ☑ **portable electrical equipment** – tools, plugs and cables designed for DIY and domestic use are not suitable for site conditions. You should use cordless tools or those that operate from a 110 volt supply system, earthed so that the maximum voltage does not exceed 55 volts. Regularly inspect power tools and take them out of service if they are damaged. Tools should be serviced by qualified electricians. Do not carry out makeshift repairs

- ☑ **residual current (trip) devices** – where mains voltage (230/240 volts) is used, the risk of injury is high if equipment, tools or leads are damaged or there is a fault. Residual current or trip devices (RCDs) can ensure that the current is cut off promptly and safely if the equipment makes contact with any live part

- ☑ **lighting systems** protect cabling and bulbs against breakage. If a bulb breaks, the exposed filament may present a hazard. Have a system for checking bulbs regularly to maintain electrical safety and to keep the site well-lit.

The effective isolation of circuits

Making sure the power is off

If a worker is working next to electrical circuits and they are not competent to check if the power is off, they must ask a competent person to do it for them, and watch them doing it. If they have any doubts about the method used, they should double-check with someone they know to be competent.

When checking that the power is off the competent person should be sure that the:

☑ device being used is suitable for the purpose of isolation

☑ isolator being used to turn off the power is working correctly and reliably

☑ switch being used is the only way that the circuit can be fed with electrical power

☑ switch being used is locked in the off position and cannot easily be turned on again

☑ equipment and method being used to check for voltage works and is reliable

☑ isolation has been successful by confirming the circuit is no longer live.

Some electrical systems and equipment must be earthed before it is safe to work near them. Check whether this is necessary, and if it is, ensure that this is done properly.

 ESC Best practice guide No. 2, Issue 2 – *Guidance on the management of electrical safety and safe isolation procedures for low-voltage installations.*

Making sure the power stays off (secure isolation)

If the electrical power has been turned off to allow work to be carried out safely, it is essential that the power stays off until the work is finished.

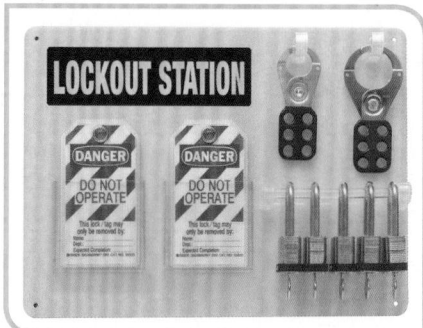

The person doing the work must make sure that they are in control and stay in control throughout the job. A good way is to have the only key to the switch or a locked room or cabinet containing the switch. Removing a fuse may seem to be a safe way of isolating a circuit but someone else could insert another one. Displaying notices could be equally or more ineffective as people often ignore them. If the person doing the job has any doubts that the electricity may be turned on again without them agreeing, they must know that they have the authority to stop work without delay or checking with a supervisor first.

Locating hidden electrical wiring

The presence of electrical wires may not be obvious at the location where work is to be carried out but, as others have found out in the past, that does not mean that there are not any there. Even if some wiring is visible, there may be others that are buried within or hidden by the fabric of the building. Electrical wiring may sometimes look like pipes, and may be a range of colours.

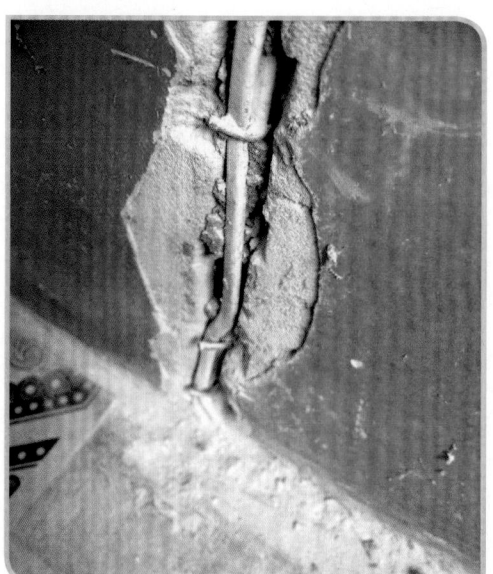

Before anyone is allowed to start drilling or cutting into surfaces the person in charge of the job must:

☑ look for the presence of electrical wires and any other hazards (such as asbestos). Remember to look on both sides of walls

☑ inspect plans of the electrical installation, and use these to find electrical wiring

☑ use a suitable cable detector if competent, or get a competent person to do it. Remember that some cable detectors will not find a wire carrying a small or no current – consult the user guide

☑ identify nearby electrical equipment or installations and try to establish from which direction the wiring runs to these

☑ identify and provide equipment that will minimise the risks during the work

☑ ensure that suitable personal protective equipment (PPE) is identified and used

☑ make it clear to the person doing the job that they must stop work and check with their supervisor if they have any doubts as to the safety of what they are about to do.

Permit to work

Permit to work systems are essential to ensure safe working where live electrical supplies, cables and equipment exist, particularly in installation, maintenance or construction work.

The Electricity at Work Regulations requires employers to implement safe systems of work in circumstances where a person could be exposed to live conductors or equipment. A permit to work system must be a part of that safe system. In the case of construction sites, permits to work are more commonly used whilst the site electrical distribution system is itself being worked on, or connections made to it, thereby potentially exposing live parts.

Tight control of the permit system is essential if its integrity is to be maintained. A competent and authorised person, often the electrical contractor's site manager, must be appointed to raise and co-ordinate the issue of permits. Other people who will be involved in completing parts of the permit and signing accordingly are:

- ☑ anyone who has been involved in making the work area and system to be worked on safe

- ☑ the person directly in charge of the workers doing the work.

 Companies will design their own permits to suit their needs, but for an example of a typical permit refer to Appendix A.

Some companies use permits printed on carbonised paper, which provide identical second or even third copies, where the company's record keeping system demands them.

Most permits contain provisions for the physical locking off of switches, and the retention or display of keys or permits.

One copy of the permit must be retained for the duration of the work by the person to whom it is issued. Before apparatus is made live again, the permit must be returned for cancellation. At cancellation, it must be countersigned by both the holder and the authorised person.

The authorised person should keep a record in the job file of the issued permits and their cancellation.

Before work starts, the authorised person should ensure that the permit to work will cover the making safe of the part of the system to be worked on, from all possible sources of supply.

If the work is handed over from one competent person to another, the permit is to be endorsed by the authorised person and transferred to the second operative.

 Under no circumstances should anyone work on, maintain, repair or otherwise adjust high-voltage apparatus, except in accordance with the instructions and terms of a formal permit to work.

 HSE publication Electricity at work, safe working practices (HSG85).

Monitoring contractors

In addition to electrical contractors, many other trades, examples of which are below, will have an electrical element to their work:

- ☑ heating and ventilation engineers

- ☑ lift and escalator engineers

- ☑ plumbers

- ☑ fire detection and control engineers

- ☑ security and CCTV engineers.

The activities of such contractors and others installing electrical circuits, or simply connecting to electrical equipment installed by others, must be carefully monitored to ensure that they do not jeopardise electrical safety or leave an installation in a dangerous condition.

The person in charge of the site, or someone else appointed to do so, must:

- ☑ inspect the risk assessments of these contractors to establish if their work could possibly adversely affect the safety of others working nearby, or who might otherwise be affected by their work

- ☑ inspect any written scheme of work (method statement) to establish if any element will conflict with other works

- ☑ periodically liaise with the contractors to establish if the risk assessment should be reviewed and updated

- ☑ co-ordinate work activities as necessary to make sure that no-one is put at risk unnecessarily

- ☑ ensure that higher risk work is carried out in accordance with a permit to work system

- ☑ monitor the work of the contractors on a periodic basis to make sure it is carried out in accordance with the method statement and any permits

- make sure that the equipment used by the contractors is suitable for the job in hand, particularly in higher risk situations (such as working in cramped conditions where there is a lot of earthed metalwork or in a damp or wet environment, for example inside a tank)

- make sure that the contractors implement a strict locking-off procedure where there is potential for them or others to come into contact with live parts due to circuits being made live again whilst work is still being carried out

- where necessary ensure that appropriate signage is displayed, but also appreciate that signage in itself is not an adequate safety measure

- ensure that contractors do not allow their combustible waste materials to accumulate in areas where it could become the fuel in the event of an electrical fire.

Particular care is needed in respect of any alterations and extensions to existing installations (for example, in renovation work), particularly in the identification of circuits where some circuits could remain live for at least part of the work.

With regard to **electrical contractors** working on site, as far as is practical, the site management team must assure themselves that:

- the contractor has compiled an accurate assessment of the risks to their employees and other people who may be affected by the work

- the people at risk are aware and know what to do to protect themselves

- an objective decision has been taken over whether the job can be carried out with the circuit(s) live or dead

- the work will be properly planned, which includes the contractor informing site management of the circuit(s) to be worked on, and the implications for others (for example, if they have to disable a fire-detection system)

- the job will be adequately supervised, with permanent accompaniment where necessary (see paragraph below)

- the contractors will implement a permit to work system where justified by the risks

- a written system of working (method statement) will be produced, communicated to those doing the job, and followed

- the contractor will provide briefings to their employees and to others, as necessary

- the contractor has engaged only competent employees

- the contractor will provide the correct tools and test equipment

- the contractor's employees will be provided with suitable and sufficient PPE.

Where it is necessary to work on live equipment, it will usually be necessary for the person doing the work to be accompanied by another person. It is essential that this person:

- can recognise the signs of danger

- is able to administer first aid for electric shock

- can otherwise give assistance in the event of an emergency

- knows how to switch off the supply

- can assist in restricting access to the area.

Appendix A – Typical example of a permit to work

1. Project details

Permit no.   Site:

2. Issue

To: , the person in charge of this work.

I hereby declare that the following high-voltage apparatus in the area specified is dead, has been isolated from all live conductors and is connected to earth.

Treat all other electrical apparatus in the area as dangerous.
The apparatus is efficiently connected to earth at the following points:

The points of isolation are:

Arrangements for the display or retention of the keys to locking-off devices are:

Caution notices have been posted at the following points:

Safety locks have been fitted at the following points:

Description of the work to be carried out:

Diagram of work/reference drawings

Signed: Time: Date:

3. Receipt

I accept responsibility for carrying out the work on the apparatus detailed on this permit to work and no attempt will be made by me or by people under my charge to work on any other apparatus in the area.

Signed: Time: Date:

Note: After signing the receipt, the permit to work should be retained by the person in charge at the place where the work is being carried out until the work is complete and the clearance has been signed.

4. Clearance

The work for which this permit to work was issued is now suspended*/completed* and all people under my charge have been withdrawn and warned that it is no longer safe to work on the apparatus detailed on this permit to work.

All work equipment, tools, test equipment, and so on have been removed. Additional earths have been removed.

The work is complete*/incomplete* as follows:

Signed: Time: Date:

5. Cancellation

The permit to work is cancelled.

Signed: Time: Date:

* Delete as applicable

04

Temporary works

The requirement to manage temporary works can be misunderstood and many believe it is only required on large projects or for complex work. However, temporary works are likely to form a key part of any construction project.

A recent survey suggests that many projects fail to appoint a person to manage temporary works.

This leaves projects open to risks such as injuries or fatalities, the failure or collapse of both temporary and permanent works, damage to adjacent premises, and the consequent delays and increased costs.

This chapter aims to raise awareness of temporary works and the legal requirements to manage them.

Introduction	52
Characteristics of temporary works	53
Responsibilities	53
Hazards arising from temporary works	54
Good practice	55
Use of equipment and materials	56
What can go wrong?	56
Briefing and receiving data	56
Generic checklist	57
Useful reference documents	57

4.1 Introduction

An important element of all construction projects relates to those items used to assist in the construction, but which do not form part of the final (permanent) works.

These are wide ranging and include, for example:

- ☑ site hoardings and signboards
- ☑ temporary access roadways and working platforms for plant
- ☑ temporary earthworks
- ☑ scaffolding and other proprietary systems used for access or support
- ☑ excavations and excavation supports
- ☑ propping systems
- ☑ formwork.

04

Although, on completion, it is the permanent works that receive attention, without temporary works being properly thought out and managed, the project will not be successful.

Effective, safe and perhaps imaginatively designed temporary works solutions can bring significant benefit and add value to projects in terms of safety, certainty, productivity, efficiency, quality, completion times and cost.

On the other hand, poorly planned, designed, constructed, supervised and managed temporary works leave projects open to risks (such as injuries or fatalities, the failure or collapse of both temporary and permanent works, damage to adjacent premises, and the consequent delays and increased costs).

Two other terms are related to temporary works:

- ☑ falsework, which is the temporary support given to structures until they are able to sustain their own loads
- ☑ formwork, which is the temporary form/mould (usually steel or timber) used to contain concrete until it has attained sufficient strength to withstand its own weight.

Hence, temporary works are important for several reasons, they:

- ☑ often form a significant part of the overall cost of the project
- ☑ have the potential to cause delay and additional cost if not thought through in adequate detail
- ☑ are often safety-critical (for example, if they fail, there is a high probability that someone will be hurt or killed)
- ☑ often have important characteristics that do not apply to permanent works *(refer to 4.2)*.

As for all aspects of construction projects it is important that, at all stages:

- ☑ it is clear who is responsible for what
- ☑ all relevant parties on site are aware of this demarcation
- ☑ all parties have adequate competence, resource and information to fulfil their role.

This is particularly critical at interfaces (such as between temporary works and permanent works, between different elements of temporary works or where there are abnormal loads in the permanent works during construction).

Consider the following situation. The permanent works foundation is to be used as a base for a tower crane. Some modifications of this foundation are required to accommodate the tower crane fixings.

 Tower crane

Element	Designation	Comment
Foundation	Permanent works	Used as temporary works to found tower crane (with permanent works designer approval).
Foundation adaptation	Temporary works	Included to facilitate fixings; may become permanent works if it is not removed on completion (with permanent works designer approval).
Fixings into base	Temporary works	Co-ordinated with foundation layout, reinforcement details and bolt pocket locations.
Crane base grillage	Temporary works	
Tower crane	Plant	

The elements described above will involve several parties: permanent works designer, temporary works designer, contractor (foundation), supplier (fixings), supplier (crane). Unless the design and construction interfaces between these organisations and activities are adequately managed, and considered in advance of the work, delay or failure could result.

4.2   Characteristics of temporary works

Temporary works often has characteristics that are not present in permanent works or which present themselves differently.
For example:

Construction accuracy	Although some temporary works have specified/recommended accuracy (specifically in respect of how upright they should be), some do not. Experience shows that, generally, accuracy is less likely to be achieved with temporary works than with permanent works. However, it can be important in order to achieve the assumed strength and robustness.
Misalignment of components	Assemblies made up of small components (such as proprietary falsework towers) may incorporate misalignments between sections.
Reuse	Unlike the permanent works, temporary works components are reused and hence the risk of damage, fatigue cracking or distortion should be recognised and managed.
Changes	Unauthorised changes (for example, in the layout or by removal of components that obstruct trades) can seriously compromise the safety of temporary works.
Abuse	Temporary works can be prone to abuse in the form of overloading, impact and poor quality control (such as welding), unless adequately managed.
Utilisation	As temporary works are designed for a specific task they are usually loaded to their full design load. Permanent works are rarely loaded to this extent.

Site management procedures should recognise these characteristics to ensure that none occur to an extent detrimental to the effective use or safety of the temporary works being used.

4.3   Responsibilities

Responsibilities for temporary works arise in two ways: through the contract and via the statutory law.

Contract

Although the main contractor will have the overall responsibility for temporary works, it is important that all sub-contracts are clear as to what obligations are passed on to others and how sub-contractors are to interact with other sub-contractors and the main contractor. Contracts should require the use of good practice approaches (such as British Standards, industry guides, and so on). For further information on avoiding ambiguity and dispute, and to ensure high standards are attained, refer to 4.5 below.

Site managers will play an important role by ensuring this interaction occurs in a timely manner, that decisions are recorded and that designers (of permanent or temporary works) are consulted when appropriate. Although most of this action will be undertaken by the temporary works co-ordinator (TWC) it is important that the site manager maintains an overview and that the interface between site manager and TWC is set out in company procedures.

Statute

Statutory requirements are legally binding and they override any contractual stipulations. There is no differentiation between temporary works and permanent works under the law: any hazardous work must be managed safely. The key requirements, which stem from the Construction (Design and Management) Regulations (CDM), are set out, in summary, in the table below.

Co-ordination, co-operation and communication	All parties are obligated to co-ordinate, co-operate and communicate to ensure that temporary works are safe, and will not cause unnecessary ill effects upon the health of those involved.
This requirement is common sense. It will not only help to avoid accidents and ill health but also is an essential ingredient for a successful project. Contract requirements need to set out how this can be achieved (such as site meetings and information flow mechanisms). **Risk thrives at interfaces.**	
Competency	It is obligatory on all parties to be satisfied that they have the competency to carry out the tasks assigned to them, and for the engaging party to be equally satisfied.
The engagement of a sub-contractor or designer who is not capable of safe or efficient working, or lacks experience, will sooner or later create a liability. It is important to have control over any further sub-contracting by sub-contractors themselves.	
Timing	All parties must be afforded sufficient time to plan, mobilise and execute the works. This includes those involved in the design or execution of temporary works. Hence good project planning is essential.
It is essential that all parties have adequate time to plan, mobilise and execute their role. Early consideration to the brief, information, constraints, sequencing, and so on, will pay dividends.	
Pre-construction data	The main contractor will have received data from the CDM co-ordinators or designers; some of this may be relevant to temporary works design or execution. If so it is important that it is passed to those sub-contractors or designers who are involved.
One of the recurrent complaints from sub-contractors is that they do not receive such data.	

Construction phase health and safety plan	This is the health and safety management document containing data and procedures relating to, amongst other things, temporary works.
Those elements of the plan that may be relevant to others must be passed to them by the main contractor.	
Inspections	Some temporary works (such as scaffolding and falsework, cofferdams and excavations) are required to have statutory inspections before use, after amendments or any significant adverse event.

Other regulations will also apply, as appropriate, (such as the Provision and Use of Work Equipment Regulations (PUWER), the Lifting Operations and Lifting Equipment Regulations (LOLER) and the Work at Height Regulations. All of these have inspection requirements.

4.4 Hazards arising from temporary works

04

Temporary works do not produce hazards that differ significantly from the permanent works. Generic hazards include:

Safety	Health
Structural adequacy	Manual handling
Work at height	Operational management
Falling objects	
Operational management	

Others will apply on specific projects.

 Operational management failure (safety)

A façade scaffold collapsed in Milton Keynes in 2006 causing the death of a worker, and injuring several others, because of poor operational site management.

Specifically:

- ☑ failure to inspect the scaffold on a regular basis
- ☑ unauthorised changes
- ☑ overloading
- ☑ insufficient ties.

Each of these issues may have been considered small in themselves, but cumulatively, and over time, they caused a tragic failure.

4.5   Good practice

Good practice, drawn up by industry itself, will help not only in the management of a safe site, but also in creating a productive site. Good practice may be divided into management and technical.

Management

The accepted core document, in place for more than 30 years, is BS 5975: *Code of practice for temporary works procedures and the permissible stress design of falsework*. This code should be embedded in all contracts to avoid any dispute or uncertainty as to the expected procedures. The key items are shown below.

Designated individual	There should be one person in each organisation who establishes and implements the procedures (temporary works design and construction), including the appointment of competent temporary works co-ordinators. Site managers should be familiar with these procedures.
Temporary works co-ordinators (TWC)	On each contract the main contractor should appoint one of its own personnel to act as TWC. It is important that the duties are in writing and made known. The TWC is responsible for ensuring that all aspects of the organisation's procedures relating to the co-ordination and management of temporary works are implemented on site. A schedule of TWC duties is provided in BS 5975 (Clause 7.2.5). It is preferable that the TWC is not the person responsible for day-to-day progress of the temporary works on site. Where this is unavoidable, the TWC should ensure that decisions relating to temporary works are safety-based and not influenced by other commercial concerns.
Temporary works supervisors (TWS)	On larger or more complex projects it may be desirable for the appointment, from sub-contractors, of one or more TWS to assist the TWC. It is important that the duties are in writing and made known.
Temporary works register	All sites should have a register of the temporary works giving: ■ a brief description ■ which parties are designing and executing the work ■ significant dates. The first entry is likely to be site hoarding.
Permits to load/unload	No temporary works should be loaded or unloaded without the authorisation of the TWC.
Information flow	The code stresses the importance of good information flow and co-ordination. Specifically, designers should always have a written brief.

There are occasions when choosing a solution with greater initial cost may have overall benefits that outweigh this expense. For example:

- ☑ use of prefabricated staircase assemblies to gain vertical access, in lieu of ladders. Staircases allow quick access, multiple usage, and the carrying of tools

- ☑ use of proprietary barrier systems allows quick installation

- ☑ formwork with integrated working platforms allows instant, safe and effective access.

Technical

BS 5975 also contains rules for design. Temporary works should be designed to these rules or to the Eurocodes (BS EN 12812) by competent persons with experience in temporary works design. Detailed advice is outside the scope of this chapter.

All temporary works should be constructed from drawings and sketches authorised for use by the TWC. Some key watch-points, not requiring explicit technical expertise, include:

- ☑ adequate foundations to falsework (if it doesn't look right, it probably isn't)

- ☑ lateral bracing at forkhead level (although some systems and arrangements do not need bracing it is better to check if none are present)

- ☑ all scaffolding requires a formal engineered design, unless it is a basic scaffold, as defined in TG20

- ☑ general standard of construction (such as verticality, alignment)

- ☑ adequate protection to those working in excavations.

4.6　Use of equipment and materials

Temporary works uniquely utilises materials that may have been used previously. It should:

- come from a reputable source
- be authenticated, when relevant
- come with guidance if its safe use is dependent upon the manner in which it is used
- be inspected (usually prior to delivery) for condition, cracks and distortion, depending upon the component.

The contractor ordering this equipment should have procedures in place to ensure these points are recognised and actioned.

It is particularly important, when using proprietary equipment, to be satisfied that the component is the genuine article.

4.7　What can go wrong?

Most temporary works, following statutory requirements and good practice, are executed without any problem. Nonetheless, there are numerous examples of failure where significant cost, delay and human suffering have resulted.

The most common category of failing is lack of management. This is shown in the table below.

Aspect	Example
General	Insufficient oversight by the main contractor (which will have responsibilities notwithstanding any contractual sub-letting).
	Failure to appoint a TWC or to provide adequate technical back-up.
Change control	Unauthorised changes (such as removal of members to allow access for another trade).
Loading	Stacking of materials on working platforms that are only designed for access or light loads.
Time	Insufficient time allowed for elements of the supply chain to undertake their task. This often happens at sub-sub-contact level.
Information	Poor appreciation by the instructing party of the information required by designers and others to deliver a compliant (and safe) output.
Lateral support	Insufficient ties into adjacent structures to provide the necessary lateral support.
Sheeting	Sheeting scaffolds and other above-ground structures (for protection or advertising), which have not been designed for such action.

4.8　Briefing and receiving data

Briefing

It is important that those being engaged as temporary works contractors or designers are fully briefed. BS 5975 sets out requirements (Section 8), as does BE EN 12812 (Section 6) but only for design class B2. It is important to check that these clauses are sufficient for the particular needs and to appreciate that they do not always apply.

Advice should be sought where the temporary works are beyond the experience of site management.

Receiving data

Equally important is that those engaged to design or construct temporary works provide information on any limitations or requirements relating to their work that might impact on others. BE EN 12812 (Section 9) provides a list of required data but only for Classes B1 and B2. As above it is necessary to be satisfied that this is sufficient for the specific case.

 Receipt of key data

- Lateral stability assumptions (such as vertical assemblies relying on the permanent works).
- Pour rate assumed (for vertical formwork).
- Whether the structure may be sheeted.
- Size of tie bolts assumed.
- (Batter) slope inclination for excavations.

4.9 Generic checklist

It is not possible to produce specific checklists, as temporary works come in a wide range of forms and all are influenced by site-specific situations. However, the following provide an overall reminder.

 Is the proposal safety-critical (if it failed, could anyone be hurt or have their health affected)?

☑ If 'YES' all organisations (and individuals) have statutory responsibilities. Clear procedures are essential.

☑ If 'No', a problem can nonetheless still cause delay or direct financial loss. Hence, it is a sensible contractual precaution to follow the same guideline principles.

 Is there a TWC appointed, acting in accordance with BS 5975?

☑ If 'YES' ensure the interface between the TWC and site management is clear and operational. If you are the TWC, ensure you know your obligations and whether you may need to seek assistance.

– If you are also responsible for site management ensure you are able to exercise the TWC duties independently from other management pressures.

☑ If 'No' you should refer the matter to the designated individual.

Some small sites can produce substantial risk (such as refurbishments involving structural alterations, basement constructions and deep excavations).

4.10 Useful reference documents

☑ *Code of practice for temporary works procedures and the permissible stress design of falsework* (BS 5975:2008 plus Amendment A1 2011).

☑ *Guide to good practice for scaffolding with tubes and fittings* (NASC TG20.08 plus Supplement 1).

☑ *Temporary works – Principles of design and construction* (Thomas Telford 2012).

 Temporary Works Forum.

05

Plant and work equipment

Over the last five years an average of 50 people have been killed each year in the construction industry. A significant number of these fatalities were caused by plant and work equipment. The majority could have been avoided by effective planning and control of plant use, adequate checking, inspection and maintenance of the plant and equipment, and thorough training, assessment and briefing of personnel.

This chapter gives an overview of the legal requirements for plant and work equipment and the steps required to ensure that these obligations are met, so that work equipment can be used safely and efficiently.

Introduction	60
Key requirements	60
Legislation	60
General	62
Abrasive wheels	65
Portable fixing tools	69
Woodworking machines	73
Compressors	76
Pumps	77
Training and competence of personnel	77
Medical fitness	77
Maintenance, checks and inspections	78
Appendix A – Further information	79

Plant and work equipment

5.1 Introduction

All plant and tools used on construction sites are defined as work equipment by the Provision and Use of Work Equipment Regulations (PUWER), and have the potential to cause harm. Reducing the risk of harm caused by work equipment requires the following steps.

- ☑ Assessment of the hazards and risks involved in using work equipment.
- ☑ Implementation of measures to eliminate or reduce those risks.
- ☑ Ensuring that operators of work equipment are trained and competent.
- ☑ Ensuring that work equipment is checked, maintained and inspected.

 Problems with plant and work equipment operations often occur because of poor communication, both during planning and briefing of operators and users of work equipment.

5.2 Key requirements

- ☑ The term 'work equipment' is very wide ranging and refers to any item of equipment, machinery or tools being used to carry out work.
- ☑ The word 'used' means any activity involving the work equipment, including starting, stopping, repairing, modifying, maintaining, servicing or cleaning.
- ☑ Examples are an excavator, a crane, a hammer, an angle grinder and a cartridge tool.
- ☑ All items of work equipment must comply with certain legal requirements.
- ☑ Broadly speaking, the effort necessary to comply with the requirements will depend upon the complexity of the equipment and its potential to cause harm (for example, a trowel will not require the same level of inspection as a passenger goods hoist).
- ☑ The law also requires anyone who uses an item of work equipment to be trained and competent to do so.
- ☑ The effort and time needed to achieve the required level of competence will depend upon the complexity of the equipment and its potential to cause harm.
- ☑ Work equipment must be maintained and inspected as necessary to ensure that it can continue to be used safely.
- ☑ Certain work equipment must also be subjected to thorough examination.

5.3 Legislation

The following is a brief summary of the legislative requirements for mobile plant operations.

 For more detailed information on legislation refer to Section A *Legal and management*.

The Provision and Use of Work Equipment Regulations

The Provision and Use of Work Equipment Regulations (PUWER) are concerned with such matters as safeguarding of dangerous parts of machinery, provision of appropriate controls, training of operators and maintenance of work equipment, including cranes and lifting equipment.

PUWER places duties on any person who has control to any extent of:

- ☑ work equipment
- ☑ a person at work who uses, supervises or manages the use of work equipment
- ☑ the way in which work equipment is used at work (including maintenance).

PUWER applies to employers in respect of work equipment provided for, or used by, their employees, self-employed persons and other persons (such as visitors).

The Lifting Operations and Lifting Equipment Regulations

The Lifting Operations and Lifting Equipment Regulations (LOLER) deal with the specific risks arising from the use of work equipment (including lifting accessories) to lift loads. They build upon PUWER and apply to the same groups of people.

LOLER requires that:

- all lifting operations are planned, supervised and carried out safely
- specific requirements are applied to the lifting of people
- pre-use checks and inspections at appropriate intervals are carried out on lifting equipment
- lifting equipment is thoroughly examined by a competent person on specified occasions and at specified intervals.

The Pressure Systems Safety Regulations

The Pressure Systems Safety Regulations deal with the specific risk arising from pressure systems, both fixed and portable. The regulations set out requirements for:

- design and construction
- provision of information and marking
- installation
- use
- maintenance, modification and repair
- examination.

The Work at Height Regulations

The Work at Height Regulations impose health and safety requirements for work at height. These include:

- organisation and planning
- hierarchy of control
- competence and supervision
- steps to be taken to avoid risk from work at height
- selection of work equipment
- inspection of work equipment.

05

Aa The regulations define work at height as:

- work in any place, including a place at or below ground level
- obtaining access to or egress from such place while at work, except by a staircase in a permanent workplace, where, if measures required by these regulations were not taken, a person could fall a distance liable to cause personal injury.

The Construction (Design and Management) Regulations

The Construction (Design and Management) Regulations place duties on duty holders, including clients, designers and contractors, for the planning, management and monitoring of health, safety and welfare in construction projects and of the co-ordination of the performance of these duties by duty holders. These include a duty on every person working under the control of another to report anything that they are aware is likely to endanger health or safety.

Certain individual regulations have implications for the way in which plant and work equipment operations are carried out, such as:

- there must be safe places of work, including getting to and from the place of work
- traffic routes must be suitable for the vehicles that will have to pass over them (for example, dumpers must be used and moved in a way that does not put pedestrians at risk)
- there must be suitable and sufficient lighting for every place of work and traffic route.

Personal Protective Equipment at Work Regulations

These regulations impose health and safety requirements for the provision of, and use by, persons at work of personal protective equipment (PPE). The regulations require that:

- employers ensure suitable PPE is provided, without charge, for their employees
- self-employed persons ensure suitable PPE is provided for them
- employers and self-employed persons meet specific requirements for the training, selection, use, storage and maintenance of PPE
- employees report to their employer the loss of, or any obvious defect in, PPE.

Control of Vibration at Work Regulations

These regulations require employers to assess the vibration risk to their employees and eliminate risk or reduce exposure. Employers must also:

- provide information to their employees
- keep records of risk assessments and control actions
- keep records of health surveillance
- regularly review and update risk assessments.

Control of Noise at Work Regulations

The Control of Noise at Work Regulations require employers to:

☑ assess the risks to their employees from noise at work

☑ take action to reduce the noise exposure that produces those risks

☑ provide their employees with hearing protection if the noise cannot be reduced enough by using other methods

☑ make sure the legal limits on noise exposure are not exceeded

☑ provide their employees with information, instruction and training

☑ carry out health surveillance where there is a risk to health.

Control of Substances Hazardous to Health Regulations

The Control of Substances Hazardous to Health (COSHH) Regulations require employers to control substances that are hazardous to health by:

☑ finding out what the health hazards are

☑ deciding how to prevent harm to health (risk assessment)

☑ providing control measures to reduce harm to health

☑ making sure control measures are used

☑ keeping all control measures in good working order

☑ providing information, instruction and training for employees and others

☑ providing monitoring and health surveillance in appropriate cases

☑ planning for emergencies.

Supply of Machinery (Safety) Regulations

The Supply of Machinery (Safety) Regulations are the UK's implementation of European Union Directive 2006/42/EC the Machinery Directive, which requires that all machinery (including lifting accessories) supplied into the European Union, meets the essential health and safety requirements detailed in Schedule 2 of the regulations. Each machine must be accompanied at the time of supply by an EC declaration of conformity, declaring that the machinery fulfils all the relevant provisions of the regulations.

 Plant, first supplied after 1 January 1995, must be CE-marked and meet the essential health and safety requirements of the Supply of Machinery (Safety) Regulations. Consequently, most items of lifting equipment are designed to a harmonised European Standard (such as EN 474 5 for excavators, EN 1459 for telehandlers and EN 12001 for concrete pumps).

British, European and ISO standards

Standards do not generally have the force of law. The application of a standard is almost always voluntary, although standards are very often used in support of legislation, and compliance with a standard is sometimes quoted in legislation as offering a route to discharging legal obligations. A good example of this is the references to the BS 7121 series in the guidance to LOLER.

British standards are generally restricted to Codes of Practice (CoPs) for safe use of equipment (such as BS 7121-1:2006 *Safe use of cranes*), whilst European (EN) standards cover requirements for basic principles (Type A), common product requirements (Type B) and specific product requirements (Type C) (such as EN 474 6 *Earth-moving machinery. Safety – Requirements for dumpers*).

International Standards (ISO) cover both the safe use and specification of lifting equipment. They do not have any legal status but are often taken as good practice and are cited as normative references in some EN product standards.

5.4   General

The building, construction and civil engineering industry uses a vast range of plant and equipment, all of which has to comply with PUWER. It is all referred to as work equipment and includes all:

☑ hand tools (such as hammers and screwdrivers)

☑ powered tools, including electric and pneumatic (such as hand drills and circular saws)

☑ lifting equipment and accessories (covered under PUWER as well as having requirements under LOLER)

☑ testing and laboratory equipment (such as cube crushers)

☑ complex structures and machines made up of other components and equipment (such as scaffolds).

Some types of powered hand tools, such as engine-powered cutting-off machines and chainsaws, have the potential to cause severe personal injury unless they are used by trained and competent persons in appropriate circumstances.

Another type of equipment commonly used in the construction industry that has the potential to cause harm if not properly used is mechanical equipment that operates through the application of leverage or torque. This includes jacks, winches and various cutting and bending tools that incorporate manually operated mechanisms.

Tools and equipment operated by air also cause significant injuries due to failure of the tools or the connections to the compressor.

All items of plant are classified as work equipment, including static and mobile equipment, pedestrian-controlled equipment, ride-on equipment and remote-controlled equipment. Plant used in construction operations on site includes static plant used in the actual construction work (such as mixers and pumps).

General requirements applicable to all work equipment

Suitability for purpose

All equipment that is used to carry out a work activity must be suitable for that work.

Improvisation is dangerous and can lead to serious accidents occurring. Both a handheld circular saw being used instead of a router to cut grooves or rebates in timber, or a dumper being used to transport persons, have the potential to create dangerous situations.

All work equipment must be regularly maintained in an effective state, in an effective working order and in good repair. Work equipment that is covered by LOLER must be subjected to thorough examinations.

 For further information refer to Chapter C07 Lifting operations.

Conformity with EU requirements

Employers should ensure that any work equipment that is in use or acquired, either new or second-hand, has a CE-mark. This indicates that it complies with the relevant European Directive and has been manufactured to appropriate standards.

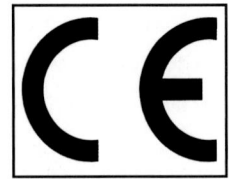

CE-mark

'Grey' imports

Machines originally supplied from outside the EU frequently do not comply with the requirements of the Machinery Directive and are not CE-marked. If such machines are brought into the EU they cannot be used until they have been modified to meet EU requirements. This is a time-consuming and costly process that often negates the benefit of purchasing second-hand machines from outside of the EU.

Types of work equipment

Mobile plant

This includes excavators, dumpers, forklifts, telehandlers, rollers, mobile elevating work platforms (MEWPs) and mobile cranes. Mobile plant may either be controlled by the operator riding on the machine or they may be pedestrian controlled.

 For specific details on mobile plant refer to Chapter C06 Mobile plant and vehicles.

Static plant

This includes items such as construction hoists *(refer to Chapter C08 Lifting equipment)*, compressors and pumps (covered later in this chapter), batching plants, concrete mixers, and rebar benders and cutters.

Lifting equipment

Both mobile and static plant may be designed as lifting equipment for lifting operations. This includes mobile cranes, tower cranes, MEWPs, hoists, telehandlers and excavators used for lifting.

 For further information refer to Chapter C07 Lifting operations and Chapter C08 Lifting equipment.

Manually operated handheld plant and work equipment

In recent years, the mechanisation of techniques that were traditionally seen as being achievable only by using non-mechanical equipment has caused an upsurge in the range of equipment that is available.

Selection of the correct equipment for the job in hand is vitally important. Choosing modern equipment that reduces the risk of injury or ill health is fundamental to creating safer working environments.

The environment in which the equipment is used also has a bearing on the safety of the operative. In certain circumstances it may be safe to use hand tools in a confined space, but to use powered equivalents could have fatal results.

Handheld power tools, whether powered electrically, by internal combustion engine, hydraulically, by cartridge or compressed air, are covered by the definition.

As the use of these types of tool has increased, so has the potential for serious injury. Old type, hand-operated smoothing planes could cause serious cuts if wrongly used, but those injuries bear no comparison with the injuries that could occur when wrongly using their modern electrical equivalent.

Cutting chases in a wall using an older type cutting disc produces unacceptable amounts of dust. Modern equipment that is fitted with a dust suppression mechanism is safer and much healthier.

Also included within this category is the type of equipment that requires human effort in its operation (such as jacks, bar-bending machines, pipe-threaders and other machines where the principles of leverage or torque are utilised).

Many jobs (such as nailing tiling battens on a roof), which traditionally would have been completed by using a hammer, are now carried out by nail guns powered by gas canisters. Equipment of this type is open to abuse, which can result in horrific consequences. It is possible to propel a nail in free flight from a nail gun, giving it the lethal potential of a firearm.

 For further information refer to Portable fixing tools later in this chapter.

Hand tools

The general requirements of PUWER apply as much to hand tools as they do to more complex items of work equipment. Unfortunately, this is often not appreciated by hand tool users, who tend to only deal with problems when they occur, rather than eliminating hazards in the first place.

Two examples are:

☑ cold chisels with burred-over mushroom heads can result in a person losing an eye when a burr breaks off during use

☑ a hammer head becoming detached from its shaft can cause a serious injury to the user or a person nearby.

In both examples, the potential to cause harm can be substantially reduced if a system of regular checks, inspection and maintenance, as required by the regulations, is instigated.

Non-mechanical access equipment

Scaffolds

If incorrectly erected or exposed to misuse, scaffolds can also be the cause of accidents.

Such equipment must:

☑ be suitably designed

☑ comprise suitable components that have been inspected prior to use

☑ be regularly inspected every seven days or after alteration, damage or high winds, the results of the inspection recorded, and proactive maintenance regimes put into place

☑ not be interfered with or altered by untrained individuals.

Many accidents have occurred due to installation of scaffold with damaged equipment (such as split boards and bent tubes).

 For further information on access scaffolding refer to Chapter D04 Scaffolding.

Ladders and other wooden access equipment

Work equipment made from wood will not last forever and will deteriorate with age and use. Regular inspection of the equipment is essential for safety, will prolong its useful life and give an early indication of deterioration. It is commonplace for inspections of ladders and steps to be formally recorded, with each ladder or step being given a specific identifying number.

A key issue with wooden ladders and steps is that they must not be painted or treated with anything that would hide any faults or defects.

The regular inspection of wooden builders' steps must include the hinges that connect the support stays and the restraining rope that controls the opening of the steps, as well as the condition of the timber.

Wooden extension ladders have ropes, pulley blocks and clips that fit over rungs. These are vital to the safe use of these ladders and, therefore, must again be regularly inspected.

The simple wooden pole ladder must be checked to ensure that the wire ties beneath certain rungs are in place and tight. Rungs must be checked to ensure they are still firm and do not twist, and the stiles checked to ensure they are not split or twisted.

All work equipment has the potential to be the cause of accidents. Obviously, the potential and the consequences differ between types of equipment.

Management systems for the training and instruction of operators, the inspection of equipment and the recording of those inspections, must be in place and complied with.

 For further information on the selection and use of ladders and stepladders refer to Chapter D03 Common access equipment.

5.5　Abrasive wheels

☑ Abrasive wheel machines of all types have the potential to cause severe injury if they are not used with care.

☑ Anyone who uses an abrasive wheel machine must be trained and competent to do so.

☑ The potential for danger arises not so much from the machine itself but from the grinding wheel or cutting-off disc used with the machine.

☑ Many accidents are caused by the abrasive wheel being rotated faster than it was designed to go, which results in it breaking up (bursting) at high speed.

☑ It is essential to check the compatibility of the abrasive wheel or cutting-off disc with the machine to which it is fitted.

☑ The fitting of any abrasive wheel or cutting-off disc to a machine (mounting) must only be carried out by someone who is trained and competent to do so.

☑ The person who is trained and competent to mount abrasive wheels or cutting-off discs need not be the same person who is competent to operate the machines.

☑ Using an abrasive wheel machine has the potential to cause occupational health problems and usually the wearing of appropriate PPE will be required.

Abrasive wheels are potentially dangerous if not used correctly. Most accidents result from selecting the wrong type of wheel or from over speeding. It is essential that:

☑ the right abrasive wheel for the job is chosen

☑ it is correctly mounted by a competent person on a compatible machine

☑ it is run at the correct speed and guards are fitted

☑ eye protection is used.

In most circumstances abrasive wheels rotate at very high speeds and contact with the revolving wheel can cause serious injury. When using a grinding wheel, a stream of hot, abrasive particles is thrown off, which can cause injury, particularly to the eyes. Finally, there is always a risk of the wheel disintegrating or bursting as it revolves. Fragments of the wheel can be projected a great distance, at great speed and in all directions.

Types of abrasive wheel

An abrasive wheel is generally defined as a wheel, cylinder, disc or point having abrasive particles, and intended to be power driven. It may consist entirely of abrasive particles, or be of metal, wood, cloth, felt, rubber or paper, with a surface covered with abrasive material. It may also be formed of a ring or segments of abrasive materials. These types of abrasive wheels are used for shaping material via grinding operations.

Other types of abrasive wheel are those used for cutting rather than grinding operations. These are circular metal blades, usually with diamond impregnated tips, used for cutting through concrete, steel, and so on.

Choosing the correct wheel

Two-thirds of accidents involving abrasive wheels are the result of using the wrong type of wheel for the job in hand. Had the manufacturer's recommendations been complied with then all these accidents would have been avoided.

Abrasive wheels should comply with the requirements of BS EN 12413 and BS ISO 525.

Many types and grades of abrasive wheel are available, and the correct selection is important. As a general rule, soft grade wheels are most suitable for use on hard materials and hard grade wheels are for use on soft materials. Coarse grains are for the rapid removal of material and fine grains are for polishing.

The use of an unsuitable wheel may result in the wheel face becoming loaded as the pores are clogged by the material being removed. If the wheel is too hard or too fine it may become glazed or polished. The consequence, in both cases, may be that the operative will press too hard, in an attempt to get the work done, and cause the wheel to break.

It is important that only reinforced, resin-bonded abrasive wheels should be used with portable grinding machines.

Abrasive wheels should be marked to conform to Annex A of BS EN 12413.

Maximum permissible speed

The maximum permissible speed in revolutions per minute (rpm) and metres per second (m/s) specified by manufacturers should be marked on every abrasive wheel larger than 80 mm in diameter, or on the blotter or identification label that is sometimes attached to it. Since it is not practicable to mark smaller wheels, the maximum permissible speed in rpm of wheels 80 mm in diameter or less should be stated in a notice posted in a position where it can easily be read. For speeds of 50 m/s and above, colour-coded stripes will appear on the wheel.

Restrictions of use

Annex A of BS EN 124133 and BS ISO 5255 specify how wheels should be marked to indicate specific restrictions for use. These are:

- ☑ RE1: Not permitted for handheld and manually guided grinding
- ☑ RE2: Not permitted for handheld cutting-off machines
- ☑ RE3: Not suitable for wet grinding
- ☑ RE4: Only permitted for totally enclosed working areas
- ☑ RE6: Not permitted for face grinding.

Shelf life

All organic bonded wheels for handheld applications will bear a use-by date of three years from the date of manufacture.

Traceable number

A code number should be marked on the wheel to indicate the source and manufacturing details of the wheel.

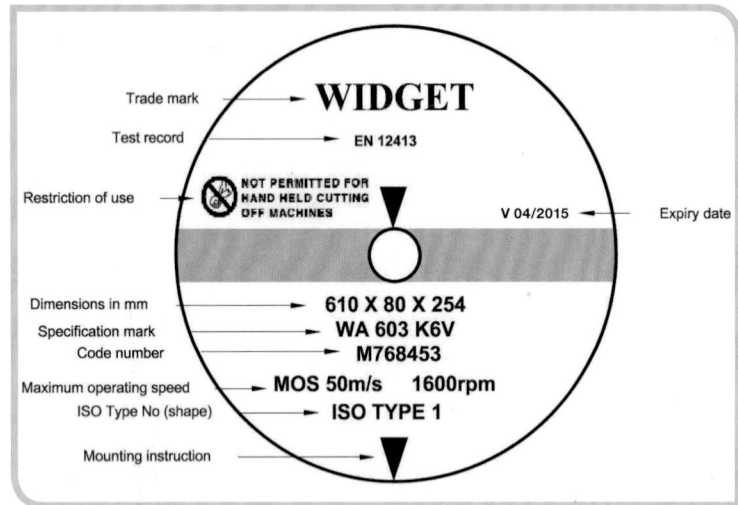

Abrasive wheel marking

Wheels bursting

The two main causes of abrasive wheels bursting are:

- ☑ over-speeding
- ☑ the incorrect mounting of wheels.

Over-speeding

Abrasive wheels must not be run in excess of the maximum permissible speed recommended by the manufacturer. This should be clearly marked in rpm on all wheels over 80 mm (approximately three inches) in diameter.

For smaller wheels, a notice stating the maximum speed permissible should be displayed on or adjacent to where the machine is being operated. Any type of record may be kept, from computer database to a written record. The only restrictions are that a hard copy of the information must be available on request.

Speed of spindle

Every power-driven machine for use with abrasive wheels should have a notice fixed to it, specifying the maximum and minimum spindle speeds.

Machines that are not marked with their spindle speed must not be used.

Sometimes these markings are very small. If this is the case, consideration should be given to painting or engraving the spindle speed clearly on the machine.

Always keep the markings clean and in good condition so that they are easy to read.

Care must be taken to see that the maximum speeds are never exceeded. Governors, or other devices to control or limit speed, must be properly maintained and in good working order.

The speed of wheels may be checked using stroboscopic timing lights.

Peripheral speeds

Care must be taken to operate the wheel at the optimum speed recommended by the manufacturer.

As an abrasive wheel wears down, its peripheral speed is reduced and this, in turn, reduces its efficiency.

A wheel operated at too low a speed will not cut properly and there will be a tendency to press the work piece hard against the wheel. This may damage the wheel and cause it to burst.

Mounting of wheels

In order to be able to demonstrate compliance with legislation, abrasive wheels should only be mounted by a trained and competent person appointed to this duty by their employer.

Maintenance

In addition to checks immediately before and after each use, every machine should be regularly and frequently serviced by a competent person in accordance with the manufacturer's instructions. A record of this maintenance should be kept.

It is good practice to record the type and serial number of all abrasive wheel machines in a maintenance log, together with the date each machine is due for service. When servicing has been carried out, ensure that details of any completed work are entered in the log, together with the date that the next service is due.

All records should be kept up-to-date.

Training

Training for the mounting of abrasive wheels must only be given by a competent person, which often involves attending an external course. It must cover the grades, types and marking of wheels, the use, hazards, speeds, storage, handling, inspection, testing, dressing, adjustments and the functions of associated components (such as flanges, blotters, bushes and locking nuts).

 Details of suitable training courses and training providers can be found on the British Abrasive Federation's website.

Diamond blades

As with bonded abrasive wheels, people working with diamond blades must be properly trained and competent. Most of the safe procedures and precautions for using bonded abrasive wheels on handheld machines apply to diamond blades. Additional advice and information can be obtained from suppliers and manufacturers.

Diamond blades are directional and must be mounted so that they rotate in the direction marked on the blade. They are designed to cut different materials, which must be strictly adhered to.

Diamond blades can significantly deteriorate and become unsafe if they are used to cut the wrong type of material. Reputable manufacturers provide inspection guides for their blades.

A worker used a concrete blade to cut a series of post holes through an asphalt surface to receive concrete fence posts. As a result the blade failed and several 50 mm long segment blade tips broke off at high speed, two of which embedded deep within his knee cap. He suffered high blood loss, was airlifted to hospital and the tips were removed during reconstructive surgery. He was off work for over six months and never fully recovered. Providing an additional asphalt blade would have avoided the accident.

Diamond blades can be used on handheld machines at peripheral speeds of up to 100 m/s, provided that the machine is designed for this speed and the marked maximum permissible operating speed of the blade is not exceeded.

Under no circumstances must the blade be allowed to overheat.

Periodically, it may be necessary to redress the blade by making cuts in a special dressing block or abrasive block. These wheels can last a comparatively long time. Before use and with the power disconnected, make a special point of checking the condition of the spindle bearings, as these can deteriorate considerably during the lifetime of a diamond cutting wheel.

In-use considerations

Guards – fixed and handheld machines

The guard should be designed, and sufficiently robust, to contain any fragments in the event of the wheel bursting.

The guard must be securely attached to the body of the machine, properly adjusted and maintained.

The guard or shield supplied by the manufacturer must be adjusted to permit exposure of the minimum amount of wheel or disc to enable the job to be carried out. It must not be left off or altered in any way.

Defects

Employees are required to report any defects in work equipment, including abrasive wheels, guards or tool rests, to their employer.

Tool rests

Rests should be secured and adjusted so that they are as close as practicable to the wheel and no more than 3 mm away. If the gap between the wheel and the rest is too great, the work piece may become trapped and an accident may result.

It is good practice to continue to display cautionary notices concerning the dangers of abrasive wheels, wherever abrasive wheels are used or changed. This also serves as a useful reminder to employees of the training they have received.

Health considerations

Protection of eyes

During cutting or grinding processes, a stream of dust or abrasive particles and hot sparks is thrown off. These can cause serious injury to the eyes.

Because there is an obvious risk of eye injuries when an abrasive wheel is being used, eye protection should be provided in accordance with PPE Regulations (goggles, a face shield or visor, to BS EN 166).

For further information refer to Chapter B06 Personal protective equipment.

Respiratory protection

Depending upon what material is being cut, it is possible that the user of an abrasive wheel may be vulnerable to inhaling hazardous dust. With fixed machinery (such as bench grinders or fixed concrete saws) it may be possible to reduce airborne dust to a safe level by such measures as:

- ☑ installing a fixed local exhaust ventilation system (for example, in workshops)
- ☑ purchasing abrasive wheel machines that incorporate a facility for wet cutting or the attachment of a standalone dust extraction/collection unit.

If such dust suppression measures are not practical, it will be for the employer, or the person to whom the responsibility is delegated, to assess the hazardous nature of the dust and provide suitable respiratory protective equipment (RPE), consulting a supplier of PPE if necessary to establish what is needed.

For further information refer to Chapter B06 Personal protective equipment.

Vibration

The very nature of carrying out grinding or cutting activities using abrasive wheels is likely to subject the person doing the job to a degree of hand-arm vibration. In extreme cases, hand-arm vibration can lead to permanent and disabling injuries. Employers must assess the risk to employees who carry out such work and put preventative and protective measures in place to ensure that the health of employees who carry out this type of work is not adversely affected.

For further information on control of vibration refer to Chapter B14 Vibration.

Noise

Grinding and cutting operations using abrasive wheel machines will inevitably result in an increased level of noise, both from the machine itself (for example, a petrol-driven disc cutter) and from contact between the cutting disc or grinding wheel and the material being worked upon. In many cases, the level of noise generated will exceed the lower exposure action value, meaning that, unless other control measures can be put in place, personal hearing protection must be made available and worn. Depending upon the level of noise and the proximity of other people, it may be necessary for them also to wear the hearing protection.

 For further information on control of noise refer to Chapter B13 Noise.

Other safety considerations

- ☑ The machine must have an efficient starting and stopping device that is easily accessible and can be readily operated.

- ☑ The floor area of the workplace must be kept in good condition, free of loose material, and should not be slippery.

- ☑ Abrasive wheels should be properly stored, flat and preferably in their boxes, and in accordance with the manufacturer's guidance. Care must be taken to see that any labels are retained, and not soiled or defaced so as to make them illegible.

 For detailed information on abrasive wheels refer to the Health and Safety Executive (HSE) publication *Safety in the use of abrasive wheels* (HSG17).

5.6 Portable fixing tools

Portable fixing tools use the power of an explosive charge or a gas propellant (from cartridges or a gas canister) to drive a fixing device into position in a base material. They are particularly useful if there are a large number of repetitive fixings to be made, where a portable fixing tool reduces the time and labour expended in this area. However, the resemblance of the tools to the shape and action of a gun can lead to their misuse, especially by young and inexperienced workers.

They can be extremely dangerous if used incorrectly. Operatives must be trained and competent and be of a sufficiently mature and responsible disposition.

Poor technique, or the use of incorrect equipment, will result in poor or defective fixing. The tool, type of cartridge or fuel cell, type of fixing and the base material must all be compatible.

In most cases, items of additional PPE, in addition to helmet, boots and hi-vis, will have to be worn.

At the end of the job all unused cartridges must be accounted for.

 It should always be remembered that portable fixing tools are potentially lethal if they are used recklessly or incompetently.

The safe use of cartridge-operated tools

A cartridge-operated tool works by using a firing cap or cartridge to provide propellant to drive a fixing home. The primary factors that will ensure the proper and safe use of cartridge tools are:

- ☑ adequate information, instruction, training and supervision

- ☑ competent and responsible users

- ☑ the compatibility of the base material, the type of fixing and the cartridge strength

- ☑ restricting access to the work area during fixing activities

- ☑ the provision and use of appropriate PPE

- ☑ carrying out activities in accordance with BS 4078-1, Code of practice for safe use

- ☑ using cartridge-operated tools that comply with BS 4078-2.

 Cartridge tools must not be used in areas where a flammable atmosphere or risk of dust explosion may exist.

Types of tool

There are two main types of cartridge-operated tool:

☑ **indirect-acting** where the driving force is transmitted to the fixing by means of the expanding explosive gas acting on a piston

☑ **direct-acting** where the explosive force of the cartridge acts directly on the fixing, driving it along the barrel into the wall or material.

Power level of tools

Cartridge tools are generally classed as high power and low power:

☑ **low power** is defined as giving the pin a kinetic energy not greater than 3.5 m/kg/f and a velocity not greater than 98.5 m per sec

☑ **high power** applies to any values greater than those above. Using high power tools can result in dangerous through-shoots. This is where the fixing is fired right through the material.

Most of the commonly available tools are low power and indirect acting. These are by far the safest. There are high-power tools for special applications, and some old, high-power (direct acting) tools are still in use.

Hammer-activated tools are nearly always low power.

Some modern tools have provision for varying the power level (within the low power range) by means of an adjustment that changes the size of the gas expansion chamber. There are also interchangeable pistons for different fixings or depths of penetration. Tools incorporating these features require a smaller range of cartridges.

Safety devices

All tools should incorporate a contact pressure safety device, which prevents them being fired unless the muzzle is pressed hard against the workface. They should always incorporate a drop-firing safety device that prevents the tool from firing when it is dropped onto a hard surface.

In addition, some tools are equipped with an unintentional firing safety device. This prevents the tool from firing if the trigger is pulled before the tool is pressed against the work surface.

It should only be possible to fire the tool when it is correctly pressed against the work surface.

Cartridges

Any premises or any place where the cartridges for a cartridge tool are stored may need to be licensed. Checks should be made with the local police station or Local Authority as to whether this is necessary and, if so, where such a licence can be obtained.

Cartridges are designed for specific brands or types of tool and are not interchangeable, even if they are of a similar type or appearance. They are available in different strengths. It is preferable to start with a lower strength cartridge for a test fixing and then change to a more powerful cartridge if the depth of penetration is not sufficient.

BS 4078 requires the strength of the cartridges to be marked on the packaging and each cartridge to be colour-coded to indicate its strength.

The colour codes set out in BS 4078 are as follows:

Cartridge strength	Colour
Extra low (XL)	Brown
Low (L)	Green
Low/medium (LM)	Yellow
Medium (M)	Blue
Medium/high (MH)	Red
High (H)	White
Extra high (XH)	Black

It should be noted that the code is not universally followed, and that colour-coding alone must never be relied on as an indicator of the cartridge strength. Cartridges should be retained in the packaging (which identifies their strength) and not carried loose. Both cartridges and fixing nails are now available on plastic strips.

Proper controls must be put in place to account for all dispensed and unused cartridges. Fully dispensed cartridges in single or strip form are not classed as hazardous waste and can be disposed of in accordance with normal rules of non-hazardous waste.

Unused or unserviceable cartridges that cannot be fired are hazardous and in no circumstances should be exposed to fire or heat, or be subject to mechanical impact.

For the purpose of waste classification, unused cartridges often have a hazardous European waste code entry of *16 04 01* Waste ammunition*, but this should be checked in each case from the safety data provided by the supplier of the cartridge.

The supplier should be contacted to discuss suitable arrangements for the return/disposal of any unused or unserviceable cartridges. Cartridges should be returned to their original packaging so that they can be properly identified.

Suitability of base materials

Attempting to fix into unsuitable materials with cartridge tools is dangerous. Before firing the first fixing, a simple test should be made by driving a fixing of the intended type into the base material with a hammer. The result will show whether the material is suitable. No attempt should be made to fix into unsuitable materials. The table below provides general guidance.

Material	Result	Conclusion
Plaster, plywood and lightweight blocks	Sinks in easily	Too soft
Marble, some rock, hardened steel and weld metal	Fixing blunted	Too hard
Glass, glazed tiles, slates and some cast-iron	Material cracks or shatters	Too brittle
Sound wood, concrete and mild steel	Clear impression of fastener point	Suitable

Hazards in use

Hazards from the use of cartridge tools generally arise from one or more of the following three factors:

- ☑ lack of competence, knowledge or training
- ☑ misuse, whether this be deliberate or due to ignorance of proper use
- ☑ poor maintenance, rendering the equipment defective or unsafe.

Two conditions that specially need to be guarded against are through-penetration, where the fixing goes through the material emerging in free flight on the other side, and ricochet, possibly towards the operator, where the fixing is deflected after firing.

Causes of through-penetration

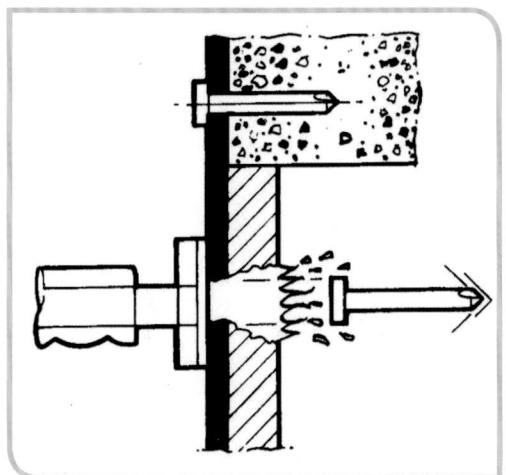

- ☑ Cartridge too powerful for the job being undertaken.
- ☑ Fixing into voids in the structure.
- ☑ The material being fixed into is too thin.
- ☑ Changes in the type or consistency of the material being penetrated.
- ☑ Not establishing the density of the material being fixed into.

To avoid these hazards:

- ☑ check the suitability of the material for cartridge-fired fixing
- ☑ if necessary, make a trial fixing using a low-powered cartridge
- ☑ check the area behind the material or structure into which the fixing is being fired, and guard the area so as to prevent the access of unauthorised persons
- ☑ use an indirect acting tool.

Penetration due to a change in the type of material

Causes of ricochet

- ☑ Firing into the hole of a previously attempted fixing.
- ☑ Attempting to fix into excessively hard materials (such as hardened steel or welded areas).
- ☑ Cartridge tools not held square onto the work surface, causing the pin to strike at an angle and then be deflected.
- ☑ Attempting to fix too near to an edge.
- ☑ Hitting a reinforcing rod or dense aggregate hidden just under the surface.

To avoid ricochets:

- ☑ fixings should be at the recommended distance (or greater) from failed attempts
- ☑ do not fix into unfamiliar materials without first checking their suitability for cartridge fixing

Ricochet due to firing too near to edge

- ☑ tools should be at right angles to the work surface. The whole rim of the splinter guard should be firmly placed against the workface so as to stabilise the tool and not leave gaps.

The risk of ricochet is reduced by the use of low-powered, indirect acting tools. If high powered tools are used, there is a risk that the fixing can be deflected and come back towards the operator.

General precautions

Recoil

Recoil of a cartridge tool can lead to loss of balance if working from an unstable workplace. In this instance, only low power tools should be used. Operators not familiar with cartridge tools, or with the type of tool to be used, should test the tool for recoil before use. In all circumstances, an adequate and safe footing is a necessity. Makeshift platforms should not be used.

Misfires

In the event of a misfire, the cartridge tool should be kept pressed in position against the workface for at least 30 seconds, to allow for any delayed detonation. Following this time period, the cartridge must then be removed strictly in accordance with the manufacturer's instructions. Cartridges that have misfired should be stored in a metal box and returned to the supplier.

  Misfired cartridges should not be removed from the tool by levering under the rim. Some types are rim detonated and could be fired by this action. Only the proper extraction tool, as supplied by the manufacturer, should be used.

Loading of tools

Loading should be carried out immediately prior to use. Once the tool is loaded, it must never be pointed towards other people or at any part of the operator's body. Unused cartridges must be removed from the tool as soon as possible.

Storage and issue of tools

Only responsible and competent persons should supervise and check the acquisition, issue, use, return and maintenance of cartridge-operated tools.

Cartridge-operated tools and cartridges should be stored in a place that is secure, dry and cool. The issue of such tools and cartridges should be strictly controlled, and licensed if necessary. The following points should be clearly noted and understood:

☑ cartridge tools should only be stored in an unloaded state

☑ different strengths of cartridge should be clearly identified and kept separate

☑ the use of different makes of equipment on one site should be limited as far as possible

☑ the manufacturer's instructions on the safe use of the cartridge tool should be available.

Gas-powered tools

Lighter duty gas-powered tools can be used for the fixing of timber and other low density materials. These fixing tools are generally lighter in weight and use a battery and fuel cell, either propane or other gas, to act as a propellant rather than a cartridge. The fuel cell, typically a small aerosol canister, is mounted within the tool. The safety issues that need to be considered when using a gas-powered tool are:

☑ operators must be trained. Usually this can be provided by the supplier of the equipment. Operators must also be in possession of the relevant equipment instructions with which they must be familiar

☑ the tool and the fuel cells must not be exposed to extremes of heat nor used within a flammable atmosphere

☑ during use, harmful fumes are expelled and therefore the tool should be used in a well-ventilated area

☑ when firing, the operator must be in a stable position and holding the tool at right angles to the work

☑ firing must not take place when others are behind the work. As with cartridge tools, through-penetration can occur

☑ if a malfunction occurs, unlike when using a cartridge tool, the tool can usually be fired again. However, the manufacturer's instruction manual should be consulted

☑ because of the mode of operation and speed of use, the tool can become hot (reference should be made to warnings of hot areas on the tool)

☑ fuel cells are a pressurised container and the propellant will remain in the fuel cell

☑ the fuel cell must not be damaged, pierced, punctured, burnt or opened, even after use

☑ fuel cells should be disposed of in accordance with local regulations for aerosol products.

Personal protective equipment

Personal protective equipment, complying with the relevant British Standards, should be used by operatives using cartridge-operated and gas-operated tools, as follows:

- [x] eye protection to BS EN 166-B must be provided and worn at all times when handling cartridge-operated tools, their cartridges or gas-operated tools

- [x] noise levels will vary with the make of tool but all tools create a high intensity, short duration noise. Suitable hearing protection should be worn

- [x] safety helmets to BS EN 397 should be worn while cartridge tools are in use.

The safety of other persons in the vicinity of where cartridge-operated or gas-operated tools are being used, a factor which should have been covered in the risk assessment, must be considered and all necessary precautions taken.

 For further information refer to Chapter B06 Personal protective equipment.

5.7   Woodworking machines

- [x] Woodworking machines are classified as work equipment and must therefore comply with certain legal requirements.

- [x] Many items of woodworking equipment, with their partially exposed blades or cutters, have the potential to cause serious personal injury if they are not properly used and maintained.

- [x] Users of woodworking machinery must be trained on each type of machine that they are required to operate and be judged as competent by their employer.

- [x] Handheld, bench-mounted and free-standing woodworking machines can all be found on sites; all types present particular hazards to the operator and, in some cases, other people.

- [x] The use of woodworking machines also has the potential to cause occupational health problems if appropriate preventative measures are not taken.

Several hundred accidents on different types of woodworking machinery are reported annually to the HSE. Of these, approximately 40% occur on circular saws and 25% on planing machines, both of which may be in use on construction sites. Woodworking machine cutters can inflict very serious injuries and it is essential that the regulations for guarding them are strictly observed. Neglect or ignorance of the regulations governing the use of such machinery creates the conditions in which accidents occur.

Importantly:

- [x] the use of woodworking machines

- [x] contact with some hardwoods used, and

- [x] contact with the dust produced

all have the potential to cause occupational health problems.

This chapter makes particular reference to circular saws and planing machines, since these are most commonly used on site in the construction industry.

Types of machine

The following non-exhaustive list gives examples of different types of woodworking machine.

- [x] Circular saws.

- [x] Sanding machines.

- [x] Bandsaws.

- [x] Routing machines.

- [x] Planing/thicknessing machines.

- [x] Chainsaws.

- [x] Mortising machines.

- [x] Tenoning machines.

- [x] Vertical spindle moulding machines, including high-speed routing machines.

- [x] Multi-cutter moulding machines having two or more cutter spindles.

- [x] Trenching machines.

- [x] Boring machines.

- [x] Automatic and semi-automatic lathes.

Health considerations

Hearing protection

Woodworking machines can be particularly noisy when in use and the noise generated will be a significant hazard to health unless adequately controlled. Ideally, the level of noise will be controlled by means other than issuing PPE, although in practice this will often not be possible on construction sites.

 For further information on control of noise refer to Chapter B13 Noise.

Vibration protection

In the context of using woodworking machines, the predominant problem is considered to be hand-arm vibration.

Respiratory protection

Woodworking machines inevitably produce dust that may affect the operator and persons in the vicinity. The dust should be controlled by effective extraction or collection systems. Where this is not possible suitable PPE should be provided.

 For further information on control of dust refer to Chapter B10 Dust and fumes.

Eye protection

Depending on the machine being used and the nature of the work being carried out, it may be necessary for machine operators (and possibly anyone assisting them) to wear eye protection (such as goggles) or a full-face shield of a suitable impact-resistant grade.

Skin protection

It may be necessary to provide operatives with suitable gloves to protect against skin damage whilst handling timber, particularly unplaned timber. Furthermore, the skin of a small number of persons is adversely affected by the natural oils that occur in some woods, notably cedar.

 For further information refer to Chapter B06 Personal protective equipment.

Controls

Every machine must be fitted with start and stop controls that can be quickly and easily operated by the machinist.

Braking

An essential safety feature of most woodworking machinery is the provision of an automatic brake.

This is to ensure that, if there is a risk of an employee coming into contact with tooling during the rundown period, the machine stops within 10 seconds or less, as defined by CEN standards.

Retrofitting of brakes

All work equipment should be provided with the necessary controls that bring the equipment to a safe condition in a safe manner. To achieve this, a risk assessment should be carried out to determine whether the rundown time should be reduced and the retrofitting of brakes to a machine is necessary. Retrofitting should have been completed by 5 December 2008.

 For further information on the retrofitting of brakes refer to the HSE's *Retrofitting of braking to woodworking machines* (Woodworking information sheet No. 38).

Guarding cutters – general

Cutters include saw blades, chain cutters, knives, boring tools, detachable cutters and solid cutters. Cutters must be guarded to the greatest practicable extent, having regard to the work being done.

Guards must be of substantial construction, properly secured and adjusted, and maintained constantly in position while cutters are in motion.

Adjustments must not be made to any guard whilst the cutters are in motion, unless safe means (that is mechanical adjusters) are provided for those adjustments to be made.

The shape and size of guards may change as technology develops alternative safeguards, if these are at least as effective as before.

Every dangerous part of any woodworking machine must be securely fenced, unless it is in such a position or of such construction that it is as safe to every person on the site as it would be if it were fenced.

Portable, electrically-powered saws

Portable, electrically-powered saws should always be disconnected from the electrical supply before any adjustments, repairs, cleaning or any type of maintenance is carried out.

Whenever possible, to reduce the risk from electric shock, all portable, electric tools should operate from a 110 volt supply and be earthed or double insulated. The mains input to the 110 volt transformer should be protected by a residual current device (RCD), commonly known as a power breaker.

Portable, electrically-powered saws must never be carried by their supply cable. Furthermore:

 when operating, the supply cable must always be kept clear of the saw blade

 the power plug must be examined each time, prior to use, for damage and security of the cable

 all electrically-powered saws should be examined regularly by a competent electrician.

Care should be taken to ensure that the spring loaded, lower blade guard returns to cover the blade after every cut. This guard, also known as the swivel guard, is designed to uncover the saw teeth when material is being cut then automatically covers the saw teeth when the saw is withdrawn. This guard must never be wired in the open position.

Chainsaws

05

Due to their high potential to cause injury, the use of chainsaws on building and construction sites is not generally recommended. While they are not illegal, site rules may prohibit their use.

Where chainsaws are used on site, they must be used only by operatives who are fully competent, have received specific and nationally approved training, and who are certificated to carry out the intended operation.

A specific risk assessment should be carried out for the operation and a written method statement produced covering the operation, including the need for full PPE, safe working at heights and, if necessary, a workplace safely away from other workers.

For specific guidance on the use of chainsaws refer to the HSE's leaflet *Chainsaws at work* (INDG 317).

Other woodworking equipment

For guidance on the safe use of other specific types of woodworking equipment refer to the HSE's woodworking information sheets, which can all be downloaded, without charge, from its website:

Circular saw benches – Safe working practices (WIS 16)

Safe use of handfed planing machines (WIS 17)

Safe use of vertical spindle moulding machines (WIS 18)

Safety in the use of narrow band saws (WIS 31)

Safe use of power-operated cross-cut saws (WIS 35)

Safe use of manually operated cross-cut sawing machines (WIS 36).

For comprehensive guidance on the safe use of woodworking machinery refer to the HSE publication *Safe use of woodworking machinery – Approved code of practice and guidance* (L114).

5.8   Compressors

Air compressors are used in construction as a power source for a range of tools and equipment. They can be either diesel or electric powered, trailer mounted or static, and range in output from 60 cfm* to 900 cfm, with working pressures of between seven and 12 bar (100 to 170 psi).

* cfm = cubic foot per minute of free air delivered.

Selection

When selecting a compressor for a particular application the following points should be taken into account.

- ☑ How many tools are going to be run from the compressor?
- ☑ What is the total airflow required?
- ☑ What is the working pressure required?
- ☑ Does the compressor need to be trailer mounted for ease of movement?
- ☑ Where will the compressor be located?
- ☑ Are diesel fumes an issue?
- ☑ Are there any noise limitations?
- ☑ How long will the compressor be required?

Compressed air safety

A compressed air system presents a range of hazards.

- ☑ Unintended release of pressure from the air receiver, piping or a loose hose-tool connection.
- ☑ Hoses that become disconnected from a tool, whipping in an uncontrolled fashion.
- ☑ Noise from compressed air leaks and pneumatic machinery.
- ☑ Hand-arm vibration from pneumatic tools (this is also a hazard with electric tools).
- ☑ Hot discharge pipes.
- ☑ Moving parts of compressor.
- ☑ Trip hazard from trailing air hoses.

The risks associated with the use of compressors and air tools can be reduced by:

- ☑ ensuring that users are trained in safe working practices
- ☑ providing users with, and encouraging the wearing of, the appropriate PPE
- ☑ selecting low vibration tools from reputable suppliers
- ☑ fitting anti-whip checks across all hose connection points
- ☑ considering the replacement of quick disconnect hose connections with safer two-stage disconnect components
- ☑ maintaining the system as required by the Pressure Systems Safety Regulations.

 When compressed air is misused, it can cause serious injury or even death

A boilermaker was making repairs on a boiler. Upon emerging from the firebox, he disconnected the air hose from a riveting gun and began to blow dust from his clothes. There was one spot on his jacket sleeve that was so embodied in the fabric that the air did not readily remove it. In order to direct more air into the spot, he placed his index finger over the end of the air hose to partially close the opening. Air entered his finger through a small puncture wound, causing swelling and pain. Foreign material, apparently made up of dust and soot from the air, and oil from the compressor, was later removed from the wound. Even with proper medical treatment, gangrene set in and the finger had to be amputated.

As shown by this accident, using compressed air to blow dust or dirt off clothing or the body is a very dangerous practice. A strong blast of air can dislodge an eye from its socket, rupture lungs, intestines or an eardrum. Air forced into the bloodstream can even cause death.

 For further guidance on the use, maintenance and examination of compressors and compressed air systems refer to the HSE's publications *Safety of pressure systems – Approved code of practice (L122)* and *Compressed air safety* (HSG39).

5.9 Pumps

Pumps are used in the construction industry for a number of tasks (such as dewatering excavations, pumping bentonite for diaphragm walls and pumping sludge or sewage). Pumps can be diesel, electric or air powered and range in capacity from around 2 m³/hr to 1,200 m³/hr. They may be trailer or skid mounted and available in silenced versions, and are also available as submersible units.

Selection

When selecting a pump for a particular application the following points should be taken into account.

- ☑ What type of fluid is being pumped?
- ☑ What is the flow required?
- ☑ What are the suction and delivery heads required?
- ☑ Does the pump need to be trailer mounted for ease of movement?
- ☑ Where will the pump be located?
- ☑ Are diesel fumes an issue?
- ☑ Are there any noise limitations?
- ☑ How long will the pump be required?

Providing the pump supplier with this information will assist in getting the correct pump for the application.

For detailed guidance on the safe use of concrete pumps refer to Construction Plant-hire Association's *Code of practice for the safe use of concrete pumps.*

5.10 Training and competence of personnel

It is essential that all personnel involved in the planning, supervision and carrying out of tasks with plant or work equipment are adequately trained and competent for their role. For larger and more complex items of plant there are a number of nationally recognised card schemes, which provide evidence of training and, in the case of the Construction Plant Competence Scheme (CPCS), competence. It is however the responsibility of each employer to ensure that their employees and those working under their control are competent to undertake the tasks they have been allocated.

It is also important that plant operators and work equipment users are familiar with the specific machine they are operating. Plant and work equipment comes in many shapes and sizes with significant differences in control layouts and operating characteristics. It is therefore essential that operators are given adequate familiarisation on an unfamiliar type or model of machine or equipment before they begin operations. This is generally carried out by an experienced person employed by the equipment owner.

Records should be maintained for all familiarisation training, clearly indicating the make and model covered.

Details of the Construction Plant Competence Scheme (CPCS) can be found online.

5.11 Medical fitness

People who operate plant and use work equipment have the potential to injure both themselves and other people in the workplace and the surrounding area. Ensuring that construction plant operators and work equipment users are medically fit to operate is primarily an issue for their employers, who have a duty to ensure that any employee is physically and mentally capable of undertaking the tasks they are required to carry out. Others in the construction sector, such as principal, main and sub-contractors, will also have an interest in ensuring that plant operators have an appropriate level of fitness.

For detailed guidance on medical fitness refer to the Strategic Forum for Construction Plant Safety Group's best practice guide – *Medical fitness to operate construction plant.*

5.12 Maintenance, checks and inspections

Maintenance, checks and inspections of plant and work equipment are essential if they are not to deteriorate over time, break down and ultimately fail. All maintenance should be carried out by a competent person who is familiar with the equipment and has the knowledge and experience to detect and repair existing or potential faults. The maintenance should be in accordance with the manufacturer's instructions and carried out at the recommended intervals.

All plant and work equipment should have a pre-use check carried out daily or at the start of each shift and any defects reported to a supervisor. This is normally undertaken by the operator or user, who should be trained to carry out the checks.

In addition to pre-use checks, inspections should be carried out at appropriate intervals, either as part of the maintenance process or at more frequent intervals. The frequency of inspections should be guided by the manufacturer's instructions and will depend on assessment of the risk of failure of the equipment, taking into account the:

☑ type, class and complexity of equipment. Some types require weekly maintenance, others less frequent maintenance

☑ frequency that a piece of work equipment is used. Equipment in regular use will probably require more frequent maintenance than equipment used infrequently

☑ equipment's potential to cause serious harm. Powered machinery with the potential to cause serious harm (for example, a circular saw) will require more regular attention than a hammer

☑ likely deterioration of work equipment when not in use

☑ the environment that the equipment is used in. An excavator used in a civil engineering project (such as sea defence work during the winter) will have the potential to deteriorate faster than an identical machine used in a less hostile environment.

The results of all checks and inspections should be recorded and there should be a system in place to ensure that all reported defects are rectified and recorded.

 Each item of plant or equipment should have a history file containing all records of checks, maintenance and inspection, so that maintenance trends can be established and adequate maintenance demonstrated in the event of an accident.

Appendix A – Further information

Legislation

The Provision and Use of Work Equipment Regulations

    HSE books *Safe use of work equipment* (L22)

The Lifting Operations and Lifting Equipment Regulations

    HSE books *Safe use of lifting equipment* (L113)

The Pressure Systems Safety Regulations

    HSE books *Safety of pressure systems* (L122)

The Supply of Machinery (Safety) Regulations

Standards

Powder actuated fixing systems. Code of practice for safe use (BS 4078-1:1987)

Powder actuated fixing systems. Specification for tools (BS 4078-2:1989)

Code of practice for the safe use of concrete pumps (BS 8476:2007)

Cartridge-operated hand-held tools. Safety requirements. Fixing and hard marking tools (BS EN 15895:2011)

Safety requirements for bonded abrasive products (BS EN 12413:2007+A1:2011)

Bonded abrasive products. General requirements. Part 1: Specification for general features of abrasive wheels, segments, bricks and sticks (BS ISO 525:1999)

HSE Woodworking information sheets

Circular saw benches – Safe working practices (WIS 16)

Safe use of hand-fed planing machines (WIS 17)

Safe use of vertical spindle moulding machines (WIS 18)

Safety in the use of narrow band saws (WIS 31)

Safe use of power-operated cross-cut saws (WIS 35)

Safe use of manually operated cross-cut sawing machines (WIS 36)

PUWER 98: Retrofitting of braking to woodworking machines (WIS 38)

HSE books

A guide to the Reporting of Injuries, Diseases and Dangerous Occurrences Regulations 1995 (L73)

Safe use of woodworking machinery – Approved code of practice and guidance (L114)

Safety in the use of abrasive wheels (HSG 17)

Compressed air safety (HSG 39)

The safe use of vehicles on construction sites (HSG 144)

Protecting the public: Your next move (HSG 151)

Construction site transport safety: Safe use of site dumpers (Construction information sheet No. 52)

Strategic Forum for Construction Plant Safety Group

Medical fitness to operate construction plant (Best practice guide)

Safe use of quick hitches (Best practice guide)

Safe use of telehandlers in construction (Best practice guide)

05

Construction Plant-hire Association

Guidance on lifting operations in construction when using excavators (Best practice guide)

Work at height whilst loading and unloading transport (Best practice guide)

Code of practice for the safe use of concrete pumps

Technical information notes

 All HSE publications can be downloaded without charge from the HSE website. All Strategic Forum for Construction Plant Safety Group and Construction Plant-hire Association publications are available to download without charge from the CPA's website.

05

06

Mobile plant and vehicles

In the 11 years from 1997 to 2009 there were 108 fatalities in construction where someone was struck by a moving vehicle and 81 due to being trapped by something collapsing or overturning. A significant number of these fatalities were caused by mobile plant and the majority could have been avoided by effective planning and control of mobile plant operations, adequate checking, inspection and maintenance of the plant, and thorough training, assessment and briefing of personnel.

This chapter gives an overview of the legal requirements for mobile plant operations and the steps required to ensure that these obligations are met so that mobile plant can be used safely and efficiently.

Introduction	82
Key requirements	82
Legislation	82
Types of mobile plant	82
Planning and use of mobile plant	83
Training and competence of personnel	87
Medical fitness	87
Supervision	88
Maintenance, checks and inspections	88
Appendix A – Further information	89

6.1 Introduction

The use and movement of mobile work equipment, whether over site roads or within specific areas, involves different and continually changing hazards. These have the potential to cause harm, such as persons being:

- ☑ struck or run over
- ☑ thrown from moving plant or equipment
- ☑ crushed by moving plant or equipment.

 Problems with mobile plant operations often occur because of poor communications, both during planning and briefing of operators.

6.2 Key requirements

- ☑ Many accidents occur with mobile plant because they were not properly planned in advance.
- ☑ Mobile plant should only be operated by trained and competent persons who have been properly briefed on the task to be carried out.
- ☑ The rated capacity of any item of mobile plant must never be exceeded.
- ☑ Mobile plant designed for specific operations must only be used for those operations. The design limitations and permitted modes of operation specified by the manufacturer must be complied with.
- ☑ All mobile plant must be adequately maintained.
- ☑ All mobile plant must be subjected to a schedule of inspections and, where appropriate, thorough examinations.
- ☑ Attention must also be paid to site features, such as overhead cables, excavations, unstable ground conditions and traffic routes.

6.3 Legislation

 For more detailed information on legislation refer to Section A *Legal and management*. For a brief summary of the legislative requirements for mobile plant operations refer to Chapter C05 Plant and work equipment.

 Mobile plant, first supplied after 1 January 1995, must be CE-marked and meet the essential health and safety requirements of the Supply of Machinery (Safety) Regulations. Consequently, most items of lifting equipment are designed to a harmonised European Standard (such as EN 474-5 for excavators, EN 1459 for telehandlers and EN 280 for MEWPs).

6.4 Types of mobile plant

By definition, mobile plant is plant that moves around a construction site, generally under its own power, and is controlled by an operator. Mobile plant is sub-divided into the three areas listed below.

Ride-on plant

Ride-on plant is where the operator sits/stands on the machine or in a cab (examples being rollers, excavators, loading shovels, rough terrain cranes, crawler cranes, self-propelled MEWPs, road planers, asphalt spreaders and dumpers).

Plant that is not designed to carry passengers should be provided with a notice clearly stating 'No passengers'.

People can only be carried if the vehicle has been designed for such a purpose. Passengers and drivers must not be carried unless proper seating, strongly and correctly connected to the main structure of the vehicle, is provided.

Where passengers are permitted to be carried, additional restraining devices must be provided.

Where on-board work activities have to be carried out, seating should be provided, if possible, with work platforms fitted with suitable barriers or guard-rails to stop operatives falling from the equipment whilst it is in motion.

Pedestrian-controlled work equipment

This type of equipment relies heavily on the experience and competence of the operative for its safe operation. Small pedestrian-operated rollers, vibrating plate compactors and surface grinders are among the types of equipment within this category.

Common accidents involving pedestrian-controlled equipment occur when operators of small vibrating rollers are crushed between the machine and adjacent obstructions. This is one reason why the regulations require efficient stop controls to be fitted. It is also essential that operators are provided with, and wear, strong protective footwear to prevent their feet from being injured.

Lifting equipment

For further information on the lifting aspects of mobile plant that is also lifting equipment (such as mobile cranes, lorry loaders, mobile elevating work platforms, telehandlers and excavators used for lifting) refer to Chapter C07 Lifting operations and Chapter C08 Lifting equipment.

6.5   Planning and use of mobile plant

The Management of Health and Safety at Work Regulations require that all tasks carried out at work are subject to a risk assessment to identify hazards and assess the risks associated with the task. Planning a safe site should begin before the construction phase. There are specific duties placed on all of those involved within the construction process, including clients, designers, CDM co-ordinators and contractors. The planning process for the use of mobile plant is similar to that for most other tasks and consists of the following steps:

1.   identifying the task to be undertaken

2.   identifying the hazards associated with the task

3.   carrying out a risk assessment

4.   identifying control measures

5.   developing the method to be used

6.   recording the planning in a method statement (including any contingency activities for rescue)

7.   communicating the plan to all persons involved

8.   reviewing the plan before the task starts and incorporating any changing circumstance.

Practical measures for safe workplaces

Practical measures that should be considered to ensure that mobile plant and equipment can be used safely on site are:

- pedestrian routes should be established on site to provide safe pedestrian access to work areas
- pedestrian routes should be segregated from mobile plant and vehicles, either by a safe distance or by physical barriers
- traffic routes should be planned in order to minimise congestion and risk of collision. These routes should be kept free of obstructions and properly maintained, with access points restricted and clearly marked
- appropriate speed limits should be introduced
- one-way traffic systems should be implemented, if possible and appropriate
- parking places should be designated for delivery vehicles and other vehicles left temporarily on site
- the operating area should be clear, as far as possible, on all sides
- where excavation is taking place, operators must know the location of any overhead power lines, underground cables, sewers, ducts or services before digging operations commence
- trenches and excavations should be fenced or otherwise guarded
- ground conditions should be stable and sufficiently level for the operations being carried out and the equipment used
- where equipment fitted with outriggers or stabilisers is used, the load-bearing capacity of the ground should be assessed so that the imposed loads do not exceed this capacity
- where site vehicles are employed in tipping material into excavations, baulks of timber or other effective blocks should be provided to prevent the vehicle over-running the edge
- excavations may have to be provided with extra support or shoring to prevent the weight of adjacent vehicles causing a collapse (surcharging).

For detailed guidance on the measures to be taken in planning for the use of mobile plant refer to the HSE's guidance *The safe use of vehicles on construction sites* (HSG144).

Material unloading and loading

Materials that are unloaded or tipped from plant should be deposited in planned locations where they will not cause an obstruction or hazard.

A signaller should assist the driver during any tipping operation to ensure that it is safe to tip and that there are no other hazards to be encountered during the operation.

Operatives must not remain on vehicles that are being loaded unless the vehicle is equipped with a reinforced cab or falling object protective structures (FOPS).

Operatives working with plant or vehicles, or on sites where there are regular vehicle movements, should be provided with the appropriate PPE, which should include high-visibility clothing.

Selection of mobile plant

Every employer must ensure that the work equipment is constructed or adapted to be suitable for the purpose for which it was provided.

In selecting the work equipment, every employer shall take account of the working conditions and the risks to the health and safety of persons who are in the vicinity of where the work equipment is to be used.

The design of some vehicles presents hazards (such as restricted visibility and lack of driver protection) from the effects of overturning, noise and vibration. Some old designs of site dumpers allowed the vehicle to be knocked easily into gear as the driver dismounted.

Choosing the right machine for the job is an essential part of effective mobile plant management. The equipment selected needs to be capable of performing its designated tasks safely. The following are important factors to consider:

- ☑ stability under all foreseeable operating conditions
- ☑ safe access to and from the cab and other working locations on the vehicle
- ☑ effective braking systems
- ☑ adequate visibility for the driver all around the vehicle
- ☑ headlights, a horn, windscreen wipers and warning devices (such as reversing alarms)
- ☑ physical guards to protect dangerous parts (such as power take-off shafts, chain drives, trapping points and exposed exhaust pipes)
- ☑ protection for the driver from work hazards (such as working at height and falling from the vehicle, falling objects and the effects of the vehicle overturning)
- ☑ protection for the driver from the weather, noise, vibration, noxious fumes and dust.

Manufacturers' specifications need to be considered when choosing vehicles for construction and civil engineering work. In particular, load and stability limits need to be taken into account when choosing vehicles for use on uneven and sloping ground. Some vehicles, especially those involved in lifting operations (such as some lift trucks and telescopic handlers) require flat, compacted surfaces to operate safely.

Braking systems

Effective braking systems, including parking brakes, are essential for the safe use of vehicles. Parking brakes should be fitted on trailers over 0.75 tonnes maximum gross capacity. Where parking brakes are not fitted, trailer wheels need to be chained or locked to prevent movement when the trailer is parked. Wheel chocks should be used to prevent unintended vehicle and trailer movements when parked on sloping ground. Trailers with maximum gross weights between 0.75 tonnes and 3.5 tonnes should have at least an overrun brake (such as an inertia brake), while trailers over 3.5 tonnes should be fitted with braking systems linked to the towing unit.

Roll-over protective structures

Where there is the risk of mobile work equipment rolling over it should be fitted with roll-over protective structures (ROPS) (such as reinforced cabs or a roll-cage), to stop mobile equipment doing anything more than falling onto its side, thereby minimising the risk of a person being crushed. The cabs or roll-cages should give adequate clearance for operatives to escape if the equipment does completely overturn.

Where there is a risk of an operator being thrown then crushed by equipment rolling over, a suitable restraining system (such as a seat-belt) should be fitted and worn by the operator.

This requirement may also apply to equipment fitted with a fully enclosed cab if there is a risk of a person who is thrown from their seat being injured by coming into contact with the inside of the cab's structure.

Restraining systems must be fixed to a strong anchorage point on the main structure of the equipment.

In areas of limited access, ROPS may be removed only if a suitable and sufficient risk assessment has been carried out and there is no risk of overturning.

06

Telehandler cabs are provided with seat-belts to restrain the operator and reduce the risk of serious injury in the event of the machine overturning. A survey of telehandler accidents in the UK carried out by the Health and Safety Executive (HSE) shows that in seven years there were at least 72 lateral overturns of telehandlers. In three cases the operator was killed by being ejected from the cab and crushed; in a further two cases the operator was ejected from the cab and received serious crushing injuries. Had three of these operators been wearing their seat-belts they would probably have lived.

Falling object protective structures

Where there is the risk to persons operating mobile work equipment of being struck by falling material, overhead protection or reinforced cabs must be fitted to stop any falling material striking the operator.

ROPS and FOPS cab

Prevention of unauthorised start-up

It must not be possible for self-propelled mobile work equipment to be started by unauthorised persons when the vehicle is parked. Additionally, it must be possible to isolate the drive mechanism. This can be achieved by simple measures (such as the removal of ignition keys or starting handles), the use of more sophisticated systems (such as key pad or smart card isolators) or remotely controlled telematics systems.

Lighting and warnings

When self-propelled mobile work equipment is used in the dark or in reduced visibility, lights must be fitted and used to enable the work area to be adequately illuminated. In addition, amber flashing beacons that give warning of the presence of the vehicle should be fitted and used. It is required that some types of construction vehicles are fitted with audible reversing warning devices or similar devices (such as CCTV).

All-round visibility

Accidents involving mobile plant and pedestrians frequently involve poor visibility where the plant operator has not seen the pedestrian or bystander. Current standards aim to ensure that the operator of the plant or vehicle has all-round vision from the operating position.

All-round visibility

It is generally accepted that the operator should be able to see, at all times, an object positioned one metre above ground level and one metre away from the plant through 360° visibility. This can usually be achieved by the use of aids (such as additional mirrors, convex mirrors or CCTV).

Where this is not possible, consideration should be given to providing a competent, qualified signaller working exclusively with the plant operator.

Forward-tipping dump trucks

Amongst mobile plant, forward-tipping site dumpers are worthy of special note because they are involved in a disproportionately high number of plant-related accidents. This applies to both rigid-frame and articulated dumpers.

Forward tipping dumper

The common causes of these accidents are:

- overturning on slopes, rough ground and at the edges of excavations
- travelling with a high-lift skip in the raised position
- the driver failing to observe pedestrians who are then run over by the front wheels
- the driver being thrown from the vehicle whilst travelling over rough ground
- driver error due to lack of experience and training, including accidental operation of the controls.

Efforts to reduce dumper accidents should focus on:

- effective site management and control of how dumpers are operated generally
- selecting the correct machine for the job
- ensuring that machines are routinely inspected, serviced and withdrawn from use if unsafe
- ensuring that only trained, competent drivers are allowed to operate dumpers, which includes removing the key when not in use
- ensuring that site roads are suitable and safe for the use of dumpers.

For detailed guidance on the safe use of forward-tipping dump trucks refer to the HSE's *Construction site transport safety: Safe use of site dumpers* (Construction information sheet No. 52).

Quick hitches

The quick hitches fitted to excavators and other earthmoving plant make a valuable contribution to the construction process by enabling buckets and other attachments to be attached and detached rapidly, as required. Unfortunately there have been a significant number of accidents involving the use of quick hitches, which have included a number of fatalities.

When using quick hitches some precautions (listed below) should be observed. These precautions are applicable to all types of quick hitch – manual, semi-automatic and all fully automatic types, including those that lock onto both pins. All types of quick hitch can be safely used by competent people within a safe system of work. This will involve planning, training, instruction, communication, supervision and maintenance. However, all types of quick hitch may fail if they are not used and maintained correctly.

Site management should familiarise themselves with the different types of quick hitches, and any related company policy to assess and monitor what contractors should be doing to manage the risk.

- Keep other workers away from the machine's working range. Never work under the bucket or attachment and ensure that the operator isolates the controls if there are other workers in the machine's working range. Ensure that your site supervisors enforce this rule.
- Make sure that your operators are aware of their personal and legal responsibility to use all quick hitches safely. Serious misuse of quick hitches should always be treated as gross misconduct, which could well lead to dismissal or individual prosecution.
- Check that all operators confirm that the quick hitch is properly engaged every time they change an attachment. It is essential that this is done by close inspection at the quick hitch, which will normally entail the operator getting down from the cab. It is best practice to make this a requirement for all quick hitches.
- Check that site supervisors understand that the operator has to fully confirm that the quick hitch is properly engaged. Make sure site supervisors allow operators time to do this.
- Check that site supervisors monitor that operators are confirming proper engagement, by spot checks.
- Check that machines are in good order, and all quick hitches are included in the maintenance plan and subject to proper maintenance.
- Check that operators and maintenance personnel have specific instructions for the combination of machine, quick hitch and attachment.
- Confirm that operators are competent to use the specific quick hitch in accordance with the manufacturer's instructions and the safe system of work.
- Forbid practices such as pick and place that involve moving attachments without properly engaging the locking devices.

Using quick hitches with other attachments

Contractors may want to use quick hitches with attachments other than a bucket in normal configuration. However, if a specific application (such as the fitting of vibratory hammers or reversing of buckets) is not explicitly allowed by the manufacturer, the user should assume that it is not allowed, and should not use the quick hitch for this attachment or application. Quick hitches should only be used with attachments and in applications as specified by the manufacturer.

It is essential that operators get out of the cab to physically ensure that all quick hitches are securely locked before starting work with a newly attached attachment.

For detailed guidance on quick hitches refer to the Strategic Forum for Construction's *Safe use of quick hitches on excavators* (Best practice guide).

Concrete pumps

All concrete pumping pours should be planned to ensure that they are completed safely and that all significant foreseeable risks have been taken into account. Planning should be carried out by personnel who have the appropriate expertise. In cases of repetitive concrete pours, this planning may only be necessary in the first instance, with periodic reviews to ensure that no factors have changed.

For detailed guidance on the safe use of concrete pumps refer to the Construction Plant-hire Association's *Safe use of concrete pumps* (Best practice guide).

6.6   Training and competence of personnel

It is essential that all personnel involved in the planning, supervision and carrying out of mobile plant operations are adequately trained and competent for their role. There are a number of nationally recognised card schemes that provide evidence of training and, in the case of the Construction Plant Competence Scheme (CPCS), competence. It is, however, the responsibility of each employer to ensure that their employees and those working under their control, are competent to undertake the tasks they have been allocated.

It is also important that mobile plant operators are familiar with the specific machine they are operating. Mobile plant comes in many shapes and sizes, with significant differences in control layouts and operating characteristics. It is therefore essential that operators are given adequate familiarisation on an unfamiliar type or model of machine before they begin operations. This is generally carried out by an experienced person employed by the equipment owner.

Records should be maintained for all familiarisation training, clearly indicating the make and model covered.

Details of the Construction Plant Competence Scheme (CPCS) can be found online.

6.7   Medical fitness

People who operate plant have the potential to injure both themselves and other people in the workplace and the surrounding area. Ensuring that construction plant operators are medically fit to operate is primarily an issue for their employers, who have a duty to ensure that any employee is physically and mentally capable of undertaking the tasks they are required to carry out. Others in the construction sector (such as principal, main and sub-contractors) will also have an interest in ensuring that plant operators have an appropriate level of fitness.

For detailed guidance on medical fitness refer to the Strategic Forum for Construction Plant Safety Group's *Medical fitness to operate construction plant* (Best practice guide).

06

6.8   Supervision

An essential part of the safe use of mobile plant is supervision of the plant operator. The responsibilities of the supervisor are, each day, to re-brief the operator and others on the task and ensure they are put to work safely. The supervisor should take this opportunity to:

- ☑ reinforce the key elements of the safe system of work, including:
    - strict adherence to exclusion zones
    - the correct safe methods when fitting/removing attachments with a quick hitch
    - consulting the operator and others regarding any issues/comments they have in adhering to or the effectiveness of the safe system of work and, where appropriate, instigate changes

- ☑ check that the operator has undertaken the relevant daily checks

- ☑ check the required maintenance has been undertaken

- ☑ ensure the inspection/maintenance log/check sheet has been completed and signed. The supervisor's signature on the check list/log may be used as verification that they have carried out the check.

As part of the supervisor's ongoing duties, they must, throughout the day, monitor that the safe system of work is being adhered to, including maintenance of exclusion zones, that no-one is working below attachments at any time and quick hitches are being used as manufacturer's recommendations, including the correct use of any safety pins or locking devices.

The supervisor should regularly check that the manufacturer's manual for operating the machine is in the cab, that any relevant decals are displayed in the cab and/or on the machine and that the next service date by a fitter has not expired. The daily checklist for the machine will provide evidence of some of these points.

6.9   Maintenance, checks and inspections

Maintenance, checks and inspections of mobile plant are essential if it is not to deteriorate over time, break down and ultimately fail. All maintenance should be carried out by a competent person who is familiar with the equipment and has the knowledge and experience to detect and repair existing or potential faults. The maintenance should be in accordance with the manufacturer's instructions and carried out at the recommended intervals.

All mobile plant should have a pre-use check carried out daily or at the start of each shift and any defects reported to a supervisor. This is normally undertaken by the operator who should be trained to carry out the checks.

In addition to pre-use checks, inspections should be carried out at appropriate intervals, either as part of the maintenance process or at more frequent intervals. The frequency of inspections will depend on assessment of the risk of failure of the equipment and should be guided by the manufacturer's instructions.

The results of all checks and inspections should be recorded and there should be a system in place to ensure that all reported defects are rectified and recorded.

 Each item of mobile plant should have a history file containing all records of maintenance, inspection and thorough examination, so that maintenance trends can be established and adequate maintenance demonstrated in the event of an accident.

Appendix A – Further information

Standards

Code of practice for safe use of MEWPs (BS 8460:2005)

Other publications

HSE books

The safe use of vehicles on construction sites (HSG144)

Protecting the public; Your next move (HSG151)

Construction site transport safety: Safe use of site dumpers (Construction information sheet No. 52)

Strategic Forum for Construction Plant Safety Group

Medical fitness to operate construction plant (Best practice guide)

Safe use of quick hitches (Best practice guide)

Safe use of telehandlers in construction (Best practice guide)

Construction Plant-hire Association

Guidance on lifting operations in construction when using excavators (Best practice guide)

Work at height whilst loading and unloading transport (Best practice guide)

Safe use of concrete pumps (Best practice guide)

Technical information notes

 All HSE publications can be downloaded without charge from the HSE website.

All Strategic Forum for Construction Plant Safety Group and Construction Plant-hire Association publications are available to download without charge from the CPA's website.

06

06

07

Lifting operations

Each year there are, on average, 17 fatalities and a significant number of major and minor injuries in the construction industry due to lifting operations. In addition, there are many more incidents that lead to property, material and equipment damage, resulting in costly delays. The majority of these could have been avoided by effective planning and control of the lifting operations, adequate selection, maintenance, inspection and through examination of lifting equipment and thorough training, assessment and briefing of personnel.

This chapter gives an overview of the legal requirements for lifting operations and the steps required to ensure that these obligations are met so that lifting operations can be carried out safely and efficiently. The requirements for installing, using, checking, maintaining, inspecting and thoroughly examining specific types of lifting equipment and lifting accessories are covered in Chapter C08 Lifting equipment.

Introduction	92
Key requirements	92
Legislation	92
Planning of lifting operations	93
Control of lifting operations	97
Training and competence of personnel	98
Medical fitness	98
Lifting persons	99
Siting of lifting equipment	99
Operation of lifting equipment	103
Maintenance, checks and inspections	105
Thorough examination	106
Appendix A – Definitions	108
Appendix B – Case study of lifting operation categorisation	109
Appendix C – Recognised hand signals	111
Appendix D – Information to be contained in a report of thorough examination	113
Appendix E – Wind strengths and effects (Beaufort scale)	114
Appendix F – Further information	115

7.1   Introduction

Experience has shown that lifting operations can be a hazardous work activity if not properly planned and carried out. Safe lifting operations will depend upon:

☑ the availability of suitable lifting equipment, which is properly maintained

☑ the provision of adequate information, instruction, training or supervision for everyone involved

☑ thorough pre-planning of each lifting operation

☑ compliance with safe systems of work, as detailed in risk assessments and method statements (lifting plan).

Although regulations require that safe systems of work are developed, accidents that have occurred during lifting operations indicate that all too often these are not in place or, if they are, they are not complied with.

Lifting operations have the potential for death and serious injury to both site workers and members of the public off site. In addition to the terrible cost in human suffering, accidents have a financial cost. There is a very strong business case for improving safety performance.

 Problems with lifting operations often occur because of poor communications, both during planning and when lifting.

7.2   Key requirements

☑ Many accidents occur during lifting operations because they were not properly planned in advance.

☑ All lifting operations must be carried out by, and under the control of, trained and competent persons who have been properly briefed on the lifting plan.

☑ The rated capacity of any item of lifting equipment or lifting accessory must never be exceeded.

☑ All lifting equipment and lifting accessories used for lifting operations must be adequately maintained.

☑ All lifting equipment and lifting accessories used for lifting operations must be subjected to a schedule of inspections and thorough examinations.

☑ In addition to the lifting equipment and lifting accessories used, attention must also be paid to site features (such as overhead cables, unstable ground conditions and adjacent properties).

☑ When using a hired crane, a contract lift will transfer the majority of the legal responsibility for carrying out the lifting operation in a safe manner to the contract lift company.

 The collapse, overturning or failure of any load bearing part of a hoist, crane or other lifting equipment is a notifiable dangerous occurrence, even if nobody is injured.

 For further information refer to Chapter A13 Accident reporting and investigation.

7.3   Legislation

A brief summary of the two main legislative requirements for lifting operations and lifting equipment are listed on the following page.

 For detailed information on legislation refer to Section A *Legal and management* and for other related legislation refer to Chapter C05 Plant and work equipment.

The Provision and Use of Work Equipment Regulations

The Provision and Use of Work Equipment Regulations (PUWER) are concerned with such matters as safeguarding of dangerous parts of machinery, provision of appropriate controls, training of operators and maintenance of work equipment, including cranes and lifting equipment.

PUWER places duties on any person who has control to any extent of:

- ☑ work equipment
- ☑ a person at work who uses, supervises or manages the use of work equipment
- ☑ the way in which work equipment is used at work (including maintenance).

PUWER applies to employers in respect of work equipment provided for, or used by, their employees, self-employed persons in respect of work equipment they use and other persons (such as visitors).

The Lifting Operations and Lifting Equipment Regulations

The Lifting Operations and Lifting Equipment Regulations (LOLER) deal with the specific risks arising from the use of work equipment (including lifting accessories) to lift loads. They build upon PUWER and apply to the same groups of people.

LOLER requires that:

- ☑ all lifting operations are planned, supervised and carried out safely
- ☑ specific requirements are applied to the lifting of people
- ☑ pre-use checks and inspections at appropriate intervals are carried out on lifting equipment
- ☑ lifting equipment is thoroughly examined by a competent person on specified occasions and at specified intervals.

 Lifting equipment first supplied after 1 January 1995 must be CE-marked and meet the essential health and safety requirements of the Supply of Machinery (Safety) Regulations. Consequently, most items of lifting equipment are designed to a harmonised European Standard (such as EN 13000 for mobile cranes, EN 14439 for tower cranes or EN 280 for MEWPs).

07

7.4   Planning of lifting operations

The siting, setting up and use of lifting equipment for lifting operations requires careful planning if all these activities are to be carried out safely and efficiently. One person with sufficient training, practical and theoretical knowledge and experience should be appointed to be responsible for planning and supervising the tasks. This person is known as the 'competent person' in LOLER or the 'appointed person' in BS 7121.

Lifting operations, no matter how large or small, must be properly planned

The competent (appointed) person must ensure that the planning for each task includes the following:

- ☑ identifying the task to be undertaken
- ☑ identifying the hazards associated with the task
- ☑ carrying out a risk assessment
- ☑ identifying control measures
- ☑ developing the method to be used
- ☑ recording the planning in a method statement (including any contingency activities for rescue)
- ☑ communicating the plan to all persons involved
- ☑ reviewing the plan before the task starts and incorporating any changing circumstances.

Lift categories

To enable lifts to be planned, supervised and carried out effectively, three categories of lift are detailed below. The category into which a particular lift will fall depends on the assessment of the hazards associated with both the environment in which the lift is to be carried out and those associated with the load and lifting equipment.

As shown in the table, increases in either and both environmental or load complexity (the 'complexity index') will lead to the lift being allocated a higher category. Having identified the hazards associated with a particular lift, a hierarchy of control measures should be applied to eliminate or control those hazards.

<table>
<tr><td rowspan="3">Environmental complexity (E)</td><td>3</td><td>*Complex*</td><td>*Complex*</td><td>*Complex*</td></tr>
<tr><td>2</td><td>*Intermediate*</td><td>*Intermediate*</td><td>*Complex*</td></tr>
<tr><td>1</td><td>*Basic*</td><td>*Intermediate*</td><td>*Complex*</td></tr>
<tr><td></td><td></td><td>1</td><td>2</td><td>3</td></tr>
<tr><td></td><td></td><td colspan="3">Load complexity (L)</td></tr>
</table>

Relationship between complexity index and lift category

The case study in Appendix B shows examples of where the same basic lifting task will fall into different lift categories, depending on differing environmental or load complexities.

Basic lift

For a basic lift the duties of the competent (appointed) person should include the following.

☑ Establishing the complexity of the lifting operation, including load and environmental complexity:
- load complexity will include characteristics such as weight, centre of gravity and presence of suitable lifting points. This can be established by a reliable source of information, measuring and weighing the load, or calculation

 Where the weight of the load cannot be accurately established, the notional weight must be multiplied by an appropriate factor (typically 1.5) to allow for possible inaccuracies.

- consideration of environmental hazards at the location of the operation will include the access and egress required for the lifting equipment and the suitability of the ground to take the loads imposed by the lifting equipment during preparation for the lift and during the lift itself.

☑ Selecting the lifting equipment, based on the load characteristics (including weight of the load and any lifting accessories); the maximum height of lift and the maximum radius required. The rated capacity of the lifting equipment should be specified by the manufacturer/installer in the user information supplied with the lifting equipment. In cases where the lifting equipment has been derated at time of thorough examination, the rated capacity stated on the current report of thorough examination, issued by the competent person, should be used. Manufacturer's sales leaflets and model classifications marked on the machine should not be relied on for the rated capacity of specific lifting equipment.

☑ Ensuring that the lifting equipment is not operated in wind speeds in excess of those given in the instruction manual for the lifting equipment. The wind area of the load should also be taken into account to ensure that its movement in the wind does not present a hazard.

☑ Ensuring that the lifting equipment has been thoroughly examined at least within the previous 12 months (or six months for the lifting of persons), inspected and checked before use. It is essential that the report of thorough examination, which confirms that the equipment is safe to use, is available.

 The report of thorough examination for the lifting equipment should be carried with the machine.

☑ Selecting appropriate lifting accessories, including their method of attachment to the load, configuration and any protection used to prevent damage.

☑ Ensuring that lifting accessories have been thoroughly examined, at least within the previous six months, inspected and checked before use. It is essential that the report of thorough examination is available to confirm that the lifting accessories are safe to use.

☑ Ensuring that a system for reporting and rectifying defects is in place.

☑ Designating a suitable person to check the lifting accessories and any lifting points that are provided on the load to ensure they are free from any obvious defect before attaching the load to the lifting equipment.

☑ Ensuring that the outcomes of the planning process are recorded in a risk assessment and method statement, which should be signed by the competent (appointed) person.

07

In many instances a basic lift may be covered by a generic risk assessment and a generic method statement, provided that no additional hazards are identified on site.

☑ Selecting and defining the roles of the members of the lifting team. In many instances it may be possible to combine some of the roles of members of the lifting team.

☑ Briefing all persons involved in the lifting operation to ensure that the safe system of work described in the method statement is understood. All persons involved in the lifting operation should be instructed to seek advice from the competent (appointed) person if any change is required to the lifting operation, or if any doubts about safety arise. If one or more handlines/taglines are required to give more control of the load, the competent (appointed) person should designate persons to handle the lines.

☑ Checking, if numerous loads are to be lifted over a long period, that no changes are required in the safe system of work.

☑ Ensuring that there is a crane (lift) supervisor designated to direct personnel and that the operation is carried out in accordance with the method statement.

The competent (appointed) person and crane supervisor should be aware of the limits of their knowledge and experience concerning lifting operations and, when conditions exceed these limits, further advice should be sought.

Intermediate lift

For an intermediate lift the duties of the competent (appointed) person should include the following, in addition to the duties listed above.

 Intermediate lifts were previously called standard lifts in the BS 7121 series – this led to confusion between basic and standard lifts, hence the change from standard to intermediate.

☑ Identifying all significant hazards in the operating area, including any areas required for access or setting up of the lifting equipment.

 This may involve the competent (appointed) person visiting site if there are any concerns about the detail and quality of the information with which the competent (appointed) person has been provided.

☑ Ensuring that a site/task-specific risk assessment and method statement, detailing control measures for the identified risks, is prepared.

☑ Liaison with any other person or authority, as required, to overcome any hazard, by including any necessary corrective action or special measures in the safe system of work.

☑ Determining any requirement for personnel in addition to the lifting equipment operator (such as a slinger, signaller or dedicated crane (lift) supervisor).

☑ Consideration of the effect of the lifting operation on surrounding property or persons, including the general public. This should lead to arranging for appropriate action to minimise any adverse effects, and to giving appropriate notice to all persons concerned.

Complex lift

For a complex lift the duties of the competent (appointed) person should include the following, in addition to the duties listed above.

☑ Identifying all exceptional hazards in the operating area, including any areas required for access or setting up of the lifting equipment. This will require the competent (appointed) person to visit the location of the planned lifting operation as part of the planning process.

☑ Liaison with any other person or authority, as required to overcome any hazard, by including any necessary corrective action or special measures in the safe system of work.

☑ Ensuring that the method statement includes the exact sequence of operations when lifting the load.

☑ Preparing a sufficiently detailed and dimensioned drawing of the site, lifting equipment and the load, identifying the load path, pick up and set down areas, together with the position of any exceptional hazards in the area. The information provided should be sufficient to enable the operator to position the lifting equipment accurately.

It is good practice for the competent (appointed) person to be present on the site during a complex lift.

Case study

The case study in Appendix B illustrates the way in which both the complexity of the load being lifted and the environment in which the lift is taking place affect the overall complexity of the lift. The case study takes a typical construction lifting operation, the lifting of timber roof trusses. Three different situations are evaluated with examples of the hazards encountered and the control measures required to eliminate or reduce those hazards to an acceptable level. It should be noted that this is an example only and does not identify all the hazards that may be present in a given circumstance.

Identifying the task to be undertaken

As the first stage in the planning process, the task to be undertaken should be clearly identified, together with the location and sequence.

Certain lifting operations require particular care and attention. Further advice can be found in BS 7121 Part 1. The competent (appointed) person should be familiar with these and plan the lift accordingly.

Site surveys

The planning of a lift using lifting equipment may involve a site survey, carried out by the competent (appointed) person or their representative. This involves visiting the location where the task is to be carried out so that both the task and any hazards involved can be identified. For simple tasks the remainder of the planning process may be completed at the same time, whilst for more complicated jobs the person carrying out the survey may need to complete the process off site. The survey should include assessment of ground conditions.

A further site visit may be required prior to the lifting operation being executed to ensure no changes have been made to the environment.

Identifying the hazards associated with the task

The hazards associated with the task should be identified. These might be associated with the location where the work is to be carried out, the nature of the lifting equipment, the load to be lifted or the people associated with the task or located in the vicinity.

Carrying out a risk assessment

Having identified the hazards associated with the task, a risk assessment should be carried out to identify who might be harmed, the chance of them being harmed and the consequences of any harm. This assessment should be recorded.

Identifying control measures

Once the risk assessment has highlighted the risks involved in the task, the procedures and measures required to control them should be identified.

Developing the method to be used

Having identified the hazards, evaluated the risks and worked out the control measures required to carry out the task safely, these components should be developed into a coherent plan. Any contingency measures and rescue procedures should be included in the plan.

Selection of lifting equipment and lifting accessories

A proprietary manhole lifting attachment

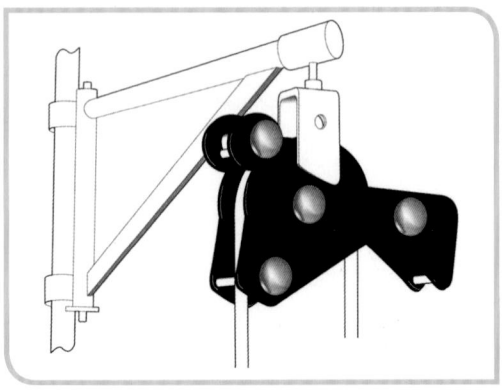

Inertia braked gin wheels are now common practice and far safer than traditional gin wheels

LOLER requires that lifting equipment and lifting accessories are of adequate strength and stability for the load being lifted. When selecting lifting equipment and lifting accessories for a particular task consider the:

- ☑ weight, dimensions and characteristics of the loader and the loads to be lifted

- ☑ operation, speed, radii, height of lift and areas of movement

- ☑ number, frequency and types of lifting operation

- ☑ space available for lifting equipment access, deployment, operation and stowage, including the space required for correct deployment of stabilisers

- ☑ control position that will be most suitable for the lifting operation. The control position should be selected to ensure that the operator has an adequate view of the load path and is adequately protected from crushing hazards

- ☑ need for motion-limiting devices (such as slewing arc or height limiters)

- ☑ effect of the operating environment on the lifting equipment.

Recording the planning in a method statement

Once the plan has been developed it should be recorded in a method statement. The length and detail of this document depends on the complexity of the task to be undertaken and on the risks involved. A simple, low risk job (such as a routine delivery and unloading of bulk materials or blocks to site) might only require the use of a brief, generic method statement, whilst a more complex and high risk job (such as delivering, unloading, and assembling and lifting into position a loading platform on a construction site) would require a more detailed job specific method statement. The method statement covering all planned lifting on a site is often referred to as the lift plan.

The method statement should include a lifting schedule, listing each type of item to be lifted together with the following information:

- ☑ item description
- ☑ weight
- ☑ dimensions
- ☑ lifting points/method
- ☑ type of lifting accessories to be used and configuration
- ☑ pick up and landing locations referenced to the site plan.

Telehandlers should have, and follow, a lifting plan

 For an example of a lift plan and lift schedule template refer to Section G *Checklists and forms.*

Communicating the plan to all persons involved

One of the most important aspects of successful planning is to ensure that the contents of the plan are communicated effectively to and between all parties involved, taking account of language differences. Arrangements should be made to ensure that copies of any method statements are given to the appropriate people and that others involved in the job are fully briefed. Similarly, any changes to the plan should be communicated to all parties.

Reviewing the plan before the job starts

Immediately before a job starts, the risk assessment and method statement should be reviewed to check if any aspects of the job have changed and the effect that these changes could have on the safety of the operation. If any modifications to the plan are required these should be communicated to all those involved. The competent (appointed) person should amend the method statement (lift plan) and initial any significant changes.

 For further guidance on planning of lifting and installation refer to:

- ☑ *Code of practice for safe use of cranes – Part 1 General and Part 3 Mobile cranes* (BS 7121)
- ☑ *Safe use of lifting equipment – Lifting Operations and Lifting Equipment Regulations 1998 Code of practice* (L113)
- ☑ HSE leaflet *Guide to risk assessment* (INDG 218)
- ☑ HSE leaflet *Five steps to risk assessment* (INDG 163)
- ☑ CIRIA publication *Crane stability on site* (C703).

7.5   Control of lifting operations

When a lifting operation is undertaken it is essential that it is adequately controlled by suitably trained and competent people. Depending on the complexity of the lift the following roles may be involved.

- ☑ **Competent (appointed) person** – although the competent (appointed) person has overall responsibility for the lift, they may choose to supervise the operation themselves or delegate the role to a crane (lift) supervisor.
- ☑ **Crane (lift) supervisor** supervises the lifting operation on behalf of the competent (appointed) person, working to the approved method statement or lift plan. If circumstances require any change to the method statement, this must be approved by the competent (appointed) person.
- ☑ **Operator** operates the lifting equipment within its permitted duties in accordance with the method statement and as instructed by the crane (lift) supervisor.
- ☑ **Slinger/signaller** connects lifting accessories to the load, initiates lifting by signalling to the operator, observes the path of the load to its destination, signals to the operator and detaches lifting accessories once the load is safely landed.

Combination of roles

In certain circumstances it may be possible to combine some of the roles of members of the lifting team (illustrated in the table below). However, the table should not be taken as definitive for every circumstance. Role combination should only take place following review of the lifting operation by the competent (appointed) person.

It should be noted that a competent (appointed) person is required to plan all lifting operations. It is good practice for them to be present on the site during a complex lift.

In some circumstances it may be appropriate for the competent (appointed) person to also assume other roles (such as crane supervisor, slinger/signaller or operator).

The combination of roles requires that the person undertaking the combined role has achieved the necessary competence for each role.

Combination of lifting team roles

Activity	Role	Lift category		
		Basic	Intermediate	Complex
Planning	Competent (appointed) person	Required	Required	Required
Site visit	Competent (appointed) person	Not essential	May be required	Required
Lifting operation	Competent (appointed) person	Not essential	May be required	Required
	Crane (lift) supervisor	Roles may be combined	Roles may be combined	Required
	Operator			Required
	Slinger/signaller		Required	Required

Note: This table is for guidance. It is the competent (appointed) person's responsibility to determine the combination of roles for each lifting operation following a site-specific risk assessment that takes account of the load, the lifting equipment and the site environment.

Signalling methods

Communication between the various people involved in the lifting operation should be clear and unambiguous. This can be by recognised hand signals *(refer to Appendix C)* or voice communication using portable radios. Slinger/signallers should be provided with distinctive PPE (such as fluorescent hard-hat covers) so that they are immediately identifiable to the lifting equipment operator.

For further information on radio communications for lifting operations refer to the Construction Plant-hire Association's Technical information note TIN 017.

7.6 Training and competence of personnel

It is essential that all personnel involved in the planning, supervision and carrying out of lifting operations are adequately trained and competent for their role. There are a number of nationally recognised card schemes that provide evidence of training and, in the case of the Construction Plant Competence Scheme (CPCS), competence. It is, however, the responsibility of each employer to ensure that their employees and those working under their control, are competent to undertake the tasks they have been allocated.

It is also important that lifting equipment operators are familiar with the specific machine they are operating. Lifting equipment comes in many shapes and sizes, with significant differences in control layouts and operating characteristics. It is therefore essential that operators are given adequate familiarisation on an unfamiliar type or model of machine before they begin lifting operations. This is generally carried out by an experienced person employed by the lifting equipment owner.

For further guidance on training and competence refer to BS 7121 Parts 1, 3, 4 and 5.

7.7 Medical fitness

People who operate plant have the potential to injure both themselves and other people in the workplace and the surrounding area. Ensuring that construction plant operators are medically fit to operate is primarily an issue for their employers, who have a duty to ensure that any employee is physically and mentally capable of undertaking the tasks they are required to carry out. Others in the construction sector (such as principal, main and sub-contractors) will also have an interest in ensuring that plant operators have an appropriate level of fitness.

For detailed guidance on medical fitness refer to the Strategic Forum for Construction Plant Safety Group's *Medical fitness to operate construction plant* (Best practice guide).

7.8   Lifting persons

Some items of lifting equipment (such as mobile elevating work platforms (MEWPs) or suspended cradles) are specifically designed for the lifting of persons and this type of equipment should be used wherever possible.

 For further guidance on MEWPs refer to Chapter C08 Lifting equipment.

The Approved Code of Practice to Regulation 5 of LOLER says:

 The raising and lowering of people by work equipment, which is not specifically designed for the purpose, should only be undertaken in exceptional circumstances, when it is not practicable to gain access by less hazardous means. Where it is necessary to use such work equipment then you should ensure that all necessary precautions are taken to ensure safety, including appropriate supervision.

If people are being lifted by lifting equipment not specifically designed for the purpose, steps must be taken to ensure that:

- ☑ the carrier is constructed to prevent a person using it from being crushed, trapped or falling from the carrier, either during lifting or carrying out work from the carrier
- ☑ fall protection PPE is worn
- ☑ the equipment is equipped with suitable devices to prevent the carrier falling
- ☑ a person trapped in a carrier is not exposed to danger and can be rescued in the event of the lifting equipment breaking down.

 If a person-riding basket or carrier suspended from a crane is being used, BS 7172 Part 1 Clause 23 gives detailed advice.

7.9   Siting of lifting equipment

The area where lifting equipment is to be sited must be carefully assessed to ensure that it is suitable before the equipment is taken to site and put into service. During this assessment, the following points should be considered.

Clearances

The area chosen must be of a sufficient size to enable the lifting equipment to be manoeuvred into position, set up or installed, operated and stowed, with sufficient clearances between the lifting equipment and surrounding structures, as detailed in the manufacturer's operation and instruction manual. This is to ensure that trapping points are not created and that damage does not occur to either the lifting equipment or the surrounding structures. The guidance to LOLER specifies a minimum gap (0.6 m) for areas into which persons may enter.

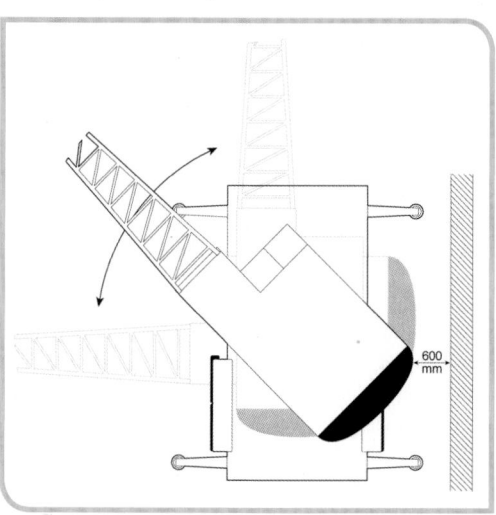

Ground conditions

 Insufficient consideration and assessment of ground conditions has been found to be a major cause of accidents with lifting equipment.

The stability of most mobile lifting equipment relies on the ground on which it stands being able to safely absorb the loads imposed by the machine. Most lifting equipment manufacturers supply information on the loads imposed by the machine on the ground in the various operating and set-up configurations of the equipment. These generally consist of:

- ☑ maximum vertical load per stabiliser (or wheel for free-on-wheels machines)
- ☑ dimensions of stabiliser support plate (pad)
- ☑ ground-level pressure on stabiliser support plate.

An assessment of the ability of the ground to accept these loads should be made by a competent person.

This assessment may indicate that the ground has insufficient bearing capacity to accept the loads imposed by the lifting equipment, in which case additional measures will need to be taken before the equipment can be set up. These may include using timber sleepers, proprietary mats or, in extreme cases, concrete pads to spread the applied load to an acceptable bearing pressure.

Where timber is to be used it is important that the timber sections employed are of sufficient dimensions and strength to transmit the applied loads to the ground and that the timbers are pinned together to form a grillage. The use of individual loose timbers has been found to be a major cause of accidents.

It is essential that any stabilisers are deployed in the manner specified by the lifting equipment manufacturer.

When siting the lifting equipment, consideration should be given to the length of time that the equipment will be erected in one position and the likely deterioration of the supporting ground or foundation over time (such as timber rotting, undermining by water or frost, drying out and adjacent excavations).

Some of the hazards that need to be considered when assessing the ground include:

- ☑ underground services
- ☑ paved areas
- ☑ uncompacted fill
- ☑ open excavations
- ☑ high water table

- ☑ basements
- ☑ cellars
- ☑ proximity to canals and rivers
- ☑ changes to site conditions during construction
- ☑ slope and camber of ground.

Details of any foundation or load spreading arrangements should be recorded in the method statement by the competent (appointed) person.

 For further guidance on assessment of ground conditions and lifting equipment foundations refer to the CIRIA publications:

- ☑ *Crane stability on site* (C703)
- ☑ *Tower crane stability* (C654).

Overhead hazards

When siting lifting equipment care must be taken to ensure that the extending structure will not contact or approach overhead hazards (such as power lines, communications cables or overhead structures).

Pre-planning of safe working procedures is important. The first step in avoiding danger is to find out whether there is any overhead electric line:

- ☑ within or immediately adjoining the work area, or
- ☑ across any route to it.

Information may be available from the local electricity supplier about location of their lines.

 If any such lines are found it should be assumed that they are live unless or until this has been proved otherwise by their owners.

If there are any electric lines over the work area, near the site boundaries, or over access roads to the work area, consult the owners of the lines so that the proposed plan of work can be discussed. Allow sufficient time for the line to be diverted or made dead, or for other precautions to be taken, as described below.

If the lines can only be made dead for short periods, then the passage of tall plant and, as far as is possible, other work around the lines should be scheduled at these times.

Liaison between the persons responsible for the work and the owner(s) of the lines should be continued until the work has been completed.

 Further advice on siting lifting equipment near to overhead power lines can be found in the HSE's *Avoidance of danger from overhead electric power lines* (Guidance note GS6).

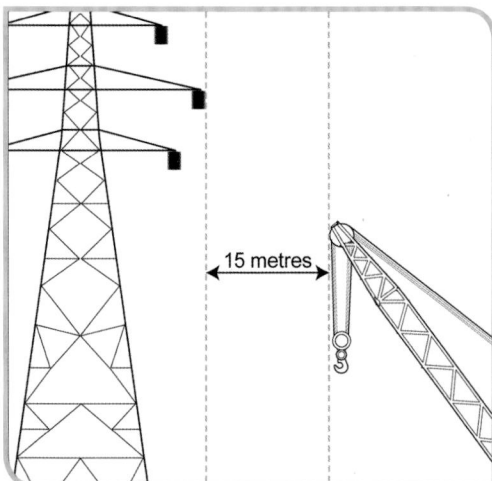

15 metres

As a guide, the minimum safe working distance between the lifting equipment (usually the tip of the jib) and the power cable is:

☑ 9 m if the cables are suspended on wooden poles

☑ 15 m if the cables are suspended on metal pylons.

Both measurements should be taken from a point on the ground directly below the outermost cable to the tip of the jib when it is nearest to the cable.

Noise

Some locations where lifting equipment is used may have restrictions on noise, particularly at night, and the competent (appointed) person should ensure that any such restrictions are taken into account in the planning process.

Exhaust gas emissions

If lifting equipment powered by an internal combustion engine is to be used in a confined space the competent (appointed) person should consider the effect of vehicle exhaust gas emissions on persons in the vicinity and take appropriate measures (such as forced ventilation or the use of fume extraction ducts).

Proximity to railways and airports

If the lifting equipment is to be sited adjacent to a railway or in the vicinity of an airfield or airport the competent (appointed) person should contact the operator of the facility as they may well impose restrictions on the height, lifting capacity and use of the lifting equipment.

The competent (appointed) person should consult the aerodrome/airfield manager for permission to work if a crane is to be used within 6 km of the aerodrome/airfield and its height exceeds 10 m or that of the surrounding structures or trees.

 The Air Navigation Order makes it an offence to act recklessly or negligently in a manner likely to endanger aircraft.

 Further guidance on the use of lifting equipment in the vicinity of airfields is given in:

☑ *Cranes and planes – A guide to procedures for operation of cranes in the vicinity of aerodromes.* Airport Operators Association (AOA)

☑ *A voluntary code of practice for the safe use of cranes in and around airports.* Off-highway Plant and Equipment Research Centre.

Access and egress to and from the site

It is important when siting lifting equipment to ensure that there is adequate access to the set-up position for both the machine and any supporting transport. It is equally important to ensure that adequate egress will be available when the lifting equipment is removed from site.

A self erecting tower crane was being used for lifting on a refurbishment project in a town centre. The crane stood in a courtyard for the duration of the project and the only way into the courtyard was through a single archway, which was just high enough to allow the folded SETC to pass below. During construction a beam was inserted at the top of the arch to support a wall being constructed above. When it was time to remove the crane from site it was found that the headroom had been reduced to such an extent that the crane could not pass through the archway. The only way to remove the crane was to dismantle it at considerable cost and inconvenience to the site.

Wind

The lifting equipment supplier/manufacturer will be able to advise on the maximum in-service and out of service wind conditions for the specific model of lifting equipment to be used. It should be borne in mind that this is a design maximum wind speed and the operator may decide to take the crane out of service at a lower speed due to the type of load being lifted or difficulty in controlling the crane. The operator has the primary responsibility for making the decision, in conjunction with the appointed person or crane supervisor. The operator's decision to take the crane out of service should not be overridden by site management under any circumstances.

The wind forces exerted on both an item of lifting equipment and any load suspended from it may be quite large and affect both the strength and stability of the lifting equipment, and safe handling of the load. It is not always appreciated that these forces are due to wind pressure, not wind speed, and consequently, if the wind speed doubles, the wind pressure increases by a factor of four. This means that a small increase in wind speed can have a significant effect on the safe operation of the lifting equipment.

Wind speeds should be monitored by either the anemometer installed on the lifting equipment (such as tower cranes and large mobile cranes and MEWPs) or the use of handheld anemometers, bearing in mind that wind speed increases with height and that the wind pressure on the load may increase as it is lifted. All operating personnel should be aware of the maximum in-service wind speed for the particular lifting equipment being used. This value may need to be significantly reduced when lifting loads with a large wind sail area.

Tower cranes normally have a maximum in-service design wind speed of 45 mph (20 m/s, 72 kph), but following a review of in-service wind speeds by the CPA Tower Crane Interest Group, involving tower crane suppliers, major contractors and the Health and Safety Executive (HSE), the industry-recommended maximum wind speed at which tower cranes operating in the UK must be taken out of service is 38 mph (16.5 m/s, 60 kph). This takes into account the time required to take the crane out of service and the difficulty of lifting large area loads in high winds.

For mobile cranes, the duty charts will specify the maximum wind speed at which the mobile crane must be taken out of service. This value will vary with the specific make and model of crane and also the duty on which it is rigged, but normally has a maximum value of 31 mph (14 m/s, 50 kph) and is frequently below this value.

For further information on wind speeds and how they may be estimated by use of the Beaufort scale, refer to Appendix E.

For specific guidance on the effect of loads with large wind sail areas on limiting wind speeds, refer to the Liebherr publication *Influence of wind on crane operations* which can be downloaded from its website free of charge.

Radio communication systems

Lifting equipment often works on congested construction sites where the signaller is out of sight of the lifting equipment operator (blind lifts) and the standard hand signals specified in BS 7121 cannot be used. As an alternative, handheld VHF/UHF radios are often used. This, however, can lead to a number of problems that may interfere with the clear communication vital for safe lifting operations, such as:

- ☑ loss of signal and thus communication, leading to loss of control of the lifting operation
- ☑ interference from radios on adjacent sites, which can lead to loss of communication or directions to the lifting equipment operator
- ☑ a misunderstanding between the lifting equipment operator and the signaller, leading to problems, such as a load being lifted before the slinger has their hands clear, loads colliding with a building and the load being lowered before people are clear of the landing area.

If communication is lost during a lifting operation, the operator must stop immediately until communication is regained.

For further detailed guidance on the siting of lifting equipment refer to:

☑ *Code of practice for safe use of cranes – Parts 1, 3, 4 and 5* (BS 7121)

☑ *Code of practice for the safe use of construction hoists* (BS 7212)

☑ *Code of practice for the safe use of mast climbing work platforms* (BS 7081)

☑ *Code of practice for the safe use of mobile elevating work platforms* (BS 8460)

☑ CIRIA publication *Crane stability on site* (C703).

7.10 Operation of lifting equipment

Lifting equipment should be operated by operators who have been trained and assessed as competent.

Manuals and signs

All operations should be carried out in accordance with the manufacturer's operating instruction manual, a copy of which should be with the lifting equipment at all times. Checks should be made by the supplier to ensure that the manual:

☑ is the correct manual for the lifting equipment supplied

☑ conveys information to the users in a simple and understandable format and is in a language (normally English) that is readily understood by the operator.

All signs, labels and decals on the lifting equipment must be clear, legible and in a language (normally English) that is readily understood by the operator. A rated capacity chart for the specific lifting equipment must be readily available to the operator.

Pedestrian lifting equipment operation

The operation of some types of lifting equipment (such as lorry loaders and self-erecting tower cranes) is frequently carried out by a pedestrian operator at ground level, using remote controls that may be hard wired or a wireless data transmission system. Whilst pedestrian control provides flexibility with the possible combination of roles there are several potential disadvantages that must be taken into account in planning the lifting operations. The operator may:

☑ be at risk of tripping and falling when trying to move around the site over uneven ground whilst concentrating on controlling the lifting equipment. Pedestrian operated lifting equipment should only be controlled whilst the operator is stationary

☑ not have a good view of the load and any obstructions. Consequently the operator must always have the lifting equipment jib or boom and load in sight at all times, unless they are working under the direction of a signaller who has a clear view of the load and load path.

Radio remote controls

To prevent unauthorised use, the operator of lifting equipment that is controlled by transmitted signals (such as radio signals) should retain the control station (transmitter) in their physical possession or remove the key from its key-lock switch and, for short periods, retain the key in their possession. For longer periods, or when the lifting equipment is not in use, the transmitter should be kept in secure storage.

When the transmitter is fitted with a belt or harness, the operator should be wearing the harness before switching on the transmitter so that accidental operation of the lifting equipment is prevented. The transmitter should only be switched on when operating the lifting equipment and should be switched off before removing the harness.

Rated capacity

The rated capacity (safe working load) of lifting equipment should not be exceeded, except when testing the lifting equipment under the supervision of a competent person.

Care should be taken to prevent pendulum swinging of the load by careful control of the operating motions to match the swing of the load and to keep it under control at all times.

Rated capacities apply only to freely suspended loads. The hoisting, slewing, telescoping, or raising and lowering motions of lifting equipment should not be used to drag a load under any circumstances. Before lifting a load, the hook and hoist rope should be vertically above the centre of gravity of the load. Failure to observe these points can adversely affect the stability of the lifting equipment or introduce loadings (stresses) into the lifting equipment structure for which it has not been designed and, even with a rated capacity indicator/limiter fitted, a sudden structural failure or overturn can occur without warning.

It is essential that all lifting equipment is clearly marked to indicate its rated capacity. Where the rated capacity depends on the lifting equipment's configuration (such as changing radius) it shall be clearly marked to indicate its rated capacity for each configuration. As an alternative, information that clearly indicates its rated capacity for each configuration should be kept with the lifting equipment.

07

Lifting equipment designed for lifting persons should be clearly marked to indicate that it is equipment for lifting persons, whilst lifting equipment not designed for lifting persons, but which might be used in error, must be clearly marked to indicated that it is not designed for lifting persons.

Most lifting equipment with a rated capacity not less than 1,000 kg or an overturning moment not less than 40,000 Nm is fitted with a load control device that will sense when the rated capacity has been exceeded and prevent further movement. These devices vary between different types of lifting equipment and on cranes are generally known as rated capacity limiters (RCL). Cranes are also fitted with rated capacity indicators (RCI), which indicate approach to overload and overload.

 Effective lift planning should ensure that the rated capacity of lifting equipment is never exceeded. The RCL or load control device should never be used to establish the weight of a load.

Handling of loads near persons

When loads have to be handled in the vicinity of persons, extreme care should be exercised and adequate clearances allowed. The route of the load should be planned to prevent lifting over persons. Operators and signallers should pay particular attention to possible dangers of persons working out of sight.

All persons should be instructed to stand clear of the load being lifted. When lifting from a stack, all persons should be instructed to stand away from the stack in case adjacent materials or objects are displaced. This also applies to the removal of part loads from the deck of a vehicle.

Where possible, lifting of loads over highways, railways, rivers, or other places to which the public have access, should be avoided. If this is not possible, permission should be obtained from the appropriate authority and the area kept clear of traffic and persons.

Multiple lifting

Multiple or tandem lifting (carrying out a lift with more than one piece of lifting equipment attached to the load) should always be planned and carried out with great care. A multiple lift is always classified as complex. Multiple lifts are generally only carried out with mobile cranes. Consequently the term *crane* will be used here, rather than lifting equipment.

Weight of the load

The total weight of the load and its distribution should be either known or calculated. Where the information is taken from a drawing, due allowance should be made for manufacturing tolerances.

Centre of gravity

Owing to the variable effect of manufacturing tolerances, variable density, and so on, the centre of gravity of the load might not be known accurately and the proportion of the load being carried by each machine could therefore be uncertain.

Weight of the lifting accessories/attachments

The weight of the lifting accessories/attachments should be part of the calculated load on the cranes. When handling heavy or awkwardly shaped loads, the deduction from the rated capacity of the lifting equipment to allow for the weight of the lifting accessories/attachments might be significant. The weight of the lifting accessories/attachments, and hook blocks, where appropriate, and its distribution should therefore be accurately known.

In cases where the hoist ropes are reeved around pulleys that are part of a specially designed lifting accessory/attachment (such as a lifting beam) the weight of the removed hook block and hook may be taken into consideration when determining the net weight of the lifting accessories/attachments.

Capacities of the lifting accessories/attachments

The distribution of the forces that arise during the lifting operation, within the lifting accessories/attachments should be established. The lifting accessories/attachments used should, unless specially designed for the particular lifting operation, have a capacity margin well in excess of that needed for its proportioned load.

 Special lifting accessories/attachments might be necessary to suit the maximum variation in distribution and direction of application of loads or forces that can occur during multiple lifting.

Synchronisation of lifting equipment motions

If the variations in the direction and magnitude of the forces acting on the crane during the multiple lift are to be kept to a minimum, it is essential that the crane motions are synchronised.

Lifting equipment/cranes of equal capacity and similar characteristics should therefore be used whenever possible. In practice, there is always some variation due to differences in response to the activation of the control system.

The rated capacity of a crane is calculated on the assumption that the load is raised and lowered in a vertical plane. The crane structure is designed to withstand any lateral loads imposed by accelerations in the various crane motions, but it is unsafe to rely on this lateral strength to withstand horizontal components of 'out-of-vertical' lifts.

If the cranes have dissimilar characteristics, it is unlikely that the motions will be accurately synchronised. Therefore, an assessment should be made of the effect of variation in verticality of the hoist ropes that could arise from inequalities of speed, together with a determination of the means for keeping such inequalities to a minimum.

Instrumentation

Instruments are available to monitor the angle of the load and verticality and the force in any hoist rope constantly throughout the lifting operation. The use of such instruments and the restriction of the motion speeds, together with the strict use of one motion at any one time, can assist in the control of the loads on the cranes within the planned values.

Supervision

One competent person should be in attendance and in overall control of a multiple crane operation. Only this person should give instructions to personnel operating or driving machines, except in an emergency when a commonly recognised stop signal may be given by any person observing a situation leading to danger.

If all the necessary points cannot be observed from one position, other personnel should be positioned at various points to observe and report to the person in charge of the operation.

It is essential that adequate means of signalling between the person in charge of the operation, the operators of the cranes, and the slingers and signallers are provided.

Recommended rated capacity during lifting

As all the factors cannot be accurately evaluated, an appropriate down-rating should be applied to all the cranes involved. The down-rating might need to be 20% or more.

7.11 Maintenance, checks and inspections

Maintenance, checks and inspections of lifting equipment are essential if it is not to deteriorate over time, break down and ultimately fail. All maintenance should be carried out by a competent person who is familiar with the equipment and has the knowledge and experience to detect and repair existing or potential faults. The maintenance should be in accordance with the manufacturer's instructions and carried out at the recommended intervals.

All lifting equipment should have a pre-use check carried out daily or at the start of each shift and any defects reported to a supervisor. This is normally undertaken by the operator who should be trained to carry out the checks.

In addition to pre-use checks, inspections should be carried out at appropriate intervals, either as part of the maintenance process or at more frequent intervals (such as the weekly inspection of mobile cranes). The frequency of inspections will depend on assessment of the risk of failure of the lifting equipment and should be guided by the manufacturer's instructions.

It is particularly important to ensure at frequent intervals that the load control device or RCL on lifting equipment is functioning correctly.

The results of all checks and inspections should be recorded and there should be a system in place to ensure that all reported defects are rectified and recorded.

Each item of lifting equipment should have a history file containing all records of maintenance, inspection and through examination, so that maintenance trends can be established and adequate maintenance demonstrated in the event of an accident.

For further guidance on maintenance and inspection refer to BS 7121 Part 2.

7.12   Thorough examination

Types of thorough examination

There are four situations where thorough examination is required by LOLER:

- ☑ before being put into use for the first time
- ☑ after installation on a new site, installation in a new location on the same site or where significant changes have been made to the lifting equipment (such as an extension of a tower crane jib)
- ☑ periodically while in service
- ☑ after exceptional circumstances have occurred.

 A thorough examination before first use is not required for new lifting equipment where the user has received an EC declaration of conformity that was made not more than 12 months before the lifting equipment is first put into service.

Frequency

LOLER place a duty on employers to ensure that all lifting equipment and lifting accessories are subjected to a schedule of thorough examinations by a competent person at intervals not exceeding:

- ☑ six months for lifting equipment used for lifting persons and all lifting accessories
- ☑ 12 months for other lifting equipment.

The competent person carrying out the thorough examination may, however, decide, for a variety of reasons, that a schedule of more frequent examinations is appropriate.

A thorough examination must also be carried out after any other event (such as damage or overloading) likely to have affected the safety of any lifting equipment or accessories or where the equipment has been out of use for a long period.

Furthermore, where the safety of lifting equipment depends upon the way it has been installed (as for the many items of temporary lifting equipment used on construction sites (such as hoists and tower cranes) it must be thoroughly examined after assembly and before being put into service at a new site or a new location on the same site or after alteration on the same site.

Competent person

The competent person carrying out thorough examinations must have sufficient practical and theoretical knowledge and experience of the lifting equipment to enable defects and weaknesses to be detected, and their importance in relation to the safety of the equipment to be assessed.

It is essential that the competent person is sufficiently independent and impartial to allow objective decisions to be made. This does not mean that competent persons must necessarily be employed from an external company. If employers and others within their own organisations have the necessary competence then they can use it. However, if they do, they must ensure that their in-house examiners have the genuine authority and independence to ensure that examinations are properly carried out and that the necessary recommendations arising from them are made objectively. This means that through examinations of lifting equipment should not be carried out by the person carrying out maintenance or installation of that lifting equipment. In practice, lifting equipment where the consequence of failure is greatest (such as tower cranes, mobile cranes, MEWPs and hoists) are generally thoroughly examined by a third party.

Reporting

Once a thorough examination has been completed the competent person must:

- ☑ immediately inform both the user and the owner of the lifting equipment of any defect in the lifting equipment, which in their opinion is, or could become, a danger to persons
- ☑ as soon as is practicable make a report of the thorough examination in writing to both the user and the owner of the lifting equipment
- ☑ where there is, in their opinion, a defect in the lifting equipment involving an existing or imminent risk of serious personal injury, send a copy of the report as soon as is practicable to the relevant enforcing authority.

 Reports of thorough examinations must contain the information contained in Schedule 1 of LOLER, which is reproduced in Appendix D.

Retention of reports

LOLER requires that reports of thorough examination are kept for minimum specified periods, depending on the type of thorough examination, as shown in the table below.

Type of equipment	Type of thorough examination	Retention period
Lifting equipment	Before first use	Until the user ceases to use the equipment
Lifting accessories	Before first use	Two years after the report is made
Lifting equipment	After installation at a new site	Until the equipment is removed from site
Lifting equipment and lifting accessories	Periodic	Until the next periodic thorough examination report is made or the expiration of two years, whichever is later
Lifting equipment and lifting accessories	Intermediate inspections	Until the next report is made

 Each item of lifting equipment should have a history file containing all records of maintenance, inspection and through examination, so that maintenance trends can be established and adequate maintenance demonstrated in the event of an accident.

Testing

LOLER specifies that testing, including overload testing, is part of thorough examination and is carried out at the discretion of the competent person.

The design of some lifting equipment and the use of high tensile materials mean that damage may be caused by conventional overload tests. Consequently, it is important that the competent person carrying out the thorough examination or testing takes account of the manufacturer's instructions and, if necessary, consults the manufacturer before starting testing.

 Overload testing is not mandatory and is only carried out when required by the competent person.

 For further guidance on through examination refer to BS 7121 Part 2.

Appendix A – Definitions

Competent (appointed) person. A person who has the competence, adequate training, authority and experience to take overall responsibility and control of a lifting operation, having been formally appointed in writing by the management of the organisation(s) that require the load to be moved.

Competent person. (For the purposes of inspection and examination) a person who has the practical and theoretical knowledge, together with actual experience of what they are to examine, so as to enable them to detect errors, defects, faults or weaknesses, which it is the purpose of the examination or inspection to discover; and to assess the importance of any such discovery.

Crane co-ordinator. A person who plans and directs the sequence of operations of cranes to ensure that they do not collide with other cranes, loads and other equipment (for example, concrete placing booms, telehandlers and piling rigs).

Crane (lift) supervisor. A person who controls the lifting operation and ensures that it is carried out in accordance with the appointed person's safe system of work.

Crane operator. A person who operates the crane for the purpose of moving and positioning loads or erection of the crane.

Lifting accessory. A lifting beam or frame, chain sling, rope sling or similar gear, a ring, link, hook, interlocks, plate clamp, shackle, swivel or eyebolt, and any loose equipment that is used with lifting gear.

Lifting equipment. A piece of work equipment for lifting or lowering loads, including a crab, winch, pulley block or gin wheel (for raising or lowering), a hoist, crane, shearlegs, excavator, dragline, piling frame, aerial cable way, aerial ropeway or overhead runway, goods hoist, mobile elevating work platform (MEWP), scissor lift, vehicle hoist, ropes used for access, forklift truck, lorry loader and passenger lift.

Mobile crane. A crane capable of travelling under its own power, but does not include cranes that travel on a line of rails.

Plant and equipment. Any plant, equipment, gear, machinery, apparatus or appliance, or part thereof.

Rated capacity. The load that any item of lifting equipment (such as a crane or hoist), or any accessory for lifting is designed to lift for a given operating condition (such as configuration or position of load). Rated capacity was formerly known as safe working load (SWL).

 On certain types of crane, for example mobile cranes, the rated capacity includes the weight of the hook block and all the lifting gear. The weight of these should be deducted from the declared rated capacity of the lifting equipment to obtain the net load that can be safely lifted.

Rated capacity indicator/limiter RCI/L. Device(s) that warns of the approach to overload and prevents the crane from being overloaded as described in BS EN 12077 2.

Thorough examination. An examination by a competent person in such depth and detail as the competent person considers necessary to enable them to determine whether the equipment being examined is safe to continue in use.

Appendix B – Case study of lifting operation categorisation

Example activity – Lifting of a generating set and fuel tank with a lorry loader

Situation 1		Straightforward off load on to level ground beside lorry.	
Environment – 1	Load – 1	Example hazards	Example control measures
Lift categorisation – Basic 		Overturning of lorry loader or failure through overloading of the lorry loader attachment or lifting accessory.	Accurately assess the weight of the load. Accurately assess the maximum radius at which the load can be lifted. Correctly select the lorry loader and lifting accessories.
		Overturning of the lorry loader through ground bearing failure.	Assessment of ground conditions and use of spreader pads.

Lifting team	Planning requirements
▪ Appointed person prepares generic risk assessment and method statement. ▪ Operator takes the role of crane supervisor, slinger/ signaller and operator.	▪ Generic risk assessment and method statement. ▪ On-site review of risk assessment and method statement by crane supervisor.

Situation 2		Lifting a generating set and fuel tank in a pedestrian area with narrow access and restricted view of load.	
Environment – 2	Load – 1	Example hazards	Example control measures
Lift categorisation – Intermediate 		Overturning of lorry loader or failure through overloading of the lorry loader attachment or lifting accessory.	Accurately assess the weight of the load. Accurately assess the maximum radius at which the load can be lifted. Correctly select the lorry loader and lifting accessories.
		Overturning of the lorry loader through ground bearing failure.	Assessment of ground conditions and use of spreader pads.
		Operator has restricted view of load.	Use separate slinger/signaller (including use of two-way radio if required).
		Ingress of personnel. Lifting near or over persons.	Cordon area off with physical barriers. Utilise site personnel to monitor the area. Close area to public access. Perform lift out of hours.

Lifting team	Planning requirements
▪ Appointed person prepares task and/or site specific risk assessment and method statement. ▪ Operator takes the role of crane supervisor and operator. ▪ Separate slinger/signaller.	▪ Task and/or site-specific risk assessment and method statement. ▪ On-site review of risk assessment and method statement by the crane supervisor. ▪ Cordoning off of lift area by site. ▪ Agreement between operator and site to fulfil duties of controlling cordoned off area.

Situation 3	Lifting a generating set and fuel tank in an electrical sub-station with overhead cables and unpaved ground.		
Environment – 3	**Load – 1**	**Example hazards**	**Example control measures**

Lift categorisation – Complex	Example hazards	Example control measures
	Overturning of lorry loader or failure through overloading of the lorry loader attachment or lifting accessory.	Accurately assess the weight of the load.
		Accurately assess the maximum radius at which the load can be lifted.
		Correctly select the lorry loader and lifting accessories.
	Overturning of the lorry loader through ground bearing failure.	Assessment of ground conditions and use of spreader pads.
	Ingress of personnel.	Cordon area off with physical barriers.
	Lifting near or over persons.	Utilise site personnel to monitor the area.
	Electricity cables.	Have power switched off.
	Blind lift.	Dedicated slinger/signaller.

Lifting team

- Appointed person prepares site specific risk assessment and method statement.
- Separate crane supervisor oversees lifting operation.
- Dedicated slinger/signaller required.
- Operator takes the role of operator only.

Planning requirements

- Site-specific risk assessment and method statement.
- On-site review of risk assessment and method statement by the crane supervisor.
- Cordoning off of lift area by site.
- Agreement between operator and site to fulfil duties of controlling cordoned off area.

Appendix C – Recognised hand signals

OPERATIONS START
(FOLLOW MY INSTRUCTIONS)

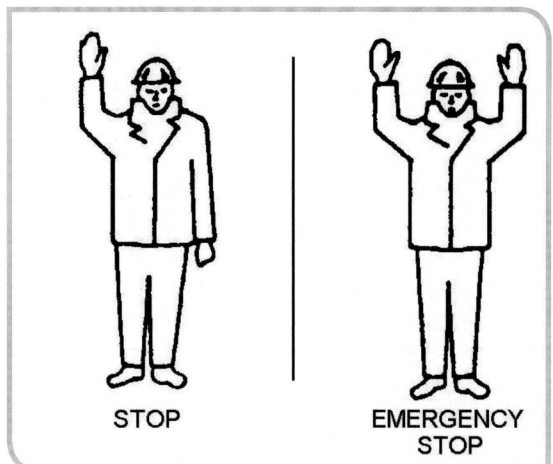

STOP

EMERGENCY
STOP

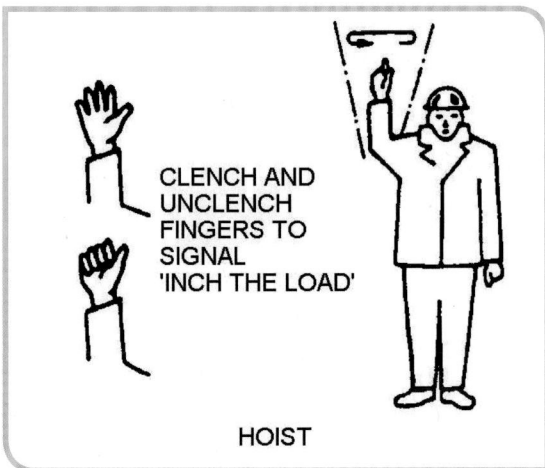

CLENCH AND
UNCLENCH
FINGERS TO
SIGNAL
'INCH THE LOAD'

HOIST

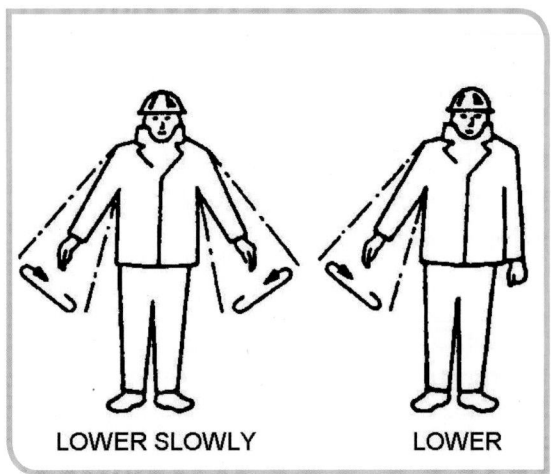

LOWER SLOWLY

LOWER

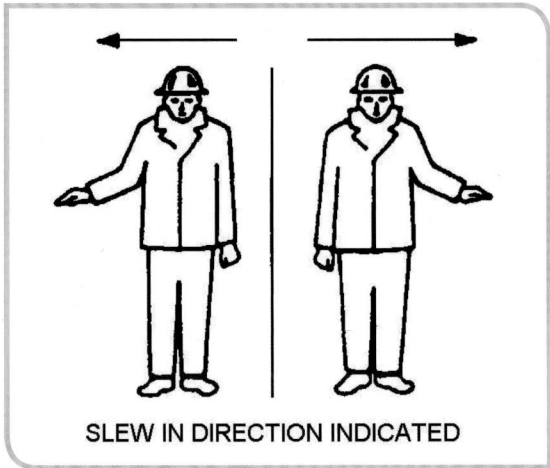

SLEW IN DIRECTION INDICATED

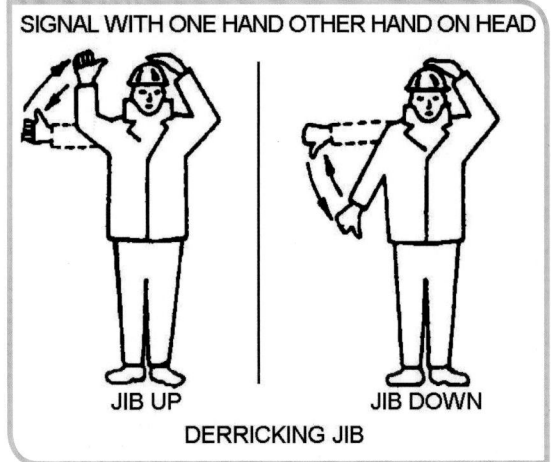

SIGNAL WITH ONE HAND OTHER HAND ON HEAD

JIB UP

JIB DOWN

DERRICKING JIB

07

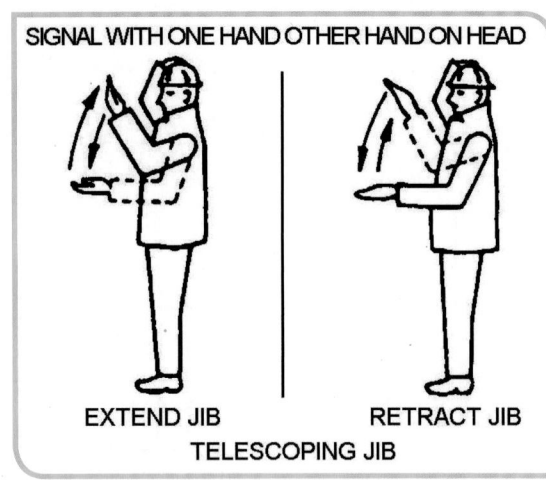

SIGNAL WITH ONE HAND OTHER HAND ON HEAD

EXTEND JIB   RETRACT JIB

TELESCOPING JIB

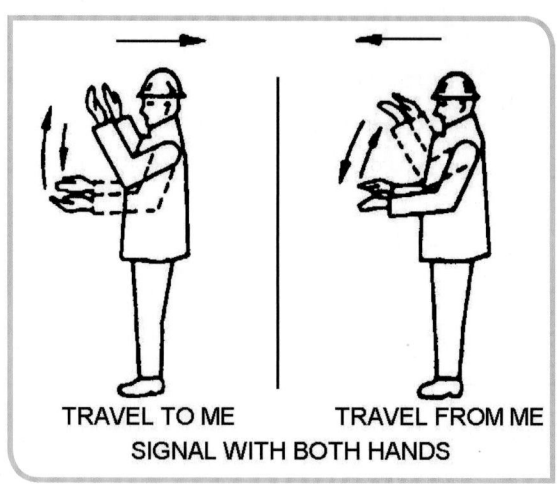

TRAVEL TO ME   TRAVEL FROM ME

SIGNAL WITH BOTH HANDS

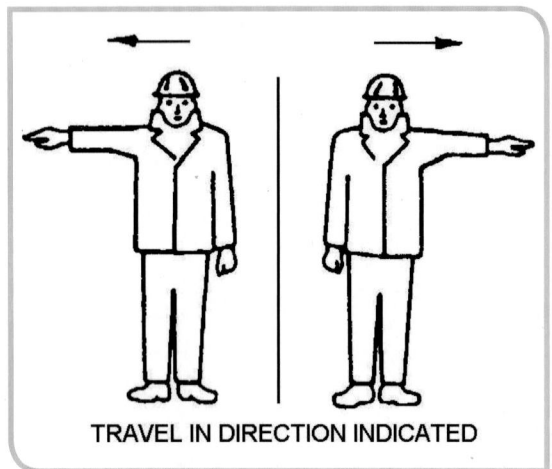

TRAVEL IN DIRECTION INDICATED

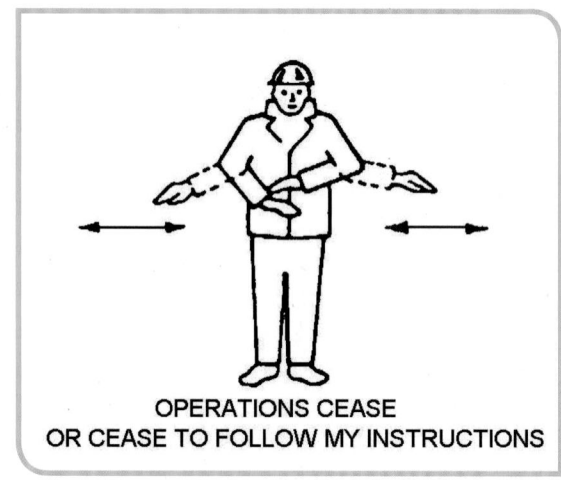

OPERATIONS CEASE
OR CEASE TO FOLLOW MY INSTRUCTIONS

The signaller should stand in a secure position, where they can see the load and can be seen clearly by the lifting equipment operator, and they should face the operator if possible. Each signal should be distinct and clear. These signals have been reproduced from BS 7121-1 *Safe use of cranes – General*.

Appendix D – Information to be contained in a report of thorough examination

1. The name and address of the employer for whom the thorough examination was made.

2. The address of the premises at which the thorough examination was made.

3. Particulars sufficient to identify the lifting equipment including, where known, its date of manufacture.

4. The date of the last thorough examination.

5. The safe working load of the lifting equipment or (where its safe working load depends on the configuration of the lifting equipment) its safe working load for the last configuration in which it was thoroughly examined.

6. In relation to the first thorough examination of lifting equipment after installation or after assembly at a new site or in a new location:

   ☑ that it is such a thorough examination

   ☑ (if such be the case) that it has been installed correctly and would be safe to operate.

7. For a thorough examination of lifting equipment other than a thorough examination relating to the circumstances in 6 above:

   ☑ whether it is a thorough examination:
      – within an interval of six months under regulation 9(3)(a)(i)
      – within an interval of 12 months under regulation 9(3)(a)(ii)
      – in accordance with an examination scheme under regulation 9(3)(a)(iii)
      – after the occurrence of exceptional circumstances under regulation 9(3)(a)(iv)

   ☑ (if such be the case) that the lifting equipment would be safe to operate.

8. In relation to every thorough examination of lifting equipment:

   ☑ identification of any part found to have a defect, which is or could become a danger to persons, and a description of the defect

   ☑ particulars of any repair, renewal or alteration required to remedy a defect found to be a danger to persons

   ☑ in the case of a defect which is not yet but could become a danger to persons:
      – the time by which it could become such a danger
      – particulars of any repair, renewal or alteration required to remedy it

   ☑ the latest date by which the next thorough examination must be carried out

   ☑ where the thorough examination included testing, particulars of any test

   ☑ the date of the thorough examination.

9. The name, address and qualifications of the person making the report; whether they are self-employed or, if employed, the name and address of their employer.

10. The name and address of a person signing or authenticating the report on behalf of its author.

11. The date of the report.

07

Appendix E – Wind strengths and effects (Beaufort scale)

Wind force number	Description of wind	Wind effect locally	Speed (mph)	Speed (m/sec)
0	Calm.	Calm, smoke rises vertically.	1	0–1
1	Light air.	Direction of wind shown by smoke drift, but not by wind or weather vanes.	1–3	1–2
2	Light breeze.	Wind felt on face. Leaves rustle. Wind or weather vanes move.	4–7	2–3
3	Gentle breeze.	Leaves and small twigs in constant motion. Wind extends light flags.	8–12	3–5
4	Moderate breeze.	Wind raises dust and loose paper. Small branches move.	13–18	5–8
5	Fresh breeze.	Small trees in leaf begin to sway. Little crested wavelets form on inland waters.	19–24	8–11
6	Strong breeze.	Large branches in motion. Umbrellas used with some difficulty.	25–31	11–14
7	Near gale.	Whole trees in motion. Becoming difficult to walk against the wind.	32–38	14–17
8	Gale.	Twigs break off trees. Progress is generally impeded.	39–46	17–21
9	Strong gale.	Chimney pots, slates and tiles may be blown off. Other slight structural damage may be caused.	47–54	21–24

Appendix F – Further information

Legislation

The Provision and Use of Work Equipment Regulations

HSE books *Safe use of work equipment* (L22)

The Lifting Operations and Lifting Equipment Regulations

HSE books *Safe use of lifting equipment* (L113)

Standards

Code of practice for safe use of cranes — Part 1: General (BS 7121-1:2006)

Code of practice for safe use of cranes — Part 2: Inspection, testing and examination (BS 7121-2:2003)

Code of practice for safe use of cranes — Part 3: Mobile cranes (BS 7121-2:2003)

Code of practice for safe use of cranes — Part 4: Lorry loaders (BS 7121-4:2010)

Code of practice for safe use of cranes — Part 5: Tower cranes (BS 7121-2:2003)

Code of practice for safe use of construction hoists (BS 7212:2006)

Code of practice for the installation, maintenance, thorough examination and safe use of mast climbing work platforms (MCWPs) (BS 7981:2002)

Code of practice for safe use of MEWPs (BS 8460:2005)

Strategic Forum for Construction Plant Safety Group

Medical fitness to operate construction plant (Best practice guide)

Safe use of quick hitches (Best practice guide)

Safe use of telehandlers in construction (Best practice guide)

Avoiding trapping and crushing in MEWPs (Best practice guide)

Tower crane working conditions (Best practice guide)

Tower crane operations – Minimum competency requirements (Best practice guide)

Guidance on the planning and liaison process for the erection, climbing and dismantling of tower cranes

Construction Plant-hire Association

Guidance on lifting operations in construction when using excavators (Best practice guide)

Maintenance, inspection and thorough examination of construction hoists (Best practice guide)

Work at height on construction hoists (Best practice guide)

Transporting scaffolding in construction hoists (Best practice guide)

Safeguarding requirements for landing gates on goods-only hoists (Best practice guide)

Transport platforms – Installation, use, maintenance, inspection, examination and testing (Best practice guide)

Work at height whilst loading and unloading transport (Best practice guide)

Safe use of lorry loaders (Best practice guide)

Maintenance, inspection and thorough examination of mobile cranes (Best practice guide)

Crane hire and contract lifting (Best practice guide)

Work at height on mobile cranes (Best practice guide)

Risk assessment and method statement for a contract lift (Best practice guide)

Climbing of tower cranes (Best practice guide)

Maintenance, inspection and thorough examination of tower cranes (Best practice guide)

Safe use of top slew tower cranes (Best practice guide)

Safe use of self-erecting tower cranes (Best practice guide)

Tower crane operator's handbook

Technical information notes

Construction Industry Research and Information Association (CIRIA)

Crane stability on site, 2003 (C703)

Tower crane stability, 2006 (C654)

Airport Operators' Association (AOA)

Cranes and planes – A guide to procedures for operation of cranes in the vicinity of aerodromes

Off-highway Plant and Equipment Research Centre

A voluntary code of practice for the safe use of cranes in and around airports

Lifting Equipment Engineers' Association

Code of practice for the safe use of lifting equipment

 All HSE publications can be downloaded without charge from the HSE website.

All Strategic Forum for Construction Plant Safety Group and Construction Plant-hire Association publications are available to download without charge from the CPA's website.

07

08

Lifting equipment

Each year there are, on average, 17 fatalities and a significant number of major injuries in the construction industry due to lifting operations. The majority of these could have been avoided by effective planning and control of the lifting operations, adequate selection, maintenance, inspection and through examination of lifting equipment, and thorough training, assessment and briefing of personnel.

This chapter gives an overview of the requirements for installing, using, checking, maintaining, inspecting and thoroughly examining specific types of lifting equipment and lifting accessories. The general principles of planning and carrying out lifting operations, and undertaking maintenance and through examination, are covered in Chapter C07 Lifting operations.

Introduction	118
Key requirements	118
Mobile cranes (wheeled and crawler mounted)	118
Tower cranes	121
Lorry loaders	123
Mobile elevating work platforms	123
Construction hoists	128
Telehandlers	135
Excavators used as cranes	141
Lifting accessories	145
Appendix A – Further Information	149

8.1 Introduction

Experience has shown that lifting operations can be a hazardous work activity if not properly planned and carried out. Safe lifting operations will depend upon:

- the availability of suitable lifting equipment, which is properly maintained
- the provision of adequate information, instruction, training or supervision for everyone involved
- thorough pre-planning of each lifting operation
- compliance with safe systems of work, as detailed in risk assessments and method statements (lifting plan).

Although regulations require that safe systems of work are developed, accidents that have occurred during lifting operations indicate that all too often these are not in place or not complied with if they are in place.

Lifting operations have the potential for death and serious injury to both site workers and members of the public off site. In addition to the terrible cost in human suffering, accidents have a financial cost. There is a very strong business case for improving safety performance.

This chapter is intended to provide advice to non-specialists on the implications that utilising lifting equipment on site will have for them. The content is therefore restricted to information considered relevant for site managers, project managers and others who may become involved in hiring-in lifting equipment or ensuring it is safely used on site. As a consequence, the inclusion of technical information on, for example, the technicalities of lifting equipment construction maintenance, inspection and thorough examination, has been limited.

By way of illustration, whilst it is reasonable to expect a site manager to know when a piece of lifting equipment should be thoroughly examined, detail of the content of such examinations is beyond the scope of this chapter.

Problems with lifting operations often occur because of poor communications, both during planning and when lifting.

8.2 Key requirements

- Many accidents occur during lifting operations because they were not properly planned in advance.
- All lifting operations must be carried out by, and under the control of, trained and competent persons who have been properly briefed on the lifting plan.
- The rated capacity of any item of lifting equipment or lifting accessory must never be exceeded.
- All lifting equipment and lifting accessories used for lifting operations must be adequately maintained.
- All lifting equipment and lifting accessories used for lifting operations must be subjected to a schedule of inspections and thorough examinations.
- In addition to the lifting equipment and lifting accessories used, attention must also be paid to site features (such as overhead cables, unstable ground conditions and adjacent properties).
- When using a hired crane, a contract lift will transfer the majority of the legal responsibility for carrying out the lifting operation in a safe manner to the contract lift company.

The collapse, overturning or failure of any load-bearing part of a hoist, crane or other lifting equipment is a notifiable dangerous occurrence, even if nobody is injured. For further information refer to Chapter A13 Accident reporting and investigation.

8.3 Mobile cranes (wheel and crawler mounted)

Mobile cranes are lifting equipment that can move under their own power between lifting positions. They are either mounted on wheeled or crawler chassis.

- Wheeled mobile cranes are generally mounted on either truck crane chassis or all-terrain chassis. Truck cranes are generally restricted to travelling on metalled roads and well-compacted ground on site whilst all-terrain cranes can travel on both public roads and over most site conditions. Some all terrain wheeled cranes may have a limited ability to lift and travel with a load (pick and carry duties). Wheeled mobile cranes range in capacity between 25 tonnes and 1,200 tonnes.
- Crawler mobile cranes require transporting to site in component form on a low loader and other vehicles. Once the crane has been rigged it can travel around the site with ease and lift and travel with a load. Crawler mobile cranes range in capacity between 40 tonnes and 3,000 tonnes.
- Mini cranes are generally mounted on small crawler chassis and may be fitted with outriggers to provide stability. Some are fitted with cabs for the operator and have pick and carry duties. Mini crane capacity is generally in the range of one tonne to eight tonnes.

Hired cranes

In construction, mobile cranes are generally hired by the user on site from the crane owner. There are two ways of doing this:

- ☑ hiring a crane (hired crane)
- ☑ employing a contractor to carry out the lifting operation (contract lift).

The difference between the two options is summarised below.

Hired crane (hired and managed)

The employing organisation should:

- ☑ carry out all work in accordance with BS 7121
- ☑ supply the competent (appointed) person
- ☑ plan the lift and operate a safe system of work
- ☑ ensure that the crane hired is of a suitable type and capacity
- ☑ check the credentials of the crane company and certification supplied.

The crane owner has a duty to provide a:

- ☑ crane that is properly maintained, tested and certified
- ☑ competent operator.

Contract lift (fully contracted)

The employing organisation should specify:

- ☑ that all work is to be undertaken in accordance with BS 7121
- ☑ that the lifting contractor is to supply the competent (appointed) person
- ☑ the dimensions and weight of the load to be lifted
- ☑ the ground bearing capacity
- ☑ what other information and/or services will be provided to the lifting contractor by the employing organisation.

The lifting contractor is responsible for:

- ☑ supplying the competent (appointed) person
- ☑ planning the lift, and operation of a safe system of work
- ☑ organisation and control of the lifting operation.

 If an individual or organisation does not have expertise in lifting operations they should not hire cranes but should opt for a contract lift. Before entering into a contract, users should satisfy themselves that the contractor has the necessary competence to carry out the work.

 For further detailed guidance on crane hire and contract lifts refer to the Construction Plant-hire Association's *Crane hire and contract lifting* (Best practice guide).

Planning and use of mobile cranes

The planning and carrying out of lifting operations with mobile cranes should be carried out in accordance with Chapter C07.

Maintenance, checks and inspections of mobile cranes

Mobile cranes should be checked, maintained and inspected in accordance with 7.11 of Chapter C07.

08

In addition, when planning and carrying out maintenance activities on mobile cranes it should not be forgotten that when travelling on the road, the condition of the crane chassis – brakes, suspension, steering, lights, wheels, tyres, and so on, will have a significant effect on the safety of the crane driver and other road users. Although mobile cranes are currently exempt from both the Commercial Vehicle Operators Licensing and Plating and Testing Regulations, the Road Vehicles (Construction and Use) Regulations (Reg. 100) require that they should:

> at all times be in such condition ... that no danger is caused or is likely to be caused to any person in or on the vehicle or on a road.

As a mobile crane has the potential to cause as much damage in a road traffic accident as any other large vehicle, it is best practice to follow the recommendations set out in the manufacturer's service manual. These normally set maintenance intervals based on both engine hours run and distance travelled, whereby the first parameter reached determines the need for maintenance.

Failure to maintain the chassis of a mobile crane adequately may put the crane operator and other road users at risk from issues such as:

- [x] poor brake performance or failure leading to increased braking distances and an inability to stop in time
- [x] insufficient tyre tread grip leading to increased braking distances
- [x] hydraulic fluid leaks from the suspension system leading to contamination of the road surface and potential loss of control for other road users
- [x] tyre blow-outs leading to loss of control of the crane
- [x] steering system failures leading to loss of control of the crane
- [x] lighting failures leading to the operator not being able to see clearly and other road users not being able to see the crane
- [x] wiper, washer and demister failures preventing the crane operator from seeing clearly
- [x] failure of the vehicle suspension system
- [x] failure of the crane chassis
- [x] security of outrigger plates, covers, guards and other potentially loose items.

It is essential that the chassis of a mobile crane is effectively cleaned before maintenance and inspection is carried out, to ensure that defects can be detected.

For further detailed guidance on the maintenance of mobile cranes refer to the Construction Plant-hire Association's *Maintenance, inspection and thorough examination of mobile cranes* (Best practice guide).

Thorough examination of mobile cranes

The thorough examination of mobile cranes should be carried out in accordance with 7.12 of Chapter C07.

Four year testing of mobile cranes

In the past, mobile cranes in the UK have frequently been subjected to overload testing at four yearly intervals, in addition to the periodic thorough examinations required by the Lifting Operations and Lifting Equipment Regulations (LOLER). This is a legacy from the requirements of the old Construction (Lifting Operations) Regulations, which were repealed when LOLER was introduced in 1998.

The Approved Code of Practice (ACoP) to LOLER states that any testing is at the discretion of the competent person carrying out a thorough examination and that the competent person will decide on the nature of the test and the method of carrying it out.

Advice from the Health and Safety Executive (HSE) confirms that four yearly overload testing is no longer a legal requirement and repeated overload testing itself may be dangerous as it may create the conditions for additional faults or even failure during testing.

In the HSE's view the most appropriate method of assessing the condition of a mobile crane is to adopt a defined scope for thorough examination. This is where a specific examination schedule is drawn up for the machine being examined by a competent person, which details the parts of the mobile crane that should be thoroughly examined and the supplementary reports and tests that should be carried out.

For further detailed guidance on the defined scope for the thorough examination of mobile cranes refer to the Construction Plant-hire Association's *Maintenance, inspection and thorough examination of mobile cranes* (Best practice guide).

8.4 Tower cranes

Tower cranes fall into three main categories:

- ☑ top slew tower cranes, which are controlled from a cab at the top of the mast and are erected and dismantled using a large mobile crane for which provision has to be made in terms of space and stable ground conditions. Top slew tower cranes are further sub-divided into saddle jib and luffing jib types

- ☑ self-erecting tower cranes, which are controlled from ground level, often using remote controls, and are self-erecting and folding

- ☑ vehicle mounted tower cranes, which are often controlled remotely from the ground and need to be treated as a mobile crane.

Tower crane installation

When contemplating the erection of a tower crane on site the following points should be taken into account.

- ☑ All tower cranes require suitable foundations. For top slew tower cranes particularly, both static and travelling, the foundations will require careful design by a competent engineer.

- ☑ Some tower cranes are tied to an adjacent structure for support. The ties and their connections to the crane and the supporting structure will require careful design by a competent engineer.

 For detailed guidance on the design and installation of tower crane bases and ties refer to the Construction Industry Research and Information Association's *Tower crane stability*.

- ☑ On sites where more than one tower crane is erected, there may be overlapping arcs of operation when slewing; anti-clash devices may be fitted or crash radios utilised.

- ☑ As a result, the cranes should be erected with their jibs at different heights; crane slewing operations will have to be co-ordinated.

- ☑ The required airspace must be confirmed with regard to the proximity of adjacent structures, overhead power lines or other obstructions.

- ☑ The requirement for airspace may need to be discussed with any local airport to establish that there will be no intrusion into, or unacceptably near to, aircraft flight paths.

- ☑ There may be a requirement for an aircraft warning light or beacon on the highest point of the crane; the colour intensity and whether it is on steady or flashes will depend upon the local rules for any flight path affected.

- ☑ Electrically powered tower cranes will require a heavy duty power supply and the crane must be effectively earthed to protect against electrical faults and lightning strikes, including earthing of the appropriate rails. The requirements of the Electricity at Work Act apply to all electrically powered tower cranes and their power supply.

- ☑ In many cases they have the capacity to over-sail adjacent properties and areas to which the public have access; arrangements will have to be made with the appropriate authorities.

- ☑ Where the right to over-sail adjacent property is not given, it may be necessary to:
  - rearrange siting of the tower crane(s)
  - review the type of crane required (for example, a luffing jib crane might be the only solution).

 For further detailed guidance on the erection, climbing and dismantling of tower cranes refer to the British Standard *Safe use of cranes – Tower cranes* (BS 7121-5) and the Construction Plant-hire Association's *Climbing of tower cranes* (Best practice guide).

08

Planning and use of tower cranes

The planning and carrying out of lifting operations with tower cranes should be in accordance with the principles set out in Chapter C07. In addition, the following points should be taken into account.

☑ High winds can temporarily stop tower crane operations; each crane should be fitted with an anemometer (wind-speed indicator).

☑ In high winds, tower cranes must be left in free slew with their hooks raised.

☑ A plan for rescue from height must be in place in the event of an accident or incident (for example, the operator becoming ill). The emergency services have no obligation to carry out such rescues and are often not able to assist because of the height of the rescue and because of restricted access for large vehicles (such as fire service turntable ladders).

 For further detailed guidance on rescue from height on tower cranes refer to the Construction Plant-hire Association's Technical information note TIN 013.

Tower cranes must be secured against unauthorised access, including climbing the tower and unauthorised use.

A lifting plan, approved by the competent (appointed) person, must be in place.

 For further detailed guidance on the safe use of tower cranes refer to:

☑ *Safe use of cranes – Tower cranes* (BS 7121-5)

☑ Construction Plant-hire Association's (Best practice guide):
  – *Safe use of top slew tower cranes*
  – *Safe use of self-erecting tower cranes.*

Maintenance, checks and inspections of tower cranes

Tower cranes should be checked, maintained and inspected in accordance with 7.11 of Chapter C07.

Thorough examination of tower cranes

The thorough examination of tower cranes should be carried out in accordance with 7.12 of Chapter C07.

 For further detailed guidance on the maintenance, inspection and thorough examination of tower cranes refer to the Construction Plant-hire Association's *Maintenance, inspection and thorough examination of tower cranes* (Best practice guide).

Tower crane register

The Notification of Conventional Tower Crane Regulations requires conventional tower cranes used on construction sites to be notified to the HSE.

A conventional tower crane is defined in the regulations as a slewing jib-type crane with jib located at the top of a vertical tower and which is assembled on a construction site from components. This includes, but is not limited to, such cranes with horizontal or luffing jibs and slewing rings at the base or top of the tower. These tower cranes are usually installed (and dismantled) with the assistance of another crane and, as a result, are sometimes referred to as assisted erected cranes.

All conventional tower cranes erected on construction sites need to be notified to the HSE (that is, all such cranes used to construct new buildings and structures or refurbish or demolish existing ones).

The duty to notify does not apply to other types of tower crane (such as self-erecting tower cranes) or any other types of crane (for example, mobile cranes). Nor does the duty apply to tower cranes on sites other than construction sites.

The responsibility for notification rests with either the principal contractor or the contractor appointed by the principal contractor to provide all on-site crane services.

Notification to the HSE must take place within 14 days of a thorough examination being carried out:

☑ following the crane's installation and before being put into use for the first time on a particular site

☑ when the crane is reconfigured on site (for example, when the height of the mast is altered)

☑ when the crane stays on site long enough for the existing thorough examination to expire

☑ if exceptional circumstances liable to jeopardise the safety of the crane have occurred.

For further detailed guidance on the tower crane register refer to the HSE publication INDG 437.

8.5 Lorry loaders

In recent years lorry loaders have developed significantly, to the stage where they are able to carry out many of the tasks traditionally undertaken by mobile and tower cranes. When used safely they make a valuable contribution to the carrying out of lifting operations. However, it should not be forgotten that all lifting operations must be planned and executed to the same standard, irrespective of the type of lifting equipment being used.

Unfortunately over the past few years there have been a significant number of accidents involving the use of lorry loaders, which have tragically included fatalities. These could have been prevented by correct planning, supervision, use and maintenance. In addition to the terrible cost in human suffering, accidents have a financial cost. There is a very strong business case for improving safety performance.

Types of lorry loader

A lorry loader is a commercial vehicle or trailer fitted with a loader crane. Loader cranes have a column that slews about its base and a boom system that is attached to the top of the column.

Typical lorry loader

Lorry loaders were originally designed to load and unload goods onto and off the body of the vehicle on which they were mounted so that deliveries and collections did not have to rely on other loading and unloading facilities.

Modern lorry loaders have developed to the stage where they are able to carry out many other lifting operations on site. Lorry loaders are rated in terms of load movement and are available in sizes from 0.5 tonne metre to 84 tonne metre.

When in use, the lorry loader is generally stabilised by two stabilisers mounted on the loader crane base. In the past loader crane controls were mounted at the base of the column, but today they are normally portable wireless units that allow the operator greater flexibility of movement and help to keep the load in view.

Planning and use of lorry loaders

The planning and carrying out of lifting operations with lorry loaders should be in accordance with the principles set out in Chapter C07.

Maintenance, checks and inspections of lorry loaders

Lorry loaders should be checked, maintained and inspected in accordance with 7.11 of Chapter C07.

Thorough examination of lorry loaders

The thorough examination of lorry loaders should be carried out in accordance with 7.12 of Chapter C07.

For detailed guidance on the safe use of lorry loaders refer to the Construction Plant-hire Association's *Safe use of lorry loaders* (Best practice guide).

8.6 Mobile elevating work platforms

Mobile elevating work platforms (MEWPs) are designed to provide temporary working platforms which, when people are in the work platform, can be easily adjusted for height and outreach. They can also be easily moved from one location to another and are particularly suitable for tasks where the use of a ladder would be unsafe and the erection of a scaffolding platform too time-consuming or impracticable in relation to the job to be done.

Sizes and capabilities of MEWPs vary considerably. Small, one-person machines are available, with a maximum safe working load of 120 kg, and working heights of a few metres, whilst at the other end of the scale, work platforms may be 4 m x 2 m or more and have safe working loads in excess of 1,000 kg. Extending boom heights exceeding 100 metres are obtainable and the outreach of some units can approach 40 metres.

08

Types of mobile elevating work platform

The basic types of MEWP elevating structure (the part that lifts the work platform) are:

- scissor lifts
- vertical lifts
- telescopic booms
- articulating and telescopic booms or multi-boom articulated.

These elevating structures may be mounted on chassis that are:

- towable units
- vehicles
- self-propelled (wheeled or crawler)
- pedestrian controlled.

Scissor lift

This type of MEWP gives a substantially vertical lift. The work platform may be fitted with a sliding extension that will give a small amount of outreach.

Vertical lift

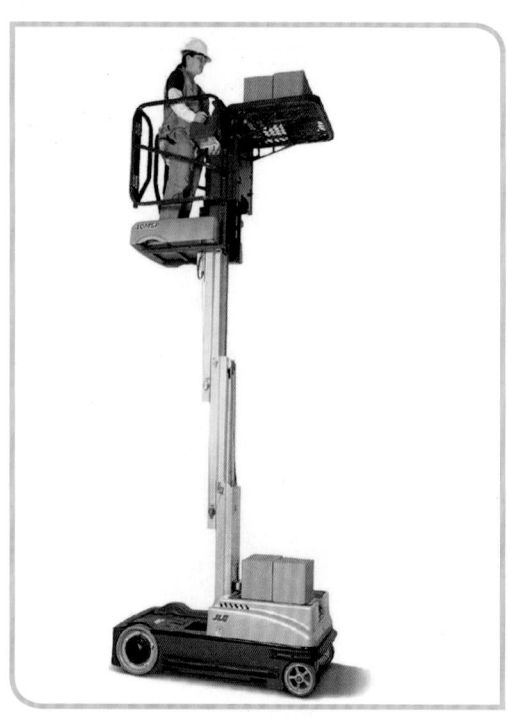

This type of MEWP gives vertical lift only and is generally used for small, lightweight machines for indoor use only.

Telescopic boom

This type gives both vertical height and outreach and the telescoping function gives smooth and fine control near structures. The work platform may also be able to swivel in the horizontal plane and is mounted on a fly jib for additional manoeuvrability. Boom-type MEWPS are sometimes known as cherry pickers.

Articulating and telescopic or multi-boom articulated

These types of MEWP may be mounted on a road-going vehicle chassis or a self propelled wheeled or crawler chassis. They give a wide range of reach and height. Vehicle-mounted MEWPs are nearly always equipped with outriggers and specialised types are available (for example, machines that enable access to the underside of bridge arches from the roadway above).

Units mounted on a self-propelled chassis have a 'travel while elevated' ability and may have four-wheel drive. Rough terrain MEWPs have been specially developed for construction site work.

Planning and use of MEWPs

The planning and carrying out of lifting operations with MEWPs should be in accordance with the principles set out in Chapter C07. In addition the points below should be taken into account.

Entrapment of people on the platform

In certain circumstances (such as working at height amongst steelwork) there is an increased risk to people in the work platform of a MEWP of becoming trapped, and in some cases crushed, between the platform and a fixed obstruction. There have been a number of such incidents in the UK over the past few years, several of which have resulted in fatalities. Job planning should consider this hazard and, where required, additional measures should be taken, including:

- ☑ consideration of additional safety devices on the MEWP
- ☑ devising and implementing a rescue plan for people trapped at height
- ☑ briefing of operators and other people in the work platform.

This issue has been highlighted by the HSE as a result of several accidents in which MEWP operators had become injured and immobilised but were unable to release themselves, having become trapped between the machine (such as the top guard-rail or controls) and a fixed structure (often structural steelwork).

For comprehensive guidance on avoiding entrapment refer to the Strategic Forum for Construction Plant Safety Group's (Best practice guide) *MEWPs – Avoiding trapping/crushing injuries to people in the platform.*

Emergency controls

Both ground and work platform controls should be checked as part of the pre-use inspection to ensure they are working correctly. This check should also include the emergency lowering controls, which are provided to enable the work platform to be safely recovered to ground level and all emergency stop controls.

The operator, or their supervisor, should ensure that a responsible person, who is familiar with the emergency lowering system, is always in close proximity to the MEWP, to lower the work platform in the event that rescue is required.

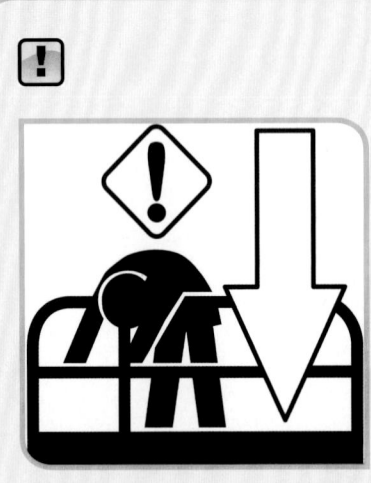

Even experienced operators sometimes have difficulty locating the emergency descent controls that every MEWP is fitted with.

This decal is a practical visual aid and a prime example of an industry initiative to make access equipment even safer.

Emergency descent systems can be found on all types of MEWPs. They differ in terms of where they are located on specific machines and how they operate.

The decal should be positioned to clearly indicate the location of the emergency descent controls. Operators should ensure that somebody at ground level is properly trained on how to use the controls in an emergency.

Personnel must never attempt to climb out of an elevated MEWP if the emergency back-up system fails to work, but should stay in the work platform until rescued by other means.

 This decal is available to download free from the IPAF website.

Overturning

☑ Check for soft ground, drains and other unsuitable ground conditions before deploying the outriggers or stabilisers; check for the hazard before siting the machine.

☑ Beware of overloading, especially if the work platform is being used at maximum outreach to remove fans, motors or other heavy loads. Always observe the safe working load.

☑ Be careful when operating on a slope, even if the machine is properly levelled with the stabilisers or outriggers.

☑ Always check that the machine is stable before operating.

☑ Be careful when travelling with the work platform raised, especially on poor ground conditions.

☑ Never attempt to travel while the outriggers or stabilisers are deployed, unless the machine is designed for this purpose.

☑ Be careful not to collide with any obstruction or other vehicle.

☑ Some modern machines are fitted with a tilt sensor, which, if activated, only enables the work platform to be lowered.

Fall protection

The following refers predominantly to the use of boom-type MEWPs although, in some circumstances, parts could also be relevant to the use of scissor or other vertical lifts. Personal fall protection systems fall into two categories:

☑ work-restraint systems

☑ fall-arrest systems.

Work-restraint system

Whereas fall-arrest equipment allows a person to fall but arrests the fall before the person hits the surface below, work-restraint equipment prevents the fall from happening.

The main feature of work-restraint equipment is that a shorter lanyard is used, which restricts the operator's limit of travel to the confines of the work platform.

Lanyards should be carefully selected, taking into account the features of the machine on which they are to be used, to ensure that the user cannot get into a situation where a fall could occur. The lanyard must always be attached to a designated anchor point in the work platform.

A fall-arrest lanyard **can** be used for restraint but a restraint lanyard may **not** be used for fall arrest.

Fall-arrest system

Where a decision has been taken to rely on fall-arrest equipment as a means of preventing injury, it will be necessary for the operator to wear a full body harness and a lanyard equipped with an energy absorber. Vital considerations are:

☑ the height at which work is being carried out must be such that it allows the lanyard to arrest the fall and the energy absorber to deploy before the wearer hits the surface below. A minimum working height of 6.75 metres is recommended if fall-arrest is to operate successfully

☑ the anchor point on the machine must have been designed to withstand the shock-loading of arresting a fall. Many anchor points fitted to MEWPs are only rated for work restraint. If the anchor point is not marked with its rating, contact the manufacturer to find it out

☑ users of harness and lanyard must have been trained in their use, inspection and care

☑ in arresting a fall, a boom-type MEWP will flex, which could eject other occupants and materials out of the basket. This could also overturn the machine if it is operating at maximum outreach

☑ a check must be made that the structure has no projecting features that the falling person would strike during the fall

☑ how the person who has fallen will be rescued after the fall has been arrested. This may be as simple as another operator gently lowering the boom of a MEWP using the ground level controls until the fallen person is at ground level.

An exception to wearing a harness whilst operating a MEWP is when the machine is working over or near to water.

 A safety harness must never be attached to anything outside the work platform; operation of the controls in this situation could leave the user suspended in mid-air (see illustration).

 For further information on the use of personal fall protection equipment in MEWPs refer to the HSE's *Preventing falls from boom-type mobile elevating work platforms* (MISC 614).

 For advice on the inspection of harnesses and lanyards refer to the HSE's information sheet *Inspecting fall-arrest equipment made from webbing or rope* (INDG 367).

Working over, or near to, water

There could be a danger of drowning where a MEWP, particularly an articulating boom-type machine (cherry picker), is being used over, or near to, water. It is possible that the work platform of such a machine could come to rest underwater if it were to topple over. It is essential, therefore, that the occupant(s) of the work platform:

☑ do **not** clip on to the anchorage point, as would happen normally (or elsewhere around the working platform)

☑ do wear life jackets.

In such circumstances:

☑ even though the machine toppling would have a traumatic effect on the user(s), they still might have a chance of being able to swim to, or scramble back onto, dry land

☑ a risk assessment must be carried out to determine and implement effective fall prevention measures that would normally be covered by wearing a harness and lanyard.

08

Restricted or enclosed spaces

- ✓ Extra care is needed when working in, or manoeuvring into, restricted or confined spaces to avoid collisions and/or entrapment. A full and precise understanding of all controls is essential.

- ✓ If the MEWP has an internal combustion engine, remember that the exhaust fumes will cause a hazard in any confined or enclosed space.

- ✓ Batteries for units should not be charged in enclosed spaces. There is a hazard of explosive hydrogen gases being given off.

- ✓ Liquefied petroleum gas (LPG) powered vehicles should not be refuelled in a confined space. Any spillage of fuel will quickly and dramatically expand into a large gas cloud. The gas will then accumulate at the lowest point and create an explosive hazard.

Interference with MEWPs in public places

- ✓ Whenever MEWPs are used in public places, additional precautions should be taken to ensure segregation between members of the public and the machine. This may be by the use of barriers or posting marshals around the machine.

- ✓ Additional interlocks or guards may be necessary to prevent the operation of, or tampering with, ground level controls by unauthorised persons or children.

- ✓ Care should be taken against the risk of entrapment as a result of inquisitive people, and especially children, getting too close or underneath. Scissor lifts are particularly hazardous.

For further detailed guidance on the planning and safe use of MEWPs refer to:
- ✓ *Code of practice for the safe use of MEWPs* (BS 8460)
- ✓ HSE's Construction information sheet *Selection and management of mobile elevating work platforms* (CIS 58).

Maintenance, checks and inspections of MEWPs

MEWPs should be checked, maintained and inspected in accordance with 7.11 of Chapter C07.

Thorough examination of MEWPs

The thorough examination of MEWPs should be carried out in accordance with 7.12 of Chapter C07.

8.7   Construction hoists

Hoists of various types are widely used on construction sites. These range from high capacity passenger/goods hoists, goods only hoists, transport platforms, inclined hoists, scaffold hoists and trestle/beam hoists, to the humble gin wheel.

Passenger/goods hoists, goods only hoists, transport platforms and inclined hoists, where the load is guided, are often referred to as construction hoists, to distinguish them from scaffold hoists, trestle/beam hoists and gin wheels, where the load is not guided.

As pressure increases to become more efficient and reduce manual handling, hoists are an increasingly vital part of many construction operations. The smooth and rapid movement of persons and materials assists in efficient management of projects. Even where other methods of moving materials around site are to be used (for example, by a tower crane) it is not unusual to find a hoist used solely to assist the scaffold erection process.

The number and type of scaffold hoists and trestle/beam hoists available for hire has increased significantly and their use will require a lifting plan to be drawn up by a competent person. This plan must consider possible exclusion zones under the hoist in the event of the load dropping, safe slinging methods, the appropriate lifting accessories, and so on. These are a different set of risks compared with, for example, loads being carried in the enclosed platform of a goods hoist.

Risks can arise from a late decision to use a hoist to solve a previously unforeseen problem during the construction phase. For example, if planning to use a hoist tied to a scaffolding system that is already in place but which was not originally designed to take the additional loadings, there is a need for careful planning and possibly discussions with the scaffold designer before simply allowing a hoist to be hired and fixed to the scaffold.

Except for manually operated hoists and any that have an independent power supply, the requirement for a dedicated power supply to the hoist must also be considered. Most hoists are electrically powered, so the Electricity at Work Regulations will apply to the installation. The electrical power requirements may result in the need for generators, which must be of adequate capacity. This introduces potential noise, fuel storage and spillage issues.

Types of hoist

A wide range of hoists are used on construction sites. The main types are described below.

Passenger/goods hoists

- [✓] Have a rack and pinion drive mechanism.
- [✓] Are tied to an adjacent structure.
- [✓] Can be erected to lifting heights of up to 250 metres.
- [✓] Can travel at up to 100 metres per minute.
- [✓] Are operated from inside the cage.
- [✓] Are available in a wide range of cage sizes, up to 1.5 metres wide x 4.6 metres long.
- [✓] Are available with payloads of up to 3,200 kg.

Goods only hoists

- [✓] Generally have a rack and pinion drive mechanism.
- [✓] Are tied to an adjacent structure.
- [✓] Can be erected to lifting heights of up to 100 metres.
- [✓] Can travel at up to 40 metres per minute.
- [✓] Are operated from outside the cage.
- [✓] Are available in a wide range of cage sizes, from 1.4 metres wide x 0.8 metres long, to 1.5 metres wide x 6.0 metres long.
- [✓] Are available with payloads from 200 kg up to 2,500 kg.

Transport platforms

Transport platforms are dual-purpose machines that either carry goods only, in which case they are operated from outside the platform, or carry passengers, in which case they are operated from inside the platform and are restricted to a speed of 12 metres per minute.

Inclined hoists

- ☑ Generally have a wire rope drive mechanism.
- ☑ Are supported by an adjacent structure.
- ☑ Can be erected to lifting heights of up to 40 metres.
- ☑ Can travel at up to 25 metres per minute.
- ☑ Are operated from outside the platform.
- ☑ Have platforms of about 0.7 metres x 0.8 metres.
- ☑ Are available with payloads up to 250 kg.

Scaffold hoists

Scaffold hoists are not hoists in the true sense, in that the load is not guided, as is the case with a goods or passenger/goods hoist. They are in fact small cranes that are generally attached to scaffolding, having a small swinging jib on which is mounted a wire rope winch.

Scaffold hoists:

- ☑ have a lifting capacity of up to 250 kg
- ☑ have a standard lifting height of up to 50 metres
- ☑ can lift at up to 25 metres per minute.

Trestle/beam hoists

Trestle/beam or gantry hoists consist of a runway beam mounted in a trestle structure, with a wire rope winch mounted on the beam. The beam is cantilevered over the edge of a building roof or floor, enabling materials to be lifted from ground level.

Trestle/beam hoists:

- ☑ have a lifting capacity of up to 1,000 kg
- ☑ have a standard lifting height of up to 25 metres
- ☑ can lift at up to 20 metres per minute.

Planning and installation of hoists

The installation of hoists requires good planning and co-ordination and must be undertaken by competent individuals. All hoists must be supplied and, where appropriate, erected, altered and dismantled by companies or people who are fully aware of the legal requirements and the relevant British and European Standards. Special attention must be given to ground conditions to ensure adequate support for the hoist. The forces imposed on the structure by the hoist, its loads and inclement weather, particularly high winds, must also be taken into account. Hoist operators must be adequately trained, competent and authorised and should be specifically responsible for ensuring that the hoist is not overloaded or otherwise misused.

Pre-planning (construction hoists)

When it has been decided (possibly as early as the tender stage) that a construction hoist will be required on site, requirements must be quantified with regard to:

- [x] consideration of the locations for siting the hoist

- [x] the loads to be carried in terms of size and weight and whether goods only or both goods and passengers are to be carried

- [x] the likely loading on the structure and whether any enabling work or structural changes are required

- [x] any constraints in the position where the hoist can be erected and whether other features (such as scaffolds) must be modified to accommodate the hoist

- [x] the loading on the hoist's foundations.

At an appropriate point both the user of the hoist (for example, the principal contractor) and the supplier of the hoist should each assign a competent (appointed) person who must liaise with each other to ensure that all aspects of the hoist selection, delivery, erection and use are carried out safely. The user's competent (appointed) person may need to rely upon the experience and competence of the supplier's competent (appointed) person in order to fulfil their responsibilities.

The detailed requirements of these roles, both of which require specific training and previous relevant experience, are considered to be outside the scope of this chapter. If necessary, refer to BS 7212:2006.

A full and detailed risk assessment should be carried out before a hoist is positioned. A method statement can then be developed, which must then be agreed with the user.

Site survey

Prior to delivery of the hoist it will be necessary for both competent (appointed) persons to visit the site to establish the practicalities of installing it. During the site survey the supplier's appointed person will determine the appropriate type of hoist required, based upon criteria and information on the intended usage of hoist provided by the user's appointed person.

The findings of the survey will determine the optimum position for the hoist, based upon such factors as:

- [x] co-location with materials storage areas

- [x] avoidance of hazardous features (such as overhead cables)

- [x] the need for safe access at all levels

- [x] the need for safe access to the cage or platform at ground level

- [x] the need for foundations and drainage

- [x] suitable locations on the building structure for the attachment of ties.

In selecting the most appropriate hoist, the supplier's appointed person will have to take into account such factors as:

- [x] the space constraints of the area

- [x] access implications relating to the size and weight of the hoist components

- [x] ground conditions and suitable locations on the building structure for the attachment of ties

- [x] the proximity of site features (such as overhead power lines, railway tracks and adjacent public thoroughfares)

- [x] other work that will take place whilst the hoist is in place and how the site might change during this period

- [x] foreseeable extremes in weather conditions.

Erecting, altering and dismantling hoists

Hoists that rest on the ground must only be erected on a firm base, adequately supported and secured. All materials supporting the hoist must be strong enough to support the weight of the completed hoist structure and its maximum load, and be free from defects.

The erection of the hoist must be carried out in accordance with the manufacturer's instructions and a method statement that has been discussed with and approved by the user, as the proposed method and timing may impact upon other site activities.

Potential problems caused by the loadings that hoists can put on the adjacent structure have already been outlined under the heading of the CDM Regulations (refer to Chapter C07 Lifting operations).

In many ways, erection, alteration and dismantling are potentially the most hazardous activities associated with hoists on site. Anyone not directly involved in erecting the hoist should keep clear of the area.

Planning how the hoist will be erected and deciding who is responsible for what is key to implementing a safe system of work. This is particularly important where the hoist will be built in conjunction with the erection of a scaffold. It is essential that the erection, and later modification and dismantling, of hoists are properly planned, adequately supervised and carried out in a safe manner by competent persons.

Where the hoist is attached to and supported by a scaffold, the scaffold must be designed to take account of the imposed loadings. This becomes more important where the use of a larger capacity hoist is being considered.

Hoists should be erected by competent personnel holding a CSCS card and an NVQ in Hoist installation, Level 2 or 3.

08

Use of part-erected hoists

It is common practice for scaffolders to build three or four lifts of scaffold, raising the components by hand, followed by the hoist company erecting the hoist to the height of the scaffold. Further erection of the part-completed hoist is co-ordinated with the scaffold contractors so that it can be used for hoisting scaffold components, as it follows the scaffold up. In such circumstances, normal safe working practices may not be practical.

The rules regarding the interlocking of landing gates cannot be applied when some of the gates have not been installed. Detailed guidance is available and it is strongly recommended that anyone faced with this situation on their site obtains and reads it.

The guidance is published jointly by the National Access and Scaffolding Federation and the Construction Plant-hire Association and is available from both organisations.

For further detailed guidance refer to the Construction Plant-hire Association's *Transporting scaffolding in construction hoists* (Best practice guide).

Work at height

Some work at height is unavoidable when carrying out the erection, maintenance, alteration or dismantling of hoists. Work at height must always be planned in accordance with the hierarchy set out in the Work at Height Regulations.

For further detailed guidance refer to the Construction Plant-hire Association's *Work at height on construction hoists* (CHIG 0901).

Alteration

Alteration of hoists (such as increasing or decreasing the height) should be planned and carried out in the same way as erection.

Dismantling

Dismantling operations should be planned and carried out in the same way as erection. Care should be taken to ensure that adequate time is allowed in the construction programme to ensure that dismantling can be carried out without time pressures on the dismantling team. Before dismantling starts it is essential to ensure that the hoist is in a satisfactory condition for safe dismantling.

Safety of hoistways, platforms and cages

Where necessary to prevent injury, hoistways and/or the hoisting machinery must be segregated by a substantial enclosure at ground level. Suitable barriers must be installed at all other access points, over the full height of travel, and wherever persons could be struck by any moving part, to prevent injury and/or falls.

Consideration must be given to the area around the base of the hoist with regard to loading and unloading materials, and whether a ramp or pit is required to facilitate access to the platform.

The area between the cage or platform and the host structure (the threshold) must be suitably protected to prevent any person or material falling through the gap at each landing.

Landings and gates

Where access to a construction hoist is required at several levels, consideration must be given to the space requirements at each landing with regard to loading and unloading the hoist. It is essential that each landing and threshold (the area between the platform and landing) can withstand the loads that will be imposed, with particular emphasis on items, such as pallet trucks, which can impose significant point loading.

The mechanical or electrical features of the hoist should ensure that:

☑ the gates at any landing point cannot be opened unless the cage or platform is at that landing point

☑ the cage or platform cannot be set in motion unless all of the landing gates are closed and locked.

For further detailed guidance on landing and gating requirements for goods hoists refer to the Construction Plant-hire Association's *Safeguarding requirements for landing gates of goods-only hoists* (Best practice guide) (CHIG 0401).

Handover

Once erected, the hoist will be subjected to a thorough examination, after which the supplier's appointed person should arrange to formally hand over the hoist to the user's appointed person.

The user's appointed person should arrange for all trained operators to be present at the handover of the hoist to receive:

☑ familiarisation training on the use of the hoist in normal operations

☑ instruction on what to do in emergency situations

☑ instruction on how to carry out the daily, pre-use inspections and weekly inspections.

A handover report, containing details of the instruction given, should be passed to the user's appointed person.

 For detailed guidance on the planning and installation of construction hoists refer to the *Code of practice for safe use of construction hoists* (BS 7212).

Planning and use of construction hoists

The planning and carrying out of lifting operations with construction hoists should be in accordance with the principles set out in Chapter C07. In addition, the points below should be taken into account.

Operation of hoists

It is essential that only operators who have been trained in the use of the hoist are allowed to operate it. The operator should:

☑ know the rated load of the hoist

☑ be able to accurately assess the weight and distribution of any load brought on to the hoist, and therefore identify if it is overloaded

☑ have access to accurate wind-speed figures and be aware of any limitations placed on the hoist

☑ be able to lower the hoist to the next landing in the event of a power failure (passenger carrying hoists only)

☑ carry out daily, pre-use checks and weekly inspections, and take the appropriate follow-up action as necessary. On some complex hoists, it may be necessary for the weekly inspection to be carried out by an employee of the hoist company.

Each hoist should only be capable of being operated from one position at any one time. Where, as in the case of a goods only hoist, the operator is not carried on the platform, they must have a clear view at all levels from the operating position or, if they have not, arrangements must be made for signals to be given to them at each level.

Whatever the system of signalling used, it must be distinct and clear to the person being signalled.

It is reasonable to expect that the hoist operator and the person(s) giving signals are at least 18 years of age. It is not illegal for younger people to do this work, but under regulations a specific risk assessment would need to be carried out to ensure that immaturity had been considered. Irrespective of their age, hoist operators must be trained and competent, unless under constant supervision by a competent person for the purpose of training.

Safety notices

The platform of a goods hoist must carry a notice stating:

☑ the safe working load

☑ that passengers must not ride on the hoist

☑ any restrictions regarding load position and concentration.

Cages for passenger hoists must carry a notice stating:

☑ the safe working load

☑ the maximum number of passengers that can be carried

☑ any restrictions regarding load position and concentration.

Landing gates for goods only hoists must carry a notice stating:

☑ goods only hoist

☑ no passengers

☑ keep gates closed

☑ rated load in kg.

Landing gates for passenger/goods hoists must carry a notice stating:

☑ keep gates closed

☑ rated load in kg.

08

Carriage of persons in hoists

No person should be carried by a hoist, unless it is a designated passenger/goods hoist or transport platform and it is provided with:

☑ gates that shut to prevent persons falling out or being trapped between the cage and any other part

☑ an efficient interlocking device, which ensures that gates can only be operated when the cage is at the landing place, and that the cage cannot be moved until the gate is closed

☑ an efficient automatic overrun device to ensure the cage will come to rest at its lowest and highest points of travel.

The construction of the cage or platform must be such as to protect passengers from falling objects. No person should be allowed to travel in a hoist that is designated a goods only hoist.

Security of loads

All loads must be secured to prevent any part from slipping and falling.

Loose materials (for example, bricks and slates) must be lifted in a properly designed box, cage or other container. The platform of a goods only hoist should have sides with a minimum height of 0.6 metres or 1.1 metre high, if persons can access the platform during loading or unloading.

 For detailed guidance on the planning and installation of construction hoists refer to *Code of practice for safe use of construction hoists* (BS 7212).

Maintenance, checks and inspections of construction hoists

Construction hoists should be checked, maintained and inspected in accordance with 7.11 of Chapter C07.

Thorough examination of construction hoists

The thorough examination of construction hoists should be carried out in accordance with 7.12 of Chapter C07.

 For further detailed guidance on the maintenance, inspection and thorough examination of construction hoists refer to the Construction Plant-hire Association's *Maintenance, inspection and thorough examination of construction hoists* (Best practice guide).

Specific requirements for scaffold hoists, trestle/beam hoists, inclined hoists and gin wheels

Scaffold hoists, trestle/beam hoists and inclined hoists are now commonly used throughout the construction industry. They can be easily transported to the site, are quickly erected and require little operating space. They may be fitted with buckets, skips, platforms or cages.

Different models allow for basic height variations of between eight metres and 30 metres, although much greater heights can be reached with extensions. Load capacity varies with the model but lifting capacity of 500 kg is not uncommon.

This equipment all comes within the scope of LOLER and, although free standing, are subject to the same provisions as construction hoists that are tied to a structure.

Scaffold cranes or barrow hoists

These are lifting equipment within the meaning of the regulations and, as with all lifting equipment, must not be overloaded.

The attachment of scaffold hoists to scaffolds is critical and must be carried out in accordance with the manufacturer's instructions. Scaffold hoists should not be attached to scaffolds unless they have been designed to take the loads imposed by the scaffold hoist.

Maintenance, inspection and thorough examination should follow the requirements for construction hoists.

Trestle/beam hoists

These are lifting equipment as defined by LOLER.

They rely for their stability on counterweighting at the rear of the trestle frame and it is essential that adequate counterweights are supplied. Counterweight is often provided by filling bins attached to the frame with sand or gravel.

Before using the hoist, checks should be made to ensure that sufficient material has been added to the bins and that they are in good condition so that the ballast cannot leak out.

Maintenance, inspection and thorough examination should follow the requirements for construction hoists.

Inclined hoists

These are lifting equipment within the meaning of the regulations. They are particularly useful for trades such as bricklaying and traditional roofing and indeed, on a larger project, they have the potential to eliminate a significant amount of manual handling.

Inclined hoists are also known as roof tile or brick carriers. New developments include telescopic and slewing functions. Load capacities go up to 200 kg and lateral extensions may be up to 35 metres.

Inclined hoists are specifically designed for use at angles between 10° and 85°, and they may also incorporate a hinged section to allow the hoist to follow the pitch of a roof.

They also provide flexible solutions to the problems of removing demolition waste in refurbishment situations. As they are in effect a conveyor-belt system, care needs to be taken to ensure that the guards to the rollers are in place to ensure that fingers and/or clothing cannot be dragged in. These are so called 'in-running nips' and particularly where the motor driving the hoist is powerful the potential for serious injury is significant.

Maintenance, inspection and thorough examination should follow the requirements for construction hoists.

Gin wheels

In many cases provision has to be made to raise tools and light materials manually with a rope and gin wheel or single block. Whilst these are still in common use, modern variants are available and incorporate an automatic locking mechanism to prevent the load from going into free-fall if the hoisting rope is accidentally released.

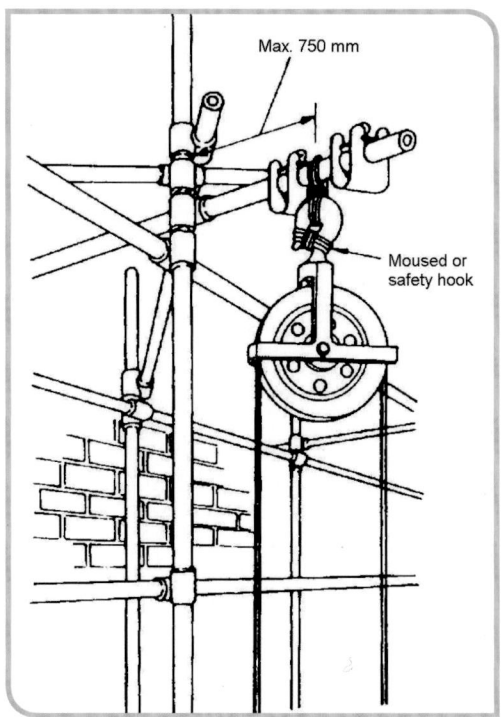

Gin wheel

The following provisions and requirements apply to gin wheels connected to a scaffold.

☑ Any scaffold tubes and hooks should be strong enough to take the load that is to be lifted and be properly secured to prevent movement.

☑ All ropes should comply with the relevant BS EN standards and fit the wheel correctly. They should be marked with a tag confirming their safe working load.

☑ Preferably, the gin wheel should be suspended from a ring-type fitting passed over the end of the supporting tube and secured against lateral movement by scaffold fittings. If using a hook type, it should be properly lashed and moused (see diagram on left).

☑ Any joints in standards should be made with sleeve couplers.

☑ Gin wheels should be suspended not more than 750 mm from the outer scaffold standard.

☑ Hooks used for supporting materials should be safety hooks and spliced into the rope.

☑ The maximum load should be no more than 50 kg at 750 mm from the outer scaffold standard.

Whilst of simple construction, gin wheels are categorised as lifting equipment so must be thoroughly examined before use and then at least every 12 months, with a test certificate issued.

Similarly, the lifting accessories used (such as the rope, hook and shackles) must be thoroughly examined before use and then at least every six months.

Given the scope for the harsh treatment of this type of equipment, all parts of a gin wheel assembly should be thoroughly examined at least every six months.

The extent of any thorough examination should reflect the risks that would arise from its failure.

8.8 Telehandlers

Telehandlers (also known as rough terrain telescopic handlers or variable reach trucks) make a valuable contribution to the construction process by enabling materials to be unloaded from delivery vehicles, transported around construction sites and placed at height (reach). They are versatile machines that can be fitted with a wide range of attachments (such as buckets, skips, work platforms and crane jibs). Unfortunately, there have been a significant number of accidents involving the use of telehandlers, which have tragically included a number of fatalities.

As with all lifting equipment the safe use of telehandlers requires selecting of the right equipment, which has been adequately maintained, planning the operation effectively and having a trained and competent operator.

Types of telehandlers

Telehandlers fall into two broad categories, non-rotating and rotating.

Non-rotating

These machines comprise a powered wheeled chassis onto which is mounted a telescopic boom, pivoted on the chassis, which can be elevated from below the horizontal to an angle approaching the vertical. The outer end of the boom is fitted with a fork carriage and forks for handling unit loads. Levelling of the forks in the longitudinal plane, as the boom elevation changes, is carried out automatically.

Typical non-rotating telehandler

These machines are able to transport loads from one part of a site to another and place the load at height. On construction sites, the wheels are generally fitted with lug grip tyres to enable the chassis to negotiate unpaved ground. Various drive and steering configurations are available (such as two-wheeled drive, four-wheeled drive, pivot steer, rear-wheel steering and four-wheeled steering).

Many telehandlers are fitted with stabilisers that are deployed when the machine is stationary to provide additional stability and enhance the machine's lifting capacity. Telehandlers are often fitted with a feature that allows the chassis to be levelled laterally, where appropriate, before the boom is raised, when the machine is standing on uneven ground.

Rotating

Rotating telehandlers have all of the features of the non-rotating type, but with the addition of a rotating or slewing superstructure on which the boom and operator's cab are mounted. These machines also have outriggers fitted at either end of the chassis that enable the entire chassis to be lifted clear of the ground for maximum stability.

Typical rotating telehandler

The main advantages of these machines over the non-rotating type is compact chassis size, enhanced lifting height, increased stability and ease of placing loads without moving the chassis.

Telehandler attachments

Telehandlers are very versatile machines which, in addition to lifting of unit loads on forks, can be fitted with a wide range of attachments, such as:

- ☑ sideshift forks
- ☑ sweepers
- ☑ block grabs
- ☑ tipping skips

- ☑ crane hooks
- ☑ crane jibs
- ☑ buckets (general purpose and material handling)
- ☑ integrated access platforms.

It is essential that all attachments are compatible with the telehandler with which they are to be used. Where necessary and appropriate, the telehandler manufacturer should be consulted where third-party attachments are to be used.

Quick hitches

Some telehandlers are fitted with quick hitches or quick couplers, which enable attachments to be changed easily and rapidly. They fall into two types:

- ☑ **mechanical quick hitch** where the hitch is engaged with the attachment, using the boom functions combined with fork carriage tilt. Once the quick hitch and attachment are engaged, a locking pin is inserted and secured with a retaining pin

- ☑ **hydraulic quick hitch** that is engaged in the same manner as the mechanical quick hitch but the locking pin is engaged hydraulically using the controls in the telehandler cab.

Both types of quick hitch can allow the attachment to become detached from the quick hitch if the manual locking pin is left out or the hydraulic locking pin fails to engage fully. There have been several serious injuries caused by falling attachments and misuse.

08

It is essential that operators get out of the cab to physically ensure that all quick hitches are securely locked before starting work with a newly attached attachment.

 For further detailed guidance on quick hitches refer to the Strategic forum for construction's *Safe use of quick hitches on excavators* (Best practice guide).

Planning and use of telehandlers

The planning and carrying out of lifting operations with telehandlers should be in accordance with the principles set out in Chapter C07. In addition the points below should be taken into account.

Visibility

Restricted visibility when the boom is raised or when large loads are carried, as well as poor segregation have been identified as a major cause of accidents involving pedestrians and telehandlers. Telehandlers are often fitted with aids to improve visibility and the operator's awareness of people in the vicinity of the telehandler. These aids should be in good working order and properly adjusted. It is the operator's responsibility to check the condition of all secondary aids to visibility and **not to use the machine** if they are not present or not working correctly. It is the supervisor's responsibility to fully support the operator in this action.

Some parts of a telehandler work cycle present particular challenges. A suspended load, for example, will clearly block some forward view, but the raised boom may also obscure the view to the side. If a telehandler is to lift suspended loads on site, the physical dimensions of the loads and their effect upon visibility must form part of the risk assessment.

If a telehandler is used to load or unload a truck, the partially raised boom will obstruct the view to the forward offside and may block the wing mirror that gives visibility to the rear offside. The safest way of using a telehandler to load/offload is to keep the machine stationary and use the telescopic facility of the boom, rather than using the wheels. The driver of the truck should remain in a designated safe location for such operations.

Whilst the principal contractor has the primary responsibility to ensure adequate segregation and the supervisor must ensure that it is enforced, it is remains the operator's responsibility to look around and check for the absence of pedestrians before moving and whilst manoeuvring and travelling. If the operator cannot see clearly, they should seek assistance or leave the cab to look around to confirm it is safe to continue the procedure.

Travelling on inclines, slopes and gradients

The telehandler must only operate on slopes/gradients at a speed designated by the site, taking into account ground conditions, to ensure that the operator has full control at all times.

Traffic routes should be on consolidated ground or may be temporary roadways giving equivalent safety. The slopes/gradients given in the table below are to assist planners in the preparation of traffic routes. They are the maximum gradients on which a telehandler can travel while being operated when crossing sites **in the standard travelling mode and at walking speed**. The standard travelling mode of a telehandler is with the boom retracted, the load/fork arms lowered to provide a clearance of 300 mm and not more than 500 mm (see manufacturer's instruction manual) from the ground to the upper faces of the fork arms, and the fork arms fully tilted rearwards.

Slope	%	Gradient	Angle
Maximum down slope			
Maximum up slope	15%	1 in 6.66	8.5°
Maximum lateral slope			

Operation on any traffic route with a greater slope or in a travelling mode different to the above should be subject to a site-specific risk assessment.

 Consolidated ground is firm ground capable of accepting the mass of a loaded telehandler without significant deformation.

Stability of the telehandler

The stability of telehandlers and their loads are affected by the conditions of the ground on which they must stand when loading or unloading.

The area selected by the planners as a static loading area must be large enough to accommodate all the wheels of the telehandler and stabilisers or outriggers when fitted. The area should be of consolidated firm ground or surfaces giving similar levels of safety. It should be capable of accepting the mass of the loaded telehandler without significant deformation and be substantially level in both planes to ensure lateral and longitudinal stability when lifting operations are being carried out. Substantially level ground is defined as ground with a gradient of ideally 1% (1 in 100 gradient, 0.6°) but not more than the standard drainage slope of 2.5% (1 in 40 gradient, 1.4°).

When determining the area to be used for the unloading of lorries and the storage of materials, care should be taken to ensure the ground is consolidated and substantially level. The area provided must be large enough that the telehandler will not need to make tight turns with an elevated load.

A telehandler may be used for loading/unloading operations in areas which are not substantially level if they are used within their design capabilities. Where the achievement of a substantially level loading/unloading area is not reasonably practicable a risk assessment will be necessary.

 A telehandler fitted with level indicators can indicate where a machine can be used for loading/unloading on lateral (side) slopes. Under these circumstances the operator can carry out the risk assessment by referring to the level indicator before raising the telehandler boom above its standard travelling mode position.

 When a telehandler is not fitted with a level indicator the risk assessment should be carried out by a person who has access to the telehandler manufacturer's information and who has the necessary competence to specify the limiting boom height and extension figures that should not be exceeded.

Telehandlers become less stable in a lateral or sideways direction as the boom and load are raised and, because telehandlers normally have freely oscillating rear axles, the tipping lines form a triangle, rather than the rectangle of machines supported on outriggers (such as rotating boom telehandlers and mobile cranes). This has the effect of reducing lateral stability, particularly with the boom raised. These effects are shown in the diagrams below.

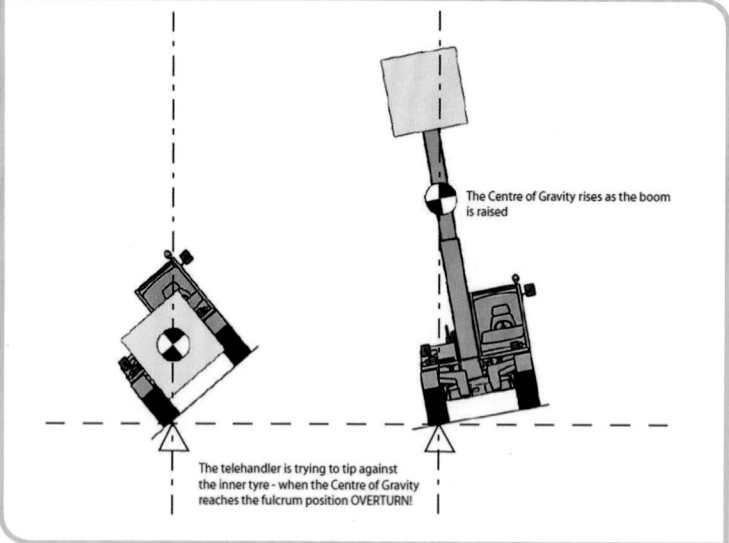

Lateral stability

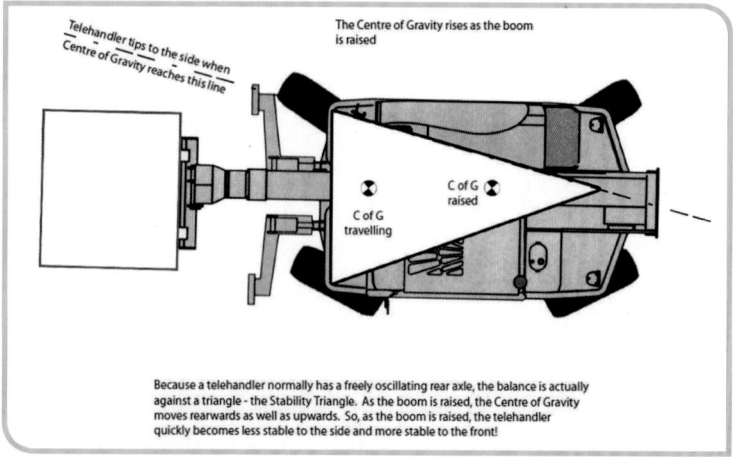

Typical stability triangle for non-rotating telehandle

When travelling with a load, the load should always be kept as near to the ground as possible.

Tyres play a vital part in the stability of telehandlers. Stability and load carrying capacity can be adversely affected by issues such as:

- ☑ use of tyres that are not approved by the telehandler manufacturer
- ☑ mixing of tyres from different manufacturers
- ☑ incorrect ply rating
- ☑ differences in diameter of tyres on the same axle due to differential wear
- ☑ low tyre pressure
- ☑ high tyre pressure
- ☑ uneven tyre pressure
- ☑ poor repairs.

Wearing of seat-belts

Telehandler cabs are provided with seat-belts to restrain the operator and reduce the risk of serious injury in the event of a machine overturning. A survey of telehandler accidents in the UK carried out by the HSE shows that in seven years there have been at least 72 lateral overturns of telehandlers.

In three cases the operator was killed by being ejected from the cab and crushed; in a further two cases the operator was ejected from the cab and received serious crushing injuries. Had three of these operators been wearing their seat-belts they would probably have lived.

 It is vital that operators of telehandlers wear the seat-belt provided at all times – it could save their lives.

Stability of the load

When using a telehandler for loading or unloading a vehicle or stack, care must be taken to ensure that the load on the vehicle or stack is stable. Unless the correct sequence of loading or unloading is followed there is risk of the load becoming unstable with the potential for injury to persons in the vicinity.

Use of a wider fork carriage

- ☑ Loading should always be carried out with unloading in mind.
- ☑ Vehicles should always be loaded from the front or as directed by the vehicle driver, working from side to side and distributing the load evenly.
- ☑ Unloading should be carried out by reversing this sequence.
- ☑ When loading uncoupled articulated trailers, the first part of the load should be placed over the rear axle before loading from the front of the trailer.
- ☑ Care should also be taken to ensure that the part of the load on the vehicle or stack is not dislodged by contact with the telehandler carriage, forks or other attachments.
- ☑ During loading and unloading measures, such as exclusion zones or barriers, should be put in place to ensure that personnel are kept clear of falling loads.

- ☑ Before lifting a load it should be assessed to ensure that it will be stable and secure during lifting.
- ☑ The forks should always be evenly spaced on either side of the centre of gravity of the load.
- ☑ Long or irregularly shaped loads may have a centre of gravity that is close to the edges of the forks and may well result in the load falling during lifting.
- ☑ Long loads can be easier to control where a wider fork carriage is used and personnel should be kept clear of the load. They should **not** be asked to steady the load.

 The practice of undercutting, where the load is lifted on the ends of the forks, rather than back at the heel, closest to the fork carriage, is often used when the load is to be placed adjacent to a wall or another item. This practice will reduce the rated capacity of the telehandler and may affect the stability of the load as its centre of gravity may be near or beyond the end of the forks.

08

Use of lifting hooks or crane jibs for suspended loads

Many telehandlers can be fitted with a lifting hook or crane jib for lifting suspended loads. However, before carrying out lifting of suspended loads the operation should be reviewed to ensure that a telehandler is the most appropriate piece of lifting equipment for the task.

The lifting of suspended loads should always be carried out with a telehandler that is fitted with a suitable lifting hook or attachment. If this can be shown to be not reasonably practicable, it is essential that any other method is justified by a robust risk assessment, taking account of the hierarchy of control.

Any lifting hook or crane jib should be marked with a rated capacity (safe working load) that must not be exceeded; the rated capacity of the hook may be less than the rated capacity of the telehandler or vice versa. It is important that the lower of the two values is used to determine the rated capacity of the combination.

When working out the total weight of the load to be lifted the weight of the lifting hook or crane jib and any lifting accessories (shackles, slings, and so on) must be taken into account.

Telehandler manufacturers supplying lifting hooks and crane jibs for their own machines will generally provide reduced rated capacities where suspended loads are being lifted and carried. This is intended to reduce the risk of overload or overturn due to displacement of the load through travelling, boom movements or the effect of wind.

Extreme care should be taken when travelling with a suspended load as any movement of the load will alter the load radius and may affect the stability of the telehandler.

Basic telehandler operator training does not include the lifting of suspended loads, the lifting of persons or the use of other attachments. If such tasks are to be carried out the employer must ensure that the operator is suitably trained and assessed as competent. This can normally be carried out by a local training provider.

Use of telehandlers for the lifting of persons

Telehandlers are primarily intended for lifting materials and not people. However, they can be used with working platforms to allow people to work at height. It is generally accepted that, in conjunction with a telehandler, an integrated working platform provides a higher level of safety than a non-integrated type and should be used for the lifting of persons on construction sites, where a MEWP is not available.

Non-integrated platform attachments must not be used for planned tasks on construction sites.

Integrated work platform

Maintenance, checks and inspections of telehandlers

Telehandlers should be checked, maintained and inspected in accordance with 7.11 of Chapter C07. In addition the points below should be taken into account.

Tyre repair, replacement and maintenance

This section applies to pneumatic tyres only. Foam-filled tyres are not user serviceable.

Tyre pressure check

- ☑ Tyre pressures should be marked on the telehandler chassis adjacent to each wheel.

- ☑ Pressures should be checked daily when the tyres are cold.

- ☑ The recommended tolerance for tyre pressures is -0% to +5%.

- ☑ The pressure of all tyres on a machine should be equal.

- ☑ Air should be added, if required, inflating to the pressure specified in the manufacturer's manual.

- ☑ Personnel inflating tyres should stand a minimum of three metres away from the tyre and outside the likely explosion trajectory to avoid injury in the event of a failure. This will require at least three metres of airline between the nozzle and airline trigger mechanism.

- ☑ Personnel should ensure that they stand to one side of the tyre facing the tread when inflating.

- ☑ Tyre valves should be checked to ensure that they are not leaking. Valve stem caps should always be replaced.

 A real life example of tyre issues

A telehandler operator had been checking the tyre pressures on his machine. Having completed the checks, he was walking away from the machine and one of the tyres exploded. Subsequent investigation revealed that the tyre, which had recently been replaced, was 14 ply with a 3.5 tonne load rating rather than the manufacturer's specification of 16 ply with a six tonne rating.

The contractor also found that the tyre had been ordered from their approved supplier by asking for a tyre for that model of telehandler, without any mention of ply or load rating. A subsequent check of other machines found that 30% were fitted with incorrect tyres.

Tyre damage

All tyres should be inspected daily. The tread and side walls should be checked for:

- ☑ bulges and separation

- ☑ cuts.

For pneumatic tyres, when any cut, rip or tear is discovered that exposes sidewall or tread area cords in the tyre, measures must be taken to remove the product from service immediately. Arrangements must be made for replacement of the tyre or tyre assembly.

Tyre and wheel replacement

Replacement tyres should be the same size, ply and brand as originally installed. Refer to the appropriate parts manual for ordering information. If not using an approved replacement tyre, the replacement tyres must have the following characteristics:

- ☑ same size as the original

- ☑ equal or greater ply and load rating as the original

- ☑ tyre tread contact width equal or greater than original

- ☑ wheel diameter, width and offset dimensions equal to the original

- ☑ approved for the application by the telehandler manufacturer (including inflation pressure and maximum tyre load).

Unless specifically approved by the telehandler manufacturer, foam-filled or ballast-filled tyre assemblies must not be replaced with pneumatic tyres.

Due to size variations between tyre brands and reduction in diameter due to wear, both tyres on an axle must be replaced at the same time with identical tyres. If tyres on opposite sides are different sizes the telehandler boom will not be vertical when the machine is standing on level ground. This will cause the combined centre of gravity of the telehandler and load to move sideways, which may lead to instability.

Thorough examination of telehandlers

The thorough examination of telehandlers should be carried out in accordance with 7.12 of Chapter C07.

8.9   Excavators used as cranes

The use of excavators for lifting operations, particularly on construction sites, has become more common over the last few years. Excavators and backhoes are designed for rapid earth moving and are not designed for lifting operations as their principal function. When planning a lifting operation, consideration should be given as to whether an excavator is the most appropriate machine, taking into account the type of lift and the duration of the task.

The use of an excavator or backhoe for lifting creates additional hazards for personnel in the vicinity. Under normal circumstances, personnel are kept away from the working area around the bucket of an excavator, as this is considered to be a hazardous area. Where the excavator is used for object handling, however, the slinger has to be in the danger area in order to hook the load onto the hooking device. This puts the slinger at risk of being struck by the load, bucket or excavator arm if the excavator moves without warning.

08

Planning and use of excavators used as cranes

The planning and carrying out of lifting operations with excavators should be in accordance with the principles set out in Chapter C07. In addition the points below should be taken into account.

Excavator requirements when used for lifting

The design of earthmoving machinery for lifting (object handling) is covered by the European standard BS EN 474 Parts 1, 3, 4 and 5.

Any earthmoving machine designed for object handling should have a rated object-handling capacity table available inside the cab. If a rated object-handling capacity table is not available then the machine should not be used for object handling.

 Handling attachments (for example, grab) that do not require the assistance of a person for hooking or guiding are considered to be part of normal earthmoving operations and do not require warning devices and a rated capacity table.

An earthmoving machine used for lifting operations must be fitted with a load hooking device. If the load hooking device is a hook then this should have a clip or other device that prevents a sling slipping off the hook. Many quick hitches provide a load hooking device in the design of the hitch.

If the rated lifting capacity for an excavator or the backhoe portion of a backhoe/loader is greater than one tonne (or the overturning moment is greater than 40,000 Nm) then the machine must be fitted with:

☑ a boom-lowering control device on the raising boom cylinder(s) that meets the requirements of ISO 8643:1997

☑ an acoustic or visual warning device that indicates to the operator when the object-handling capacity or corresponding load moment is reached.

A change in the definition of rated object handling capacity in the latest version of EN 474 has affected new excavators manufactured and CE-marked after 29 December 2009. It requires any new excavator that has a rated capacity of over one tonne, and which is going to be used for lifting, to be fitted with an RCI and check valves.

Previously some manufacturers had been marking the excavator for a rated lifting capacity of one tonne even though it had a rated capacity in excess of this. Excavators manufactured and CE-marked before 29 December 2009 are not affected by these changes.

 Loaders and the loader portion of a backhoe/loader do not require a boom lowering control device or acoustic/visual warning devices.

 Where a risk assessment shows that there is a significant risk of overloading and/or overturning on machines with a rated capacity of one tonne or less, a rated capacity indicator may be required. (Refer to LOLER ACoP and Guidance paragraph 122.)

Suitable slings must be available to attach the load to the excavator. Slings and other lifting accessories should be CE-marked, and marked with the rated capacity (SWL).

Whilst BS 7121 may not specifically refer to excavators used as cranes, compliance with all the appropriate parts of BS 7121 would assist in the provision of safe systems of work as required by Section 2(2) of the Health and Safety at Work Act 1974.

Quick hitches

The quick hitches fitted to excavators and other earthmoving plant make a valuable contribution to the construction process by enabling buckets and other attachments to be attached and detached rapidly, as required. Unfortunately, there have been a significant number of accidents involving the use of quick hitches, which have included a number of fatalities.

When using quick hitches the following precautions should be observed. These precautions are applicable to all types of quick hitch (manual, semi-automatic and all fully automatic types), including those that lock onto both pins. All types of quick hitch can be safely used by competent people within a safe system of work. This will involve planning, training, instruction, communication, supervision and maintenance. However, all types of quick hitch may fail if they are not used and maintained correctly.

☑ Keep other workers away from the machine's working range. Never work under the bucket or attachment and ensure that the operator isolates the controls if there are other workers in the machine's working range. Ensure that your site supervisors enforce this rule.

☑ Make sure that your operators are aware of their personal and legal responsibility to use all quick hitches safely. Serious misuse of quick hitches should always be treated as gross misconduct, which could lead to dismissal or prosecution.

☑ Check that all operators confirm that the quick hitch is properly engaged every time they change an attachment. It is essential that this is done by close inspection at the quick hitch, which will normally entail the operator getting down from the cab. It is best practice to make this a requirement for all quick hitches.

- ☑ Check that site supervisors understand that the operator has to fully confirm that the quick hitch is properly engaged. Make sure site supervisors allow operators time to do this.

- ☑ Check that site supervisors monitor that operators are confirming proper engagement, by spot checks.

- ☑ Check that machines are in good order, and all quick hitches are included in the maintenance plan and subject to proper maintenance.

- ☑ Check that operators and maintenance personnel have specific instructions for the combination of machine, quick hitch and attachment.

- ☑ Confirm that operators are competent to use the specific quick hitch in accordance with the manufacturer's instructions and your safe system of work.

- ☑ Forbid practices such as pick and place (moving attachments without properly engaging the locking devices).

Using quick hitches with other attachments

Contractors may want to use quick hitches with attachments other than a bucket in normal configuration. However, if a specific application, such as the fitting of vibratory hammers or reversing of buckets, is not explicitly allowed by the manufacturer, the user should assume that it is not allowed, and should not use the quick hitch for this attachment or application. Quick hitches should only be used with attachments and in applications as specified by the manufacturer.

 It is essential that operators get out of the cab to physically ensure that all quick hitches are securely locked before starting work with a new attachment.

 For further detailed guidance on quick hitches refer to the Strategic Forum for Construction's *Safe use of quick hitches on excavators* (Best practice guide).

Lifting of persons with excavators

Excavators should not be used under any circumstances for the lifting of persons as they are primarily designed for excavating with a bucket and consequently are capable of operating speeds and movements that make them totally unsuitable for the lifting of persons.

Load attachment

Where the hooking device (the point on the machine designed for connection of the load) is not part of the bucket, the bucket should (where possible, and unless the manufacturer's instructions specify otherwise) be removed in order to improve visibility and reduce the weight being lifted. If the bucket is retained, then the weight of both the bucket and quick hitch has to be added to the load when determining whether the load is within the rated capacity.

 When attaching lifting slings to the hooking device or lifting point care should be taken to ensure that the slings and their attachments are able to hang free at all times.

Attachment using a shackle may limit rotation if, for example, a pipe suspended from the slings is to be turned end to end

Using a swivel to overcome this problem

 If the quick hitch is tilted backwards and/or the dipper arm is raised, the master link of the sling and any attachments may bend or twist – possibly leading to damage or failure.

Hitch tilted backwards with master link subject to bending

Hitch tilted backwards with master link subject to twisting

 Chain and master link can hang freely without obstruction.

 For further guidance on planning and carrying out lifting operations with excavators refer to the Construction Plant-hire Association's *Guidance on lifting operations in construction when using excavators*.

Maintenance, checks and inspections of excavators used as cranes

Excavators should be checked, maintained and inspected in accordance with 7.11 of Chapter C07.

Thorough examination of excavators used as cranes

The thorough examination of excavators used as cranes should be carried out in accordance with 7.12 of Chapter C07. In addition the points below should be taken into account.

Thorough examination of quick hitches

Quick hitches used for lifting fall under the thorough examination requirements of the Lifting Operations and Lifting Equipment Regulations (LOLER), whilst those not used for lifting fall under the inspection requirements of the Provision and Use of Work Equipment Regulations (PUWER).

The periodic examination and/or inspection of quick hitches forms a vital addition to planned preventive maintenance. It provides evidence of the adequacy of a maintenance regime and highlights any deficiencies, leading to improved reliability and safety of the hitch being used.

The requirements for examination and/or inspection vary with the type of hitch. Consequently the type of examination/inspection and the frequency at which it occurs is a decision for the competent person carrying out the examination/inspection.

 For information on the legal minimum requirements for quick hitches see the current version of the HSE's Sector information minute 02/2007/01. In all cases, seek guidance from the competent person regarding the most appropriate regime for a particular hitch.

The nature and extent of both LOLER thorough examinations and PUWER inspections are risk based and since the risks associated with quick hitch failure are similar for lifting and non-lifting duties, best practice requires that all quick hitches:

☑ that remain permanently fitted to a machine, are thoroughly examined and/or inspected at the same time as the base machine

☑ suitable for lifting (fitted with a lifting eye), which are regularly removed from the machine (as interchangeable equipment), are subjected to a periodic thorough examination at intervals not exceeding six months.

All quick hitches subject to thorough examination must be permanently marked with a unique identification number. If a quick hitch does not have such a number, the owner/user must ensure that one is applied.

Reports of thorough examination should contain the details required by Schedule 1 of LOLER. *(Refer to Appendix D of Chapter C07 Lifting operations.)*

Thorough examinations should be carried out by competent persons who have the genuine authority and independence to ensure that examinations are properly carried out and that the necessary recommendations arising from them are made impartially.

Thorough examination/inspection following major alteration, damage or incident

If the quick hitch has been subjected to major alteration, repair, damage or has been involved in an incident, it should be thoroughly examined/inspected before it is put back into service.

 Examples of a major alteration include alteration of attachment mechanisms, attachment of lifting eyes, modification of pin bores, application of heat, and so on.

8.10 Lifting accessories

08

Ropes, chains, eye bolts and slings are all examples of lifting accessories. They must be clearly marked with their safe working load.

All lifting accessories must also be:

☑ properly constructed and maintained

☑ free of any defect or damage likely to affect their strength

☑ regularly maintained and inspected

☑ thoroughly examined

☑ securely attached to the lifting equipment (for example, the crane) and the load

☑ used within their safe working load.

Accessories used for lifting must be inspected and thoroughly examined at a maximum of six monthly intervals, with records kept as specified in Chapter C07.

Marking

All lifting accessories must be clearly marked with their rated capacity (SWL) and carry an identifying mark. Where this is not possible then a coding system (such as a tag or colour code) should be used to allow the user to determine the safe working load. A lifting accessory may also be marked with its own weight, which is a consideration when assessing the total load to be lifted.

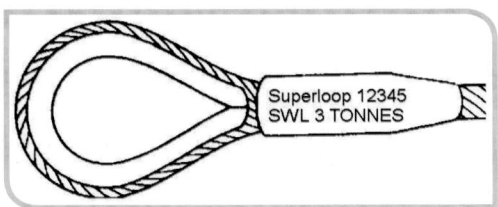

Where the rated capacity (SWL) depends on the configuration of a lifting accessory (such as a two leg chain) then the rated capacity (SWL) for each configuration should be clearly marked on the equipment using a tag or by a chart available at the point of use.

Overloading

Lifting accessories must never be overloaded except under test conditions authorised by an experienced and competent person.

Preventing damage

The edges and corners of a load should be packed to prevent sharp edges damaging lifting ropes, chains or slings.

Hooks

All hooks used for lifting must be fitted with a safety catch, or should be moused, or otherwise shaped to prevent the sling eye or load coming off the hook.

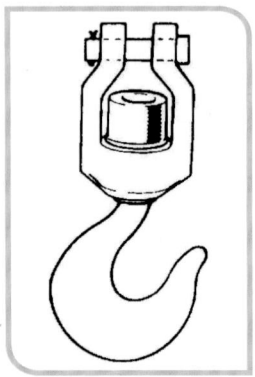
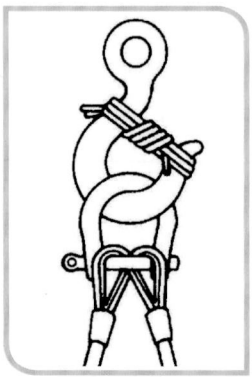
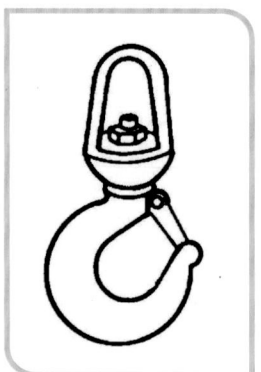
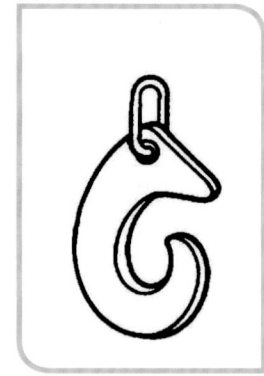

Open top swivel hook   *Moused hook*   *Hook with spring*   *'C' hook with link-loaded safety catch*

Slings

Slings must be attached correctly to the lifting equipment by an approved method, either by securing the ring directly onto the hook if size permits, or by use of a suitable shackle, fitted with the pin of the shackle on the hook and the load suspended from the bow.

The correct method of slinging will vary with the types of load, the different materials or items lifted. It is essential to see that the load is secure. Care must be taken to see that slings are not damaged, and suspect or defective slings must be discarded.

Dog ropes or tag lines, securely attached to the end of the load, should be used when handling long or large loads, to direct the load into position and prevent it spinning. Tag lines should be as short as possible.

Multiple slings (two-legged, three-legged, and so on) must be connected by a ring or shackle and the load properly distributed so that no leg is overloaded. Chandelier lifting (using each leg to lift a load at different heights) must not be undertaken when using multi-legged slings as this would place the slinger in danger when detaching the load.

When in use, the angles between sling legs should be less than 90°. At angles greater than this, the strain on each leg increases very rapidly to a point where they may break because of overloading.

With a simple two-legged parallel sling, the load on each leg is half the total load. As the angle between sling legs increases, the load on each sling leg increases to approximately double at an angle of 120°.

With a sling angle of 90°, the rated capacity (SWL) of the sling should be at least 43% greater than the nominal weight of the load.

e.g. The load in each sling leg increases as the angle between the sling legs is increased as shown in the diagram below

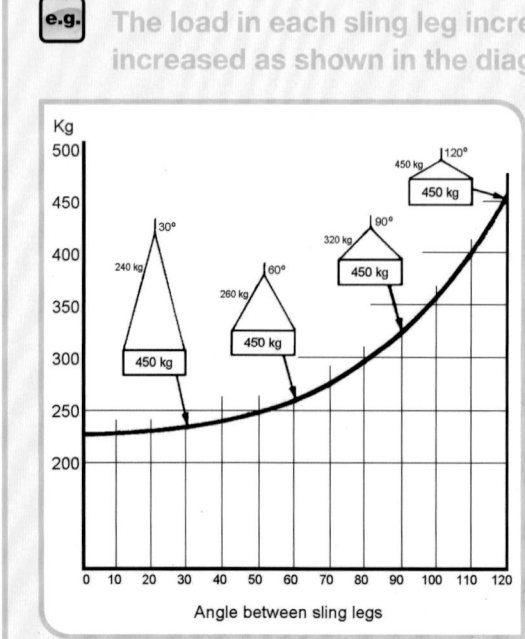

Repaired lifting accessories

Any lifting accessory (chain, sling, and so on) that has been altered or repaired by welding must be thoroughly examined and tested before taking it back into use. The record of thorough examination should be kept until at least the next scheduled thorough examination.

Knotted ropes, chains or slings and those that have been shortened or joined by nuts and bolts through the links must not be used.

Any lifting accessory that is thought to have suffered a loss of strength, been damaged or overloaded, or is otherwise defective, should be withdrawn from use and quarantined. The equipment should be scrapped or re-examined by a competent person who will recommend that either it can be put back into service or must be disposed of.

Construction of slings

Slings are available in a wide range of styles made from many different materials to suit particular purposes.

Chain slings are made from various grades of steel. They can stretch and the links, rings or hooks may become distorted and fracture if subject to excess stress.

Chain slings should only be shortened by using the correct shortening clutches. Chains must not be knotted or joined by nuts and bolts. Hooks must be of the 'C' type or fitted with a safety latch.

Wire rope slings are made from drawn steel wire. Each leg of the sling will have an eye formed at either end. Wire rope slings may be damaged when kinked sharply or if put under stress when twisted. Steel wire rope may be damaged by corrosion through poor care and storage.

Wire rope slings must not be made up on site using bulldog grips.

Wire ropes and slings are of many different types of construction, each having properties related to usage. It is therefore important, when ordering an item, to specify the intended use.

Fibre rope slings might be made from natural fibres (manila, sisal, hemp) or synthetic fibres. Slings made from natural fibres can be prone to rotting. Only purpose-made slings, clearly marked with their rated capacity (SWL), should be used on site.

On no account should slings be fabricated from lengths of rope found lying around the site. Fibre rope slings are more easily cut or damaged, and should be visually examined by a competent person every time before use to ensure they are serviceable. Natural fibre ropes should not be used for making up slings on site.

Synthetic fibre ropes do not rot but can be affected by some chemicals. Care should be taken to avoid contamination with alkalis or acids. Suspect or contaminated synthetic fibre ropes and slings must not be used.

Flat lifting slings are used where special lifting operations are required and afford a certain amount of protection to the load.

Flat and round slings may be made of woven synthetic materials (such as nylon, polyester, polypropylene and Terylene) with 'eyes' sewn in, or plastic-coated wire mesh, or formed by a series of plaited wire ropes between two end fittings. These might also be covered with a plastic material. All woven materials are prone to damage and should be regularly checked for serviceability. Slings should be protected from sharp edges and placed evenly about the load, not twisted. Care must be taken to see that the rated capacity (SWL) is not reduced by having a sling angle greater than 90°.

Shackles

Two types of shackle are commonly used in lifting operations. They are the bow type shackle and dee type shackle, both of which are available with threaded or plain pins.

Only bow type shackles may be used to suspend a load from a hook. The shackle must be positioned with the pin across the hook and the load suspended from the bow. If necessary, spacers should be fitted over the pin to centralise the shackle on the hook.

Overloading, out-of-balance loads and misuse can distort shackles; they should be checked regularly for shape and wear.

Eyebolts

Eyebolts are made to screw into or through a load and may be plain (dynamo) or have collars, with or without links. The plain eyebolt is good only for vertical loading. Even when a collared eyebolt is used, the safe working load is reduced if the load to which it is attached initially lifted at an angle.

Collared eyebolts with links may be used providing the angle of load to the axis of eyebolt thread does not exceed 15°. Over 15°, safe working loads must be derated in accordance with BS EN ISO 3266 *Forged steel eyebolts Grade 4* for general lifting purposes.

When installed, the collar must be at right angles to the hole, should be in full contact with the surface, and be properly tightened.

The load should always be applied in the plane of the eye, never in the other direction. If necessary, washers or shims should be inserted below the collar to ensure that the eye is correctly aligned when tight.

Extreme care must be taken to ensure that metric threaded eyebolts are not inserted in imperial threaded holes. Although these might appear to match, it is an interference fit only, and the mechanical strength may be almost nothing.

Bulldog grips (wire rope grips)

Bulldog grips, if used properly to make an eye with a thimble, provide a simple and effective means of securing the ends of wire ropes instead of splicing or socketing. The final rated capacity (SWL) will be about 75% of that of the wire. It is essential that the correct size and type of grip is used, that the wire is clean and that the correct torque is applied when tightening the grips.

Bulldog grips must be fitted with the 'U' bolt on the dead or tail end of the line (non-load-bearing end). There must be no deviation from this practice.

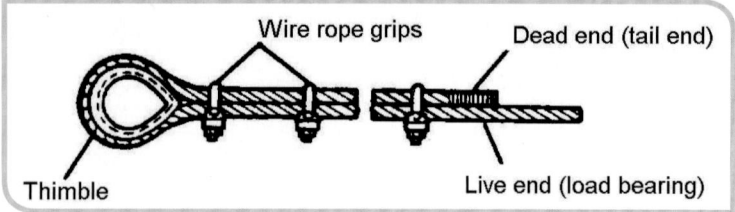

Correct method of fitting wire rope grips

 The number of wire rope grips shown in the above illustration is insufficient. The figure is schematic only.

Wire rope grips meeting the requirements of BS EN 13411 are efficient when correctly installed by a competent person. Generally, when using wire rope grips, the previous numbers of grips should be used and they should be tightened to the relevant torque. However, in all cases, the manufacturer's recommendations, in addition to the advice given in the standard, should be closely followed.

Maximum nominal rope diameter (mm)	Required number of wire rope grips	Tightening torque required (Nm)
5	3	2.0
6.5	3	3.5
8	4	6.0
10	4	9.0
12	4	20.0
14	4	33.0
16	4	49.0
19	4	68.0
22	5	107.0
26	5	147.0
30	6	212.0
34	6	296.0
40	6	363.0

The wire should be in good condition and all threads and nuts should be suitably greased.

The first bulldog grip should be fitted as close as possible to the thimble and, thereafter, at a spacing of no greater than six times the rope diameter.

Nuts must be tightened to the relevant torque:

☑ when the rope is assembled

☑ when taken into use

☑ on the application of the load

☑ at periodic intervals when in continuous use.

If the above criteria are not followed, then the strength of the eye and thimble will be considerably reduced. If the criteria are neglected for an extended period, the eye and thimble may fail.

Wire rope grips must not be used to make lifting slings, long splices, or to join two wire ropes, other than with thimbles or eyes.

For intermediate diameters of rope, the next larger size wire rope grip should be used, except as follows:

☑ the size 5 mm grip should only be used on a nominal 5 mm diameter rope

☑ for 11 mm diameter rope, use four 10 mm rope grips tightened to a torque of 14 Nm.

Maintenance, checks and inspections of lifting accessories

Lifting accessories should be checked, maintained and inspected in accordance with 7.11 of Chapter C07.

Thorough examination of lifting accessories

The thorough examination of lifting accessories should be carried out in accordance with 7.12 of Chapter C07.

Appendix A – Further information

Legislation

The Provision and Use of Work Equipment Regulations

> HSE books *Safe use of work equipment* (L22)

The Lifting Operations and Lifting Equipment Regulations

> HSE books *Safe use of lifting equipment* (L113)

Standards

Code of practice for safe use of cranes — Part 1: General (BS 7121-1:2006)

Code of practice for safe use of cranes — Part 2: Inspection, testing and examination (BS 7121-2:2003)

Code of practice for safe use of cranes — Part 3: Mobile cranes (BS 7121-3:2003)

Code of practice for safe use of cranes — Part 4: Lorry loaders (BS 7121-4:2010)

Code of practice for safe use of cranes — Part 5: Tower cranes (BS 7121-5:2003)

Code of practice for safe use of construction hoists (BS 7212:2006)

Code of practice for the installation, maintenance, thorough examination and safe use of mast climbing work platforms (MCWPs) (BS 7981:2002)

Code of practice for safe use of MEWPs (BS 8460:2005)

Strategic Forum for Construction Plant Safety Group

Safe use of quick hitches (Best practice guide)

Safe use of telehandlers in construction (Best practice guide)

Avoiding trapping and crushing in MEWPs (Best practice guide)

Tower crane working conditions (Best practice guide)

Tower crane operations – Minimum competency requirements (Best practice guide)

Medical fitness to operate construction plant (Best practice guide)

Guidance on the planning and liaison process for the erection, climbing and dismantling of tower cranes

Construction Plant-hire Association

Guidance on lifting operations in construction when using excavators (Best practice guide)

Maintenance, inspection and thorough examination of construction hoists (Best practice guide)

Work at height on construction hoists (Best practice guide)

Transporting scaffolding in construction hoists (Best practice guide)

Safeguarding requirements for landing gates on goods-only hoists (Best practice guide)

Transport platforms – Installation, use, maintenance, inspection, examination and testing (Best practice guide)

Work at height whilst loading and unloading transport (Best practice guide)

Safe use of lorry loaders (Best practice guide)

Maintenance, inspection and thorough examination of mobile cranes (Best practice guide)

Crane hire and contract lifting (Best practice guide)

Work at height on mobile cranes (Best practice guide)

Risk assessment and method statement for a contract lift (Best practice guide)

Climbing of tower cranes (Best practice guide)

Maintenance, inspection and thorough examination of tower cranes (Best practice guide)

Safe use of top slew tower cranes (Best practice guide)

Safe use of self-erecting tower cranes (Best practice guide)

Tower crane operator's handbook

Technical information notes

Construction Industry Research and Information Association (CIRIA)

Crane stability on site, 2003 (C703)

Tower crane stability, 2006 (C654)

Airport Operators' Association (AOA)

Cranes and planes – A guide to procedures for operation of cranes in the vicinity of aerodromes

Off-highway Plant and Equipment Research Centre

A voluntary code of practice for the safe use of cranes in and around airports

Lifting Equipment Engineers' Association

Code of practice for the safe use of lifting equipment

 All HSE publications can be downloaded without charge from the HSE website.

All Strategic Forum for Construction Plant Safety Group and Construction Plant-hire Association publications are available to download without charge from the CPA's website.

Index

abrasive wheels 65–69
access 4
    see also exclusion zones; gates; guards and guarding;
    pedestrian routes; security; traffic routes
access equipment 64–65
    see also hoists; ladders; mobile elevating work platforms;
    scaffolding
access for emergency services 15, 16, 21, 22, 31
access restriction for fixing tool work 69, 71
access to excavations 5
access to multi-storey buildings 26
access to site offices 5
access to/for plant and equipment 84, 94, 95, 101–102,
131, 132
airports 101, 121
appointed persons see competent/appointed persons
arson 12, 13, 17, 21
articulating and telescopic boom MEWPs 125
asbestos 3, 8
assisted erected cranes 122

barrow hoists 134
base materials for cartridge-operated tools 71
basic lifts 94–95
Beaufort scale 114
bitumen boilers 22, 40
bonfires 17, 20–21
brakes 74, 84
brick carriers see inclined hoists
bulldog grips 147–148
buried services 2, 43, 83
    see also utility services
burning see bonfires; fire; hot work

carbonaceous material fires 38
cartridge-operated tools 69–72
CE marks 62, 63, 82, 93, 142
chain slings 147
chainsaws 75
chandelier lifting 146
cherry pickers 124
cleaning and cleanliness 3, 7
    see also tidiness; waste management
clearances for flammable materials storage 23, 24
clearances for lifting equipment 99, 101, 104, 121
clearances for site accommodation 29
clothes care and changing facilities 5, 19
co-operation 8, 53
co-ordination 48, 53
colour-coding of abrasive wheels 66
colour-coding of cartridges 70
colour-coding of electrical distribution equipment 44–45
colour-coding of fire extinguishers 27
combustible metals fires 28, 39
communication 4, 15, 93, 97, 102
    see also radio communication/control; signals and signalling
competence 8, 53, 77, 86, 87, 98
competency cards 8, 77, 87, 98
competent/appointed persons for hired cranes 119
competent/appointed persons for lifting operations and
equipment 61, 93, 94–95, 96, 97, 98, 101, 102, 106, 108, 122,
131, 133
complex lifts 95, 98, 104
compressors 63, 76
concrete pumps 86
confined spaces 24, 27, 101, 128
Confined Spaces Regulations 24
Construction (Design and Management) Regulations 8, 15,
53, 61
construction hoists see hoists
construction phase plans 2, 6, 15, 54
consultation 8
contract lifts 119

contractors 12, 48–49, 53, 55
control of lifting operations 97–98
Control of Noise at Work Regulations 62
Control of Substances Hazardous to Health Regulations 62
Control of Vibration at Work Regulations 61
conventional tower cranes 122
cooking appliances 13, 19, 23, 28, 30, 40
crane co-ordinators 108
crane jibs on telehandlers 140
crane (lift) supervisors 95, 97, 98, 102, 108
crane operators 108
cranes 92, 104
    see also excavators as cranes; hired cranes; mobile cranes;
    scaffold cranes; scaffold hoists; tower cranes
cutting and cutting equipment see diamond blades; hot work;
woodworking machines

dangerous occurrence notification 92
Dangerous Substances and Explosive Atmospheres
Regulations 24
demolition 3, 11
diamond blades 67
Disability Discrimination Act 30
drainage 4, 7, 83, 131
drinking water supplies 4
dumpers see forward-tipping dump trucks
dust see respiratory protection

electric shock 42, 49
electrical fires 39–40, 49
electrical power requirements 43, 44
electrical safety posters 42
electrical work and equipment 13, 17, 20, 23, 24, 27, 28, 41–50
Electricity at Work Regulations 43, 48, 121, 128
electricity distribution 2, 13, 20, 44–46
electricity supply 4, 5, 43–44, 74, 121, 128
emergency controls 125–126
    see also safety devices; start/stop controls
emergency lighting 31
emergency procedures 5, 6, 10–11, 16, 30, 122, 125, 126,
127, 133
    see also electric shock; fire action plans; fire drills; first aid
emergency routes and exits 6, 7, 15, 16, 18, 21, 25, 26, 29–30
emergency services 6, 8, 15, 16, 18, 21–22, 26, 31, 122
enclosed spaces 24, 27, 101, 127–128
enforcement of fire safety law 37
entrapment on MEWPs 125, 128
environmental factors 7
    see also pollution
examination see inspection; thorough examination
excavations 5, 55, 83
excavators as cranes 63, 141–145
exclusion zones 128, 139, 142
exhaust gas emissions 101, 127
explosive substances 11, 16, 17, 24–25
    see also LPG
eye protection 7, 65, 68, 73, 74
eyebolts 147

fall-arrest and suspension equipment 99, 126–127
fall prevention 4, 132
    see also guards and guarding
falling object protection 84, 85, 134
falsework 52, 55
fibre rope slings 147
finished surfaces protection 20
fire, nature of 38–40
fire action notices 15, 18, 29
fire action plans 13, 14, 15–16, 26, 30, 36
fire alarms 5, 6, 7, 15, 16, 18, 21, 26, 29, 31
Fire and Rescue Service see emergency services
fire blankets 28, 30
fire detection systems 15, 16, 18, 24, 27, 29

fire drills 15, 16, 18, 30
    see also emergency procedures
fire extinguishers 6, 7, 14, 20, 22, 24, 25, 26–28, 30, 40
fire-fighting equipment 15, 16, 19, 21, 22, 26–28, 30
fire hazards 12–13, 14, 16–17
fire hose reels 28
fire marshals 14, 15, 21
fire prevention and control 6, 7, 9–40
fire risk assessments 12–14, 26, 32–35
fire risk management 11–16, 17–22, 26, 36
fire wardens 6, 14, 30
first aid 6
    see also electric shock
fitness 77, 87, 98–99
flammable materials 6, 12, 13, 16, 17, 20, 21, 22, 23–25, 28
    see also LPG
flammable materials fires 39, 40
flammable materials signs and notices 7, 23, 24, 25
flammable materials storage 4, 12, 13, 16, 17, 19, 21, 23, 24–25, 29
    see also fuel storage
flat lifting slings 147
food preparation 5
foot protection 83
formwork 52, 55
forward-tipping dump trucks 86
foundations 121, 131
    see also ground conditions
frequency of thorough examination 106
fuel storage 16, 25, 40, 128
    see also flammable materials storage
fuels 4, 7, 13, 25, 128
    see also gas-powered tools; gases; LPG

gantry hoists see trestle/beam hoists
gas-powered tools 72
    see also hot work
gases 13, 19
    see also exhaust gas emissions; flammable materials
gates 2, 3
gates of hoists 132, 133, 134
generators 4, 43, 128
gin wheels 135
gloves 7, 74
goods hoists 129, 133, 134
'grey' imports 63
ground conditions 2, 5, 83, 94, 96, 100, 126, 130, 131, 137–138
    see also buried services; foundations; siting of lifting
    equipment
guards and guarding 5, 65, 68, 73, 74, 75, 83, 84
    see also access; security

hand-arm vibration 68, 74, 76
hand-held plant and equipment 63–64
    see also abrasive wheels; hand tools; portable tools/
    appliances; woodworking machines
hand signals see signals and signalling
hand tools 13, 20, 62, 64
handover of hoists 133
hazard identification 47–48, 94, 95, 96, 131
hazardous vapours 27
hazardous waste 7, 8, 70
head protection 72
Health and Safety (Safety Signs and Signals) Regulations 25, 30
hearing protection 7, 62, 69, 72, 73, 74
heating 4, 5, 13, 19, 23
hidden wiring location 47–48
high-visibility clothing 84
higher risk projects 13, 18, 21, 22, 25–26, 29
hired cranes 119
hoists 63, 92, 128–135
hooks 103, 104, 135, 140, 142, 146, 147
hose reels 28

hot work 12, 13, 15, 16, 22, 40
housekeeping see cleaning and cleanliness; tidiness; waste
management
human factors 8

inclined hoists 130, 134, 135
incomplete hoists 132
induction training 6, 7, 13, 15, 18, 28, 42
inspection of electrical equipment 13, 20, 75
inspection of emergency routes and exits 15
inspection of excavations 5
inspection of fire extinguishers 27
inspection of flammable gas/liquid distribution systems 13
inspection of lifting accessories 145, 148
inspection of lifting equipment 93, 94, 105, 119–120, 122, 133, 134, 140–141
inspection of LPG equipment 24
inspection of plant and equipment 64, 77–78, 86, 88
inspection of quick hitches 86, 87, 144–145
inspection of scaffolding 5, 64
inspection of temporary works 54
intermediate lifts 95
isolation of electrical circuits 43, 47, 49

ladders 5, 64
landings of hoists 132
life jackets 127
lift categories 93–95, 109–110
lift supervisors 95, 97, 98, 102, 108
lifting accessories 145–148
    see also hooks; slings/slinging
lifting equipment 4, 62, 63, 82, 84, 94, 96, 97, 104, 108, 117–150
    see also ground conditions
lifting of persons 61, 99, 104, 134, 140, 143
    see also mobile elevating work platforms; passengers
lifting operations 2, 61, 91–116
Lifting Operations and Lifting Equipment Regulations 54, 60–61, 63, 93, 96, 99, 120, 134, 144, 145
    see also thorough examination
lifting plans 93–97, 98, 100, 101, 119, 122, 128, 131, 133, 137, 141–144
lighting 13, 16, 18, 20, 23, 31, 46, 61, 85
liquefied gases fires 39
    see also LPG
load complexity 93–94
load control devices 104, 105
lorry loaders 123
LPG 7, 16, 23–24, 128
    see also liquefied gases fires

maintenance of abrasive wheels 67
maintenance of compressed air equipment 76
maintenance of electrical equipment 20
maintenance of fire extinguishers 27
maintenance of flammable gas/liquid distribution systems 13
maintenance of lifting accessories 148
maintenance of lifting equipment 105, 119–120, 122, 140–141
maintenance of plant and equipment 63, 77–78, 86, 88
maintenance of PPE 7
maintenance of quick hitches 86, 142–143
maintenance of traffic routes 83
Management of Health and Safety at Work Regulations 12, 83
manually operated hand-held plant and equipment 63–64
manuals 88, 103
marking of lifting equipment/accessories 103–104, 145
materials for temporary works 55
materials storage and lay-down areas 2, 4, 84, 131
medical fitness 77, 87, 98–99
method statements 48, 49, 75, 83
    see also lifting plans
misfires 72
mobile cranes 63, 102, 104–105, 108, 118–120

mobile elevating work platforms 5, 63, 123–128
    see also lifting of persons
mobile plant and equipment 63, 81–89, 142
    see also forward-tipping dump trucks; lifting equipment;
      mobile elevating work platforms; pedestrian-controlled
      equipment; traffic routes; vehicles
mounting of abrasive wheels/diamond blades 67
multi-boom articulated MEWPs 125
multistorey buildings 22, 26
multiple lifting 104–105
multiple slings 146

noise 7, 43, 62, 68–69, 73, 101, 128
    see also hearing protection
non-rotating telehandlers 136
Notification of Conventional Tower Crane Regulations 122

overhead cables 2, 43, 83, 100–101
oxy-fuel sets 13

parking 3, 83
    see also start-up prevention
parking brakes *see* brakes
part-erected hoists 132
passenger/goods hoists 129, 133, 134
passengers 82, 93, 94
    see also lifting of persons
pedestrian-controlled equipment 83, 103
pedestrian routes 3, 83
    see also traffic routes
permits for bonfires 17, 20
permits for electrical work 48, 49, 50
permits for hot work 13, 15, 16, 22
permits for temporary works 55
personal protective equipment 6–7, 49, 61, 65, 69, 72–73, 75,
76, 84, 98
    see also respiratory protection
Personal Protective Equipment at Work Regulations 61
plant and equipment 3, 13, 17, 44–45, 55, 59–80, 108
    see also electrical work and equipment; lifting equipment;
      mobile plant and equipment
pollution 6, 7, 24, 43, 128
    see also exhaust gas emissions; waste management
portable tools/appliances 5, 13, 20, 46, 69–73, 74–75
    see also fire extinguishers; hand tools
power breakers *see* residual current devices (RCDs)
pre-construction information for temporary works 53
Pressure Systems Safety Regulations 61, 76
protected species 3, 7
protective footwear 83
Provision and Use of Work Equipment Regulations 54, 60, 62,
92–93, 144, 145
pumps 63, 76–77
    see also concrete pumps

quick hitches 86–87, 88, 136–137, 142–145

radio communication/control 98, 102, 103, 123
railways 101
rated capacities of lifting equipment 94, 103–104, 105, 108,
133, 135, 140, 142, 143, 145, 146, 147
rated capacities of mobile plant and equipment 82
recoil 72
records of abrasive wheels 67
records of emergency lighting tests 31
records of fire prevention and control 12, 14, 16, 27, 29
records of lifting equipment/accessories 94, 96, 97, 105, 145
records of plant and equipment 61, 64, 77–78, 87, 88
records of temporary works 55
repaired lifting accessories 147
reports on lifting operations 106–107, 113, 145
rescue procedures *see* emergency procedures
residual current devices (RCDs) 45, 46, 74

respiratory protection 7, 27, 68, 74
responsible persons 11, 12, 15, 31
restraint systems 82, 84, 85, 126, 139
restricted spaces 24, 27, 101, 127–128
retrofitting of brakes 74
ricochet 71
ride on plant 82
risk assessments for abrasive wheel work 68
risk assessments for electrical work and equipment 46, 48, 49
risk assessments for fire 12–14, 26, 32–35
risk assessments for lifting operations and equipment 93,
94–95, 96, 100, 105, 131, 133, 137, 138, 140, 142
risk assessments for plant and equipment 77, 83, 84, 88, 127
risk assessments for pollution 7
risk assessments for portable fixing tools 73
risk assessments for woodworking machines 74, 75
risk assessments for work at height 4
risk assessments for work over water 127
risk management 11–16, 17–22, 26, 36, 46, 83
roads 2, 3, 4, 20, 86
    see also traffic routes
roll-over protective structures (ROPS) 84
roof tile carriers *see* inclined hoists
rotating telehandlers 136
rough terrain handlers *see* telehandlers

safe working loads *see* rated capacities
safety devices 70, 74, 134, 135, 146
    see also emergency controls; residual current devices
      (RCDs); start/stop controls; warnings and warning devices
safety harnesses *see* fall-arrest and suspension equipment
safety helmets 73
safety representatives 8
scaffold cranes 134
scaffold hoists 128, 130, 134
scaffolding 5, 55, 62, 64, 131, 132, 135
scissor lifts 124, 126, 128
seat belts *see* restraint systems
security 3, 23, 24, 29, 85, 103, 122, 128
    see also arson; start-up prevention
shackles 146, 147
signals and signalling 84, 85, 97, 98, 102, 105, 111–112, 133
signs and notices 6, 7
    see also fire action notices
signs and notices for abrasive wheels 66, 68, 69
signs and notices for electrical work and equipment 42, 49
signs and notices for escape routes 18, 30, 31
signs and notices for flammable materials 7, 23, 24, 25
signs and notices for hoists 133
signs and notices for lifting equipment 103
site accommodation/offices 3, 5, 6, 7, 8, 16, 29–31, 35, 46
    see also temporary buildings
site organisation 1–8
site surveys 96, 131
Site Waste Management Plans (SWMPs) 7
siting of lifting equipment 99–103, 121, 130–131
    see also ground conditions
skin protection 74
skips *see* waste management
slingers/signallers 97, 98, 102
slings/slinging 5, 141, 142, 143, 146, 147
smoke alarms 29
smoking 13, 17, 19, 23
speeds of abrasive wheels 66–67
speeds on traffic routes 83
spillages *see* pollution
stability of telehandlers 137–139
standard lifts *see* intermediate lifts
standards 62
start-up prevention 85
start/stop controls 69, 74, 83
    see also emergency controls; safety devices
storage of abrasive wheels 69

storage of cartridge-operated tools 72
storage of flammable materials 4, 12, 13, 16, 17, 19, 21, 23, 24–25
storage of fuels 16, 25, 40, 128
storage of hazardous waste 7
storage of materials 2, 4, 84, 131
storage of PPE 7
sub-contractors for temporary works 53
suitability of base materials 71
suitability of plant and equipment 63
supervision 49, 69, 86, 88, 92, 99, 105, 142
Supply of Machinery (Safety) Regulations 62, 82, 93

tandem lifting see multiple lifting
telecommunications facilities 4, 5
telehandlers 63, 85, 135–141
telescopic boom MEWPs 124
temporary buildings 5, 16, 29, 35
    see also site accommodation/offices
temporary lighting 13
temporary works 2, 51–57
testing of cartridge-operated tools 71, 72
testing of electrical work and equipment 13, 45, 46
testing of emergency lighting 31
testing of fire alarms and detection systems 15, 18, 29
    see also fire drills
testing of fire-fighting appliances 15, 27
testing of lifting equipment 103, 107, 120, 147
testing of LPG pipework 23
testing of portable tools/appliances 5, 13, 20, 46
thorough examination of excavators as cranes 144–145
thorough examination of hoists 133, 134
thorough examination of lifting accessories 94, 135, 145, 147, 148
thorough examination of lifting equipment 61, 63, 93, 94, 106–107, 108, 113, 135
thorough examination of mobile cranes 120
thorough examination of mobile plant and equipment 82
thorough examination of quick hitches 144–145
thorough examination of tower cranes 122
through penetration by cartridge-operated tools 71, 72
tidiness 4, 13, 16, 17, 18, 19, 29, 69, 83
    see also cleaning and cleanliness; waste management
timber-frame structures 11, 13, 22, 25–26, 29
tool rests for abrasive wheels 68
tools see hand tools; plant and equipment
tower cranes 52, 63, 102, 121–123
traffic routes 3, 7, 61, 83, 137
    see also roads
training at induction 6, 7, 13, 15, 18, 28, 42
training for abrasive wheel work 65, 67
training for compressed air work 76
training for electrical safety 43
training for fall-arrest equipment use 127
training for fire extinguisher use 6, 14, 20, 22, 26, 27, 28, 30
training for fire prevention and control 14, 16, 28, 30, 31
training for lifting operations 92, 98, 130, 133, 140
training for plant and equipment 77, 86, 87
training for pollution control 7
training for portable fixing tool use 69, 72
training for woodworking machine use 73, 75
transport platforms 129
trestle/beam hoists 128, 130, 134

utility services 4
    see also buried services

variable reach trucks see telehandlers
vehicles 5, 81–90, 128
    see also fuels; mobile plant and equipment; parking; traffic routes
ventilation 23, 24, 27, 68, 72, 101
vertical lift MEWPs 124, 126

vibration 61, 68, 74, 76
visibility 84, 85, 133, 137
    see also lighting
voltages 44

warnings and warning devices 84, 85, 142
waste management 7–8, 13, 16, 17, 19, 24, 29, 49, 70
    see also bonfires; cleaning and cleanliness; pollution
water 2, 28
    see also drinking water supplies
water safety 127
weather protection 5, 23
welding see hot work
welfare facilities 5, 46
wildlife 3, 7
wind 2, 20, 94, 102, 114, 122, 130, 133
wire rope grips 147–148
wire rope slings 147
woodworking machines 73–75
work at height 4–5, 132
Work at Height Regulations 54, 61, 132
work equipment see plant and equipment
work over water 127
work-restraint systems 126
    see also restraint systems

Contents

Introduction   iii

How to use GE 700   ix

01 The Work at Height Regulations   **1**

02 Safe working on roofs and at height   **15**

03 Common access equipment   **35**

04 Scaffolding   **49**

05 Fall arrest and suspension equipment   **73**

06 Frame erection   **89**

07 Excavations   **97**

08 Underground and overhead services   **107**

09 Confined spaces   **119**

10 Dangerous substances   **133**

Index   **159**

Introduction

Construction site safety covers all aspects of current health, safety and environment issues in the building and construction industry. It is designed to help managers, supervisors and small businesses understand how they should comply with, and put into practice, their legal, moral and social responsibilities.

Construction site safety (GE 700)   iv

About the construction industry   iv

Further supporting information from
CITB-ConstructionSkills   vi

Acknowledgements   vii

Construction site safety (GE 700)

Construction site safety is a leading publication within the construction industry, based on current construction health, safety and environment legislation, guidance and best practice. It will assist in the crucial areas of:

- ☑ accident prevention
- ☑ the avoidance of occupational ill health
- ☑ environmental good practice.

The content has been written with the site manager in mind, with a balance between outlining the requirements of relevant legislation and providing practical guidance on how to comply.

It is divided into the standard structure, which is used across all core CITB-ConstructionSkills publications:

Section A	**Legal and management**
Section B	**Health and welfare**
Section C	General safety
Section D	**High risk activities**
Section E	**Environment**
Section F	**Specialist activities**

Each section within *Construction site safety* is contained within a separate book.

There is also a new additional supporting book:

Section G	**Checklists and forms**

Section G is a collection of information (such as forms and checklists) that can be used on a day-to-day basis when running a site.

The content of *Construction site safety*, which is developed with construction industry experts, is revised annually to take into account the latest changes in legislation and new or updated health, safety and environment industry guidance and best practice.

There is a companion website that will keep users informed of legislation changes, content updates and links to further guidance.

Construction site safety is also available to purchase online or on CD-ROM.

Construction site safety is the official supporting publication for the CITB-ConstructionSkills Site Management Safety Training Scheme (SMSTS), a five-day course for construction site managers.

About the construction industry

Approximately 2.1 million people are employed in the UK construction industry. It includes housing, utilities, repair and maintenance, refurbishment, shop fitting, demolition, roofing, mechanical and electrical, plumbing and highways maintenance.

It is made up of 175,000 construction firms and 90% of companies employ less than 10 workers.

Construction workers (just like you) will die due to work-related ill health. Work-related respiratory disease covers a range of illnesses that are caused or made worse by breathing in hazardous substances (such as construction dust) that damage the lungs.

4,000 people die each year from asbestos-related lung diseases.

500 people (and more each year) are dying from silica-related lung diseases (dust from cutting blocks, kerbs, and so on). Many more suffer from occupational asthma or are forced to leave the industry due to work-related ill health.

Each year there are an estimated 36,000 new cases of work-related ill health with rates of musculoskeletal disorder significantly higher than average.

On average 50 workers are killed each year due to accidents. The biggest killer (around half) is due to falls from height.

Each year approximately 2,500 are seriously injured (broken bones, fractured skull, amputations) and 5,700 have reportable injuries.

The most common cause of injuries is due to manual handling and slips, trips and falls. 60% of all work at height injuries are due to falls from below head height.

Why so many accidents?

Many reports of present day construction accidents and ill health make depressing reading because simple actions were not taken to prevent them. In many cases, those planning the jobs totally failed to consider the health or safety of the people carrying out the work (and possibly others who were affected) and to actively manage the situation.

Common examples of such events include:

☑ the increasing number of workers who suffer from cancers and life changing illnesses from breathing and skin complaints. Some of these force the sufferer to give up work, because exposure to dangerous substances such as dust, are not even considered, let alone prevented or controlled

☑ the deaths and serious injuries that occur because people fall from height. Often basic actions (like using temporary work platforms on fragile roofs, installing edge protection or using a safety harness and lanyard clipped to a strong-point) were simply not taken

☑ workers being buried in collapsed excavations because the sides were unstable or not supported

☑ workers being killed or injured by construction plant because pedestrians were not kept out of the plant operating area.

Achieving a reasonable standard of on-site health and safety need not be difficult. Where the work to be carried out is relatively uncomplicated and familiar, the precautions that need to be taken are in many cases simple and common sense or may require just a little investigation or reading. The crucial decision for anyone with responsibility for on-site health and safety is to know when they have reached the limits of their knowledge and capabilities and therefore need the assistance of someone with specialist knowledge.

Caution should also be exercised when a job is not going to plan and there is the temptation to resort to improvised methods of working. If the person in control is not at ease with the way that things are going they should stop the job, step back and think things through carefully before deciding upon a course of action.

Health and Safety Executive (HSE) research has shown that workers are most vulnerable during their first few days on site.

Setting out

Construction is an exciting industry. It is constantly changing as projects move on and jobs get done. As a result of this a building site is one of the most dangerous environments to work in.

But many accidents that occur on sites can be avoided if everyone on site works together. So a free film *Setting out* explains what the site must do and what you must do to stay healthy and safe at work.

 For further information or to view *Setting out* refer to the CITB-ConstructionSkills website.

This film is essential viewing for everyone involved in construction, and should be watched before sitting the CITB-ConstructionSkills' Health, safety and environment test. The content of the film is captured in summary here, and these principles form the basis for the behavioural case study questions, which are a new element of the test from Spring 2012.

Part 1: What you should expect from the construction industry

Your site and your employer should be doing all they can to keep you and their workforce safe.

Before any work begins the site management team will have been planning and preparing the site for your arrival. It is their job to ensure that you can do your job safely and efficiently.

Five things **the site** you are working on **must do**:

☑ know when you are on site (signing in and out)

☑ give you a site induction

☑ give you site-specific information

☑ encourage communication

☑ keep you up-to-date and informed.

Part 2: What the industry expects of you

Once the work begins, it is up to every individual to take responsibility for carrying out the plan safely. This means you should follow the rules and guidelines as well as being alert to the continuing changes on site.

Five things you **must do**:

☑ respect and follow the site rules

☑ safely prepare each task

☑ do each task responsibly

☑ know when to stop (if you think anything is unsafe)

☑ keep learning.

Every day the work we do improves the world around us. It is time for us to work together to build an industry that puts its people first. By working together we can build a better industry that respects those who work in it.

Introduction

Introduction

Working Well Together

The Working Well Together (WWT) campaign is an industry-led initiative that helps support micro and small businesses improve their health and safety performance. The campaign undertakes a variety of activities, including health and safety awareness days, designer awareness days, breakfast and evening events, roadshows and regional WWT groups.

 To find out how the WWT campaign can help you and your company refer to its website.

Further supporting information from CITB-ConstructionSkills

CITB-ConstructionSkills has a wide range of products, publications and courses that could help to improve your health, safety and environment knowledge.

 To discover more about CITB-ConstructionSkills and the services, publications and courses offered visit the CITB-ConstructionSkills website.

Health, safety and environment publications

Site managers	GE 700 *Construction site safety* (printed, CD and online)
	RACD *Risk assessment and method statement manager*
	SA 03 CD *Health, safety and environmental auditing system*
	DVDs Range of topics including scaffold inspection, worker engagement and sustainability
Supervisors	GE 706 *Site supervision simplified* (printed, CD, online)
	GT 700 *Toolbox talks* (printed, CD, online)
	GT 701 *Safety critical communication toolbox talks* (printed)
Operatives	GE 707 *Safe start*
Health safety and environment test	GT 100 *Health, safety and environment test for operatives and specialists* (printed, DVD, online)
	GT 200 *Health, safety and environment test for managers and professionals* (printed, DVD, online)

Site Safety Plus courses

Directors	Directors role for health and safety course – one day
Site management	Site Management Safety Training Scheme (SMSTS) – five days
Plant managers	Plant Management Safety Training Scheme (SMSTS) – five days
Supervisors	Site Supervisors' Safety Training Scheme (SSSTS) – two days
Operatives	Health safety and environment awareness – one day
Environment	Site Environmental Awareness Training Scheme (SEATS) – one day
Behavioural safety	Achieving Behavioural Change (ABC) – one day
Shopfitting	Site safety for shopfitters and interior contractors – three days

National Construction College

The National Construction College is focused on creating a highly skilled, safe and professional UK construction workforce.
To achieve this, it has more first-class instructors in more locations than any other construction training provider in Europe and offers free professional advice on finding the right training for individuals and companies.

Acknowledgements

CITB-ConstructionSkills wishes to acknowledge the assistance offered by the following organisations in the preparation of this edition of GE 700:

- ☑ Access Industry Forum
- ☑ Arco
- ☑ Balfour Beatty
- ☑ Britannia Safety and Training
- ☑ Civil Engineering Contractors Association
- ☑ Combisafe
- ☑ Construction Plant Association
- ☑ Drilling and Sawing Association
- ☑ eBrit Services Ltd
- ☑ Environment Agency
- ☑ Environmental and Waste Consulting
- ☑ Federation of Master Builders
- ☑ Health and Safety Executive
- ☑ Henry Boot
- ☑ Highways Term Maintenance Association
- ☑ Home Builders Federation
- ☑ J Breheny Contractors Ltd

- ☑ Lead Paint Safety Association
- ☑ MJ Fuller and Associates
- ☑ Makers Construction Ltd
- ☑ May Gurney
- ☑ Montpellier International Consulting
- ☑ National Access and Scaffolding Confederation
- ☑ National Association of Shopfitters
- ☑ National Construction College
- ☑ National Federation of Demolition Contractors
- ☑ Persimmon Homes
- ☑ Prospect – The Union for Professionals
- ☑ Scafftag
- ☑ Temporary Works Forum
- ☑ Union of Construction, Allied Trades and Technicians (UCATT)
- ☑ Unite
- ☑ Wates
- ☑ Willmott Dixon

And a special thank you to:

- ☑ Carillion
- ☑ Costain
- ☑ Morgan Sindall
- ☑ Skanska

How to use
GE 700

The following information sets out how to use
Construction site safety. Each section is contained
within a separate book, which has been designed
to provide simple navigation for the end user. It also
explains the companion website, which is a significant
addition for keeping users informed of legislation
changes, content updates and links to further guidance.

Construction site safety structure   x
How to navigate   x
Use of icons   x
Companion website   xi

Construction site safety structure

Construction site safety is divided into the standard structure that is used across all core CITB-ConstructionSkills publications:

Section A	**Legal and management**
Section B	**Health and welfare**
Section C	General safety
Section D	**High risk activities**
Section E	**Environment**
Section F	**Specialist activities**

Within *Construction site safety* each section is contained within a separate book.

There is also a new additional supporting book:

Section G	**Checklists and forms**

This new section is a collection of information that can be used on a day-to-day basis when running a site. The forms, checklists and guidance within Section G follow the same structure as in Sections A to F.

How to navigate

Each section contains a main contents page at the start of the section, followed by the introduction, a detailed chapter contents list at the start of each chapter and an index at the back (but there is no index within Section G).

Chapters have been numbered according to the section you are in. Therefore, chapter one of Section A is numbered 01, chapter two of Section B is numbered 02 and so on. However, references to chapters within other sections will be referred to as A01, B02, and so on.

At the start of each chapter there is a short overview of what the chapter is about.

This is followed by the chapter contents list.

Use of icons

A set of icons emphasises key points within the text and also directs readers to further information. The icons are explained below:

www.	Website/further info	!	Important	"	Quote
e.g.	Example	👍	Best practice	Aa	Definition
?	Question	👎	Poor practice	☑	Checklist
💡	Ideas	✋	Caution	▶	Video
📝	Notes	👥	Consultation		
★	Favourite	🔍	Guidance/case study		

Companion website

A companion website has been created to support *Construction site safety* and it contains up-to-date information on:

- ☑ the current edition of each section (book)
- ☑ news (such as legislation changes, industry guidance and best practice)
- ☑ any minor amendments or updates to the current editions
- ☑ web links/phone numbers/addresses
- ☑ details of CITB-ConstructionSkills' publications and courses.

 This icon indicates that further information (such as useful websites and links) can be found on the companion website at www.citb-constructionskills.co.uk/GE700companion

Rather than printing individual weblinks in each section, which can become out of date, the relevant website will be stated alongside the icon (for example, for more information refer to the CITB-ConstructionSkills website). The actual weblink can then be found on the companion website, referenced to the relevant section and chapter.

The companion website will be regularly updated, to ensure that relevant information (such as weblinks) are current.

 Save the companion website address to your favourites, so it is always available when you need it.

01

The Work at Height Regulations

Falls from working at height still remain the largest cause of fatal and major accidents in the construction industry. Many falls are from less than two metres high.

Many accidents are caused by the poor selection and use of access equipment, or because no fall prevention measures were provided.

This chapter outlines what the regulations are about, what they require, what needs to be done and by whom.

Introduction	2
Key points	3
Requirements, interpretation and duties (Regulations 2 and 3)	4
Organisation and planning of work (Regulation 4)	5
Competence (Regulation 5)	5
Avoidance of risks from work at height (Regulation 6)	5
Selection of equipment for work at height (Regulation 7)	7
Requirements for particular work equipment (Regulation 8)	7
Fragile surfaces (Regulation 9)	9
Falling objects (Regulation 10)	9
Danger areas (Regulation 11)	9
Inspection of work equipment (Regulation 12)	9
Inspection of places of work at height (Regulation 13)	10
Schedules 1 to 8	10

The Work at Height Regulations

1.1   Introduction

The intent of the regulations is to reduce the number of deaths and injuries resulting from falls, and so improve the safety performance of the industry. The Work at Height Regulations came into force in 2005. It implements the EC Temporary Work at Height Directive and applies to all sectors of industry.

It covers all circumstances where a person:

- ☑ is working at height
- ☑ is gaining access to, or egress from, such a place of work, either above or below ground
- ☑ could fall a distance liable to cause personal injury (that is, any distance whatsoever).

These regulations do not apply to fixed staircases, but of course other legislation does.

Common examples of tasks carried out within the construction industry classified as work at height include:

- ☑ working on a scaffold
- ☑ working from a mobile elevating work platform (MEWP)
- ☑ being on the back of a lorry
- ☑ working close to an excavation or a cellar opening
- ☑ working on staging or trestles
- ☑ using a mobile tower
- ☑ using ladders or stepladders.

Many other jobs in the construction industry also involve working at height and are covered by the regulations.

The evaluation by the Health and Safety Executive (HSE) of reports of accidents that occurred through working at height show that common factors include the failure of:

- ☑ all parties to recognise that there was a problem
- ☑ management to provide a safe system of work
- ☑ management to ensure that the safe system of work was followed
- ☑ management to provide adequate information, instruction, training or supervision
- ☑ the injured worker to use appropriate equipment
- ☑ management to provide safe plant and equipment
- ☑ collective protection to take priority over personal protection.

 HSE research using 2005/06 statistics as a baseline up to 2010/11 demonstrate that, since the introduction of the Work at Height Regulations:

- ☑ fatal fall injuries are down by 25%
- ☑ major fall injuries are down by 12%
- ☑ over three-day fall injuries are down by 20%.

However, of 294 fatal accidents, 135 were still falls from height (46%).

In 2010/11, of 50 fatalities to workers, 17 were from falls from height (34%).

In 2011/12 (provisional), of 49 fatalities to workers, 27 were from falls from height (55%).

 The HSE website has many resources, including a dedicated work at height section, which includes the Work at Height Regulations (INDG 401).

1.2 Key points

☑ Falls from height are the main source of fatalities and injuries to construction workers.

☑ Falls from low heights (below two metres) are the cause of many deaths and injuries.

☑ Working at height is defined as working at any height from which a fall could cause personal injury.

☑ Work at height must be carried out in accordance with the Work at Height Regulations, which require that such work is:
  - avoided if it is reasonably practicable to do the job another way
  - carried out using appropriate equipment to prevent falls
  - organised so that the distance and possible consequence of any fall are minimised
  - risk-assessment based
  - properly planned and supervised by a competent person(s)
  - carried out by competent operatives
  - collective protection (for example, guard-rails) to take priority over personal protection (safety harnesses) at all times.

Dutyholders must:

■ avoid work at height where they can;

■ use work equipment or other measures to prevent falls where they cannot avoid working at height; and

■ where they cannot eliminate the risk of a fall, use work equipment or other measures to minimise the distance and consequences of a fall should one occur.

 The Access Industry Forum website contains information and guidance, including a working at height video knowledge base, which includes a series of online videos of experts explaining the requirements for various topics (such as edge protection and fall prevention, scaffolding, MEWPs, safety nets, ladders and mobile access towers). It also contains a series of video toolbox talks.

There is a huge range of access equipment available to meet every need of the construction industry, and advice can be sought from a variety of means, including the Access Industry Forum, whose members include:

☑ ATLAS – steeplejacks and lightning protection installers

☑ BSIF – British Safety Industry Federation

☑ EPF – Edge Protection Federation

☑ FASET – Fall Arrest Safety Equipment Training

☑ IPAF – International Powered Access Federation

☑ IRATA – Industrial Rope Access Trade Association

☑ Ladder Association

☑ PASMA – Prefabricated Access Suppliers' and Manufacturers' Association

☑ SAEMA – Specialist Access Engineering and Maintenance Association (Suspended access)

☑ WAHSA – Work at Height Safety Association (Fall protection).

1.3 Requirements, interpretation and duties (Regulations 2 and 3)

Requirements of the regulations

The key provisions of the regulations are that employers should:

☑ where it is reasonably practicable, avoid the need to carry out work at height

☑ where such work cannot be avoided, select the most appropriate equipment for the work and to prevent falls

☑ reduce the distance of, and potential consequences of, any fall

☑ ensure that the work is properly planned, risk-assessment based and carried out safely

☑ ensure the work is carried out by trained and competent persons who are adequately supervised.

The use of a ladder or stepladder is not prohibited by the regulations; however, a greater degree of consideration must be given to using an alternative means of access before selecting a ladder or stepladder for use. A decision to use this type of access equipment must be justified by the findings of a risk assessment that clearly shows that, given all of the circumstances, it is reasonable to use such equipment rather than safer types of access equipment.

Some clients and main contractors are being very rigid in their views by not allowing ladders or stepladders on their sites, as they see this as importing an unnecessary risk. The tendency of some contractors and sub-contractors to turn up at site with a ladder or stepladder with which to do their work, without justifying why safer alternative equipment is not to be used, may now be over, on some sites at least.

It is to be hoped that these regulations will be a further stimulus to architects and designers to design out work at height for the construction and ongoing maintenance of buildings, or at least make safe working at height easier, to further contribute to safety in the industry.

Interpretation of the regulations (Regulation 2)

Below are the most important definitions from within the regulations.

☑ *Access and egress* includes ascent and descent.

☑ *Fragile surface* means a surface which would be liable to fail if any reasonable foreseeable load were to be applied to it. This will obviously include the weight of a person or any work equipment or materials.

☑ *Ladder* includes any fixed ladder or stepladder.

☑ *Personal fall protection system* means:

– a fall prevention, work restraint, work positioning, fall arrest or rescue system other than a system in which the only safeguards are collective safeguards

– rope access and positioning systems.

☑ *Suitable* means suitable in any respect, which it is reasonably foreseeable will affect the safety of any person.

☑ *Work at height* means work in any place, including a place at or below ground level, along with access to it and egress from it (except by a staircase in a permanent workplace) where, if the measures required by these regulations were not taken, a person could fall a distance liable to cause personal injury.

☑ *Working platform*:

– means any platform used as a place of work or as a means of access to or egress from a place of work

– includes any scaffold, suspended scaffold, cradle, mobile platform, trestle, gangway, gantry and stairway, which is used as a place of work.

Reasonably practicable

The term *reasonably practicable* is used in the regulations. It has the same meaning as it does in The Health and Safety at Work Act and elsewhere. Therefore, an employer can look at what the risks in a task involving work at height actually are, and what it would cost to avoid them. If it would cost a great deal of money, or use of other resources to avoid a very small risk, then it may not be reasonably practicable to avoid it.

Application and duty of employer (Regulation 3)

The requirements of the regulations that are imposed:

☑ on an **employer** apply to work carried out by their employees and by any other person(s) under the employer's control, to the extent of that control

☑ apply to **self-employed** persons, together with persons under their control, to the extent of that control

☑ apply to persons who are **not self-employed**, in relation to work being carried out for them and under their control, to the extent of their control.

This last provision covers clients and customers who are having work carried out for them, and the degree to which this point applies depends upon the degree and extent of control that they have over the person(s) carrying out the work. A major client would obviously have more control over a contractor or sub-contractor than would a domestic customer who is perhaps having a roof retiled or gutters cleaned.

Duties of employees

The regulations also apply to employees in that they have duties under Regulation 14. These duties are similar to, and in addition to, their duties under other acts and regulations. In particular, in these regulations, employees must:

☑ report any activity or defect relating to work at height that they know is likely to endanger the safety of themselves or that of any other person

☑ use any work equipment or safety device provided for work at height in accordance with any training and/or instructions that they have received.

Given the legal status of health and safety regulations, failure by an employee to comply with the above is an offence which could, in the appropriate circumstances, be dealt with in a court of law, although company disciplinary procedures may be the preferred method.

Unsafe work at height – many factors could have lead to these employees thinking it was an acceptable risk

1.4 Organisation and planning of work (Regulation 4)

It is the responsibility of every employer to ensure that all work at height is properly planned, appropriately supervised and carried out in a safe manner, taking into account adverse weather conditions that could jeopardise the health and safety of employees. Planning must include the selection of appropriate work equipment, and planning for any emergencies or any rescue.

An employer will probably meet most of the requirements of this regulation if they have carried out and properly implemented a suitable and sufficient risk assessment.

 For a work at height flowchart refer to Section G *Checklists and forms*.

1.5 Competence (Regulation 5)

Employers must ensure that no person engages in any activity concerning work at height (including the organisation and planning of the work, and selection of the work equipment) unless they are competent to do so or, if they are being trained, that they are being supervised by a competent person.

The level of supervision is important. The supervisor will need to be able to intervene, physically or by virtue of their authority, if an unsafe situation begins to develop and rectify the situation or stop the work in progress. The less experience an employee has of working at height, the greater will be the appropriate level of supervision required.

While there is no definition of *competence* in the regulations it may be taken to mean:

☑ a person who has practical and theoretical knowledge of the appropriate aspects of work at heights, together with actual experience of what they are to do, which will enable them to ensure that all necessary planning and assessments have been prepared, and safety precautions taken, so that the work may be carried out safely, or that they may work safely.

If they will be inspecting work equipment then *competence* may be taken to mean:

☑ a person who has practical and theoretical knowledge, together with actual experience of what they are to examine, which will enable them to detect errors, defects, faults or weaknesses that it is the purpose of the examination or inspection to discover and to assess the importance of any such discovery.

Training is an element of the competence necessary to work at height. Similarly, those who deliver such training must also be competent to do so.

 To assist trainers in this respect British Standards published the *Code of practice for the delivery of training and education for work at height and rescue* (BS 8454).

1.6 Avoidance of risks from work at height (Regulation 6)

This is one of the key regulations and specifically requires employers to ensure that risk assessments carried out take account of work carried out at height.

 For further information refer to Chapter A05 Risk assessments and method statements.

The Work at Height Regulations

In addition, the regulation requires that:

> every employer shall ensure that work is not carried out at height where it is reasonably practicable to carry out the work safely otherwise than at height.

This clearly requires the employer to carry out a detailed study or assessment of all the ways in which the work could be carried out. If a way can be found to carry out the work other than at height, then the employer should do so, provided that it is reasonably practicable.

A good example of how this can be achieved was demonstrated during the construction of an over-bridge. The bridge deck was completed on flat ground before the spoil was excavated from below it, thus virtually eliminating the need for working at height and reducing the height at which people had to work when constructing the upper parts of the structure.

Ground-level fabrication is another way of eliminating, or at least reducing, some tasks that have been traditionally carried out at height.

The fact that falls from height often result in fatal or serious injuries should weigh heavily in any risk assessment in deciding if an alternative to working at height is reasonably practicable.

When assessing risk or developing a safe system of work, the hierarchy in the flowchart below must be followed.

Hierarchy for working at height

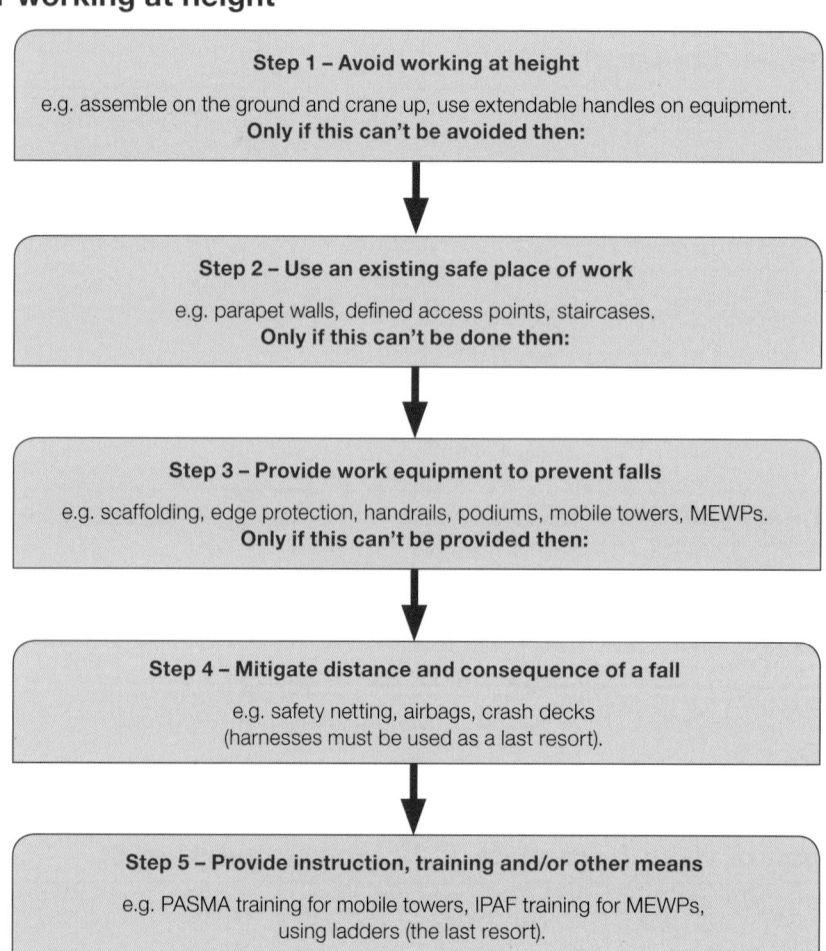

1.7   Selection of equipment for work at height (Regulation 7)

In selecting work equipment for use in work at height there is an absolute requirement for the employer to select work equipment or other measures that will give collective protection to employees as a whole, rather than just individual personal protection for one person.

For example, a guard-rail will protect everyone (collective), whereas a safety harness only protects the wearer (personal). (This is also the advice given in the HSE guidance on the Personal Protective Equipment at Work Regulations.)

This regulation requires that employers follow current best industry practice when selecting equipment for work at height. In particular, employers are required to take account of:

- ☑ working conditions and risks to the safety of the persons at work
- ☑ access and egress and distances to be negotiated
- ☑ distance and consequences of any potential fall
- ☑ duration and frequency of use of the work equipment
- ☑ need for and ease of evacuation and rescue in any emergency
- ☑ any additional risks posed by the installation, use, or removal of the work equipment, and any evacuation or rescue from it
- ☑ any other provisions of the regulations.

Any work equipment which is selected must:

- ☑ be appropriate for the work intended to be carried out
- ☑ have dimensions and load-bearing characteristics
- ☑ allow passage of persons and materials without risk
- ☑ be the most suitable equipment for avoiding risks while working at height.

Current industry practice

Where a trade or occupation has historically used ladders, stepladders, trestles and other similar work equipment, the regulations do not prohibit their continued use provided that the provisions of the Work at Height Regulations are properly complied with.

In such circumstances employers will have to be in a position to demonstrate that:

- ☑ the work at height has been properly planned and cannot be avoided or done any other way that is reasonably practicable
- ☑ the most suitable work equipment is proposed to be used, and a risk assessment shows that the remaining risks are low
- ☑ appropriate steps have been taken to mitigate the effects of any fall, should one occur (for example, guard-rails on trestles)
- ☑ employees are competent and properly supervised.

Risk assessments should be very thorough but proportionate to the risks inherent in the work that is to be done.

It may, however, be the case that a client or main contractor will not allow, or will control through a permit system, certain types of ladders, stepladders or some types of trestles on their premises or site. That is their prerogative and it may mean that alternative ways need to be found to carry out some activities.

1.8   Requirements for particular work equipment (Regulation 8)

This regulation and Schedules 2 to 6 of the regulations cover the provision of:

- ☑ guard-rails, toe-boards, barriers and similar means of protection
- ☑ working platforms (such as scaffolds and trestles)
- ☑ safety nets, airbags and other collective means of arresting falls
- ☑ personal fall protection systems
- ☑ work positioning systems
- ☑ rope access and positioning systems
- ☑ fall-arrest systems
- ☑ work restraint systems
- ☑ ladders.

In respect of guard-rails, the main guard-rail must be installed to at least 950 mm above the work surface or the edge from which a person may fall (previously 910 mm).

Although there is no statutory minimum height for toe-boards, both BS EN 12811-1 and TG20 recommend a minimum of 150 mm. They must be suitable and sufficient to prevent the fall of persons or materials. In line with current industry practice it is anticipated that scaffold boards on edges will continue to be used in most circumstances.

The maximum distance or gap between the top of a toe-board and the mid guard-rail, or between the mid guard-rail and the top guard-rail, is 470 mm.

Where brick guards or similar items are used as a means of protection, then they must be:

☑ placed so as to prevent the fall of persons or materials

☑ of a suitable size and strength

☑ placed or secured so that they do not become accidentally displaced.

Gap between handrails no more than 470 mm

At least 950 mm high

Toe-board minimum of 150 mm high

Guard-rails may be removed on a temporary basis for the movement of materials, provided that suitable and effective alternative fall protection measures are put in place for the duration of the work, and that the guard-rails are replaced as soon as possible after the work is completed.

There is also provision in the regulations for the creation of danger areas (refer to Regulation 11).

Where employers can demonstrate that they are complying fully with current industry best practice and HSE codes of practice or guidance, then in the majority of situations they will meet most of the requirements of the Work at Height Regulations. Their risk assessments for working at height will then essentially be a comparison between what they are already doing to control the risks and what is regarded as best practice, then implementing further control measures if necessary.

The use of scaffolds

The current industry guidance is based on the content of the British Standard: Temporary work equipment. Part 1. Scaffold – Performance requirements and general design (BS EN 12811-1).

Additional practical guidance is produced by the National Access and Scaffolding Confederation (NASC), which sells the Guide to good practice for scaffolding with tubes and fittings (TG20) and Preventing falls in scaffolding (SG4). Both of these documents are accepted by the scaffolding industry and the HSE as essential in ensuring that scaffolding is designed and erected in a safe manner, in compliance with the Work at Height Regulations.

 NASC has a large number of technical (TG) and safety (SG) guidance notes that are accepted by the HSE as scaffolding industry best practice. These are available to purchase online.

The use of ladders, stepladders and trestles

Ladders may be used for access to and egress from the place of work, and ladders, stepladders and trestles may be used to work from, provided that all of the requirements of the Work at Height Regulations are properly complied with.

The primary objective of the regulations is to eliminate work at height (and so the possibility of falls) and, where that is not possible, to ensure that all work at height is carried out safely and that the work equipment being used (such as a ladder or stepladder) is appropriate, suitable and safe for the work.

In deciding to use a ladder for access or egress, or a ladder, stepladder or trestle for work at height, the employer must have carried out an assessment and found that it is not reasonably practicable to use any safer means, and that a risk assessment has shown that the risks from using the ladder, stepladder or trestle are low.

Ladders should be used in accordance with manufacturers' instructions. They must be the right ladder for the job, positioned at the correct angle, placed on a firm level surface, and secured or otherwise prevented from slipping or moving. Users should face the ladder at all times when climbing up or down, have both hands free, and not be carrying anything that would interfere with their safety or balance.

Ladders may be used as a place of work, subject to the above, and if it is light work and of short duration. Users should be trained in how to work safely on ladders (for example, not to overreach).

When stepladders are to be used to carry out work they should be of a suitable size and type. Generally, stepladders should be placed facing the work. They should not be used side-on to the work in any situation where a sideways load could be applied. Again, the work should be light and of short duration.

Podium steps are a product that was developed as a result of the Work at Height Regulations and are in simple terms a stepladder with a secure working platform with guard-rails and toe-boards in place. They are available in various sizes and heights and many are fitted with castors to make them more mobile.

Trestles should be of sound construction, and properly set up on a surface that will bear their weight, as well as any loading of persons or materials. If they are adjustable using telescopic adjustment, they should have high tensile pins in the adjusters. If they are fitted with wheels or castors, they should have brakes or other suitable devices on the wheels or castors.

Trestles should be fitted with guard-rails and toe-boards, where appropriate.

 The Ladder Association in consultation with the HSE and with the support of the DTI has produced *Risk assessment guidelines for leaning ladders and for stepladders.*

1.9 Fragile surfaces (Regulation 9)

The general requirement is that employers must ensure that no person passes across or near, or works on, from or near any fragile surface when it is reasonably practicable to carry out the work safely without their having to do so.

Where this requirement cannot be met, then the employer must:

- ☑ provide and ensure that there are suitable and sufficient platforms, coverings, guard-rails or other similar means of support or protection, which must be capable of supporting any foreseeable load or loading
- ☑ where the risk of a fall still remains, take suitable and sufficient steps to minimise the distance and consequences of any fall, should it occur
- ☑ place prominent warning notices at the approach(es) to any fragile material
- ☑ where such notices cannot be used, ensure that employees (and others as appropriate) are made aware of the fragile materials by other means.

1.10 Falling objects (Regulation 10)

Along with much else in the Work at Height Regulations, the requirement in this regulation follows current best practice in that employers must take suitable and sufficient steps (including prohibiting the throwing down of materials) to prevent, so far as is reasonably practicable, the fall of any materials or objects that are likely to cause any injury to any person. Suitable steps will include the use of such items as brick guards, toe-boards and debris nets.

Where such falls cannot be prevented, or in the interests of safety, suitable and sufficient measures must be taken to prevent persons from being hit by falling objects or materials. This will cover the use of protective fans, boarded or roofed walkways and exclusion zones at ground level.

Materials on scaffolds and working platforms must be stored so that they cannot fall or pose a risk of injury to anyone by their collapse, overturning or unintended movement.

1.11 Danger areas (Regulation 11)

Following on from Regulation 10 and building on its requirements, in any workplace where there is a risk of any person falling or of persons being struck by falling objects, then employers must take all reasonably practicable steps to prevent any unauthorised access to that area (such as putting up physical barriers and appropriate warning signs). Any signs must comply with the Health and Safety (Safety Signs and Signals) Regulations.

1.12 Inspection of work equipment (Regulation 12)

This regulation only applies to work equipment to which Regulation 8 and Schedules 2–6 apply, and closely follows the current requirements in the Provision and Use of Work Equipment Regulations as regards the inspection of work equipment.

Where the safety of work equipment used for working at height (for example, a scaffold) depends upon how it has been installed or assembled, then it must not be used in that place or elsewhere until after it has been inspected by a competent person. Throughout the regulations, *inspection* means any visual or more rigorous inspection, and any appropriate testing that a competent person decides is necessary.

All work equipment exposed to conditions causing deterioration that may result in dangerous situations must be inspected. This will ensure that it remains safe and that any deterioration can be detected and remedied.

Inspections must take place:

- ☑ at suitable intervals
- ☑ after each time that exceptional circumstances have occurred that are liable to have jeopardised the safety of the work equipment.

In addition to these requirements, any working platform that is used for construction work, and from which a person could fall more than two metres, must not be used unless it has been inspected in that position within the previous seven days. A mobile working platform (such as a mobile scaffold tower or a MEWP) must have been inspected within the previous seven days.

Employers must ensure that no work equipment (other than lifting equipment for which an identical provision applies under the Lifting Operations and Lifting Equipment Regulations), whether it is purchased, brought in or hired in, is used unless they have evidence that the last inspection required by this regulation was carried out.

If there is no evidence of the last inspection then the work equipment cannot be used on site until an inspection is carried out.

These formal inspection(s) should not be regarded as a substitute for any routine pre-use checks that should be carried out by the user.

What is a suitable interval should be decided by a competent person, based on the results of risk assessments, and then be reviewed in the light of experience.

The purpose of an inspection is to identify whether the work equipment is safe to use, and that any defect or deterioration is detected and repaired. If this is not possible, the work equipment should be removed from service before it becomes an unacceptable risk.

The results of every inspection must be recorded and kept on site until the construction work is completed, and after that they must be kept at one of the company offices for three months. The detail of the inspection must be recorded before the end of the working day, and the report delivered within 24 hours. Lifting equipment that has had a thorough examination under the provisions of LOLER is treated as having had an inspection under these regulations.

The regulations do not specify a format for the results of the inspections. Provided that the required information is recorded, and is readily available, then an employer may adopt their own recording system. Any computer-based system should be secure and cannot be interfered with. Systems may also be in the form of a register.

1.13 Inspection of places of work at height (Regulation 13)

So far as is reasonably practicable, every employer must ensure that the surface of every place of work at height, every parapet and any permanent rail or other such fall prevention measure be inspected visually prior to each use. While there is no requirement to record such inspections, a simple record would provide evidence that they have been carried out.

1.14 Schedules 1 to 8

There are eight schedules to the regulations. Much of the information contained in the schedules is virtually identical to current requirements and/or guidance so if employers are actively working to current standards and guidance then there is little extra for them to do.

Schedule 1 – Regulation 6(4)(a)

The requirement in this schedule is for existing places of work at height and means of access or egress to and from such places to be stable, of sufficient size and strength and with edge protection as necessary. Ladders in particular must rest on stable, strong surfaces.

A place of work is to be properly constructed, used and maintained so as to prevent the risk of tripping, slipping or being trapped between it and adjacent surfaces. It should have no gaps through which materials could fall and injure someone.

Schedule 2 – Regulation 8(a)

This covers the requirements for guard-rails, toe-boards, barriers and similar means of protection *(refer to Regulation 8)*. The remainder of the requirements are unchanged other than the fact that the top guard-rail must now be at least 950 mm above the edge from which any person might fall (with the proviso of 910 mm for guard-rails that were in place at the time the Work at Height Regulations came into force), and the removal of any specific height at which guard-rails and toe-boards must be fitted.

Schedule 3 – Regulation 8(b)

This covers the requirements for working platforms. Part 1 deals with requirements for all working platforms, and Part 2 covers the additional requirements for scaffolding.

Part 1 – All working platforms

Working platforms must be erected and used so that components cannot become displaced and cause danger to anyone. They must be suitable for the work, and of sufficient strength and rigidity. If they are altered or modified (by a competent person) they must remain safe and stable.

Any supporting structure for a working platform must itself be suitable and of sufficient strength and stability while being erected, used or dismantled. It must be prevented from slipping or moving, and if it has wheels or castors, they must be capable of being locked or similar. Working platforms and supporting structures must not be overloaded.

Part 2 – Additional requirements for scaffolding

As regards the additional requirements for scaffolding strength and stability, calculations must be carried out unless it is being assembled in conformity with generally recognised standard configurations (for example, a TG basic scaffold). If the scaffold is not a TG20 basic scaffold then design calculations will need to be provided by the scaffolding contractor that usually will include detailed drawings.

If prefabricated scaffolding materials are being used, (for example, ladder beams and hop-up platforms) then design calculations will be required to substantiate these products used in conjunction with the specific scaffold.

Depending on the complexity of the scaffold, an assembly, use and dismantling plan (commonly referred to as a method statement) shall be drawn up by a competent person. This may be a standard or generic plan, supplemented with specific details as appropriate. A copy of the plan must be kept for the use of any persons concerned with the erection, use or dismantling of the scaffold.

The size and layout of the scaffold must be appropriate and suitable for the work to be performed, and it must also permit the work and passage of persons to happen safely. (NASC TG20 gives details on specific scaffold dimensions, layouts and load bearing capacities.)

When a scaffold is not available for use during erection, alteration and/or dismantlement, then warning signs in accordance with the Health and Safety (Safety Signs and Signals) Regulations need to be displayed (scaffold tagging systems are available for this task) and physical barriers to prevent access to the scaffold, or part of the scaffold, put in place.

 Scaffolding may only be assembled, dismantled or significantly altered under the supervision of a competent person and by persons who have received appropriate and specific training.

 The Construction Industry Scaffolders Record Scheme (CISRS) has a card scheme in place for scaffolders.

Schedule 4 – Regulation 8(c)

This schedule covers the requirements for collective safeguards for arresting falls. Collective safeguards include safety nets, airbags, landing mats and any similar devices or arrangements. All must be suitable and of sufficient strength to be able to safely arrest or cushion a fall.

These safeguards may only be used:

☑ where a risk assessment has shown that the work to be done can be carried out safely while the safeguard is being used, and without influencing its effectiveness

☑ where the use of safer work equipment is not reasonably practicable

☑ if a sufficient number of employees (or others) have received adequate training specific to the safeguard, including rescue procedures.

A key requirement is that if the safeguard is designed to be attached to a building or a structure then the safeguard, the structure and all anchorages must be suitable and of sufficient strength for any foreseeable load that a fall might impose on it.

Airbags and landing mats must be suitable for the purpose intended, and they must be stable.

If a safeguard is designed to distort when arresting a fall, it must give sufficient clearance from the ground or adjacent structures to avoid injury to a person whose fall is being arrested.

Schedule 5 – Regulation 8(d)

This schedule covers the requirements for personal fall protection systems (Part 1), work positioning systems (Part 2), rope access and positioning techniques (Part 3), fall arrest systems (Part 4) and work restraint systems (Part 5).

 Much of the information in this schedule is quite technical and it is of paramount importance that employees are, or have been fully trained on, and are competent in, the use of any of the fall protection systems available to them. There is not sufficient detail within this brief explanation of the schedule to train a person on the requirements, or for them to gain sufficient knowledge to be regarded as competent.

All safety harnesses, lanyards and other fall prevention or fall arrest equipment must comply with the appropriate British and European standards.

The Work at Height Regulations

Part 1 deals with the requirements for all personal fall protection systems. See Interpretation of the regulations *(refer to 1.3 of this chapter)* for the definition of personal fall protection systems.

Current guidance is that the requirements set out in this schedule apply to all rope-based activities for work at height, including industrial rope systems and any other similar activity when carried out as a work activity. The schedule requires that:

- ☑ a personal fall protection system shall only be used if a risk assessment has shown that the work can be done safely while it is being used, and that the use of other, safer work equipment is not reasonably practicable
- ☑ the user and a sufficient number of others have been trained in its use and in rescue procedures
- ☑ it shall be suitable and of sufficient strength for the purpose for which it is to be used and will withstand any foreseeable loading
- ☑ it fits the wearer and is correctly fitted or worn
- ☑ it is designed to minimise injury to the user in the event of a fall, and is such that the user will not fall or slip out of it should they fall
- ☑ it is designed, installed and used so as to prevent unplanned or uncontrolled movement of the user.

Any anchorage point must be suitable and of sufficient strength to support any foreseeable loading. If designed to do so, the equipment must be securely attached to at least one such anchorage point when in use.

Part 2 deals with the additional requirements for work positioning systems, which may only be used if:

- ☑ the system includes a suitable backup system for preventing or arresting a fall
- ☑ the system includes a line as a backup system and the user is connected to it
- ☑ where it is not reasonably practicable to do either of the above, then other suitable measures are taken to prevent or arrest a fall.

Part 3 deals with the additional requirements for rope access and positioning techniques, which may only be used if:

- ☑ it has two separate lines: the working line and a safety line
- ☑ the user has a safety harness that is connected to both the working line and the safety line
- ☑ the working line has safe means of ascent and descent, and a self-locking device to prevent falling
- ☑ the safety line has a mobile fall protection system that is connected to, and travels with, the user
- ☑ subject to the type and length of work, and the findings of a risk assessment, it has a seat with appropriate accessories.

However, if a risk assessment has demonstrated that a second line would entail a higher risk to the user, then, provided that appropriate safety measures have been taken, a single rope may be used.

Part 4 deals with the additional requirements for fall arrest systems. It requires that they must have a suitable energy absorber (often called a shock absorber and which is usually either a folded metal strip that deforms, or tear-away stitched webbing), or other suitable means of limiting the force applied to the user's body if they fall. In addition, a fall arrest system must not be used if there is any risk of a line (a rope or a lanyard) being cut, or where there is no safety zone or clear zone to allow for any swinging or pendulum effect after a fall, or in a way that hinders the system's safety performance or makes its use unsafe.

Part 5 deals with the additional requirements for work restraint systems (often a safety harness with a very short lanyard), and requires that they are designed so that they are used correctly to prevent the user from getting into a position where they could fall.

Schedule 6 – Regulation 8(e)

Requirements for ladders

This schedule contains a new and specific requirement on the use of ladders and stepladders for work at height. Employers and the self-employed must ensure that a ladder or stepladder is only used for work at height if a risk assessment has shown that the use of more suitable work equipment is not justified because of the low risk and the short duration of the work, or because of existing features on site that cannot be altered.

The remainder of the schedule is in line with current industry best practice and does not contain any further new or changed requirements.

Briefly, the requirements are:

- ☑ the surface on which a ladder rests must be stable and of sufficient strength
- ☑ the ladder is strong enough for loads that may be put on it
- ☑ the ladder is placed so that it is stable during use
- ☑ a suspended ladder is attached in a secure manner so that it does not swing
- ☑ portable ladders are prevented from slipping by being secured at or near their top or bottom, or with anti-slip or stability devices, or other effective means
- ☑ access ladders are long enough to provide a handhold when getting off at the top, unless other handholds have been provided
- ☑ sections on interlocking or extension ladders are prevented from movement while in use
- ☑ mobile ladders are prevented from moving before being stepped on

☑ where reasonably practicable, rest platforms are provided where a run of ladders rises a vertical distance of more than nine metres

☑ ladders are used in such a way that a secure handhold and secure support are always available to the user

☑ the user can maintain a safe handhold while carrying a load.

This last point is qualified for stepladders in that:

> in the case of a stepladder the maintenance of a handhold is not practical when a load is carried, and a risk assessment has demonstrated that the use of a stepladder is justified because of the low risk and the short duration of the work.

Footing ladders

For advice on footing ladders, refer to Chapter D03 Common access equipment.

Schedule 7 – Regulation 12(7)

This schedule states the details to be recorded in a work equipment inspection report (for example, scaffold inspection).

The details are:

☑ the name and address of the person for whom the inspection was carried out

☑ the location of the work equipment inspected

☑ a description of the work equipment inspected

☑ the date and time of the inspection

☑ details of any matter identified that could give rise to a risk to the health or safety of any person

☑ details of any action taken as a result of any matter identified in the point above

☑ details of any further actions considered necessary

☑ the name and position of the person making the report.

Reports of inspection have to be kept on site until construction work is completed and then at the employer's offices for three months.

Schedule 8 – Regulation 19

This schedule outlines various other regulations or parts of them that are revoked by the coming into force of the Work at Height Regulations.

02

Safe working on roofs and at height

There is no such thing as a safe height; anyone who is off the ground is at risk of falling. The hazard exists on working platforms, scaffolds, ladders, flat and pitched roofs, open steelwork and any area where work is being done in proximity to fragile materials, openings, holes and roof edges.

Ladders, stepladders and trestles (or lightweight staging) are among the most commonly used pieces of access equipment on site and, perhaps, the most misused.

Most building and construction workers have used them at some time and it is essential that safe working practices should be followed if accidents are to be avoided.

Introduction	16
Key points	16
The stages of a roofing project	17
Access arrangements	23
Best practice solutions	27
Other considerations	30
Legislative requirements	33

Safe working on roofs and at height

2.1   Introduction

Before reading this chapter, it is strongly recommended that readers familiarise themselves with Chapter D01 The Work at Height Regulations. There have been a number of major improvements in safety standards and practices, with regard to working at height. For example, the almost standard practice of profile roofing workers using safety nets on new build, along with the use of powered access for steel workers, have been significant steps forward in construction health and safety.

Every year, work at height remains by far the largest cause of death in the construction industry.

Roof work, including work on fragile roofing materials, gives rise to a substantial number of fatal and serious accidents.

It needs to be emphasised, however, that there is not just the actual roof working to be considered, but the whole process: planning the job, creating a safe access, the safe storage of equipment and materials, and so on.

There is no such thing as a safe height; anyone who is off the ground is at risk of falling. The hazard exists on working platforms, scaffolds, ladders, flat and pitched roofs, open steelwork and any area where work is being done in proximity to fragile materials, openings, holes and roof edges.

In many respects, maintenance, repair and working for domestic clients may offer greater challenges to providing a safe working environment. The work is typically of shorter duration than new build, and often carried out directly for a client who is ignorant of the required standards. This does not lessen either the need for safe working methods or compliance with the law.

Compliance with well-established safety procedures and existing legislation could save many lives and prevent many injuries. Most accidents could be avoided, given the provision of appropriate equipment and the adequate information, instruction, training and supervision of those who use it.

The photo shows various work at height solutions in practice, including a MEWP with cantilever platform, proprietary edge protection mesh barriers and scaffold guard-rails to the roof perimeter.

Guard-rails and toe-boards are required on all working platforms where a risk assessment indicates that any person would be injured as a result of the fall.

Various work at height solutions

For additional information refer to:
Chapter D01 The Work at Height Regulations,
Chapter D03 Common access equipment,
Chapter D04 Scaffolding,
Chapter D05 Fall arrest and suspension equipment, and
Chapter F05 Working over or near to water.

2.2   Key points

- ☑ Those who work on roofs are, by the nature of their work, at risk of falling if appropriate measures are not taken.

- ☑ Those who plan, supervise or carry out roof work must be competent to do so.

- ☑ A risk assessment and, where considered necessary, a method statement, must be compiled for all such work.

- ☑ Integral features of roofs (such as a steep pitch, valleys, fragile cladding or roof lights) can increase the risk of falling.

- ☑ Falls through fragile roofing materials continue to be the cause of many deaths and injuries.

- ☑ Bad weather can have a significant impact on the risk control measures that have to be taken.

- ☑ Ideally work will be carried out from a stable working platform, fitted with guard-rails and toe-boards, all of which comply with the requirements of the Work at Height Regulations.

- ☑ Where such fall prevention measures cannot be used, effective fall arrest measures must be put in place, ideally collective measures (such as safety nets or other soft landing systems).

- ☑ Those who work on roofs must also take into consideration the safety of anyone passing below to protect them from falling materials or tools.

- ☑ Ladders, stepladders and lightweight staging are all easily transported means of access to work at height. They can all be used safely in certain conditions.

- ☑ The danger comes when one of them is used for a job for which it is not suitable; this particularly applies to ladders and stepladders.

- ☑ All persons that are working at height must have received adequate training in systems of work and any equipment that they are planning to use for access.

- ☑ Although newer and safer equipment is available, these can still present serious risks if not used correctly.

- ☑ The nature and duration of the job will be significant factors in determining the most appropriate type of access equipment to use for work at height.

- ☑ The HSE's evaluation of accidents resulting from work at height shows that inappropriate access equipment, provided by management and used by workers, is a significant factor.

- ☑ Falls from low heights (a height below two metres) are the cause of many fatalities and major injuries.

 For further information refer to the HSE website.

2.3 The stages of a roofing project

There are various stages to any roofing project:

- ☑ design
- ☑ selection of contractors/staff
- ☑ planning
- ☑ carrying out the work
- ☑ post-completion information (at the end).

 The Access Industry Forum website contains information and guidance, including a working at height video knowledge base, which includes a series of online videos of experts explaining the requirements for various topics (such as edge protection and fall prevention).

Design

Notes on designers taking account of the health and safety of persons who will have to do the job and then maintain, clean and demolish the roof appear previously in this chapter.

 For further information refer to Chapter A03
Construction (Design and Management) Regulations.

Selection of contractors/staff

Where a company is using its own employees to carry out roof work, it is essential that several factors are taken into consideration. Both training and operational work on roofs can be hazardous, strenuous work, often involving:

- ☑ work at considerable heights for long periods of time
- ☑ work outdoors, usually in hot, cold or wet weather and possibly high winds
- ☑ repetitive materials handling
- ☑ reaching, stretching and maintaining balance in awkward postures whilst carrying loads on varying roof terrains.

This means that fitness to work is particularly important and needs to be considered by the employers. The advisory committee on roof work suggests that it is vital that people working on roofs do not suffer from:

- ☑ any neurological condition likely to cause seizures
- ☑ weakness of limbs
- ☑ loss of balance, including vertigo (dizziness from being at height)
- ☑ any heart or lung condition likely to be aggravated by strenuous work
- ☑ any disability/impairment of limb function
- ☑ any other disease, disability or the effects of medication, alcohol, drugs or toxic substances (lead and so on) likely to impair mental or physical activity, especially at a height
- ☑ temporary ailments (such as influenza) or other conditions that may affect judgement
- ☑ uncorrected sight problems
- ☑ a physique that would be unsuitable for the work.

Safe working on roofs and at height

Obviously an employer needs to be aware of The Equality Act with regard to the above. It is very strongly suggested that employers should establish a policy on fitness for work, and ideally that this should be implemented before taking on any new staff. So-called fitness to work medicals are not new and many sectors already use them for their staff (for example, holders of PSV driving licences (bus drivers)). Often a local GP can carry out these medicals or will know where they can be done.

> A 50-year-old roofer was killed when he fell from the edge of a pitched roof. He was understood to have been carrying out extensive work to repair the roof following storm damage. There was no edge protection and the access ladder was not secured.
>
> A 60-year-old employee was killed when he fell through a fragile roof as he was helping to install a ventilation duct for a spray booth.
>
> A self-employed builder, aged 52, fell while he was trying to repair damage to the asbestos cement roof of an industrial unit. He fell through a fragile roof light.

Planning

Planning the work should include consideration of the progression of the work with regard to:

- ☑ site-specific risks
- ☑ weather conditions
- ☑ emergencies (including rescue)
- ☑ safe means of access and egress
- ☑ materials handling and storage.

Site-specific risks

The site-specific risks could include:

- ☑ working above public areas (such as shopping malls or public streets)
- ☑ the difficulties in delivering materials and transferring them to roof level
- ☑ the presence of site traffic or road traffic on a public road
- ☑ awkward working environments (such as occupied houses or factories)
- ☑ emergency situations (such as rescuing someone who has fallen and is suspended at high level in a safety harness)
- ☑ vent pipes that may suddenly shower unsuspecting roof workers with anything ranging from high pressure steam to noxious chemicals
- ☑ nesting seagulls or other species of bird that will aggressively defend their territory
- ☑ the presence of accumulated pigeon droppings.

Weather conditions

It goes without saying that the weather can have a significant impact upon the intention to carry out roof work and may ultimately be the reason for the start of a job being delayed, or it being suspended part-way through.

Heavy rain, high winds, frost or snow might make it unsafe for operatives to work at height.

> Five-day weather forecasts, which include temperature, wind speed and direction, are available from several websites.

The only note of caution is that the forecast wind speed is given for ground level. The wind speed can be considerably higher at height (for example, if installing a glass atrium roof on top of a multistorey tower block).

If a roofing job has started and the weather is forecast to be changeable, with perhaps extremes of conditions, it will be essential to monitor the forecast so that work can be halted before it becomes unsafe to continue.

Wind speeds in excess of 25 mph can create unsafe working conditions. Winds can funnel and eddy around buildings, causing turbulence, which again may make working places unsafe. In cold weather conditions, the wind will effectively lower the temperature considerably – this is known as the wind chill factor.

Work involving the handling of sheeting and cladding requires extra care in windy conditions, when a sheet may act like a sail, causing the person holding it to lose their balance.

Guidance suggests that the following activities should cease when the average wind speeds shown are exceeded:

17 mph – handling lightweight materials and any materials over five metres long or rolls of felt

23 mph – general roofing activities.

Windforce number	Description of wind	Wind locally	Speed mph	Speed m/sec
0	Calm	Calm, smoke rises vertically.	1	0–1
1	Light air	Direction of wind shown by smoke drift, but not by wind or weather vanes.	1–3	1–2
2	Light breeze	Wind felt on face. Leaves rustle. Wind or weather vanes move.	4–7	2–3
3	Gentle breeze	Leaves and small twigs in constant motion. Wind extends light flags.	8–12	3–5
4	Moderate breeze	Wind raises dust and loose paper. Small branches move.	13–18	5–8
5	Fresh breeze	Small trees in leaf begin to sway. Little crested wavelets form on inland waters.	19–24	8–11
6	Strong breeze	Large branches in motion. Umbrellas used with some difficulty.	25–31	11–14
7	Near gale	Whole trees in motion. Becoming difficult to walk against the wind.	32–38	14–17
8	Gale	Twigs break off trees. Progress is generally impeded.	39–46	17–21
9	Strong gale	Chimney pots, slates and tiles may be blown off.	47–54	21–24

Beaufort wind scale for use on land (Numbers 1-9)

For further information refer to the National Federation of Roofing Contractors' guidance booklet, *Roofing and cladding in windy conditions.*

For further detailed guidance refer to the HSE's guidance, HSG 33.

Emergencies (including rescue)

Several types of emergency (such as a fire) could occur either at ground level or at height, which requires that an emergency evacuation of the whole site or the roof be carried out. For this reason the planning stage must ensure that safe access and egress will be available at all times. Depending upon the nature of the job it may be necessary to have more than one access/egress route.

If the site layout necessitates that the asphalt/bitumen boiler has to be sited on the roof, the question will have to be asked as to whether it is still possible to get off the roof safely if a fire occurs.

It may be necessary to deal with medical emergencies where someone becomes incapacitated at height through illness or injury and is unable to make their way back to ground level. In such circumstances, the local fire and rescue service (FRS) may have to be involved to effect a safe rescue.

Carrying out roof work will often involve the use of fall-arrest equipment (such as safety nets or safety harness and lanyard). Anyone who falls will have to be rescued promptly, particularly if they are suspended in a harness.

For further information refer to Chapter D05 Fall arrest and suspension equipment.

Safe means of access and egress

The means of gaining access to height and safely working there will depend upon many factors (such as the nature of the roof structure, whether there is room to erect a scaffold or bring in a MEWP and even the length of time that the job is expected to take).

Some common means of gaining access to height or actually working at height are:

- ☑ ladders
- ☑ mobile access equipment
- ☑ fixed or mobile towers
- ☑ stair towers
- ☑ independent scaffolds.

Safe working on roofs and at height

Materials handling and storage

Part of the planning process will involve taking decisions on:

☑ what roofing materials are required and possibly where they can be stored safely at ground level

☑ a safe means of transferring roofing materials to height and in what quantities

☑ avoiding the overloading of any part of the roof by stacking materials prior to installation

☑ the safe storage of sheet materials if they are to be stored for any length of time, particularly during windy weather

☑ the safe distribution of materials around the roof during installation

☑ the safe transfer of waste materials back to ground level.

Further notes on the safe stacking of materials on roofs are included later in this chapter.

Carrying out the work

To a large extent, the risks of doing the job, the risk-control measures that will be necessary and therefore the way in which the work is carried out will depend upon the type of roof.

Flat roofs

On flat roofs, falls most frequently occur from:

☑ the edge of a completed roof

☑ from the leading edge where work is being carried out

☑ through openings or gaps

☑ through fragile material.

A roof with a pitch of less than 10° is classed as a flat roof. Safe access to the roof, and to any working place on that roof, must be provided and maintained.

If there is no parapet or similar barrier to stop anyone from falling, edge protection must be provided. This may take the form of standard guard-rails and toe-boards or, providing nobody will approach the edge, a barrier set back from the edge.

Where works are to be undertaken that could result in materials or equipment falling onto people passing below, protective measures must be taken. This can range from adding netting, close boarding or debris fans to scaffolds or establishing exclusion zones. These could range from permanently fenced-off areas to simply having someone stopping people from accessing the drop zone at critical times.

There will be times when operatives need to work at exposed leading edges but it is not reasonably practical to install guard-rails or other fall prevention measures. In these circumstances, it will be necessary to install or provide fall-arrest systems. The most suitable type of fall-arrest system will be indicated by a risk assessment. Where safety nets, air bags or other soft landing systems are used, they will provide collective safety for anyone working above them who falls.

Alternatively, it may be decided that operatives should wear a safety harness with a lanyard clipped to a strong anchor point or a horizontal running line. The effectiveness of this system depends upon the training of operatives in the use of the equipment and the operatives actually clipping on.

When a safety harness and lanyard is used, consideration must be given to the position of the anchor point, which ideally will be above the head-height of the user. Where the anchor point is at ankle level, for example, there will be more slack in the lanyard and the fall will be further before it is arrested. It has been calculated that in some circumstances a person could fall up to 5.5 metres before the fall is arrested. In this situation, where the person is working less than 5.5 metres above ground level, impact with the ground would occur before the fall could be arrested.

Currently questions are being asked about the effectiveness of inertia reel block systems if there is a horizontal pull.

For further information refer to Chapter D05
Fall arrest and suspension equipment.

The use of this type of equipment has become more common as it is not as restrictive as a fixed line system. If this method is proposed it is suggested that advice is sought from the manufacturers to check they advise that inertia reels are appropriate.

Sometimes, guard-rails have to be moved or removed to enable work to be undertaken. If this is to happen:

☑ an equally effective safe system of work must be in place and maintained, which will prevent falls of persons or materials

☑ the guard-rails must be replaced or re-erected as soon as practical.

Some flat roofing systems will involve the use of various chemicals or hot works and the liberation of fumes or solvents may occur. Consideration to the Control of Substances Hazardous to Health (COSHH) Regulations should be given as well as the significant possibility of fire, explosion or burns from hot bitumen.

Traditional pitched roofs

On traditional pitched roofs, most falls occur:

- ☑ from the eaves, by slipping down then falling from the roof

- ☑ into the structure during truss erection

- ☑ from gable ends during salvage prior to demolition

- ☑ through fragile roofing materials, particularly fragile roof lights

- ☑ when passing along valley gutters with fragile materials alongside the access way.

Working at height in a safe environment

A sloping roof is defined as any roof having a pitch of more than 10°.

Work on pitched roofs should only be carried out:

- ☑ by persons who are physically capable and adequately trained

- ☑ using roof ladders or a temporary work platform equipped with guard-rails and toe-boards as necessary and securely fixed to prevent it slipping (homemade roofing ladders, created from bits of spare batten and angle iron or the like, do not comply with any regulations and are illegal)

- ☑ providing that either a suitable catch barrier or a working platform with guard-rails is erected at the eaves of the building.

This requirement applies to any work on a sloping roof, including access to, and egress from, other workplaces.

If the steepness of the roof is such that it prevents a secure foothold, a working platform must be erected. Roofs pitched at over 50° should be regarded as steep, as should shallower slopes if they are slippery.

There has always been an issue over work of short duration, and when it becomes necessary to provide edge protection – this is normally considered to be 30 minutes. This is not 30 minutes on one tile, and then another 30 minutes on another, but 30 minutes in total.

The construction method used in Scotland is different to that in other parts of the UK. The pitch of the roof is often steeper and, as opposed to purely installing a felt and batten roof, often the roof is fully boarded before being slated or tiled over. The HSE has expressed various concerns over the use of so-called slater's heels. These are boards pegged into the timber that are used to give a more comfortable stance. These, on their own, do not provide a safe access system, and additional fall protection is required.

Catch barrier

Curved roofs

When working on a curved roof (such as a glass barrel-vault structure) providing:

- ☑ the roofing material is load-bearing, and

- ☑ there is a secure anchorage at the apex of the roof

it is usually necessary to employ rope access techniques (such as work-positioning or abseiling). It is essential that any such system incorporates a self-locking device to prevent the uncontrolled descent of anyone who loses their footing.

Additionally, proprietary rubber steps are available that follow the exact contour of a curved roof, with sections being joined to extend the overall length. These steps must be regarded as a foothold only, as they are not equipped with a handrail. They must therefore only be used in conjunction with another form of fall protection (such as a fall-arrest block).

Where there is a risk of falling through a curved roof, consideration should be given to installing safety nets inside the roof.

Safe working on roofs and at height

Profiled roofs

These range from a single asbestos cement sheet on an outside toilet to the latest continuously extruded system formed in situ to cover large portal frame buildings. The systems will differ in complexity and range from single skin through to composite factory-produced units.

New build profiled installation will normally be carried out over a system of safety nets that provide fall protection.

 For further information refer to Chapter D05
Fall arrest and suspension equipment.

There are other means of providing safe access for roofs. Traditionally for new build systems this was called leading edge protection and used working platforms in the form of lightweight staging. This system advances along the roof in line with, or previously, in advance of the installation of the roof sheets.

If a double skin roof system is being installed, the inner sheet or liner tray must be fixed by at least four fixings before it can be stood on.

Metal profile roof sheets are therefore still fragile until they have been fixed. Furthermore, many roof-light assemblies, which are often installed as part of a profiled roof system, are also fragile. This will necessitate proprietary work platforms (such as Youngman boards) that are used to enable safe access.

Edge protection should be provided in accordance with BS EN 13374.

Edge protection systems are selected primarily based on the gradient of the surface for which they are to provide protection. The performance requirements for the various classes are detailed within the standard BS EN 13374.

☑ **Class A** provides protection to flat surfaces and slopes generally up to 10°. It provides resistance to static loads and is based on the requirements to support a person leaning against, walking beside, and possibly stumbling against the edge protection.

☑ **Class B** provides protection to flat surfaces and slopes, generally up to 30°, and to even steeper slopes with short slope lengths. It provides resistance to both static and low dynamic loads and is based on the requirements to support a person leaning against, walking beside, possibly stumbling against and sliding down a sloping surface towards the edge protection.

☑ **Class C** provides protection to steeply sloping surfaces, generally up to 45°, and up to 60° for five metre slopes. It provides resistance to high dynamic loads only and is based on the requirements to contain a person sliding down a steeply sloping surface.

Any working platform must comply with the Work at Height Regulations and be a minimum of 600 mm wide with hand-rails on one or both sides, depending on whether a fall can occur. This does create practical difficulties in terms of moving them, due to their bulk and weight.

In a new build situation it can be possible to run the boards on a wheeled system, referred to as purlin trolleys. However, unless the steelwork designer has allowed for this, parts of the frame (called sag rods) often prevent the trolleys moving.

The only other option therefore is to physically step on the roof and lift the stagings. A five metre platform with guard-rails weighs about 50 kg. Given that the platforms should be joined together, then physically moving them does offer challenges. Also, how the stagings are put in place to start with can often be an issue. It is not a safe system of work to simply carry the staging up the steelwork. They may need to be craned up and positioned at the same time as the packs of sheets.

Fragile roofs

Fragile roofing materials include asbestos, glass, plastic, cement sheets and similar brittle surfaces.

Roof lights should be fixed with red coloured fixings to indicate their presence. These should be introduced where none is fitted and roof lights are replaced.

As far as the strength of the materials is concerned, the appearance of fragile roofs is often misleading. Surface coatings, dirt or moss may conceal the fragile nature of the material, thereby giving a false appearance of soundness to glass, plastic, asbestos, and so on. Even if the roof is clad in a load-bearing material, roof lights are often fragile.

Asbestos and various plastic materials are particularly brittle and will shatter without warning.

Many deaths and serious injuries have occurred as a result of roof workers falling through fragile surfaces. Most of the falls could have been easily prevented had a risk assessment been carried out and a safe system of work developed. Even if the falls did occur, the deaths and injuries could have been prevented by the use of safety nets or another soft landing system.

Ideally, another way of carrying out the job can be found that does not require anyone to work on or near to fragile roofing materials. However, in many cases, this may not be practical.

Temporary working platform

If it is necessary to pass across a fragile roof, a roof-board complete with a guard-rail should be used to spread the weight and provide a good handhold. Depending upon the job, it may be necessary to use more than one roof-board: one to support the person, whilst the other is moved to a new position.

The practice of trying to walk the line of the bolts or the line of the purlins is very dangerous and must not be attempted. Where walkways with a handrail are not an integral part of the roof structure, a safe system of work must be devised.

Walkways near fragile surfaces (in valleys, parapets, gutters or channels) must be provided with suitable guard-rails or, if not, the fragile surface should be overlaid with a load-bearing material to prevent the possibility of anyone falling through.

Warning signs must be fixed at all approaches to roofs constructed with fragile materials. This is a requirement of the Work at Height Regulations. Such signs must comply with the Health and Safety (Safety Signs and Signals) Regulations.

Where such signs are not fixed in place, it is essential that the presence of fragile material is identified in advance and those doing the job are made aware of it by other means.

Post-completion information

Where a project is notifiable under the Construction (Design and Management) Regulations, a health and safety file will have to be compiled for the project. The purpose of this document is to provide useful health and safety related information for anyone who, at a later date, has to maintain, clean, demolish or use the structure as a place of work.

Depending upon the nature and complexity of the roof structure installed, the roofing contractor may have to supply information for inclusion in the health and safety file.

Even if a project is not notifiable, it will often be necessary for the roofing contractor to provide the client with (health and safety) information about the roof structure.

2.4   Access arrangements

Stair towers

Stair towers are a far more effective and safe means of access. They help speed up access, production and enable the workforce to carry materials and equipment far more safely than ladder access. Many companies now default to stair towers, unless a risk assessment deems that ladder access is suitable for the situation (such as short or infrequent access).

A purpose-built scaffold stair tower

A ladder safety gate

Ladders

Ideally, access to a scaffold will be via a purpose-built stair tower. However, where the decision is taken to use a ladder, the scaffold should be designed to incorporate internal ladders. If an external ladder is used it should be positioned along the face of the scaffold rather than at right-angles to it. Ladder gates should be installed at access points.

Safe working on roofs and at height

A ladder must not be used as an access to, or egress from, a workplace unless it is reasonable to do so, taking into account the work being carried out, its duration and the risks to the safety of any person arising from the use of the ladder.

If the vertical height of a ladder is over nine metres, safe landing areas or rest platforms should be provided at suitable intervals.

Landing places

All landing places must be of adequate dimensions.

If a person is liable to fall from a height that would result in injury, landing places must be provided with:

- ☑ a guard-rail at a height of not less than 950 mm
- ☑ an intermediate guard-rail
- ☑ a toe-board
- ☑ a gap not exceeding 470 mm between the toe-board and guard-rail, or between any two guard-rails
- ☑ an intermediate guard-rail if standard, light-gauge brick guards are used.

Roof ladders

Roof ladders should be erected as follows.

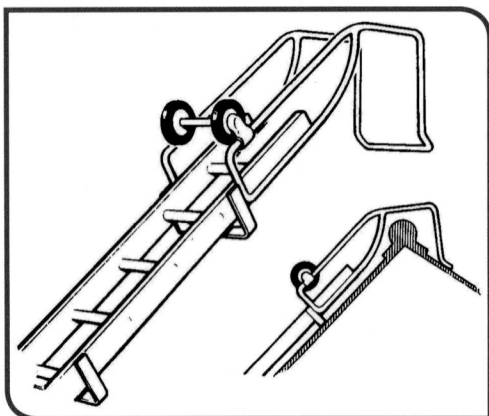 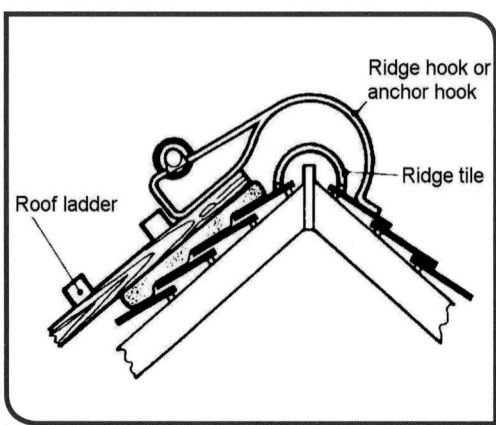

First, a standing ladder is erected for access to the eaves of the roof. It should extend at least one metre or five rungs above the eaves of the roof and be properly secured, but not to the guttering, downpipes or any other plastic or fragile material.

The roof ladder should then be brought up and pushed up the roof on its wheels, with the anchor hook or ridge hook uppermost.

Once over the ridge, the ladder is turned over and the hook engaged. It may be necessary to secure the ladder with a rope if ridge tiles are unsound.

Ideally, where it is necessary to use a roof ladder, access to the lower end of it will be from a working platform at the eaves.

Where access is from a free-standing ladder, the safety points on ladder safety, outlined previously in this chapter, must be observed.

Roof ladders must be:

- ☑ only used by persons who are competent to use them
- ☑ positioned to enable easy and safe transfer between:
  - – any other ladder used to get to the eaves and the roof ladder
  - – the roof ladder and the place of work
- ☑ designed for the purpose
- ☑ of good construction, strong enough to enable the planned work to be carried out and regularly inspected
- ☑ adequately supported to take the user's weight without damaging the roof
- ☑ securely fixed to the sloping part of the roof by means of a ridge hook placed over the ridge. Ridge hooks must not bear down on ridge tiles or capping tiles.

Eaves and stop ends

On steep roofs, those over 50°, a working platform at the eaves is essential, preferably with an additional third handrail or toe-board. It is also important to provide suitable edge protection which could withstand the impact of a person or materials falling or rolling down the roof at speed.

Mobile access platforms

Mobile access platforms are often used as an alternative to ladders, scaffolds and cradles.

The range of equipment includes MEWPs, forklift trucks equipped with work platforms and mast climbing work platforms (MCWPs).

Each of these types of equipment can be suitable for carrying out particular types of roof work. For example, using a telescopic boom MEWP (cherry picker) might be a suitable and safe way of accessing a job that would otherwise require someone having to cross a fragile roof. This is particularly important for inspection work. Truck-mounted cherry pickers now have sufficient reach to enable inspection of nearly all buildings to be made without having to directly access the roof.

Where people are working from these platforms, calculations of the real loads must be made. Typically an allowance for each person of 100 kg covers operative and tools. If materials are to be carried as well, then the weight must be estimated to ensure that the platform is not overloaded.

Finally, thought must be given to emergencies, and how aerial rescue could be carried out if necessary.

Mobile elevating work platform

Easily moved from place to place, MEWPs are particularly suitable for short duration tasks requiring a work platform.

Work platforms may be towable units, lorry or trailer-mounted, or self-propelled. If they are used on public roads, the Road Traffic Acts apply in respect of licences, insurance, construction and use.

Also, it must not be overlooked that MEWPs are classified as lifting equipment within the Lifting Operations and Lifting Equipment Regulations, and, as the task is so-called 'man riding', the inspections must be at six-monthly intervals.

Working platforms on forklift trucks

Forklift trucks equipped with work platforms may be used for access to limited heights, usually for maintenance work. The platform or cage must be designed for the purpose, fitted to the forklift truck in a manner that prevents it from becoming accidentally detached, and comply with the Work at Height Regulations.

If the use of a forklift truck for this purpose becomes part of an established pattern of work, consideration should be given to introducing a purpose-built mobile platform.

In the eyes of the HSE, the use of so-called non-integrated work platforms on forklift trucks is not seen as a particularly safe practice. The HSE is very concerned about the use of rough terrain telescopic forklifts.

These are very commonly used on demolition sites when stripping roofs for salvage or removing asbestos cement sheets. To be able to use them, as a minimum the platform and forklift must have the following:

- ☑ be tested under LOLER every six months
- ☑ a plate in the basket displaying information about loading and so on
- ☑ harness points identified
- ☑ dipper ram controls isolated
- ☑ signage on the forklift confirming that it is suitable for the use.

Crane and man-riding basket

One way to overcome the access difficulties associated with fragility is simply not to land on the roof at all. It is possible to use man-riding baskets from a mobile crane. The crane itself would normally be expected to be fitted with a dead man's handle so that the driver cannot inadvertently lower the basket to the ground, and must be on power lower as opposed to free fall. This may rule out some older crawler cranes.

All physical parts of the system will require thorough examination under LOLER every six months. It would be expected for the operatives to be harnessed in and typically the harnesses are attached to the hook block of the crane, which offers a second level of safety – so-called redundancy.

Mast climbing work platforms

With this equipment, the platform or cradle rises up one or more static masts in a similar way to a hoist, providing a temporary work platform at height, usually on the side of a building. Some of the procedures to be observed in their erection and use are that they should be:

- ☑ erected only by skilled and competent persons

- ☑ used only by trained operatives

- ☑ inspected daily before use, by the user

- ☑ regularly inspected by a competent person and records maintained of the inspection

- ☑ thoroughly examined every six months

- ☑ clearly marked with the safe working load and permitted numbers of persons allowed on the platform at each configuration.

They should not be used as a substitute for using stairs or a passenger lift for travelling to higher levels.

For further information refer to:
Chapter D05 Fall arrest and suspension equipment,
Chapter C05 Plant and work equipment, and
Chapter C07 Lifting operations.

Access to chimneys

Various purpose-designed, lightweight stagings are available for work on or around chimneys. Alternatively, tube and fitting scaffolding should be erected or a MEWP used. Under no circumstances should work be carried out on a chimney without the use of a properly constructed and stable working platform.

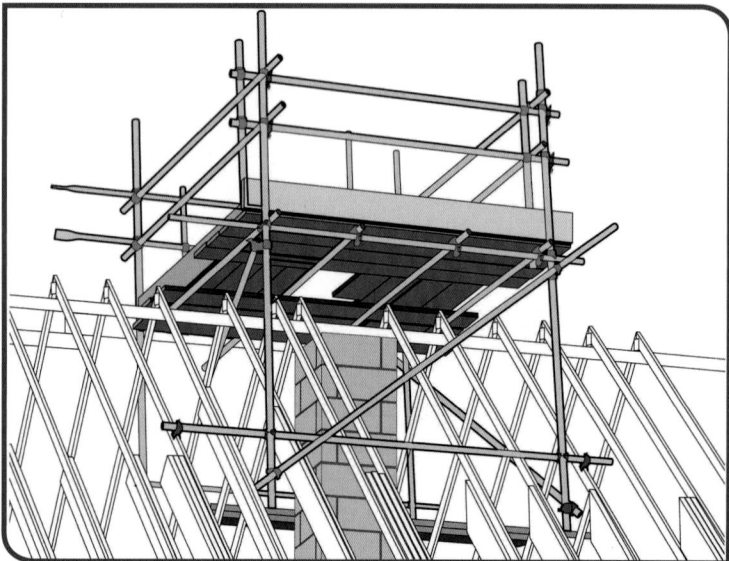

Special scaffolds (such as roof saddles) must be designed in accordance with NASC Guidance Note TG20.

2.5 Best practice solutions

The following are commercially available systems commonly used in the construction industry.

Edge protection

Steel mesh barriers

Steel mesh barrier systems are designed for simple assembly and can be adapted to suit site requirements.

Fast frame system

The fast frame system is a bespoke system designed to satisfy the specific needs of the high-rise steel frame industry.

Containment solutions

To address the hazard of loose building materials or dropped tools falling outside of the construction area, there is a broad range of high quality containment solutions.

Net barrier system

Net barrier systems offer a flexible edge protection solution to all manner of roof construction.

Counterweight system

Rapid, versatile, freestanding edge protection for flat roof construction and renovation projects, which uses a secure counterweight system.

Telescopic transoms

Telescopic transoms can be slid back and inner boards removed to accommodate the progress of the façade works.

02

Fall safety

Loading systems

Designed for the loading and unloading of material from flat-bed lorries.

Personal fall protection

Designed to secure a person to an anchorage point, so that a fall from height is either totally prevented or safely arrested.

Safety net fans

Safety net fans are a new innovation in high-rise protection, specifically designed to catch falling objects, debris and people.

The safety net fan utilises the Class B1 net and comes with 60 x 60 mm mesh and 20 x 20 mm debris net as standard, which has been proven to arrest falls of up to 100 kg from a height of six metres, conforming to EN 1263-1&2 *(Safety nets)*.

The elasticity of the net, together with a slight deformation of the frame, ensures that the impact of a fall is absorbed, considerably decreasing the risk of injury or objects falling to street level. Items do not bounce out or shatter, which can harm people and property below.

Fall arrest

A zero factor fall-arrest system is designed to prevent falls from height.

It provides total safety when placing:

- ☑ decking panels
- ☑ edge protection
- ☑ slab edges
- ☑ stop-ends

and generally all situations that may arise during the form-working process, where there is a risk of a fall from height.

It is easy to assemble and use.

Temporary access – working platforms

Cantilevered platform

Used to provide a working platform and walkway around wall forms and partition walls.

Hanging platform

Creates a working platform around the edge of roofs and structures.

The hanging platform offers a modular, quickly installed working platform system that can be fixed around the full outer perimeter of structures.

Lightweight, and fitted to allow high level access without the need to restrict the area below, the system consists of a console that is suspended or attached to the structure using a range of supports, and into which boardwalks are fixed to create a walkway.

Platform shoe

Provides anchorage of working platforms in lift shafts and similar structural situations.

Temporary access – stairways

Stairways

There is a wide range of stairways that are quick and easy to install, and offer safe, temporary access between levels on construction sites.

They should be designed and tested to meet the access performance requirements within the standard *Temporary works equipment – performance requirements and general design* (EN 12811).

Universal stair

Ladder replacement stair

Universal stair provides temporary access between levels in scaffolds or construction sites and for building stair towers in both traditional and system scaffolding. The staircase units fold for transport, are easily assembled and automatically adjust to a wide range of lift heights.

The ladder replacement stair provides compact stairway access within traditional and system scaffold structures, offering an easy solution for replacing the use of traditional ladders on site.

(The above images are reproduced with the kind permission of Combisafe International Ltd.)

www. For further information visit the Combisafe website.

2.6   Other considerations

Stacking materials on roofs

Care must be taken at all times when stacking material on or at roof level. Attention should be given to the:

- ☑ size of the load involved
- ☑ types of material involved
- ☑ methods of raising the load, whether manually or mechanically
- ☑ means of communication (signals) and the competence of the slinger or signaller
- ☑ position authorised for stacking materials
- ☑ distribution of the loads (loading plan)
- ☑ maximum load or stack size
- ☑ loading limitations of the roof
- ☑ adequate support or packing to the truss

- ☑ protection of the existing roof surface and any weather-proofing
- ☑ prevention of the displacement of loads that should be secured against:
  – the wind, especially split bundles and sheets
  – sliding down sloping roofs (sheet stop).

Permission to load roofs

Permission to place a load on a roof structure must be obtained from either:

- ☑ owners or occupiers
- ☑ the architect or a consultant engineer, or
- ☑ the main contractor.

Danger areas

Under the Work at Height Regulations there is a specific legal requirement to ensure the safety of:

- ☑ those working at height (from falls)
- ☑ others who may be working or passing below (from falling objects), by the creation of danger areas, either around the high-level workplace and/or below it.

This is achieved by preventing unauthorised access into any danger area, so far as is reasonably practicable, by the use of equipment (such as barriers and appropriate signs).

Employers may find in particular situations that it is not practical to create a permanent exclusion zone beneath the work being carried out above. In these circumstances a solution would be to deploy safety marshals at the lower level to enforce exclusion from the danger area as and when it is necessary.

In such circumstances it is essential that an effective means of communication be established between those working at height and the workers controlling the danger area.

Roof trusses

The placement and installation of roof trusses and their associated bracing has the potential to be a very hazardous activity and a safe system of access and protection must be planned and implemented. The risk assessment should have considered these and all other aspects of the work.

Safe access within the trusses

The design of safe access into a roof truss system should be undertaken by the truss designer or the architect, and information passed to the contractor. This will then form part of the overall risk assessment.

A safe working platform around the perimeter of the roof should be erected and, where access is required within the trusses, safe access provided. This can be achieved by boarding out the bottom chord of the trusses, so long as they are stable and capable of taking the imposed loads.

Safety nets can be used, provided a safe clearance distance can be achieved below the net. However, it is difficult to arrange a strong fixing for a net on a new-build house. The most common fall protection systems in use in house building are bean bags, air bags or crash decks.

There are a number of proprietary soft-landing systems available in which the fall-arrest bags simply interlock to provide a cushioned landing if someone falls.

Crash decks could be as simple as a tower scaffold under the place of work. They do need to be moved periodically so that they remain under the place of work and of course they are nowhere as comfortable to land on as a soft-landing system.

Openings, corners, breaks, edges and joisting in a floor

Where reasonably practicable, edge protection, in the form of guard-rails and toe-boards, must be provided if people have to work close to what would otherwise be an unprotected edge, where:

- ☑ a person who fell would be injured as a result of the fall
- ☑ material, tools or equipment could fall
- ☑ the work is over water, other liquid or dangerous material.

All holes in floors must be similarly guarded or securely covered. The covering must be of a suitable material, securely fixed and clearly marked 'hole below'.

Open joists through which a person could fall must be boarded over to provide safe access to a working place.

Guard-rails, toe-boards and covers may be removed to allow access for people and materials, but must be replaced as soon as possible. This does not apply to demolition work unless it is left unattended.

Working over water

Where there is a risk of persons falling from a structure into water, a secure form of fencing, barrier or fall arrest equipment (preferably safety nets) must be provided. This can be briefly removed for access and the movement of materials, but must be replaced as soon as possible.

Other points to be considered include:

- ☑ ensuring that a risk assessment has been carried out
- ☑ if possible, providing a suitable working platform
- ☑ safety nets, if used, must be properly erected and periodically inspected
- ☑ warning notices must be placed near to all edges
- ☑ adequate lighting must be provided as necessary
- ☑ special care must be taken in inclement weather (such as fog, frost, snow and rain)
- ☑ special attention must be paid to the possibility of tides or storm surges changing water levels or flow rates
- ☑ life jackets must be provided, and worn by all operatives involved in working over water

☑ preferably only operatives who can swim should be used

☑ suitable rescue equipment must be provided, maintained and operated by trained and competent staff

☑ frequent checks must be carried out to ensure that the correct number of personnel can be accounted for

☑ all persons must work in pairs, or in larger groups, as necessary (no lone-working)

☑ all persons must be trained in the procedures for raising alarms and in rescue drills.

 For further information refer to Chapter F05 Working over or near to water.

Managing asbestos in roofwork

Asbestos-containing materials have been widely used in roof construction. It is an absolute legal requirement for all roof-workers and specifiers to attend an asbestos awareness course unless all their work is entirely on new build. If they will carry out any work on asbestos then they will need additional practical training.

 HSE maintains a list of organisations that can carry out this training.

A method statement will be required for any work with asbestos and this requirement makes no exception for the number of employees. The method statement must be written by someone who is deemed competent with regard to asbestos and who understands the Control of Asbestos Regulations.

All asbestos-containing materials removed from roofs will be classed as hazardous waste (special waste in Scotland) and will need to be disposed of by a registered waste carrier to a licensed tip.

Whilst the construction of a new roof will not pose any asbestos problems, the replacement, repair, refurbishment or demolition of an existing roof might well have asbestos implications.

Under the Control of Asbestos Regulations an employer must assume all materials are asbestos-containing unless they can prove otherwise. Whilst it is not difficult to recognise asbestos cement roof sheet, determining if a particular existing roofing felt contains asbestos and whether soffits are asbestos cement or asbestos insulation board is normally more problematic. All commercial clients have a duty to be able to provide information on the presence of asbestos and should be able to give both designers and contractors a copy of their asbestos management plan. Domestic clients have no such obligation and it is down to the contractor to find out if there are any asbestos-containing materials.

The presence of bats

Bats commonly roost in roof space and it is vital that contractors are aware of their obligations.

All species of bat and their breeding sites or resting places (roosts) are protected under Regulation 39 of the Conservation (Natural Habitats) Regulations and Section 9 of the Wildlife and Countryside Act.

It is an offence for anyone intentionally to kill, injure or handle a bat, to possess a bat (whether live or dead), disturb a roosting bat, or sell or offer a bat for sale without a licence. It is also an offence to damage, destroy or obstruct access to any place used by bats for shelter, whether they are present or not.

The presence of pigeons

The accumulated droppings of pigeons, if disturbed into airborne dust and then inhaled, can cause severe respiratory problems. It is anticipated that this will mainly be a problem during refurbishment and repair work, or demolition.

If during the early visits to site it is evident that pigeons have been, or are present, measures must be taken to clean up the droppings before work starts, using a safe system of work, and to discourage the return of the birds.

2.7 Legislative requirements

The Work at Height Regulations

The relevant requirements of these regulations with regard to roof work are considered to be:

- ☑ employers to ensure that work at height is planned, supervised and carried out in a safe manner by competent persons

- ☑ work at height to be carried out using appropriate work equipment, particularly that which provides collective fall protection

- ☑ suitable and sufficient steps to be taken to prevent falling objects that are likely to cause injury to any person

- ☑ consideration for the weather conditions

- ☑ where appropriate, the need to plan how the rescue of someone who has fallen but is suspended might be achieved

- ☑ where there is a risk of a person falling or being struck by a falling object, steps to be taken to prevent unauthorised access into that area

- ☑ ensure the work is carried out by trained and competent persons who are adequately supervised.

[!] Competence is the key

Demonstration of competence is a key requirement of the Work at Height Regulations, and successful completion of the Ladder Association's industry standard training course contributes significantly to providing that proof of competence.

 For further information on this course, and the regulations, refer to the Ladder Association and legislation websites.

In the context of roof work, the definition of personal protective equipment (PPE) includes items of fall-arrest equipment (such as safety harnesses and lanyards).

In deciding which type to issue, the employer must take into account the risk that the PPE is being used for, and also ensure that the PPE will fit the wearer and allow them to work comfortably.

The employer must ensure that employees have been given adequate and appropriate information, instruction and training to enable them to understand the risks being protected against, the purpose of the PPE and the manner in which it is to be used.

Whilst the employer must take reasonable steps to ensure that any PPE supplied is used, the employee in turn must ensure that they use the equipment provided in accordance with instruction and training given and know the procedures for reporting loss or defects to their employer.

The Construction (Design and Management) Regulations

The regulations place legal duties on several categories of duty holder, each of which has the potential to reduce the risks to health and safety during and after the construction phase.

Designers

The definition of *designer* under the Construction (Design and Management) Regulations (CDM) is extremely wide and many contractors will also be designers. A common scenario would be where the client simply asks the contractor to sort out a leaking roof and the contractor designs the solution.

Whoever devises the specification for the work is likely to be considered a designer. This is very important as the designer has a legal duty to consider health and safety issues in relation to not only carrying out the work, but also the maintenance, cleaning and eventual removal (demolition) of the roof.

In common with all aspects of design, the person carrying out the design should be sufficiently knowledgeable of the construction process to specify how the work can be carried out safely.

Roofers working on industrial type buildings are commonly faced with the problem of fragility. This may be because the roof itself is made of a fragile material (such as asbestos cement sheets) or simply because the roof lights are not load bearing. As the standard specification for roof lights is 10% by area, this represents a significant amount of fragile roof surface.

The HSE states quite categorically that stringent effort should be made by designers to ensure that fragile roof lights are not specified. The Advisory Committee for Roofwork (ACR), which is the lead authority in the UK on roofwork health and safety and represents all the relevant trade associations, has published jointly with the HSE definitive guidance on what constitutes fragile material.

This is found in the so-called *Red book – ACR 001:2011 (Fourth edition)*. This book details tests that manufacturers should carry out on profiled roof sheets. Anyone who specifies this type of roofing must be aware of the contents of this book and ensure the materials they specify meet the standards where possible.

02

When designing roofs, designers should also consider such things as ongoing maintenance activities (for example, how roof lights and gutters can be cleaned safely) and whether the safe access for this type of work can be designed-in at the design stage.

Clients

Under the regulations the client must provide relevant pre-construction information to other parties (such as the main contractor, or the principal contractor and CDM co-ordinator where the project is notifiable) to enable the job to be planned so that it can be carried out safely. The client, along with other duty holders, must take reasonable steps to ensure that all parties involved are competent to do what is required of them.

The main type of information that would be relevant for roof work would be the presence of asbestos, areas of damage, loading limitations of the roofing material, the existence of fall-restraint systems, the location of safe access routes where known, as-built drawings where available and so on.

It should be noted that the client may not be aware of such factors as damaged areas of the roof or the existence (or lack) of safe access routes. The client may assume that the job will be carried out by a method that is neither practical nor safe. They commonly expect roofing contractors to be able to access places and do tasks that they would simply not allow their employees to do.

Competence

The Approved Code of Practice (ACoP) to the CDM Regulations contains guidance on competence. It refers to management systems and access to health and safety advice, training and historic performance. There is also a number of trade associations for roofing companies that could be consulted or comment upon queries on competence. These include:

☑ National Federation of Roofing Contractors (NFRC)

☑ Flat Roofing Alliance (FRA)

☑ Single Ply Roofing Association (SPRA)

☑ Mastic Asphalt Council (MAC)

☑ Rural and Industrial Design and Building Association (RIDBA).

 For information on the regulations and for additional resources refer to the HSE or the individual websites.

Whilst membership of these organisations by itself does not guarantee either good health and safety practices or quality, they do all vet members and operate a dispute resolution service, which may be a useful facility.

 The Advisory Committee for Roofwork is a body dedicated to making working on roofs safer. It was established in 1998 and is made up of nominees from HSE, trade associations and organisations involved in roof work that provide the experience of many years of involvement in working on roofs in the advice given in their documents.

 Refer to the Access Industry Forum's website for some useful online videos.

03

Common access equipment

The purpose of this chapter is to give an understanding of the use of, and health and safety requirements for, common access equipment.

While the chapter gives relevant information, training in the actual system to be used will be necessary before a person can be regarded as competent.

It is important that anyone reading this chapter has a good understanding of the requirements of the Work at Height Regulations.

Introduction   36
Key points   36
Ladders and stepladders   36
Podium steps/mini mobile towers/pop-ups   41
Lightweight staging and trestle scaffolds   41
Mobile towers   42
Other access equipment   46
Legislative requirements and further information   47

3.1   Introduction

Access equipment, system scaffolds and the components of mobile scaffold towers are generally of a modular layout. They comprise standards with welded node connectors to which ledgers and transoms are fastened, usually with proprietary wedges or rings (rather than loose coupler connections) or frames with both standards and transoms welded into one unit.

The safety requirements of system scaffolds are broadly similar to traditional scaffolds, but there are some significant differences.

3.2   Key points

☑ When selecting suitable access equipment, the working at height hierarchy should be followed.

☑ The modular construction of system and tower scaffolds could increase the temptation for unqualified persons to tamper with them. Site managers must be aware of this and monitor the situation.

☑ Mobile tower and access equipment must be subjected to statutory inspections with reports raised where appropriate.

☑ All mobile towers must be properly erected, stable, suitable for their purpose and equipped with toe-boards and guard-rails on all working platforms.

3.3   Ladders and stepladders

Traditionally, ladders and stepladders have been used as:

☑ the way of getting up to or down from a place of work at height (for example, the means of access to a roof or scaffold)

☑ a place of work at height (work carried out whilst standing on a ladder or stepladder (for example, painting first floor windows)).

The Work at Height Regulations require that employers give adequate consideration to the safety of the user before selecting a ladder or stepladder as either a means of access to height or as a place of work at height.

Sherpamatic-type steps with safe working platform and additional outriggers

In deciding whether or not a ladder or stepladder should be used, the employer must carry out a risk assessment and be able to demonstrate that it is not reasonably practicable to use an alternative, safer means of access and that the risks from using the ladder or stepladder are low.

HSE guidance is that ladders and stepladders should only be used as a place of work when the nature of the work:

☑ is of short duration (a few minutes rather than hours)

☑ is of a light nature (requires no heavy lifting, carrying or a destabilising pressure applied by the user or equipment in carrying out the work – minimal manual handling)

☑ allows one hand to be available at all times for holding on to the ladder or stepladder

☑ requires nothing to be carried that would cause instability of the ladder, stepladder or user

☑ does not necessitate using the top third of the ladder or stepladder.

Additionally, when stepladders are used as a place of work they should be positioned so that the user faces the work as the stepladder is climbed. A stepladder must not be positioned so that the user is side-on to the work, where the nature of the work would apply a sideways pressure and cause the stepladder to become unstable.

Ladders should:

☑ be set up at an angle of 75° (one metre out for every four metres up)

☑ be positioned on a firm, level surface

☑ not be vulnerable to impact by pedestrians or traffic

☑ be used in accordance with the manufacturer's instructions

☑ be the right ladder for the job

☑ be inspected before use to ensure there are no defects

☑ ideally, be lashed at or near the upper point of rest by the stiles, not the rungs

☑ extend at least one metre above the stepping-off place unless an alternative handhold is provided that enables a safe transfer between ladder and stepping-off place

☑ be secured at the bottom or footed* if lashing at the top is not possible

☑ not be rested against fragile or flexible items (such as plastic guttering); a ladder stay or stand-off device must be used, as necessary

☑ never be painted to an extent that the paint could conceal defects

☑ be subjected to a schedule of periodic inspections with written inspection reports kept, be individually identifiable and proof of inspection demonstrated

☑ be visually checked by the user for obvious defects before use and not used if found to be defective.

Users should face the ladder at all times when climbing up or down, and not carry anything that would interfere with their safety or balance.

HSE research has shown that, to be most effective, the person footing a ladder should stand on the bottom rung with both feet at all times. Even then, footing is not an effective method of stopping a long ladder from slipping sideways and, furthermore, two people are on the ladder, which goes against good practice. Ideally a ladder will only be footed when it is climbed for the first time for the purpose of tying it off.

03

Types of ladder

Standing ladders are a single stage ladders up to six metres in length.

Pole ladders are a variant of the above type, but with the stiles having been made from a long, whitewood pole cut down the middle to give even strength and flexibility. Lengths can vary up to a maximum of 10 metres.

The practice of shortening a pole ladder to fit a particular situation should be discouraged. The only time shortening a pole ladder is acceptable is when an end is damaged. Care must be taken to ensure that the fabric of the ladder remains stable if a tie wire is removed.

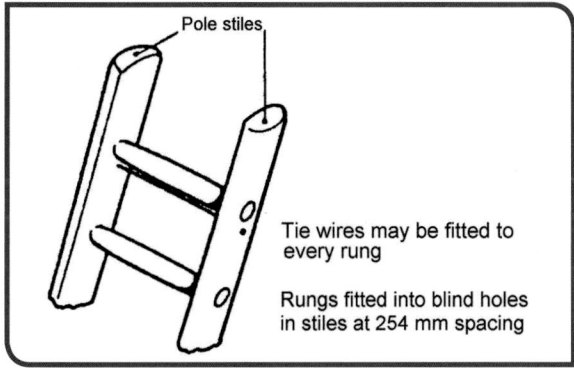

Pole stiles

Tie wires may be fitted to every rung

Rungs fitted into blind holes in stiles at 254 mm spacing

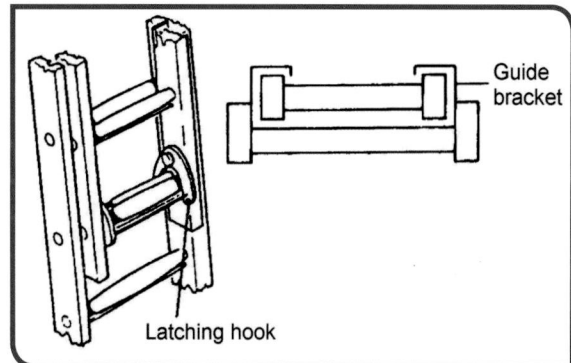

Guide bracket

Latching hook

Extension ladders consist of two or three sections coupled together and extended by sliding over or inside each other.

Longer multi-stage ladders are extended by means of a rope and pulley. A three-section ladder, fully extended, may reach over 16 metres.

Stepladders are of various types, have flat rectangular treads and are usually free standing.

Platform stepladders have a built in working platform, and newer models can have wheels for ease of movement, handrails and restraint chains. Due to the platform, these are usually a better option for activities that are regularly carried out at the same height.

Roof ladders are a ladder with a hook on the top end of it for securing over the ridge of a roof.

Aluminium and steel ladders are available in various types. Their main advantage is that they are light and weather resistant. They can be prone to slipping at the base if the rubber or wooden feet are not properly maintained.

Classes of ladder (BS 1129:1990, BS 2037:1994 and BS EN 131)

Portable ladders, steps, trestles and lightweight staging are covered by BS 1129:1990, BS 2037:1994 and BS EN 131.

A **duty rating** indicates their suitability of use.

☑ **Class 1. Industrial**. Heavy duty – can be used frequently and in the tough conditions that can be found on site. These are the only ladders that are recommended for use on site.

☑ **Class 2. Light trades**. Medium duty – can be used only in good conditions. Suitable for light trade purposes. (This class of ladder is now covered by BS EN 131.)

☑ **Class 3. Domestic**. Light duty – suitable only for domestic and household use.

 Class 2 and 3 ladders are not recommended for general use on site.

All ladders should be marked with a unique identification number and the class or duty rating. For more comprehensive guidance refer to the HSE's guidance document INDG402.

Inspection of ladders

Every ladder should be inspected on a regular basis and should carry an identification mark, as detailed above. A written record should be kept of all inspections, defects and repairs.

03

 The frequency of inspections should be determined by considering the use, duration and environment in which they will be used. It is common for ladders that are used regularly to be thoroughly inspected every three months.

Ladders should not be used if defective in any way and, if damaged beyond repair, they should be destroyed.

During the inspection of ladders, attention should be paid to the following points. There should be no:

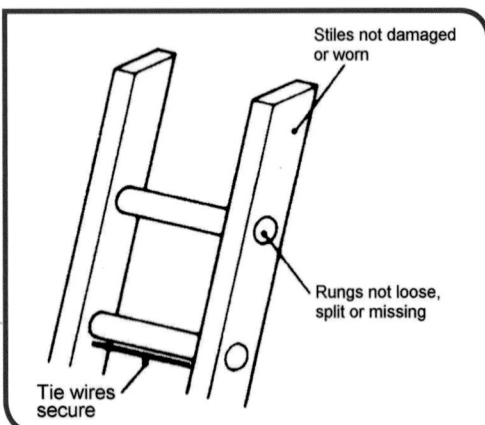

Stiles not damaged or worn

Rungs not loose, split or missing

Tie wires secure

☑ damaged or worn stiles, particularly at the head or foot of the ladder

☑ broken, missing, loose or worn rungs

☑ mud or grease on the rungs

☑ rungs supported solely by nails, screws or spikes

☑ movement in the rungs or stiles

☑ decayed timber, or corroded fittings

☑ insecure tie wires

☑ warping, sagging or distortion; check that the ladder stands firmly.

The condition of any ropes and cords, along with pulleys, hinges and any other fittings, should be checked for fraying to ensure that they are all secure with no sign of damage.

Carrying a ladder

A short ladder may be carried comfortably by having it vertical against the shoulder and holding one of the lower rungs, using the other hand to hold the stile. Longer ladders should be carried horizontally by two people. Care should be taken in negotiating corners and obstacles.

Ladders must not be taken into the vicinity of overhead power lines unless a permit to work has been issued. Even then, extreme care should be taken with the head of the ladder so that it is not allowed to get close to the overhead power lines.

Timber ladders generally do not conduct electricity (unless wet) but aluminium ladders are extremely conductive, and are dangerous to use in close proximity to overhead lines.

Erecting and lowering ladders

The procedure for erecting a ladder, when the ladder is flat on the ground, is as follows.

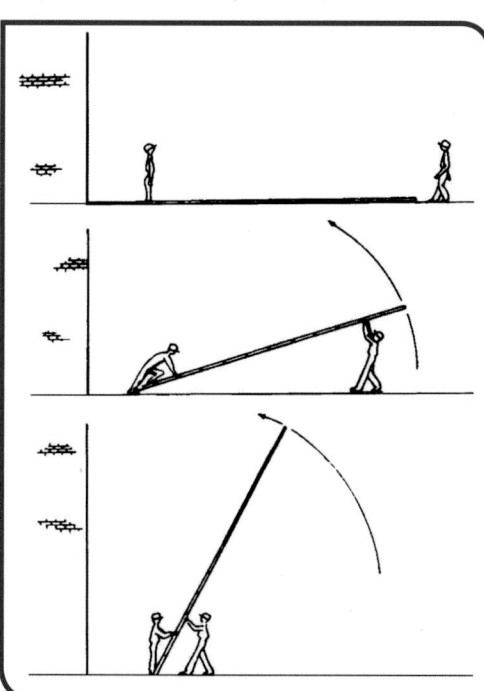

☑ One person stands on the bottom rung while the other takes position at the head of the ladder and takes hold of the top rung, raising the ladder off the ground.

☑ Then, rung by rung, that person moves towards the foot of the ladder, lifting as they go. The person at the foot grasps the lower rungs as soon as possible and draws the ladder towards them, steadying it at the same time.

☑ The sequence is reversed when lowering.

☑ Short ladders may be raised by one person placing the foot of the ladder against a wall or fixture and pushing the ladder upwards, starting at the top, walking, under-running and raising the ladder as they go.

03

Extension ladders

Extension ladders are raised one section at a time and slotted into position. The minimum recommended overlap on extension ladders is shown in the table below.

Closed length	Approximate no. of rungs	Overlap of rungs
Under 5 metres	Under 18	2
5–6 metres	18–23	3
Over 6 metres	Over 23	4

Latching hooks must be properly engaged.

 Ordinary ladders must never be lashed, tied or spliced together in an attempt to make an extension ladder.

Roof ladders

Roof ladders should be erected as follows.

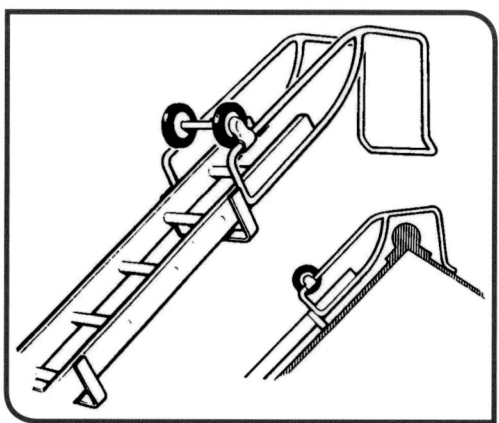
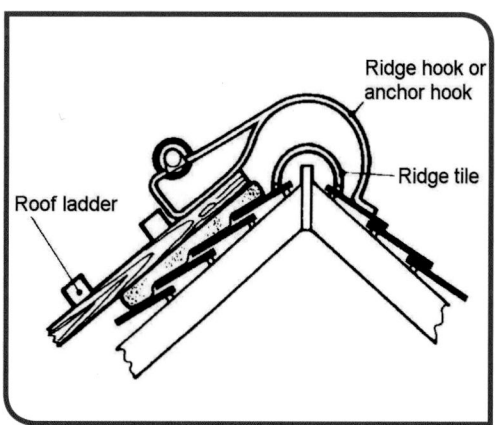

First, a standing ladder is erected for access to the eaves of the roof. It should extend at least one metre or five rungs above the eaves of the roof and be properly secured, but not to the guttering, downpipes or any other plastic or fragile material.

03

The roof ladder should then be brought up and pushed up the roof on its wheels, with the anchor hook or ridge hook uppermost.

Once over the ridge, the ladder is turned over and the hook engaged. It may be necessary to secure the ladder with a rope if ridge tiles are unsound.

Ideally, where it is necessary to use a roof ladder, access to the lower end of it will be from a working platform at the eaves.

Where access is from a free-standing ladder, the points on ladder safety (outlined previously in this chapter) must be observed.

Roof ladders must be:

- ☑ only used by persons who are competent to use them
- ☑ positioned to enable easy and safe transfer between:
  – any other ladder used to get to the eaves and the roof ladder
  – the roof ladder and the place of work
- ☑ designed for the purpose
- ☑ of good construction, strong enough to enable the planned work to be carried out and regularly inspected
- ☑ adequately supported to take the user's weight without damaging the roof
- ☑ securely fixed to the sloping part of the roof by means of a ridge hook placed over the ridge. Ridge hooks must not bear down on ridge tiles or capping tiles.

Storage of ladders

Ladders, especially if made of wood, deteriorate when exposed to the weather for prolonged periods. Where indoor storage is not available, they should be covered or stored in a protected, well-ventilated position. They should not be exposed to steam pipes, boilers or other sources of radiant heat.

Ladders should be stored on racks, supported on the stiles only, with sufficient supports to prevent them from sagging. They must not be hung from the rungs or stiles.

Aluminium ladders should be kept away from wet lime or cement, which may corrode them.

Pulleys and hinges should be lubricated and the condition of ropes and cords checked.

Any damage or deterioration should be noted and made good before further use.

Stepladders

Many of the general rules for the safe use of ladders also apply to stepladders. In addition, the following points should be considered.

- ☑ Stepladders are not to be used if a fall from one would cause the user to be injured (based upon a risk assessment).
- ☑ The treads (or steps), hinges, bolts, screws and fixings must all be sound and secure.
- ☑ Retaining cords or hinges should be of equal length and in good condition.
- ☑ The stepladder must be stable when open and standing on a level base.
- ☑ The legs of stepladders should be positioned as far apart as the retaining cord or hinges allow, with all four legs firmly and squarely on the ground.
- ☑ Wherever possible, the stepladder should be positioned so that the person climbing it is facing the work to avoid twisting and possible instability.
- ☑ Unless the design permits, the knees of the person using the stepladder should be kept below the top step.
- ☑ The user should not work from the top third of a stepladder unless it has been designed for this purpose.

If it is not practicable to maintain a handhold when a load is being carried, a risk assessment must demonstrate that the use of the stepladder is justified because of the:

- ☑ low risk
- ☑ short time the stepladder is to be in use.

3.4   Podium steps/mini mobile towers/pop-ups

The use of this type of equipment is preferred to stepladders in most circumstances as it provides a small but stable working platform, complete with guard-rails. This type of access equipment has the advantage over a stepladder in that it allows the user to work in a safer manner facing any side of the working platform without it becoming unstable.

Podium in use, correctly assembled, wheels locked and displaying inspection tag

Podium steps and mini towers are lightweight in construction and some types will fold flat for transportation. They are designed to be wheeled through a standard-sized door. Some types of this access equipment can be fitted with outriggers to increase stability.

Whilst providing a high degree of safety in most situations, there are a number of specific hazards with the use of this type of equipment and the employer should ensure the following precautions are considered in selecting and using podium steps.

- ☑ There are many differing types of podium steps with different arrangements of use. Some are just wheeled platforms and others have specific installation requirements. The instructions for each individual podium must be available and understood by the user.

- ☑ The height of the working platform should be assessed: too low and the user will not reach; too high and the user may be inclined to work from the steps rather than the platform.

- ☑ Where adjustable height platforms are in use, ensure that the user is trained in how to adjust the platform and handrails to ensure protection.

- ☑ Brakes must be used whilst the platform is in use and users must not be permitted to pull themselves along from the top of the podium.

- ☑ Podium steps, like any other access equipment, must have an individual identifying mark and be subject to frequent inspection.

 For further information about low level access equipment and training refer to the PASMA website.

Push around vertical (PAV)

Push around verticals, commonly called pop-ups, are an increasingly popular and versatile item of access equipment. These are a category covered by IPAF's PAL card (powered access licence).

3.5   Lightweight staging and trestle scaffolds

Modern trestle systems

More modern trestles are similar in many ways to system scaffolding, including the fact that guard-rails and toe-boards are an integral part of the working platform. The spacing of the supports is fixed by the system design, which enables platform boards to fit snugly without overhanging or overlapping.

All lightweight staging should be marked with the maximum permitted distributed loading. This can be done by either specifying the maximum number of persons, allowing for their tools and equipment, or by specifying the maximum safe weight.

Common access equipment

Guidelines are that:

- ☑ trestles must be set on a firm, level base

- ☑ only one working platform is installed

- ☑ guard-rails, barriers and toe-boards are required where a fall would cause a personal injury, as indicated by a risk assessment

- ☑ if a guard-rail is removed (for example, to allow materials to be stacked on the working platform) the guard-rail must be replaced as soon as practicable

- ☑ scaffold boards used on trestles to form a working platform must be of a consistent length and of equal thickness

- ☑ the trestle assembly must be completely stable when in use

- ☑ a safe means of access to the working platform must be provided (for example, a ladder that is of sufficient length, properly positioned and securely lashed)

- ☑ where locating pins are used, they should be of the correct size and type and not rebar off-cuts or other makeshift items.

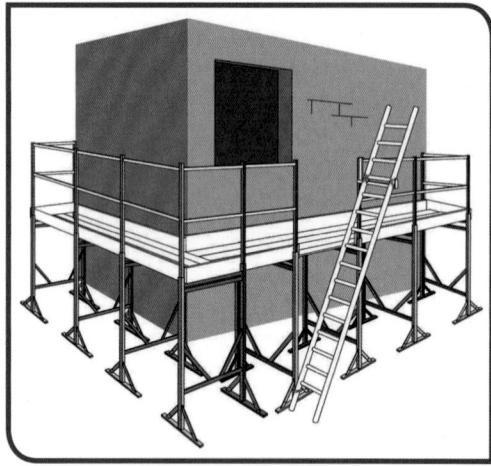

A modern trestle system with handrails, toe-boards and safe ladder access

 The use of loose scaffold boards, supported on split-head trestles with no means of preventing falls that could cause an injury to the user, is totally unacceptable and should not be considered as an option for working at height.

3.6 Mobile towers

The use of lightweight aluminium mobile towers on construction sites is a popular alternative to the use of traditional tube and fitting towers. However, these systems have some limitations and should only be used when they can satisfy both legislative and general site requirements.

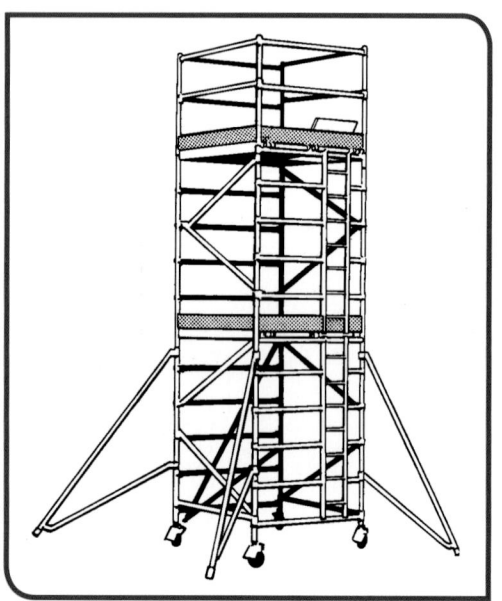

Five different items make up a basic mobile aluminium tower:

- ☑ frames

- ☑ braces

- ☑ platforms

- ☑ legs

- ☑ wheels or castors.

General conditions and provisions

The same points that arise from the Work at Height Regulations in relation to the safe erection and use of system scaffolds apply to mobile towers but, in addition, the following points should be particularly noted.

The Prefabricated Access Suppliers' and Manufacturers' Association (PASMA) has developed two methods of installing guard-rails that do not require the erector to stand on a working platform until the guard-rail frames have been installed:

☑ advanced guard-rail system

☑ through-the-trap (3T method).

The **advanced guard-rail** system involves the use of specially manufactured, hinged guard-rail frames that can be raised and slotted into position from below.

The **3T method** involves the erector only passing through the platform trapdoor far enough to be able to locate the guard-rail frames in place. In many cases, safe erection of the guard-rail sections can be achieved with the erector sitting on the platform with their legs through the trap and their feet supported on the ladder section below.

Both of these methods are approved by the HSE.

Materials

Mobile towers may be constructed from steel, but are principally aluminium.

All components must be free from any welding defects, dents, bends or distortion, or any corrosion that could prevent their safe use. Platform boards must be free from holes, cracks, splits or any delamination that would affect their safe use.

Competence

Any person erecting a mobile tower must be competent to do so, having received adequate training or, if not fully competent, be under the supervision of an experienced and competent person.

The tower must start off and remain vertical as it is built and used.

> For further information about training in mobile towers refer to the PASMA website.

Maintenance

All aluminium mobile towers are work equipment and, as such, come under the requirements of the Provision and Use of Work Equipment Regulations.

As such, mobile towers (including individual components) must be suitable for the job in hand and properly maintained.

Preparation and planning

A risk assessment should be carried out to determine whether or not a mobile aluminium tower scaffold is a suitable item of work equipment for the type of work that is to be carried out and the environment in which it is intended to be used.

Factors that should be considered when deciding whether or not it is safe to use a mobile tower are shown below.

The ground surface

Is the surface sufficiently level to use a mobile tower, if there is no adjustment on the legs for levelling the tower? A tower scaffold should not be erected if it cannot be levelled and therefore made stable.

Mobile towers only have a small area of each wheel in contact with the ground and therefore each wheel imposes a high loading at each point of contact. Is the surface strong enough to take the loading? It may be possible to use sole boards on soft ground to effectively spread the load and allow a mobile tower to be used, providing that there is no chance of the tower sinking, tilting or otherwise becoming unstable.

Are there any features (such as drain covers or underground pipes) that may not be able to take the direct or indirect loading imposed by one or more wheels?

The weather (outdoor use)

Aluminium tower scaffolds are lightweight structures that can become unstable in moderately high winds.

Has a check of the weather been made for the period that the tower will be erected?

Is it possible to tie-in the tower to the structure against which it is to be erected?

If any doubt exists on the limitations of the tower in high winds, has the manufacturer or supplier been consulted?

03

Overhead power lines

Are there any lines that are close enough to render the use of a metal scaffold unsafe?

Remember, it is not necessary to touch a high-voltage cable to get a shock. Many overhead power lines are not insulated and the electricity can arc through the air to an adjacent metal object.

Pre-assembly inspection

The competent person who is to erect a mobile tower should check that all the components are present and undamaged and ensure that they are all from the same manufacturer/supplier, and are for the same type of tower.

A check should be made that the castors and wheels rotate and swivel freely and that they have a functioning locking device (brake).

Safety during use

Stability

Due to their lightweight nature, stability can be a problem with aluminium tower scaffolds, the more so the higher they are built.

The old rules of thumb (3½:1 for towers used inside a building, or 3:1 for towers used outside) for height-to-base ratio are no longer acceptable. Individual manufacturers carry out tests on their products to enable them to provide specific guidance on height-to-base ratios, including circumstances where the installation of outriggers will be necessary. Such guidance should be available to the competent person erecting the tower.

As general guidance, it should be assumed that stabilisers will be required if an aluminium tower is to have a working platform higher than three metres above ground level.

In addition to the dimensions of the erected tower scaffold, there are several other factors that can affect its stability.

☑ Ground conditions (covered earlier in this chapter).

☑ Sheeting (outside) – will increase the wind-loading on a tower scaffold. In many instances it will not be acceptable to sheet a tower scaffold unless it can be tied-in to the structure.

☑ Overreaching – if this is so severe that the centre of gravity is moved to a point outside the base area of the scaffold, it will overturn. It is far safer to move the tower scaffold.

☑ Work activity – any work that involves applying a sideways pressure to the adjacent structure (for example, water-jetting) at a point that is high on the tower will create an equal and opposite pressure that may overturn the tower. In many cases, tying-in the tower to the adjacent structure may overcome this problem.

☑ Hoisting materials – if heavy items are hoisted up the outside of the tower, it could become unstable and overturn. Again, tying-in the tower to the adjacent structure may overcome this problem.

☑ Climbing the tower – access to the working platform should be gained by using the built-in stair or ladder sections. If a vertical ladder is built into an end frame of the tower, the person climbing the ladder must do so on the inside of the tower. Climbing the outside could overturn the tower. Never gain access to the working platform by leaning a ladder against the tower.

Tying-in a tower scaffold

Care should be taken to avoid couplers causing damage to the aluminium tubing and, accordingly, only special couplers should be used. Advice on the horizontal and vertical frequency of ties will be supplied by the manufacturer or supplier or, in the case of substantial or linked towers, the scaffold designer.

The working platform

The access hatch to the working platform must be closed as soon as everyone working from the tower is on the working platform.

The working platform must be fully boarded unless a design feature of the scaffold enables safe access and egress and effective guard-rails and toe-boards to be installed around a partially boarded platform.

The requirement for the minimum width of working platform was removed when the Work at Height Regulations came into force. These state that a working platform must be of sufficient dimensions for the safe passage of people, plant and materials with due regard to the type of work being carried out. However, BS EN 12811-1 recommends that platforms on all types of scaffold should not be less than 600 mm wide.

Gaining extra height

Placing stepladders and ladders on the working platform of a mobile tower to gain additional height is particularly dangerous and must be prohibited. Adjustable legs are only to be used for levelling, and not to gain additional height. If additional height is needed then a further lift should be added, providing this is within the manufacturer's height limitations.

The brakes

The wheel brakes must be locked in the ON position at all times when the tower is not being moved. The lightweight nature of aluminium tower scaffolds presents the potential for unattended towers to be moved by the wind if the brakes are not applied, particularly where they are used on exposed floor slabs at height.

Moving a tower scaffold

The tower must not be moved whilst anyone is on the working platform. Any item that could fall or cause the tower to be unstable whilst being moved, taking into account the condition of the floor surface, must also be removed. A tower scaffold must only be moved by pushing or pulling at the base.

The tower must never be moved by:

- ☑ towing it with a vehicle

- ☑ a person who is on the platform pulling the tower along using an adjacent structure.

Avoiding collisions

Suitable barriers should be erected to prevent people or vehicles from accidentally colliding with a tower scaffold, particularly where it is erected in a public place.

It may be necessary to create a safety zone around a tower simply because of the nature of the work being carried out above.

Loading capacity

The capacity of each platform and tower structure is often shown on labels attached to the frame of the mobile tower, or will be in the manufacturer's assembly guide. Never exceed the recommended loading levels as this may cause the tower to become unstable.

Incomplete towers

Where the proper erection of a mobile tower has not been completed, it should not be left unattended without the display of a notice stating 'Scaffold incomplete. Do not use.'

Inspection and reporting

Where the tower constitutes a working platform, it must be inspected by a competent person:

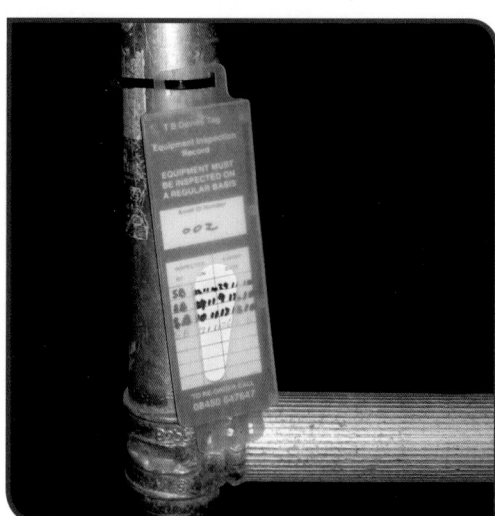

- ☑ after assembly but before being used for the first time

- ☑ after any substantial addition, dismantling or other alteration and after any event that is likely to have affected its strength or stability

- ☑ at regular intervals not exceeding seven days since the last inspection (towers with a platform at two metres or more)

- ☑ at suitable intervals, depending on the frequency and conditions of use (towers with a platform at less than two metres).

A written record is required each time the tower is inspected, as outlined above, but not after it has simply been moved to another location. A pre-use inspection might be required if, for example, it is necessary to remove and refit components to get past an obstruction.

For towers with a platform at two metres or more, this written record must be more than simply a scafftag system.

Wind strength

Aluminium structures are very vulnerable to the strength of the wind. It is recommended by many manufacturers that if the wind reaches a speed of 17 mph then all work should cease on the tower.

If the wind speed is likely to reach 25 mph, the tower should be tied-in to a rigid structure. If there is a possibility of the wind reaching speeds approaching or in excess of 40 mph, the tower should be dismantled.

Operators should be aware of the possibility of sudden high winds in exposed or gusty conditions.

It must be remembered that winds at high levels are often higher than at ground level. The wind speed can also increase as it funnels between buildings or other solid structures.

For further information on Beaufort wind scales refer to Chapter D02 Safe working on roofs and at height.

Training

Training for any operation on a construction or building site is a requirement of the regulations. Adequate training must be provided for scaffolding or any other task where any risk to the health and safety of employees, or other persons affected by their actions, is present. This applies equally to mobile towers.

> www. Training courses are available from CITB-ConstructionSkills, National Construction College, as well as from manufacturers and suppliers. Certificates should be provided as proof of training.

03

3.7   Other access equipment

There is a huge range of access equipment and solutions available to meet every need of the construction industry.

Proprietary access systems

A proprietary access system incorporating ladder access, working platform, guard-rails and hoist

Hop ups

Generally speaking hop ups, up to 600 mm high, are suitable for most applications, especially wet trades (such as plastering) that involve constant stepping up and down. Other solutions with handrails are available, but it is important to balance risk of falls against risk of musculoskeletal injuries if other solutions restrict or make movement awkward.

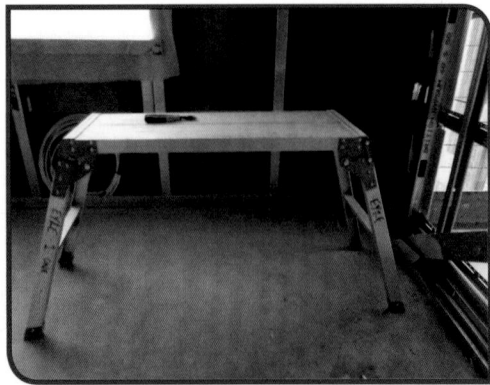

3.8   Legislative requirements and further information

The Work at Height Regulations

These regulations govern all work activities carried out at height in all industrial sectors. While recent legislation has moved towards being goal-setting rather than being prescriptive, the schedules of the Work at Height Regulations still contain a number of key dimensional and prescriptive requirements.

A key difference between these regulations and the Construction (Health, Safety and Welfare) Regulations is that there is no longer a two-metre rule. The height at which guard-rails and toe-boards must be fitted is determined solely by the findings of a risk assessment. The requirement now is that an employer must:

> take suitable and sufficient measures to prevent, so far as it is reasonably practicable, any person falling a distance liable to cause personal injury.

Experience has shown that falls from less than two metres can cause serious and fatal injuries.

For detailed information on the following requirements refer to Chapter D01 The Work at Height Regulations.

☑ Organisation and planning of work at height.

☑ The avoidance of risks from working at height.

☑ The competence of those who work at height and are involved with work equipment used for working at height.

☑ General principles for the selection of work equipment for working at height.

☑ Requirements for particular work equipment.

☑ Work on or near fragile surfaces.

☑ Danger areas.

☑ The inspection of work equipment used for working at height.

☑ The inspection of places of work at height.

☑ The duties of persons at work in relation to work at height.

For further information refer to the HSE's website.

There is a huge range of access equipment available to meet every need of the construction industry, and advice can be sought from a variety of means (such as the Access Industry Forum). Members include:

☑ ATLAS – Steeplejacks and Lightning Protection Installers

☑ BSIF – British Safety Industry Federation

☑ EPF – Edge Protection Federation

☑ FASET – Fall Arrest Safety Equipment Training

☑ IPAF – International Powered Access Federation

☑ IRATA – Industrial Rope Access Trade Association

☑ Ladder Association

☑ PASMA – Prefabricated Access Suppliers' and Manufacturers' Association

☑ SAEMA – Specialist Access Engineering and Maintenance Association (Suspended access)

☑ WAHSA – Work at Height Safety Association (Fall protection).

03

04

Scaffolding

The purpose of this chapter is to give readers an understanding of the safety issues that relate to the use of scaffolds, particularly where site managers or other readers have to manage scaffolding operations and assess the suitability of scaffolds that have been erected by others.

While its content will provide relevant basic information, training in the actual techniques of scaffolding will be necessary before a person can be regarded as competent in the erection, alteration or dismantling of any scaffolding whatsoever.

Introduction	50
Key points	51
Planning and design	52
Basic scaffold considerations and components	54
Working platforms, guard-rails, decking and access	60
Other considerations	63
Inspection and handover	66
System scaffolds	67
Appendix A – Inspection report	71

4.1 Introduction

It is very important that anyone reading this chapter has a thorough understanding of the Work at Height Regulations because they outline the legal requirements and sound principles of safely working at height. The majority of guidelines for good practice in scaffolding can be found in the safety and technical guidance notes of the National Access and Scaffolding Confederation (NASC).

This chapter will provide you with a basic knowledge of what to look for in the scaffold contractors you employ and the scaffolds that are erected. It will not confer competence in scaffolding techniques or scaffold inspection.

 Please refer to the Construction Industry Scaffolders' Record Scheme (CISRS) website for details of training schemes within the scaffolding industry.

04

The main British and European Standard for tube and fitting scaffolding is BS EN 12811 (Part 1) *Scaffolds – Performance requirements and general design.* Readers are directed to the range of NASC publications, particularly *Guide to good practice for scaffolding with tubes and fittings* (TG20).

Although this chapter applies to tube and fitting scaffolding, it is important to note that all proprietary scaffolding equipment (such as system scaffolding, beams, modular transom units and hop-up brackets) must be manufactured and tested to the relevant British and European Standards (for example, BS EN 12810).

They must also be used in accordance with the manufacturers' instructions or the scaffold should be designed by a competent engineer.

 Please refer to NASC's website for details of guides and publications.

NASC technical guidance

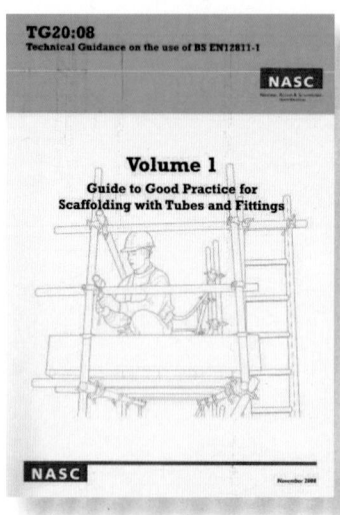

Throughout this chapter, wherever TG20 appears in the text, it refers to the NASC publication *Guide to good practice for scaffolding with tubes and fittings.*

Competent persons

The term *competence* is used in the Work at Height Regulations. However, there is no legal definition in the regulations for the word competence or the term *competent person.*

For the purposes of **scaffold inspection**, a competent person may be defined as:

 a person who has practical and theoretical knowledge, scaffold inspection training and actual experience of what they are to examine, in respect of a scaffold, so as to enable them to detect errors, defects, faults or weaknesses that it is the purpose of the examination or inspection to discover; and to assess the importance of any such discovery.

As regards the competence of individuals in relation to the erection of scaffolds, competence may be taken to mean:

 a person who has practical and theoretical knowledge, together with actual experience of scaffolding, and has acquired, or who is being supervised while being trained to acquire, a recognised qualification in scaffolding.

Record schemes

An example of a recognised qualification is the record card of CISRS.

Users of proprietary products must also ensure that scaffolders have received appropriate training (such as manufacturer's training) or a recognised qualification (such as the system scaffold product training scheme (SSPTS)), which is endorsed on the CISRS record card.

Construction Industry Scaffolders' Record Scheme

NASC operates CISRS.

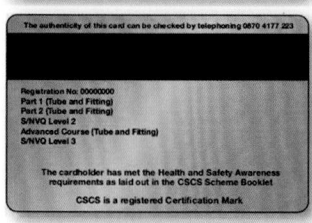

In this scheme, which is administered by CITB-ConstructionSkills, all registered scaffolders are issued with an identification card that details their grade qualifications.

It covers trainee (Part 1), scaffolder (Part 2 and VQ Level 2) and advanced scaffolder (VQ Level 3).

04

 For further details refer to the NASC website.

4.2   Key points

☑ Scaffolds must only be erected, altered or dismantled by operatives who have been trained to do so and are competent, or are under the direct supervision of someone who is.

☑ Employers who engage the services of scaffold contractors should look for proof of competence via schemes such as CISRS.

☑ The main piece of legislation that applies to scaffolding is the Work at Height Regulations.

☑ Scaffolds are subject to statutory inspections, with reports of inspections raised where appropriate.

☑ All scaffolds must be properly erected, stable, tied to the structure as appropriate, suitable for their purpose and equipped with toe-boards and guard-rails on all working platforms.

☑ The BS EN 12811 series of standards were introduced in 2004 and are supported by TG20.

☑ NASC's *Preventing falls in scaffolding and falsework* (SG4) (latest version) is the accepted industry standard to which all scaffolding contractors should be working.

☑ SG4 (latest version) is essential reading for site managers in order for them to understand how scaffolders should be erecting and dismantling structures safely.

☑ In some circumstances scaffold contractors must hold a licence to work with asbestos.

 NASC also has some online video learning aids that can be referred to.

☑ Overview of scaffolding terms.

☑ Explaining scaffold handover certificates and inspections (includes free online test).

☑ Explaining scaffold record cards and who can do what (includes free online test).

☑ The use of ladders in scaffolding (includes free online test).

☑ Preventing falls in scaffolding (SG4) (includes free online test).

☑ Technical guidance on the use of BS EN 12811-1 (TG20:08) (in two parts – includes free online test).

☑ Recommended scaffolding criteria for pavement licences (includes free online test).

4.3   Planning and design

Planning for a scaffolding contract

When selecting a scaffolding contractor you must check that they are competent and consider:

- ☑ the competence of their management and operatives for the type of work

- ☑ a proven track record for the type of work

- ☑ their past health and safety performance

- ☑ the allocation of sufficient physical and human resources to service the contract (for example, scaffolding equipment, transport, qualified scaffolders and supervision)

- ☑ whether they are regulated through membership of a recognised organisation (such as NASC).

04

Before engaging a specialist scaffolding contractor, it is advisable to prepare information on the intended use of the scaffolds for the contractor to take into account. *(For further information refer to Client's brief (TG20).)*

Before the erection of any scaffold, the following points must be clearly defined.

- ☑ What is the scaffold for?

- ☑ Is it to be a standard scaffold, as defined in TG20?

- ☑ Exactly where is it to be erected?

- ☑ What materials are to be used?

- ☑ Can safe access be provided for the erection and use of the scaffold?

- ☑ How many working platforms will there be?

- ☑ Is the ground condition where the scaffold is to be erected suitable?

- ☑ How and where can the scaffold be tied-in and what bracing will be required?

- ☑ What loadings will be imposed upon the working platforms, and on the scaffold as a whole?

- ☑ Will the scaffold be sheeted?

Scaffold design

The Work at Height Regulations require all scaffolds to be calculated unless constructed to a generally recognised standard configuration. This means tube and fitting scaffolds must be a standard scaffold, as defined in TG20 Volume 1 Section 2. Otherwise the scaffold **must** be designed and calculated by a competent engineer.

Further sections of Volume 1 and Volume 2 of TG20 provide information for engineers to design and calculate **special scaffolds** in tube and fittings.

Scaffolding contractors should have suitable arrangements in place to manage and control the erection, alteration and commissioning of special scaffolds (such as issuing drawings, managing variations to the design, inspection and handing over designed scaffolds).

It should be noted that for all **standard scaffolds** erected, a simple procedure must be followed to determine the maximum safe height as required by TG20. This basic calculation is intended to be carried out by those planning and organising scaffolding and not necessarily an engineer.

 For further information, including a comprehensive list of types of scaffold for which a design is necessary, refer to the Health and Safety Executive (HSE) website.

Fall prevention and protection while scaffolding

While a scaffold structure is actually being built, the scaffolders do not always have the protection afforded by guard-rails and toe-boards until they have installed them. They rely upon the use of personal fall protection equipment (harnesses) to arrest a fall during this time.

In order to assist employers, NASC has produced *Preventing falls in scaffolding and falsework* (SG4) (latest version). This is the accepted industry standard to which all scaffolding contractors should be working.

Under the heading *Step 1 – Planning for work at height,* the guidance states:

 scaffolding contractors should consider measures that prevent falls from height, such as providing adequate work platforms with suitable guard-rails or other collective measures, before resorting to fall arrest equipment (such as harnesses).

Devices and systems of work that provide collective fall protection, such as advanced guard-rail systems and step-ups, are now available for certain scaffolding operations. These collective measures enable scaffolders to provide guard-rail protection in advance of erection and to maintain fall protection for alterations and dismantling. Such systems do not completely eliminate the risk of a fall in all circumstances and NASC still recommends the use of personal fall protection equipment.

Scaffolding plans must also consider the rescue and recovery of a scaffolder suspended by their personal fall protection equipment.

04

Using a scaffolding step to install advanced guard-rails following SG4

 For further information on rescue planning refer to NASC's Safety guidance note SG19.

Personal fall protection equipment used for scaffolding should be inspected:

☑ by the user before use

☑ thoroughly by a competent person every three months and recorded

☑ thoroughly at other intervals if the need is identified via a risk assessment.

 For further information on the inspection of fall protection equipment refer to NASC's Safety guidance note SG16.

 To ensure compliance with the above requirements:

☑ scaffolders and their supervision should be trained in the requirements of SG4 (latest version) and the rescue plan

☑ site managers and others who run construction sites should check that the scaffold contractors coming on to their sites have been adequately trained in the requirements of SG4 (latest version).

4.4 Basic scaffold considerations and components

Scaffold features

Foundations

The foundations for all scaffolds must be of adequate strength to support and disperse the load. On hard surfaces (such as steel and concrete of sufficient strength and thickness) standards may be placed directly on the surface, although it is generally preferable to use a base plate that is 150 mm x 150 mm in size. Sheeting or proprietary plastic treaders can also be used to protect sensitive floors from damage or marking.

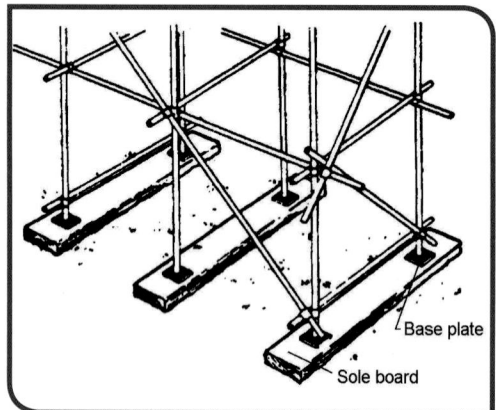

On other surfaces, the load should be spread by using base plates and sole boards. The soil or ground beneath the sole board should be level and properly compacted.

When a sole board is used on hard ground, the area beneath any one standard should be at least 10,000 mm². If a timber sole board is used, it must be not less than 35 mm thick.

On soft or disturbed ground, the sole board area should not be less than 17,000 mm². Each sole board should support two standards.

Sole board minimum dimensions should be:

☑ on hard ground – 450 mm x 225 mm x 35 mm

☑ on soft ground – 760 mm x 225 mm x 35 mm.

Bricks, blocks and scraps of odd timber must not be used as sole boards.

On sloping ground, steps should be cut into the ground to accept base plates or sole boards (see below). If the slope exceeds 1:10, an engineer should check that the ground has sufficient stability.

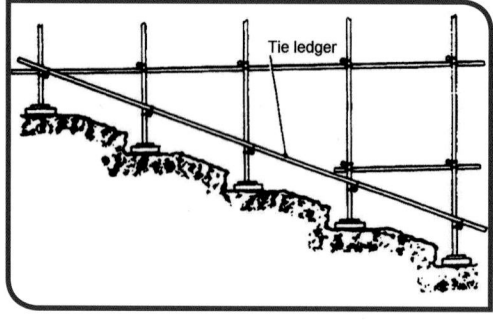

Scaffolds founded on roofs or other suspended surfaces will need special consideration for the loads imposed. An assessment and calculations may need to be made by an engineer to ensure the loads can be supported, or whether temporary supports (shoring) will be required. Alternative scaffolding materials (such as aluminium) can also be used to reduce the loads imposed by the scaffolding.

! All special scaffolds will require design input under TG20.

Materials

Scaffold tubes and fittings must comply with BS EN 39:2001 (older tubes to BS 1139). Ends should be cut square and clean, free from any bends or distortion, corrosion, lamination splits or surface flaws.

Fittings must comply with BS EN 74:2005. Fittings should not have worn threads or damaged bolts and excess surface oil that may reduce friction grip.

All scaffold boards should comply with BS 2482:2009 and should not be warped, twisted, split or badly worn, painted or otherwise treated so as to conceal any defects.

Standards

Standards should be:

☑ placed vertically

☑ spaced closely enough to provide an adequate support *(refer to TG20 Table 1 Load classes)*

☑ on a base plate and sole boards to prevent displacement

☑ near to ledgers

☑ positioned so that joints are staggered, ensuring there are no more than three joints in any one bay.

Ledgers

Ledgers should be:

☑ horizontal and fixed securely to the inside of standards with right-angled, load-bearing couplers

☑ fitted so that joints are staggered, and not situated in the same bay

☑ positioned so that joints in ledgers are in the end thirds of the bay, adjacent to the standards.

Putlogs and transoms

The length of putlog tubes and transoms will vary to suit the width class of the scaffold in accordance with TG20 Table 7.

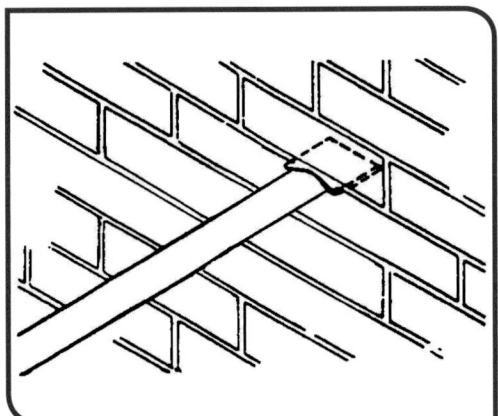

In order to avoid injury to site workers (and in some circumstances, the public), the outermost ends of the putlogs or transoms should not project an unnecessary distance beyond the face of the scaffold and/or should be shielded by the use of purpose-made protective plastic cups or other suitable protection.

Where appropriate, transoms should be long enough to butt up against the supporting structure and enable the attachment of façade bracing tubes.

Putlogs should be:

- ☑ securely fixed to ledgers or standards with right-angled or putlog couplers

- ☑ supported with the blade placed in the mortar bed joint of the brickwork, and pushed right into the wall to provide a sufficient support (see above). The blade should be horizontal and bedded approximately 75 mm into the brickwork.

When putlogs are used on existing buildings for tasks such as refurbishment or repointing, each putlog blade can be installed either with the flattened end located in a vertical joint (pert) or the horizontal bed in the brickwork.

04

Boarded lifts

Width

While the Work at Height Regulations do not specify a minimum width of a boarded lift, the recommended minimum width in accordance with BS EN 12811-1 is 600 mm.

Lift height

BS EN 12811-1 requires a minimum headroom height of 1.75 m on working lifts.

Under TG20, the maximum lift height is two metres for standard putlog and independent tied scaffolds.

Where pedestrian access is required under the first lift, a 2.7 m base lift is permissible, provided that the scaffold is tied at the first level to alternate standards.

Transom (or putlog) spacing

The spacing of transoms or putlogs for boarded lifts will be determined by the standard or grade of scaffold board used and the load class of scaffold required.

The spacing between transoms or putlogs must not result in an unsupported length of board greater than that specified in Table 8 of TG20.

Loading

It is essential that scaffolds are not loaded beyond their maximum design load. Materials should be distributed as evenly as possible with heavy items (such as piles of bricks) positioned adjacent to standards. (*Refer to Table 1 of TG20.*)

Non-boarded lifts

For scaffolds up to 15 metres high, transoms and putlogs used for non-boarded lifts should be fixed at every pair of standards, including the pair at each end of the scaffold, to either the standards with right-angled couplers, or to the ledgers with putlog couplers, and should be within 300 mm of the ledger and standard connection. For scaffolds higher than 15 metres, specialist guidance should be sought.

 SG4 requires all platform boards to be correctly supported as part of the safe system of work. Transoms provided as temporary board supports on non-boarded lifts must be left in place for alterations and dismantling.

Ledger bracing

Ledger bracing on standard scaffolds should usually be fixed to alternate pairs of standards to all lifts.

BS EN 12811-1 requires unimpeded access along the working lift. For this to be achieved in tube and fittings, reference needs to be made to TG20 Volume 2 and the structure classed as a special scaffold.

Ledger bracing should be fitted on alternate pairs of standards, except where the width of the bays is 1.5 metres or less. If so, they may be fitted on every third pair.

Ledger bracing should be fitted to:

- ☑ ledgers or standards using load-bearing fittings, which will have a minimum slip resistance of 5 Kn

- ☑ the full height of the scaffold

- ☑ start at base plate level (unless a pavement lift is required).

Scaffolding

Façade bracing

Façade bracing runs parallel to the face of the building or structure and is also known as longitudinal, face or sway bracing. It is fixed to the outside standards for independent tied scaffolds.

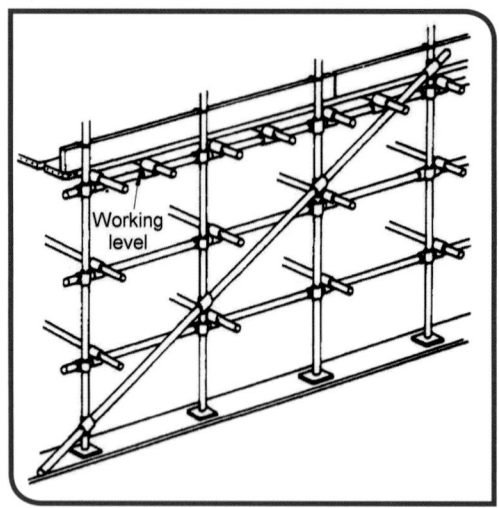

Façade braces can be attached to transoms with right-angled couplers at every lift, or to every standard using swivel couplers.

Façade bracing must be fixed to every sixth bay and set at an angle between 35–55°. All joints should be made with sleeve couplers. However, when joint pins are used, a splicing tube should overlap by a minimum of 300 mm and be fixed with two swivel couplers on either side of the joint.

There are three standard façade bracing patterns:

☑ zigzag across two bays (ledger braced)

☑ continuous for wider façades

☑ zigzag across one bay only*.

* Plan bracing is required for this form of façade bracing (refer to plan bracing below).

Plan bracing

Plan bracing is required horizontally across the scaffold on all standard scaffolds taller than eight metres where the façade bracing is fixed across one bay only *(refer to façade bracing above).*

Plan braces are fixed to the standards with right-angled couplers, except where headroom is critical, when it may be fixed with swivels to the ledgers.

Plan bracing should be fitted every eight metres (four lifts) vertically and every twelfth bay to correspond with the façade bracing.

 For greater detail on the fitting of plan bracing refer to TG20.

Scaffold ties

A tie secures the scaffold to the supporting structure and is provided to resist the inward and outward movement of the scaffold and also to give some additional longitudinal stability.

Ties are generally designated as moveable or non-moveable, the terminology being self-explanatory. Where possible, ties should be left undisturbed until the scaffold is dismantled. Where it is necessary for ties to be removed, even for a short period, the scaffold will be less stable and the fitting of additional temporary ties will be necessary unless the initial tie-pattern was designed to allow for the temporary removal of some ties.

Ties must not be removed by anyone other than a competent scaffolder or someone who is under the direct supervision of one. The removal of scaffold ties must be carried out in compliance with a method statement.

Scaffolds fitted with debris netting, sheeting and tarpaulins will be subjected to extra loading due to wind pressure and will require the scaffold designer to increase the number and frequency of ties, or the tie capacity.

Ties often pass through openings into the building, although alternative methods of tying can be employed.

Generally, each tie must have a minimum tensile or compressive capacity of 6.1 Kn, although designers can consider heavy duty ties at 12.2 Kn and light duty ties at 3.5 Kn.

Layout and frequency of ties

Ties should be evenly distributed over the scaffold, both horizontally and vertically, with a vertical spacing of no more than four metres.

TG20 offers alternative tie patterns. If these minimum tie patterns cannot be achieved, the pattern will need to be calculated by an engineer. At least 50% of ties must be fixed to ledger braced standards.

The density of ties will be decided by the scaffold designer based on all the factors that have the potential to affect the loading on the scaffold.

Full details of tying scaffolds are included in TG20.

Rakers

For lower level and domestic scaffolds, where it is not possible to install normal ties, the stability of a scaffold can be achieved by the use of rakers. A single, unjointed raking tube, not more than 6.4 metres in length, may be coupled at the top to the ledger at the second lift, extending at an angle not greater than 75° to the horizontal (4:1). The foot of the raking tube must be well founded and must always be tied back to the main scaffold. This arrangement can be used in place of a single tie.

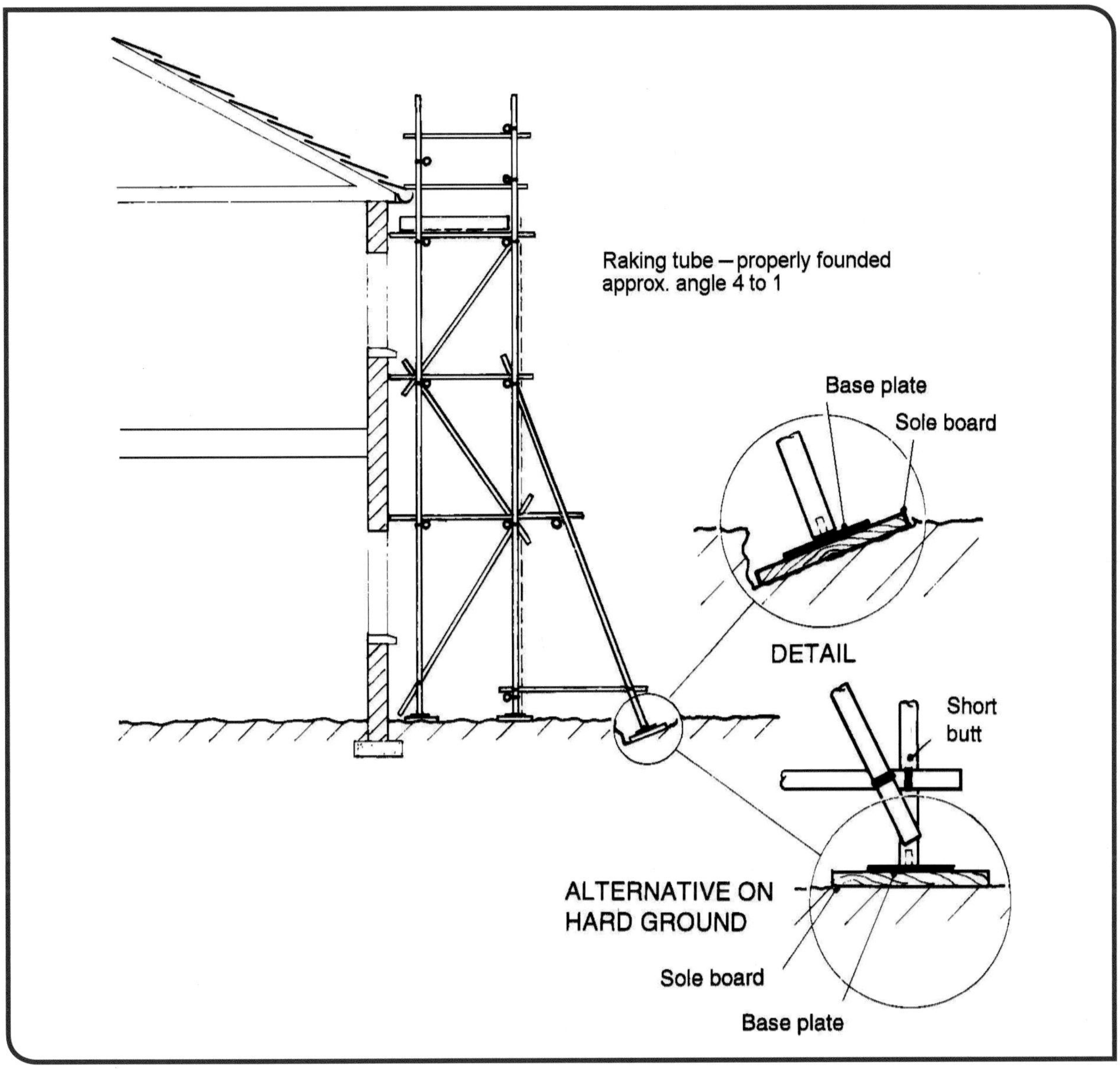

Raking tube — properly founded
approx. angle 4 to 1

Base plate
Sole board

DETAIL

Short
butt

ALTERNATIVE ON
HARD GROUND

Sole board

Base plate

Components fitted during the erection of the scaffold to comply with the guidance given in NASC's SG4 publication, have been omitted from the diagram for clarity.

Freestanding access scaffolds

Freestanding access scaffolds for modern methods of construction (such as timber frame structures) require calculations to be made for stability. These scaffolds would therefore be classed as special scaffolds.

Engineers can utilise alternative methods of achieving stability (such as buttressing, kentledge (ballast or counterweights), guys and ground anchors). Returns around corners, access towers and loading bays can also be taken into account by engineers when calculating stability.

For further information refer to NASC's *Safe systems of work for scaffolding associated with timber frame construction* (SG28).

Types of tie

Through tie

This type of tie relies on a tube, usually placed vertically inside an opening or window in a building. The tie tube should preferably rest on the sill, as close to one edge of the opening as possible.

Through ties should be placed as close as possible to the window reveal and secured with right-angled couplers.

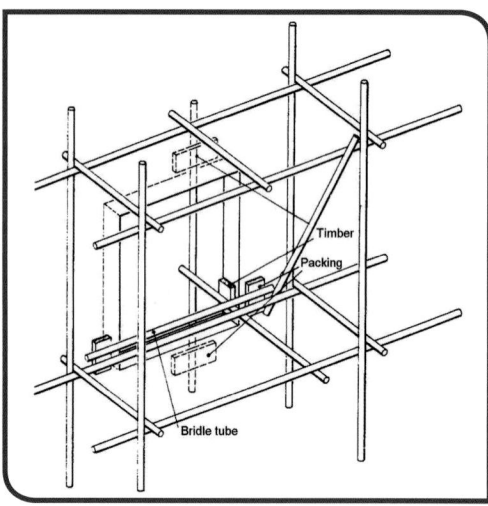

Through tie (couplers not shown for clarity)

Reveal tie

In cases where it is not possible to open windows or leave them open, or where it is impractical to fit other types of tie, a reveal tube may be wedged or jacked tight between the opposing faces of the window opening. Timber packing should be thin (10 mm) to reduce the possibility of timber shrinkage, and approximately 75 mm x 75 mm. It should be checked frequently for tightness.

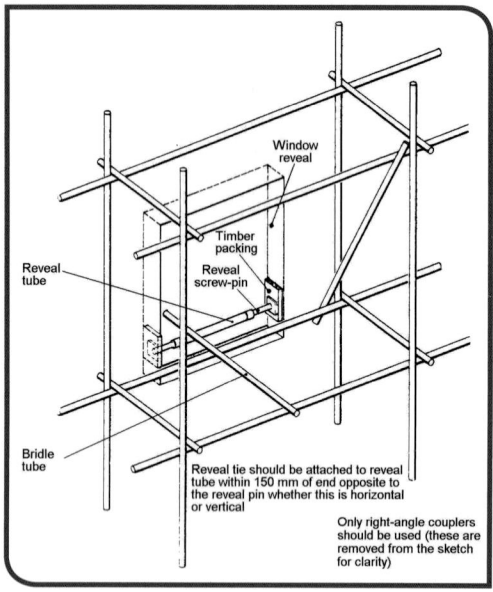

Reveal tie

A bridle tube should then be attached to the reveal tube with a right-angled coupler, within 150 mm of the end opposite to the reveal pin (whether this is horizontal or vertical). The bridle tube is usually fixed to the scaffold in two places with right-angled couplers, although other satisfactory arrangements may be used.

It should be noted that reveal ties generally depend entirely upon friction for their integrity and therefore:

☑ they should be checked frequently for tightness

☑ their use is limited to a maximum of 50%.
(Refer to NASC guidance TG20.)

Box tie

This forms an assembly of tubes and couplers around columns or other parts of a building. It should preferably be at the level of the scaffold lift and joined to both inside and outside ledgers or uprights.

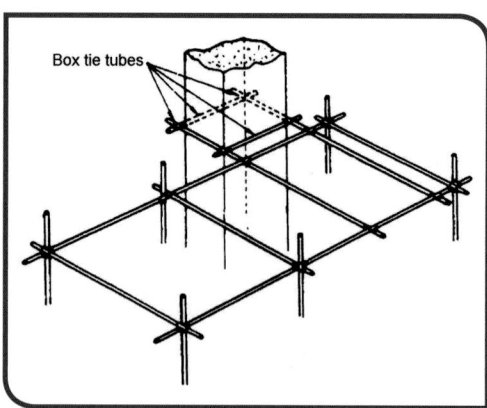

Box tie

Lip ties

These are an alternative form of tie, where box ties cannot be used. They take the form of an L-shaped arrangement of tubes and couplers, which hook the scaffold behind elements of the building (such as parapets). Lip ties do not resist inward or sway movement of the scaffold; adjacent butting and sway transoms should be used to prevent this.

Cast-in or drilled-in anchorages

A selection of screwed plates, eyes, sockets and nuts are available for setting into concrete during pouring. These may be used as anchorages.

There is a wide range of drilled-in anchorages available, also known as masonry anchors.

The accepted industry standard for the selection, use and testing of masonry anchors is NASC's *Anchorage systems for scaffolding* (TG4).

Masonry anchors must be used in accordance with the manufacturer's instructions. Scaffolders who install these anchors should be trained in accordance with those instructions.

TG4 requires two levels of testing:

☑ **preliminary testing**, wherever there is doubt about the base materials, to help select the correct type of anchor

☑ **proof testing**, to check the installation and that the required tensile loads can be achieved. A minimum of three ties must be tested and 5% (1 in 20) thereafter. Ties must be tested to 1.5 times the required tensile load (for example, 6.1 kN tie requires a 7.6 kN tensile test load).

If any anchor fails the test the cause must be investigated and the test frequency increased to 10%. A test report should be provided with the test results as part of the handover process.

Ring bolts are produced in two sizes, a:

☑ ring of 50–55 mm internal diameter, through which a scaffold tube could be passed

☑ smaller ring for use with wire or steel banding ties, which should be turned around a node point of the scaffold or otherwise prevented from slipping.

The strength and pull-out capabilities of all cast or drilled anchorages must be confirmed before use.

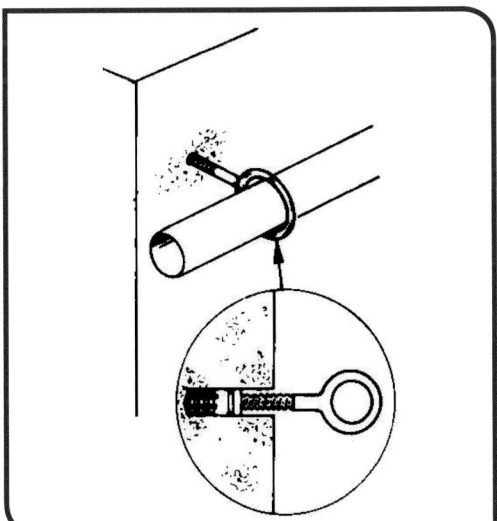

Ring bolts

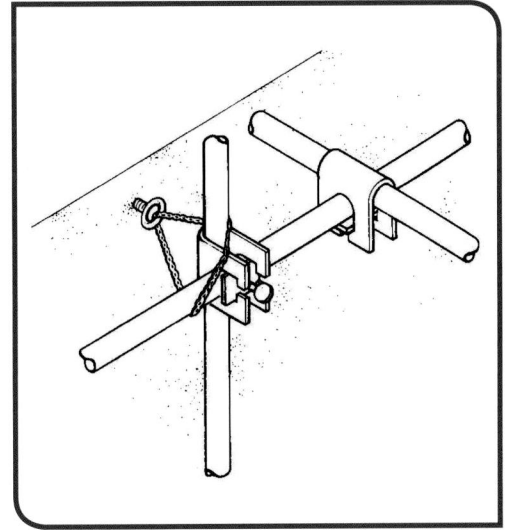

Ring bolt with 6 mm wire rope

Wire or steel banding ties

Scaffolding may be secured to the building using a small ring bolt with 6 mm wire rope threaded through the ring and around a scaffolding member with a minimum of three turns. Steel banding of the equivalent strength may be used for the same purpose.

This method does not prevent movement inwards; butting or sway transoms should be used to prevent this.

Some architectural features of a structure may be of sufficient strength for attaching wire or banding ties, although they must not be used until their suitability has been verified, by testing if necessary. If there is any doubt, they must not be used and an alternative method of tying must be found. Rainwater guttering and soil pipes must never be used for the attachment of ties.

When viewed in plan, tie tubes or banding ties should be set at right-angles to the building.

Information regarding design loads for ties can be obtained from the NASC guidance TG4.

Scaffold boards

The minimum amount by which any scaffold board should overhang any putlog or transom must be no less than 50 mm.

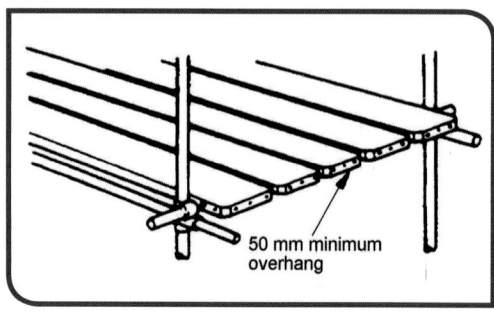

50 mm minimum overhang

The maximum overhang varies with the thickness of the scaffold board used. (*For further information refer to Table 8 of TG20.*)

All scaffold boards that comply with BS 2482:2009 should:

- ☑ be free from splits, shakes, excessive knots, paint, oil or concrete
- ☑ be usually 225 mm wide and not less than 220 mm
- ☑ not be painted or otherwise treated to conceal defects
- ☑ be banded or nail-plated at ends
- ☑ be supported by putlogs or transoms at the appropriate spacings

- ☑ overhang at least 50 mm but not more than four times the thickness of the board, unless secured from tipping
- ☑ be guarded against the wind causing the boards to lift
- ☑ be secured to prevent movement if short boards less than 2.13 metres are used.

4.5   Working platforms, guard-rails, decking and access

All working platforms and decking should be closely boarded to their full width and free from tripping hazards. Where reasonably practicable, overlapping boards should be avoided. Where an overlap is unavoidable, the lapped board should be secured to prevent movement and, if necessary, bevelled pieces should be installed.

The platform should be of an adequate width for the work to be carried out and safe passage of people. The suggested widths, as shown in Table 7 of TG20, may be taken as current industry guidance.

When material is deposited on a platform, a clear passage must be maintained for access.

The space between the inner edge of a working platform and the adjacent structure should be kept as small as possible to prevent falls. However, there can be circumstances in which this gap has to be wider. This is usually due to the nature of the work being carried out (for example, to enable the craning-in of sections of curtain wall between the scaffold and the building under construction or where there is only primary steelwork inside the scaffold).

This is known as the service gap.

In such circumstances, suitable compensatory measures must be taken if there is a risk of people falling, or people being struck by falling objects. For example:

- ☑ use of inner guard-rails and toe-boards
- ☑ segregation of the areas below the scaffold and post warning signs
- ☑ areas of the scaffold designated as danger areas, where access is restricted by guard-rails and warning signs
- ☑ use of personal fall protection equipment (harnesses).

The space between scaffolding boards should be kept as small as possible and in any case should not exceed 25 mm.

Boards should be securely fixed and present no risk to any person below.

 For further information refer to NASC's Safety guidance note SG29.

---

e.g.

In this photograph, telescopic transoms have been used to create an inner three-board-wide working platform, to close off the gap that is required to accommodate the façade. Scaffolders can then slide back the transoms and remove the boards, as required, to accommodate the progress of the façade works.

Gangways and runs

All gangways and runs should be:

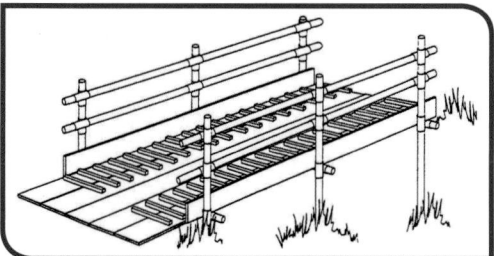

✓ 600 mm wide (three boards) if used for barrowing and the passage of materials

✓ preferably horizontal, but where this is not possible they may slope up to a maximum gradient of 20% (one unit vertical to five units horizontal) without the requirement for stepping laths.

If the gradient is unavoidably over 20%, or if the conditions are slippery, stepping laths must be provided. Whilst there is no recommended distance between stepping laths, a 300 mm separation is suggested. Stepping laths may incorporate a maximum central gap of 100 mm for barrow wheels.

Guard-rails

Guard-rails are just one of the options an employer may consider as a suitable and sufficient measure or means of protection when a person could fall any distance liable to cause them personal injury. As guard-rails are generally a collective measure, by offering protection to everyone, they are to be preferred to other measures that only protect individuals (such as safety harnesses).

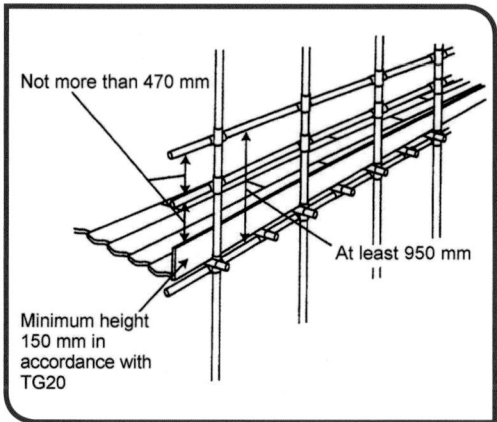

Not more than 470 mm

At least 950 mm

Minimum height 150 mm in accordance with TG20

A change brought about by the Work at Height Regulations is that, in relation to work at height in construction work, a main or top guard-rail must now be 950 mm above the edge (or above a working platform) from which any person is liable to fall.

The only exception is for a guard-rail that was fixed in place at 910 mm before the regulations came into force.

A second guard-rail (or mid guard-rail) may be placed approximately halfway between the top edge of the toe-board and the top guard-rail, so that there is no gap larger than 470 mm between the guard-rails or between the mid guard-rail and the toe-board.

All guard-rails must be fixed inside the standards with right-angled couplers to each standard.

Guard-rail connections, returns or corners should also be made using load-bearing couplers.

Brick guards should always be installed where there is a possibility of materials toppling from working platforms. If using the common type of brick guard, mid guard-rails should also be fitted.

There will be occasions when it is possible to fall from the working platform into the structure under construction. In these cases, it will be necessary to consider installing guard-rails to the inner edge of working platforms or using other fall prevention/arrest measures.

Temporary removal of guard-rails

Where it is necessary to load out scaffolds with bulk materials and so on, ideally there will be a purpose-built loading bay with a lifting safety gate or similar. Where this is not the case, it is permissible to temporarily remove guard-rails and toe-boards provided that:

✓ unless other work is stopped, other equally effective fall prevention/arrest measures are put in place (such as safety harnesses) whilst there is an exposed edge

✓ once the loading has been completed, the guard-rails and toe-boards are replaced immediately.

The removal and refitting of guard-rails and toe-boards must only be carried out by a competent scaffolder or someone who is under the direct supervision of a competent scaffolder.

Toe-boards

Toe-boards must be:

✓ fitted in conjunction with all guard-rails

✓ a minimum height of 150 mm in accordance with TG20

✓ fixed inside the standard, at a minimum of two positions.

Access to scaffolds

The Work at Height Regulations require employers to specify the use of existing structures as a means of access to height (for example, lifts or a permanent staircase) in preference to temporary measures (such as ladders).

Whilst ladders have been the commonly used means of access to scaffolds, the use of other, safer means of access (such as stair towers) should now be considered in preference.

Scaffolding

04

BS EN 12811 recommends that where extensive work is carried out, stairways should be provided for access, and for taller scaffolds consideration should be given to the use of a passenger hoist.

 Where passenger hoists are used, then additional non-mechanical access must also be provided in case of breakdown or emergencies

NASC recommends the following hierarchy of access from TG20.

1. Stairways.

2. Ladder access bays with single lift ladders (to reduce the potential fall distance).

3. Ladder access bays with multiple lift ladders.

4. Internal ladder access with protected ladder traps.

5. External ladder using a safety gate.

Where a ladder protrudes through a working platform (known as a ladder trap) the remaining width of the platform must be at least 450 mm (two boards wide).

 For further information refer to NASC's Safety guidance note SG25.

Ladder access

Straight ladders used for access to a scaffold must:

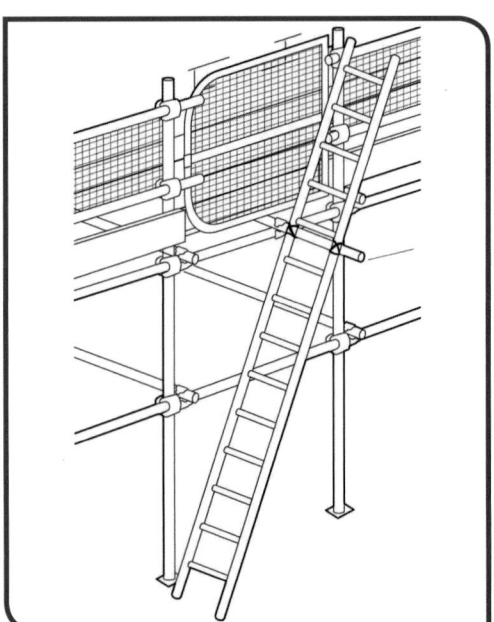

External access ladder and safety gate

- ☑ be manufactured to BS EN 131/BS 1129
- ☑ not be defective in any way
- ☑ not be painted or treated in any way that might hide defects
- ☑ be placed on a firm footing, with each stile equally supported
- ☑ be so positioned that there is sufficient space at each rung to give an adequate foothold
- ☑ be positioned approximately at an angle of 75°, that is, one measure horizontal to four measures vertical
- ☑ be secured at the top using square lashings or a proprietary ladder clamp. For longer ladders, additional ladder supports (stays) can be used to prevent the ladder deflecting when used. The stay must not obstruct the rung of the ladder
- ☑ extend approximately one metre above the working platform, unless there is another adequate handhold
- ☑ be provided with suitable rest platforms if rising more than nine metres
- ☑ be the right way up (tie wires or bars positioned under the rungs).

Shorter ladders, which provide access to only one lift, are recommended.

Where scaffolds are designed with internal ladders, working platforms must be provided with access holes for each ladder. Such access holes should be at least 450 mm wide (across the platform) and not less than 600 mm in the other direction.

 The access hole should be protected with a ladder trapdoor.

Landing platforms

Landing platforms should:

- ☑ be fitted with guard-rails and toe-boards, as previously detailed
- ☑ not be used for the storage of materials
- ☑ be installed at a maximum vertical height of nine metres and multiples thereof
- ☑ be equipped with access holes of similar dimensions to working platforms, as detailed above.

 Lateral gaps in guard-rails and toe-boards for access and egress must be kept to a minimum and protected with a ladder safety gate.

4.6   Other considerations

Incomplete scaffolds

Where the erection of a scaffold has not been completed, physical measures must be taken to restrict access to the scaffold (for example, remove or board over the access ladder(s) and warn people of the fact that the scaffold is not safe to use). The method of warning will usually be 'scaffold incomplete' signs at each point of access.

Good example of warning incorporated into a physical barrier

On larger scaffolds that are substantially complete, it may only be necessary to deny access to the part of the scaffold that remains incomplete, providing:

- ☑ the part of the scaffold that is complete is safe to occupy
- ☑ all access points from the completed part of the scaffold, beyond which the scaffold is incomplete, are clearly defined by warning signs and access to the incomplete part of the scaffold is effectively prevented with guard-rails or other barriers.

Loading of scaffolds

Any working platform on a scaffold should not be loaded so that it gives rise to a danger of collapse or to any deformation that could affect its safe use.

Any scaffold, or part of it, that is to be loaded by mechanical means (such as crane or forklift truck), must be specially designed and calculated as a loading bay or tower.

The scaffold should be checked periodically to ensure that the loads are within the permissible limits. *(Refer to Table 7 of TG20.)*

Loads on scaffold fittings

BS EN 74 Part 1 contains specifications for scaffolding couplers, including the slip-load of scaffold fittings. Load-bearing fittings (such as right-angled and swivel couplers) have much higher slip values than non-load-bearing items (such as putlog clips).

Other considerations are:

- ☑ scaffold fittings must not be oily or greasy as this will cause reduced frictional resistance between the tube and the fitting

- ☑ the correct spanner or podger must be used, and used in the correct manner, otherwise the screw threads may be overstressed

- ☑ scaffold fittings and tubes must be free from corrosion or other obvious defects.

Hoisting of materials

When working at heights, various items of lifting equipment or ancillary lifting equipment will usually be required. These may include block and tackle, motorised winches, wire ropes, chains or slings.

Goods and passenger hoists should not be tied to the scaffold unless specially designed and calculated for the purpose.

Accessories

There are many proprietary accessories for scaffolding, from covers to protect employees from snagging themselves on fittings along access routes, to filling the gap between two scaffold boards created by a standard.

Plastic protective shields cable tied around fittings on staircase, including plastic end caps on tubes

Use of scaffolds by other employees

Scaffolds erected for one employer may (provided that permission has been sought and given) be used by employees of another company, as long as the second employer is satisfied that the scaffold is safe for its intended use and conforms to the regulations.

Protection of the public

Protection of the public and other persons against falling materials should be provided by the use of nets, brick guards, toe-boards, protective fans, and so on.

Scaffold in a public place

Local Authority permission will normally be required for scaffolds to be built on the pavement or footpaths. These can cause particular problems to people with physical and visual disabilities, unless adequate steps are taken to reduce contact hazards with such items as tube ends and threads on fittings.

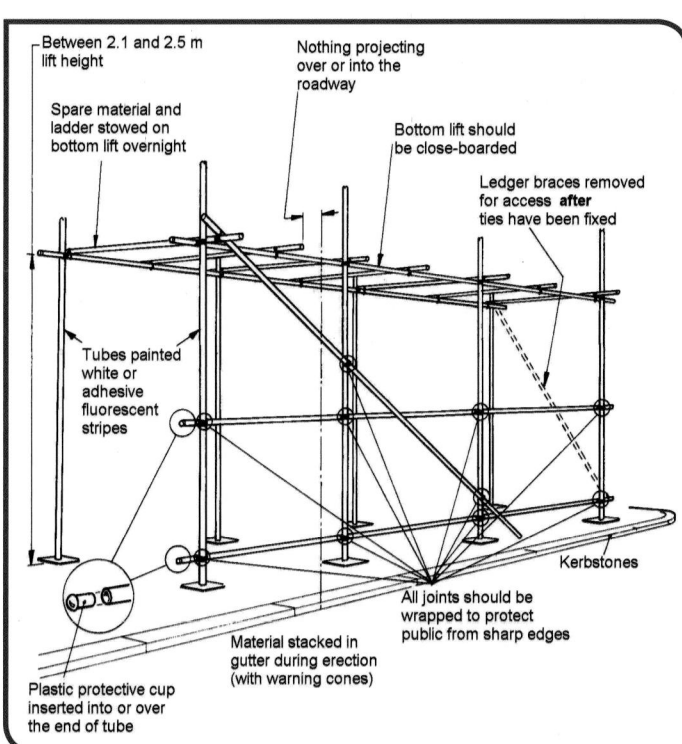

Between 2.1 and 2.5 m lift height

Nothing projecting over or into the roadway

Spare material and ladder stowed on bottom lift overnight

Bottom lift should be close-boarded

Ledger braces removed for access **after** ties have been fixed

Tubes painted white or adhesive fluorescent stripes

Kerbstones

All joints should be wrapped to protect public from sharp edges

Material stacked in gutter during erection (with warning cones)

Plastic protective cup inserted into or over the end of tube

04

This can usually be achieved by cladding the run of standards or binding the scaffold poles and fittings with suitable padding and/or brightly coloured bunting and tape.

All joints should be wrapped to protect the public and other persons from sharp edges, and plastic protective cups should be placed in or over the ends of tubes.

In most cases the scaffold will need to be designed to allow for ledger braces to be omitted at ground level so that members of the public can pass under the scaffold.

The bottom or pavement lift of the scaffold should be at a height no greater than 2.7 metres. The lift above pavement gantries must be fully close boarded, with a double layer of scaffold boards and a layer of impervious sheeting.

It is not sufficient to warn the public of the hazard just by placing safety signs on the scaffold, even if they meet the requirements of the Health and Safety (Safety Signs and Signals) Regulations. Employers must have acted to reduce the hazard as far as reasonably practicable.

To ensure the scaffold is not struck by vehicles, no part of it should be allowed to project into the roadway, unless appropriate measures are taken, such as traffic control or a road closure. The provision of lighting at night may also be necessary.

Supplementary lights should be installed on the scaffold where it has been erected in a place to which the public has access (whether pedestrians or vehicles), unless the level of background lighting after dark is thought to be sufficient.

 The HSE has produced a scaffolding protocol for Local Authorities that issue licences for scaffolding on the public highway.

Licences for work with asbestos

The Control of Asbestos at Work Regulations states that work with asbestos includes work that is ancillary to the removal, repair or disturbance of asbestos or materials containing asbestos. Erecting, altering or dismantling scaffolding are some activities covered under this regulation.

In such circumstances, scaffolding contractors must hold the appropriate HSE asbestos licence if their scaffolding will:

☑ form the framework from which an enclosure will be built for the purpose of working with asbestos

☑ provide access for work when it is foreseeable that asbestos is likely to be disturbed by the erection of the scaffold.

Generally, any scaffolding work is likely to require a licence if it is in:

☑ the vicinity of asbestos, or asbestos-containing materials which are in poor condition

☑ contaminated environments

☑ live asbestos enclosures.

The regulation requires the person in control of non-domestic premises to locate, identify and manage the presence of asbestos or asbestos-containing materials in those premises. This will usually require an asbestos survey to be carried out and the findings recorded in an asbestos register.

Where it becomes evident that work could result in the disturbance of the fabric of the building, the scaffold contractor should consult the asbestos register to establish the likelihood of exposure. Where there is doubt, professional advice should be sought.

 Even unlicensed scaffolders should be provided with asbestos awareness training due to the nature of the work they carry out. Licensed scaffolders will require more rigorous, in-depth training.

 For further information on asbestos and the procedure for obtaining a licence refer to Chapter B09 Asbestos.

Scaffolding

4.7   Inspection and handover

Inspection

All scaffolds and working platforms (together with all other protective measures) are work equipment for the purposes of the Work at Height Regulations and so the inspection requirements of the regulations apply, which state:

 every employer shall ensure that where the safety of work equipment depends on how it is installed or assembled, it is not used after installation or assembly in any position unless it has been inspected in that position.

This clearly applies to all scaffolds, including mobile and static tower scaffolds.

The inspection must be carried out by a competent person. An employer may wish to have a commercial arrangement with a scaffolding contractor in order to carry this out.

There is a further requirement in that every employer must ensure that work equipment exposed to conditions that may cause any deterioration liable to result in dangerous situations is inspected at suitable intervals, and also when any exceptional circumstances that are liable to jeopardise the safety of the work equipment have occurred.

In addition, employers must ensure that working platforms used for construction and from which a person could fall more than two metres are not used in any position unless they have been inspected in that position within the previous seven days.

It is common for proprietary inspection tags to be used to provide a status report for the scaffold.

Inspection of places of work at height

An additional requirement as regards inspection (or checking) is that every employer must ensure, so far as it is reasonably practicable, that every surface, parapet, permanent rail or other such fall protection measure of every place of work at height are checked before each use.

While there appears to be no requirement to record these checks, the prudent employer should do so to prove (for example, to the HSE or clients) that they have in fact been done.

Reports

Where an inspection has been carried out, a written report of the findings of the inspection must be made before the end of the working period.

The person who prepares the written report must provide a copy within 24 hours to the person on whose behalf the inspection was carried out. The report, or a copy of it, must be kept on the site where the inspection was carried out until the construction work is completed, and then kept at the company offices for three months.

Employers are free to design their own inspection report forms or purchase pads of them from commercial suppliers.

In either case they must include:

- ☑ the name and address of the person for whom the inspection was carried out
- ☑ the location of the work equipment inspected
- ☑ a description of the work equipment inspected
- ☑ the date and time of the inspection
- ☑ details of any matter identified that could risk the health or safety of any person
- ☑ details of any action taken as a result of any matter identified above
- ☑ details of any further actions considered necessary
- ☑ the name and position of the person making the report.

04

While it is not explicit in the regulations, where someone has carried out an inspection of a scaffold and believes that it is not safe to use, they must inform the person for whom the inspection has been carried out that the scaffold is unsafe. The scaffold must not then be used until it has been made safe.

 An example of an inspection report form can be found in Appendix A.

Handover

When each scaffold is completed, a competent employee of the scaffolding contractor will inspect the scaffold for compliance with regulations, codes of practice and this policy and then complete a scaffold handover certificate. This should conform to the current NASC template *Handover of scaffold structures* (SG35) (latest edition) as a minimum and ensure that the client's representative receives a copy. Where applicable, the green insert of a tag-type inspection system (if used) shall be completed and located at the access point of the scaffold, and the first entry made in the statutory scaffold inspection register by the competent person.

4.8   System scaffolds

04

Basic system scaffolding considerations

Before undertaking the erection of a system scaffold, the following points must be clearly defined.

Who will erect the scaffold?

Scaffolds must only be erected, altered or dismantled by, or under the direct supervision of, a competent person.

Users of proprietary systems must also ensure that scaffolders have received appropriate training (such as manufacturer's training) or a recognised qualification (such as the system scaffold product training scheme (SSPTS)), which is endorsed on the CISRS card.

This competence scheme is available for most of the primary scaffold systems used in the UK.

Where will it be erected?

Care will be required in the initial setting out of the system scaffold as far as leg or jack adjustment and the positioning of fixed length ledgers are concerned.

Measuring the length of the building and then positioning the first frames or standards and ledgers in relation to door openings will be important.

Are the ground conditions suitable?

Bay lengths may often differ from those associated with tube and fitting scaffolding, which can cause loads to be concentrated in particular spots. Initial ground inspection and levelling is essential to reduce the amount of jack levelling and adjustment required during scaffold erection. As with tube and fitting scaffolds, care should be taken with regard to manholes, slopes and the general load-bearing capabilities of the area on which the system scaffold is to be placed.

04

What materials are to be used?

The availability of space for the standards and the width of the working area are prime considerations in deciding which type of scaffold should be used. An allowance must be made for the fact that heavy or bulky materials may be deposited on the scaffold.

Stability of the scaffold structure

The scaffold structure must be of sufficient strength and rigidity when erected and, if appropriate, secured or tied-in to the structure against which it is built to ensure stability.

If the scaffold is later adapted or altered, this must be done in such a way as to ensure that the scaffold structure remains stable.

Can safe access to the working place be provided?

System scaffolds provide a variety of options for safe access to the working place (such as pole ladders, internal ladder systems or staircase towers). A decision must be made at an early stage in order that provision may be made for the particular type of access required.

How many working platforms will there be?

Platforms may have to be installed at every level, whether or not they are working places. This is a feature of some types of system scaffold. However, it is often the case that only one or two may be used as working places, and in such cases the manufacturer's recommendations must be followed as to whether or not platforms can be omitted.

How and where will the scaffold be tied in?

The principle of tying a system scaffold to the supporting structure is the same as for a tube and fitting scaffold. The pattern of ties and the frequency of their use will vary between manufacturers, and the different types of system scaffold will often incorporate their own proprietary ties instead of the conventional through ties or Hilti rings that are used on tube and fitting scaffolds.

It may be necessary to tie-in the scaffold at different places compared to tube and fitting scaffolds, and so consideration should be given to the exact locations available.

What bracing will be required?

Ledger bracing is not generally required in system scaffolds. This has the benefit of providing a clear walk-through at platform level. However, the frequency of façade bracing will vary from product to product, and plan bracing may be required if tie or anchor positions are not readily achievable or if deemed necessary by a designer.

Unauthorised alteration

Due to their design features, most types of system scaffold are generally easier to alter than a tube and fitting scaffold. This makes unauthorised alteration (for example, the removal of a guard-rail or the repositioning of a working platform) that much easier.

Unathorised alteration can make a scaffold an unsafe place of work for the unwary and possibly breach the scaffold design criteria from a stability point of view.

It is for site management to make clear to anyone who has to work on a system scaffold that unauthorised alteration must not be carried out and that appropriate actions will be taken against individuals who do so.

System scaffold specifications

Materials

Components should be free from any weld defects, bends, distortion or corrosion that may affect the safe functioning of the items. Many scaffold systems are galvanised, so the risks from corrosion are reduced.

Fittings employed for tying and adaptations to the scaffold should be free from worn threads and damaged bolts.

Foundations and levelling

The requirement for any supplementary support or load-spreading capability will depend upon:

- ☑ the nature of the surface on which a system scaffold is to be erected
- ☑ the weight of the scaffold itself
- ☑ loading that will be imposed upon the completed scaffold by materials, people and equipment.

In most cases, the installation of either base plates alone, or base plates plus sole boards, will be sufficient.

On system scaffolds, the ledgers and transoms connect to the standards at fixed points so there is not the degree of vertical adjustment that there is with tube and fitting scaffolds.

Because of the difficulty of levelling a system scaffold as erection progresses, all such scaffolds should be properly levelled and located at the first level. If this is done correctly, components should be vertically self-aligning, but great care must be taken to check the initial vertical alignment at the base.

Platform decking

As the scaffold frames and components have been designed by the manufacturer to meet the legislative requirements then, if used in accordance with the manufacturer's assembly instructions, platform span and thickness requirements will be met.

Types of platform

There are several different types of platform available for use with system scaffolds:

☑ conventional scaffold boards (225 mm x 38 mm x 3.9 m) (plus steel and aluminium versions of similar dimensions)

☑ timber battens (typically 225 mm x 60 mm x 2.5 m)

☑ decking platforms of plywood and aluminium (650 mm x 50 mm x 2.5 m or 3 m or 3.5 m)

☑ steel decking platforms (330 mm x 50 mm x 2.5 m or 3 m).

Only scaffold boards, whether timber, steel or aluminium, require supporting at 1.2 m or 1.5 m centres. Other decking products have been generally designed to span distances of up to 3 m or 3.5 m. The manufacturers of the various types of decking will provide specific guidance.

04

Reaction to windspeed

All decking platforms should be secured against the possibility of wind uplift. There are several types of fitting and straps available to achieve this. Design features (such as locking devices to prevent wind uplift) are increasingly built into proprietary platforms.

Platform widths

Whilst there is now no **legal** minimum width of a working platform, it is supposed that the minimum of 600 mm, as specified in BS EN 12811-1, will remain as the standard minimum.

The actual width chosen will depend largely upon the nature of the application (for example, bricklaying will not be suitable on a 750 mm-wide scaffold, but painting and cladding may be well suited to this width).

Ledger bracing

Additional ledger bracing is not generally required within system scaffolds due to the inherent stiffness of the joints. However, if the system scaffold is to exceed the design boundaries of a standard scaffold, the layout should be specified by a competent scaffold designer.

Longitudinal or façade bracing

The requirement for longitudinal or façade bracing will be specified by the manufacturer or scaffold designer, and will vary from product to product.

Ties

The need for ties on a system scaffold is the same, in principle, as on a traditional scaffold.

However, a system scaffold has different characteristics (for example, its components are shorter and lighter) so the tie pattern will need to be specified by the manufacturer, or a competent scaffold designer. Requirements for ties may vary from product to product.

Increasingly, new methods of tying are being used to replace conventional through ties or Hilti rings. Eyebolt and plastic plug type ties are now used on some systems.

Sheeting of scaffolds

Caution must always be exercised before a decision is taken to sheet any scaffold. The sheeting of any scaffold increases the wind-loading on it. The requirement for additional ties will be determined by the manufacturer or a competent scaffold designer.

Access

Requirements are as per tube and fitting scaffold. However, most system scaffolds have designed access components.

Concentrated loads

Where concentrated loads, pallets of bricks or tiles are to be placed on the scaffold, loading towers may be required. These specially designed and braced scaffolds provide support for concentrated loads, the weight of which would be excessive on standard scaffold working platforms.

Incomplete scaffolds

Where a loading tower constructed in a system scaffold is erected adjacent to the working scaffold, the two structures should be securely tied both to each other and to the building.

Scaffolding

Safe places of work, and stability of working platforms

Any working platform on a scaffold must:

- ☑ have safe access to it and egress from it
- ☑ be of suitable and sufficient strength and rigidity for the purpose for which it is to be used
- ☑ be erected and used so that none of the components can come loose or be displaced and endanger anyone
- ☑ be stable when being erected, used and dismantled
- ☑ be of sufficient dimensions to permit safe passage of persons and materials, and provide a safe working area for the work that is to be done there
- ☑ have a suitable (non-slip) surface so as to prevent slipping or tripping
- ☑ not have any gaps through which a person or materials could fall
- ☑ be used and maintained so that persons cannot be caught between the working platform and any adjacent structure
- ☑ be dismantled in such a way as to prevent accident displacement.

Appendix A – Inspection report

Report of inspection on *scaffolding, *work equipment or working platform

*(*delete as appropriate)*

The Work at Height Regulations

Inspection carried out on behalf of: ....

Inspection carried out by (name and position): ....

Address of site (or location of work equipment): ....

Date and time of inspection	Description of place of work, or part inspected	Details of any matter identified giving rise to the health and safety of any person	Details of any action taken as a result of any matter identified	Details of any further action required

Scaffolding

05

Fall arrest and suspension equipment

Where a risk assessment has identified that the risk of falls from height cannot be eliminated by the installation of barriers, guard-rails or other similar measures, the use of fall-arrest equipment may then be the best option.

Safety nets or the use of other soft-landing systems are preferred to the use of safety harnesses and lines, as they protect the whole area and all persons working above them. They do not rely on individual workers wearing a safety harness and lanyard connected to a secure anchorage point.

Introduction	74
Key points	74
Safety nets	75
Other soft-landing systems	79
Safety belts, harnesses and lanyards	79
Suspension trauma	84
Rope access (abseiling)	84
Boatswain's chairs	85
Cradles	86
Appendix A – Safety nets – Safety checklist	88

Fall arrest and suspension equipment

5.1 Introduction

In situations where people and traffic pass below others working at height, a safety net used in conjunction with a fine-mesh debris net will protect those below from falling tools and materials, as well as providing fall arrest for the people working at height.

Where safety nets cannot be rigged for any reason, and it is not practical to use another form of soft-landing system, it may be necessary to resort to the use of a safety harness and lanyard.

In the first instance work/fall restraint should be considered (technique used to prevent the worker from falling). If the worker is required to move around an area where they have the potential to fall then fall arrest should be used (technique used to reduce distance and consequences of a fall).

☑ It is imperative that operatives have been trained in the use and care of the equipment and wear it correctly.

☑ When operatives are working in fall-arrest equipment, consideration must be given to the clear space beneath the work area required to allow the energy absorber within the lanyard to operate effectively. A two-metre lanyard anchored at foot level will require approximately 6.75 metres of clear space beneath to prevent injury. This distance is made up of the two-metre lanyard, 1.75 metre energy absorber, two-metre body height and one-metre safety margin.

☑ A secure anchor point must be available.

☑ The person working at height must actually clip on.

Whichever system is used for minimising injury from falling, whether it is safety nets, another soft-landing system or harness and lanyard, the system must be:

☑ designed to provide a safe system of work

☑ installed by competent persons

☑ maintained, inspected and supervised to ensure it is used correctly.

For further information also refer to:
Chapter D01 The Work at Height Regulations,
Chapter D03 Common access equipment,
Chapter D04 Scaffolding, and
Chapter F05 Working over or near to water.

In the first instance, where practicable, falls should be prevented by the use of collective control measures; these include the use of edge protection, parapets, scaffold, temporary towers and mobile elevating work platforms (MEWPs) – all forms of fall prevention.

5.2 Key points

☑ In situations where the prevention of falls from height cannot be guaranteed, it is essential that measures are put in place to ensure that any fall that does occur is arrested, without injury to the person who has suffered the fall.

☑ In many cases safety nets are the preferred method of arresting falls because:

– they provide what is termed *collective fall protection*

– if rigged immediately below the work area, they limit the height of the fall to the minimum and recovery of the faller should not be a problem

– they are a soft-landing system that should cause no injury to the person who has fallen.

☑ Safety nets can suffer wear and damage and must be inspected periodically.

☑ Other forms of soft-landing systems (such as airbags or beanbags) also offer collective protection and are more appropriate for some types of work.

☑ If fall protection is to be achieved using a safety harness and lanyard, the wearer must be trained in fitting and adjusting the harness and selecting the appropriate lanyard and a secure anchorage.

☑ Harness and lanyard offer personal fall-arrest protection only.

☑ Some items may need a regime of inspections and thorough examinations under the Lifting Operations and Lifting Equipment Regulations (LOLER).

☑ The HSE has issued warnings regarding the:

– severe and rapid wear to webbing lanyards arising from them being abraded over concrete edges

– dangers associated with the misuse of retractable-type fall arrestors.

Personal suspension equipment (such as rope-access equipment and a boatswain's chair) must only be used by people who have been trained and are competent. For rope access, training can be achieved through BS 7985:2009 or the Industrial Rope Access Trade Association (IRATA).

www. For further information refer to the HSE's website.

5.3   Safety nets

The use of nets has become widespread throughout the industry particularly on new build steel frame structures. They have revolutionised safety in roof work. Figures quoted by the trade association FASET (Fall Arrest Safety Equipment Training) suggest that upwards of 50 people a year are caught in their members' nets. The fatal accident rate in industrial roofing has been massively reduced with the introduction of nets.

Yet the use is not without risk. It is vital that site managers appreciate that they have an important role in the safe provision of nets on their sites, and that this is best done by making sure that the net provider is following the best practice guidance for the sector.

05

Anyone involved in construction will appreciate that costs are important. Nets are an area where complying with best practice means testing, inspection, record keeping and storage facilities are required to ensure that the net itself is fit for use. It is important that the end users appreciate that a safe net is not simply about whether the net erectors have a training records card, but also look deeper to check that the net itself has been checked and inspected.

There are a number of British Standards relating to safety nets. They should be manufactured to the requirements of BS EN 1263-1 and erected in accordance with BS EN 1263-2. This latter standard gives information on the installation and use of safety nets.

A further standard, BS 8411, which was first published in 2007, contains construction-specific information and more importantly a list of duties for the parties usually involved in construction projects. This includes CDM co-ordinators, designers, engineers, principal contractors, scaffold contractors and anyone having on-site responsibility for the integrity of safety net installations.

Safety nets installed prior to roof works commencing

This standard specifies that anyone who is planning the installation of a safety net system should take into account the:

- experience and competence of the net erectors
- sequence and type of work being carried out during installation and removal
- sequence of construction work to be carried out whilst the nets are in position
- provision of effective anchorages
- means of access for erecting and removal
- access for inspection, debris removal and temporary repair
- clearance distances below the net
- protection of anyone below
- recovery of anyone who has fallen into the net.

Modern safety nets are efficient at saving lives and preventing injury. They are an energy-absorbing system designed to minimise the consequences to the person who has fallen. Safety nets should be erected as close as possible to the working level to minimise the height of any fall that may occur.

There are two types of net manufacture:

- **knotless**, which provide energy absorption by permanent plastic deformation (stretching) of the net material
- **knotted**, which is generally a heavier and older type of net, providing energy absorption by tightening at the knots and permanently deforming.

Safety nets are manufactured in square or diamond mesh, with two mesh sizes: 60 mm and 100 mm. The 100 mm is the normal mesh size used in the UK.

All safety nets should carry an identification label. This includes the date of manufacture, the net type, class and size, and reference to the BS EN 1263-1. It should also carry a unique serial number for record purposes and traceability.

Recent sector guidance has created a more rigorous regime for tagging nets. Any nets purchased after 1 January 2008 should have a tag showing their repair history and any net that is older than 12 months should have a tag showing that it has been tested within the last 12 months.

Fall heights

The positioning of a safety net system is critical to minimise the height of falls that may occur. Although safety nets are designed for a maximum fall height of six metres, the maximum fall, if installed directly under the workplace, should be under one metre.

When nets are installed, the maximum amount of sag in the net should be no more than 10% of the bay width.

When a load or person falls into a correctly erected net, the net material will deform as it absorbs the energy from the fall.

It is therefore critical to provide adequate clearance below the net, to allow the deformation to occur without the load or person striking the ground or some other object.

If a person were to fall two metres into a net between five metres and nine metres wide, the total deformation, including the erection sag, may be between 2.6 metres and 3.5 metres, depending on the width of net. It is essential to check the manufacturer's specification to ensure that there is adequate clearance below the planned net position.

Competence

The way in which safety net systems are installed is critical. Not only must those installing the net system be trained and competent, so must the people who carry out the routine inspection of safety nets.

The issue of competence is important, as a handover certificate should be issued. Under the sector guidance, the minimum competence to issue a handover certificate would be someone holding a CSCS experienced worker card, signifying that they have the appropriate experience and training. Consequently, anyone holding only an IRATA card plus a certificate of training should not be regarded as fully competent.

Always receive a handover certificate from the riggers for each section of netting as it is completed.

There are industry-agreed standards and qualifications for training in the rigging and inspection of safety nets. The training of inspectors is aimed at site management staff as well as professionals within the industry.

 Information on the providers of such training is available from Fall Arrest Safety Equipment Training (FASET).

FASET guidance

FASET's website contains the latest technical and safety information, guidance and bulletins for the selection, installation and use of safety nets. These are freely available on their website and should be consulted before selecting and installing nets (for example, understanding what the maximum numbers of workers above a safety net are, and how to attach safety nets to temporary edge protection).

Guidance includes:

01	Why specify a FASET member?
02	Safety net test records.
03	The testing of safety nets for UV degradation.
04	Safety net labels and record keeping.
05	General arrangement for repairing both knotted and knotless safety nets.
06	Repairs to a knotless safety net.
07	Repairs to a knotted safety net.
08	Tagging of safety net repairs.
09	On-site safety net temporary repair.
10	Maximum permissible gaps.
11	Gathering and map; under-rolling.
12	Joining safety nets together.
13	Testing requirements for safety net attachment devices.
14	Not available
15	Incorrect safety net support clamps – single Gravlock.
16	Attaching safety nets to temporary edge protection.
17	Number of workers above a safety net.
18	Loading of safety nets.

Installation

 FASET's *The selection of access methods to install and dismantle safety netting* can be freely downloaded from their website and site managers should familiarise themselves with it in order to manage and monitor the installation team.

FASET recommended hierarchy for work at height

There are four methods of access currently recommended for rigging and de-rigging safety nets, which should be considered in the following order.

1. Rig/de-rig safety nets remotely – using remote attachment devices.

2. Rig/de-rig using powered access – (MEWPs).

3. Rig/de-rig using ladders – (recommended maximum height 4.5 metres).

4. Industrial climbing access techniques.

 FASET does not recommend the use of scaffold towers or hop ups for the rigging and derigging of safety nets under normal rigging conditions. There may be rare and isolated occasions for specific work where towers may be appropriate, having taken due regard of this document, and the hierarchy set out within it. Where such occasions arise, the rigging contractor must prepare a suitable specific risk assessment taking account of the rigging conditions and the additional control measures required. Towers must always be erected in accordance with the manufacturers'/suppliers' instructions by trained personnel.

05

Periodic testing

Safety nets are provided with short lengths of test cord attached to the net. These cords carry the net's unique serial number and are so fitted that they receive the same environmental exposure as the net material. At yearly intervals, a test cord should be detached from the net and sent back to the manufacturer so that it may undergo a tensile failure test, to monitor the degradation of the net material through exposure to sunlight. Typically a net is made with three so-called test diamonds. The presence or absence of these gives the site manager a clear indication as to whether the basic testing regime is in place.

Inspection

Where safety net systems are erected, they should be inspected on a weekly basis by a competent person to ensure that they are still in a safe condition, fixed correctly and will provide the fall arrest capability if required.

Inspections should be carried out more frequently if circumstances indicate that the integrity of the net system is in doubt.

A net should also be inspected after a person or substantial load has fallen into it, to determine whether it should remain in service or be replaced. In some cases, it may be necessary to seek specialist advice.

It is recommended that the findings of all inspections are recorded.

Care of nets

Care should be taken to reduce to a minimum unnecessary wear and mechanical damage likely to weaken the net. Materials must not be stacked on it, and deliberate jumping into it or dropping of objects onto it must be prohibited, as permanent deformation may occur.

The following sources of damage or wear should be avoided as far as possible:

- ☑ dragging the net over rough surfaces
- ☑ contact between the net and sharp edges
- ☑ an accumulation of debris in the net
- ☑ any sparks from hot work, welding, grinding, burning operations, hot gases from blowlamps, or hot ash from chimneys or furnaces
- ☑ chemical attack
- ☑ any form of radiation.

Special care should be exercised and precautions taken to prevent the net and any supporting framework from being struck by loads on moving vehicles or by the vehicles themselves.

Regular inspection is necessary to ensure that the nets remain serviceable. The net manufacturer should be consulted when there is any doubt about the suitability of nets for use in hazardous conditions, after any known contamination or when deformation has occurred.

When erecting nets in the vicinity of electricity lines or overhead power cables, the appropriate authority should be consulted before work starts.

Maintenance

Nets must always be inspected after use and before storing to identify any damaged areas. Glass, metal, grit and other debris should be removed to prevent abrasion.

If contaminated by acids or alkalis, nets should be thoroughly washed, preferably by hosing, and allowed to dry naturally away from heat.

If areas of damage are found, or chemical damage is suspected, contact the manufacturer to obtain a list of competent people able to repair or clean the nets.

Storage

- ☑ Nets should be stored away from heat, chemicals and solar radiation.
- ☑ Nets should be stored in dry conditions.
- ☑ Nets should be stored to minimise vermin attack.
- ☑ Wet nets should be dried naturally.
- ☑ Storage cupboards should be well ventilated.
- ☑ Nets should be turned periodically to allow air circulation.
- ☑ If stacked, nets should be packed up clear of the ground.

Rescue from a net system

Where the net is erected as close as possible below the work area, many of the situations where persons enter a net will be minor step-ins, with the person able to climb out unaided.

On other occasions, a person may fall a considerable height into a net. They may fall onto materials lying in the net, or strike their head or body on, for example, structural steelwork during the fall.

When such accidents occur, extreme care must be taken during the rescue of the person lying injured in the net. Due to the stretching nature of the net, it is possible that any rescuer entering it could inadvertently and unavoidably cause further injury to the victim.

It is therefore essential that companies using safety net systems have, as part of their risk assessment process, emergency procedures written for:

- ☑ treating first aid needs whilst the injured person is in the net
- ☑ emergency recovery from a rigged net system.

Procedures for both the above are included in the standard industry training courses for net riggers or net inspectors.

05

5.4 Other soft-landing systems

Alternative soft-landing systems are an effective alternative to safety nets in some circumstances.

Designed to be used in buildings with a storey height of up to 2.5 m, one type of system comprises large polypropylene bags (typically 2.5 m long x 0.55 m wide x 0.55 m deep) that are packed with polystyrene chippings or another energy-absorbing material. The depth of the bags both cushions a fall and reduces the distance of that fall (by the depth of the bag).

The bags are linked together with plastic snap clips to completely fill the area over which protection is required. They can also be used on the first or subsequent floors while trusses are being installed or in the roof space when fixing bracings.

An alternative system that may be considered in appropriate circumstances is the use of air-filled bags. Similar to the above, bags of varying sizes may be clipped together to completely fill the area over which fall-arrest protection is required. Airbags require an air compressor running all the time that fall arrest is required, to maintain the pressure in the air bag system. These devices work on the principle of a controlled rate of constant inflation and leakage so that the airbags will absorb the energy of someone falling onto them without bouncing.

Whilst soft landing systems do not prevent falls, they are very effective in eliminating injuries in falls of less than two metres.

5.5 Safety belts, harnesses and lanyards

If fall prevention measures (for example, working platforms, barriers, guard-rails) or collective fall arrest measures (safety nets or other soft landing systems) are not practical, an alternative safe system of work must be employed. This safe system may require the use of safety harnesses and lanyards, but it should be a last resort. Whereas safety nets and other soft-landing systems are collective measures (in other words, they automatically provide protection for everyone working above them), safety-harness systems only protect the user, and only then if the equipment is used correctly.

Care must be taken when planning to use a safety harness, lanyard and energy-absorbing system since, depending on where the lanyard is anchored, a person may fall around four metres before the fall is arrested.

One of the limitations of using such fall-arrest equipment is that it only protects a person if they adjust and wear the harness properly and connect the lanyard to an appropriate and secure point. The use of any such system requires a high degree of training, competence and supervision.

Training

Training should only be carried out by competent trainers, following industry and HSE guidelines. Training should refer to the manufacturer's instructions and should emphasise the importance of following those instructions. Ideally training should be delivered to BS 8454, British Standard for the delivery of work at height training.

It should cover the selection, fitting, adjustment, maintenance and use of the safety belt or harness, and explain the choice and use of suitable anchorage points. Employees should not be permitted to use the equipment before adequate instruction has been received, and they have been judged to be competent in its use.

Safety belts and harnesses are wrongly regarded by some workers as an encumbrance and a restriction on their freedom of movement. The fact that a safety belt or harness can prevent serious injury or even save a life is often ignored.

The problems arising from such attitudes can and must be solved by applying the principles of good health and safety management. These include educating employees in the need for the equipment, training them in its use, ensuring it is provided and, through adequate supervision, ensuring it is always used.

Types of belt or harness

While the British Standard that defined the various types of belt and harness has been replaced by a European Standard, the common construction industry terminology for these pieces of equipment is as shown below.

A – Pole belt

B – Chest harness

C – General purpose safety harness

D – Safety rescue harness

Selection of equipment

The correct selection of a safety harness or safety belt is important. If a person falls more than 600 mm when using a safety belt, serious injury can be sustained due to a heavy load being exerted on the spine and internal organs. Safety belts should only be used for pole access or other similar specialist access needs.

If any doubt exists concerning the suitability of a piece of equipment for a particular task or type of work, further information and advice should be sought from the manufacturer.

Whatever type is chosen, it should give a high degree of safety allied to mobility and wearer comfort.

Fall arrest and suspension equipment

The main characteristics of the types of appliance, together with an indication of their uses, are given below.

A – Pole belt. A simple waist belt for use by pole linespeople and for other similar tasks. They are not intended for situations where a drop may exceed 600 mm.

B – Chest harness. A safety belt with shoulder straps, for use where a lanyard and anchorage point limit the drop to a maximum of 600 mm. It must be worn quite tightly to prevent any slippage after a fall.

Both A and B above are for very specific and restricted use only.

C – General purpose safety harness. A full body harness with thigh and shoulder straps. In the event of a fall, a person is suspended in a reasonably upright position from the attachment point. If the harness is of the right size and properly adjusted, the wearer cannot fall out.

D – Safety rescue harness. Designed to be worn by anyone in a confined space or location where they may be overcome or incapacitated and need to be rescued. A safety rescue harness looks similar to Type C, but will support a person almost upright for rescue purposes. It is intended for a maximum drop of 600 mm.

Harnesses and lanyards come under the inspection and maintenance requirements of a number of regulations, the main one being BS EN 365:2004 *PPE against falls from a height.*

A competent person should draw up a schedule for testing and examination, which is likely to also include a requirement for thorough examinations at six-monthly intervals and user checks each time the equipment is used. The six-monthly examination is a detailed visual examination, typically following cleaning where the harness is checked for contamination by oils and other solvents as well as abrasion and damage. The user, pre-use check is simply to make sure that all the bits are still there and there are no obvious defects.

Type of lanyard

There are several types of lanyard, each intended for a particular purpose.

Fall-arrest lanyards incorporate an energy-absorbing feature to reduce the shock loading on the body, termed the *impact force*, of the person who has fallen when the fall is arrested.

Twin tailed lanyards are a type of fall-arrest lanyard that allows greater mobility at height by enabling the repositioning of one tail at a time so that the user is constantly clipped on.

However, this type of lanyard can pose additional risks to safety if it is not used correctly. If only one tail is clipped to a secure anchorage and the second tail is not located correctly, then during a fall the second tail could loop over a fixed object and arrest the fall before the energy-absorber has deployed, which may cause severe personal injury.

The second tail must never be clipped back on to the user's harness unless it is fitted with purpose-fitted parking points that will break away from the harness if the second tail comes under tension. Alternatively, the second tail can be either left to hang free or **(on this type of lanyard only)** be simultaneously clipped to the same secure anchorage. If there is any doubt about these lanyards' safe use, the supplier or manufacturer should be consulted.

Restraint lanyard with full body harness for MEWP operator

Restraint lanyards are used as a means of limiting the range of movement of the wearer in order to stop them falling from an exposed edge (for example, allowing maintenance to be carried out on a gutter on the edge of a roof). The worker can reach the gutter but the lanyard is not long enough to allow the worker to physically loose contact with the structure, thus preventing a fall from the roof.

These lanyards are not designed to arrest falls and have no energy-absorbing feature. Sometimes two of these may be worn at the same time, with each lanyard fixed to a clip on either side of the harness (EN 358) to make the harness what is termed a work positioning harness.

Irrespective of the type of lanyard used, they are only effective if the free end is securely anchored to a suitable anchorage point.

Manufacturers and suppliers will advise on the appropriate type of lanyard for particular work situations.

Selecting the anchorage point

When working in fall arrest, in order to limit the drop, the anchorage points should always be as high as possible above the person and as near to vertical as possible in order to avoid the pendulum effect.

Anchorage points must be capable of withstanding the anticipated shock loading.

Consideration should also be given to how persons would be rescued following an arrested fall, particularly when work is from high structures. Some harness manufacturers also produce rescue systems that enable a single rescuer to raise a suspended person back to the working platform or safely lower them to ground level.

Markings on belts and harnesses

Safety belts and harnesses must be clearly and indelibly marked or permanently labelled with the:

- ☑ British Standard, or European Standard, to which it conforms:
    - – EN 361 – Basic full body harness
    - – EN 358 – Side D rings for work positioning
    - – EN 13 – Waist D ring for abseiling
    - – must also include CE-marking if it is to be used as PPE within Europe
- ☑ name, trademark or other means of identification of the manufacturer
- ☑ year in which the harness or belt was manufactured – maximum working life of 5–10 years, depending on the manufacturer
- ☑ type of belt or harness
- ☑ manufacturer's serial number
- ☑ company serial number, or other recognition system, for recording maintenance and inspections.

Under LOLER, the safe working load would also be required, and it would be common to see some form of marking that indicates that the harness has been tested.

Markings on lanyards

Lanyards that are not permanently attached to belts or harnesses must be clearly and indelibly marked or permanently labelled with the:

- ☑ British Standard, or European Standard, to which it conforms:
    - – EN 354 – Lanyard
    - – EN 355 – Energy absorber
    - – must also include CE-marking if it is to be used as PPE within Europe
- ☑ name, trademark or other means of identification of the manufacturer
- ☑ year of manufacture
- ☑ manufacturer's model number
- ☑ company serial number, or other recognition system, for recording maintenance and inspections.

 Ideally, lanyards will have a label with the words (or similar): for maximum safety attach the free end to a point as high as possible above you and avoid looping the lanyard around small joists and angles with narrow edges.

Lanyards should preferably be permanently attached to belts so that longer lanyards cannot be substituted.

Shock absorbers

If a person wearing a harness and lanyard falls, there is a considerable shock loading to the body impact force – the further the fall, the greater this force.

A shock-absorbing lanyard

The maximum distance a person can fall will depend on the height of their anchor point and length of lanyard: the higher the anchor, the shorter the lanyard and the less fall distance. In a worst-case scenario with a two-metre lanyard (maximum length under EN 354) anchored at foot level, the area of clear space beneath the person required is 6.75 metres. This is made up of the following:

- ☑ 2 m lanyard length
- ☑ 1.75 m energy absorber extension
- ☑ 2 m body height
- ☑ 1 m safety.

Shock absorbers in the form of tear-away stitching, stretch springs or a deforming metal strip are built into fall-arrest lanyards as a means of reducing the shock loading.

Once a lanyard has been used to arrest a fall and the energy-absorber has been deployed, it must be discarded.

Arrester devices

These devices are similar in operation to the inertia reel safety seat-belts fitted in cars.

The safety harness is attached to a self-reeling cable, which is securely anchored. The wearer is free to move normally but, in the event of a sudden movement (a fall) the locking device is brought into operation.

The HSE has issued a warning that these devices are often being used in situations for which they were not designed and have not been tested.

Most inertia reel-type arresters are only designed to safely arrest someone who has fallen from a position directly below, or very close to, the anchorage point (which should be above the head height of the user). They are not designed to compensate for the pendulum effect that will occur when the faller is a significant horizontal distance from the suspension point. In these circumstances, the HSE has warned that there is a far greater risk of a fatality.

Certain manufacturers now produce inertia reels that can be used on the horizontal; however these have to be specifically requested at the time of purchase/hire. They will come with some form of labelling clearly stating that they are for use on the horizontal.

A typical misuse would be to see a line rigged along the ridge of an industrial roof with inertia reels fixed to it by karabiners. The work being carried out is not actually on the roof but on a lower level, resulting in the safety lines being stretched, and possibly abraded, across the lower edge (eaves) of the pitched roof.

Using a proprietary fall-arrest system

The issue is that most examples of this type of device are not tested for over-the-edge type falls in which the retractable lanyard is pulled tight across the edge of a surface (for example, a roof sheet or floor slab) by the weight of the fallen person. In these circumstances it has been reported that the lanyard could snap or fail to limit the height of the fall to a safe distance.

If this is the proposed work method, then advice needs to be taken from the manufacturer that the equipment will work satisfactorily in this manner.

Various other types of fall arrester are often incorporated as a permanent fixture into the structure being built (such as a traveller on a pre-tensioned vertical cable). There are also proprietary systems where the lanyard is attached to a traveller that moves along a pre-positioned and tensioned horizontal or vertical steel cable. This permits movement around corners and past obstacles without the need to unclip.

Advice should be sought on the best type to be used for the job to be done. Again, these devices are likely to require inspection under the Lifting Operations and Lifting Equipment Regulations. Where the client provides this equipment as is common in many cases, care still needs to be taken that it has been inspected and checked as required and that the users understand how it works.

 For further information refer to the HSE's website.

Storage

While not being worn, appliances should be stored in a cool, dry place and not subjected to direct sunlight. The use of purpose-designed cabinets, which allow ventilation, is recommended. If the appliances get wet, they should be dried thoroughly, but avoid drying by direct heat or sunlight.

The equipment should not be subjected to unnecessary strain or pressure and must be kept free from contact with sharp implements, corrosives and other possible causes of damage. Recommended cleaning instructions should be followed.

Inspection

Research carried out for the HSE in 2002, involving synthetic fibre webbing lanyards, confirmed potential causes of degradation.

A 1 mm cut in the edge of a lanyard was shown to result in up to a 40% loss of strength, depending on the make of lanyard being used for the test. Most users do not appreciate the possible loss of strength as they assume that there is a proportional strength-to-width relationship; so in their eyes a 1 mm nick on a 25 mm flat sling is not really significant.

A further study in 2006 investigated the resistance of the webbing material (used to make harnesses and lanyards) to abrasion by various types of surface, including concrete and angle iron. The findings of this study revealed that severe abrasion of the material, and a significant reduction in its strength, occurred after a small number of cycles of abrading the material across concrete. Abrasion across angle iron also degraded the material but at a significantly slower rate.

The wearer must make a visual inspection of safety equipment before use. The equipment should be examined by a competent person at least once every six months (three months for frequently used equipment) and a record kept.

Safety belts, harnesses and lanyards should be examined by a competent person after a fall or other circumstances in which the equipment has been deployed, before it is reissued for use.

Safety belts, harnesses and lanyards should be taken out of use if found to be damaged or defective.

Under most circumstances, knots in lanyards would be considered a significant problem. Typically, a knot is presumed to reduce the strength of a lanyard by 50%.

Particular attention should be directed to the points below.

- ☑ **Webbing and leather.** Examine for cuts, cracks, tears or abrasions, stretching and distortion, damage due to deterioration, contact with heat, acids or other corrosives and rot.

- ☑ **Snap hooks.** Examine for damaged or distorted hooks, faulty springs, strained jaws, hairline cracks and corrosion.

- ☑ **Buckles.** Carefully examine the shoulders of buckles; inspect for open or distorted rollers, undue wear, hairline cracks and corrosion.

- ☑ **Sewing.** Examine for broken, cut or worn threads, open seams and failed stitching.

- ☑ **Lanyards, ropes and chains.** Examine for damage or signs of wear and, in the case of hawser-laid ropes, inter-strand wear, unravelling extension and fusion. In the case of kernmantle rope, check for cuts, abrasions, flat spots, permanent kinks and visible signs of the inner core.

For webbing lanyards, specific attention should be given to:

- ☑ cuts of 1 mm or more to the edge of the lanyard (for example, as a result of being choke-hitched around steelwork)

- ☑ surface abrasions to surface or edges and damaged stitching

- ☑ a knot in the lanyard other than the manufacturer's

- ☑ results of chemical attack

- ☑ damaged or deformed fittings

- ☑ partially deployed energy-absorbers.

 For full details refer to the HSE publication INDG367 (02/09 reprint) and Appendix 5.

- ☑ **Unauthorised modifications.** Examine equipment for homemade attachments or adaptations. Impress on the wearers that their lives could depend on the continued efficiency and durability of their safety equipment and that, by frequent personal inspections, the possibility of equipment failure will be reduced to a minimum.

Records

A card or history sheet should be kept for each harness and lanyard, and particulars of all examinations and other details of interest recorded. Each harness and lanyard should be marked with an individual serial number for identification purposes. The harness ID, if being written in pen, should not be placed directly on the webbing tape as this can weaken the material.

Dead weight anchor devices

The use of dead weight anchors in accordance with European and British Standards BS EN 795 and BS 7883 (Class E) has become an acceptable means of providing a safe fall-arrest anchor device on flat roof surfaces, particularly where it is not possible to penetrate the roof surface.

However, the increased usage and range of devices developed over recent years has revealed a number of factors not previously considered.

To ensure the safety of users, the BSI technical committee dealing with this subject, supported by the HSE, has prepared the following points that should be considered.

- ☑ Has the dead weight anchor device been designed and tested in accordance with the Personal Protective Equipment Directive?

- ☑ Have the BS EN 795 and BS 7883 tests been carried out in accordance with the latest version of BS 7883?

Prior to the above, testing was only carried out on dry roof surfaces. If there is any possibility that a dead weight anchor may be used in wet conditions (for example, if it starts to rain, or after rain, with water trapped under the anchor device or in its path of travel) then it must have been tested for use in wet conditions on the relevant type of roof covering.

While many dead weight anchor devices have been tested for use on single-ply membrane roofs, it has recently been found that the performance of some (and, possibly all) is far less satisfactory on embossed membranes rather than on plain, smooth membranes.

Fall arrest and suspension equipment

This is thought to result from the reduced contact surface area between the anchor device and the roof surface. This effectively reduces the amount of friction.

Anyone who wishes to use a dead weight anchor device on an embossed membrane surface or a surface that is not smooth should seek advice from the anchor device manufacturer before proceeding.

The attention of users is drawn to the fact that no standard, at present, specifies tests for fall-arrest systems when a full body harness is connected via:

- ☑ a retractable fall arrestor to a dead weight anchor device using a connector

- ☑ an energy-absorbing lanyard to a dead weight anchor device using connectors.

Users who wish to connect such a system to a dead weight anchor device are advised to seek confirmation from the manufacturer of the retractable fall arrestor or energy-absorbing lanyard that their products are safe to use in this way.

5.6   Suspension trauma

One of the effects of being suspended in a harness is a tightening of the leg straps that bear the body weight of the suspended person. This can affect the blood circulation in the legs and cause the suspended person considerable discomfort, possible kidney failure and eventually unconsciousness and death. This is known as suspension trauma. It is essential that someone suspended in a harness is recovered in the shortest possible time.

 Current guidance from the HSE is to have someone removed from suspension within 10 minutes if they are immobile.

However, suspension trauma can start within five minutes. A fallen person can become unconscious with 10 minutes and die within 15 minutes.

Fall victims may be able to slow the onset of suspension trauma by relieving the pressure on their legs by pushing down vigorously with the legs, by positioning their body in a horizontal or slight leg-high position, by using their pole rope to make an improvised sit harness, or if there is something nearby upon which the feet can be rested, by standing up. Also onset can be slowed by the victim moving their legs to maintain circulation. However, the design of the harness and injuries sustained during the fall may prevent these actions being taken.

Harness accessories include stirrups that are secured out of the way by Velcro during normal use but can be lowered after a fall to enable the person to effectively stand up in the harness.

The HSE has advised that the often-quoted view that anyone who has been suspended in a harness, become unconscious and then rescued must not be put in the standard recovery position, **is in fact untrue** and could be dangerous. The person must be placed in a horizontal position, preferably the standard recovery position. It is essential that the emergency services are summoned immediately if it becomes apparent that there could be a medical emergency situation. Throughout any rescue normal first aid protocols take priority.

It should be noted that a recovered conscious person should remain in the sitting position for at least 30 minutes. Anyone who has been suspended for more than 10 minutes **must** go to hospital as soon as possible.

Harness fall recovery

Many of the companies who manufacture and supply harnesses and lanyards also produce systems for rescuing a person who is suspended in a harness.

Depending upon the design of the equipment, sometimes a single person is able to attach the rescue system to the D-ring of the fallen person's harness and either lower them to ground level or raise them back up on to the working platform in a controlled manner.

This type of rescue equipment is classified as lifting equipment under the Lifting Operations and Lifting Equipment Regulations.

5.7   Rope access (abseiling)

This technique is only to be carried out by fully trained and competent persons. It is generally suitable for inspection and other similar activities but not for general construction work, except in exceptional circumstances. An example might be the rigging of safety nets where it is not reasonably practicable to do it by using other means of access (such as a MEWP or another form of working platform).

The Work at Height Regulations require that (generally) anyone carrying out roped access uses a system that incorporates two separately anchored lines: the working line, which is the means of access, and a safety line, which prevents a fall if the working line fails.

This requirement may be ignored in exceptional circumstances where:

- ☑ the risk assessment shows that the use of a second line would increase the risk to the person

- ☑ effective alternative safety measures are taken.

The person must be connected to both lines by automatic locking devices that prevent an uncontrolled descent should the person lose control of their actions.

The ropes, harnesses and other equipment are covered by the six-monthly thorough examination and inspection requirements set out in the Lifting Operations and Lifting Equipment Regulations as they apply to equipment used for the lifting of persons.

Protection must be installed if there is a danger of materials or equipment falling onto persons below.

It is essential that only persons trained and competent in the use of rope-access equipment, to current industry standards (IRATA/BS 7985:2009), are allowed to carry out such activities.

 The trade association that governs the rope access industry is IRATA. Its contact details can be found online.

A second group of specialists, steeplejacks, commonly use rope access. It is vital to remember that steeplejacking is completely covered by the Work at Height Regulations, and there are no exemptions for them.

 For advice on the relevant standards and training, it is suggested that you contact the Steeplejack and Lightning Protection Training Group.

5.8   Boatswain's chairs

05

Boatswain's (or bosun's) chairs should only be used where the work is of a relatively short duration and where no other means of access or working (such as a suspended scaffold) is practicable.

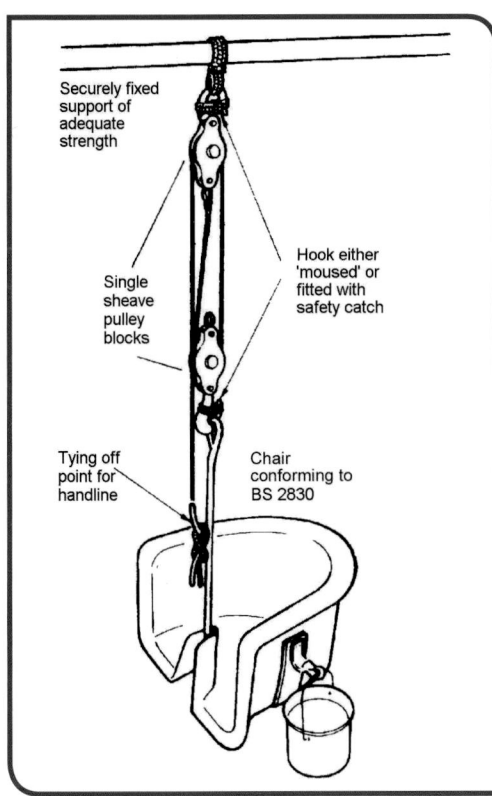

Securely fixed support of adequate strength

Single sheave pulley blocks

Hook either 'moused' or fitted with safety catch

Tying off point for handline

Chair conforming to BS 2830

A person in a boatswain's chair is extremely vulnerable. They are suspended high above the ground and, if anything goes wrong, the chances are that they are beyond rapid or immediate help. The risk assessment should cover rescue procedures should an emergency occur.

The installation and use of a boatswain's chair must be supervised by an experienced and competent person. Only properly trained and competent operatives should be permitted to use them. The regulations must be strictly observed.

The traditional non-British Standard boatswain's chair is still used by specialist trades (such as steeplejacks and lightning conductor engineers). Operatives need to be fully trained and competent before being permitted to use and work from it.

Where possible, consideration should be given to the provision of a second safety line connected to a harness being worn by the operative. In this way, should there be a problem with the boatswain's chair, this safe system of working will prevent a fall. It may not always be possible and if this is the case, then the reason for this should be recorded as part of the work at height risk assessment.

(An independently anchored safety line and safety harness are not shown in the diagram.)

Boatswain's chair

Rigging

In the construction industry, a boatswain's chair should always be rigged with a pair of single sheave pulley blocks, having a safe working load of at least 225 kg. Outriggers and other supports must be strong enough, and be securely fastened down. Where weights are used, a safety factor of four is required.

A boatswain's chair is classified as a roped access system under the Work at Height Regulations. Therefore, the system should be rigged with a separately anchored safety line complete with an automatic locking device attached to the user of the seat that prevents or limits a fall should the primary suspension system fail.

Fall arrest and suspension equipment

Chair

A boatswain's chair should meet the following requirements:

- ☑ compliance with BS 2830. A certificate of compliance should be available from the manufacturer
- ☑ be of a recommended size:
  - between 450 mm and 610 mm wide
  - not less than 225 mm deep
  - have a back not less than 250 mm high
- ☑ if the chair has a single central leg or suspension member, this should be without sharp bends and be securely fixed to the seat as far back as practicable, so that the user sits with one leg at either side
- ☑ be provided with a safety harness to prevent the occupant falling out
- ☑ the back and the suspension member should be placed so that no-one can fall out
- ☑ the suspension point must be at least 500 mm above the seat, with provisions for suspension. No part should be able to become detached
- ☑ be made for a safe working load of 115 kg. A proof test of 150 kg is recommended.

Protection of the public

When the risk assessment identifies that work from a boatswain's chair will take place above areas where people may be present, adequate protection must be installed to prevent them being injured from falling equipment or materials. This is reinforced by the requirement for the creation and management of danger areas under the Work at Height Regulations.

Lifting equipment

All ropes and chains used should be thoroughly examined before their first use for any sign of chafing or wear, and then every six months. They must be securely attached to the chair and to the anchor. Swivel connections should be used to prevent spinning.

Fall ropes should not be less than 18 mm in diameter. They should be tied off correctly in the working position. The rope must not be removed from the cleat while the chair is in use. A controlled descent is achieved by removing the locking-hitch from the rope in the tied-off position and easing it around the cleat.

All lifting equipment and ancillary equipment must conform to the Lifting Operations and Lifting Equipment Regulations

Hooks

Hooks should be moused, C-shaped or fitted with a spring-loaded device to prevent the displacement of the load.

5.9   Cradles

Cradles, which come within the category of suspended access equipment, may be used for window cleaning, painting, exterior maintenance and inspection.

They may be permanently rigged and attached to the roof, or be a temporary installation that can be dismantled. Safe access to the cradle must be provided, either at ground or roof level. Cradles, as man-riding equipment, must be inspected at appropriate intervals under LOLER and subjected to six-monthly thorough examinations.

Two main types of cradle in use within the construction industry are:

- ☑ those 3.2 metres or less in length, suspended on pulley blocks with natural or synthetic fibre ropes
- ☑ those more than 3.2 metres in length, suspended on wire ropes controlled by hand-operated or power winches that are mounted on the cradle.

Both types can be installed as:

- ☑ **fixed cradle** rise and fall only
- ☑ **travelling** capable of moving horizontally across the workface as well as rising and falling.

General

Care must be exercised when planning works at elevated positions, where the safe distance from electric cables may be reduced. The risk assessment should specify appropriate distances and precautions.

Only competent and properly trained personnel should be employed in the erection and use of cradles.

All equipment must be thoroughly examined at six-monthly intervals and tested in compliance with the relevant legislation and standards, and proper records must be kept.

The public should be warned of operations.

Specification for suspended access equipment (suspended chairs, traditional steeplejacks' seats, work cages, cradles and platforms) for use in the building, engineering construction, steeplejack and cleaning industries (BS 2830).

Management information

British Standard BS 5974:2010 recommends that both the supplier and the user appoint a competent person to co-ordinate and oversee the safe installation, use and dismantling of the equipment.

Temporary suspended access equipment (TSAE) may be motor or manually operated but manual hoisting is not recommended for operation above 15 metres.

 Cradles are a highly specialised area and expert advice must be sought before commencing work.

The erection of a cradle must be carried out and supervised by an experienced, competent person, who is familiar with the type of equipment being erected.

05

Appendix A – Safety nets – Safety checklist

Safety checklist

Before use	Yes	No	N/A
1. Has a risk assessment been carried out?			
2. Are the safety nets rigged to minimise the height of any fall such that an uninjured person can simply climb out?			
3. If not, have emergency rescue procedures been established?			
4. Have checks been made to ensure that freefall distances are not more than specified?			
5. Have the safety nets been rigged by trained and competent persons?			
6. Is the use of safety nets to be supervised by competent persons?			
7. Have safety nets been inspected prior to current use?			
8. Are complete and proper records kept of all inspections and examinations?			
9. Has the safety net system been inspected within the previous week?			
10. Are all anchors and supports secure?			
11. Is the safety net clear of all debris?			
12. Have checks been made to ensure that nothing is positioned under the net to reduce the minimum clearance distance required?			

During use	Yes	No	N/A
1. Is the net being kept clear of debris?			

2. Are the safety nets inspected:
  – after a fall
  – for the effects of contamination
  – every seven days during use to ensure that the safety net is not damaged and that the anchorage points and ties are sound?			

After use	Yes	No	N/A
1. Are safety nets inspected for any damage following use and before being stowed away?			
2. Are any defects reported promptly and correctly?			
3. Are repairs only carried out by a competent person?			
4. Are adequate records maintained as to the use and condition of safety nets?			
5. Are safety nets dried and stored correctly?			
6. Are the annual condition tests being undertaken?			

06

Frame erection

The building and construction industry as a whole has an unacceptably high accident rate, and workers involved in handling and erecting steelwork are in the group that suffers one of the highest fatality and serious injury rates within the industry.

The majority of fatal accidents are as a result of falls from height. In addition, many serious accidents occur due to workers being struck by falling materials.

Introduction	90
Key points	90
Design and planning	91
Other considerations	92

6.1 Introduction

According to the British Constructional Steelwork Association (BCSA), the increased use of mobile elevating work platforms (MEWPs) in recent years has reduced the need to put operatives onto the steelwork, which has resulted in a significant reduction of fall-arrest accidents reported to the Health and Safety Executive (HSE).

 For further information on BCSA refer to their website.

The erection of structures can be both difficult and dangerous. The principal hazard and cause of injury is falls from height, while either working from, or gaining access to, working positions. Other hazards include structural instability during erection, lifting operations and moving plant.

Reading this chapter will not give you the competence to erect structures. It will, however, inform you of the common hazards and how, through practical measures, the risks arising from those hazards can be effectively controlled, enabling the work to be carried out safely.

6.2 Key points

☑ The majority of jobs that involve erecting steelwork will also involve working at height, and exposure to the associated potential hazards.

☑ A schedule of erection should be in place to ensure the safe erection and stability of the structure until it is complete.

☑ All steel erection must be the subject of a risk assessment and carried out in accordance with a method statement.

☑ Ideally, the erection of steelwork will be carried out in such a way that those doing the job are on a stable working platform at all times, be that a scaffold or a mobile elevating work platform (MEWP). Operatives having to go onto the steelwork should be a last resort.

☑ Designers should consider fitting steelwork with proprietary edge protection before it is lifted into place at height as a collective fall prevention measure.

☑ Ground conditions must be suitable to take the weight of MEWPs, cranes and their loads.

☑ Designers have the potential to ensure that the erection of steelwork can be carried out safely (for example, designing-in lifting eye attachment points, or specifying ground-level fabrication).

☑ The erection of steelwork will usually involve extended crane operations, the use of MEWPs in and around the new structure, lorry movements, steel laydown areas and possibly a lorry-park, all of which must be planned for when the site is first set up.

☑ All lifting operations, including the use of cranes and MEWPs, must be carried out by, and under the control of, competent persons.

☑ The presence of overhead power cables and the possible need to manually align steelwork components for connection are other potential hazards associated with the erection of steelwork.

Dutyholders must:

- avoid work at height where they can;

- use work equipment or other measures to prevent falls where they cannot avoid working at height; and

- where they cannot eliminate the risk of a fall, use work equipment or other measures to minimise the distance and consequences of a fall should one occur.

 Falls from height are the biggest cause of fatal accidents at work within the UK.

 For additional information and resources regarding work at height refer to the HSE's website.

6.3 Design and planning

Key items that should receive attention include the following.

Structural stability

The structure must be stable at all times, from when the first piece of steelwork is put into position until it is completed.

Temporary supports (such as bracing, guys or stays) must be used during the erection of any structure that may be unstable or liable to collapse before it is completed. Additionally, where any work is carried out that is likely to adversely affect the foundations or stability of any existing building or structure (or one under construction), all practicable precautions (such as shoring) must be taken.

Temporary structures

Any temporary structure must be of good construction, adequate strength and stability, made of sound materials, free from obvious defects and be properly maintained.

Safe means of assembly or making connections

Assembly of steelwork components or making connections should be planned so that erectors can do as much of the work as possible at ground level.

Where erectors have to work at a height, provision must be made for safe means of access to the connecting points and any other working places. Ideally, work will be carried out from MEWPs operating on a suitable floor surface. However, where this is not possible, design consideration should be given to:

- ☑ ensuring there is adequate working space and a suitable work platform for a crane

- ☑ connections between steelwork components that are simple to make off site, ground-level assembly or fabrication to reduce work at height

- ☑ the provision of fixed work platforms and ladders

- ☑ the provision of anchorage points for safety nets and fall prevention and arrest devices.

Steelwork components

The size, weight and shape of individual steelwork components will influence safe handling and erecting. The designer should therefore consider the following steps:

- ☑ marking components as an aid to identification (also to prevent costly mistakes)

- ☑ optimising the length of structural members in an attempt to reduce the number of connections at height

- ☑ calculating the weights of components to assist in the estimation of safe crane capacities and the location of cranes

- ☑ identifying the positions where components should be lifted

- ☑ indicating centres of gravity where these are not readily evident.

6.4   Other considerations

Site features

Potentially hazardous features that will conflict with health and safety should be identified. Some typical examples include the following items.

Overhead electric cables

If there are any overhead power lines near the proposed erection site, the local electricity company should be consulted. Either the power lines should be made dead, temporarily rerouted or other suitable precautions taken to prevent any close approach to, or contact with, live overhead lines.

 For further information on the regulations and for additional resources refer to the HSE's website.

Other site features that require attention

These features include:

- ☑ lack of space for the handling and storage of steelwork
- ☑ restricted (crane) oversailing rights
- ☑ restricted area(s) for vehicle movements
- ☑ low resistance to ground-bearing pressures
- ☑ poor access onto the site
- ☑ any buildings close to the site that may affect the erection process
- ☑ any rights of access that may bring members of the public close to the erection site
- ☑ ground contamination from previous use of the land.

Other contractors and their activities

Certain activities or processes on, or adjacent to, the site may have the potential to adversely affect the health and safety of workers on site. For example, noxious gases, vapours or dusts may be given off from chimneys, stacks, tank vents and ventilation ducts. These may not cause a problem at ground level but may affect steelwork erectors working at height.

Managing the safe erection of steelwork

Following a detailed risk assessment of the work activity, the next step in ensuring safe working practices in erection is the preparation of a method statement. This important document should detail the proposed erection scheme and should form part of the health and safety plan for the project.

Method statements

The amount of detail required in a method statement will depend on how big or complex the job is. However, method statements should be written for even small steel erection jobs. It is clear evidence that attention has been given to design and planning aspects, as well as being a plan to ensure that the project is completed without risks to health and safety.

A typical method statement should include:

- ☑ details of how the project will be managed and health and safety risks eliminated, avoided or reduced
- ☑ information on the site, including any hazardous features (such as overhead electric power lines) and what effect these will have on the project
- ☑ details of plant requirements (such as cranes, MEWPs and other lifting equipment) and the competencies required to operate them
- ☑ arrangements for the safe receipt, off-loading, storage and handling of steelwork components on site
- ☑ details on where and how steelwork will be assembled prior to erection
- ☑ the sequential method of erecting the structure and how stability will be ensured at all times
- ☑ how activities, such as slinging, lifting, unslinging and the initial and final connecting of steelwork components, will be carried out safely
- ☑ the safety precaution to prevent falls from height. For example, arranging for as much assembling as possible to be done at ground level, minimising the number of connections to be made at a height
- ☑ the means of providing safe access and a safe place of work by methods such as mobile towers, temporary platforms and walkways
- ☑ details of the means of communication during lifting operations

☑ any requirement for safety nets, safety harnesses and fall-arrest devices (provisions for design features should be specified, for example, attachment points for ladders, safety nets and fall-arrest devices)

☑ how people will be protected from falling objects. For example, use of screens, fans and debris nets, installation of barriers and warning notices at ground level

☑ a contingency plan for dealing with any problems that may arise

☑ the expected level of competence of the people undertaking the work.

 For further information refer to Chapter A05
Risk assessments and method statements.

Site access and egress

The main or principal contractor should check that all of the vehicles associated with the erection or dismantling of steelwork can access and egress the site safely. It is envisaged that the vehicles will mainly be cranes and delivery lorries (delivering steel and MEWPs).

A safe location for lorries to park must be identified and communicated to the steelwork contractor if their lorries may have to wait to be admitted to the site to be unloaded. This area must not be immediately outside the site or on any access road, if doing so would create an unacceptable obstruction or other hazards for passing traffic or pedestrians. On larger sites space should be allocated as a dedicated lorry or trailer park.

On sites where there is simply not space to park large vehicles, appropriate arrangements (such as a road or lane closure) must be made for delivery lorries (and possibly the mobile crane) to be parked on the public highway adjacent to the site boundary for the off-loading of steel.

Where there is a loading/unloading bay for only a single lorry, a strict schedule of delivery times must be written, communicated to the steel delivery contractors and adhered to. In this instance it is highly advisable to identify a lorry holding area, to which lorries that miss their slot can be sent pending the allocation of another unloading slot.

Every effort should be made to avoid the need for vehicles to reverse, particularly out of the site gate and back on to a public road. Where this is not possible, suitable precautions must be taken (for example, the use of one or more signallers or an alternative traffic-control system).

Where it is considered unsafe for vehicles and pedestrians to use the same site entrance, one or more separate pedestrian entrances must be provided, clearly indicated and kept free of obstruction.

Housekeeping

Construction sites must, so far as is reasonably practicable, be kept in good order and a reasonable state of cleanliness.

Platforms, gangways, floors and other places must not be obstructed by loose materials.

Projecting nails or similar sharp objects in timber or other materials must be removed or knocked down to prevent injury.

Materials must be stacked safely.

 For further information and additional resources refer to the HSE's website.

Lighting

The following areas must be adequately and suitably lit:

☑ every working place

☑ access to working places

☑ where lifting operations are in progress

☑ all dangerous openings.

Protection from falling material

At any place where people work, steps must be taken to prevent them from being struck by any falling material or article.

Scaffold components, tools and other objects must not be thrown or tipped down from a height where they are liable to cause injury, but should be properly lowered.

06

Lifting and slinging

Competent people must be used to operate lifting equipment and give signals in line with either BS 7121 or the Health and Safety (Safety Signs and Signals) Regulations.

All critical lifts, including tandem lifts, should be carefully planned and supervised and, where appropriate, a lifting plan should be developed for more complex operations.

Appropriate precautions must be taken to ensure the stability of lifting appliances when used on soft, uneven or sloping ground. These could include measures such as ground levelling, use of mats or hard standing.

The load must not exceed the safe working load of the lifting appliance (allowance should be made for the weight of lifting slings, beams, and so on).

Any load that approaches the safe working load of a crane should be carefully raised a short distance and the operation stopped to check safety and stability before continuing.

If more than one lifting appliance is used to raise or lower a load, a competent person must supervise the operation, which must be arranged so that no lifting appliance is loaded above its safe working load or is made unstable.

Suitable packing should be used to prevent the edges of the load from damaging the slings.

Loads should be lifted and lowered slowly to avoid any shock loading. The use of hand lines, fixed near the ends of the load, will help to prevent the load spinning when being lifted or lowered.

Loads should be lowered onto timber battens to protect slings and enable them to be removed easily.

 For further information refer to:
Chapter C07 Lifting operations,
Chapter C08 Lifting equipment,
The Lifting Operations and Lifting Equipment Regulations, and
Code of Practice for Safe Use of Cranes (BS 7121).

 For further information and for additional resources refer to the HSE's website.

06

Off-loading, stacking and storage of steelwork

A safe means of access and a safe workplace must be provided when off-loading components from delivery lorries. Two examples of recently developed safety systems are:

This example of unloading reinforcement shows the use of a fall-arrest unloading device and pre-slung loads

☑ tensioned steel wire running the length of the lorry trailer, at above the head-height of anyone standing on the trailer. Each slinger wears a safety harness and a restraint lanyard, the free end of which is clipped to the tension steel wire. In the event of a trip or stumble, the slinger is prevented from falling from the trailer

☑ a 'U' shaped inflatable airbag or a beanbag that fits around the back and sides of the trailer to act as a soft-landing system, should anyone fall off the trailer.

Many accidents have occurred during the off-loading of lorries when the load-securing mechanism was released. This is because the load was either not stable when loaded or because it moved and became unstable during the journey.

The stability of the load on the lorry, or in the stack, must be ensured at all times. Suitable timber wedges or packing pieces can be used as an aid to stability.

Precautions should be taken to prevent slingers being struck by the load. For example, taking up a safe position off the lorry before the load is lifted.

The stack must be constructed so that components can be removed without risk of someone being trapped or struck.

There may be an advantage in using a suitable transportable storage rack (stillage) for smaller components.

Anyone not directly involved in the off-loading activity should not be allowed into the area.

 Pedestrians and vehicles should be kept apart where practicable.

Safe means of access and safe place of work

To comply with the Work at Height Regulations, consideration must be given to reducing the need to work at height, for example by:

☑ doing as much of the connecting work at ground level or from erected floor decks, as the work progresses

☑ using a releasing device so that lifting gear can be released remotely

☑ ensuring that, wherever possible, inspection and testing is carried out at low level.

When people must work at height, consideration should be given to:

☑ installing permanent or temporary handrails, stairways, ladders, walkways and floor decking, so that these can be used by erectors as the work progresses

☑ providing hard standings or floor slabs so that mobile access platforms can be used

☑ providing temporary access and working platforms, including scaffolds, lightweight staging and purpose-built platforms with safe means of access

☑ working from MEWPs.

Whilst the increased use of MEWPs has brought about safer working at height, it has also created the need to ensure that:

☑ MEWP operators are adequately trained and competent

☑ ground conditions on the site are properly surveyed and prepared to enable the safe use of such heavy plant without risk of sinking or overturning.

Steel erection in progress using a mobile crane, two MEWPs and edge protection being attached to steelwork at ground level before being lifted in to position

Traditionally, scaffolding was the main form of edge protection and could only be installed, modified or removed by trained scaffolders, after the steelwork was in place. However, the development of various types of system edge protection has provided opportunities for pre-installing edge protection before work at height commences. The use of such systems can also eliminate the need for successive trades to install their own edge protection and then remove it when leaving site, only for it to be replaced by the next trade's edge protection. The elimination of such duplication has obvious safety benefits.

It may be appropriate in some circumstances to use other means of access to height, such as the use of roped access techniques, which must be carried out by trained and competent persons. Alternatively, access may be achieved by using a man-riding basket suspended from a crane.

There may be occasions when it is necessary to use fall-arrest rather than fall-prevention measures, with safety nets or other soft-landing systems being the preferred method of fall arrest. BCSA has stated that the increased use of safety nets has had a significant beneficial effect on the steel construction industry's accident rate.

06

 For further information refer to Chapter D02 Safe working on roofs and at height, and Chapter D05 Fall arrest and suspension equipment.

Edge protection

Consideration should be given to how edge protection for the following activities will be provided. One option is to use proprietary edge protection, which can be fitted directly to the steelwork at ground level and lifted with the steelwork into position. This can save time, or reduce the risk for installing edge protection at height.

Beam straddling

There may be occasions where the work cannot be done from a MEWP or other platform and erectors may have to work from the steel. This is known as beam straddling. This form of access is only permissible for specific short-duration jobs where the beam is of I-beam section.

A full body harness with a twin-tailed lanyard system may be used. However, users must ensure that this system is used correctly and that the second leg is not attached to the user's harness, as this may interfere with the operation of the energy absorber.

Consideration must be made as to suitable anchor points to which the harness lanyard can be attached. The erector can sit astride the flange with the sole and heel of each foot resting on the bottom flange and both hands able to grasp either side of the top flange.

Alternatively, proprietary beam-gliding devices are available to improve mobility.

The risk assessment must consider how anyone carrying out this practice is going to be rescued following a fall.

The use of a safety harness or lanyard requires a minimum clearance below the high-level place of work to allow the lanyard to function properly in arresting a fall. Expert advice should be sought.

Frame erection

 For further information on safe working at height refer to Chapter D01 The Work at Height Regulations.

The safe system of work must also ensure the operative's safety:

☑ whilst getting up to the place of work and down again

☑ during the period of time at high level before the operative is able to clip on.

If access has to be made inside a structural steel box section or any configuration of steelwork where ventilation is poor, it should be treated as a confined space and appropriate precautions taken. The atmosphere should be tested by a competent person, before entry is made, to ensure that there is sufficient oxygen present. Continuous monitoring for oxygen deficiency is strongly recommended.

Tests for flammable or toxic gases or vapours and oxygen enrichment should be carried out as appropriate, depending on the proposed work activity. (For example, oxypropane cutting or burning may lead to a build up of toxic gases or toxic metal fumes, or there may be a leakage of propane or oxygen.)

 For further information refer to Chapter D09 Confined spaces.

The weather

A regular weather forecast should be obtained by the manager in charge of the erection programme. Erection should not take place where weather conditions impose an adverse effect, such as:

☑ ice, frost or snow

☑ rain or dew

☑ wind strengths

☑ poor visibility (fog, mist or glare).

If erection work is stopped, measures should be taken to ensure that the structure remains stable.

After a stoppage due to the weather, stability of the structure should be checked before work is allowed to restart.

The stability of structures

Steel erection, by its very definition, involves creating structures, which these regulations require to be stable at all times. In particular:

☑ all practicable steps must be taken to ensure that no person is put at risk by the collapse of any structure that may become unstable or weakened

☑ structures must not be loaded to an extent that they become unsafe

☑ any temporary means of supporting a permanent structure must be:
   – designed and maintained to withstand any stresses and strains that are put on it
   – only used for the purpose for which it was designed, installed and maintained
   – not overloaded so as to render it unsafe.

Traffic routes and vehicles

Prior to, and during, steel erection, deliveries of steel on articulated lorries will be a feature of many jobs. In the context of this chapter, these regulations place a legal duty on the person in charge of the site to ensure:

☑ that pedestrians and vehicles can move safely and without risks to health, so far as is reasonably practicable

☑ there are sufficient traffic routes, all of which must be suitable for the vehicles using them

☑ there is sufficient segregation between pedestrians and moving vehicles but where this is not reasonably practicable:
   – other means of protection are provided
   – a means of warning pedestrians of the approach of vehicles, where the pedestrians would otherwise be at risk, is provided

☑ that (vehicle) loading bays have one exit for the exclusive use of pedestrians

☑ appropriate signs are erected in the interests of health and safety

☑ steps are taken to prevent the unintentional movement of any vehicle

☑ each vehicle must be operated in a safe manner with its load arranged safely

☑ every vehicle is fitted with means of warning persons who may be at risk when the vehicle is moving.

07

Excavations

This chapter gives some practical guidance on factors to be considered when planning excavations, the setting up of the work and safe working within them. This will include the elements to consider, such as soil composition, depth, support structures and emergency evacuation.

Good planning and correct preparation for excavations are essential, as seven to 10 people are killed each year in collapsed trenches, most of these less than 2.5 metres deep.

Introduction	98
Key requirements	98
Excavation support	100
Excavation safety	103
Underground cables and services	105
Inspections and reports	106
Excavators used as cranes	106

7.1   Introduction

Most construction work will involve a form of excavation, for foundations, sewers or drainage. These will vary in depth but are always a high risk activity as they can be affected by diverse factors (such as rainwater) or hot weather, which will increase the amounts of materials being removed.

Many accidents occur when the excavation looks in good condition with its sides clean and self-supporting, with no defects to be seen.

Some excavations may need to be classed as confined spaces, and will therefore need additional precautions.

Neither the shallowness of an excavation nor the appearance of the ground should be taken as indicators of safety. Accident reports suggest that **far too often** such assumptions are made incorrectly.

 The HSE inspector served a prohibition notice for this excavation, which was 1.9 metres deep and unsupported

The contractor was fined £10,000 and the HSE was awarded £8,000 costs. In addition the supervisor was fined £1,000 and the HSE was awarded £800 costs.

The method of excavation can vary, even a short distance from a previous excavation. Workers will often have to improvise and use their knowledge and skills to overcome unforeseen obstructions and different ground conditions. It is important that supervisors and their workers are trained and competent to ensure excavation work is completed in a safe way.

7.2   Key requirements

You need to complete a **risk assessment** for any works that are to be undertaken, and this must be done by a competent person.

This risk assessment must take into consideration the potential for the sides to collapse, that someone may be injured and the possible need for a support structure.

Try to ensure the risk assessment seeks to eliminate or reduce the risk at source (such as using trenchless techniques and having the sides battered or stepped).

Risk, from the following hazards, must also be taken into consideration:

- ☑ collapse of the sides
- ☑ underground services
- ☑ contaminated ground
- ☑ fall of persons, materials, plant or equipment into the excavation
- ☑ confined spaces – poisonous/explosive atmospheres or lack of oxygen
- ☑ flooding
- ☑ overhead services

- ☑ moving plant – injury to persons
- ☑ lifting operations
- ☑ undermining adjacent structures or services
- ☑ surcharging the excavation, meaning applying pressure to the sides (for example, planning vehicle routes or material storage areas too close to the excavation).

 For details on safety awareness for working around excavations refer to Section G *Checklists and forms*.

Control measures described in the risk assessment should include:

- ☑ protection of person(s) installing the support system
- ☑ safe exposure, and if necessary, support of underground services
- ☑ safe access and egress from the excavation
- ☑ adequate ventilation of the workspace
- ☑ arrangements to dewater the trench if necessary
- ☑ inspections of the excavation by a competent person
- ☑ consideration for the stability of adjacent structures or land
- ☑ arranging for guarding and lighting where necessary.

A collapse captured while taking site record photos

The excavation was 1.8 metres deep and the collapse took less than two seconds. The method was to dig and pour with no-one entering. Due to heavy rain, this method was abandoned and trench support installed. The section that broke away weighed about one tonne and it can be seen how easily a serious or tragic accident could happen.

07

7.3 Excavation support

Soil stability

There will always be water present during excavations, even if only moisture in the soil, and this is an additional hazard to be considered, as shown in the illustration below.

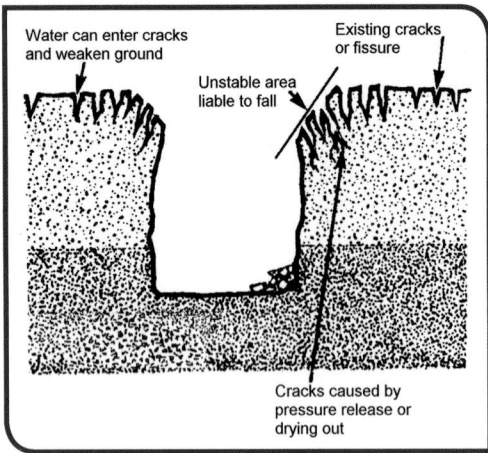

Firm or stiff clay-type ground

Soils that are akin to fine sand flow easily; however, those like stiff clay stick together better.

Do not rely on any soil, whatever its structure, to support its own weight. If it cannot be battered or stepped, then alternative support will be essential.

Loose and fractured rock will also need support.

Trenchless techniques

Persons planning construction work should also be aware of alternative techniques that may be able to eliminate totally or partially the need for excavations.

Examples of the trenchless techniques include boring, directional drilling and pipe jacking – some will need excavation pits at each end to launch and retrieve equipment.

Battering or stepping excavations

This will depend on the nature of the soil, and could be a mix of materials. You will need to take into consideration the water content, and the increase/decrease of this while the excavation is open.

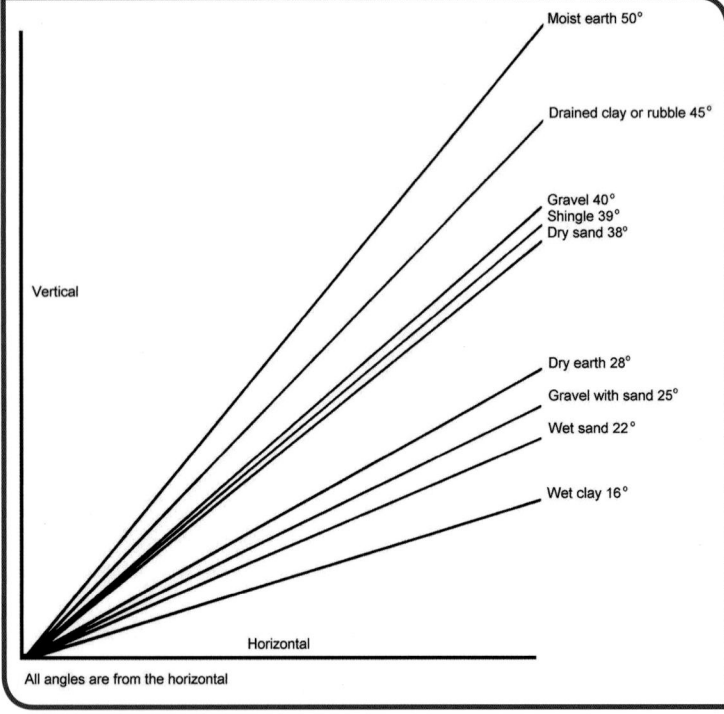

Examples of stepped excavations

Trench supports

The type of support will depend on:

- ☑ the type of excavation
- ☑ the nature of the ground
- ☑ groundwater conditions
- ☑ surcharge of sides of excavation.

Under CDM a client or principal contractor may require excavations to be supported.

A survey should be carried out for all but shallow trenches, to determine the type of soil and other ground conditions; this will then show what support will be required. This survey must be carried out by a competent person.

A specialist engineer will be required for large or complex excavations.

Materials for support must be available before excavation work is started, and be of good quality and well maintained; they must also be fixed securely.

All erection, dismantling and alteration of any support must be under the supervision of a competent person.

07

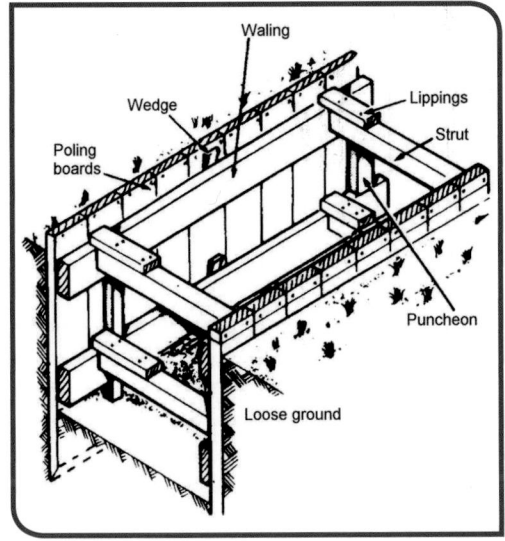

Close-boarded excavation

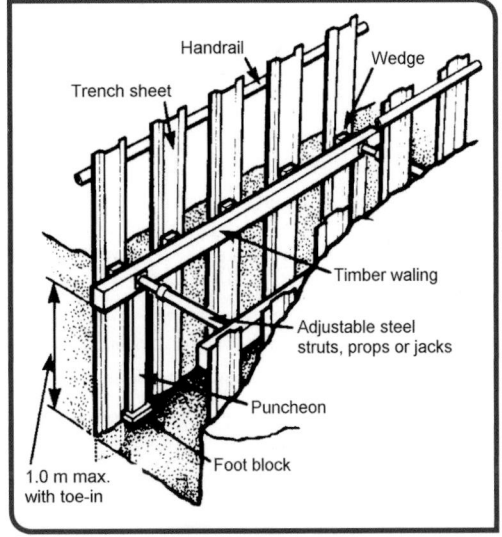

Open sheeting using steel sheets and jacks

Types of support systems

Timber shuttering, steel trench and adjustable props should be used; the props can be mechanical or hydraulic.

A temporary framework of support of a protective box/cage type may be required to protect workers. This can be moved forward as timbering progresses.

Safe working in a deep excavation using trench boxes, tied ladder and height of boxes extends one metre to form edge protection

Proprietary support systems are available and include:

- ☑ **shields,** which are two vertical plates braced permanently apart, intended as temporary localised protection for workers and they can be dragged along as work progresses

- ☑ **trench boxes,** which are modular and are lowered in, and form a permanent support for the trench sides; they can be extended in height and width

- ☑ **plate lining systems** have metal plates that slide into position between vertical soldier posts at preset intervals; the posts counteract stress from trench sides.

You need to be aware that any of the above support systems can cause problems when buried services cross the line of the trench being excavated.

The use of a hydraulic waling frame is better used in the above case, as spaces can be left between the metals sheets once they are in position.

Hydraulic frames are ideal when excavating pits and manholes as they can be extended in both length and width.

Inspection and maintenance of support systems

Excavations must be closely monitored when first opened and sides are unsupported.

Little movements of 6-12 mm are usually the only sign of weakening in cohesive soils – be aware of them, as they can pass unnoticed but they mean something is wrong.

Movement can be seen from slight distortion in the timbering, bowing of poling boards and walings, or signs of local crushing.

The ground can also dry out and shrink, which loosens timbering. Timber can be displaced by the ground absorbing additional moisture.

- ☑ Avoid damage to struts or walings when moving loads into or out of the excavation.

- ☑ Check timber regularly – it can dry out, shrink or rot.

- ☑ In bad weather spoil heaps can slump and loose boulders or masonry can fall into the excavation.

- ☑ A guideline is that the distance from the edge of the trench and the bottom of the spoil heap must not be less than the depth of the excavation.

- ☑ Do not allow heavy vehicles near the edge of an excavation unless the support work has been designed to permit it.

Adjacent structures

- ☑ Take care not to affect the stability of any neighbouring structure or features.

- ☑ Take into account the Party Wall Act and any permissions or restrictions.

- ☑ Take precautions to protect workers (and others) before and during excavation works.

🔍 An unsupported excavation

This excavation was only about 650 mm deep and it was left unsupported overnight. There was heavy rain during the evening and the team returned to find this and the existing cast iron gas main at risk.

7.4   Excavation safety

Access

There must be safe means of getting into and out of an excavation (access and egress).

If the workers use ladders then these must be fit-for-purpose and strong enough. They must be on a firm, level base, secured to prevent slipping, and if no handhold is available, extended to at least one metre (five rungs) above the top of the excavation.

Safe access into a deep excavation, together with all round secure edge protection

 Climbing in or out using walings, buried services or struts must be prohibited. This must be specifically covered in the safe system of work and/or method statement.

Guarding excavations

Suitable steps must be taken to prevent any person, vehicle, plant or equipment, or any accumulation of earth or other materials, from falling into an excavation.

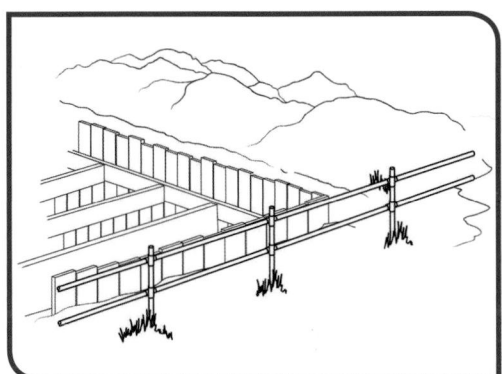

☑ Physical barriers (not pin-and-rope or rolls of orange plastic mesh) should be used to keep materials, plant and equipment away from the edges.

☑ When barriers are removed, they should be replaced as soon as possible.

☑ Edges of an excavation should be lit during darkness, particularly if close to public road and spaces.

☑ If excavation work is carried out on the highway, Local Authority approval is required and appropriate signing and guarding complying with the Traffic Signs Manual, Chapter 8, and the Code of Practice for Safety at Street Works and Road Works must be utilised.

☑ Ensure adequate hazard warning lighting is used when it is dark or during foggy conditions.

 If plastic, Chapter 8-type barriers are used, they must be installed to be robust enough to stop a person if they fell or leant against them. This is particularly important if they are being used to protect the public.

 For further information on guarding excavations refer to Chapter F01 Street works and road works.

07

Vehicles and plant

Plan your traffic routes so that no vehicles or plant go near excavations, other than those that need to be in that area.

Be aware of surcharging when heavy items of construction plant are near to an excavation – where this cannot be avoided, it must be considered in the design of the support system that will be installed.

Stop blocks must be used if vehicles are required to tip into an excavation. Ensure these are placed far enough away to avoid the edge of the excavation being damaged.

Use a signaller to give directions to the vehicle driver/plant operator.

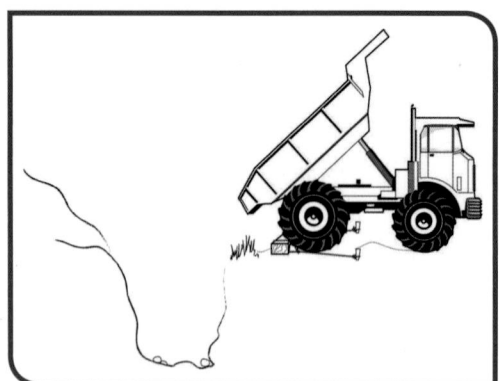

Stop blocks should be used, where appropriate

Safe segregation of excavation work and plant

 For further guidance refer to the HSE's publication *The safe use of vehicles on construction sites* (HSG 144), which can be downloaded free from the HSE's website.

 For further information on vehicles and plant refer to Chapter C06 Mobile plant and vehicles.

Site lighting

There must be suitable and sufficient lighting at every workplace, the approaches to it and on traffic routes.

You must pay particular attention to ensuring there is adequate lighting for access points, openings and lifting operations.

Ventilation

Excavations must be kept clear of suffocating, toxic or explosive gases. Gases can seep through the soil and accumulate in the bottom of the excavation.

Gases that are heavier than air (such as plant exhaust emissions) can leak or roll into an excavation and displace the air, which can lead to asphyxiation.

Leakage of propane and butane from liquefied petroleum gas (LPG) cylinders is potentially very dangerous; the gases will sink to the lowest point and form an explosive concentration that cannot disperse naturally.

The excavation will need to be checked and continuously monitored for the presence of gases and purged before entry by workers if these are found.

 For further information on ventilation refer to Chapter B07 The Control of Substances Hazardous to Health (COSHH).

Confined spaces

If an excavation is classified as a confined space, tests for toxic gas or oxygen depletion must be carried out before work starts and continuously as work progresses.

It is also recommended that the work should be subject to the issue of a permit to work certificate.

You must ensure that every workplace or approach is safe and without risks to health. There must be a sufficient supply of purified air. The most common method of ventilation is to blow clean air into the excavation in sufficient volume to dissipate any gas and provide adequate breathable air.

07

e.g. **Examples of safe systems in practice**

Deep manhole excavation with good access and edge protection

Deep manhole excavation with good access and edge protection

Protected shallow excavation

Drag boxes with guard-rail attachments and ladder access

Remote controlled trench compactor avoiding the need to enter the excavation

Designated bucket changing area

Fencing along utility trench

07

 For further information refer to Chapter D09 Confined spaces.

7.5   Underground cables and services

Before any excavation works take place, you must ensure buried services (such as gas, electricity, water and telecommunications) have been identified.

Many injuries each year are caused by accidental contact with underground services.

You must have controls in place to reduce the risk of injury from underground cables or other underground services.

 For further information refer to Chapter D08 Underground and overhead services.

7.6　Inspections and reports

An inspection of an excavation must be carried out by a competent person:

☑ at the start of each shift during which work is to be carried out

☑ after an event that is likely to have affected the stability of the structure

☑ after the accidental fall or dislodgement of any material.

The competent person must be satisfied that work can be carried out safely.

A report must be prepared, which includes the:

☑ name and address of the person on whose behalf the inspection was carried out

☑ location of the work being inspected

☑ description of the place of work, or part of that place of work inspection, including plant and equipment or materials

☑ date and time of the inspection

☑ details of any matter identified that could give risk to the health and safety of any person

☑ details of any action taken as a result of any matter identified

☑ details of any further actions considered necessary

☑ name and position of the person making the report.

The report must be written before the end of the shift during which it was completed and a copy provided within 24 hours to the person on whose behalf it was undertaken.

A copy of the report must be kept on site until the work is completed and for three months from the date of completion.

You do not need to do more than one written report in any period of seven days. However, it is advisable that a daily record of inspection is kept (for example, in the site diary).

There is no statutory form for inspections and it can be kept electronically. However, you must be able to produce a hard copy for an HSE inspector, if so requested.

Details of what the report should contain can be found in the CDM Regulations.

 For an example of an inspection report refer to Section G *Checklists and forms*.

7.7　Excavators used as cranes

Excavators are mobile work equipment and subject to the provisions of the Provision and Use of Work Equipment Regulations.

Using them for lifting operations in connection with excavation works will make them subject to the Lifting Operations and Lifting Equipment Regulations.

All work is subject to a suitable and sufficient risk assessment, subsequent control measures and capabilities of the work equipment.

The risk assessment must take into consideration that the slinger taking the load on and off will be in what should be regarded as a hazardous area and much nearer to the machine than usual.

Be aware that the slinger is at risk of being struck by the load, bucket or excavator arm if the excavator moves or slews rapidly.

When using slingers, good communication and constant vigilance are essential.

The risk assessment must establish the suitability of the machine, taking into account the additional weight of the bucket and quick hitch in addition to the load.

If appropriate the bucket should be removed and this will improve the operator's view.

The safe working load must be marked on the machine and lifting accessories.

Chains and slings must, under no circumstances, be placed around or on the teeth of the bucket in lieu of a suitable attachment point.

A purpose-made point on the machine must be used for attaching lifting accessories.

 For further detailed guidance refer to Chapter C08 Lifting equipment.

08

Underground and overhead services

This chapter provides practical guidance on factors to be considered when preparing to work with, or near to, underground and overhead services

On the majority of occasions a licensed utility company will carry out this type of work. However, existing services, whether known or unknown, remain a risk on nearly all projects.

Always bear in mind that drawings are not always accurate. Therefore positions may not be correct and there may even be some that have not been charted.

This chapter also includes practical guidance on some of the hazards and the subsequent risks of working, or coming into contact, with overhead power lines.

Introduction	108
Underground services	108
Digging	111
Damage to buried services	114
Overhead services	115
Appendix A – Permit to work on high voltage equipment	118

8.1   Introduction

Buried services are, to a great extent, out of sight and out of mind until, perhaps, there is a fault or another reason to excavate. Every year people are injured and some killed due to accidental contact with buried services, such as electricity cables and gas pipes.

In every case, the damage and injury could have been avoided if the proper procedures had been followed. The statistic of 70,000 instances of damage and 150 injuries per year show that there is considerable room for improvement.

Coming into contact with overhead services kills many people and causes even more serious injuries each year. This also includes the lines serving the railway network (*for further information refer to Chapter F02 Trackside safety*).

This chapter includes items of plant or equipment (for example, cranes and scaffold poles) that may come into contact with overhead power lines (OHPLs).

 The health and safety construction phase plan will provide information about hazards specific to a site, and must include locations and types of underground and overhead services that can be found in the area.

8.2   Underground services

Risks and costs of damage

The most common injury is from contact with electrical cables. These often carry high voltages and on many occasions death and/or major burns have resulted.

 In the event of an electrical emergency telephone CableSafe.

Damage to gas pipes can cause leaks, which can result in fire and/or explosions. This can happen even when their location is known (such as contact by excavator bucket).

Damage to water and telephone cables is often less evident but still potentially serious and can affect, for example, places dependent on those services (such as hospitals and persons requiring the emergency services).

If plant under your control damages a fibre optic cable, for example, this could result in a long section needing to be replaced, costing thousands of pounds.

 In the event of a gas leak, suspected gas leak or any other emergency relating to gas, immediately ring the gas emergency services.

 The HSE's guidance document *Avoiding danger from underground services* (HSG47) can be downloaded from the HSE's website.

Types of buried services

The ones you will find most commonly are gas, water, electricity and telecommunications; but you will need to locate drains and sewers as they are also buried services.

There are other services that may not be known about or detected other than through investigation before digging or excavation is started; these include cable television, hydraulics, private telecommunications and street lighting cables.

In some cases, depending on the location, you will also need to investigate for petroleum and fuel oils (large bore, deep pipelines linking major installations).

If work in the vicinity of gas transmission pipelines is being considered, the local gas company will be able to provide details of suitable procedures.

 For further information on types of buried services refer to Chapter C03 Electrical safety and Chapter F01 Street works and road works.

Colour-coding of buried services

There is national agreement between the utility groups for colour-coding of services. Full information can be obtained from NJUG guidelines on the *Positioning and colour-coding of underground utilities apparatus*.

You will, however, need to bear in mind that large numbers of pipes and services have been laid over the last 100 years, and include a mixture of materials and colours.

The table below highlights the different services that may have similarly coloured pipes or cables.

Pipe or cable	Service(s)
Black PVC	Electricity, water and telecoms
Blue PVC	Water
Grey PVC	Water and telecoms
Red PVC	Electricity
Natural PV	Telecoms
Yellow PVC	Gas

Note: all plastic, polythene and polyvinylchloride pipes are shown above as PVC.

The table below shows the pipe or cable material used by the different services.

Pipe or cable	Service(s)
Cast iron	Gas and water
Steel	Gas and water
Braided steel	Electricity
Yellow steel	Gas
Copper	Water
Lead or lead covered	Electricity and water
Asbestos	Water
Hessian wrapped	Electricity

08

☑ The coal authority has laid some yellow PVC electric cable.

☑ Black PVC must always be assumed to be live electricity until proved otherwise.

☑ All cast iron and steel must be assumed to be carrying gas until proved otherwise.

☑ Ducts may well contain any one of the services, irrespective of type or colour of the duct.

Checking for buried services

Before doing anything yourself, check with all public and private utilities for existence of services in the area you are planning to work in and ensure these routes are clearly marked on your plans.

The local electricity or gas company will give advice by telephone. BT operates a similar type of service and those wishing to make such enquiries should phone and select the option 'dial before you dig'.

Underground and overhead services

Be careful when you read plans; reference points may have been moved, surfaces regraded, services moved without authority and not all connections may be shown.

On old brownfield sites you can find abandoned services and buried metallic items (such as tram lines and cast iron pipes); these can distort survey results.

When you have identified routes, mark them with paint, tape or markers but **not** metal spikes, which might penetrate a cable or pipe.

Remember the exact position will only be known when the buried service is uncovered.

Changes in colour of the surface material (sometimes known as tracks) may indicate where a service trench can be found. Absence of markers posts is not evidence that there are no buried services.

Shallow service

Never assume that services have been installed at the recommended depth – they are often shallower.

Never assume that when you have located a service that it is the only one, there may be others adjacent to, above or underneath it.

Beware of services encased in concrete bases, structures or in the concrete backing to kerbs.

Beware of services rising over obstructions, culverts, bridges, and so on. They are often much shallower in these locations.

Indications that buried services do exist include the presence of:

- ✓ lamp posts
- ✓ illuminated traffic signs
- ✓ telephone boxes

- ✓ concrete or steel manhole covers
- ✓ hydrant and valve pit covers.

 An electricity cable was damaged by the floor saw used to cut the road prior to excavating a new service trench. Although a CAT survey had located the cable, it was discovered that it was directly under the asphalt sub-base, which was 270 mm thick.

Use of cable and pipe locators

Be aware that the cable avoidance tool (CAT) and generator should be used together, otherwise you will only have half the picture. Equipment should be regularly serviced, at intervals not exceeding 12 months.

 Recent developments in technology include depth read-outs.

08

A CAT will find most electricity cables whilst power is flowing through them, but it may not work:

- ☑ if the cable has been disconnected
- ☑ when the loading on a three-phase supply is evenly distributed
- ☑ if the current is so small it is beyond the detection capability of the tool
- ☑ if no current is flowing as the device is inactive (such as street lighting in the daytime).

Radio frequency can be used to detect electricity cables that have not been found by power detection, but its limitations can be geographical and it can also pick up other metal objects.

The **transmitter and receiver** (inductive or conductive) method is good when there is no current in services being sought.

 Conventional cable locators will not find plastic pipes.

A **generator** (genny), when attached to an exposed part of a pipe or cable, will provide a signal for a CAT to track; it is important to continue to use the locator as the excavation progresses.

Metal detectors can detect hidden flat metal covers, joint boxes, and so on, but can miss cables or pipes. The deeper these objects are buried, the less chance of detection.

Ground penetrating radar is a portable hand transmitter that can sweep the area of land where there are thought to be buried services. The transmitter will display variations in the materials below the surface and can show where land has been disturbed.

An operative properly trained in the use of radar equipment can detect the majority of buried services and this result should then be compared with existing plans.

Information on all cables and pipes detected should be recorded and passed to the CDM co-ordinator for inclusion in the client's health and safety file. You must ensure co-ordinates, lines and levels of newly installed services are included.

8.3   Digging

08

Permit to work and permit to dig

Where necessary, a formal permit to work system should be employed.

 For a copy of a sample permit to dig refer to Section G *Checklists and forms*.

This will show precautions to be taken, what has been done and what is required.

The permit to work also enables the person in charge to check that all the conditions have been met before work commences.

 Some sites operate a system where a copy of the permit to dig is held by the worker in an armband. This allows site management and supervisors to monitor that excavation work is being undertaken under a permit.

Permit in armband

Digging methods

Depending upon the potential hazards, it may be necessary to use a permit to work system before commencing any digging. On some sites a specific permit to dig system is used, and many main contractors operate a mandatory permit to dig or break ground.

Trial holes should be dug by hand to establish the exact location and depth of service; do not assume the service runs a direct line or same depth between two trial holes.

Do not use power tools or excavators within 500 mm. Hand digging must be adopted using insulated tools (such as spades or shovels).

Power tools can be used to break paved surfaces but be careful to avoid over-penetration as services near buildings may have been laid shallowly.

Do not use power tools directly over an indicated line of a cable unless it has been made dead or steps have been taken to avoid damage.

The sides of an excavation must be suitable to allow services to pass through. You may need to support services in these surroundings.

 Never assume that a service is dead – always treat it as live until confirmed otherwise.

☑ Before and during excavation

☑ Check with all utilities and landowners before starting work.

☑ Assume the presence of services when digging, even though nothing is shown on plans.

☑ Use detection devices and keep a close watch for signs of buried services (such as marker tape or tiles).

☑ Although there are recommended minimum depths for all services, they may be closer to the surface than normal, especially in the vicinity of works, structures or other services.

☑ Markers (such as plastic tape, tiles, slabs or battens) may have been displaced and will not necessarily indicate the exact location of the buried service.

☑ Some electric cables and water pipes look alike, as do some gas pipes and water pipes. Ensure each pipe is properly identified before starting work on them.

☑ Services could be easily damaged by a fork or a pickaxe forced into the ground, but careful use of insulated spades and shovels enables services to be safely uncovered.

☑ Depending upon the risk assessment, those that are likely to encounter live services on a regular basis should wear flame resistant clothing, gloves and light eye protection.

☑ Carefully lever out rocks, stones and boulders.

☑ Over-penetration of the ground or surface with handheld power tools is a common cause of accidents.

☑ If an excavator or digger is being used near any service, take extra care to prevent accidental damage. Where possible, no-one should be near the digger bucket while it is digging.

☑ Ensure the excavator operator and others excavating are informed of the presence of suspected services.

☑ If the service is embedded in concrete or paving material, the owner should de-energise it, otherwise make it safe or approve a safe system of work before it is broken out.

☑ Always assume closed, capped, sealed, loose or pot-ended services are live or charged, not dead or abandoned, until proved otherwise.

☑ Follow the guidelines and advice issued by the electricity, gas, water and telecommunication industries.

☑ Where possible, carry out the final exposure of buried services in a way that prevents any damage (such as using a compressed air lance).

08

Hand digging near live services

 For further information refer to Chapter D07 Excavations.

Piling and drilling

A safe system of work must be devised and implemented before any piling or drilling takes place.

If you think there are services nearby, their position must be exposed by hand digging first.

Exposure and protection

If you expose a service in a trench, protect it with wood or other suitable materials.

Services crossing trenches need support to avoid stress. Seek advice from the relevant utility company if you are unsure.

Never use services crossing in a trench as footholds, anchorage or climbing points.

Backfilling

When backfilling a trench **do not** dump hard core, surplus concrete, rock, rubble and flint onto a service pipe or cable, as it may damage it.

Use suitable material and ensure it is compacted with care to avoid shocking the service pipe or cable.

Warning tape should then be placed above the service at approximately 300 mm.

If gas service pipes have been exposed, advice on backfilling should be obtained from the local gas company.

Emergency works

Emergency works often mean there is no time to contact the utility companies. However, this work can be carried out safely if:

- ☑ the area is marked out carefully
- ☑ detectors are used correctly
- ☑ trial holes are dug by hand
- ☑ the practice of safe digging is followed.

Pipelines

 Information on working adjacent to buried pipelines and the location of buried pipelines around the UK can be found on the Linewatch and Linesearch websites.

Working in the roadway

Unless you are a licensed utility company, you may not work in the footway, carriageway or any verge. If you are working in the roadway, you must comply with the New Roads and Street Works Act.

 For further information refer to Chapter F01 Street works and road works.

08

8.4 Damage to buried services

Damage to buried services **must** be reported to the owner/occupier immediately. When such damage causes an emergency situation, call the **police**, **fire** and/or **ambulance** services as necessary.

Gas

 For gas emergencies phone the gas emergency services.

If a gas leak is suspected, contact the police, fire brigade and gas supply company immediately. If there is a dangerous situation and the emergency services have not arrived, try to evacuate the immediate area including, if necessary, the occupants of nearby properties to an upwind position. As far as possible, prevent anyone from smoking and keep traffic clear of the area.

 If the gas escape catches fire, do not attempt to extinguish the flames.

Depth of cover

The normal minimum depth of cover for gas mains operating in the low and medium pressure ranges is:

- ☑ 600 mm in footways or verges
- ☑ 750 mm in carriageways.

These figures may vary since each gas company can have its own standards.

Electricity

 For electricity emergencies phone CableSafe.

Avoid contact with any damaged cable or apparatus. If you are operating a machine do not attempt to disentangle any equipment. If at all possible, jump clear of the machine, ensuring that you do not make contact with the vehicle and ground at the same time.

If this is not possible, stay exactly where you are. As far as possible, do not touch any metallic part of the vehicle and shout for help. If you are able, inform the electricity company or ask someone else to do so. Keep people away.

Depth of cover

The depth at which electricity cables or ducts are usually installed in the ground is decided by the need to avoid undue interference or damage.

Depending on the type of cable and the power that it may be carrying, the depth of cover may vary from 450–900 mm.

However, existing services can be found at any depth. It is not uncommon for them to have as little as 50 mm cover.

In all cases where the depth of cover is likely to increase or decrease, the service owner must be consulted.

Other services

Leave a damaged service well alone and inform the owner.

 Some cables are automatically re-energised by the local sub-station after a short time following the supply tripping out due to damage. Do not assume that a damaged cable will remain dead.

In conclusion

- ☑ **PLAN** the work.
- ☑ **LOCATE** the buried services.
- ☑ **DIG** using a safe method of work.

8.5   Overhead services

Electricity supplies above 33,000 volts are usually routed overhead. Supplies below this voltage may be either overhead or underground.

Care should be taken when dumping, tipping waste, regrading, landscaping, or when in planned or unplanned storage areas, not to reduce these minimum clearances, which are:

- ☑ 400 kV   7.3 m
- ☑ 275 kV   7.0 m
- ☑ 132 kV   6.7 m
- ☑ 33-66 kV   6.0 m
- ☑ 11-33 kV   5.2 m

except for roads where the minimum is 5.2 m, or in accessible places where minimum height may be reduced to 4.6 m.

Working near overhead services (overhead power lines)

You must consult the local electricity company before any work is started and a safe system of work must be planned and implemented.

There may be other suppliers who have to be notified (such as Local Authorities, National Grid and other electricity companies).

The regulations need power lines to be **dead** or suitable precautions taken to prevent danger before any work takes place.

You may need to wait for the supplier to isolate or re-route to enable the work to take place.

You must take practical steps to prevent danger from any live cable or apparatus and this should include the placing of substantial and highly visible barriers. You can barrier one side only if you only need access from one side but if the line crosses the site, you will need to place barriers on both sides.

If there is a danger to people with scaffold poles or other conducting objects then the barriers should exclude people and mobile plant.

08

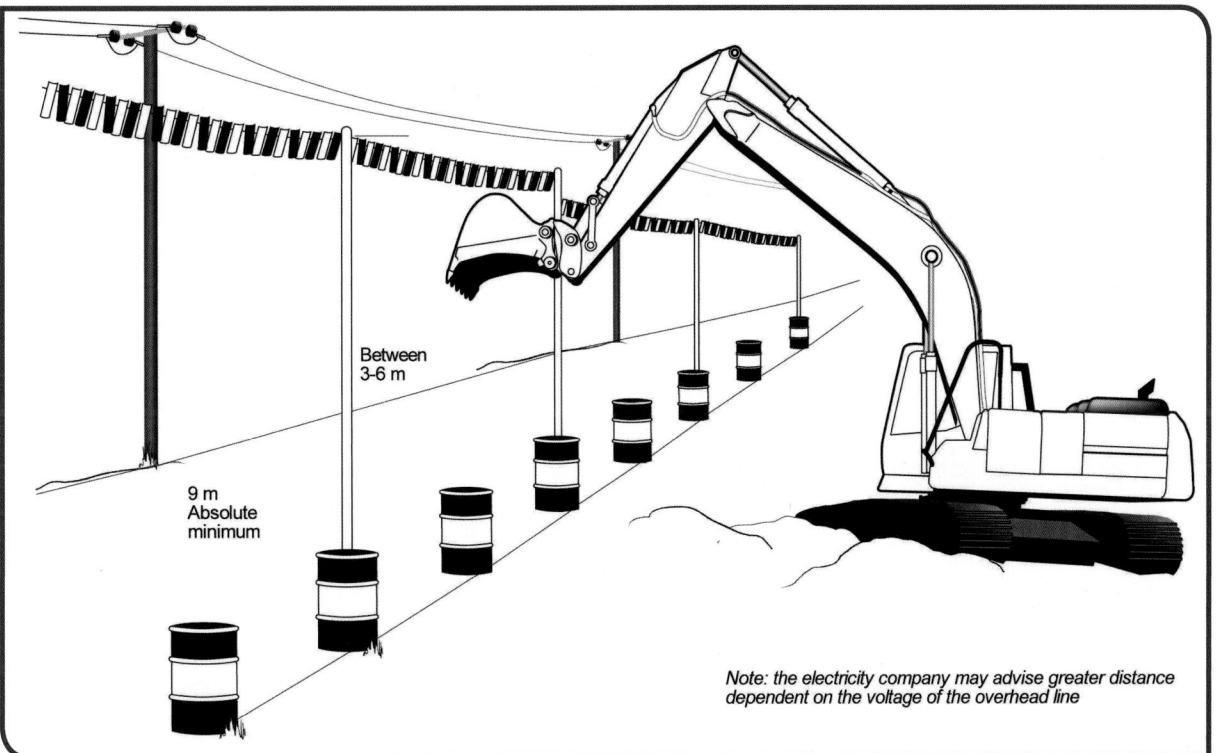

Between 3-6 m

9 m Absolute minimum

Note: the electricity company may advise greater distance dependent on the voltage of the overhead line

Isolating the area containing the overhead services

Any ground-level barriers should consist of:

☑ a stout post and rail fence

☑ a tension wire fence, earthed at both ends, with flags on the wire. The fence is earthed in consultation with the electricity company

☑ large steel drums (for example 200 litre oil drums) filled with rubble or concrete, and placed at frequent intervals

☑ an earth bank, not less than one metre high and marked by posts to stop vehicles

☑ substantial timber baulks to act as wheel stops.

Do ensure that post and oil drums are made as distinctive as possible by being painted with red and white stripes. Red and white flags or hazard bunting can be used on wire fences.

Do not store materials between the overhead services and the ground level barriers, even if the work is only going to last a short while.

Ensure all work is carried out under the direct supervision of a responsible supervisor (someone who is familiar with all the hazards that need to be taken into consideration).

 It must be assumed that all overhead lines and cables **are live** unless advised otherwise by the electricity company.

Safe working near overhead services

Ensure that everyone working on site is aware that no work should take place:

☑ until the electricity company is consulted for advice

☑ within nine metres of overhead power lines on wood, concrete or steel poles

☑ within 15 metres of overhead power lines on steel towers.

All personnel must be aware that the distances above are measured horizontally at ground level, from directly below the outermost conduction.

It is essential that ongoing liaison is maintained between the contractor and the electricity company.

If the overhead lines have not been diverted or made dead, have all practicable steps been taken to provide adequate barriers to comply with the regulations?

Have arrangements been made for the passage of tall plant at specific times where overhead power lines have been made dead?

Electricity carried by overhead cables, which are generally uninsulated:

☑ will flow though any metal object that comes into contact with them (such as a metal ladder, a scaffold pole or a raised excavator bucket)

☑ may jump through the air (arc) to anything nearby that will conduct electricity.

When plant needs to go under the overhead services

If plant needs to pass under the overhead lines then the danger must be reduced. This can be done by restricting the access way to the minimum possible width.

The following precautions are also recommended.

☑ Keep the number of access passageways to a minimum.

☑ Fence it to define its route and erect goal posts at each end.

☑ Construct the goal posts from non-conducting material and highlight them.

☑ Give warning notices on either site of the passageway.

☑ Give information to drivers on clearance height and instructing them to lower jibs, tipper bodies, and so on, and to keep below this height whilst crossing.

☑ If lighting is needed, place at ground level and project upwards towards the conductors.

☑ Place additional notices on the approaches to the crossing – approximately 30 metres prior to the approach.

☑ Ensure the access route's surface is kept level and firm, and well maintained to prevent undue tilting or bouncing of equipment whilst moving under the power lines.

 For further information refer to the HSE's guidance note GS6.

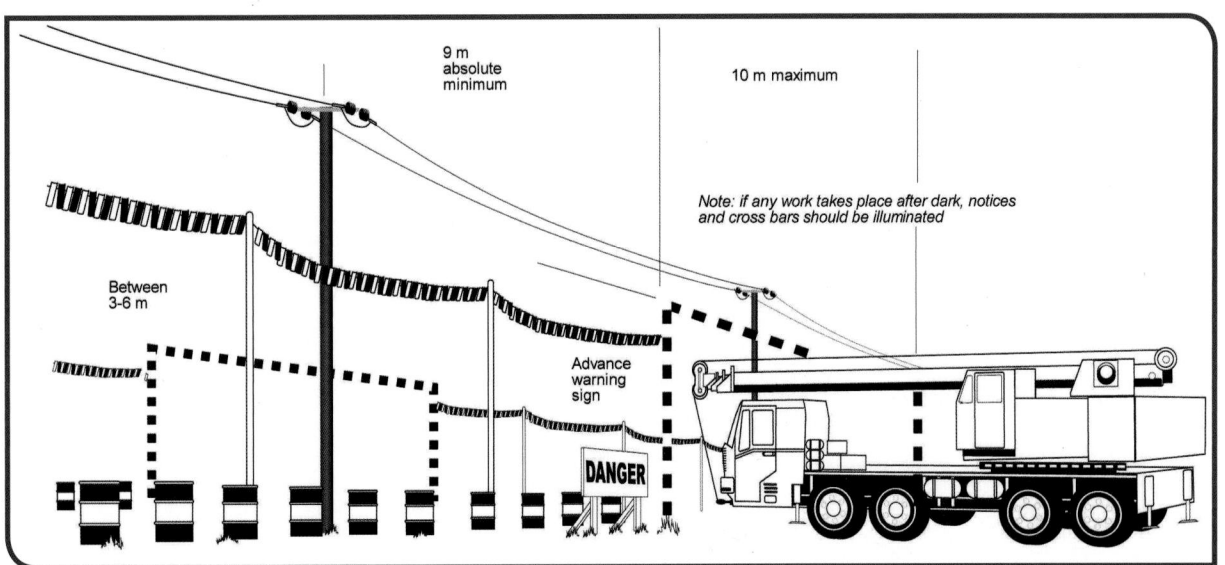

9 m
absolute
minimum

10 m maximum

*Note: if any work takes place after dark, notices
and cross bars should be illuminated*

Between
3-6 m

Advance
warning
sign

DANGER

Building under overhead services

Risks will be increased, either by the existence of buildings where work needs to be undertaken on or in it, or where buildings are being erected under overhead power lines.

If the services cannot be made dead or diverted then the following precautions are strongly recommended.

☑ Consult the owner of the line as to how the work should be done.

☑ Appoint a competent supervisor to oversee the work and ensure it is carried out safely.

☑ Avoid any equipment that can reach the overhead services or is near enough to cause a flashover (such as scaffold poles and ladders).

☑ Ideally, erect a horizontal barrier of timber or other insulating material over the construction site. (Lines may have to be made dead prior to this roof being installed.)

 Electricity can kill. The correct information, instruction, training and supervision can help to keep workers, and others coming into contact with them, alive.

08

Appendix A – Permit to work on high voltage equipment

No.

Issued to .... Job ....

I hereby declare that it is safe to work on the following high voltage apparatus, which is dead, isolated from all live conductors and is connected to earth

....

All other apparatus is dangerous.

Switching and isolating. The apparatus is disconnected from all live conductors by the following operations

....

Earthing. The equipment is earthed at the following points

....

Danger notices are posted at ....

Automatic fire extinguishing control has been rendered inoperative at ....

Other precautions ....

Signature .... Date .... Time ....
(Authorised person)

I hereby declare that I accept responsibility for carrying out work on the apparatus detailed on this permit and that no attempt will be made by me, nor by any person under my control, to carry out work on any other apparatus.

Signature .... Date .... Time ....

Note: after signature for work to proceed, this receipt must be signed by, and the permit to work retained by, the person in charge of the work until work is suspended or completed and the clearance section has been signed.

This is to certify that the work authorised above has been completed or stopped and that all workers under my charge have been withdrawn and warned that it is no longer safe to work on the apparatus specified on this permit to work and that gear, tools and additional earthing connections are all cleared. Automatic fire extinguishing control has been restored.

Permit to work is hereby cancelled.

Signature .... Date .... Time ....
(Authorised person)

08

09

Confined spaces

Every entry into a confined space is potentially hazardous. Accidents in confined spaces are a major source of deaths at work, killing on average around 15 people each year in a wide range of industries, including the construction industry.

Some confined spaces are easy to identify (such as closed tanks, vessels and sewers). Others are less obvious but may be equally dangerous, including basement-level boiler rooms or toilets, as well as open-topped tanks, vats, silos or other structures that become confined spaces during their manufacture.

Introduction	120
Key points	120
Dangers in confined spaces	121
Information, instruction and training	123
Safe working	123
Legislative requirements	130
Appendix A – Permit to work certificate example	132

9.1 Introduction

Accidents are caused by a combination of factors arising from a lack of awareness, inadequate supervision and a lack of training. The situation is often made worse by heroic but ill-conceived rescue attempts, founded on insufficient planning and knowledge, which may lead to multiple fatalities. It is essential, therefore, to be able to identify confined spaces and the hazards associated with entering and working in them.

Within confined spaces a *specified risk* can mean a risk of:

- ☑ serious injury to any person at work, arising from a fire or explosion
- ☑ the loss of consciousness of any person at work arising from an increase in body temperature
- ☑ the loss of consciousness or asphyxiation of any person at work arising from gas, fumes, vapour or the lack of oxygen
- ☑ drowning of any person at work arising from an increase in the level of liquid
- ☑ asphyxiation of any person at work arising from a free-flowing solid or the inability to reach a respirable environment due to entrapment by a free flowing solid.

Some places may become a confined space only occasionally, perhaps due to the type of work to be undertaken (such as a room during paint spraying). A confined space may not necessarily be enclosed on all sides; some confined spaces (such as vats, silos or deep excavations) may have open tops. Places not usually considered to be confined spaces may become confined spaces because of a change in the condition inside or a change in the degree of enclosure or confinement.

The expression *confined space* could also refer to the following examples: ducts, vessels, boreholes, building voids and enclosures for the purpose of asbestos removal. This list is not exhaustive, and application of the Confined Spaces Regulations in any of these places will depend on the presence of a reasonably foreseeable risk of serious injury from a hazardous substance or condition within the space or nearby.

Examples of confined spaces that may be encountered during construction activities are:

- ☑ cellars or an inadequately ventilated basement room
- ☑ boilers, boiler flues or chimneys
- ☑ manholes, sewers, drains or excavations
- ☑ ceiling voids or ducts
- ☑ caissons or cofferdams
- ☑ loft spaces or plant rooms
- ☑ any room or enclosed space with poor ventilation, as these can become a confined space (for example, painting a room or power floating in a large hanger using petrol-powered equipment).

There are many more examples of confined spaces and the hazards will vary with the location, the type of work being carried out, and the equipment or substances used.

9.2 Key points

- ☑ Working in confined spaces has the potential to be very hazardous unless the appropriate controls are put in place.
- ☑ Many people have died as a result of work in confined spaces not being adequately planned, organised or safely carried out; many of them were would-be rescuers.
- ☑ Ideally carry out the work without anyone having to enter a confined space.
- ☑ Confined spaces are not just sewers and ducts; under the regulations many other work areas could also be classified as confined spaces.
- ☑ A risk assessment must be carried out for all work in a confined space.
- ☑ Where the findings of the risk assessment reveal significant risks to health or safety, it will normally result in a method statement being written.
- ☑ Any plan of the work must consider the method of rescuing the people in the confined space should the situation become unsafe.
- ☑ Entry to a confined space should be controlled by a permit to work and, where considered necessary, a separate permit to enter.
- ☑ Any training may need to be specific for the type of confined space – a sewer entry course may not be appropriate for someone who has to work in a hot roof space. Training should extend not only to those entering confined spaces but also to managers, supervisors, emergency personnel, and so on.

The use of respiratory protective equipment (RPE) is common in confined space work and users must be face-fit tested and trained in its use, general care and maintenance.

 Unplanned or poorly planned work in confined spaces has the potential to kill – reading and understanding this chapter is not a substitute for adequate training and experience.

> **!** Take great care identifying what is and what could be a confined space. Many confined space accidents occur in work areas that have simply not been identified as potential confined spaces.

9.3 Dangers in confined spaces

Oxygen deprivation and suffocation

The air that we breathe contains around 21% oxygen and, at that level, people can work without difficulty. A falling level of oxygen will create an increasingly serious situation if breathing apparatus is not worn. Generally, the following symptoms are experienced at the corresponding level of oxygen depletion:

Oxygen depletion	Symptoms
19%	Tiredness (normal acceptable minimum level for working).
17%	Judgement (decision making) is affected.
12%	Respiration is affected and fatigue experienced.
10%	Light-headedness and increasing breathing difficulties.
8%	Nausea and possible collapse.
6%	Respiration stops and death follows within minutes.

Oxygen deprivation may be the result of:

 the displacement of oxygen by gas leaking in from elsewhere, or the deliberate introduction of purge gas (for example, nitrogen or argon)

 the displacement of oxygen by a naturally occurring gas (such as methane)

 oxidisation, rusting or bacterial growth using up the oxygen in air

 oxygen being consumed by people working and breathing, or by any process of combustion

 welding and other hot works

 the prior discharge of a fire extinguisher containing carbon dioxide or other asphyxiating gas.

09

Hazards of excess oxygen

An oxygen-enriched atmosphere is, in itself, a major hazard. Organic materials (such as oil and wood) become highly combustible, and ordinary materials (such as paper and clothing) will burn with exceptional ferocity.

An increase of only 4% oxygen is sufficient to create a hazard and this may occur inadvertently. In oxyacetylene and oxypropane processes, sometimes not all of the oxygen supplied to a cutting torch is consumed. Some may be released, increasing the atmospheric oxygen above the normal 21%.

The oxygen enrichment of the atmosphere in a confined space also results from the practice of using oxygen to sweeten or enrich the atmosphere when it has become oppressive, stale, hot, fume-filled or otherwise unpleasant. This is a very dangerous practice and must be prohibited.

Another way in which the atmosphere may become oxygen-enriched is through leakage from torches or hoses during meal breaks or overnight. For this reason, they should be removed at each breaktime. The deliberate kinking or nipping of an oxygen hose while changing a torch does not usually cut off the supply completely and can result in the release of substantial quantities of oxygen.

If excess oxygen is discovered, the space must be quickly evacuated and ventilated until normal levels of oxygen are regained.

Toxic atmospheres

However much oxygen is present in the atmosphere, if there is also a toxic gas present in sufficient quantity it will create a hazard.

Some of the many toxic gases that may be encountered include:

☑ hydrogen sulphide, usually from sewage or decaying vegetation

☑ carbon monoxide, from internal combustion engines, or any incomplete combustion, especially of liquefied petroleum gases (LPG)

☑ carbon dioxide, from any fermentation, or being naturally evolved in soil and rocks, or coming from the combustion of LPG

☑ fumes and vapours, from chemicals such as ammonia, chlorine, sodium, and from petrol and solvents.

Whenever a toxic gas (or any gas, fume or vapour that may be hazardous to health) is thought to be (or known to be) present, then an assessment of the risk to health must be made under the provisions of the Control of Substances Hazardous to Health (COSHH) Regulations and the appropriate control measures must be put into place to eliminate the hazard or control the risks.

Petrol and diesel engines create carbon monoxide, which is an extremely toxic gas.

Liquid petroleum gas-powered engines create an excess of carbon dioxide, which is a suffocating hazard. The use of any form of internal combustion engine within a confined space must be prohibited, unless a specifically dedicated exhaust extraction system is operative.

Flammable atmospheres

Some gases and vapours need to only be present in very small quantities to create a hazard. A few of the major sources of explosive and flammable hazards are:

☑ petrol or liquefied petroleum gas, propane, butane and acetylene. These are explosive in the range of 2% upwards in air. The hazard is normally created by a spillage or leakage

☑ methane and hydrogen sulphide, which are naturally evolved from sewage or decaying organic matter. These are explosive in the range of 4% upwards in air

☑ solvents, acetone, toluene, white spirit, alcohol, benzene, thinners, and so on. These are explosive in the range of 2% upwards in air. The hazard generally results from process plants and/or spillage

☑ hydrogen and other gases evolved from processes such as battery charging.

In an explosive or flammable atmosphere, a toxic or suffocating hazard may also exist.

Other causes of a hostile environment

Apart from the hazards dealt with above, other dangers may arise from the use of electrical and mechanical equipment, from chemicals, process gases and liquids, dust, paint fumes, welding and cutting fumes.

Extremes of excess heat and cold can have adverse effects and may be intensified in a confined space. Consideration must be given to the timing of what would otherwise be considered standard work. During hot weather, roof spaces and other types of confined spaces may reach temperatures that will lead to a dangerous increase in body temperature.

If work cannot be planned to avoid this (for example, by starting early) then physical measures (such as cooling and reducing the time spent working in the confined space) must be introduced following an assessment by a competent person.

Further dangers exist in the sheer difficulty of getting into or out of, and working in a confined space. The potential hazard of an inrush of water, gas or sludge due to a failure of walls or barriers, or leakage from valves, flanges or blanks, must all be considered at the risk assessment stage.

Depending upon the work activity, any space can become a confined space, including lofts, lifts or inspection pits, service risers and unventilated rooms, even if they are large spaces

9.4 Information, instruction and training

The information, instruction and training given to employees must enable them to carry out work safely and without risks to their health. The extent of training needed will vary according to circumstances and the type of space being entered.

Any entry into a confined space requiring the use of breathing apparatus would require a full breathing apparatus and rescue course. However, training to enter a bund around a large diesel tank where the risks are less significant (such as fumes and possible drowning in diesel) would not require such an intensive course, and indeed adopting the use of breathing apparatus in this instance may be entirely inappropriate.

Training should involve demonstrations and practical exercises. It is important that trainees are familiar with both equipment and procedures before working for the first time in confined spaces.

Practical refresher training should be organised and available. The frequency with which refresher training is provided will depend upon how long it is since the type of work was last done, or if there have been changes to methods of work, safety procedures or equipment.

 No person should enter a confined space unless they are trained and competent to do so safely.

The training needs for confined space working should be considered for each of the four categories of employee. These categories are:

☑ supervisors

☑ employees entering confined spaces

☑ people employed as attendants outside of confined spaces

☑ rescue teams.

Some of the roles identified may be carried out by the same person.

Prior to working in a confined space, there is currently no legal requirement to have obtained a specific standard of training. However, there has been discussion between the utility companies, who are the clients for much of the sewer-entry work, with regard to recognising each other's training standards.

 Tunnelling offers more specific challenges and the Pipe Jacking Association and British Tunnelling Society websites should be consulted for the latest updates on training standards.

9.5 Safe working

Safe working in a confined space can only be achieved by the use of a permit to work system, in which each step is planned and all foreseeable hazards are taken into account. Such a system, backed up by adequate rescue facilities, should enable work to be carried out safely.

At the planning stage it will be necessary to determine:

☑ whether an entry into the confined space is required, or whether an alternative method of doing the work exists

☑ if an entry is necessary, whether it can be carried out without the use of breathing apparatus

☑ whether the entry must be made with the use of breathing apparatus.

In respect of the final point, it should be emphasised that entry into a confined space using breathing apparatus should not be made routinely or undertaken as a matter of convenience, where the use of isolation and mechanical or forced ventilation would achieve a safe atmosphere.

If it is decided that the work can be done without anyone entering the confined space, provided that a safe system of work exists and the confined space has been isolated from potential sources of hazard, the work can proceed. It is important to avoid systems or plant being re-energised while work is proceeding and everyone involved should be advised accordingly.

Once it has been decided that people must enter a confined space, a preliminary meeting should be held with all concerned, and effective lines of authority and communication established in order to minimise any risk of subsequent misunderstanding.

The exact routine to be followed will vary, depending on the type of confined space to be entered. The provisions and precautions required for entry into a large, empty surface water tank will obviously be different from those needed for entry into a narrow service duct containing pipes and valves, but the fundamental principle of a safe system of work applies to these and other cases. The risk assessment, as mentioned previously, will have identified many of the above points and should be used as the basis for developing the safe system of work.

09

It is stressed that all personal protective equipment (PPE) in general, and RPE in particular, must have been specified by a competent person who is clearly aware of all of the circumstances surrounding its use.

If the fire and rescue service forms a part of the rescue plan, they must be given a warning that a confined space entry is to be made. This will give them the opportunity to assess the risks to their own staff and identify any equipment they might need.

Isolation

The confined space must be isolated from all possible external sources of danger to persons entering it. It is good practice to use **positive isolations** for confined space entries – this means complete separation of the plant/equipment to be worked on from other parts of the system. If this is not possible then isolation should generally be proved.

A full permit to work system should be used to record the location and types of isolation, and the hazards being guarded against.

Electrical isolation must never rely on a switch or fuse. The switch gear or fuse holder must be locked off and a warning notice applied.

 For further information refer to the permit to work systems later in this chapter.

Mechanical isolation of pipework should not rely on a single valve or on a non-return valve; these may let-by and create a hazard. Whenever possible, a section of pipe should be removed or a blank or spade should be put into a flange between the valve and the confined space and a warning notice displayed.

Isolation from mechanical and electrical equipment will often include locking off the switch and formally securing the key in accordance with a permit to work, until it is no longer necessary to control access. Lock-and-tag systems can be useful here, where each operator has their own lock and key giving self-assurance of the inactivated mechanism or system. Check there is no stored energy of any kind left in the system that could activate the equipment inadvertently.

Paddles, stirrers or agitators, whether electrically or mechanically operated, should be physically disconnected by the removal of an operating arm, and a warning notice displayed.

Cleaning

There is a variety of methods of cleaning the inside of confined spaces to remove hazardous solids, liquids or gases. Cold water washing, hot water washing and steaming will remove many contaminants, while solvents or neutralising agents may be necessary for others. If hot water or steam is used, with or without a solvent, care must be taken to ensure that adequate ventilation exists for steam pressure and that condensation does not build up to unacceptable levels.

If steam is used or water is boiled in a confined space, account must be taken of the vacuum that can be created on cooling.

When steam or solvents are used, these may create a toxic, suffocating or flammable hazard. Even though a space has been well cleaned, it must not be entered until it has been monitored.

Great care must be taken if encountering any sludge or heavy deposits that may release toxic gases if disturbed.

Purging and ventilation

Air purging and ventilation can be carried out by removing covers, opening inspection doors, or similar, and allowing ordinary air circulation, or by the introduction of compressed air via an air line. However, higher rates of air exchange can be achieved by the use of air movers, induction fans or extractor fans.

It is especially important that when an inert gas (such as nitrogen) has been used to purge or render inert a flammable atmosphere, the inert gas itself is properly purged with air.

When air purging is taking place, the flow of air should be of a sufficient volume and velocity to ensure that no pockets or layers of gas remain undisturbed.

Atmospheric monitoring

Depending on the circumstances, as a result of the assessment made under the Control of Substances Hazardous to Health Regulations, or the risk assessment made under the Management of Health and Safety at Work Regulations, continuous atmospheric monitoring may well be necessary when any work is to be done that would expose employees to any substance hazardous to health.

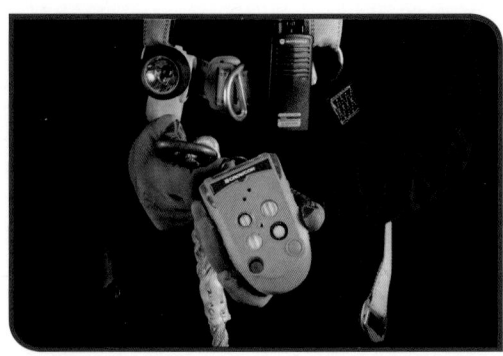

Before an entry is made into such a confined space, tests must be carried out to establish the levels of oxygen, toxic gas or flammable gas in the atmosphere.

The external atmosphere around the opening should be monitored first, and if the results are satisfactory, internal monitoring should be carried out by lowering a gas monitor into the confined space before it is occupied.

If entry into the confined space is necessary to carry out the tests, breathing apparatus or other RPE must be worn.

Suitably trained and competent personnel may use simple, reliable instruments to measure oxygen and flammable gas levels.

 The accuracy of the instruments must be assured by periodic calibration.

A satisfactory oxygen content must not in itself be relied on to indicate safety since flammable, explosive or toxic gas may exist alongside oxygen and need only be present in minute quantities to create a serious hazard.

The tests applied should take account of what the space is known to have contained, including any inert gas used to purge a flammable atmosphere, which may itself produce toxic hazards or the risk of asphyxiation. Account must also be taken of hazards arising from other sources (such as materials used for cleaning). Methane, hydrogen sulphide and carbon dioxide can all evolve naturally due to the decomposition of organic matter or, in some cases, by the effect of rainwater percolating through certain types of ground. It is necessary to test the atmosphere of a confined space at both high and low level as well as in any corners where pockets of gas may exist.

 Instances have occurred of carbon dioxide displacing oxygen at lower levels while a normal oxygen level continues to exist at higher levels of the same confined space.

The sense of smell must never be relied upon to detect gases. Some are odourless, and hydrogen sulphide, in particular, can paralyse the sense of smell to such an extent that even fatally high concentrations of the gas cannot be detected. In any case, the sense of smell varies from person to person and deteriorates with age.

Monitoring and testing equipment

Providing that the specific contaminant is known, tests can be carried out by competent persons using the individual detector tubes available for the detection of specific toxic and asphyxiant flammable or explosive fumes or gases.

The tubes have a wide range of tolerance, so readings close to an occupational exposure limit should not be acted upon until the test has been repeated and the manufacturer's standard of accuracy applied.

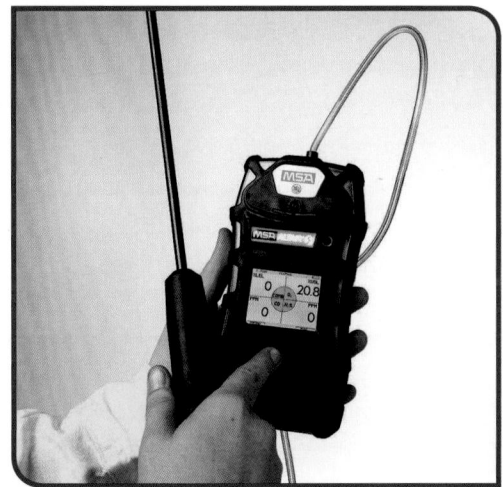

A wide range of portable gas detection equipment is available for flammable and toxic gases; some are specific to one gas (for example, hydrogen sulphide), while others can sample a range of different gases. Such instruments need to be properly calibrated.

09

Continuous monitoring

The initial monitoring and testing must establish that the confined space is safe to enter. Monitoring should then be carried out at intervals to ensure the continued safety of personnel. Tests should be repeated after any breaks (such as lunch or overnight) or after the time limit set out in a permit to work has expired.

It may be necessary to issue individual monitors to people working in a confined space, so as to give them an instant warning of low oxygen, or toxic or flammable gas hazards.

Competence of monitors

All atmospheric monitoring must be carried out by persons who are trained and competent to use the instruments and interpret the results. They must have sufficient practical and theoretical knowledge to enable them to make a valid judgement based on the results. They must be fully aware of their responsibilities in permitting an entry into a confined space.

Selection of personnel

Care is required in selecting the right people to work in confined spaces, since conditions can be difficult. They must be physically fit, agile and, most importantly, not be claustrophobic. People who suffer from asthma, bronchitis or other respiratory conditions, or whose immune system has been suppressed, must be assessed by a medical practitioner as to their suitability to work in confined spaces.

Other health conditions that might indicate that a person is not suitable for working in a confined space, or that further checks need to be made before it is allowed, are:

☑ high blood pressure

☑ partial or complete deafness

☑ lack of mobility through joint problems

☑ diabetes

☑ depression or other mental illness

☑ defective eyesight (which is not corrected by wearing glasses)

☑ sensitivity of the skin to some substances

☑ taking some types of medication.

Stamina is also required. The wearing of any form of respiratory protection tends to lead to an increase in respiration and a higher use of energy; the amount of work that can be done in confined spaces is less than that expected under normal conditions.

When respiratory protection is to be used, it should be remembered that facial hair and spectacles often prevent a respirator from fitting properly and thus achieving the assumed degree of protection.

Face-fit testing should be carried out to ensure that the chosen mask fits the wearer. This can be achieved quantitatively using a 'portacount' for half or full-face masks or qualitatively using bitter/sweet solutions for half or disposable masks.

Communications

Adequate and effective communications must exist between those inside and those outside the confined space, so that, in the event of an incident, a warning can be given and the space evacuated or those inside rescued. The system needs to be fail-safe, ensuring that, if a reply is not received or a scheduled call not made, the procedure for rescue starts immediately.

When a confined space is relatively small, so that the person entering it cannot move far from the entry point and there are no other factors that could hinder effective communication, the method of communication may be relatively simple (such as a pre-arranged system of tugs on the safety rope, which must be fully understood by all involved). However, if the nature of the confined space, the job to be carried out and other factors necessitate the person travelling some distance from the entry point, a more elaborate communication system might be required.

Factors that could hinder effective communication and may need to be considered in the risk assessment are the:

☑ level of noise inside or outside the confined space, which may or may not be associated with the confined space work

☑ physical nature of the confined space or the presence of substances that could reduce visibility

☑ distance between the point of entry and the place of work

☑ presence of workers with little or no understanding of English.

Depending upon the findings of the risk assessment, prior communication with the emergency services regarding the location and nature of the work might be considered necessary.

All types of respiratory protection affect verbal communication to some degree and, whatever method of communication is chosen, it should be tested and proved outside the confined space before entry is made.

Work equipment

Due to the potential for a flammable or explosive atmosphere in confined spaces, selecting tools and other work equipment with which the work can be carried out safely is essential.

If there is any possibility of flammable gas existing in a confined space, even below the lower explosive limit (LEL), all tools must be of a non-sparking material and all lighting and electrical equipment must carry British Approvals Service for Electrical Equipment in Flammable Atmospheres (BASEEFA) approval. Smoking and naked lights must be strictly prohibited and care must be taken to avoid the generation of static electricity with the consequent risk of sparks.

 For further information refer to the BASEEFA website.

Fire safety

Hot works must not be carried out in a confined space unless atmospheric testing has confirmed that flammable or explosive gases are not present and the findings of a risk assessment show that it is otherwise safe to do so.

Where there is still a residual risk of fire, appropriate fire extinguishers may need to be kept in the confined space at the entry point.

Where hot works are being carried out inside a confined space, the operative carrying out the work must also have a suitable and serviceable fire extinguisher at the place of work. In the event of a fire, the local fire service should be called in case the fire cannot be contained or extinguished.

First aid

Appropriate first-aid equipment and trained first aiders should be provided and available for emergencies and to provide first aid until professional medical help arrives.

Rescue

The arrangements for the rescue of persons in the event of an emergency, both in terms of trained persons and equipment, need to be suitable and sufficient. The arrangements must be in place before any person enters or works in a confined space.

In some circumstances (for example, where there are prolonged operations in confined spaces and the risks justify it) there may be advantage in prior notification to the local emergency services (for example, local fire or ambulance service) before the work is undertaken. However, reliance on the emergency services alone will not be sufficient to comply with the regulations. Employers must put in place adequate emergency arrangements before the work starts.

Proper and effective rescue training is quite hard and arduous and is not to be undertaken lightly. Persons selected for such training need to be physically fit and able to adapt to situations as they arise during a rescue.

If a person is **injured** in a confined space that has been certified safe to enter without respiratory protection, an entry can be made to rescue and remove them straight away.

When a person **collapses** in a confined space and the cause is not known, irrespective of whether or not the confined space was certified fit for entry without respiratory protection, no-one must enter unless they are wearing breathing apparatus. The collapse may have been due to deterioration in the atmosphere within the confined space. The first duty of any rescuer is to ensure that they do not become a casualty themselves.

Each year, would-be rescuers who are insufficiently trained or equipped die by going into confined spaces where a person has collapsed.

This point is illustrated in the following two case studies.

09

 Case study 1

At Carsington Reservoir, four men, all aged between 20 and 30 and physically fit, died in an open-topped inspection shaft. Naturally evolved carbon dioxide had displaced the oxygen. No tests were made before entry. The first man down collapsed and the three other men climbed down to their deaths in futile attempts to rescue him.

An HM Inspector of Factories working in the Public Utilities National Industry Group of the Health and Safety Executive (HSE) wrote about this major accident and stressed:

'It should be manifestly obvious that confined spaces working is one activity where shortcuts in safety cannot be permitted. The deaths of these four men will be more tragic if the lessons of this incident are not fully learnt'.

 Case study 2

When an engineer collapsed in a sewer, a rescuer entered without breathing apparatus and was overcome. A second person made a similarly vain attempt to reach the victims. When the rescue team from the fire and rescue service arrived they had to remove bodies of the two would-be rescuers before they could get to the engineer. By then it was too late and he had died. Had everyone waited for the fire and rescue service, the engineer might have lived and the rescuers would not have needlessly died.

Rescue equipment

Every person entering a confined space wearing breathing apparatus must also wear a safety harness. The harness must be attached to a lifeline, attended by a person outside the confined space.

The harness must be one that is suitable for confined space rescue, in that it must enable an unconscious person to remain in an upright position whilst being hoisted.

An unsuitable harness will allow the unconscious person to bend at the waist, making recovery through a narrow opening difficult or impossible.

This equipment forms part of a safe system of work for any entry into a confined space. Properly used, it may enable a rescue to be carried out successfully without the need for a rescuer to enter the confined space.

Rescue equipment must include some means of lifting or pulling a person up from a confined space, since it is virtually impossible for the average person to achieve this solely by muscular effort. There are a variety of tripods, winches, blocks and tackles which, when used in conjunction with a safety harness, enable a person to be lifted quickly and safely out of a confined space.

If lifting is envisaged as part of a rescue scenario, then as indicated earlier in this chapter, the equipment and accessories will be subject to the Lifting Operations and Lifting Equipment Regulations. This would mean testing and inspection in accordance with the schedule drawn up by the competent person. In practice, harness, lines and accessories (such as carabiners) should be subjected to a formal thorough examination by a competent person every six months and be checked by the user weekly and before each use. Tripods, hoists and other lifting devices need to be load tested every six months in the same way that a scissor lift used for lifting people would.

Dependent on circumstances, rescue equipment may have to include first-aid equipment, oxygen or resuscitation packs and rescue breathing apparatus. A secure line of communication to the emergency services may also be required.

Respiratory protective equipment

RPE must be selected by a competent person, be CE-marked and be suitable for the type of hazard against which it is to protect the wearer.

A wide range of RPE is available from various manufacturers. The equipment functions on the basis of two distinct principles, outlined below.

Purifying the air breathed. The air inhaled is drawn through a filter or medium that removes the harmful substance or pollutant. The nature of the filtering agent depends on the type of pollutant to be dealt with. These types are commonly called **respirators.**

The simplest form of respirator is the dust mask, a preformed cup made of filtering material that fits over the nose and mouth to filter out nuisance dust. These masks give no protection against harmful or toxic gases or fumes and the protection factor of the mask may not offer adequate protection against the level of airborne dust that can be experienced in a confined space.

More complex types have filter cartridges that may be general for various types of dust or fume, or specific to a particular substance.

Supplying clean air. The air can be supplied straight through an air line via a pump or compressor or, alternatively, the person may carry compressed air in cylinders. These types are known as **breathing apparatus.**

An alternative type of breathing equipment is the self-rescue set. This consists of a small compressed air bottle, the necessary hoses and valves and a face piece. Self-rescue sets can be carried by operatives who enter confined spaces where the air is initially safe to breathe.

Should the air quality deteriorate, the face piece is placed over the nose and mouth and the air valve opened. The air bottle supplies fresh air to the operative whilst an escape from the confined space is made. The air bottle of a self-rescue set has a duration of typically 15-20 minutes.

 Care must be taken to select the correct type of protection for the conditions. Respirators (as opposed to breathing apparatus) do not protect against oxygen-deficient atmospheres and should not be used in any atmosphere dangerous to life. RPE should not be used unless all other methods of control or protection have been examined and it is established that the use of RPE is the only reasonably practicable solution.

09

The HSE publication *Respiratory protective equipment at work – A practical guide* (HSG 53) sets out the nominal protection factor for each type of respirator and describes their limitations; it should be carefully consulted in cases of doubt.

Respirators can only be used for protection against the gases or dusts for which they are specifically intended. It is important to note that dust masks and canister and cartridge respirators have a limited period of usage before becoming saturated with the contaminant. They may also have a limited shelf life, indicated by a use-by date.

Permits

Permit to work

Every entry into a confined space must be made under a permit to work, whereby a competent person must be satisfied that all necessary precautions have been taken and provisions made to secure the safety of those entering the confined space, before signing the permit to work. The signed permit thus gives an assurance that work may safely take place.

Permits should only be issued by named, authorised persons, who must sign them. Such persons must be competent, have authority and possess sufficient practical and theoretical knowledge and actual experience of working conditions to enable them to judge whether everything necessary has been done to ensure the safety of personnel. It is quite common for several authorised persons to sign a permit to work, each certifying that they have taken the necessary actions with regard to their own area of responsibility (for example, electrical isolation and atmospheric testing). Where a permit to work system involves the use of padlocks and keys (for example, for locking-off electrical isolators or other sources of energy) the keys must stay with an authorised person until such time as the permit is returned for cancellation.

Permit to enter

Depending upon the nature of the confined space and the inherent risks of carrying out the work, some companies may choose to run a separate permit to enter system.

An example of when such a system might be used is where all preparatory work is carried out to meet the requirements of the permit to work and then the permit to enter is issued when final pre-entry checks of the atmosphere have been carried out.

Such a system would cover situations where:

☑ a single permit to work covers the duration of the whole job, but

☑ successive shifts of workers are each authorised to enter the confined space under a newly raised permit to enter.

Access and egress

A safe way in and out of the confined space should be provided and, wherever possible, allow quick, unobstructed and ready access (such as a fixed, vertical ladder inside an underground chamber that terminates just below the entry/exit point at ground level).

The means of escape must be suitable for use by the individual who enters the confined space so that, ideally, they can quickly escape in an emergency. However, it must be accepted that in many cases the entry/exit point will be of a restricted size that will not necessarily allow an easy escape route in an emergency, particularly if the person who is escaping is wearing a compressed air cylinder. The means of achieving a prompt escape or rescue must be considered in the risk assessment.

Suitable means to prevent access (for example, a locked hatch) should also be in place when there is no need for access to the confined space. There should be a safety sign that is clear and conspicuous to prohibit unauthorised entry alongside openings that allow for safe access.

Conclusion

For work to be done safely in a confined space, great care has to be taken over the detail of each step of the procedure. Common causes of accidents are:

☑ failing to identify confined spaces

☑ inadequate risk assessments

☑ poorly trained and equipped workers

☑ failing to put in place adequate emergency arrangements before work starts

☑ failing to carry out an initial check of air quality

☑ failing to set up a safe system of work, including continuous air monitoring, based around a permit to work system

☑ failing to follow an established safe system of work

☑ deviations in conditions rendering the risk assessment/safe system invalid

☑ incorrectly using RPE

☑ using the incorrect type of RPE

☑ failing to use safety harnesses and lifelines

☑ ill-conceived and badly executed rescue attempts.

All such accidents are avoidable. If an accident does occur, it demonstrates that a breakdown has occurred in the supposed safe system of work.

9.6 Legislative requirements

The Confined Spaces Regulations

These require employers to plan work so that entry to confined spaces is avoided so far as is reasonably practicable (for example, by doing the work from outside). They also require a safe system of work to be developed and implemented if entry to a confined space is unavoidable, and adequate emergency arrangements, which will also safeguard rescuers, to be put in place before work starts.

Duties to comply with the regulations are placed on:

☑ employers in respect of work carried out by their own employees and work carried out by any person (for example, a contractor) insofar as work is, to any extent, under the employer's control

☑ the self-employed in respect of work carried out by any other person insofar as work is, to any extent, under the control of the self-employed person.

The key duty under Regulation 4 is a complete prohibition of any person entering a confined space to carry out any work for any purpose whatsoever, where it is reasonably practicable to carry out the work by any other means.

If entry into a confined space is necessary then a risk assessment by a competent person, under the Management of Health and Safety at Work Regulations, is required. The outcome of the risk assessment will then provide the basis for the development of a full and effective safe system of work, including rescue arrangements.

These regulations are supported and explained by an approved code of practice (ACoP) and guidance notes. The competent person responsible for carrying out the risk assessment, or otherwise planning work in a confined space, should be familiar with the principles outlined in the document.

 For the definition of reasonably practicable refer to Chapter A01 Health and safety law.

 The complete regulations and the ACoP and guidance notes can be viewed online.

The Construction (Design and Management) Regulations

These regulations place a legal duty on designers, when preparing their designs, to carry out design risk assessments and design out risk, so far as it is reasonably practicable.

In the context of this chapter, designers should carry out their design work so that no-one has to enter a confined space during construction work, maintenance or cleaning of the structure or during its demolition. The regulations place a duty on the designer, when preparing their designs, to consider the users of any workplace.

Also, within the context of this chapter, these regulations place legal duties on contractors, including principal contractors, with regard to:

☑ safe places of work

☑ excavations

☑ prevention of drowning

☑ prevention of risk from fire, explosion, flooding and asphyxiation

☑ emergency procedures

☑ fresh air.

 For further information refer to Chapter A03 Construction (Design and Management) Regulations.

The Provision and Use of Work Equipment Regulations

These regulations require that an employer only supplies work equipment that is correct and suitable for the job and ensures that the equipment is maintained and kept in good working order.

Where the use of the equipment involves a specific risk to the health and safety of employees, the use of the equipment must be restricted to specified workers.

The Personal Protective Equipment at Work Regulations

These regulations require that, where a risk has been identified by a risk assessment and it cannot be adequately controlled by other means, which are equally or more effective, then the employer must provide and ensure that suitable PPE is used by employees.

In essence, PPE may only be used as a last resort after all other means of eliminating or controlling the risk have been considered and are found to be not reasonably practicable to implement. In practice, however, unless it is possible to carry out the work without entry into the confined space, the wearing of PPE will usually be necessary.

In deciding which type to issue, the employer must take into account the risk that the PPE is being used to protect against, and ensure that the PPE will fit the wearer and allow them to work safely. Where the use of RPE is necessary, face-fit testing to establish the suitability of the RPE for the wearer is required. If more than one item of PPE is being used, the employer must make sure that individual items of PPE are compatible and suitable for the task that is to be undertaken.

Whenever PPE is to be issued, the employer must ensure that employees have been given adequate and appropriate information, instruction and training to enable them to understand the risks being protected against, the purpose of the PPE and the manner in which it is to be used.

Whilst the employer must ensure that PPE is supplied and used, the employee has a duty to properly use the equipment provided, follow the information, instruction and training that they have been given, and know the procedures for reporting losses or defects to their employer.

In the context of this chapter, in addition to the more commonly used PPE, confined space working will often require the use of appropriate RPE and rescue equipment (such as a safety harness and line).

 For further information on the Personal Protective Equipment at Work Regulations refer to Chapter B06 Personal protective equipment.

The Lifting Operations and Lifting Equipment Regulations

Access to and egress from many confined spaces is made by lowering or raising a person vertically through the entry/exit point, including during practice or actual rescues.

In these circumstances:

☑ safety harnesses and rescue lines must be regarded as lifting accessories

☑ the tripod hoist or other type of winch must be regarded as lifting equipment used for lifting persons and, as such, requires thorough examination on a six monthly basis under the Lifting Operations and Lifting Equipment Regulations (LOLER).

However, if the rescue involves a sideways or inclined drag along, for example a duct, then there would be no lifting and LOLER would not apply, however PUWER would.

 For further information on the Lifting Operations and Lifting Equipment Regulations refer to Chapter C07 Lifting operations.

Other legislation

Other legislation that can have an impact upon how work in confined spaces is planned, organised and carried out are the:

☑ Control of Substances Hazardous to Health Regulations (refer to Chapter B07)

☑ Work at Height Regulations (refer to Chapter D01)

☑ Dangerous Substances and Explosive Atmospheres Regulations (refer to Chapter D10).

09

Appendix A – Permit to work certificate example

(Reproduced from Entry into confined spaces (GS5), by permission of HMSO.)

Confined spaces permit

Serial no. CS.........

Authorisation by permit co-ordinator

Project Name/No:	Permit Date:
Contractor:	Permit Start Time:
Contractor's Supervisor:	Permit Finish Time:

Confined space location and description, including any plant or processes:

Hazards

The following processes within the confined space have been WITHDRAWN from service:			
Electrical power	Yes/No	Pressure systems	Yes/No
Mechanical power	Yes/No	Liquids/flowing substances	Yes/No
Relevant isolation permit no:			
There exists the potential for the following hazards to be present:			
Flammable substances	Yes/No	Ingress/presence of liquids	Yes/No
Oxygen enrichment/deficiency*	Yes/No	Solids which can flow	Yes/No
Toxic gases, fumes or vapours	Yes/No	Excessive heat or cold*	Yes/No
Activities within confined space:			

Safe systems

A suitable and sufficient written safe system of work must be produced for this activity:		
Risk Assessment Document No:		Author:
Method Statement Document No:		Author:
The risk assessment/method statement* is enclosed with the original permit		Yes/No

The confined space has been assessed and the following control measures identified within the written safe system of work, are to be implemented (➤ in box):		
Removal of residues	Full Breathing Apparatus (BA)	
Use of intrinsically safe tools	Escape BA only	
Purge atmosphere before entry	First aid/emergency procedures	
Forced ventilation/extraction*	Tools and equipment checked for safe use	
Weils disease cards issued	System of communication in place e.g. radios/mobiles	
Topman only/Rescue team*	Warning signs/barriers in place	
Safety harnesses/lifelines*	Competency of work team checked	
Continued atmospheric testing - record unit type/serial no:		

Permission is granted to work within the confined space according to the safe systems.	
Name:	Position: Permit Coordinator
Signature:	Date and Time:

Part 2 – Receipt by supervisor

As the supervisor, I am familiar with the scope of work and safe systems to be implemented. A recorded briefing has been delivered to the workforce on this safe system of work:		Yes/No
Name:	Position:	
Signature:	Date and Time:	

Part 3 – Completion by supervisor

The activities authorised by this permit have finished and the confined space fully vacated.	
Name:	Position:
Signature	Date and Time:

Part 4 – Cancellation by permit co-ordinator

The activities authorised by this permit have now ceased. The cancellation of this permit now precludes any further work taking place in this confined space.		
The confined space and any plant within it, have been **returned** to service:		Yes/No
Name:	Position:	
Signature:	Date and Time:	

* delete as applicable

10

Dangerous substances

Dangerous substances are widely used on building and construction sites. The main hazards are fire and explosion, and everything possible must be done to lessen the risks.

Safety is divided into three main areas: the storage of substances, the safe handling and transport of substances and the uses to which substances are put.

Introduction   134
Key points   134
Storage of dangerous substances   134
Handling and use of dangerous substances   136
Liquefied petroleum gas   138
Fire   146
Legislative requirements   149

Appendix A – Dangerous substances safety
                  questionnaire   153
Appendix B – LPG safety questionnaire   155
Appendix C – Retrieval of orphaned
                  compressed gas cylinders   157

10.1 Introduction

This chapter does not cover the storage of explosives, which may be used in the industry for demolition and civil engineering. There are specific requirements under the Manufacture and Storage of Explosives Regulations 2005 and it is suggested that the HSE is contacted for further advice.

In most cases, the Health and Safety Executive (HSE) enforces fire safety legislation on construction sites, under the Construction (Design and Management) Regulations and the Management of Health and Safety at Work Regulations, although they also have enforcement powers under The Regulatory Reform (Fire Safety) Order.

Local Authority environmental health officers are likely to have a similar role where the work is carried out as part of a non-notifiable construction project in a premise that they enforce.

The local fire and rescue service (FRS) has responsibilities for the enforcement of fire safety in some circumstances.

10.2 Key points

☑ A risk assessment must be carried out before dangerous substances are stored, transported or used. In some cases, a method statement and/or a permit to work will also be required.

☑ Important pieces of legislation relating to this chapter are the:
- Dangerous Substances and Explosive Atmospheres Regulations (DSEAR)
- Construction (Design and Management) Regulations (CDM)
- Regulatory Reform (Fire Safety) Order (RR(FS)O) (England and Wales only)
- Fire (Scotland) Act
- Fire Safety (Employees' Capabilities) (England) Regulations.

☑ DSEAR covers the flammable or explosive properties of dangerous substances used in the workplace.

☑ There may also be health issues that are covered by the Control of Substances Hazardous to Health (COSHH) Regulations.

☑ Fire safety legislation will be enforced by the HSE or the local FRS, generally depending upon the location where dangerous substances are stored and used.

☑ People who use dangerous substances must be fully aware of their hazardous properties, adopt methods of controlling the risks and be trained in the use of portable fire extinguishers.

☑ Electrical apparatus and naked flames should not be used near flammable or explosive dangerous substances, particularly if they are being sprayed.

☑ Good ventilation is essential wherever flammable or explosive dangerous substances are used or stored.

☑ Smoking policies and waste disposal policies must be established and diligently monitored.

 Start by identifying dangerous substances on site and quantities – use the material safety data sheets and labels to identify these hazards. Also consider processes that may generate dangerous forms of substances.

10.3 Storage of dangerous substances

On most building or construction sites, dangerous substances will be used at some time during the construction phase. Depending upon the nature of the work to be undertaken it may be necessary to store bulk quantities of dangerous substances, either in:

☑ an external, secure, purpose-built compound, where site conditions allow

☑ a suitable, secure internal storeroom if, because of the nature of the site, external storage is not possible.

Alternatively, small quantities (for example, 200 ml containers upwards) will often be taken to the place of work by the person doing the job.

Where small quantities of dangerous substances for daily use are required in the workplace, metal lockable bins may be used.

Storage in the open air

Where it is necessary to store dangerous substances in bulk, a store should be built:

☑ on a concrete sloping pad with a sump to catch any leaks or spills

☑ with a low sill all around, sufficient to contain the contents of the largest can or drum stored, plus 10% (in other words, bunded)

☑ surrounded by a 1.8 metre high wire fence

☑ so that it is protected against direct sunlight

☑ at least two metres away from nearby buildings or boundaries, except that, where the boundary of the store forms part of a solid wall, cans or drums may be stacked up against that wall up to one metre from the top.

Cans or drums should be stored:

☑ so that their contents can be easily identified and removed in the event of any leak or damage

☑ on their sides and chocked to prevent movement.

Stores or bins must be kept locked and only sufficient amounts for each day's requirements should be removed, as and when needed.

They may be marked with suitable signs, such as flammable liquid or flammable gas.

Additionally, if an assessment under DSEAR shows that an explosive atmosphere may be present in a particular area, appropriate numbers of the illustrated sign must be displayed.

The sign comprises a yellow background and black graphics. Signs must conform to the Health and Safety (Safety Signs and Signals) Regulations and *Safety signs and colours* (BS 5499). All signs purchased from reputable suppliers will be to these specifications.

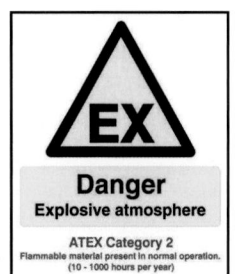

Naked flames, smoking, matches or lighters must not be allowed in the area of the store, and proper prohibition signs must be clearly displayed, as well as other signs already indicated.

Any lighting within a store must be flameproof to the appropriate standard, and under no circumstances should electrical sockets be permitted.

Where there is a need for electrical apparatus (other than lighting) within a store, the supply must be permanently wired in using intrinsically safe equipment.

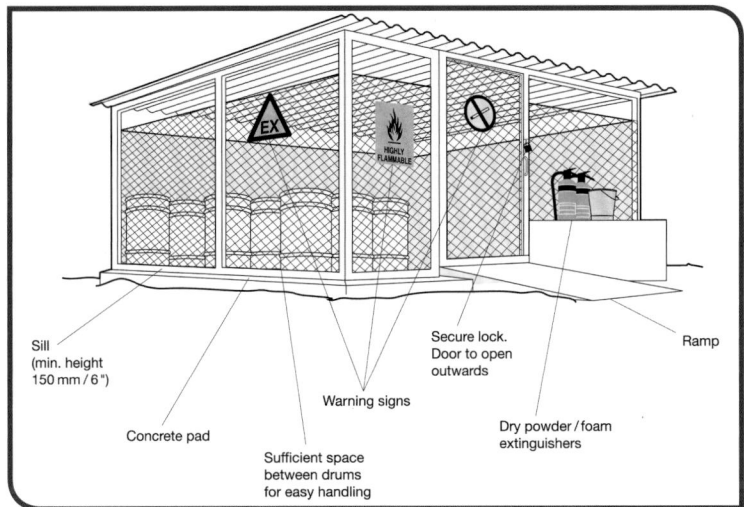

Sill (min. height 150 mm / 6")

Concrete pad

Warning signs

Sufficient space between drums for easy handling

Secure lock. Door to open outwards

Dry powder / foam extinguishers

Ramp

Example of a secure storage area

Other points to be noted.

☑ Stores should not be built below ground level because the vapours from spills and leaks will not be able to disperse (they are heavier than air).

☑ Adequate cross-ventilation at both high and low level is necessary.

☑ The store should always be kept locked when unattended.

☑ A door sill of approximately 150 mm in height should be provided to catch any leaks or spills in order to retain the liquids inside the building.

☑ A quantity of absorbent material, to soak up any spilt liquids, and a suitable container for the collection and safe disposal of the contaminated absorbent, should be provided at the store.

☑ The use of mobile phones in or immediately adjacent to the store should be prohibited. Notices to this effect should be provided and prominently displayed.

☑ Any shelves or racking in the store should be of a non-ferrous metal or other non-combustible construction.

10

Storage inside a building

A separate building should be provided, if possible, solely for the storage of dangerous substances where security or protection from the weather is required. Ideally, it will be constructed from fire-resisting materials and it should be at least two metres away from other buildings or boundaries.

A risk assessment should be carried out to determine whether the risks of storing dangerous substances in such a location are acceptable. If not, either additional control measures must be put in place or alternative arrangements made for storing the substances.

Where a separate building cannot be provided, and the store forms part of an existing structure, the surrounding walls and roof of the store must be fire-resisting and the door should be of the fire-resisting type and open outwards.

It is recommended that the maximum quantities that may be stored in cabinets and bins are no more than 50 litres for highly flammable liquids (and flammable liquids with a flashpoint below the maximum ambient temperature of the workroom/working area) and no more than 250 litres for other flammable liquids with a higher flashpoint of up to 55°C.

Other points to be noted.

☑ Stores should not be built below ground level, because the vapours from spillages and leaks will not be able to disperse.

☑ Adequate cross-ventilation at both high and low level is necessary.

☑ The store should always be kept locked when unattended.

☑ When not in use, containers of flammable liquids needed for current work activities should be kept closed and stored in suitable cabinets or bins of fire-resisting construction, which are designed to retain spills (110% volume of the largest vessel normally stored in it).

☑ A quantity of absorbent material, to soak up any spilt liquids, and a suitable container for the collection and safe disposal of the contaminated absorbent, should be provided at the store.

☑ Signs should be positioned on or near the store stating, for example, 'highly flammable' or 'flashpoint below 32°C'. All signs should conform to the Health and Safety (Safety Signs and Signals) Regulations and *Safety signs and colours* (BS 5499).

☑ Naked flames, smoking, matches or lighters must not be allowed in the store, and signs stating this must be clearly displayed.

☑ The use of mobile phones in or adjacent to the store should be prohibited. Notices to this effect should be provided and prominently displayed.

☑ Any lighting or other electrical apparatus must conform to BS EN 60079-14.

☑ Any shelves or racking in the store should be of a non-ferrous metal or other non-combustible construction.

10.4 Handling and use of dangerous substances

The use of any dangerous substance, including decanting small quantities for daily use from bulk containers, must be the subject of a risk assessment.

The findings of the risk assessment will indicate the maximum quantity of the dangerous substance that can be taken to the place of work and the safe working practices to be observed once it is there and being used.

Generally, only enough of the dangerous substance to enable the work in hand to be carried out should be taken to the place where it is to be used.

 The HSE recommends that only the minimum quantity needed for frequently occurring activities, or that required for use during a half day or one shift, should be present in the workroom/working area.

Clearly, actual quantities will depend on the work activity and also the organisational arrangements for controlling the fire risks in the workroom/ working area.

Decanting, mixing or sampling should not be carried out in a store. It should be done in the open air or in a separate room constructed of fire-resisting materials.

Funnels should be used to prevent spillage whilst decanting is taking place and drip trays should be used to catch any spillage that may inadvertently occur.

Any spillage should be soaked up using proprietary absorbents, dry earth or dry sand.

Metal bins with lids should be provided for any used absorbents to be placed in and these should be emptied regularly and carefully.

Consideration must be given to the disposal of any waste as it may well be classified as hazardous waste. Such waste must be transported by a registered carrier to a licensed landfill site. The site itself may also need to be notified to the Environment Agency, depending on how much waste is produced.

In general, where work involves the use of a dangerous substance that has the potential to create an explosive atmosphere inside a room, all electrical power should be turned off unless all electrical fittings are intrinsically safe by design. If space heating is needed, it should be flameproof and incapable of causing the ignition of any vapours present in the atmosphere.

The build-up of concentrations of vapours must be avoided and dispersed, if necessary, by natural or mechanical ventilation. If mechanical ventilation is necessary, a flameproof motor, not in the ventilation trunking, should be used.

Other points to be considered.

- ☑ Naked flames, welding and heating torches, and smoking materials should be prohibited in any area where an explosive atmosphere may be present.

- ☑ Metal bins with lids must be provided for offcuts, waste or rags, and should be emptied regularly.

- ☑ A suitable container with a lid should be used for any brushes or scrapers that require soaking, to remove residues of dangerous substances. This should be placed in a safe area well away from any possible source of ignition.

Spraying of dangerous substances

New covering materials (such as paints, varnishes and lacquers), and the techniques for applying them, have been developed, and extensive use of spray painting equipment can now be seen on construction sites.

Using a spray gun for spraying dangerous substances is most likely to introduce an airborne explosive mist into the workplace, creating a hazard both to the user and to other workers in the area. Such work must only be undertaken by fully trained and competent employees and in a situation where all appropriate precautionary measures are in place.

A risk assessment must be carried out and other controls, including permits to work and/or permits to enter (for those people involved in the job, by implication, excluding all others), implemented as necessary.

Other points to be noted.

- ☑ Identify the material carefully and always follow the manufacturer's instructions on preparation, use and application.

- ☑ Always use the correct type of spraying equipment. Never make do, just because the proper equipment is not immediately to hand.

- ☑ If alternative control measures are not available or adequate, protective clothing and respiratory protective equipment must be used.

- ☑ Always use the hygiene and washing facilities provided.

- ☑ Do not introduce ignition sources into the working area.

- ☑ Do not smoke or use naked flames in the working area.

- ☑ Always place warning signs in approaches to the area where the work is being carried out, and at entrance points to areas where dangerous substances are being used. Use physical barriers, if necessary, to stop unauthorised persons entering the area.

Empty tanks and containers

Bulk tanks and drums

Do not cut or heat any empty tanks, containers or drums unless they have been certificated as being free of flammable vapours that could explode. Current opinion recommends reducing the length of time that such certification is valid for. Under most circumstances, the cutting work should be planned to start as soon as the gas-free certificate is issued.

Special care is necessary when demolishing or dismantling disused bulk tanks. By disturbing the tank or heating the residues left inside, you may cause an explosive concentration of vapours.

Entry into any disused tank or vessel that may be regarded as a confined space should be avoided by doing the work from outside, if possible. Often, there will be a need to clean residues and if entry to a confined space is unavoidable, a safe system of work must be followed and the work carried out under a permit to work system.

Further advice on permit to work systems and entry into confined spaces is contained in the approved code of practice (ACoP) and guidance notes that support the Confined Spaces Regulations (L101) and HSE leaflet *Safe work in confined spaces* (INDG 258).

There are a number of factors to consider when the work involves large tanks. The first would be what the contents were. Oil storage tanks may have held so-called heavy fuel oil and these will undoubtedly have been insulated. It is quite likely that the insulation system will have been asbestos. If the tanks once held petrol, it may have been leaded fuel. This means that the exposure to lead fumes during cutting should be considered.

It is normal for large tanks, whether above or below ground, to be emptied and cleaned by a specialist contractor before dismantling. The contents are generally removed by a large vacuum tanker and then the inside of the tank is steam cleaned. Most of this work can be carried out from the outside and it is only to carry out the final clean that entry is required. Operatives carrying out this final clean must be trained in confined space working and provided with all the normal gas detector, rescue equipment and personal protective equipment (PPE) that would be expected for confined space working.

Having been cleaned, the tank is tested and a gas-free certificate issued. It should then be cut up as soon as possible. The risk of not doing so is that it is practically impossible to completely clean a tank, particularly where its construction incorporates internal ribs, welds and other internal features that could harbour residue of the content. These may well become fumes and if the concentration becomes high enough then the atmosphere inside the tank may become explosive if ignited.

Dangerous substances

It is important to be aware that even cold-cutting techniques (such as hydraulic shears) may cause sparks and, therefore, leaving the cutting even until the next day is simply not an option.

Industrial gas cylinder colours

While the cylinder label is the primary means of identifying the properties of the gas in a cylinder, the colour-coding of the cylinder body provides a further guide.

Cylinder shoulder – European standard colour-coding

The colour applied to the shoulder, or curved part at the top of the cylinder, signifies the European standard colour-coding.

The aim of the new standard (EN 1089-3), which has replaced the old cylinder colour scheme (BS 349), is to help improve safety standards within the gases industry.

 Cylinder identification colour-coding and labelling requirements can be downloaded for free from the British Compressed Gas Association website.

Orphaned compressed gas cylinders

Apparently empty compressed gas cylinders are often abandoned for a variety of reasons and eventually appear at waste disposal centres, where they are not welcome.

It is often possible to identify the owner of any particular cylinder as 90% of all cylinders are owned by five companies. These companies will normally take back their orphaned cylinders.

10.5   Liquefied petroleum gas

Liquefied petroleum gas (LPG) is a mixture of hydrocarbons that are a gas or vapour under normal conditions of temperature and pressure, but can be turned into a liquid by either the application of pressure or the reduction of temperature.

LPG can be found in numerous locations, in various sizes of cylinder, and can be put to a variety of uses on building and construction sites. Uses range from the heating of bitumen boilers, site huts and offices to providing a fuel for hand tools and cutting equipment.

If used properly and safely, LPG is a convenient and valuable source of energy. Misuse or carelessness can cause serious accidents.

Key points

- ☑ In some cases, the Regulatory Reform (Fire Safety) Order will only be relevant where LPG is stored off site (for example, at company premises and builders' yards). However, it will also apply to some construction sites where LPG is used in conjunction with a work process.
- ☑ LPG is normally found as a compressed liquid, usually of commercial butane or propane.
- ☑ LPG is a colourless, odourless liquid that floats on water but vaporises to form a gas that is heavier than air. A stenching agent is normally added.
- ☑ A release or spillage of LPG can form a large vapour cloud of flammable gas capable of ignition from some distance.
- ☑ LPG is stored on site in fixed tanks, refillable cylinders or non-refillable disposable cylinders (cartridges).
- ☑ Storage should be in secure, non-combustible, well ventilated areas away from other risks and sources of ignition.
- ☑ There are special requirements for vehicles and drivers covering the transportation of LPG.
- ☑ In site huts all LPG cylinders and regulators for use with fixed heaters, cookers and lighting must be kept outside and piped in using rigid copper piping.
- ☑ Staff who work with LPG must be suitably trained in the hazards and use of LPG (such as not rolling cylinders).
- ☑ In the event of a leak, do not attempt to operate electrical apparatus or switches.
- ☑ If a fire breaks out that involves LPG cylinders:
  - – immediately inform the FRS of the whereabouts of all cylinders on site, including details of whether they are full or empty
  - – if in any doubt as to the safety of the overall situation, evacuate the site and put a security cordon in place.

Liquefied petroleum gas means any commercial butane, commercial propane or a mixture of the two.

Commercial butane

This is usually stored in blue cylinders and is generally known as camping gaz or calor gas. It consists mainly of butane and butane isomers. The remaining components are predominantly propane and propane isomers, pentane and pentane isomers. Because of the low vapour pressure, butane cylinders are not generally used outside.

Commercial propane

This is usually stored in vessels or in red cylinders. It consists mainly of propane and propane isomers. The remaining components are predominantly butane and butane isomers, ethane and ethane isomers.

Liquefied petroleum gas properties

LPG is a colourless, odourless liquid or gas that normally has a smell or stench added before distribution.

As a liquid, it is lighter than water and will float before evaporating.

As a gas, it is approximately twice as heavy as air and will sink and flow into sumps and underground excavations or workings. It will also sink into drains but, because its density is approximately half that of water, it will not flow through drains that are water-trapped.

It is capable of ignition at some distance from the original leak. The resulting flame can travel back to the source of the leak.

Any release of liquid under pressure into the atmosphere results in its rapid conversion to gas. This gas has a volume of about 230 (butane) and 270 (propane) times that of the liquid.

The expansion, during a rapid release of pressure, results in a rapid drop of temperature, which for propane can approach its boiling point of -45°C. Leakage of liquid LPG will result in the release of large volumes of highly flammable gases.

For example, one litre of liquid propane spilt in a workplace will evaporate to make approximately 270 litres of gas. If it is diluted with air to 2%, this will give 13,750 cubic litres of an explosive gas/air mixture – enough to fill a room 3 m x 2.3 m x 2 m.

Properties of liquefied petroleum gases

Property	Commercial butane	Commercial propane
Density in comparison to water	0.57	0.5
Density in comparison to air	2	1.5
Litres per tonne	1,745	1,995
Boiling point	-2°C	-45°C
Pressure at 15°C	1.5 bar	7.0 bar
Expansion ratio	1:230	1:270
Levels of flammability	1.9% – 8.5%	2.0% – 10.9%

The use of LPG equipment in confined spaces, and small, poorly ventilated spaces (such as basement and sub-basement boiler houses, toilets and kitchens) can give rise to a highly flammable or explosive atmosphere, if the equipment should leak.

Flammability

Following mechanical failure of LPG equipment, or any other event that causes the release of LPG, the resulting gas will form a flammable mixture with air at gas concentrations between approximately 2% and 10%.

Ignition of released LPG, where the concentration exceeds 2%, can result in fire or, if confined, an explosion. If a leak does not ignite immediately, and the LPG and air mixture drifts from the point of release, it will gradually become more diluted.

However, should the concentration still exceed 2% and ignition occur, this could cause a flash or cloud-fire back to the point of release.

A leak of LPG may be noticed either by the smell or the noise of the gas escaping. There may also be condensation or frosting on the outside of the cylinder.

Leaks must not be traced with a lighted match or naked flame as this would almost certainly cause an explosion. Only soapy water or a proprietary leak-finding fluid should be used.

 If it is suspected that LPG has leaked inside a building, no attempt should be made to touch any electrical apparatus. Do not turn light switches, sockets or any other electrical appliance either on or off.

Open all doors and windows, if it is safe to do so, and leave immediately. Do not re-enter the building until advice has been sought and you are told that it is safe to do so.

Workplace exposure limits

The maximum levels of exposure, as stated in EH40 under the heading LPG, are:

☑ 1,000 ppm (0.1%) for long-term exposure (reference period eight hours)

☑ 1,250 ppm (0.125%) for short-term exposure (reference period 15 minutes).

During any maintenance work involving release of pressure, especially in confined spaces, care must be taken that these exposure limits are not exceeded.

10

Inhalation

LPG gas is not toxic, but at concentration levels above about 10,000 ppm (1%) in air, propane becomes a slight narcotic. At higher levels, it becomes an asphyxiant by displacing oxygen.

In a sufficiently high concentration, a person will suffocate and die.

Cold burns

The release of liquid propane onto unprotected skin will cause cold burns. This is due to the rapid vaporisation of the liquid, withdrawing heat from the affected area of the body.

The release of liquid, or significant amounts of gas at vessel pressure, can also cause the adjacent fittings to cool. This may be sufficient to cause cold burns if the fittings are subsequently touched by unprotected hands.

Suitable skin and eye protection must be worn whenever there is the possibility of a release of liquid LPG.

 In the event of a cold burn, treat as for a burn from a hot object. Flush with copious amounts of cold water and seek medical help (call 999).

Environmental hazards

A small, unignited release of LPG would not pose a serious danger to the environment.

The gas, being heavier than air, will roll and sink to the lowest point (such as a basement or excavation). This may result, if in the flammable range, in a fire or explosion, even if a naked source of flame is a considerable distance from the original leak.

A fire and explosion would be instantaneous on ignition and would be limited to immediate damage. The fire might devour only escaping LPG and then the danger will have passed with no lasting environmental damage.

The fire will burn fast and the explosion will be intense, but both may be over very quickly.

Storage

LPG can be stored on construction sites in one of three ways:

- ☑ in fixed storage tanks
- ☑ in refillable cylinders
- ☑ in non-refillable cylinders (that is, disposable cylinders).

Fixed storage tanks

Whilst most LPG used on construction sites can be found in cylinders, on some larger sites there may be a need for bulk storage. In view of the large capacity, it is essential that the positioning of any storage tank is carefully planned and discussed with the local fire prevention officer and the HSE.

LPG tanks should be positioned on a level concrete base to provide a stable foundation. For short-term installations it may be satisfactory to stand the tank on concrete slabs, but advice must be sought from the tank or gas suppliers.

Tanks should not be sited close to any ditches, cellars or drains, and delivery and emergency vehicles must easily reach them.

All access roads must be clear of obstruction and the entire area kept free from weeds and other vegetation.

Tanks over 2,250 litres liquid capacity should be electrically bonded and earthed.

All bulk storage tanks must have good, all-round ventilation. On non-secure sites, tanks should be protected against vandalism by a chain-link fence at least two metres high.

Motorway-type crash barriers should surround the installation to minimise damage by motor vehicles.

 Installations must be clearly labelled 'Highly flammable LPG. No smoking or naked lights'.

Signs must conform to the Health and Safety (Safety Signs and Signals) Regulations and *Safety signs and colours* (BS 5499). Signs purchased from reputable suppliers will be to these specifications.

Separation

Adequate separation must be maintained between bulk storage tanks and adjacent buildings or boundaries. As a guide, the distances detailed in the table below should be followed.

Separation distances of bulk LPG tanks

Gas capacity	Water capacity		Minimum distance*
Tonnes	Litres	Gallons	Metres
Under 0.2	450	99	2.5
0.2 – 1	451 – 2,250	100 – 495	3
1 – 4	2,251 – 9,000	496 – 1,980	7.5

* Minimum distance from boundaries, buildings or sources of ignition.

Where possible, LPG storage areas should not be positioned under power cables. Where this is unavoidable, the **minimum** distances between the extremities of the vessel or cylinders to the nearest cable should be:

☑ up to 1 kV – 1.5 m

☑ 1 kV or above – 10 m.

Cylinders

Handling

Care must be taken when moving cylinders around the site, especially by hand or on rough ground. A full 47 kg cylinder has a total mass of about 90 kg and, before moving by hand, requires an assessment under the Manual Handling Operations Regulations of the method to be used. Cylinders must not be rolled, even when empty.

Cylinders should be handled with care and, wherever reasonably practicable, moved using suitable equipment. They should not be moved unprotected in dumper trucks or on forklift trucks. The valve on a cylinder should not be used for lifting or to lever the cylinder into position. Damage to the valve can result in a non-controllable release of LPG under high pressure. Throwing cylinders from any height or dropping them is prohibited, as in such circumstances damage to the valve, shroud and cylinders is even more likely.

Damaged cylinders

Before use, cylinders should be examined. Any damaged or faulty cylinder should **not** be used. The cylinder should be labelled and put in a safe place for return to the supplier.

If a cylinder is found to be leaking (usually from the valve) and the leak cannot be stopped, the cylinder should be carefully removed to a well-ventilated, open space, free from sources of ignition. It should be left with the leak uppermost, marked faulty, and notices displayed prohibiting smoking or other naked lights. General access should be prevented by barriers or otherwise. The supplier of the cylinder and, if necessary, the FRS, should be informed immediately.

Under no circumstances should attempts be made to dismantle or repair defective cylinders.

Orphaned compressed gas cylinders

Whilst this advice applies to abandoned LPG cylinders, it is also valid for compressed gas cylinders that have held other gases.

Empty compressed gas cylinders may still contain some of their original content. They are abandoned for a variety of reasons and then appear at metal recyclers or council waste disposal sites, neither of which welcomes their presence. It is felt that cylinders are often abandoned because:

☑ they are empty and are too troublesome to return to the supplier

☑ the owner/supplier cannot be identified

☑ they are damaged and therefore not returnable

☑ they are at the end of their useful life.

Within the UK there is a cylinder retrieval system co-ordinated by the Liquid Petroleum Gas Association. Five major companies own around 90% of all UK compressed gas cylinders. Each company has arrangements in place to collect their own cylinders.

Where the original owners of cylinders cannot be identified because, for example, they came in from abroad or they have no ownership markings, Calor Gas will recover these cylinders. *(For details of collection companies refer to Appendix B.)*

Refillable cylinders

A level base of compacted earth, concrete or paving slabs should be provided and surrounded by a secure chain-link fence at least two metres high. A hard standing should be provided for the delivery and dispatch of cylinders. The area should be kept weed and vegetation free. If the compound is more than 12 metres square, two exits should be provided in opposite corners of the compound. If it is less than 12 metres square, one gate will suffice. Gates should open outwards and always be left unlocked when someone is in the compound. There should be sufficient shelter to prevent cylinders from being exposed to extremes of weather.

10

Dangerous substances

Signs must be clearly displayed indicating the presence of LPG, and prohibiting smoking and the use of any naked flame in the area of the store.

LPG cylinders must be stored with their valves uppermost. They must be stored away from oxygen, highly flammable liquids, oxidisers, toxic or corrosive gases or substances. A distance of at least three metres must be kept between LPG cylinders and other such substances, although they may be kept in the same compound.

LPG store

Separation

Any store for refillable LPG cylinders must be located away from boundaries, buildings, fixed sources of ignition or electrical equipment by at least the distances detailed in the table below.

LPG storage (including empties)	Separation from building/boundary
Under 1,000 kg	3 metres
1,001–4,000 kg	4 metres

The store must be sited at least three metres away from any cellars, drains or other excavations into which a leak of gas would collect.

No cylinder should be stored within 1.5 metres of any compound fencing.

If only a small compound is used (3 m² for example) cylinders may be stored against the inside of the compound fencing, providing this fence is not within three metres of any boundary.

Empty cylinders must be stored with their valves securely closed to prevent any residue of gas escaping, or air being drawn into the cylinder.

Stocks should be grouped in batches of not more than 1,000 kg and batches separated by a minimum 1.5 metre gangway.

Where lighting is necessary, it should be mounted well above ground level and not less than two metres above the cylinders.

Any equipment not in use (such as portable hand equipment) should be isolated so as not to be accessible to trespassers. Any cylinders not required should be returned to the storage compound or other secure position.

Non-refillable cylinders

Non-refillable LPG cylinders for use with small portable equipment (such as blowlamps) may be stored in a lockable, metal container.

Care should be taken when changing cylinders to ensure that connections are correctly made and that there are no leaks.

Always dispose of empty containers safely and in accordance with the manufacturer's recommendations. Do not, under any circumstances, puncture or throw empty cylinders onto a fire.

Additional storage details for small LPG containers

These are often non-refillable (for example, cartridges). However, small refillable cylinders (for example, primus) should also be stored in the same way.

Although only containing small quantities of gas, they must not be stored in occupied site huts.

They should be kept in a secure, non-combustible, well-ventilated external enclosure. The store should have warning signs: 'Highly flammable – LPG', and prohibition signs: 'No smoking/naked lights'.

The disposal of cartridges after use requires care as they still contain gas. Under no circumstances should cartridges be thrown on fires. Small numbers of empty cartridges may be disposed of by including them in normal refuse. Larger quantities should be disposed of by a specialist waste contractor.

Small refillable cylinders should be kept and returned to the supplier when empty.

Transportation of LPG cylinders on vehicles

This section details the requirements of legislation for people who occasionally carry LPG cylinders in a van, truck or similar vehicle. This is covered by the Carriage of Dangerous Goods and Use of Transportable Pressure Equipment Regulations, which implements the European agreement on carriage of dangerous substances by road, hereafter referred to as 'ADR'.

Transportation

Acetylene, LPG and other gases are commonly carried by tradespersons (such as welders, plumbers and motor vehicle repair technicians). Flammable gases are in transport Category 2. Oxygen and gases (such as carbon dioxide and argon) are in transport Category 3. Usually small load threshold exemptions will apply.

The parts of ADR which apply are that the:

☑ driver will have received general awareness, function-specific and safety training (ADR 1.3). A record of such training must be kept

☑ vehicle must be equipped with at least one 2 kg dry powder fire extinguisher, which is kept in good working order

☑ load must be properly stowed. Note that special provisions CV 9, 10 and 36 all apply in the case of these gases. In particular, CV 36 specifies:

> packages shall preferably be loaded in open or ventilated vehicles or open or ventilated containers. If this is not feasible and packages are carried in other closed vehicles or containers, the cargo doors of the vehicles or containers shall be marked with the following, in letters not less than 25 mm high: **WARNING NO VENTILATION OPEN WITH CAUTION**.

The HSE has published a leaflet *Take care with acetylene* and the British Compressed Gases Association (BCGA) has a useful leaflet on the topic of carrying gas cylinders in vehicles, as well as a wider range of publications that may be helpful. The Liquid Petroleum Gas Association (LPGA) has also published its *Carriage of LPG cylinders by road* (Code of Practice 27).

Small load exemptions (ADR 1.1.3.6)

Small load exemptions relate to the total quantity of dangerous goods carried in packages by the transport unit (usually the van or lorry, but also any trailer). It is the transport category (TC) that determines the load limits (thresholds). Many substances are assigned a packing group but these are not synonymous in all cases with the TC. The TC is given in Column 15 of Table A in ADR (Chapter 3.2). If this is not available, the table at ADR Part 1.1.3.6.3 needs to be consulted. References to load limits for the different transport categories are given in the table below. For convenience this has been amended in accordance with Regulation 19 but it needs to be used with care.

Vehicle/load	Driver training	ADR reference
All vehicles except those carrying packages under the load limit.	General training plus ADR training certificate. The certificate may be endorsed for different classes of dangerous goods or different modes (in tanks or other than tanks).	8.2.1
Any vehicle carrying packaged dangerous goods under the small load limit.	General training.	8.2.3 *(refers to Chapter 1.3).* ADR 1.1.3.6
Vehicle with small tank (up to 1 m³).	General training.	8.2.1.3 8.2.3

If a vehicle is carrying dangerous goods under the small load threshold, many of the requirements of ADR are not applicable. Some care needs to be taken, as 'what is not exempted is still required'. In most cases the remaining obligations are as follows:

☑ general training for driver (ADR 1.3.2) a record should be kept (ADR 1.3.3)

☑ carry one 2 kg dry powder fire extinguisher or equivalent (ADR 8.1.4.2)

☑ stow the dangerous goods properly (ADR 7.5.7).

Note that use of these exemptions is optional. For example, a carrier may choose to display the orange plates as long as the vehicle is carrying dangerous goods.

All vehicle marks (orange plates) must be removed when dangerous goods are not being carried. An important aspect is that packaging has to comply with the relevant standards.

Small load application

☑ LPG. This is in transport Category 2. The small load threshold is 333 kg and LPG is LQ0. The result is that all cylinders count towards the load limit, but if that is less than 333 kg, the minimum ADR requirements apply.

☑ Section 8.2 of the ADR details mandatory training for drivers. There should be a record of their training, which must be carried at all times. The level of training required depends upon the load.

10

General transportation of LPG cylinders

When loaded onto vehicles, cylinders must be kept upright and secured. Vehicles must be equipped with two dry powder extinguishers (nominally a 6 kg and a 2 kg) and a first-aid kit. They must also display warning notices.

Ideally, LPG should not be carried on vehicles with other flammable substances (such as paints and solvents). Where this is unavoidable, the other materials should be kept in a steel chest and away from the LPG cylinders. Drivers carrying more than two LPG cylinders must have received training in what to do in an emergency and carry a transport emergency card containing details of the load carried.

If a cylinder leaks during a journey, close the valve immediately. If this is not possible, move the vehicle to open ground, away from buildings and people, and inform the emergency services.

Use of LPG in cylinders

Everyone with any responsibility for the storage and transportation of LPG must understand the characteristics and hazards of the LPG product they are using.

They should understand the fundamentals of fire fighting and control of leakages. They should also have knowledge of the procedures for dealing with emergencies.

It is not possible to cover all aspects of the use and application of LPG, but the following checklist gives the main points for its safe use and handling. Please note that this list should not be regarded as exhaustive.

> ☑ **Safe use and handling of LPG**
>
> ☑ Never use or store a gas cylinder on its side, unless it is a special cylinder for use on LPG-fuelled plant and vehicles. Liquefied gas may escape, causing concentrations of gas, and operatives may suffer frostbite because of the very low temperature of the escaping liquid.
>
> ☑ Propane cylinders must never be stored indoors because any leakage will lead to large concentrations of explosive mixtures.
>
> ☑ Only hoses suitable for use with LPG installations or appliances should be used and these should be inspected frequently for wear.
>
> ☑ Cylinders must not be dropped during handling, nor brought into violent contact with other cylinders or adjacent objects.
>
> ☑ Before and after use, valve protection caps and plastic thread caps or plugs should be fitted to prevent accidental leakage.
>
> ☑ LPG cylinders should not be used below ground level as any leakage of gas will collect at the lowest point and will not disperse.
>
> ☑ Regulators must be handled with care. Damaged regulators should not be used, but should be replaced or sent for specialist repair.
>
> ☑ Hoses and fittings should be examined before use. Damaged items must be replaced.
>
> ☑ LPG cylinders are fitted with a left-hand thread or push-on connection. Union nuts and couplers have grooves on the outside corners of the nuts confirming this. Always use the correct size spanner to tighten or loosen connections. Hand-tight connections will permit leaks. Over-tightening will damage threads and cause leaks.
>
> ☑ Checks for leaks should be carried out using soapy water or other proprietary detector. **Never use a match or other naked flame.**
>
> ☑ Before connecting any cylinder of LPG to equipment, it is essential that all fires, flames or other potential sources of ignition, including any smoking materials, are extinguished. Where it is reasonably practicable to do so, cylinders should be changed in the open air.
>
> ☑ If a leak is found, the gas supply must be turned off at the cylinder immediately.
>
> ☑ Flexible hoses should be in good condition and be protected or steel braided if they are likely to be subjected to damage by abrasion. Hoses must conform to the *Specification for flexible rubber tubing, rubber hose and rubber hose assemblies for use in LPG vapour phase and LPG air installations* (BS 3212).
>
> ☑ Before use, inspections should be carried out on all LPG appliances and equipment. The inspection should cover testing for leaks, cleaning, adjusting, checking hoses, hose clips and ferrules.
>
> ☑ Empty cylinders should always be treated as new ones and returned to a properly designated central storage area for collection. Under no circumstances should an LPG cylinder, either full or empty, be left around the site or buried during site operations.

Regulators

LPG regulators should be suitable for the equipment with which they are to be used. They should be suitable for either propane or butane and be set to the correct pressure. They should be capable of passing the correct flow capacity.

It is dangerous to use regulators set at the incorrect pressure.

Bitumen boilers and cauldrons

Work with a bitumen boiler should always be supervised by a competent person.

The majority of, if not all, bitumen boilers or cauldrons are fuelled by LPG to melt the block bitumen. Such a boiler or cauldron must be sited on a level non-flammable base, away from areas where site traffic may damage hoses or gas cylinders. If avoidable, bitumen boilers should not be taken onto roofs.

Ensure that any LPG cylinder is at least three metres away from the boiler or cauldron to which it is attached. Full cylinders, not attached, should be kept at least six metres away from the boiler or cauldron and protected from heat.

Supply hoses should be checked for crushing, damage to the metal braiding or impregnation with bitumen. Any unserviceable hose must be replaced.

The sequence for lighting is as follows.

1.	Remove the burner from the boiler or cauldron.
2.	Have the source of ignition ready before turning on the gas.
3.	Light the burner, ensuring that the gas is turned on slowly.
4.	Replace the burner beneath the boiler or cauldron.

If frost forms on the outside of the cylinder, the gas flow rate is too high. Either use a smaller burner or couple two or more cylinders together by means of a manifold.

Never leave a bitumen boiler or cauldron unattended when the burner is alight, and never move a bitumen boiler or cauldron with the burner alight.

If a bitumen boiler or cauldron is overfilled, overflows or boils over, the LPG cylinder valves must be turned off immediately. Any spillage should be contained using dry sand or earth and then left until cool. No attempt should be made to remove or recover any spillage of hot bitumen.

A dry powder extinguisher, of a minimum 4.5 kg in size, should be provided whenever a bitumen boiler or cauldron is used.

Gas-operated hand tools and equipment

There are two types of LPG cylinder available for use with portable tools:

☑ disposable

☑ refillable.

Range of LPG cylinder sizes

These cylinders come in various shapes, sizes and colours, depending on the manufacturer. They range in size from the very small (0.5 kg) to the very large (47 kg).

All LPG cylinders used with portable equipment should be positioned upright and secured (if possible). Cylinders used with cutting equipment should always be placed on purpose-made trolleys.

☑ Before changing a cylinder, always make sure that all valves are closed.

☑ Hoses must never be kinked to try to shut off gas when changing torches. It does not work and can lead to a gas escape.

☑ Always replace valve protection caps and plastic thread caps.

☑ Flames from portable tools must not be allowed to play on LPG cylinders.

☑ When work has been completed, turn off the cylinder valves and allow the flame from the portable torch to burn out.

☑ Closure of torch valves rather than cylinder valves will retain gas in hoses which, if damaged, will allow gas to escape.

☑ Hoses and torches must never be put into site toolboxes while still attached to the cylinder.

☑ Manufacturers' operating pressures must be strictly observed and must never be exceeded.

☑ Do not interfere with preset pressure regulators.

Gas-powered fixing tools

Nail guns

Many of the principles for the safe use of cartridge-operated tools also apply to gas-powered fixing tools, which use a canister of pressurised gas (a fuel cell) as a propellant. Generally, gas-powered fixing tools are used for firing fixings into softer materials (such as timber). However, in untrained hands they can be as dangerous as cartridge-operated tools.

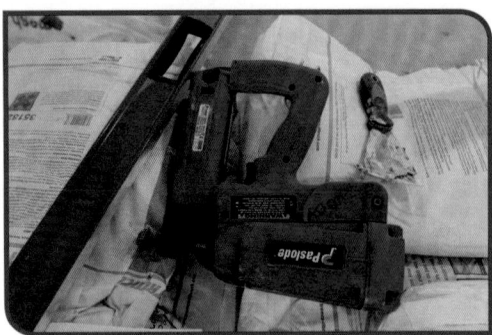

The implications of a misfire when using a gas-powered fixing tool are not as serious as when using a cartridge-operated tool and it is usually safe after a misfire to attempt to make the next fixing immediately. The battery and fuel cell must be removed prior to attempting to remove a blockage.

However, it is important to store and dispose of canisters safely, as detailed elsewhere in this chapter.

LPG for use in site huts and other small buildings

All LPG cylinders and regulators for use with fixed heaters, cookers and lighting within site huts must be kept outside and the gas supply piped in using rigid copper piping. The use of flexible hosing is permitted only between the cylinders and changeover valves or manifolds, and for the final connection to appliances, but this must be kept as short as possible.

All pipework should be exposed and easily accessible for inspection, but located to prevent accidental damage. Any work on LPG pipework or other parts of a fixed installation, including testing, must only be carried out by appropriately trained (Gas Safe registered) persons.

Ventilation for heaters and cookers must be permanent and adequate. It should be divided equally between vents at high and low level.

A two-burner cooker in a site hut needs approximately 150 mm x 150 mm ventilation. A 3 kW convector heater needs approximately 225 mm x 225 mm ventilation.

Inspections of all appliances must be carried out before use. If soot forms or smells occur do not use or allow the appliance to be used. Find out the reasons for the problem and ensure that it is corrected.

Enclosed spaces

Before using LPG equipment in an enclosed space, it is essential to carry out a risk assessment under the Management of Health and Safety at Work Regulations. It is essential to ensure that there is adequate ventilation, which may have to be forced. This is necessary to ensure full combustion and also to make certain that the products of combustion, other fumes and excess oxygen from any cutting apparatus are removed. Proper safety precautions and atmospheric monitoring should be considered.

Wherever practicable, cylinders used with operations in confined spaces should be located in a safe area, preferably in the open air. The supply pressure should be reduced to the lowest practicable level on leaving the source of supply.

Where cylinders are used below ground level, the number must be kept as small as possible. All cylinders and hoses should be removed as soon as work has finished or if it is interrupted for a substantial period, for example overnight.

LPG cylinders must not be taken into confined spaces, as defined in the Confined Spaces Regulations, unless exceptional safety precautions are taken.

10.6 Fire

Fires involving flammable liquids usually fall into one of two categories:

- ☑ flowing liquid fires
- ☑ contained liquid fires.

Powder extinguishers are the most suitable type for tackling a flowing liquid fire. The use of foam or carbon dioxide extinguishers may be effective on a small, flowing liquid fire.

Foam extinguishers are the most suitable type for use on contained liquid fires. Powder or carbon dioxide extinguishers may also be used, but operators should be aware of the short duration of small carbon dioxide extinguishers and the possibility of reignition of any residual vapours being given off when an ignition source is still present.

 Do not use a water extinguisher for any fire involving highly flammable liquids, because the water will cause a violent reaction and make the liquid overflow.

Suitable portable fire extinguishers should, wherever possible, be sited in pairs (so as to minimise the risk of failure) and in strategic positions adjacent to the store.

10

Colour of fire extinguishers

With the introduction of the British Standard *Portable fire extinguishers* (BS EN 3) there are now two colour-coding systems for portable fire extinguishers.

It is important that staff who may be called upon to use a fire extinguisher have a clear understanding of the colour-coding.

This standard states that the body of all fire extinguishers should be red with zones of colour covering not more than 5% of the surface area of the extinguisher, fixed to the extinguisher body and denoting the extinguishing agent or medium it contains.

Colour-coding by agent or medium (see below) enables a trained person to rapidly identify the type of extinguisher needed in an emergency.

Extinguishing medium	Colour of panel
Water	Red
Foam	Cream
Powder (all types)	Blue
Carbon dioxide	Black
Wet chemical	Yellow

Other information concerning its use may also be displayed on the body of the extinguisher.

The requirements of the standard are not retrospective. Fire extinguishers conforming to the older standard, BS 5423, which has been withdrawn, will continue to be found on premises and they can remain in use and be refilled until they need to be replaced. When replaced, the new extinguishers must be to BS EN 3. The one exception is vaporising liquid extinguishers (body colour green). These contained halogenated hydrocarbons (halons), which are known to be environmentally damaging. All vaporising liquid extinguishers should have been removed and properly disposed of during 2002.

The full body colour-coding of the older extinguishers is:

Extinguishing medium	Colour of extinguisher
Water	Red
Foam	Cream
Powder (all types)	Blue
Carbon dioxide	Black
Wet chemical	Yellow

In addition, a small number of extinguishers are bright silver or self-coloured metal with a designated panel stating the medium they contain. The colour-coding of the panel is the same as the above.

Training in the correct type of extinguisher to use and the safe way to operate fire-fighting equipment is essential and should be undertaken **by all** staff who work with dangerous substances. The use of the **wrong** extinguisher in the **wrong** way would have serious consequences.

 Advice on training can be obtained from extinguisher manufacturers or the local fire station.

Enforcement of fire safety legislation

The responsibility for the enforcement of fire safety legislation is split between the:

☑ HSE, or possibly the Local Authority on small non-notifiable sites, either of which would usually take enforcement action under the Construction (Design and Management) Regulations (CDM) or the Management of Health and Safety at Work Regulations (MHSAWR). However, the HSE also has enforcement powers under the RR(FS)O

☑ FRS, which would enforce their powers under the Regulatory Reform (Fire Safety) Order (England and Wales) or the Fire (Scotland) Act (Scotland only).

In most circumstances, fire safety legislation will be enforced by the:

☑ HSE on construction sites, including on-site offices and other on-site accommodation

☑ FRS where activities other than construction are taking place, for example where:

– one floor of an office block is being refurbished but the other floors remain occupied

– part of a department store sales floor is a cordoned-off construction site but the public have access to the sales floor outside of the hoarding.

Dangerous substances

In circumstances such as those described, it is usual for the HSE to enforce fire safety legislation within the confines of the site and the FRS to enforce it outside the hoardings.

However, the responsibility for the enforcement of fire safety legislation may not always be as clear cut as this. For example, the FRS is likely to take an interest in any construction site where there is a significant fire loading or there are other factors that significantly increase personal risk, for example:

☑ where the flammable nature of the partly finished structure is considered to pose a significant risk should it catch fire

☑ the flammable (or highly flammable) nature and quantities of materials and substances stored and used on the site (for example LPG)

☑ the vulnerability of adjacent premises should a fire start on site

☑ if there is a large on-site multi-floor administrative complex.

This aspect of fire safety is considered to be particularly relevant to this chapter if significant quantities of flammable or highly flammable substances are stored on site.

 For further information on legislation and other resources, including guidance and incident reports, refer to the HSE's website.

LPG

Action in an emergency

Instructions for dealing with incidents involving LPG will vary for each situation. The most important thing is to avoid endangering anyone's life. The following actions should be taken by anyone discovering a fire.

☑ In case of fire, **no matter how small**, call the FRS.

☑ Whilst waiting for the FRS to arrive, (if it can be done safely) turn off all cylinder valves to cut off the fuel supply and remove the cylinders from the area.

☑ If this action cannot be completed safely (which would starve the fire of further LPG), evacuate the site and impose a cordon to stop anyone inadvertently entering the area.

☑ Never attempt to use a water extinguisher to put out an LPG fire. Dry powder extinguishers are the most suitable type to use. The use of the wrong extinguisher in the wrong way could have serious consequences.

☑ Training in the correct type of fire-fighting equipment to use, and the safe way to operate it, should be undertaken by all staff who work with LPG. These staff must be trained to recognise when the situation is getting out of control and know when to evacuate the area.

☑ When the FRS arrives, inform the fire officer of the situation including:

– the location and contents of all cylinders

– details of any security cordon that you have implemented

– confirmation that all people who were known to be in the area have been accounted for or details of anyone that is unaccounted for

– if possible and required, offer them the data information sheet relating to the cylinder(s) involved.

Remember

☑ Cylinders fitted with pressure relief valves can produce gas jets that will extend a considerable distance.

☑ If cylinders are exposed to a severe fire or are engulfed in flames, no attempt should be made to fight the fire. **Evacuate everyone from the area.**

☑ Where a flame from a leaking gas cylinder is extinguished but the valve is still open, gas will continue to escape and there will be a danger of a gas cloud forming and the risk of an explosion.

☑ Any cylinder involved in a fire should be clearly labelled that it has been involved in a fire and removed from the area to a safe place. Telephone the suppliers – they will give advice and arrange for the cylinder(s) to be collected.

Instructions concerning emergency procedures should be clearly displayed and all employees should be made aware of them.

Data information sheets are available from product manufacturers giving advice in case of an accident involving LPG cylinders. A copy of each sheet should be available for inspection and those sheets relating to the cylinders involved should be given to the fire officer.

Fire-fighting equipment

Selected and suitable employees should be trained in the use of fire-fighting equipment.

Advice on the training of staff can be obtained from the LPG supplier or the FRS.

Portable fire extinguishers, sited in pairs to minimise the risk of failure, should be positioned at strategic points wherever LPG is stored or used. As a general guide, no fewer than two 4.5 kg dry powder extinguishers or equivalent should be provided for every 20 large cylinders (47 kg) stored.

10

Training

Most accidents involving LPG are due to ignorance of basic safety precautions.

All persons using LPG cylinders, tools or equipment should be suitably instructed in the hazards associated with LPG, and the precautions to be taken in its use.

 For an LPG safety questionnaire refer to Appendix B.

10.7 Legislative requirements

 For further information refer to Section A *Legal and management*.

The Dangerous Substances and Explosive Atmospheres Regulations

The principles of the regulations

The Dangerous Substances and Explosive Atmospheres Regulations (DSEAR) require employers to control the risks to safety from fire and explosions. The regulations apply at all places of work where:

☑ a dangerous substance is present (or is liable to be present) at the workplace

☑ the dangerous substance could be a risk to the safety of people as a result of fires, explosions or similar energetic events.

A definition of a dangerous substance is: 'any substance or mixture of substances that can put people's health or safety at risk from fire and explosion'.

Dangerous substances are:

☑ a substance or mixture of substances that is classified as explosive, oxidising, extremely flammable, highly flammable or flammable

☑ any dust, whether in the form of solid particles or fibrous materials, which can form an explosive mixture in air.

A definition of explosive atmosphere is: 'a mixture of air and one or more hazardous substances in the form of a gas, vapour, mist or dust, which will explode after ignition has occurred'.

In the construction industry, many dangerous substances are used, or created by, work activities, for example:

☑ the storage and use of solvents, adhesives and paints

☑ the storage and use of flammable gases (such as oxygen and acetylene) during cutting and welding

☑ the storage and use of LPG for work processes, heating or cooking

☑ the creation of large quantities of airborne dust (for example, as a result of wood-machining or sanding) and the handling and storage of bulk waste dust

☑ the storage and decanting of vehicle fuels and lubricants

☑ the storage and handling of liquid flammable wastes (such as fuel oils)

☑ many hot work activities (such as the hot-cutting of tanks and drums that have contained flammable materials).

 Further guidance is available on the HSE's website.

10

Employers' duties under DSEAR

DSEAR places duties on employers (and the self-employed, who are considered employers for the purposes of the regulations) to assess and eliminate or reduce risks from dangerous substances. Complying with DSEAR involves the responsibilities shown below.

Assessing risks

Before work is carried out, employers must assess the fire and explosion risks that may be caused by dangerous substances. This should be an identification and careful examination of:

☑ dangerous substances in the workplace

☑ work activities involving those substances

☑ ways in which those substances and work activities could harm people.

Dangerous substances

The purpose is to help employers to decide what they need to do to eliminate or reduce the risks from dangerous substances. If there is no risk to safety from fires and explosions, or the risk is low, no further action is needed. If there are risks then employers must consider what else needs to be done to comply fully with the requirements of DSEAR. If an employer has five or more employees, the employer must record the significant findings of the risk assessment. This is the same risk assessment required under the Management of Health and Safety at Work Regulations. There is no requirement to carry out two risk assessments, as long as the requirements of both sets of regulations are met.

Preventing or controlling risks

Employers must put control measures in place to eliminate risks from dangerous substances, or reduce them as far as is reasonably practicable. Where it is not possible to eliminate the risk completely employers must take measures to control risks and reduce the severity of the effects of fire or explosion.

The best solution is to eliminate the risk by replacing the dangerous substance with another substance, or using a different work process. In DSEAR, this is called substitution.

In practice, this may be difficult to achieve. However, it may be possible to reduce the risk by using a less dangerous substance (for example, by replacing a low flashpoint liquid with a high flashpoint one). In other situations, it may not be possible to replace the dangerous substance. For example, it would not be practical to replace petrol with another substance at a filling station.

Control measures

Where the risk cannot be eliminated, DSEAR requires control measures to be applied in the following priority order.

1.	Reduce the quantity of dangerous substances to a minimum.
2.	Avoid or minimise releases of dangerous substances.
3.	Control releases of dangerous substances at source.
4.	Prevent the formation of a dangerous atmosphere.
5.	Collect, contain and remove any releases to a safe place (for example, through ventilation).
6.	Avoid ignition sources.
7.	Avoid adverse conditions (for example, exceeding the limits of temperature or control settings) that could lead to danger.
8.	Keep incompatible substances apart.

These control measures should be proportionate to the degree of risk as highlighted in the risk assessment and be appropriate to the nature of the activity or operation.

Mitigation

In addition to control measures, DSEAR requires employers to put mitigation measures in place. These measures should be consistent with the risk assessment and appropriate to the nature of the activity or operation, and include:

☑ reducing the number of employees exposed to the risk

☑ providing explosion-resistant plant

☑ providing explosion suppression or explosion relief equipment

☑ taking measures to control or minimise the spread of fires or explosions

☑ providing suitable PPE.

Preparing emergency plans and procedures

Arrangements must be made to deal with emergencies. These plans and procedures should cover safety drills and suitable communication and warning systems, and should be in proportion to the risks. If an emergency occurs, workers tasked with carrying out repairs or other necessary work must be provided with the appropriate equipment to allow them to carry out this work safely.

The information in the emergency plans and procedures must be made available to the emergency services to allow them to develop their own plans if necessary.

Providing information, instruction and training for employees

Employees must be provided with relevant information, instructions and training.

This includes:

☑ the dangerous substances present in the workplace and the risks they present, including access to any relevant safety data sheets and information on any other legislation that applies to the dangerous substance

☑ the findings of the risk assessment and the control measures put in place as a result, including their purpose and how to follow and use them

☑ emergency procedures.

Information, instruction and training need only be provided to other people (non-employees) where it is required to ensure their safety. It should be in proportion to the level and type of risk.

The contents of pipes and containers must be identifiable to alert employees and others to the presence of dangerous substances. If the contents have already been identified in order to meet the requirements of other legislation this does not need to be done again under DSEAR.

Places where explosive atmospheres may occur

DSEAR places additional duties on employers where potentially explosive atmospheres may occur in the workplace. In relation to construction site activities, this could include bottled gas/petrol storage areas. These duties include:

- ☑ identifying and classifying (zoning) areas where potentially explosive atmospheres may occur

- ☑ avoiding ignition sources in zoned areas, in particular those from electrical and mechanical equipment

- ☑ where necessary, identifying the entrances to zoned areas by the display of signs

- ☑ providing appropriate anti-static clothing for employees

- ☑ before they come into operation, verifying the overall explosion-protection safety of areas where explosive atmospheres may occur.

Decisions on the zoning of areas and the appropriate actions to take must be made by someone who has been trained and is competent to do so.

(The above summary of DSEAR is reproduced from the HSE website under licence from The Controller of Her Majesty's Stationery Office.)

 Further guidance on DSEAR is available on the HSE's website.

Whilst the employer must, as far as possible, ensure that any PPE supplied must be worn, the employee in turn must ensure that they wear the equipment provided and know the procedures for reporting loss or defect to the employer.

In the context of this chapter, the relevance of these regulations includes the prevention of:

- ☑ inhalation of fumes and vapour given off by dangerous substances

- ☑ skin contact with dangerous substances

- ☑ eye injuries resulting from splashes of dangerous substances.

 For further information on the Personal Protective Equipment at Work Regulations refer to Chapter B06 Personal protective equipment.

The Control of Substances Hazardous to Health Regulations

The Control of Substances Hazardous to Health (COSHH) Regulations do not apply to dangerous substances by virtue of their explosive or flammable nature. However, they may apply if these substances also possess certain other hazardous properties. This would be identified as part of the COSHH assessment carried out on the substance.

 For further information refer to Chapter B07
The Control of Substances Hazardous to Health (COSHH).

The Construction (Design and Management) Regulations

Regulation 38 specifies the measures to be taken to prevent the risk from fire, explosion or any substance likely to cause asphyxiation.

Regulation 41 specifies the measures to be taken to detect and fight fires in relation to work carried out on construction sites.

In practice, the HSE is likely to use this legislation for any enforcement action against any employer and they would expect similar standards to be implemented on construction sites.

 For further information refer to Chapter A03
Construction (Design and Management) Regulations.

10

ATEX and explosive atmospheres

ATEX is the name commonly given to the two European Directives for controlling explosive atmospheres.

1. Directive 99/92/EC (also known as ATEX 137 or the ATEX Workplace Directive) on minimum requirements for improving the health and safety protection of workers potentially at risk from explosive atmospheres.

2. Directive 94/9/EC (also known as ATEX 95 or the ATEX Equipment Directives) on the approximation of the laws of member states concerning equipment and protective systems intended for use in potentially explosive atmospheres.

In Great Britain the requirements of Directive 99/92/EC were put into effect through Regulations 7 and 11 of the Dangerous Substances and Explosive Atmospheres Regulations (DSEAR).

The aim of Directive 94/9/EC is to allow the free trade of ATEX equipment and protective systems within the EU by removing the need for separate testing and documentation for each member state.

In Great Britain, the requirements of the directive were put into effect through BIS Equipment and Protective Systems Intended for Use in Potentially Explosive Atmospheres Regulations (SI 1996/192).

The regulations apply to all equipment intended for use in explosive atmospheres, whether electrical or mechanical, and also to protective systems.

Manufacturers/suppliers (or importers, if the manufacturers are outside the EU) must ensure that their products meet essential health and safety requirements and undergo appropriate conformity procedures. This usually involves testing and certification by a third-party certification body (known as a notified body) but manufacturers/suppliers can self-certify equipment intended to be used in less hazardous explosive atmospheres. Once certified, the equipment is marked by the 'EX' symbol to identify it as such.

Certification ensures that the equipment or protective system is fit for its intended purpose and that adequate information is supplied with it to ensure that it can be used safely.

Competence and training

All the above sets of regulations stipulate the need for a degree of competence in assessing certain workplace situations.

In most cases it will be necessary for the employer to provide employees with adequate information, instruction, training and supervision to enable them to carry out any work task safely and without risk to their health.

Appendix A – Dangerous substances safety questionnaire

This questionnaire has been worded so that all the correct answers are **yes**. If you answer **no** to any question, perhaps you need to give the matter some more attention.

Dangerous substances

General	Yes	No	N/A
1. Has a risk assessment been carried out?			
2. Does it indicate that other methods of managing the situation are required (such as a method statement or permit to work system)?			
3. Have employees been made aware of the significant findings of the risk assessment?			

Storage in the open air	Yes	No	N/A
1. Is the base of the store built of concrete and sloped?			
2. Is there a low level sill surrounding the base?			
3. Is there a ramp for access to the store over the sill?			
4. Is a sump provided to catch any leakages or spillages and is the capacity large enough to contain any leakages or spillages?			
5. Is there a roof or cover over the store to protect the contents from direct sunlight?			
6. Is there an adequate separation distance between the store and adjacent buildings or boundaries?			
7. Are appropriate signs displayed (for example, 'Highly flammable' or 'Flashpoint below 32°C')?			
8. Are the correct fire extinguishers provided and positioned adjacent to the store?			

Storage in buildings	Yes	No	N/A
1. Is the storage building used exclusively for the storage of dangerous substances?			
2. If the store is part of a multi-purpose building, is there adequate fire separation from the rest of the building?			
3. Are appropriate signs displayed (for example, 'Highly flammable' or 'Flashpoint below 32°C')?			
4. Is there a sill across the doorway to prevent leakages or spillages reaching the open air and is the capacity large enough to contain any leakages or spillages?			
5. Is there adequate cross-ventilation at both high and low level?			
6. Is there the required separation distance between the store and adjacent buildings or boundaries?			

Storage at the place of work	Yes	No	N/A
1. Is there a lockable metal cabinet available to store small quantities for daily use?			
2. Is it marked with the appropriate safety signs?			

Decanting	Yes	No	N/A
1. Is decanting done only in the open air or in a fire-resisting building?			
2. Is the decanting located away from any source of heat or ignition?			
3. Are dangerous substances only decanted into small, correctly marked containers with effective closures?			
4. Are funnels correctly used to assist decanting?			
5. Are drip trays positioned to catch any leakages or spillages?			
6. Are suitable absorbents or spill kits available to contain any spillage?			
7. Are metal bins available for used absorbents to be placed in?			
8. Are these bins emptied regularly?			
9. Is contaminated absorbent safely, carefully and properly disposed of?			

10

Dangerous substances (continued)

Use of dangerous substances	Yes	No	N/A
1. Where dangerous substances are used, is adequate ventilation provided?			
2. If there is a need for mechanical extraction, is the electric motor out of the line of discharge of the fumes?			
3. Are there signs stating 'No smoking' or 'Naked lights'?			
4. Are metal waste bins with lids provided for dangerous substances that are no longer required?			
5. Are the correct warning notices provided?			
6. Are serviceable fire extinguishers of the correct type provided and positioned adjacent to the workplace?			
7. Are containers with lids provided for cleaning brushes?			

Spraying	Yes	No	N/A
1. Have the materials in use been clearly identified?			
2. Are the correct precautions in relation to use and storage being observed?			
3. Is the correct spraying equipment being used?			
4. Is the correct protective clothing and equipment, including RPE, being worn?			
5. Are the necessary precautions being taken to avoid all ignition risks?			
6. Are warning notices correctly displayed?			
7. Are barriers in use if necessary?			
8. Are serviceable fire extinguishers of the correct type provided and positioned adjacent to the workplace?			

Empty tanks and containers	Yes	No	N/A
1. Are the necessary precautions being taken against the risk of explosion in storage tanks awaiting demolition or dismantling?			
2. Has an explosive gas-free certificate been obtained prior to any hot work? (Check how long the certificate is valid for.)			
3. Is a permit to work system used when work is being carried out on disused or redundant tanks?			
4. Are authorising permits to work to deal with all the confined space issues being obtained before any entry into a tank is made?			
5. Has thought been given to the possibility of contamination around the tank from leakage or spillage?			
6. Has advice been sought from a competent person before work begins?			

Fire

Emergency procedures	Yes	No	N/A
1. Are the correct types of fire extinguisher provided and suitably positioned adjacent to the store or workplace?			
2. Have the staff been correctly trained to use them?			
3. Are there procedures to call the FRS?			
4. Is there a telephone available to call the FRS?			
5. Is the address of the site displayed on prominent notices conveniently located in offices and near telephones?			
6. Are suitable absorbents or spill kits available to contain any spillage?			

Appendix B – LPG safety questionnaire

This questionnaire has been worded so that all the correct answers are **yes**. If you answer **no** to any question you may need to give the matter some more attention.

Storage

		Yes	No	N/A
1.	Has a risk assessment been carried out?			
2.	Has specialist advice been sought prior to the location of fixed or moveable storage tanks?			
3.	Is there the required separation distance between the storage tanks and adjacent buildings or boundaries?			
4.	Is the base supporting the tanks level?			
5.	Is the base paved or concrete?			
6.	Is there a chain-link fence surrounding the tank?			
7.	Are there barriers to prevent collision?			
8.	Are the correct warning signs displayed?			
9.	Are there outward opening exits from the cylinder storage compound?			
10.	Are the exits non-self locking?			
11.	Is the area kept weed free?			
12.	Are all access areas being kept clear?			
13.	Are the correct type of fire extinguishers provided?			
14.	Are all cylinders stored upright?			
15.	Are the LPG cylinders three metres from cylinders containing any other products?			
16.	Are cylinders being handled safely?			
17.	Is the LPG being grouped in not more than 1,000 kg?			
18.	Are there 1.5 metre wide gangways?			
19.	Is lighting provided?			
20.	Is lighting at least two metres above the tallest stack?			

Transportation

		Yes	No	N/A
1.	Have drivers received adequate training, as required by law?			
2.	Are cylinders transported upright and secured?			
3.	Is the vehicle equipped with the correct type of fire extinguisher?			
4.	Is the vehicle equipped with a first-aid kit?			
5.	Does the vehicle carry suitable warning notices?			
6.	If using a closed van, are all gas cylinders offloaded at the end of each journey?			

Use of LPG cylinders and appliances

		Yes	No	N/A
1.	Are valve caps and protectors replaced after every use?			
2.	Are regulators being handled carefully?			
3.	Is the correct size of spanner being used to tighten connections?			
4.	Is all equipment (such as hoses and clips) being inspected regularly for leaks?			

Bitumen boilers and cauldrons

		Yes	No	N/A
1.	Is a competent person supervising?			
2.	Is there a fire extinguisher of the correct type readily available?			
3.	Is the boiler or cauldron standing on a non-flammable level base?			
4.	Is the cylinder in use with the bitumen boiler or cauldron a minimum of three metres away?			
5.	Are any cylinders not in use a minimum of six metres away?			
6.	Are hoses inspected regularly for damage or bitumen impregnation?			
7.	Are cylinders ice-free when the boiler or cauldron is alight?			
8.	Should manifolds coupling two or more cylinders be used?			
9.	Are bitumen boilers always attended when alight?			

Hand tools

		Yes	No	N/A
1.	Are cylinders being used in the upright position?			
2.	Are purpose-made trolleys being used for cylinders used in conjunction with cutting equipment?			
3.	Are hand tools being used at the manufacturer's recommended operating pressures?			
4.	Are connecting hoses being regularly checked for wear and damage?			
5.	Are cylinder valves being turned off on the completion of work?			
6.	Is there a fire extinguisher of the correct type readily available?			

Site huts and other buildings

		Yes	No	N/A
1.	Are LPG cylinders, supplying heaters and other appliances, fixed outside the building?			
2.	Is the gas fed into the building by the provision of fixed copper piping?			
3.	Are fixed installations only installed, modified and tested by a Gas Safe registered engineer?			
4.	Is the final, short flexible hose as short as possible?			
5.	Are all pipes in use readily accessible for inspection?			
6.	Is there plenty of ventilation at high and low levels?			
7.	Are weekly inspections being carried out on all appliances?			
8.	Is there a fire extinguisher of the correct type readily available?			

Fire precautions

		Yes	No	N/A
1.	Are written procedures provided and displayed prominently?			
2.	Is there a telephone available to summon the FRS?			
3.	Are the correct types of fire extinguishers provided?			
4.	Are your staff trained in the use of fire extinguishers?			
5.	Are your staff and visitors aware of the site emergency evacuation alarm and procedure?			
6.	Are personnel aware of pressure relief valves?			
7.	Are product data sheets available?			

10

Appendix C – Retrieval of orphaned compressed gas cylinders

The cylinder retrieval arrangements in place for the major national companies are listed below.

Parent company	Collection company	Contact numbers
Calor Gas	Brooksight Ltd	Tel: 0207 731 1221 Fax: 0207 731 4155
BP	Synergy Asset Services Ltd	Tel: 01304 827 277 Fax: 01304 827 287
Flogas	In-house collection by own staff	Tel: 01132 497 140
BOC	In-house collection by own staff	Tel: 0800 111 333

1. If a cylinder is no longer needed, it should be returned to the local dealer of the company owning the cylinder.

2. Where the original owner of a compressed gas cylinder cannot be identified, contact Brooksight Ltd.

3. Until such time as they are collected, orphaned cylinders should be stored in a safe and secure manner.

4. If it is not known which company owns an LPG cylinder, the table of LPG cylinder fillers should be viewed in the 'who knows who' guidance table (available online).

5. In extreme circumstances, where all attempts to trace the owner of a cylinder have failed, the Local Authority waste disposal sites may offer a disposal service.

10

10

Index

Index

abseiling *see* rope access
access below overhead services 115, 116
access by ropes 4, 7, 12, 21, 84–85, 95
access equipment 4, 23–26, 35–47
    see also ladders; lightweight staging; mobile access
    platforms; scaffolding; staircases/stairways; stepladders;
    trestles; working platforms
access for frame erection 91, 92, 93, 94, 95–96
Access Industry Forum 3
access to confined spaces 122, 129
access to cradles 86
access to excavations 103, 104
access to LPG storage 140, 141
access to mobile towers 44
access to roofs 18, 19, 20, 21–22, 23–26, 30–31, 34
access to safety nets 75
access to work at height 2, 4, 9, 10
    see also danger areas
access to/under scaffolds 23, 24, 42, 52, 55, 61–63, 64–65, 68,
69, 70
advanced guard-rail system 43
airbags *see* soft-landing systems
anchorages 11, 12, 20, 21, 59, 74, 75, 79, 80, 91, 95
arrester devices 20, 82
asbestos 22, 32, 34, 65, 137
ATEX 152
atmospheric monitoring 96, 104, 124–126, 127, 146

backfilling 113
barriers for dangerous substances 137, 140
barriers for excavations 103
barriers for overhead services 115–116, 117
barriers for water safety 31
barriers for work at height 7, 10, 11, 20, 21, 42, 45
base plates 54, 68
bats 32
battering of excavations 100–101
beam straddling 95–96
Beaufort scale 19
birds 18, 32
bitumen boilers and cauldrons 19, 20, 145
boarded lifts 55
boatswain's chairs 85–86
box ties 58
bracing 52, 54, 55–56, 65, 68, 69
brakes 9, 10, 41, 44, 45
breathing apparatus *see* respiratory protective equipment
brick guards 8, 9, 24, 61
buried services 43, 102, 105, 108–115
burns 20, 140

cable locators 110–111
*Carriage of Dangerous Goods and Use of Transportable
Pressure Equipment Regulations* 142–144
chest harnesses 80
chimney access 26
clearances for bitumen boilers and cauldrons 145
clearances for dangerous substances storage 135, 136,
141, 142
clearances for fall-arrest and suspension equipment 11, 31, 74,
75, 76, 81
clearances for LPG equipment 141, 142, 145
clearances for overhead services 115, 116, 141
clients' duties 34
cold burns 140
colour-coding of buried services 109
colour-coding of fire extinguishers 147
colour-coding of gas cylinders 138
communications 30, 31, 92, 93, 104, 106, 123, 126, 128
competence 5, 33, 34, 43, 50–51, 52, 76, 126, 152
    see also training
competency cards 11, 51, 67, 76
confined spaces 80, 96, 98, 104, 119–132, 137, 139, 140, 146

Confined Spaces Regulations 120, 130, 137, 146
Conservation (Natural Habitats) Regulations 32
Construction (Design and Management) Regulations 23, 33–34,
130, 134, 147, 151
containers of dangerous substances 135, 137–138
    see also cylinders; tanks
contractors 33, 92, 93, 130
    see also roofing contractors; scaffolding contractors
Control of Asbestos at Work Regulations 32, 65
Control of Substances Hazardous to Health Regulations 20,
122, 124, 131, 151
cradles 4, 86–87
cranes 26, 91, 92, 93, 94, 95
    see also excavators as cranes
crash decks 31
curved roofs 21
cylinders 104, 138, 140, 141–146, 148, 157

damage to buried services 114–115
damaged LPG cylinders 141
danger areas 8, 9, 30–31, 60, 86
    see also exclusion zones
dangerous substances 133–157
    see also asbestos; LPG
Dangerous Substances and Explosive Atmospheres Regulations
131, 149–151, 152
dead weight anchor devices 83–84
debris nets 9, 20, 56, 74
decking 69, 95
    see also crash decks; scaffold boards
demolition 25, 31, 33, 137
design for frame erection 91
design of scaffolding 52, 56, 57, 64, 65, 69
designers 17, 22, 33–34, 130
digging 111–113
    see also excavations
drilling 113
dust *see* explosive atmospheres

edge protection 10, 20, 21, 22, 24, 27, 31, 74, 95
    see also brick guards; guard-rails; toe-boards
electrical safety 116, 124, 135, 136, 137, 139, 140
    see also buried services; overhead services
emergency procedures 5, 18, 19, 25, 108, 114, 130, 144,
148, 150
    see also fire safety; first aid; rescue equipment and
    procedures
emergency works 113
employees' duties 5, 33, 131, 151
enclosed spaces *see* confined spaces
energy absorbers *see* shock absorbers
enforcement of fire safety law 134, 147–149
Equality Act 18
excavations 97–106, 112, 130, 142
    see also backfilling; digging
excavators as cranes 106
exclusion zones 9, 20, 45, 60, 115
    see also danger areas
explosive atmospheres 104, 122, 125, 127, 131, 135, 137, 139,
140, 144, 148, 149–151, 152
explosive materials *see* dangerous substances
exposure limits for LPG 139
extension ladders 12, 37, 39

façade bracing 54, 56, 68, 69
fall-arrest and suspension equipment 4, 7, 11–12, 19, 20, 28, 31,
33, 34, 73–88, 91, 93, 95
fall heights 75, 76, 80
fall prevention 4, 7–8, 9, 11, 21–23, 28, 47, 52–53, 60, 66, 91,
92, 103
    see also edge protection; guard-rails
falling object protection 9, 20, 28, 60, 61, 64, 74, 75, 85, 86, 93
    see also danger areas

falls 2, 91
    see also work at height
FASET 76–77
Fire and Rescue Service 19, 124, 127, 147–148
fire extinguishers 121, 127, 143, 144, 145, 146–147, 148
fire safety 19, 20, 121, 127, 130, 135, 136, 137, 139, 140, 144, 145, 146–149
first aid 78, 84, 127, 128, 140
fitness 17–18, 126
flammable atmospheres 96, 121, 122, 124, 125, 126, 127, 139, 140
flammable materials see dangerous substances
flat roofs 20, 83–84
floors 31
forklift trucks 25
foundations 54, 68, 91
    see also ground conditions
fragile surfaces 4, 9, 20, 21, 22–23, 33, 37
frame erection 89–96
freestanding access scaffolds 57
fumes see toxic atmospheres

gangways and runs 4, 9, 23, 29, 61, 95
gas cylinders 104, 138, 140, 141–146, 148, 157
gas-powered tools 145–146
gas services see buried services
gases see atmospheric monitoring; flammable atmospheres; LPG; oxygen; toxic atmospheres
goods hoists 64
ground conditions 43, 44, 52, 67, 92, 94, 95
    see also foundations
guard-rails for mobile towers 43, 44
guard-rails for scaffolding 41, 42, 53, 60, 61, 63
guard-rails for work at height 7, 8, 9, 10, 16, 20, 21, 22, 23, 24, 31, 47, 95
guarding excavations 103

hanging platforms 29
hazardous waste 32, 136
health see medical fitness
health and safety files 23, 111
Health and Safety (Safety Signs and Signals) Regulations 9, 11, 23, 65, 94, 135, 136, 140
hoists 62, 64
hop ups 46, 77
hot work 20, 78, 121, 127, 137
hydraulic waling frames 102

incomplete mobile towers 45
incomplete scaffolding 63, 69
inertia reel block sysems see arrester devices
information provision 23, 33, 34, 111, 116, 123, 131, 150–151
inspection of cradles 86
inspection of excavations 102, 106
inspection of fall protection equipment 53, 66, 80, 82–83, 85
inspection of frame erection 95
inspection of ladders 36, 37, 38
inspection of lifting equipment 10, 25, 26
inspection of LPG equipment 144, 146
inspection of mobile towers 44, 45
inspection of places of work at height 10
inspection of podium steps 41
inspection of safety nets 75, 76, 77, 78
inspection of scaffolding 50, 66–67, 71
inspection of work equipment 5, 9–10, 13
inspection of working platforms 10, 66
isolation of confined spaces 124
isolation of electrical services 116, 124, 129

joists 31

ladder gates 23, 63
ladder replacement stairs 30

ladder traps 62, 63
ladders 4, 7, 8–9, 10, 12–13, 23–24, 36–40, 44, 61, 62–63, 77, 91, 103
    see also roof ladders; stepladders
landing mats see soft-landing systems
landing places/platforms 24, 37, 63
    see also rest platforms
lanyards see safety belts, harnesses and lanyards
ledger bracing 55, 65, 68, 69
ledgers 36, 54, 67, 68
life jackets 31
Lifting Operations and Lifting Equipment Regulations 10, 25, 26, 81, 82, 84, 85, 86, 106, 128, 131
lifting operations/equipment 10, 25, 26, 86, 93, 94, 104, 128, 131
    see also cranes; excavators as cranes; hoists; mobile elevating work platforms
lighting 31, 65, 93, 103, 104, 116, 135, 136, 142
lightweight staging 22, 26, 37, 41–42, 95
lip ties 59
liquefied petroleum gas see LPG
loading of LPG transport 143
loading of mobile towers 43, 45
loading of roofs 30, 54
loading of scaffolding 52, 55, 56, 64, 69
locating buried services 109–111
lone working 32
longitudinal bracing see façade bracing
LPG 104, 122, 138–146, 148, 149, 155–156

maintenance 33, 34, 43, 78, 80, 102, 110
man-riding baskets 26, 95
Management of Health and Safety at Work Regulations 124, 130, 134, 146, 147, 150
manual handling assessments 141
masonry anchors 59
mast climbing work platforms 26
materials handling 18, 20, 30, 44
    see also manual handling assessments
medical fitness 17–18, 126
method statements 11, 32, 56, 92–93, 94, 103
mini mobile towers 41
mobile access platforms 4, 25–26, 95
    see also mobile elevating work platforms
mobile elevating work platforms 2, 10, 25, 26, 74, 77, 90, 91, 95
mobile phones 135, 136
mobile towers 2, 10, 36, 42–46, 66
    see also mini mobile towers

nail guns 146
New Roads and Street Works Act 113
non-boarded lifts 55
notifiable projects 23, 34

off-loading of steelwork 94
openings 31, 93
    see also excavations
orphaned gas cylinders 138, 141, 157
overhead services 38, 44, 78, 86, 92, 108, 115–118, 141
oxygen 96, 104, 121, 125, 126, 140, 143

passenger hoists 62
pavement lifts 55, 64–65
permits for confined spaces 104, 123, 124, 129, 132, 137
permits for digging 111, 112
permits for high voltage equipment work 118
permits for ladders near overhead lines 38
permits for scaffolding 64, 65
permits for spraying of dangerous substances 137
personal fall protection systems 4, 7, 11–12, 52, 60
    see also safety belts, harnesses and lanyards
personal protective equipment 33, 112, 124, 131, 137, 140, 150, 151
    see also fall-arrest and suspension equipment

Personal Protective Equipment at Work Regulations 7, 131
pigeons 18, 32
piling 113
pipe locators 110–111
pipelines 108, 113
pipework 124, 146
pitched roofs 21
plan bracing 56, 68
plant and equipment 7–9, 104, 115, 116
    see also access equipment; lifting operations/equipment;
    work equipment
plate lining systems 102
platform decking 69
    see also scaffold boards
platform shoes 29
platform stepladders 37
podium steps 9, 41
pole belts 80
pole ladders 37
pop-ups 41
profiled roofs 21–22
protective clothing *see* personal protective equipment
Provision and Use of Work Equipment Regulations 9, 43,
106, 131
purging 124
purlin trolleys 22
push around verticals 41
putlogs 55, 60

rakers 56–57
'reasonably practicable' (definition) 4
records of cradles 86
records of excavation inspections 106
records of LPG transport training 143
records of risk assessments 150
records of safety belts, harnesses and lanyards 53, 83
records of safety net inspections 77
records of work equipment inspections 10, 13, 26, 36, 38,
45, 66
refillable LPG cylinders 141–142
Regulatory Reform (Fire Safety) Order 134, 138, 147
reports of inspections 66–67, 106
rescue equipment and procedures for beam straddling 95
rescue equipment and procedures for confined spaces 80, 123,
124, 127–128, 129, 130, 131, 137
rescue equipment and procedures for fall arrest equipment 75,
78, 80, 84, 85, 95
rescue equipment and procedures for scaffolding 53
rescue equipment and procedures for work at height 5, 7, 11,
12, 18, 19, 25, 32, 33
respiratory protective equipment 123, 124, 125, 126, 127,
128–129, 131, 137
rest platforms 13, 24, 62
    see also landing places/platforms
restraint lanyards 80
reveal ties 58
ring bolts 59
risk assessments for access equipment 36, 40, 42, 47
risk assessments for boatswain's chairs 85, 86
risk assessments for confined spaces 122, 123, 124, 126, 127,
129, 130, 146
risk assessments for cradles 86
risk assessments for dangerous substances 136, 137, 146,
149–150
risk assessments for excavators as cranes 106
risk assessments for frame erection 95
risk assessments for manual handling 141
risk assessments for mobile towers 43
risk assessments for personal protective equipment 131
risk assessments for roof work 16, 20, 31
risk assessments for rope access 84
risk assessments for safety nets 77, 78
risk assessments for scaffolding 53

risk assessments for work at height 4, 5–6, 8, 10, 11, 12, 13
Road Traffic Acts 25
roads 64–65, 93, 103, 113, 115
    see also pavement lifts; traffic routes
roof ladders 21, 24, 37, 39–40
roof lights 22, 33
roof trusses 31
roof work 15–34, 54, 75, 82, 145
    see also fragile surfaces
roofing contractors 17–18, 23
rope access 4, 7, 12, 21, 84–85, 95
    see also boatswain's chairs
rough terrain telescopic forklift trucks 25

safe places of work 9, 10, 70, 95, 130
safety belts, harnesses and lanyards 11, 12, 20, 26, 53, 74,
79–84, 85, 86, 94, 95, 128, 131
safety devices 21, 26, 69, 84, 85
    see also brakes
safety marshals 31
safety net fans 28
safety nets 7, 11, 20, 21, 22, 31, 74, 75–78, 88
    see also debris nets
safety zones *see* exclusion zones
scaffold boards 8, 42, 54, 60, 61, 65, 69
scaffold ties 44, 56–59, 68, 69
scaffolding 4, 8, 11, 26, 49–71, 74, 95, 115
    see also mobile towers; trestle scaffolds; work at height
scaffolding contractors 52–53, 65, 66
scaffolding handover 59, 67
scaffolding standards 54, 67
self-employed persons 4, 12, 130, 149
self-rescue sets 128
separation *see* clearances
service gaps 60
sheeting 18, 44, 52, 54, 56, 65, 69
shields for trench support 102
shock absorbers 12, 74, 81, 95
short duration work 9, 12, 13, 21, 36, 40, 85, 95
signals *see* communications
signs and notices for confined spaces 124, 129
signs and notices for dangerous substances 135, 136, 137, 140,
142, 143, 144, 151
signs and notices for excavations 103
signs and notices for fragile surfaces 9, 23
signs and notices for incomplete mobile towers 45
signs and notices for lifting equipment 25, 26
signs and notices for openings 31
signs and notices for overhead services 116
signs and notices for scaffolding 11, 53, 60, 65
signs and notices for work at height 9, 23, 31
site huts and LPG use 146
slater's heels 21
small load exemptions 143
soft-landing systems 7, 11, 20, 31, 79, 94, 95
    see also safety net fans; safety nets
sole boards 54, 68
solvents 20, 122, 124
spraying of dangerous substances 137
stability 44, 57, 68, 70, 91, 93, 94, 96, 100–102
stacking of materials 30, 94
stair towers 23
staircases/stairways 2, 4, 29–30, 62, 95
standards *see* scaffolding standards
standing ladders 37
steel banding ties 59
steelwork *see* frame erection
steep roofs 21, 24
stepladders 7, 9, 12–13, 36, 37, 40, 44
    see also podium steps
stepping laths 61
stepping of excavations 100–101
storage and work at height 9, 18, 20

storage near overhead services 116
storage of dangerous substances 134–136, 148
storage of ladders 40
storage of LPG 140–142, 144
storage of safety belts, harnesses and lanyards 82
storage of safety nets 78
storage of steelwork 92, 94
'suitable' (definition) 4
support for excavations 100–102, 112, 113
suspension trauma 84
sway bracing see façade bracing
system scaffolds 36, 50, 67–70

tanks 137–138, 140–141
testing for gases see atmospheric monitoring
testing of cradles 86
testing of dead weight anchor devices 83–84
testing of forklift trucks 25
testing of frame erection 95
testing of lifting equipment 128
testing of LPG equipment 139, 144, 146
testing of respiratory protective equipment 126, 131
testing of safety harnesses 80, 128
testing of safety nets 75, 77
testing of scaffolding anchors 59
thorough examinations 26, 80, 85, 86, 128, 131
through-the-trap (3T) method 43
through ties 57–58
ties see scaffold ties; tying-in
toe-boards for scaffolding 41, 42, 44, 60, 61, 63
toe-boards for work at height 7, 8, 9, 10, 16, 20, 21, 24, 31, 47
tools see gas-powered tools; work equipment
tower scaffolds 66, 77
     see also mobile towers
toxic atmospheres 96, 104, 122, 124, 125, 126
traffic routes 93, 94, 96, 104
     see also roads
training for asbestos work 32, 65
training for boatswain's chairs 85
training for confined spaces 123, 137
training for dangerous substances 143, 144, 150–151, 152
training for fall-arrest and suspension equipment 11, 12, 20, 74, 76, 78, 79
training for fire-fighting 148–149
training for ladder use 9
training for LPG 143, 148, 149
training for mobile towers 43, 46
training for personal protective equipment 33, 131
training for podium steps 41
training for rescue equipment and procedures 12, 32, 123
training for roof work 17, 32
training for scaffolding 50, 51, 53, 59, 67
training for work at height 5
transoms 36, 55, 59, 60, 68
transport of gas cylinders 142–144
trench boxes 102
trench supports 101–102
trenches see backfilling; digging; excavations
trenchless techniques 100
trestle scaffolds 41–42
trestles 4, 7, 9, 37
tunnelling 123
twin tailed lanyards 80
tying-in 44, 52, 68, 69
     see also scaffold ties; stability

underground services see buried services
universal stairs 30
unloading of steelwork 94

vehicles 78, 92, 93, 94, 96, 102, 104, 142–144
ventilation 96, 104, 123, 124, 130, 135, 136, 137, 140, 143, 146

walkways 4, 9, 23, 29, 61, 95
waste management 20, 32, 135, 136, 137, 142, 145
     see also orphaned gas cylinders
water safety 31–32, 130
weather 18–19, 31, 96, 122, 141
     see also wind
Wildlife and Countryside Act 32
wind 18–19, 20, 43, 45, 56, 60, 69, 96
wire banding ties 59
work at height 1–13, 15–34, 91
     see also excavations; falls; ladders; lightweight staging;
     mobile towers; scaffolding
Work at Height Regulations 1–13
Work at Height Regulations and access equipment 36, 43, 44, 47
Work at Height Regulations and confined spaces 131
Work at Height Regulations and frame erection 95
Work at Height Regulations and roof work 22, 23, 25, 30, 33
Work at Height Regulations and rope access 84, 85, 86
Work at Height Regulations and scaffolding 50, 52, 55, 61, 66
work equipment 7–9, 11–13, 66, 126–127
     see also personal protective equipment; Provision and Use
     of Work Equipment Regulations
work over water see water safety
work positioning systems 4, 7, 12, 21, 80
work restraint systems 4, 7, 12, 74
working platforms 4, 7, 10–11
     see also hanging platforms; lightweight staging; mobile
     access platforms; mobile elevating work platforms; platform
     shoes; podium steps; scaffold boards
working platforms for frame erection 9, 91
working platforms for roof work 16, 21, 22, 24, 25–26, 29, 31, 40
working platforms for scaffolding 11, 52, 53, 60–61, 62, 63, 64, 66, 68, 69, 70, 71
workplace exposure limits for LPG 139

Contents

Introduction iii

How to use GE 700 ix

01 Sustainable construction and the environment 1

02 Resource efficiency 13

03 Waste management 19

04 Energy management 49

05 Water management 57

06 Statutory nuisance 71

07 Ecology 79

08 Contaminated land 97

09 Archaeology and heritage 107

10 Site environment management systems 113

Index 131

E

Contents

i

E

Introduction

Construction site safety covers all aspects of current
health, safety and environment issues in the building and
construction industry. It is designed to help managers,
supervisors and small businesses understand how they
should comply with, and put into practice, their legal,
moral and social responsibilities.

Construction site safety (GE 700)   iv
About the construction industry   iv
Further supporting information from
CITB-ConstructionSkills   vi
Acknowledgements   vii

Construction site safety (GE 700)

Construction site safety is a leading publication within the construction industry, based on current construction health, safety and environment legislation, guidance and best practice. It will assist in the crucial areas of:

- ☑ accident prevention

- ☑ the avoidance of occupational ill health

- ☑ environmental good practice.

The content has been written with the site manager in mind, with a balance between outlining the requirements of relevant legislation and providing practical guidance on how to comply.

It is divided into the standard structure, which is used across all core CITB-ConstructionSkills publications:

Section A	**Legal and management**
Section B	**Health and welfare**
Section C	General safety
Section D	**High risk activities**
Section E	**Environment**
Section F	**Specialist activities**

Each section within *Construction site safety* is contained within a separate book.

There is also a new additional supporting book:

Section G	**Checklists and forms**

Section G is a collection of information (such as forms and checklists) that can be used on a day-to-day basis when running a site.

The content of *Construction site safety*, which is developed with construction industry experts, is revised annually to take into account the latest changes in legislation and new or updated health, safety and environment industry guidance and best practice.

There is a companion website that will keep users informed of legislation changes, content updates and links to further guidance.

Construction site safety is also available to purchase online or on CD-ROM.

Construction site safety is the official supporting publication for the CITB-ConstructionSkills Site Management Safety Training Scheme (SMSTS), a five-day course for construction site managers.

About the construction industry

Approximately 2.1 million people are employed in the UK construction industry. It includes housing, utilities, repair and maintenance, refurbishment, shop fitting, demolition, roofing, mechanical and electrical, plumbing and highways maintenance.

It is made up of 175,000 construction firms and 90% of companies employ less than 10 workers.

Construction workers (just like you) will die due to work-related ill health. Work-related respiratory disease covers a range of illnesses that are caused or made worse by breathing in hazardous substances (such as construction dust) that damage the lungs.

4,000 people die each year from asbestos-related lung diseases.

500 people (and more each year) are dying from silica-related lung diseases (dust from cutting blocks, kerbs, and so on). Many more suffer from occupational asthma or are forced to leave the industry due to work-related ill health.

Each year there are an estimated 36,000 new cases of work-related ill health with rates of musculoskeletal disorder significantly higher than average.

On average 50 workers are killed each year due to accidents. The biggest killer (around half) is due to falls from height.

Each year approximately 2,500 are seriously injured (broken bones, fractured skull, amputations) and 5,700 have reportable injuries.

The most common cause of injuries is due to manual handling and slips, trips and falls. 60% of all work at height injuries are due to falls from below head height.

Why so many accidents?

Many reports of present day construction accidents and ill health make depressing reading because simple actions were not taken to prevent them. In many cases, those planning the jobs totally failed to consider the health or safety of the people carrying out the work (and possibly others who were affected) and to actively manage the situation.

Common examples of such events include:

☑ the increasing number of workers who suffer from cancers and life changing illnesses from breathing and skin complaints. Some of these force the sufferer to give up work, because exposure to dangerous substances such as dust, are not even considered, let alone prevented or controlled

☑ the deaths and serious injuries that occur because people fall from height. Often basic actions (like using temporary work platforms on fragile roofs, installing edge protection or using a safety harness and lanyard clipped to a strong-point) were simply not taken

☑ workers being buried in collapsed excavations because the sides were unstable or not supported

☑ workers being killed or injured by construction plant because pedestrians were not kept out of the plant operating area.

Achieving a reasonable standard of on-site health and safety need not be difficult. Where the work to be carried out is relatively uncomplicated and familiar, the precautions that need to be taken are in many cases simple and common sense or may require just a little investigation or reading. The crucial decision for anyone with responsibility for on-site health and safety is to know when they have reached the limits of their knowledge and capabilities and therefore need the assistance of someone with specialist knowledge.

Caution should also be exercised when a job is not going to plan and there is the temptation to resort to improvised methods of working. If the person in control is not at ease with the way that things are going they should stop the job, step back and think things through carefully before deciding upon a course of action.

Health and Safety Executive (HSE) research has shown that workers are most vulnerable during their first few days on site.

Setting out

Construction is an exciting industry. It is constantly changing as projects move on and jobs get done. As a result of this a building site is one of the most dangerous environments to work in.

But many accidents that occur on sites can be avoided if everyone on site works together. So a free film *Setting out* explains what the site must do and what you must do to stay healthy and safe at work.

For further information or to view *Setting out* refer to the CITB-ConstructionSkills website.

This film is essential viewing for everyone involved in construction, and should be watched before sitting the CITB-ConstructionSkills' Health, safety and environment test. The content of the film is captured in summary here, and these principles form the basis for the behavioural case study questions, which are a new element of the test from Spring 2012.

Part 1: What you should expect from the construction industry

Your site and your employer should be doing all they can to keep you and their workforce safe.

Before any work begins the site management team will have been planning and preparing the site for your arrival. It is their job to ensure that you can do your job safely and efficiently.

Five things **the site** you are working on **must do**:

☑ know when you are on site (signing in and out)

☑ give you a site induction

☑ give you site-specific information

☑ encourage communication

☑ keep you up-to-date and informed.

Part 2: What the industry expects of you

Once the work begins, it is up to every individual to take responsibility for carrying out the plan safely. This means you should follow the rules and guidelines as well as being alert to the continuing changes on site.

Five things you **must do:**

☑ respect and follow the site rules

☑ safely prepare each task

☑ do each task responsibly

☑ know when to stop (if you think anything is unsafe)

☑ keep learning.

Every day the work we do improves the world around us. It is time for us to work together to build an industry that puts its people first. By working together we can build a better industry that respects those who work in it.

Introduction

Working Well Together

The Working Well Together (WWT) campaign is an industry-led initiative that helps support micro and small businesses improve their health and safety performance. The campaign undertakes a variety of activities, including health and safety awareness days, designer awareness days, breakfast and evening events, roadshows and regional WWT groups.

 To find out how the WWT campaign can help you and your company refer to its website.

Further supporting information from CITB-ConstructionSkills

CITB-ConstructionSkills has a wide range of products, publications and courses that could help to improve your health, safety and environment knowledge.

 To discover more about CITB-ConstructionSkills and the services, publications and courses offered visit the CITB-ConstructionSkills website.

Health, safety and environment publications

Site managers	GE 700 *Construction site safety* (printed, CD and online)
	RACD *Risk assessment and method statement manager*
	SA 03 CD *Health, safety and environmental auditing system*
	DVDs Range of topics including scaffold inspection, worker engagement and sustainability
Supervisors	GE 706 *Site supervision simplified* (printed, CD, online)
	GT 700 *Toolbox talks* (printed, CD, online)
	GT 701 *Safety critical communication toolbox talks* (printed)
Operatives	GE 707 *Safe start*
Health safety and environment test	GT 100 *Health, safety and environment test for operatives and specialists* (printed, DVD, online)
	GT 200 *Health, safety and environment test for managers and professionals* (printed, DVD, online)

Site Safety Plus courses

Directors	Directors role for health and safety course – one day
Site management	Site Management Safety Training Scheme (SMSTS) – five days
Plant managers	Plant Management Safety Training Scheme (SMSTS) – five days
Supervisors	Site Supervisors' Safety Training Scheme (SSSTS) – two days
Operatives	Health safety and environment awareness – one day
Environment	Site Environmental Awareness Training Scheme (SEATS) – one day
Behavioural safety	Achieving Behavioural Change (ABC) – one day
Shopfitting	Site safety for shopfitters and interior contractors – three days

National Construction College

The National Construction College is focused on creating a highly skilled, safe and professional UK construction workforce. To achieve this, it has more first-class instructors in more locations than any other construction training provider in Europe and offers free professional advice on finding the right training for individuals and companies.

Acknowledgements

CITB-ConstructionSkills wishes to acknowledge the assistance offered by the following organisations in the preparation of this edition of GE 700:

- ☑ Access Industry Forum
- ☑ Arco
- ☑ Balfour Beatty
- ☑ Britannia Safety and Training
- ☑ Carillion
- ☑ Civil Engineering Contractors Association
- ☑ Combisafe
- ☑ Construction Plant Association
- ☑ Drilling and Sawing Association
- ☑ eBrit Services Ltd
- ☑ Federation of Master Builders
- ☑ Health and Safety Executive
- ☑ Henry Boot
- ☑ Highways Term Maintenance Association
- ☑ Home Builders Federation
- ☑ J Breheny Contractors Ltd

- ☑ Lead Paint Safety Association
- ☑ MJ Fuller and Associates
- ☑ Makers Construction Ltd
- ☑ May Gurney
- ☑ Montpellier International Consulting
- ☑ National Access and Scaffolding Confederation
- ☑ National Association of Shopfitters
- ☑ National Construction College
- ☑ National Federation of Demolition Contractors
- ☑ Persimmon Homes
- ☑ Prospect – The Union for Professionals
- ☑ Scafftag
- ☑ Temporary Works Forum
- ☑ Union of Construction, Allied Trades and Technicians (UCATT)
- ☑ Unite
- ☑ Willmott Dixon

And a special thank you to:

- ☑ Costain
- ☑ Environment Agency
- ☑ Environmental and Waste Consulting
- ☑ Skanska
- ☑ Wates

How to use
GE 700

The following information sets out how to use *Construction site safety*. Each section is contained within a separate book, which has been designed to provide simple navigation for the end user. It also explains the companion website, which is a significant addition for keeping users informed of legislation changes, content updates and links to further guidance.

Construction site safety structure   x

How to navigate   x

Use of icons   x

Companion website   xi

Construction site safety structure

Construction site safety is divided into the standard structure that is used across all core CITB-ConstructionSkills publications:

Section A	**Legal and management**
Section B	**Health and welfare**
Section C	General safety
Section D	**High risk activities**
Section E	**Environment**
Section F	**Specialist activities**

Within *Construction site safety* each section is contained within a separate book.

There is also a new additional supporting book:

Section G	**Checklists and forms**

This new section is a collection of information that can be used on a day-to-day basis when running a site. The forms, checklists and guidance within Section G follow the same structure as in Sections A to F.

How to navigate

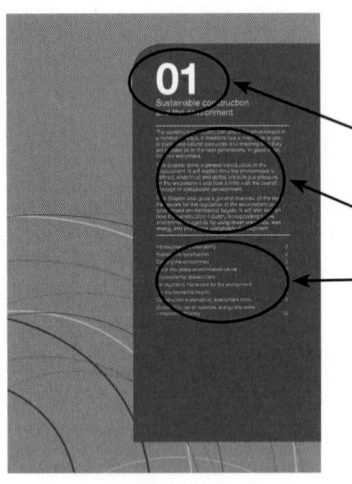

Each section contains a main contents page at the start of the section, followed by the introduction, a detailed chapter contents list at the start of each chapter and an index at the back (but there is no index within Section G).

Chapters have been numbered according to the section you are in. Therefore, chapter one of Section A is numbered 01, chapter two of Section B is numbered 02 and so on. However, references to chapters within other sections will be referred to as A01, B02, and so on.

At the start of each chapter there is a short overview of what the chapter is about.

This is followed by the chapter contents list.

Use of icons

A set of icons emphasises key points within the text and also directs readers to further information. The icons are explained below:

www.	Website/further info	!	Important	"	Quote
e.g.	Example	👍	Best practice	Aa	Definition
?	Question	👎	Poor practice	☑	Checklist
💡	Ideas	✋	Caution	▶	Video
Notes	Notes	👥	Consultation		
★	Favourite	🔍	Guidance/case study		

Companion website

A companion website has been created to support *Construction site safety* and it contains up-to-date information on:

- ☑ the current edition of each section (book)
- ☑ news (such as legislation changes, industry guidance and best practice)
- ☑ any minor amendments or updates to the current editions
- ☑ web links/phone numbers/addresses
- ☑ details of CITB-ConstructionSkills' publications and courses.

 This icon indicates that further information (such as useful websites and links) can be found on the companion website at www.citb-constructionskills.co.uk/GE700companion

Rather than printing individual weblinks in each section, which can become out of date, the relevant website will be stated alongside the icon (for example, for more information refer to the CITB-ConstructionSkills website). The actual weblink can then be found on the companion website, referenced to the relevant section and chapter.

The companion website will be regularly updated, to ensure that relevant information (such as weblinks) are current.

 Save the companion website address to your favourites, so it is always available when you need it.

How to use GE 700

01

Sustainable construction and the environment

The construction industry can affect the environment in a number of ways. It therefore has a major role to play in protecting natural resources and ensuring that they are passed on to the next generations, in good order, for their enjoyment.

This chapter gives a general introduction to the environment. It will explain how the environment is defined, what local and global impacts put pressure on the environment and how it links with the overall concept of sustainable development.

This chapter also gives a general overview of the legal framework for the regulation of the environment and government environmental targets. It will also explain how the construction industry is responding to the environmental agenda by using fewer resources, less energy and promoting sustainable development.

Introduction to sustainability   2

Sustainable construction   2

Defining the environment   3

Local and global environmental issues   3

Environmental stakeholders   5

UK regulatory framework for the environment   5

UK environmental targets   8

Construction sustainability assessment tools   9

Sustainable use of materials, energy and water
– resource efficiency   12

1.1 Introduction to sustainability

The rapid growth in population, together with ever-increasing demand for resources from economic development, are placing huge pressures on our planet. This has, in turn, led to an increase in all types of pollution and an acceleration of environmental damage. If everyone in the world lived as we do in Europe, we would need three planets to support us, because we consume resources at a much faster rate than the planet can replenish them. People, consumption and production, and the environment, are all linked and have a major impact on each other. It is important that consideration is given to how construction's contribution to future development can be achieved without causing any further damage. Sustainable living is about respecting the earths' environmental limits.

The terms *sustainability* and *sustainable development* were first established in the paper *Our common future*, released by the Brundtland Commission in 1987 for the World Commission on Environment and Development.

Sustainable development is the kind of development that meets the needs of the present generation without compromising the ability of future generations to meet their own needs.

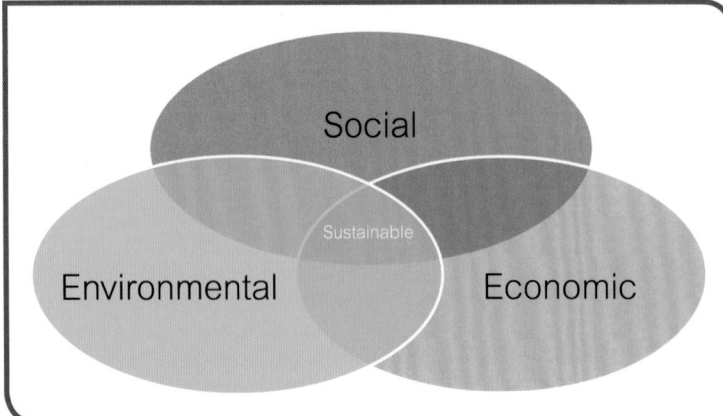

The key goal is to integrate the three key pillars of sustainability that contribute to the achievement of sustainable development.

1. **Environment** – protection and enhancement of natural resources.

2. **Society** – the wellbeing of people.

3. **Economy** – sustainable consumption and production.

Most people now recognise that economic activity cannot take place without considering the environmental impacts. For example, the extraction of aggregates for new development has a significant effect on the local environment, which must be taken into account.

The strategy of the UK Government for achieving sustainable development was first set out in its paper called *Securing the future – delivering UK sustainable development strategy*, which has four key priorities.

1. **Sustainable consumption and production** (for example, through better product design, resource efficiency, waste reduction and sustainable procurement).

2. **Climate change and energy** (for example, implementing measures to reduce carbon dioxide emissions).

3. **Natural resource protection** (for example, reducing the rate of biodiversity loss).

4. **Sustainable communities** (for example, placing sustainable development at the heart of the planning system and enabling local communities to have a say in how they are run).

Progress in achieving sustainable development is measured against a set of indicators (currently 68), which were outlined in *Securing the future strategy* where the impacts of production and consumption can have significant environmental impacts. These indicators are currently under consultation.

Environmental indicators include greenhouse gas emissions, sulphur dioxide and nitrogen oxide emissions, rivers of poor or bad quality, commercial and industrial waste, the way in which electricity is produced and fossil fuel use.

 For further information refer to the DEFRA website.

1.2 Sustainable construction

The construction industry has an important role to play in achieving these sustainable development priorities for the following reasons:

☑ the output of the construction industry is enormous; it is worth around £100 billion per year

☑ the construction industry accounts for 8% of GDP and employs three million people

☑ buildings are responsible for almost half of UK carbon emissions, half of water consumption, about one third of landfill waste and 25% of all raw materials used in the UK economy.

The construction industry has a significant opportunity to influence these issues and change the way we build. The Government's response to achieving sustainable development in construction is through the strategy for sustainable construction launched in June 2008. This joint industry and government strategy is based on a shared recognition of the need to deliver a radical change in the construction industry. The strategy includes the following 11 overarching targets.

1. **Procurement** – to achieve improved whole-life value through the promotion of best practice construction procurement and supply chain management.

2. **Design** – to ensure, through good design, that buildings, infrastructure, public spaces and places are buildable, fit for purpose, resource efficient, sustainable, future-proof to climate change, adaptable and attractive.

3. **Innovation** – to enhance the industry's capacity to innovate and increase the sustainability of the construction process and its resultant assets.

4. **People** – to increase organisations' commitment to training; to reduce the incidence rate of fatal and major injury accidents by 10% year on year from 2000 levels.

5. **Better regulation** – to reduce the administrative burden on private and public sector organisations.

6. **Climate change mitigation** – to reduce total UK carbon emissions by 80% by 2050 and by 34% by 2020; new homes to be zero carbon from 2016; new schools and public sector buildings to be zero carbon from 2018; other buildings to be zero carbon from 2019.

7. **Climate change adaption** – to develop a robust approach to adaption to climate change.

8. **Water** – to assist with the future water target to reduce per capita consumption of water in the home to an average of 130 litres per person per day by 2030.

9. **Biodiversity** – to conserve and enhance biodiversity throughout all stages of a development.

10. **Waste** – by 2012, to achieve a 50% reduction of construction, demolition and excavation waste to landfill compared to 2008.

11. **Materials** – used in construction to have the least environmental, social and economic impact.

 For further information refer to the Department for Business, Innovation and Skills (BIS) website.

The following highlight the government's and construction industry's response to improving sustainability in construction.

☑ Establishment of the Green Building Council in 2008.

☑ Improvement in building energy performance through enhanced Building Regulations in 2010 (Part L).

☑ The Waste Resources Action Programme (WRAP); halving waste to landfill commitment for clients, contractors designers and waste contractors.

☑ Implementation of Site Waste Management Plan Regulations in England.

☑ Strategic Forum for Construction baseline and action plan to reduce carbon emissions associated with construction by 15%.

☑ Strategic Forum for Construction baseline and action plan for reducing water consumption associated with construction.

☑ All new buildings on the central government estate must achieve a BREEAM rating of *excellent (refer to 1.8 for further details on BREEAM).*

1.3 Defining the environment

The environment, in its simplest terms, is where we all live, according to the World Commission on Environment and Development. More specifically, it can be defined as any physical surroundings consisting of air, water and land, natural resources, flora, fauna, humans and their interrelation.

1.4 Local and global environmental issues

Construction activities can affect the environment in a number of ways, most noticeably at a local level. However, they can also contribute to wider regional or global issues. The three media that could be affected are the atmosphere, water or land; the end result of any impact is usually described as pollution or contamination.

The use of energy, water and the depletion of natural resources also have an impact on the environment. Dust, noise and traffic are also a nuisance and can have a significant effect on the neighbourhood/local community.

Sustainable construction and the environment

Local environmental issues

The table below provides a summary of typical pollutants that cause local environmental impacts to atmosphere, land and water.

Atmosphere	Land	Water
■ Dust	■ Oils and fuels	■ Silt
■ Exhaust emissions	■ Chemicals	■ Chemicals
■ Gases or vapours	■ Lead	■ Concrete
■ Odours	■ Waste and litter	■ Contaminated water
■ Noise	■ Spillage of materials	■ Run-off
■ Light or visual amenity	■ Concrete	■ Effluent
■ Smoke	■ Asbestos	■ Oils and fuels
■ Radiation		■ Hazardous solid matter
■ Asbestos		■ Slurry

It is important that one solution to environmental pollution does not divert the problem to another medium. For example, a solution to air pollution should not lead to water contamination.

Global environmental issues

Climate change – Certain gases in the atmosphere (principally carbon dioxide, methane, nitrous oxide and chlorofluorocarbons (CFCs)) form an insulating blanket around the planet. This allows the sun's rays through, but prevents some of the heat radiated back from the earth escaping, which warms the planet. This can be likened to the role of glass in a greenhouse, hence the term *greenhouse effect*. The obvious risks of climate change on construction will be to ensure buildings are designed to adapt to higher temperatures and more erratic weather patterns, including flooding, as well as mitigating any further impacts through energy efficiency and use of renewable energy.

Resource depletion – The world's finite resources (such as coal, gas and oil) are being rapidly depleted. These resources cannot be used in a sustainable way because they are not renewable. In reality, hydrocarbons (oil-based fuels and products) are finite resources because it takes millions of years for them to form: they cannot be replaced naturally within human timescales. Metals are also a finite resource. The amount of any metal available is reflected in its price, as well as its chemical and physical usability.

Other resources being depleted that can be re-grown are forests. Water, especially clean drinking water, is being depleted and even in areas of Europe with regular rainfall this resource becomes limited after a short period of drought. Construction is wholly dependant on the use of resources; without this, development could not happen. The drive for sustainable consumption and production will inevitably increase the costs for scarce resources and lead to technological improvements in the reuse and recycling of existing materials.

Deforestation – The world's forests are being rapidly depleted by logging, slash-and-burn agriculture and development projects (such as roads, mines and dams). In the 1950s, forests covered about a quarter of the earth's surface. At the turn of the 21st century, the figure is only one sixth. A forested area of one and a half times the size of England is cut down or burned each year.

Forests are essential for a healthy world. They play an important role in regulating global climate by, for example, locking up large amounts of carbon dioxide during photosynthesis. Trees prevent erosion, flooding and the formation of deserts. Forests contain over half the world's plant and animal species and provide a home, fuel and food to many of the world's 200 million tribal people. They also provide the basis for most medicines and cures discovered to date. The construction industry uses a large amount of timber and is increasingly aware of the need to use this resource sustainably, hence why certification schemes (such as the Forestry Stewardship Council (FSC)) have been established.

Biodiversity loss – The clearing of natural ecosystems (linked groups of self-sustaining plants), which is usually a result of agricultural, industrial development or a consequence of war, undoubtedly causes great local disruption to the natural environment. One major concern about the wholesale destruction of any natural habitat, particularly tropical forest, is that many species may become extinct as the ecosystem disappears. On a wider scale migratory species, which use that particular habitat during one season (such as breeding season) might also become extinct.

The destruction of habitats has the same consequences as deforestation but also includes other ecosystems (such as wetlands, oceans, grasslands and others). Whilst irresponsible construction can have a devastating impact on biodiversity, the UK recognises that this issue has to be managed through the planning process.

Acid rain – Acid rain is a collection of loosely related environmental problems involving acid substances and hydrocarbons. Burning fossil fuels, especially coal and oil (mainly in power stations and motor vehicles) produces acid gases (sulphur and nitrogen oxides). The presence of ozone in the lower atmosphere (harmful at this height), formed by the interaction of nitrogen oxides and hydrocarbons, also contributes to the effects of acid rain.

Ozone layer depletion – The ozone layer is a thin concentration of gas in the upper atmosphere. It protects the planet by filtering out harmful ultra-violet rays from the sun. These can cause skin cancer, eye cataracts, and restrict the growth of plants and other organisms. The layer was being depleted, especially above the North and South Poles, by artificial gases that destroy ozone molecules. The main offender was a family of chemicals called CFCs (chlorofluorocarbons), which are used in industry and household goods. Another group of destructive gases is called halons. These were used in fire extinguishers designed to fight electrical fires, especially in electricity sub-stations, computer rooms and aircraft. Worldwide action on ozone-depleting substances has significantly reduced this issue.

1.5   Environmental stakeholders

Environmental management terminology often refers to *stakeholders* who, in simple terms, are interested parties who have either a direct involvement in a construction project or who may be affected by its activities. Typical environmental stakeholders for a construction project could include the following.

Stakeholder	Potential interest
Investors.	Ensure that the project's green credentials add value.
Non-governmental organisations (NGOs) (for example, Greenpeace or Friends of the Earth).	Publicise any good (but usually bad) environmental practices.
Client or client's representative.	Set the project environmental requirements.
Designer.	Ensure that the client's environmental aspirations are reflected in the project design.
Planning authority.	Approve the design, including relevant environmental requirements and set relevant planning conditions.
Local Authority.	Ensure that the works comply with statutory requirements for local air pollution control, including noise and dust and issue relevant permits.
Environment regulators.	Act as a statutory consultee in the planning process and issue relevant permits and licenses for the works (such as discharge consents).
Staff and contractors.	Ensure that the project environmental requirements are met and lead by example.
Government funded support organisations (for example, WRAP and the Carbon Trust).	Provide support, advice and best practice and drive environmental improvement.
Residents and community representatives.	Participate in the planning and consultation process and ensure that the works are carried out without causing nuisance from noise, dust, light and traffic congestion.

Early identification of all relevant stakeholders, together with regular communication and liaison are important to avoid the likelihood of any delay, legal intervention or causing a nuisance to local residents. Effective communication with the local community reduces the risk of complaint. Typical methods of communication include:

- ☑ letter drops to local residents and businesses

- ☑ visiting owners or occupiers of sensitive homes and businesses

- ☑ attending local interest group meetings

- ☑ articles in local publications and newspapers

- ☑ displaying contact boards with relevant contact details so that interested parties can comment – this is a requirement of the Considerate Constructor Scheme (*for further details refer to Chapter E06 Statutory nuisance*)

- ☑ establishing a telephone complaint line, email address or website if appropriate.

 Identify all interested parties and regularly communicate with them on relevant environmental issues.

1.6   UK regulatory framework for the environment

Construction sites have a number of legal obligations and the environment is no exception.

Environmental policy and law is based on guiding principles that define the content of any rules and regulations. These principles are firmly embedded within legal frameworks.

- ☑ **Prevention** is better than cure, so policy measures are introduced to prevent environmental harm rather than remediate environmental problems once they have occurred.

☑ **Precaution** – where there is uncertainty over the environmental science of a pressing problem then environmental protection must be prioritised rather than risk an impact occurring.

☑ **Polluter pays** principle requires that those causing (or potentially responsible for) environmental damage bear the financial costs of doing so. For example, this payment may be through remediation of contamination, investment in pollution abatement technology or clean production plant, or through environmental taxation and charges.

Legal obligations do not just originate from the UK Government, or its devolved administrations, but there are many sources of environmental law, starting at the international level, which are then transposed into European and finally UK law. In fact, most environmental law in the UK now comes from regulations made in Europe as part of the UK's membership of the European Union.

In the UK there are two general types of law:

☑ **civil law**, which covers disputes between individuals or organisations

☑ **criminal law**, which deals with offences against the state.

Laws can be statutory (detailed by the state) or, in the case of common law, be based on the development of principles through case-law precedents where a basic law is interpreted under specific circumstances and the interpretation is used thereafter.

In the UK there are three levels of regulation relevant to criminal law.

☑ **Statutes or Acts of Parliament** are documents that set out legal rules and have normally been passed by both Houses of Parliament in the form of a Bill and have received royal assent. Acts of Parliament are also often called primary legislation. The Climate Change Act 2008 is a statute.

☑ **Delegated (or secondary) legislation** can take different forms:

– statutory instruments (SIs), through which the Secretary of State can issue specific regulations

– orders issuing specific rules relating to a statute or part of a statute. For example, the Carbon Reduction Commitment Energy Efficiency Scheme Order issued under the Climate Change Act

– by-laws, which are made by the various tiers of local government, and can cover such maters as the establishment of internal drainage boards.

☑ **Guidance** – for some pieces of legislation the relevant Government department or regulator will issue guidance on the interpretation and implementation of the regulations. This may be in the form of:

– **statutory guidance** – typically in the form of a Code of Practice that sets out how to comply with the law

– **non-statutory guidance** – typically a circular from a Government department, or technical guidance from either Government or the regulator (for example, DEFRA *Non-statutory guidance for site waste management plans*).

UK policy-making departments

The main Government departments involved in developing environmental policy and legislation are outlined below. They work with the devolved administrations of Wales, Scotland and Northern Ireland to implement local environmental policy and regulation.

Department for Environment, Farming and Rural Affairs (DEFRA) is responsible for making policy and legislation, and works with others to deliver policies in the natural environment, biodiversity, plants and animals; sustainable development and the green economy; food, farming and fisheries; animal health and welfare; environmental protection and pollution control; and rural communities and issues.

Department for Energy and Climate Change (DECC) is responsible for making policy and legislation in respect to energy and climate change mitigation and adaption. The department has four key goals: save energy with the green deal and support vulnerable consumers; deliver secure energy on the way to a low carbon energy future; drive ambitious action on climate change at home and abroad; manage the UK's energy legacy responsibly and cost-effectively.

Department of Communities and Local Government (CLG) is responsible for implementing planning policy, Building Regulations and building-related environmental standards (such as the Code for sustainable homes, energy performance certificates and display energy certificates).

Department for Business Innovation and Skills (BIS) brings all areas of the UK economy together as a co-ordinating department to promote economic growth. BIS has a construction sector unit that works with the industry to improve business performance, including sustainability. BIS was responsible for joint development of the Government's Sustainable Construction Strategy launched in 2008 and more recently the Low Carbon Construction Action Plan by the Innovation and Growth Team (IGT).

The Green Construction Board is a consultative forum for Government (led by BIS) and the UK design, construction and property industry in order to ensure a sustained, high level conversation and to develop and implement a long term strategic framework for the promotion of innovation and sustainable growth. The board owns and will monitor implementation, and build on the Low Carbon Construction Action Plan.

 Further information on these departments can be found on their individual websites.

Environmental regulators

Environment agencies

☑ **England and Wales.** The Environment Agency was formed under The Environment Act of 1995 by merging The National Rivers Authority (NRA), Her Majesty's Inspectorate of Pollution (HMIP), the Waste Regulation Authorities and several smaller units from the former Department of the Environment (now DEFRA). At the same time, some of the functions of the Secretary of State were transferred to the agency making it one of the most powerful regulators in the world.

 In 2013 the Environment Agency in Wales will become a separate body linking with the Forestry Commission and Countryside Council for Wales.

The equivalent authorities elsewhere in the UK (with some differences) are:

☑ **Scotland.** The Scottish Environmental Protection Agency (SEPA)

☑ **Northern Ireland.** The Northern Ireland Environment Agency.

The Environment Agency exists to provide high quality environmental protection and improvement. This is achieved by an emphasis on prevention, education and vigorous enforcement wherever necessary. The agency's overall aim of protecting and enhancing the whole environment is intended to contribute to the worldwide environmental goal of sustainable development.

The enforcement powers of the Environment Agency are set out in its enforcement and sanctions statement and guidance, which outlines the circumstances under which it will normally prosecute. The enforcement powers available to the agency will vary according to the nature and severity of the breach, but could include:

☑ a formal warning

☑ a formal caution

☑ enforcement notices and works notices (where contravention can be prevented or needs to be remedied)

☑ prohibition notices (where there is an imminent risk of serious environmental damage)

☑ suspension or revocation of environmental permits and licences

☑ variation of permit conditions

☑ injunctions

☑ remedial works (where it carries out remedial works, it will seek to recover the full costs incurred from those responsible)

☑ criminal sanctions, including fines, prosecution and imprisonment

☑ civil sanctions, including financial penalties, which were new powers available to the agency from January 2011.

Under Section 108 of the Environment Act persons authorised by the Environment Agency (England and Wales) or Scottish Environment Protection Agency (SEPA) have the authority to enter any premises, by force if needed, with or (in an emergency) without a warrant, and to:

☑ take any equipment or materials necessary as evidence

☑ make any examination or investigation

☑ direct that the premises are left undisturbed while being examined

☑ take samples and photographs

☑ require any relevant person to answer questions and to declare the truth of the answers given and require the production of records.

The Environment Agency can also carry out formal interviews under caution in accordance with the Police and Criminal Evidence (PACE) Act. The Environment Agency's *Offence response options* document sets out the options available to every offence that the Environment Agency regulates.

 The Environment Agency's construction pages can be found online.

Local Authorities

Local Authorities are responsible for various environmental pollution control functions, including those listed below.

Air quality. Local Authorities are responsible for the management and assessment of local air quality, including the establishment of smoke control areas and the prohibition of dark smoke from chimneys under the Clean Air Act.

Contaminated land. Under the Contaminated Land Regime, Local Authorities have a duty to inspect their land, to formally classify it as contaminated land, and require it to be cleaned up by the owner/occupier. Special sites are regulated by the environmental agencies.

Local Authority Air Pollution Control (LAAPC). For less polluting processes requiring an environmental permit (in England and Wales) or authorisation (in Scotland), the control of emissions to air alone is exercised by Local Authorities. Local Authorities have a duty to give prior written authorisation for processes under their control. This includes, for example, permits for mobile crushing and screening equipment and concrete batching plants.

Nuisance. Complaints of statutory nuisance (such as noise, dust and odour) are dealt with by Local Authorities. They may serve an abatement notice where they are satisfied that a statutory nuisance exists or is deemed likely to occur or recur.

Planning. Local Authorities have the responsibility of implementing and regulating national planning policy, including environmental impact assessments, tree preservation orders (TPOs) and authorisations for hedge removal. In many cases other regulators will be a statutory consultee, as part of the planning process.

Waste controls: Local Authorities have some powers under waste legislation to stop and search waste carriers and confiscate vehicles suspected of waste crime.

Water companies. The composition and quantity of industrial discharges to sewers are controlled primarily by the regional water companies (frequently referred to as sewerage undertakers). Under the provisions of the Water Industry Act a discharge consent from the appropriate water company is required, except where all discharges are regulated under an environmental permit (England and Wales) or integration pollution prevention and control (IPPC) authorisation (Scotland).

Water consents. On 6 April 2012, when a further phase of the Flood and Water Management Act was implemented, responsibility for regulating activities on ordinary watercourses in most areas of England and Wales transferred from the Environment Agency to lead local flood authorities. Lead local flood authorities are unitary authorities where they exist and county councils elsewhere.

Other regulatory organisations

There are a number of other regulatory bodies (shown below) that have specific regulatory and advisory responsibilities that are relevant to construction sites.

Canal and River Trust. British Waterways ceased to exist in England and Wales and in its place the Canal and River Trust was set up in July 2012 to care for 2,000 miles of historic waterways. In Scotland, British Waterways continues to exist as a legal entity caring for the canals under the trading name Scottish Canals.

Cadw is the historic environment service of the Welsh Assembly Government, having responsibility for designated archaeological and heritage sites in Wales.

Countryside Council for Wales is an independent public body whose role is to sustain Wales' natural environment, both on land and at sea.

English Heritage is responsible for protecting historic buildings, landscapes and archaeological sites.

Health and Safety Executive. There is an overlap between environmental legislation and health and safety legislation, which is regulated by the Health and Safety Executive (HSE), including the COSHH Regulations and the Control of Major Accident Hazards (COMAH).

Internal Drainage Boards have powers under the Land Drainage Act (as amended) to undertake works on any watercourse within their district other than main river. A board's district is defined on a sealed map prepared by the Environment Agency and approved by the relevant ministry. In addition, boards can undertake works on watercourses outside their drainage district in order to benefit the district.

Natural England is responsible for conservation of wildlife and geology, including sites of special, scientific interest (SSSIs) and prevention of damage to habitats.

Scottish Natural Heritage is responsible for designated ecological sites, geological and geomorphological sites, and protected species.

Historic Scotland is an executive agency of the Scottish Government and is charged with safeguarding Scotland's historic environment and promoting its understanding and enjoyment.

1.7   UK environmental targets

The UK's environmental targets are held within the plethora of strategies for each environmental policy area. The list below provides a summary of the key targets for each of these policy areas.

Policy area	Target(s)
Waste	The reduction, from a 1995 baseline, of biodegradable waste going to landfill to 75% by 2006, 50% by 2009 and 35% by 2016. To achieve a target of 50% for the reuse and recycling of waste materials (such as paper, metal and glass) by 2020; the target for non-hazardous construction and demolition waste is 70%. The construction target set out in the strategy for sustainable construction is to halve waste sent to landfill by 2012 from a 2008 baseline.
Energy	To reduce carbon emissions by 80% (from 1990 levels) by 2050, with an intermediate target of 34% by 2020. The UK also has a target to provide 15% of all energy from renewable sources by 2020. The construction target set out in the strategy for sustainable construction is a 15% reduction in carbon emissions from construction processes and associated transport by 2012 compared to 2008 levels. In addition, all new homes and schools should be zero carbon (based on energy consumption) from 2018.
Water	Reduce the consumption of water through cost effective measures, to an average of 130 litres per person per day by 2030, or possibly even 120 litres per person per day depending on new technological developments and innovation. Water quality standards are also set out in the Water Framework Directive. The construction target set out in the strategy for sustainable construction is for a 20% reduction in water consumption in the manufacturing and construction phase by 2012 compared to 2008 levels.

Air quality	Objectives and target values for the protection of human health and for the protection of vegetation and ecosystems are set out in the UK National Air Quality Strategy for England, Wales, Scotland and Northern Ireland. It specifies objectives and target values for a range of pollutants including benzene, carbon monoxide and particulates.
Biodiversity	The UK is a signatory to the Convention on Biological Diversity (CBD) and is committed to the new biodiversity goals and targets 'the Aichi targets' agreed in 2010 and set out in the strategic plan for biodiversity 2011-2020. The UK has put in place a set of indicators to measure its progress on meeting these targets annually: *UK biodiversity indicators in your pocket.*

1.8   Construction sustainability assessment tools

Building Research Establishment's Environmental Assessment Method (BREEAM), the *Code for sustainable homes* and Civil Engineering Environmental Quality Assessment and Award Scheme (CEEQUAL) are all tools used by the construction and civil engineering industry to improve the sustainability of projects. Clients are increasingly requiring these standards as part of the project obligations. Many of the requirements set out in these tools are directly linked to the objectives and targets set out in the Government's strategy for sustainable construction discussed above.

BREEAM

BREEAM is an environmental assessment method for buildings. It has certified over 200,000 buildings since it was first launched in 1990.

BREEAM methodology is to assess and certify (using licensed assessors) the sustainability credentials of a building at two stages of the project life cycle:

☑ design and procurement

☑ post-construction.

For new buildings (for example, BREEAM new construction), it measures the performance in nine categories (shown below) of environmental criteria, with the relative weighting for each category shown in brackets.

1. Management	(12%)
2. Health and wellbeing	(15%)
3. Energy	(19%)
4. Transport	(8%)
5. Water	(6%)
6. Materials	(12.5%)
7. Waste	(7.5%)
8. Land use and ecology	(10%)
9. Pollution	(10%)
Total	**100%**
Innovation (additional)	10%

The management category details the requirements for a number of site-related issues, for example:

☑ **MAN 02: Construction site practices**, which requires evidence of registration and compliance with a recognised considerate contractor scheme

☑ **MAN 03: Construction site impacts**, which requires the monitoring and reporting of energy consumption, water consumption and transport of materials and waste. It requires the procurement of site timber for formwork, site hoardings and for temporary works in accordance with the Government's timber procurement policy. It also requires construction site environmental management systems to be in accordance with ISO 14001 or equivalent and to implement best practice pollution prevention practices and procedures.

It is also one of the aims of BREEAM to support innovation within the construction industry. BREEAM does this by making additional credits available for the recognition of sustainability-related benefits or performance levels that are currently not recognised by standard BREEAM assessment issues and criteria. Awarding credits for innovation enables clients and design teams to boost their building's BREEAM performance and, in addition, helps to support the market for new innovative technologies, and design or construction practices.

The overall score for the assessment will be the percentage of credits achieved in each of the nine categories, which are then weighted to provide an overall percentage score. The total score will determine the BREEAM rating in accordance with the following:

☑ outstanding   85%   ☑ good   45%

☑ excellent   70%   ☑ pass   30%

☑ very good   55%   ☑ unclassified   < 30%

Sustainable construction and the environment

To ensure that performance against fundamental environmental issues is not overlooked in pursuit of a particular rating, BREEAM sets minimum standards of performance in key areas (such as energy, water and waste). It is important to bear in mind that these are minimum acceptable levels of performance and, in that respect, they should not necessarily be viewed as levels that are representative of best practice for a BREEAM rating level. To achieve a particular BREEAM rating, the minimum overall percentage score must be achieved and the minimum standards, applicable to that rating level, complied with.

The BREEAM ratings are validated by BRE through the submission of evidence, together with the relevant fees by the licensed assessor.

 For further information refer to the BREEAM website.

Code for sustainable homes

The *Code for sustainable homes* (the 'Code') is an environmental assessment method for rating and certifying the performance of new homes. It is very similar to BREEAM and was previously called BREEAM eco-homes prior to becoming the Code.

It is a national standard for use in the design and construction of new homes with a view to encouraging continuous improvement in sustainable home building. The Code became operational in England in April 2007, and having a Code rating for new build homes has been mandatory since 1 May 2008. It is anticipated that all new homes from 2016 will be zero carbon.

The Code is not mandatory, nor is the Code a set of regulations, and care should be taken not to confuse it with zero carbon policy. The only circumstances where the Code can be required are where:

- ☑ Local Authorities stipulate a requirement in their local plans
- ☑ affordable housing is funded by the HCA (Homes and Community Agency), which requires homes to be built to Code Level 3. The Level 3 energy standard is now incorporated in the Building Regulations.

The Code covers nine categories of sustainable design, shown below.

1. Energy and CO_2 emissions.
2. Water.
3. Materials.
4. Surface water run-off.
5. Waste.
6. Pollution.
7. Health and wellbeing.
8. Management.
9. Ecology.

As with BREEAM, the Code also includes a number of management requirements in Section 8 during the construction phase that require companies to monitor, measure and set targets for emissions from the use of energy and fuels from the construction process.

Mandatory minimum performance standards are set for some issues. For three of these, a single mandatory requirement is set that must be met, whatever Code level rating is sought. Credits are not awarded for these issues. Confirmation that the performance requirements are met for all three is a minimum entry requirement for achieving a Level 1 rating. The three uncredited issues are:

- ☑ environmental impact of materials
- ☑ management of surface water run-off from developments
- ☑ storage of non-recyclable waste and recyclable household waste.

If the mandatory minimum performance standard is met for the three uncredited issues, four further mandatory issues need to be considered. These are agreed to be such important issues that separate Government policies are being pursued to mitigate their effects. For two of these, credits are awarded for increasing levels of achievement recognised within the Code.

The two issues with increasing mandatory minimum standards are:

- ☑ dwelling emission rate
- ☑ indoor water use.

The table below shows the minimum levels of dwelling emission rate to achieve the relevant Code level.

Code level	Minimum percentage reduction in dwelling emission rate over target emission rate
Level 1*	10
Level 2**	18
Level 3***	25
Level 4****	44
Level 5*****	100
Level 6******	Zero carbon home

 A Level 5 house has zero emissions from heating, hot water, lighting and ventilation. A Level 6 house has zero emissions from all energy use in the home.

The final two issues with mandatory requirements are fabric energy efficiency and lifetime homes. To achieve an overall Code rating of Level 5 it is necessary to achieve at least seven credits in Ene 2. To achieve an overall Code rating of Level 6 it is necessary to achieve at least seven credits in Ene 2 and three credits in Hea 4 – lifetime homes.

As with BREEAM, Code ratings are validated by BRE through the submission of evidence, together with the relevant fees by the licensed assessor. Assessors will assess the property during two stages (design stage and post-construction stage).

 For further information refer to the Communities and Local Government website.

CEEQUAL

CEEQUAL is an assessment scheme for civil engineering. It assesses how well project and contract teams have dealt with environmental and social issues in their work. If used during the design, construction or maintenance phases, the CEEQUAL assessment is likely to positively influence the project's or contract's environmental and social performance.

The CEEQUAL assessment scheme is available in three forms:

☑ **CEEQUAL for UK and Ireland projects** – applicable to all types of civil engineering, infrastructure, landscaping and public realm works. There are five types of award available under this form of the scheme.

☑ **CEEQUAL for International projects** – based on the 'for UK and Ireland projects' this scheme is applicable to projects anywhere else in the world. There are five types of award available under this form of the scheme.

☑ **CEEQUAL for term contracts** – specifically created for the assessment of civil engineering and public realm works that are undertaken through contracts over a number of years and in a wide geographical or operational area. There is only one award type available under term contracts.

A CEEQUAL assessment is a self-assessment process carried out by a trained CEEQUAL assessor who is usually a member of the project or contract team, rather than hired only for the assessment task. Assessors use the questions set in the CEEQUAL manuals and an online assessment tool provided by CEEQUAL to decide on and capture the scores their work deserves, and to log the evidence justifying those scores.

The CEEQUAL assessment manuals (Version 5) are laid out in nine sections, which have been weighted. More details on what each section covers are given in the *Scheme description and assessment process handbook*, which can be downloaded for free as part of the CEEQUAL manuals.

1. New project strategy.
2. Project management.
3. People and communities.
4. Land use (above and below water) and landscape.
5. The historic environment.
6. Ecology and biodiversity.
7. Water environment (fresh and marine).
8. Physical resources use and management.
9. Transport.

A fee is charged to cover the cost of the verifier and the administration and progressive development of the CEEQUAL scheme. The fee is based on the civil engineering value of the project or contracted works or, if applying early in the process, on the client's or engineer's estimate.

 For further information refer to the CEEQUAL website.

Leadership in Energy and Environmental Design

Launched by the US Green Building Council (GBC) in 1998, the Leadership in Energy and Environmental Design (LEED) standard has become widely used both within the US and around the world. In recent years, UK based client groups have begun to ask for LEED certification alongside BREEAM.

Like BREEAM, LEED is voluntary and it can be applied to any building type and any building life cycle phase. It promotes a whole-building approach to sustainability by recognising performance in key areas of energy and water efficiency, CO_2 emissions, indoor environmental quality and sustainable use of resources.

LEED credits are weighted differently, depending on their potential impact. The greatest weighting is placed on energy and atmosphere, with sustainable sites and materials and resources also receiving a high weighting.

A total of 100 base points are available, with six possible innovation in design and four regional priority points. There are four levels of achievement: certified (40-49), silver (50-59), gold (60-79) and platinum (80 and over).

There are different rating systems to cover different types of project, including new construction, LEED for existing buildings, LEED for commercial interiors, LEED for retail, LEED for schools and LEED for core and shell. Most building types are included in one or more of these systems.

LEED differs from BREEAM in a number of areas, and contractors should review requirements fully. Some key differences are:

☑ there is no need for an accredited assessor, as the US GBC assesses applications (although an extra credit is available where an assessor is used)

☑ design requirements are linked to the American ASHRAE standards whereas BREEAM relates to UK Building Regulations

☑ some credits are calculated using US specific outputs (such as US dollars saved for credits relating to energy)

☑ regional priority credits can only be obtained in the US.

RICS Ska rating online assessment tool

This tool allows property and construction professionals and Ska assessors to design, specify, rate and certify fit-out projects for environmental impact, using the Ska rating fit-out benchmark system. Use of the tool is free and open to all. Projects can be certified by qualified assessors for an additional fee.

 For further information refer to the RICS website.

1.9 Sustainable use of materials, energy and water – resource efficiency

Materials, water and energy (including transport) are all forms of resource, where efficiency of use has a considerable influence on construction times, costs and environmental impact.

Construction projects that use materials efficiently will have lower construction times and lower costs. Clearly this will lead to greater competitiveness, more repeat business and greater customer satisfaction. It also reduces the amount of resources that are taken from the planet and the amount of waste that the planet receives from construction activities.

Inefficient projects are costly, late, use excessive resources, produce too much waste, are bad for image and lead to reduced client satisfaction.

The Government's strategy for sustainable construction places a top priority on resource efficiency for the construction sector. An efficient construction project is also a reflection of the mindset of the project leadership. To achieve a resource-efficient project the project leadership must be focused around resource efficiency. This mindset then needs to be reflected throughout all levels of the project. Communication of the right behaviours within the project is therefore a high priority, starting with the leadership of a project. The right resource-efficiency mindset will be evident at all levels on a project.

 For further guidance on resource efficiency, energy management and water management refer to Chapters E02, E04 and E05 respectively.

02

Resource efficiency

The construction sector is the largest consumer of materials in the UK, and the largest producer of waste. More efficient use of materials would make a major contribution to reducing the environmental impacts of construction, including carbon emissions, landfill and the depletion of natural resources.

This chapter provides a brief introduction to the environmental and economic benefits of improved material efficiency and waste reduction. It provides guidance on the responsible sourcing of materials, chain of custody for timber and life cycle analysis.

This chapter also highlights the benefits of reusing and recycling materials, including the use of recycled aggregates.

Introduction	14
Sustainable sourcing of materials	15
Reuse and recycling of materials	16
Appendix A – Example chain of custody certificate for timber	18

02

2.1 Introduction

Construction uses huge amounts of natural resources and accounts for 25% of all raw materials used in the UK. Historically, construction has been an inherently inefficient process, arising from the bespoke nature of on-site construction. This not only wastes a lot of money, it also produces high levels of waste materials and causes excess material extraction to replace those materials that have been lost through inefficient use.

The aim of modern construction is to move to the top of the waste hierarchy (prevention) and away from where it has been traditionally placed, which is at the bottom (disposal).

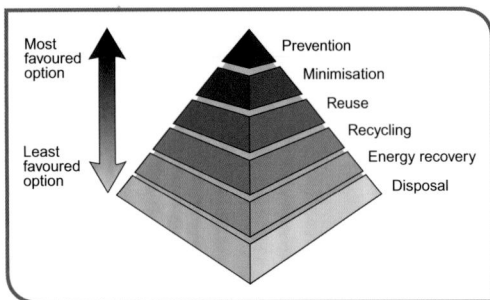

The Government has responded to these challenges by producing the strategy for sustainable construction in June 2008, introducing Site Waste Management Plans Regulations (England) in April 2008 and the Halving Waste to Landfill by 2012 Commitment. Their purpose is to drive improvements in resource efficiency throughout the construction process. The EU has also set out a roadmap for a resource-efficient Europe by 2020 (COM(2011) 571 final).

Design for manufacture and assembly (DfMA) seeks to increase material efficiency by manufacturing modules in dedicated facilities that are then assembled on site. This has the potential to achieve zero waste and much higher resource utilisation.

Site waste management plans seek to eliminate waste at the bid and design stage. They are a management systems approach to identifying where waste is likely to be produced in the construction process, and then seeking ways of introducing improvements in the process. Used effectively, they will drive improvements throughout the process.

 Practical ways for improving resource efficiency and reducing waste are covered in the three methods below

☑ Design:
  – designing the project to incorporate recycled materials
  – designing the project to suit standard product sizes and to avoid site cutting
  – designing to allow pre-assembling components off-site
  – designing to allow a cut/fill balance and by utilising surplus materials in site features (such as landscaping)
  – specifying non-hazardous and low impact materials.

☑ Procurement:
  – selecting suppliers with a good environmental track record
  – requiring sub-contractors to have a waste management policy
  – not over-ordering materials
  – reducing the amount of packaging
  – ordering materials at the size required, to avoid off-cuts.

☑ Construction:
  – avoiding over-excavation
  – storing materials to avoid damage, theft, contamination and double handling
  – segregating surplus materials for reuse elsewhere
  – crushing existing demolition waste for reuse in the works to avoid the need for virgin materials.

 WRAP has developed a number of tools for resource efficiency (net waste tool and recycled content calculator) and designing out waste (designing out waste tools) for building and civil engineering projects that are freely available on their website. The designing out waste tools sets out a simple, three-step process of **identify, investigate** and **implement,** enabling designing out waste principles to be applied in a structured way on a project.

2.2   Sustainable sourcing of materials

With the increasing focus on sustainable development, many construction companies are recognising the need to prove that their buildings are built with sustainability in mind. One element of this is in the responsible sourcing of products used in their construction and the onus of proof is increasingly being passed down to the manufacturers of those construction products. Section 13 of the strategy for sustainable construction (materials), for example, set a target by 2012 that at least 25% of products used in construction projects must be from schemes recognised for responsible sourcing.

The *Code for sustainable homes* (the 'Code') and BREEAM awards credits based on the environmental impact of materials and for materials responsibly sourced. The aim is to encourage the use of materials with lower environmental impacts over their life cycle and to recognise and encourage the specification of responsibly sourced materials for basic building and finishing components. Material sourcing is also assessed under CEEQUAL (Civil Engineering Environmental Quality Award) and LEED (Leadership in Energy and Environmental Design – developed by the US Green Building Council).

The Building Research Establishment's (BRE) *Green guide to specification* provides guidance on how to make the best environmental choices when selecting construction materials and components. The guide presents information on the environmental impacts of building elements and specifications by ranking them on an A+ to E rating scale. These environmental rankings are based on life cycle assessments (LCAs), using an environmental profile methodology. They are generic rankings that illustrate a range of typical materials.

The BRE standard BES 6001 has been published to enable construction product manufacturers to ensure and then prove that their products have been made with constituent materials that have been responsibly sourced. The standard describes a framework for the organisational governance, supply chain management and environmental and social aspects that must be addressed in order to ensure the responsible sourcing of construction products.

Independent, third-party assessment and certification against the requirements of BES 6001 then give the organisation the ability to prove that an effective system for ensuring responsible sourcing exists and adds credibility to any claims made. BES 6001 is also aligned to the Code and BREEAM so that products from manufacturers certified against this standard are able to score points against the responsible sourcing credits.

For manufacturers and suppliers, having certification to the environmental management systems (EMS) standard (ISO 14001) provides some evidence that the company has considered, and is reducing, the environmental impacts of their products. Relevant products assessed under the responsible sourcing elements of the Code or BREEAM are able to score points against credits where the certified EMS covers key processes or key supply chain processes. For example, the responsible sourcing of bricks would need to demonstrate that the certified EMS covers manufacture (key process) and clay extraction (key supply chain process) to obtain maximum points.

Timber and chain of custody

Construction uses large amounts of timber, so it is important that timber is sourced from forests that are managed in a sustainable and ethical way. Illegal logging results in soil erosion, loss of biodiversity and uncontrolled development. It is therefore important to know where timber has been sourced from.

Chain of custody (COC) is a process that provides assurance about where timber has been sourced from. This is done by certifying timber from the forest to the final point of purchase and requires an effective audit process. The process tracks timber through each stage of the supply chain, from forest and logging, through sawmill, factory and distributor, to timber merchant and contractor. This provides a level of transparency and traceability to guarantee compliance with demands for ethically sourced timber products. An example COC is included in Appendix A.

There are more than 50 certification programs addressing the many types of forests and tenures around the world.

> The two largest international forest certification programs are the Forest Stewardship Council (FSC) and the Programme for the Endorsement of Forest Certification (PEFC).

Timber and chain of custody certificate number

In 2004 the UK Government established its own central policy for the procurement of timber – central point of expertise on timber (CPET). Suppliers working for the government are expected to comply with CPET requirements and CPET policy now demands that all timber and wood-derived products must be from only:

☑ independently verifiable legal and sustainable sources, or

☑ forest law enforcement, governance and trade (FLEGT) licensed timber or equivalent sources (when the scheme is fully established).

The government has approved four timber certification schemes that meet CPET requirements:

☑ Forest Stewardship Council (FSC)

☑ Programme for the Endorsement of Forest Certification (PEFC)

☑ Sustainable Forestry Initiative (SFI)

☑ Canadian Standards Association scheme (CSA).

Schemes (such as the BRE's Environmental Assessment Method (BREEAM) and the Code) have adopted CPET requirements for the purpose of demonstrating responsible sourcing of timber.

Some large construction projects have adopted a chain of custody certification scheme themselves as best practice.

Life cycle assessment (cradle to cradle)

Life cycle assessment (LCA) is described by the United Nations Environment Programme (UNEP):

> Life cycle thinking implies that everyone in the whole chain of a product's life cycle, from cradle to grave, has a responsibility and a role to play, taking into account the relevant external effects. The impacts of all life cycle stages need to be considered comprehensively when making informed decisions on production and consumption patterns, policies and management strategies.

A good LCA will identify where in the life of a product the key impacts occur and identify what can be done to reduce or mitigate these impacts. In construction LCA is applied to both the building itself and also to the products that go into that building.

The stages in the life of a building are material extraction, processing into a product, combination of products into the building, use of the building, end of life deconstruction and material recycling. Efficient recycling of materials at end of life has now given rise to the term *cradle to cradle*.

The Royal Academy of Engineering has identified that the typical costs for owning buildings are in the ratio of one for construction costs, five for maintenance costs and 200 for building operating costs. Better investment decisions can be made by adopting whole-life costing and life cycle costing systems that are vital to setting targets, measuring and achieving long-term value and improved cost management.

Life cycle costing is a narrower assessment of the overall economic impacts of an asset, whereas the use of environmental costs in a whole-life analysis allows a true comparison between options, particularly where they are quoted as 'good' for the environment. For a major project (such as the construction of a nuclear power station) it is possible to calculate the environmental impact of making the concrete containment, the water required for refining the copper for the power plants and all the other components. Only by undertaking such an analysis is it possible to determine whether one solution carries a lower or higher environmental cost than another.

A key construction material is cement and much work has been done on cement LCA. *The cement technology road map 2009* published by the International Energy Association (IEA) and the World Business Council for Sustainable Development (WBCSD) identifies the following action areas to reduce the LCA impacts of cement.

| 1. Thermal and electric efficiency. |
| 2. Alternative fuel use. |
| 3. Clinker substitution. |
| 4. Carbon capture and storage. |

An outcome from the work on cement using LCA is lower embodied energy, where less carbon has been used in the production of the cement product. The latest technical breakthrough in cement composition has resulted in a carbon negative cement called novacem.

Novacem is based on a non-carbonate raw material, magnesium silicate, and uses a relatively low temperature production process. Overall, more CO_2 is absorbed during production than emitted. For every tonne of ordinary Portland cement replaced by novacem, CO_2 emissions will be reduced by up to 850 kg.

PAS 2050, Specification for the assessment of the life cycle greenhouse gas emissions of goods and services, produced by the British Standards Institute, is a publicly available specification that provides a consistent method for assessing the life cycle greenhouse gas emissions of goods and services.

2.3   Reuse and recycling of materials

Maximising the reuse of materials on site can significantly reduce the amount of waste generated. For example, careful cut and fill analysis can ensure ground excavated from cuttings can be used as fill material elsewhere (such as within embankments) so that no waste is sent to landfill and there is no need to procure fill.

Not only can demolition materials be processed for aggregates and fill materials, designers should aim to use other materials (such as reclaimed bricks, timber and steel sections).

Other materials that have recycled content include plastics, aluminium, steel and steel reinforcement. Eco-reinforcement is a trademark for responsibly sourced reinforcing steel. It is a third-party certification scheme developed by the reinforcing steel industry to comply with BRE's *Framework standard for the responsible sourcing of construction products* (BES 6001:2008).

Using construction materials that have been recycled and are low impact offers a number of clear environmental benefits. These include:

- ☑ demonstrating performance against corporate and sustainability policies

- ☑ reducing material costs (where locally reprocessed demolition materials are cheaper than virgin materials)

- ☑ support, to meet the requirements of planning authorities

- ☑ providing a competitive edge through differentiation

- ☑ complementing other aspects of sustainable design

- ☑ conserving finite natural resources by reducing the demand for raw materials

- ☑ conserving energy and water, as recycled materials require less processing than extracting raw materials

- ☑ reducing air and water pollution, since manufacturing from recycled materials is generally a cleaner process and uses less energy

- ☑ reducing the amount of material that would otherwise go to landfill.

Taking a whole life cycle approach, designers should also take into account the possibility of reusing or recycling materials at the end of a product's life (for example, designing for dismantling and reuse of building components).

Recycled aggregates

Aggregates include sand, gravel, crushed stone, slag, recycled concrete and more recently geosynthetic aggregates and recycled glass. The extraction of aggregates has a wide range of impacts upon the environment, including noise, vibration, vehicle emissions, visual impact and hydrogeology.

The largest volume of recycled material used as construction aggregate is presently blast furnace and steel furnace slag. At the end of the life of a building there is the potential to recycle aggregates and make them available as new construction materials. This is often the case where an existing site is being redeveloped.

There are many benefits of using recycled aggregates and these include lowering embodied energy and reducing transport if produced on brownfield sites.

On-site processing of demolition materials into aggregates is classed as a waste operation and will require an environmental permit or exemption for the treatment and reuse of the material. The WRAP quality protocol of the production of aggregates from inert waste details the requirements for ensuring that the processed materials meet end-of-waste status.

You have a responsibility to check that all relevant supplier documentation is correct to confirm that the protocol requirements have been met.

 For further information on the WRAP quality protocol refer to the WRAP website within the AggRegain section.

 For further details on reducing waste and permitting requirements associated with the treatment of demolition waste and contaminated soils refer to Chapter E03 Waste management.

Appendix A – Example chain of custody certificate for timber

Certificate

Registration schedule

03

Waste management

The construction sector produces around 100 million tonnes of construction waste per annum, which is nearly a third of all waste produced in the UK.

This chapter gives a general overview of the legal framework for the regulation of waste. It will outline how waste is defined and classified for the purpose of disposal and will introduce the waste hierarchy.

This chapter also gives you an overview of the permits that are required for the management of waste and the documentation required under the duty of care for its safe and environmentally sound disposal. It will provide an overview of various types of waste, including hazardous waste, Waste Electrical and Electronic Equipment (WEEE) and waste batteries, and provide an introduction to site waste management plans.

Introduction	20
Key requirements	20
Defining waste	21
Describing and classifying waste	21
Waste hierarchy	23
Duty of care and waste carrier registration	25
Controlled waste and transfer notes	26
Hazardous waste and consignment notes	27
Environmental permits and exemptions	29
CL:AIRE Development Industry Code of Practice (DICoP)	33
WRAP quality protocol for the production of aggregates from inert waste	34
Waste electrical and electronic equipment	35
Waste batteries	35
Site waste management plans	36
Appendix A – Six-digit European waste catalogue codes	38
Appendix B – Example of a controlled waste transfer note	39
Appendix C – Example of a hazardous waste consignment note	40
Appendix D – Waste flowcharts for the reuse of construction materials (soils and aggregates)	41
Appendix E – Waste exemption materials and thresholds	44

3.1 Introduction

Of the 100 million tonnes of construction waste produced by the construction sector per annum, a proportion of this ends up in landfill sites, which also has other environmental impacts (such as the generation of greenhouse gases) that contribute to climate change.

Waste is a by-product of the inefficient use of valuable resources that could perhaps be reused on site or recycled. The simple operation of cutting a brick in half, or sawing the end off a piece of wood, is producing waste if that half brick or off-cut is not reused or could have been avoided in the first place.

Waste costs money to produce, in terms of the materials thrown away, and also money to dispose of it and, for the skip or lorry to remove it. Landfill tax rates will continue to rise to provide a financial incentive to reduce the amount of waste being sent to landfill.

Research carried out on housing projects has indicated that the true cost of disposing of the material is around ten times the cost of the skip. This includes the cost of labour to fill it and the cost of purchasing the materials in the first place. The cost of skips on a project is typically 0.5% of the build cost. The true cost of waste and its disposal can amount to around 5% of the project costs. This is valuable lost profit for the project. Making the best use of materials and resources is therefore essential in reducing waste and its associated costs.

The incorrect or inappropriate disposal of waste (such as fly-tipping) is illegal, unsightly and can damage the environment for many years. Waste materials lying around on a building or construction site also have the potential to cause people to trip and injure themselves.

The Government has set targets for waste reduction, with waste to landfill being halved by 2012. There is a major emphasis in the Government's strategy for sustainable construction on reducing waste. Poor design, insufficient attention to the generation of waste during procurement and poor control and supervision by site management, including improper or unsafe systems of work on site, can lead to the production of waste.

Legislation imposes conditions and obligations on the building and construction industry, and on how contractors may dispose of any waste produced during work on site.

Waste regulation authorities

The principal waste regulation authority in England and Wales is the Environment Agency. The principal waste regulation authority in Scotland is the Scottish Environment Protection Agency (SEPA).

The Environment Agency and SEPA took over this function from Local Authorities and their responsibilities include dealing with the application and enforcement of waste management licences, permits and exemptions, waste carriers' licences and the duty of care regime *(refer to 3.6)*.

However, to tackle the problem of waste crime (such as fly-tipping and neighbourhood nuisance) Local Authorities are given powers, including stop and search of vehicles thought to be involved in illegal waste activity. Local Authorities are also responsible for dealing with local air pollution control (LAPC) matters related to waste (such as the issue of permits for crushing equipment).

 The improper disposal of waste is illegal and can lead to prosecution and even imprisonment. The maximum fine for waste crime is a £50,000 fine and/or imprisonment for six months.

3.2 Key requirements

☑ Producers of waste must correctly identify whether surplus materials are waste and classify it as non-hazardous or hazardous with reference to the six-digit European waste catalogue code, SIC code, and so on.

☑ Producers of waste have a legal duty of care to ensure that it is passed on to an authorised person with the correct technical competence and holding a relevant environmental permit or licence.

☑ All contractors who carry or collect construction and demolition waste should have a waste carrier's licence.

☑ All waste transfers must be supported by the correct document (a controlled waste transfer note) for non-hazardous waste. The transfer of hazardous waste requires a consignment note. Both of these documents must include a declaration that the producer of the waste has considered the waste hierarchy in deciding to dispose of the material.

☑ In England and Wales, producers of 500 kg or more hazardous waste (such as oils or asbestos) must register their premises with the Environment Agency.

☑ All waste treatment or disposal facilities should have an environmental permit (England and Wales) or waste management licence (Scotland) unless they have a registered exemption from the Environment Agency or SEPA.

☑ Where materials are treated or processed on site before being suitable for putting back into the works then consideration must be given as to whether this activity requires an environmental permit or registered exemption. Compliance with schemes, including the Contaminated Land: Application In Real Environments (CL:AIRE) code of practice or WRAP's quality protocol for the production of aggregates from inert waste could avoid the requirement of an environmental permit for reuse of the processed material.

☑ From April 2008, projects in England over an estimated value of £300,000 have had to prepare a site waste management plan (SWMP), identifying the types and quantities of waste actions to reduce these wastes. A more detailed plan is required for projects above £500,000.

03

3.3   Defining waste

The starting point on whether something is classed as waste comes from the revised European Waste Framework Directive (WFD) (2008/98/EC). It states that:

> waste shall mean a substance or object which the holder discards, intends to discard or is required to discard.

Waste is also defined in the Environmental Protection Act as:

> any substance which constitutes a scrap material, an effluent or other unwanted surplus arising from the application of any process or any substance or article which requires to be disposed of which has been broken, worn out, contaminated or otherwise spoiled.

In practice, however, this definition has been tested by EU and UK case law and whether or not a substance is waste depends on applying the right legal tests. A substance can be classed as waste even if the producer still has a use for it or if other people are prepared to pay for it. This is important because whether or not a material is waste determines whether a complex body of legal rules and restrictions govern what can be done with it.

Surplus materials are generally not waste whilst they remain in the chain of utility (they remain as the original manufactured product and do not need to be re-processed).

However, construction or demolition waste that has been generated as part of the works could be classified as waste until it has been processed (for example, crushed and screened) and recovered back into the permanent works. In these cases there will be various requirements to demonstrate that the material has achieved an **end of waste** status.

Materials that meet the end of waste test must satisfy the following criteria.

☑ The material must be converted into a distinct and marketable product.

☑ It can be used in the same way as an ordinary soil/aggregate.

☑ It can be used with no negative environmental effects.

Aggregates manufactured from construction and demolition waste complying with the WRAP quality protocol, for example, can normally demonstrate that the material has achieved an end of waste status. Likewise, complying with the CL:AIRE development industry code of practice will also help you to achieve end of waste status for the treatment and use of contaminated excavated materials.

> For further information on the CL:AIRE code of practice and WRAP quality protocol refer to 3.10 and 3.11 respectively.

3.4   Describing and classifying waste

Wastes will always fall into one of three categories; those that are:

☑ **never hazardous** (for example, clean bricks or glass)

☑ **always hazardous** (for example, insulating materials containing asbestos)

☑ **may, or may not be hazardous and need to be assessed** (for example, contaminated soils).

What makes a waste hazardous is whether it contains any dangerous substances above certain thresholds that make it display a certain hazardous property. There are 15 different hazardous properties that exist, from H1 to H15 (for example, H1 is explosive and H6 is toxic or very toxic). The threshold concentration levels for the relevant hazardous properties are defined within the Lists of Wastes Regulations.

The most appropriate method of classifying waste, where it needs to be assessed, is to identify the hazardous constituents/chemicals (dangerous substances) in the waste, determine the risk phrases and hazardous properties of these substances and then to use their concentrations to identify whether they exceed the threshold levels of any of the hazardous properties. The safety documentation supplied with any product should provide sufficient information to make this assessment. For contaminated soils, however, detailed testing would need to be carried out by competent staff.

The European Waste Catalogue (EWC) is a standard six-digit coding system that describes and categorises different types of waste. This has been transposed in England through the Lists of Wastes (England) Regulations. There are similar regulations in Wales. These waste codes are arranged in 20 chapters; Chapter 17 contains the codes for construction and demolition waste.

Appendix A includes the full Chapter 17 EWC codes relating to construction and demolition waste.

Waste management

The list of wastes refers to hazardous and non-hazardous entries. Where an entry is marked with an asterisk it is classified as hazardous waste if it meets one the following criteria.

☑ The hazardous entry makes no reference to dangerous substances (for example, 17 06 05* construction materials containing asbestos). These types of entries are always hazardous and are called **absolute entries**.

☑ The hazardous entry refers to a waste containing dangerous substances and the concentration levels of these dangerous substances exceed the threshold limits (for example, 17 05 03* soil and stones containing dangerous substances). These entries are called **mirror entries** as it depends on the concentration of dangerous substances to determine whether they are hazardous or not. Wastes containing dangerous substances below the threshold limits are non-hazardous.

---

e.g. **Typical construction wastes from Chapter 17 of the list of wastes**

☑ Bricks – 17 01 02 Non-hazardous.

☑ Concrete – 17 01 01 Non-hazardous.

☑ Wood – 17 02 01 Non-hazardous.

☑ Waste hydraulic oil – 13 01 13* Hazardous.

☑ Plasterboard – 17 08 02 Non-hazardous (but must be segregated from other wastes).

☑ Insulation containing asbestos – 17 06 01* Hazardous.

☑ Contaminated soil – 17 05 03* Will be hazardous if concentrations exceed thresholds.

☑ Mixed canteen waste – 20 03 01 Non-hazardous.

The disposal of hazardous waste arising from construction operations, or from contaminated land, is dealt with under the Hazardous Waste Regulations (in England and Wales) or the Special Waste Regulations (in Scotland), and is covered in more detail in 3.8.

 All waste transfer documentation must include the relevant six-digit code that describes that waste.

For the purpose of disposal of waste to landfill there are three classes of waste.

1. **Inert waste** that will not decompose to produce greenhouse gases (such as rubble, concrete and glass).

2. **Non-hazardous waste** that will rot and decompose, and does not contain dangerous substances (such as timber, food and paper).

3. **Hazardous waste** that has substances in sufficient concentration to make it possess one or more of the 15 dangerous properties (such as explosive (H1) or toxic (H6)) and is dangerous to human health or the environment (such as asbestos or oil).

There are strict criteria for the acceptance of waste at each of these three types of landfill site and certain types of waste, particularly contaminated soil, would have to be tested in order to demonstrate that it meets the relevant waste acceptance criteria. The landfill directive introduces a hierarchy of waste characterisation and testing known as the waste acceptance procedures. The three levels are shown below.

Level 1 – Basic characterisation. A thorough determination, according to standardised analysis and behaviour-testing methods, of the leaching behaviour and/or characteristic properties of the waste.

Level 2 – Compliance testing. A periodic testing of regularly arising wastes by simpler standardised analysis and behaviour-testing methods to determine whether a waste complies with permit conditions and whether a waste with known properties has changed significantly. The tests focus on key variables and behaviour identified by basic characterisation.

Level 3 – On-site verification. This constitutes checking methods to confirm that a waste is the same as that which has been subjected to compliance testing and that which is described in the accompanying documents. It may merely consist of a visual inspection of a load of waste before and after unloading at the landfill site.

 Before sending waste to landfill, waste producers and landfill operators must ensure that they know all of the properties of the waste, relevant to its potential for pollution or harm to health, and the options for the management of the waste.

There are certain types of waste that are banned from disposal to landfill. These must either be recovered, recycled or disposed of in other ways (for example, incineration). Banned wastes include:

☑ any liquid waste

☑ infectious medical or veterinary waste

☑ whole or shredded used tyres

☑ waste that might cause a problem in the landfill (such as hot or chemically active waste)

☑ any waste that does not meet the waste acceptance criteria for that class of landfill.

Difficult waste

The term *difficult waste* has come into common use and applies to wastes that require handling in a particular way. Examples of difficult waste include:

☑ **invasive plants**, which are waste materials, both soil and plant matter, contaminated with Japanese knotweed or giant hogweed, that can only be disposed of at sites that are specifically licensed to receive them

☑ **contaminated soil**, which is a mixture of soils, stones, rubble and polluting substances, which could be hazardous depending on thresholds, and could be a range of things left over from former use of the site

☑ **gypsum and plasterboard wastes**, which, when mixed with biodegradable waste, can produce hydrogen sulphide gas in landfill, which is both toxic and odorous.

The land filling of gypsum and other high sulphate-bearing wastes with biodegradable waste has been prohibited in England and Wales since July 2005. Previously, the Environment Agency took a pragmatic view that separate disposal of these substances is not necessary where a waste contains less than 10% of gypsum. However, this flexibility was removed from 1 April 2009 and all gypsum waste should be segregated from biodegradable waste before being sent to landfill. It should be noted that plasterboard waste itself (unless contaminated) is not hazardous waste but must be segregated.

3.5   Waste hierarchy

Article 4 of the revised WFD (2008/98/EC) requires that all reasonable measures should be taken to:

☑ prevent waste

☑ consider the waste hierarchy when you transfer waste.

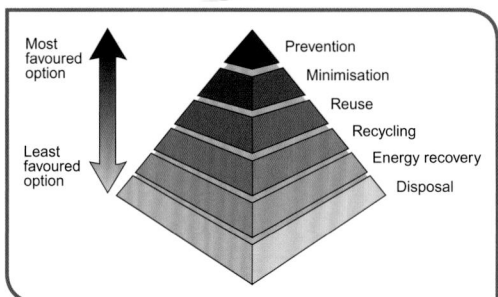

The waste hierarchy is a series of steps for dealing with waste in order of priority and signifies the relative environmental benefits that can be made at each stage.

The waste hierarchy shows that the highest priority is waste reduction or prevention so that the need for other options (such as reuse, recycling and energy recovery) would be dramatically reduced.

 The Waste (England and Wales) Regulations now require that you declare on the waste transfer documentation that you have considered the waste hierarchy in the management of the waste.

Examples of applying the waste hierarchy on a construction project for waste minimisation could include the following.

☑ Reduction/prevention:

– designing the project to suit standard product sizes and to avoid site cutting

– designing the project levels to avoid excavation materials going off site

– specification to allow the use of recycled materials

– pre-assembling components off site or using pre-cast sections

– not over-ordering materials

– reducing the amount of packaging

– ordering materials at the size required, to avoid off-cuts

– creating employee awareness of environmental matters

– requiring sub-contractors to have a waste management policy

– not over-excavating.

Waste management

☑ Reuse:
- reusing soil for landscaping
- using off-cuts of timber for alternative uses
- using brick rubble as hard-core
- investigating local environmental activities where other materials might be reused.

Office recycling

Plasterboard recycling

Segregated waste streams

Timber segregation

☑ Recycling:
- crushing waste concrete to use as hard-core
- recycling asphalt planings as road sub-base or temporary surfacing
- recycling scrap metal, glass and waste oil
- segregating waste materials to a separate well-planned area
- recycling timber off site for educational use or social enterprise (see case study on the following page)
- recycling office waste (such as paper, cans and plastics).

 The WRAP website contains a number of useful resources for designing out waste, managing waste, what materials can be recycled and organisations for doing this.

☑ Recovery:
- sending waste for composting or for energy recovery (such as timber off site to be shredded for use as biomass fuel, or composting).

☑ Disposal:
- sending canteen or office waste for disposal to a local landfill site.

 The recycling or treatment of waste on or off site is likely to require a waste management permit (England and Wales) or licence (Scotland), or registered exemption. *(Further details on waste management permitting are outlined in 3.9.)*

03

 Social enterprise for waste – National community wood recycling project

The NCWRP was founded in 2003 to help set up and develop a nationwide network of wood recycling social enterprises.

Modelled on the multi-award-winning Brighton and Hove wood recycling project, the aim of these social enterprises is to:

☑ save resources by rescuing and reusing waste timber that would otherwise be landfilled (or at very best down cycled into woodchip)

☑ create sustainable jobs and training and volunteering opportunities for local people – especially those who might be described as disadvantaged and find it difficult to get back to employment.

 The national community wood recycling project website provides further details of the project, partners and locations of where wood is being recycled.

Treatment of waste

The Environmental Permitting (England and Wales) Regulations and the Landfill (Scotland) Regulations state that non-hazardous waste must now be treated before being sent to landfill. In practical terms treatment is applying the waste hierarchy to reduce the quantity of waste that ends up in landfill.

Treatment must satisfy all three criteria of a three point test. The treatment must:

1. be a physical, thermal, chemical, or biological process (including sorting)

2. change the characteristics of the waste

3. be carried out in order to:
   – reduce the volume of the waste
   – reduce the hazardous nature of the waste
   – facilitate handling of the waste
   – enhance recovery of the waste.

On construction sites, in practical terms, this can be achieved by setting up appropriate segregated skips and separating out **(sorting)** any wastes that can be reused or recycled, which will change the **characteristics of the original waste stream**. This in turn will aid in **reducing the volume** of the waste, **facilitating the handling** of the waste and **enhancing recovery** of the waste destined for landfill.

Hazardous wastes are required to be stored and disposed of separately from non-hazardous wastes. Separating these out will **reduce the hazardous nature** of the original waste stream.

Sending your waste to a transfer station or recycling facility, for sorting and recovery prior to the residual waste being sent to landfill, will also satisfy these treatment requirements.

Excavated materials that are to be treated on or off site are generally considered to be waste and the treatment facility operator must have an appropriate environmental permit or register a waste exemption allowing that particular treatment of the excavated materials. This issue is explained in 3.9 and 3.10.

3.6   Duty of care and waste carrier registration

If you are involved in managing waste you have a legal duty of care. The duty of care applies to everyone involved in handling the waste:

☑ from the person who produces it

☑ to the person who finally disposes of or recovers it.

Duty of care is one of the main ways to combat fly-tipping and means that:

☑ waste has to be stored in a secure location and measures taken to prevent its escape

☑ waste has to be passed to an authorised person holding a valid licence or permit

☑ any waste passed to an authorised person must be supported by the relevant documentation.

E

Waste management

Registration of waste carriers, brokers and dealers (England and Wales)

The Waste (England and Wales) Regulations implements a system for the registration of:

 waste carriers (those who move waste)

☑ waste brokers (those who arrange the movement/disposal on behalf of others)

☑ waste dealers (those who use an agent to buy and sell waste).

It is possible for a single registration to cover all of these activities.

There are two classes of registration known as upper tier and lower tier.

☑ **Lower tier.** Those registered in the lower tier are known as **specified persons**. This group includes all those who are currently registered as professionally exempt. In general this refers to waste authorities, charities, voluntary organisations and those who only manage wastes from agricultural premises, animal by-product wastes or wastes from mines or quarries.

Those that are currently registered as professionally exempt will automatically be transferred to the lower tier. From the end of December 2013 anyone who normally and regularly carries their own business waste (excluding construction and demolition waste) will need to register in the lower tier.

There is currently no fee for lower tier registration; the registration will be valid until revoked or cancelled.

☑ **Upper tier.** There will be a fee payable for upper tier registration. Upper tier registration will be valid for three years unless revoked or cancelled. If you are a waste carrier, broker or dealer but you are not a specified person you will need to register in the upper tier. All those who are currently registered and not professionally exempt will automatically be transferred to the upper tier. **This includes those who carry their own construction and demolition waste. The existing renewal date will remain valid.**

> An application for registration as a carrier, broker or dealer can be made on the Environment Agency's website or by downloading the appropriate form.

Registration of waste carriers (Scotland)

The Controlled Waste (Registration of Carriers and Seizure of Vehicles) Regulations in Scotland require that if you transport waste within the UK, in the course of your business or in any other way for profit, you must register as a carrier of waste with the local waste regulation authority.

You must register even if you only carry your own company's waste or carry waste on an infrequent basis. This applies whether you are a self-employed contractor, part of a partnership or a company.

Registration only needs to be made in the area where your company has its head office. All other offices will be covered by this one registration.

Application for registration as a waste carrier must be made on the prescribed form, which is obtainable from the local waste regulation authority office.

If you have applied for registration but have not yet received the documentation, you will be deemed to be registered and may carry waste.

> The law demands that waste carriers keep a copy of their registration document on their vehicle. Do not accept photocopies of registration documents as proof of registration. If you have any doubt as to whether the carrier is registered or not, ask the appropriate waste regulation authority.

3.7   Controlled waste and transfer notes

All waste subject to the provisions of the Environmental Protection Act is known as controlled waste and includes waste from domestic, commercial and industrial premises as well as hazardous waste.

Under the duty of care waste must be passed to an authorised person (a holder of a waste carrier or waste management permit or licence).

When non-hazardous waste is transferred to an authorised person this must be supported by a controlled waste transfer note. This also applies even if you have produced and carry waste yourself. The transfer of hazardous waste must be supported by a consignment note *(refer to 3.8)*.

> Refer to Appendix B for a sample of a controlled waste transfer note.

Whenever you pass non-hazardous waste on to someone else, you will have to declare on the waste transfer note that you have applied all reasonable measures to apply the waste management hierarchy.

It is a requirement to include the appropriate 2007 standard industry classification (SIC) code on all waste transfer notes. Hazardous waste consignment notes issued before that will continue to use the 2003 SIC code.

The controlled waste transfer note must:

☑ include a declaration that you have taken all measures to apply the waste management hierarchy

☑ include the appropriate SIC code

☑ give a description of the waste, including the six-digit EWC code

☑ state the quantity

☑ state how the waste is contained, whether loose or in a container and, if in a container, the kind of container

☑ identify the carrier of the waste

☑ state the date, time and location of transfer

☑ identify the disposal site

☑ contain your signature and the signature of the authorised person receiving your waste.

You must:

☑ keep a copy of the transfer note for a minimum of two years

☑ give a copy to the disposal site representative. They will:

– sign the documents to say where, when and how the waste will or has been disposed of.

If you use a registered carrier to dispose of your waste for you, the transfer note must contain all the points described above and, in addition, state the:

☑ name and address of the carrier, their licence registration number and issuing authority

☑ place of transfer.

If you use a registered carrier to remove your waste, they will raise and distribute the necessary documentation and will:

☑ give you a copy to keep

☑ keep a copy for themselves

☑ deliver your waste and a copy of the document to the management at the disposal site.

> You must keep all controlled, non-hazardous waste transfer documentation for two years.

3.8 Hazardous waste and consignment notes

In England and Wales, all construction premises that produce, plan to produce or store 500 kg or more of hazardous waste, in any twelve month period, must be registered with the Environment Agency before the waste is removed from site. This can be done either on a paper form or electronically online on the Environment Agency's website. Registration must be renewed annually.

> Sites producing or storing less than 500 kg per year must still comply with the Hazardous Waste (England and Wales) Regulations. There is no requirement to register your site in Scotland.

The Hazardous Waste Regulations in England and Wales, and the Special Waste Regulations in Scotland, require that all hazardous waste must be segregated from non-hazardous waste. The following controls should be adopted to comply with the regulations.

☑ Different types of hazardous wastes should be segregated, as you will clearly need to identify the quantities and types on the hazardous waste consignment note.

☑ Mixing of different types of hazardous waste should be avoided as this may inadvertently create an explosive or fire risk, particularly in warm weather.

☑ The mixing of hazardous waste with non-hazardous waste to dilute the material below the threshold concentration is banned.

☑ Packaging or containers contaminated with hazardous substances should be treated as hazardous waste unless it can be shown that the concentration (including the packaging) is below the threshold limits.

Where individual products are combined to form a substance (such as adhesives and resins) then each component should be considered for its hazardous properties and disposed of accordingly. Resins are often inert when set so leaving materials to dry before disposal may make them non-hazardous.

Removal of hazardous waste

If you wish to have hazardous waste removed from site, a document called a **hazardous waste consignment note** (special waste consignment note in Scotland) must be prepared.

 For an example of a hazardous waste consignment note refer to Appendix C.

The consignment note must be prepared by the person who is originating the transfer of the waste. In Scotland, a special waste consignment note must be obtained from the local office of the Scottish Environment Protection Agency (SEPA).

The hazardous waste consignment note must include the following information:

- ☑ the premises code (where the site is required to register)
- ☑ a consignment note code*
- ☑ address of the producer
- ☑ name and address of the consignee (where the waste will be taken)
- ☑ details of the process that produced the waste
- ☑ the appropriate 2007 SIC code
- ☑ a description of the waste, including the six-digit EWC code
- ☑ the quantity
- ☑ various details on the properties of the waste, including concentrations, hazard code and proper shipping name
- ☑ the type of container
- ☑ the date and time of transfer
- ☑ your signature (consignor) and the signature of the authorised person carrying the waste
- ☑ a declaration that you have taken all measures to apply the waste management hierarchy.

* The consignment note code is a unique code for each consignment of hazardous waste and is always in the same format of six digits, followed by a forward slash, and then five further digits (for example ABC123/45678). The specific coding to be used will be determined by whether the site is registered, exempt from registering or whether the waste was fly-tipped. The table below sets out the required format for this coding.

Coding format for hazardous waste consignment notes

Type of producer	Registered	Exempt	Fly-tipped
Consignment note code format	ABC123/YYYYY	EXEAAA/YYYZZ	FLYAAA/YYYZZ
First six digits	'ABC123' is the registration number given when you registered your premises – it will have the format XXXNNN (X is a letter, N is a number, for example, ABF599)	'EXE' shows the premises are exempt	'FLY' shows the waste was fly-tipped
		'AAA' can be any letters or numbers (for example, the first three letters of the name of the waste collection business)	'AAA' can be any letters or numbers (for example, the first three letters of the name of the waste collection business)
Second five digits	'YYYYY' can be any letters or numbers (for example, HW02L)	'YYY' can be any letters or numbers (for example, the initials of the trading name of the premises)	'YYY' can be any letters or numbers (for example, the first three digits of the postcode where the fly-tipping took place)
		'ZZ' can be any letters or numbers used to give the consignment a unique code	'ZZ' can be any letters or numbers used to give the consignment a unique code
Example	For example, the consignment note code could be ABF599/HW02L	For example, if Bob's waste management were collecting the waste from a company called E B Aardvark, the consignment note code could be EXEBOB/EBA01	For example, if Bob's waste management was collecting the waste from a street with a postcode of BN1 1AB, the consignment note code could be FLYBOB/BN101

In Scotland, a copy of completed consignment notes must be received by SEPA at least 72 hours before the waste is due to leave site. Completed consignment notes are valid for 28 days after the anticipated date of collection.

 You must keep all hazardous waste documentation for three years.

3.9 Environmental permits and exemptions

Environmental permitting in England and Wales

The Environmental Permitting (England and Wales) Regulations (EPR) combine the system of waste management licensing previously regulated under the Waste Management Licensing Regulations, and the system of permitting installations in the Pollution Prevention and Control (England and Wales) Regulations. The EPR also now include the provision of permits to deal with groundwater protection and water discharges.

 For further information on water protection refer to Chapter E05 Water management.

The EPR specify which waste activities require an environmental permit and allow some waste activities to be exempt from requiring a permit (as in Schedule 3 discussed below). Certain waste operations covered by other legislation are excluded from these permitting arrangements.

An environmental permit is required for seven different classes of **regulated facility**, five of which relate to waste (the other two cover groundwater and water discharges):

- ☑ **installations** – generally these are facilities at which industrial, waste and intensive farming activities falling (mainly) under the Integrated Pollution Prevention and Control Directive are carried out. These include landfill sites

- ☑ **waste operation** – any other waste activity that is not defined as an installation will be classed as a waste operation. This includes the depositing, treatment or recycling of waste that is not exempt under the Environmental Permitting Regulations (such as waste transfer stations) including the treatment of contaminated land

- ☑ **mobile plant** – mobile equipment carrying out an activity listed in Schedule 1 of the EPR or a waste operation (such as crushers)

- ☑ **mining waste operation** – the management of mining extraction waste that may include the mining waste facility

- ☑ **radioactive substances** – the keeping and management of radioactive material (including radioactive apparatus) or the storage and disposal of radioactive waste.

 It is an offence to operate a regulated facility without the relevant permit. You could be fined up to £50,000 and imprisoned for up to five years for this offence.

Two types of permit can be applied for:

- ☑ **standard permits** for certain standard types of waste operation (such as a waste transfer station or mobile treatment plant for the treatment of waste soils). Each type of standard permit has standard rules and risk criteria that have to be met to comply with the permit

- ☑ **bespoke permits** for more complex operations that are specifically relevant to the waste facility or operation.

If you can't meet the requirements of a standard permit then you may need to apply for a bespoke permit.

Exemptions are for activities that don't need or are below the threshold limits for a permit. Many of these need to be registered (see below).

Environmental permit applications

The starting point is to understand what type of waste activity is intended to be carried out, who regulates it, and then complete an application to the appropriate regulator.

Part 2 of Schedule 1 to the EPR lists regulated facilities that are installations and mobile plant. They include Part A(1) activities that are regulated by the EA and Part A(2) and Part B activities that are regulated by Local Authorities. The EA generally regulates activities that are higher risk and can pollute more than one media (such as water and air), whereas Local Authorities regulate activities that contribute to air pollution.

Waste management

The following table defines which authority is responsible for issuing permits for regulated facilities associated with construction.

Type of regulated facility	Regulator and where to send permit applications
Installations	
Landfill sites	Environment Agency
Asphalt plant	Environment Agency
Concrete batching plants	Local Authority
Waste operation	
Waste transfer stations	Environment Agency
Use of waste in construction	Environment Agency
Mobile plant	
Mobile plant for the treatment of contaminated soils	Environment Agency
Mobile plant for crushing and screening demolition waste	Local Authority

Mobile plant for the treatment of waste soils and contaminated material is a waste operation regulated under a standard permit SR2008 No. 27 by the EA. In addition to holding the permit the operator is required to prepare a site-specific deployment form, which sets out in detail the type of technology used and specified activities at the site.

The treatment of contaminated soil and/or contaminated waters requires a mobile treatment permit (MTP).

A mobile treatment permit is used to regulate a mobile plant activity that involves treatment either in situ or ex situ. The permit sets out the type and extent of activities that can be carried out. A site-based permit has to be used where a mobile plant permit is not applicable. The environmental permit can be either a standard rules permit or a bespoke one depending upon the type of treatment and site location.

Operators who want to treat contaminated soil and/or contaminated waters using their mobile plant permit at a particular site must submit a site-specific deployment application (the deployment form and supporting information). The deployment application details site-specific information and potential impacts arising from the proposed use of the mobile plant. The operator must demonstrate that the activity will not cause pollution of the environment, harm to human health or serious detriment to local amenities.

Following treatment under a MTP the material would normally cease to be waste, providing it was excavated and treated on the site it was used or is part of a remediation cluster. Where this is not the case then an environmental permit or registered exemption would be required.

 For flowcharts providing further guidance on permitting for the use or reuse of soils or aggregates refer to Appendix D.

The regulator has four months from receipt of the permit application and all supporting information to make a determination. You have the right of appeal to the Secretary of State should your permit not be granted, or the permit is granted but you are not happy with the conditions that have been imposed. Pre-application discussions with the regulator can help in improving the quality of permit applications so early contact with them is advisable.

The Waste (England and Wales) Regulations implement a new permit condition to require waste to be managed in accordance with the waste hierarchy.

Only a person who is in control of a regulated facility may obtain or hold an environmental permit. This person is called the operator.

To obtain an environmental permit you may have to prove that you have the appropriate technical competence (see below) to be able to carry out the relevant activities and fulfil the obligations of an operator.

The regulator will consider:

- ☑ whether your management systems are adequate
- ☑ if your site is run by someone who is technically competent (see below)
- ☑ any convictions that you, or other persons in your business, may have for pollution offences
- ☑ if you have taken steps to meet the possible costs of the duties of the permit.

Technical competence

Certain types of waste management activity require the operator to demonstrate technical competence. They are called relevant waste operations. These include, for example, landfill sites, transfer stations and certain activities involving hazardous waste.

You will be able to show that you are a technically competent operator if you can satisfy one of the following.

- ☑ Compliance with an approved industry scheme. There are currently two approved schemes for operators of relevant waste operations, the:
  - CIWM/WAMITAB scheme
  - ESA/EU scheme.

☑ Holding an appropriate certificate of technical competence (CoTC) from the Waste Management Industry Training and Advisory Board (WAMITAB), which issues a range of certificates for the managers of most types of waste management site. This can be checked on the WAMITAB CoTC database.

☑ Holding a registered and validated deemed competence status (see below).

☑ You have previously completed an environmental assessment for non-CoTC activities.

Persons operating under a waste disposal licence before May 1994 have been deemed to be technically competent for that operation, and have never been required to demonstrate their technical competence. These individuals will retain deemed competence status and will now be assumed to have passed the continuing competence assessment.

Exemptions from environmental permitting in England and Wales

There are a number of exemptions from environmental permitting for certain waste activities that are not seen as a threat to the environment. The general requirements and descriptions of these exemptions are set out in Schedule 3 of the Environmental Permitting Regulations.

The Environmental Permitting Regulations have significantly changed the descriptions and references for exemptions, which are now grouped into four categories.

Refer to Appendix E for materials and quantity thresholds for U1 or T5 exemptions.

1. **Use of waste.** This includes the recovery or reuse of waste for a purpose. These exemptions will have a 'U' reference (for example, *U1 – Use of waste in construction*).

2. **Treatment of waste.** This includes the treatment of material for the purpose of recovery. These exemptions will have a 'T' reference (for example, *T5 – Screening and blending of waste for the purposes of producing an aggregate or soil and associated prior treatment*). Note that some wastes produced under this exemption may then be used under another exemption (such as the production of aggregates) that is then used under a *U1 – Use of waste in construction exemption*.

3. **Disposal of waste.** This includes the disposal of certain types of waste onto land. These exemptions will have a 'D' reference (for example, *D1 – Deposit of waste from dredging of inland waters*).

4. **Storage of waste.** This includes the storage of waste at a location other than where it was produced pending its recovery or disposal. These exemptions will have an 'S' reference (for example, *S2 – Storage of waste in a secure place*).

These exemptions generally exclude hazardous waste and there will be conditions on most exemptions granted. For example, the conditions included in the exemption might be:

☑ limits on the quantities and time periods for the temporary storage of waste produced on site for reuse on that site

☑ limits on the quantities for the spreading, on land, of waste soil

☑ that certain other precautions must be taken.

You may deal with waste under an exemption subject to the conditions imposed, but you must make sure that you do not pollute the environment or cause harm to anyone's health.

To obtain a waste management exemption under Schedule 3 of the Environmental Permitting Regulations, an application must be made, together with the appropriate fee, to the correct waste regulation authority. In most cases this is the EA.

However, if you want to crush bricks, tiles and concrete you may need to register a *T7 – Treatment of waste bricks, tiles and concrete by crushing, grinding or reducing in size* exemption with your Local Authority. Also note that the equipment will need to have a valid mobile plant permit, which must be obtained from the Local Authority in which the business is situated.

The information required varies considerably depending on the relevant exemption being applied for. Notifications for more complex exemptions will generally require a form to be completed and must be supported by information such as:

☑ name and address of applicant for the exemption

☑ location of the site where the waste activity is being carried out

☑ details of relevant planning permissions

☑ description, type and analysis of the waste

☑ intended use for the waste

☑ the relevant fee.

A number of the exemptions also have time constraints and cannot be renewed before the expiry date. For example, under a *U1 – Use of waste in construction* exemption, you cannot register the exemption more than once at any one place during the three-year period from first registration.

Paragraph 103 of the Environmental Permitting Regulations deals with transitional arrangements for existing waste exemptions that were in place before the regulations came into force on 6 April 2010.

For flowcharts providing further guidance on exemptions from permitting for the use or reuse of soils or aggregates refer to Appendix D.

Waste management licensing in Scotland

In Scotland, the existing waste management licensing system is controlled under Section 33 of Part II of the Environmental Protection Act and the Waste Management Licensing (Scotland) Regulations.

A waste management licence is required if you deposit, recover, treat or dispose of controlled waste. If you do any of these things without a licence, or a licence exemption, you could be fined and/or sent to prison.

Obtaining a full waste management licence can be a lengthy and costly exercise. To obtain a waste management licence you have to prove that you are a fit and proper person. Applications for waste management licences should be made to SEPA.

SEPA will consider:

- ☑ any convictions that you, or other persons in your business, may have for pollution offences
- ☑ if your site is run by someone who is technically competent
- ☑ if you have taken steps to meet the possible costs of the duties of the licence.

Technical competence

Under the Waste Management Licensing (Scotland) Regulations there is no longer a legal requirement for a technically competent person in Scotland to hold a certificate of technical competence (CoTC). These were previously regulated by the Waste Management Industry Training and Advisory Board (WAMITAB) under Waste Management Licensing Regulations.

CoTCs remain an appropriate qualification to demonstrate competence in Scotland and can be used on a voluntary basis. Operators in Scotland should contact their SEPA regulatory officer in the first instance to check other competence arrangements.

Waste management licence applications

An application for a waste management licence can only be made if planning permission has been granted. To obtain a waste management licence, you should apply to the waste licensing office of SEPA and ask the following questions.

- ☑ How do you apply for the licence?
- ☑ What information do they require?
- ☑ How can you show that you are a fit and proper person, including technical competence?
- ☑ How much is the application fee for the type of site you wish to run?

SEPA has four months from when all information was received to consider the application. You have the right of appeal to the Secretary of State should your licence not be granted, or the licence is granted but you are not happy with the conditions that have been imposed.

Exemptions from waste management licensing in Scotland

There are a number of waste management exemptions set out in Schedule 1 of the Waste Management Licensing (Scotland) Regulations. These exemptions generally exclude hazardous waste and there will be conditions on most exemptions granted.

For example, the conditions included in the exemption might be:

- ☑ limits on the quantities and time periods for the temporary storage of waste produced on site for reuse on that site
- ☑ limits on the quantities for the spreading, on land, of waste soil
- ☑ that certain other precautions must be taken.

You may deal with waste under an exemption subject to the conditions imposed, but you must make sure that you do not pollute the environment or cause harm to anyone's health.

To obtain a waste management exemption under Schedule 1 of the Waste Management Licensing Regulations, an application must be made, together with the appropriate fee, if appropriate, to SEPA.

The information required varies considerably depending on the relevant exemption being applied for. In Scotland, SEPA makes a distinction between simple and complex exemptions and the notification process is different for each type. Notifications for complex exemptions will generally require a form to be completed and must be supported by information such as:

- ☑ name and address of applicant for the exemption
- ☑ location of the site where the waste activity is being carried out
- ☑ details of relevant planning permissions
- ☑ description, type and analysis of the waste
- ☑ intended use for the waste
- ☑ the relevant fee.

A number of the exemptions are also required to be renewed on an annual basis. Further advice should be sought from SEPA.

3.10   CL:AIRE Development Industry Code of Practice (DICoP)

CL:AIRE (Contaminated Land: Applications in Real Environments) has developed a code of practice for dealing with the waste management aspects of contaminated land. This code of practice, developed with contributions from the development and remediation industries and the EA, is designed to help developers and construction companies to identify if they are dealing with waste and when waste is fully recovered.

Version 2 of the code of practice was launched in March 2011 with an extended scope. The scenarios now covered are:

☑ reuse of excavated materials on the site of production (contaminated and uncontaminated)

☑ direct transfer of clean, naturally occurring soils between sites

☑ reuse of naturally elevated substances in soils (such as arsenic and lead)

03

☑ cluster projects (multiple reuse at different development sites within a similar timeframe)

☑ brownfield to brownfield transfers

☑ fixed soil treatment facilities allowing the release of treated materials to the market place.

The main purpose of the code of practice is to achieve good practice across the development industry to:

☑ assess whether materials are waste or not

☑ determine when treated waste ceases to become waste

☑ provide an auditable trail to demonstrate that the code of practice has been complied with on each site.

The code of practice (CoP) specifies the implementation of a **materials management plan** (MMP) alongside a site waste management plan, together with a declaration from a competent qualified person before the commencement of the works. When the declaration is provided to the Environment Agency, demonstrating that the materials are to be dealt with in accordance with the MMP, the Environment Agency may take the view that the materials, where they are used on site, may cease to be waste. The Environment Agency has issued a position statement in regard to the CoP supporting this view but it will be up to the site to demonstrate proper controls are in place.

By complying with this CoP it may be possible to avoid the need to apply for a waste permitting exemption for the use of construction waste (U1) as highlighted above. The CoP also allows the direct transfer of uncontaminated natural excavation materials between projects without the need for a permit.

 Further advice should be sought from CL:AIRE with reference to the code of practice.

 Flowcharts providing further guidance on how the CL:AIRE CoP links with environmental permitting in regard to the use or reuse of soils, can be found in Appendix D.

03

  CL:AIRE Code of Practice – a case study

Galliford Try – Ingsbeck flood alleviation scheme

Background

The voluntary CoP developed by CL:AIRE in conjunction with the Environment Agency helps determine whether materials are classed as waste. The CoP has recently been updated (CL:AIRE CoPv2) to allow the direct transfer of naturally occurring soil materials.

Ingsbeck flood alleviation scheme is a £11 million development in Wakefield. It is spread across a number of areas and comprises the construction of new flood defence walls, channels, embankments and flood storage areas. Part of the construction involved building a new clay flood defence embankment around residential houses, which was valued at approximately £180,000. This required approximately 4,000 tonnes of clay. By applying the CoP, a materials management plan (MMP) was produced to enable the reuse of this material, which had a number of benefits, shown below.

Reduced operational costs

The use of a large volume of waste material would require the use of a standard rules environmental permit, which takes approximately four months in application and incurs costs of around £6,000 for application, subsistence and surrender, as well as the use of a technically competent manager. However, the production of the MMP took three weeks from production to sign off and only cost £500. This benefited the project by reducing programme time and cost, which significantly decreased the overall project cost by £60,000, approximately 33% of the project value.

Reduced landfill costs

The surplus material would have been destined for landfill as there was no further use on the donor site. By utilising the MMP, 4,000 tonnes of material was diverted from landfill (avoiding a £10,000 landfill gate fee for importing inert material) and further benefiting from an 80 tonne embodied carbon saving.

Reduced use of natural resources

By utilising a recycled material, this avoided the use of excavating the material from a quarry, which avoided the further use of a finite material.

Reduced regulatory effort

The use of the MMP does not require any direct involvement from the Environment Agency regulator. This frees up its resources for deployment on other tasks and allows self-regulation for the industry, whilst minimising impact and protecting the environment.

3.11 WRAP quality protocol for the production of aggregates from inert waste

This protocol is published by the waste and resources action programme (WRAP) and has been produced by the Quarry Products Association (QPA), the Highways Agency (HA) and WRAP as a formalised quality control procedure for the production of aggregates from recovered inert waste. These are referred to in the document as *recovered aggregates*.

The document has two main purposes, to:

- ☑ assist in identifying the point at which the inert waste used to produce recovered aggregates has been fully recovered, ceases to be a waste and becomes a product. *(Further information on the definition of waste and recovery is given in Section 1 of the document.)*

- ☑ give adequate assurance that recovered aggregate products conform to standards common to both recovered and primary aggregates.

The protocol seeks to ensure that recovered aggregates meet the quality and conformity requirements for European standards for aggregates. If they do then they are likely to be regarded as having been completely recovered and having ceased to be waste at that point. However, whether a substance or object is waste, in any particular situation, must still be determined in the light of all the circumstances, having regard to the aims of the WFD and the need to ensure that its effectiveness is not undermined.

You have a responsibility to check that all relevant documentation is correct to confirm that the protocol requirements have been met.

  For further information refer to the WRAP website.

  For flowcharts providing further guidance on how the WRAP quality protocol links with environmental permitting for the reuse of aggregates refer to Appendix D.

3.12 Waste electrical and electronic equipment

The Waste Electrical and Electronic Equipment Regulations (the WEEE Regulations) came into effect on 2 January 2007 and apply to England, Scotland and Wales. These regulations apply to ten categories of electrical equipment listed in Schedule 1 and generally cover all types of electrical equipment (for example, computers, power tools and microwaves). Schedule 2 lists the products that fall under each of the ten categories in Schedule 1.

A producer selling electrical equipment for non-household use (such as equipment used by a construction company) is obliged to finance the collection, treatment and recycling in an environmentally sound manner of:

☑ any waste electrical equipment replaced (with equivalent or similar function) by the electrical equipment sold, if it was originally purchased before 13 August 2005, whether supplied by this or another producer

☑ the electrical equipment the producer sold on or after 13 August 2005 when it is eventually discarded as WEEE.

The collection, treatment and recovery may be undertaken either by the producer, or by their producer compliance scheme (PCS), which they must register with. The PCS should be registered with the appropriate waste regulation authority (Environment Agency or SEPA).

Equipment distributors (retailers, wholesalers, mail order or internet dealers) do not have any specific obligations for non-household electrical equipment. However, the PCS registration information should be passed on so that the end user (such as a construction company) can properly dispose of the item at the end of its life.

End-user responsibilities for WEEE

A construction company's role in the WEEE Regulations means that, to dispose of waste electrical equipment, the following actions must be taken.

☑ It must be segregated from other types of waste for disposal.

☑ If the waste electrical equipment was purchased before 13 August 2005, and is being replaced with new equivalent equipment, then ask the producer for details of its PCS and collection arrangements.

☑ If the waste equipment is not being replaced with new equivalent equipment, or the PCS cannot be traced, then you must pay to transfer the waste equipment to an approved authorised treatment facility that can accept waste electrical equipment (such as a licensed transfer station).

☑ If it was purchased after 13 August 2005, then contact the supplier for details of the PCS and collection arrangements (if these have not been provided).

☑ Any waste transferred to an authorised collector or waste carrier must meet all of the normal requirements for duty of care (such as waste carrier's licence, transfer notes and licensed treatment facilities, for example waste transfer station) approved by the waste regulation authority.

3.13 Waste batteries

The construction industry is a large user of batteries in many types of vehicles, plant and equipment. Currently the recycling rate for portable batteries is low, at around 3%.

The Waste Batteries and Accumulators Regulations came into force on 5 May 2009 and apply to the UK. They implement the waste battery provisions of the EU Directive on Batteries and Accumulators 2006/66/EC and set out requirements for waste battery collection, treatment, recycling and disposal for all types of battery.

The regulations deal with three types of battery.

1. **Automotive batteries** used for starting or the ignition of a vehicle engine, or for powering the lights of a vehicle.

2. **Industrial batteries** used for industrial or professional purposes (such as the battery used as a source of power and propulsion to drive the motor in an electric forklift).

3. **Portable batteries** that are sealed, can be hand carried and are neither an automotive battery or accumulator nor an industrial battery. Examples of a portable battery include AA or AAA type battery or the battery used to power a laptop or mobile telephone.

Take-back of waste batteries

These regulations require that distributors of **portable batteries** (for example, retail stores) have a duty to take back waste portable batteries through facilities such as in-store waste-battery bins. This requirement does not apply to distributors who supply less than 32 kg of batteries per year.

A producer of **industrial batteries** is obliged to provide for the take-back of waste industrial batteries free of charge from the end user where:

☑ the producer has supplied new industrial batteries to that end user

☑ for any reason, the end user is not able to return waste industrial batteries to the supplier who supplied the batteries, providing the waste batteries are the same chemistry as the batteries the producer places on the market

☑ if the end user is not purchasing new batteries, and a battery with the same chemistry as the one being returned has not been placed on the market for a number of years, then the end user's entitlement is to be able to contact any producer to request take-back.

Waste management

The regulations also require that **automotive battery** producers collect, on request, waste automotive batteries free of charge, from businesses (such as garages, scrap yards, end-of-life vehicle authorised treatment facilities or civic amenity sites, such as Local Authority waste recycling centres) during any calendar year in which the producer places new automotive batteries on the market. Under the regulations producers do not have a duty to collect waste automotive batteries from individual end users.

Guidance for battery users

A key aim of the regulations is to enable end users of industrial batteries to have them treated and recycled at no cost to the end user.

End users of automotive batteries are not entitled to the free collection of their waste batteries by battery producers. Businesses (such as garages, breakdown companies and end-of-life vehicle treatment facilities) are not obliged to accept waste batteries from end users free of charge but may be prepared to do so because these businesses are entitled to a free collection service from battery producers.

As with any waste, the final holders must comply with the duty of care for waste by ensuring that all waste transfers are passed to authorised persons, together with the correct waste transfer documentation. Waste should only be carried by a licensed waste carrier.

3.14   Site waste management plans

The requirement for site waste management plans (SWMPs) on construction projects became law through the Site Waste Management Plan Regulations. The two key reasons for implementation of the regulations were to:

- ☑ improve resource efficiency and reduce waste
- ☑ prevent fly-tipping.

Preparing site waste management plans

Any client intending to carry out a construction project with an estimated cost greater than £300,000 is required to prepare a SWMP. It is likely, however; that the client may contractually delegate this responsibility to the principal contractor.

The Site Waste Management Plan Regulations require that the plan must identify the:

- ☑ client
- ☑ principal contractor
- ☑ person who drafted it
- ☑ nature of the construction work and location
- ☑ estimated cost of the project
- ☑ types and quantities of each waste expected to be produced during the project
- ☑ waste management action proposed for each of these wastes (such as reusing, recycling, recovery or disposal).

The plan must also include information on any decisions taken before the plan was prepared relating to the nature of the project, its design, construction methods or materials employed to minimise the amount of waste. The plan must also include a declaration from the client and principal contractor that:

- ☑ all waste is dealt with in accordance with the Duty of Care Regulations
- ☑ materials will be handled efficiently and waste managed appropriately.

Updating site waste management plans

The Site Waste Management Plan Regulations require that certain records are maintained. These requirements depend on whether the estimated value of the project is less than £500,000 or above £500,000. There are more detailed requirements for projects above £500,000.

For projects less than £500,000, whenever waste is removed the plan must be updated by the principal contractor to identify:

- ☑ the company or person removing the waste
- ☑ the types of waste removed
- ☑ where the waste will be taken to.

For projects above £500,000, whenever waste is removed the principal contractor must update the plan to identify the:

- ☑ company or person removing the waste
- ☑ waste carrier's registration number
- ☑ waste by providing a description along with a copy or reference to the DoC waste transfer note
- ☑ site that the waste is being taken to and whether the operator of the site holds a waste management permit under the Environmental Permitting (England and Wales) Regulations (see above).

As often as appropriate, but at least every six months, the principal contractor must ensure that the plan accurately reflects the progress of the project by:

- ☑ reviewing the plan

- ☑ recording the types and quantities of waste produced

- ☑ recording the types and quantities of waste that have been reused, recycled, sent for another form of recovery, sent to landfill or disposed of in another manner.

Finalising site waste management plans at project completion

There are also requirements under the Site Waste Management Plan Regulations to add information when the project has been completed.

For projects with an estimated value of less than £500,000, within three months of the works being completed the principal contractor must add the following information to the plan:

- ☑ confirmation that the plan has been monitored on a regular basis and the works are progressing in accordance with the plan

- ☑ an explanation of any deviations from the plan.

For projects above £500,000, within three months of the works being completed the principal contractor must add the following information to the plan:

- ☑ confirmation that the plan has been monitored on a regular basis and the works are progressing in accordance with the plan

- ☑ a comparison of the estimated quantities of each waste against the actual quantities

- ☑ an explanation of any deviations from the plan

- ☑ an estimate of the cost savings that have been achieved by completing and implementing the plan.

A copy of the SWMP should be maintained at the site office or at a location that is accessible to any contractor who has an involvement within it. Arrangements for the project site waste management plan should also be included within site inductions.

As well as being a legal requirement, implementing a SWMP can bring a number of business benefits, such as:

- ☑ wastes can be identified early and can be minimised through design and procurement practices before construction starts

- ☑ queries from the waste regulation authority can be answered simply and easily

- ☑ it can help avoid prosecution by ensuring that all wastes being disposed of ends up in the right place

- ☑ it shows how waste is managed and can demonstrate any savings made

- ☑ materials and waste are managed responsibly and are therefore less risk to the environment

- ☑ it provides valuable information for future projects on the costs and quantities of waste produced. This information can be used to set targets for reduction.

Whilst the Site Waste Management Plan Regulations do not specify how all of this information should be presented, a standard template and guidance is available from the Government's non-statutory guidance for SWMPs.

 Further advice can be obtained through the Environment Agency's Netregs service or other organisations (such as WRAP).

Appendix A – Six-digit European waste catalogue codes

Section 17 – Construction and demolition waste

A six figure EWC code for the type of waste being removed MUST be written on every waste transfer note (for example, skip/muck away tickets).

17 01 Concrete, bricks, tiles and ceramics

17 01 01	Concrete.
17 01 02	Bricks.
17 01 03	Tiles and ceramics.
17 01 06*	Mixtures of, or separate fractions of concrete, bricks, tiles and ceramics containing dangerous substances.
17 01 07	Mixtures of concrete, bricks, tiles and ceramics other than those mentioned in 17 01 06.

17 02 Wood, glass and plastic

17 02 01	Wood.
17 02 02	Glass.
17 02 03	Plastic.
17 02 04*	Glass, plastic and wood containing or contaminated with dangerous substances.

17 03 Bituminous mixtures, coal tar and tarred products

17 03 01*	Bituminous mixtures containing coal tar.
17 03 02	Bituminous mixtures other than those mentioned in 17 03 01.
17 03 03*	Coal tar and tarred products.

17 04 Metals (including their alloys)

17 04 01	Copper, bronze, brass.
17 04 02	Aluminium.
17 04 03	Lead.
17 04 04	Zinc.
17 04 05	Iron and steel.
17 04 06	Tin.
17 04 07	Mixed metals.
17 04 09*	Metal waste contaminated with dangerous substances.
17 04 10*	Cables containing oil, coal tar and other dangerous substances.
17 04 11	Cables other than those mentioned in 17 04 10.

17 05 Soil (including excavated soil from contaminated sites), stones and dredging spoil

17 05 03*	Soil and stones containing dangerous substances.
17 05 04	Soil and stones other than those mentioned in 17 05 03.
17 05 05*	Dredging spoil containing dangerous substances.
17 05 06	Dredging spoil other than those mentioned in 17 05 05.
17 05 07*	Track ballast containing dangerous substances.
17 05 08	Track ballast other than those mentioned in 17 05 07.

17 06 Insulation materials and asbestos-containing construction materials

17 06 01*	Insulation materials containing asbestos.
17 06 03*	Other insulation materials consisting of or containing dangerous substances.
17 06 04	Insulation materials other than those mentioned in 17 06 01 and 17 06 03.
17 06 05*	Construction materials containing asbestos (7).

17 08 Gypsum-based construction material

17 08 01*	Gypsum-based construction materials contaminated with dangerous substances.
17 08 02	Gypsum-based construction materials other than those mentioned in 17 08 01.

17 09 Other construction and demolition wastes

17 09 01*	Construction and demolition wastes containing mercury.
17 09 02*	Construction and demolition wastes containing PCB (for example, PCB containing sealants, PCB-containing resin-based floorings, PCB-containing sealed glazing units).
17 09 03*	Other construction and demolition wastes (including mixed wastes) containing dangerous substances.
17 09 04	Mixed construction and demolition wastes other than those mentioned in 17 09 01.

 Entries marked with * are either potentially hazardous (mirror entry) and will require testing to determine if hazardous properties are present or definitely hazardous (absolute) and must be disposed of as hazardous waste.

Appendix B – Example of a controlled waste transfer note

Duty of care: waste transfer note Keep this page and copy it for future use. Please write as clearly as possible.

Section A – Description of waste

A1 Description of the waste being transferred

List of Waste Regulations code(s)

A2 How is the waste contained?

Loose ☐ Sacks ☐ Skip ☐ Drum ☐

Other ☐

A3 How much waste? For example, number of sacks, weight

03

Section B – Current holder of the waste – Transferor

By signing in Section D below I confirm that I have fulfilled my duty to apply the waste hierarchy as required by Regulation 12 of the Waste (England and Wales) Regulations 2011   Yes ☐

B1 Full name

Company name and address

Postcode ⌊_____⌋ SIC code (2007) ⌊_____⌋

B2 Name of your unitary authority or council

B3 Are you:

The producer of the waste? ☐

The importer of the waste? ☐

The local authority? ☐

The holder of an environmental permit? ☐

Permit number

Issued by

Registered waste exemption? ☐

Details, including registration number

A registered waste carrier, broker or dealer? ☐

Registration number

Details (are you a carrier, broker or dealer?)

Section C – Person collecting the waste – Transferee

C1 Full name

Company name and address

Postcode ⌊_____⌋

C2 Are you:

The local authority? ☐

C3 Are you:

The holder of an environmental permit? ☐

Permit number

Issued by

Registered waste exemption? ☐

Details, including registration number

A registered waste carrier, broker or dealer? ☐

Registration number

Details (are you a carrier, broker or dealer?)

Section D – The transfer

D1 Address of transfer or collection point

Postcode ⌊_____⌋

Date of transfer (DD/MM/YYYY)

D2 Broker or dealer who arranged this transfer (if applicable)

Postcode ⌊_____⌋

Registration number

Time(s)

Transferor's signature

Name

Representing

Transferee's signature

Name

Representing

Appendix C – Example of a hazardous waste consignment note

Form HWCN01v111

The Hazardous Waste Regulations 2005: Consignment Note

Environment Agency

PRODUCER'S/HOLDER'S/CONSIGNOR'S COPY (Delete as appropriate)

PART A Notification details

1 Consignment note code: /

4 The waste will be taken to (name, address and postcode):

2 The waste described below is to be removed from (name, address, postcode, telephone, e-mail, facsimile):

5 The waste producer was (if different from 2) (name, address, postcode, telephone, e-mail, facsimile):

3 Premises code (where applicable):

PART B Description of the waste   If continuation sheet used, tick here ▢

1 The process giving rise to the waste(s) was:

2 SIC for the process giving rise to the waste: .   /

3 WASTE DETAILS (where more than one waste type is collected all of the information given below must be completed for each EWC identified)

Description of waste	List of wastes (EWC code)(6 digits)	Quantity (kg)	The chemical/biological components in the waste and their concentrations are:		Physical form (gas, liquid, solid, powder, sludge or mixed)	Hazard code(s)	Container type, number and size
			Component	Concentration (% or mg/kg)			

The information given below is to be completed for each EWC identified

EWC code	UN identification number(s)	Proper shipping name(s)	UN class(es)	Packing group(s)	Special handling requirements

PART C Carrier's certificate

(If more than one carrier is used, please attach schedule for subsequent carriers. If schedule of carriers is attached tick here. ▢)

I certify that I today collected the consignment and that the details in A2, A4 and B3 are correct and I have been advised of any specific handling requirements.

Where this note comprises part of a multiple collection the round number and collection number are:

                                        /

1 Carrier name:

On behalf of (name, address, postcode, telephone, e-mail, facsimile):

2 Carrier registration no./reason for exemption:

3 Vehicle registration no. (or mode of transport, if not road):

Signature

| Date | D D M M Y Y Y Y | Time | H H M M |

PART D Consignor's certificate

I certify that the information in A, B and C has been completed and is correct, that the carrier is registered or exempt and was advised of the appropriate precautionary measures. All of the waste is packaged and labelled correctly and the carrier has been advised of any special handling requirements.

I confirm that I have fulfilled my duty to apply the waste hierarchy as required by Regulation 12 of the Waste (England and Wales) Regulations 2011.

1 Consignor name:

On behalf of (name, address, postcode, telephone, e-mail, facsimile):

Signature

| Date | D D M M Y Y Y Y | Time | H H M M |

PART E Consignee's certificate (where more than one waste type is collected all of the information given below must be completed for each EWC)

Individual EWC code(s) received	Quantity of each EWC code received (kg)	EWC code accepted/rejected	Waste management operation (R or D code)

1 I received this waste at the address given in A4 on: Date D D M M Y Y Y Y   Time H H M M

2 Vehicle registration no. (or mode of transport if not road):

Name:

On behalf of (name, address, postcode, telephone, e-mail, facsimile):

3 Where waste is rejected please provide details:

I certify that waste permit/exempt waste operation number:

authorises the management of the waste described in B at the address given in A4.

Where the consignment forms part of a multiple collection, as identified in Part C, I certify that the total number of consignments forming the collection are:

Signature

| Date | D D M M Y Y Y Y | Time | H H M M |

HWCN01v111

Appendix D – Waste flowcharts for the reuse of construction materials (soils and aggregates)

Appendix D includes three flowcharts that help you decide whether use and reuse of soil and aggregate materials in construction works is a waste activity or not and what you need to do to ensure legal compliance whilst minimising the regulatory burden. These flowcharts may also assist you in completion of a SWMP when assessing reuse or recycling options during design and construction phases. These flowcharts are applicable in England and Wales.

These flowcharts are not intended to cover exhaustive criteria of waste; however they do cover the typical scenarios that are commonly faced on construction and civil engineering projects.

For simplicity, these flowcharts have been split up into three key operations (see the following pages).

Materials arising from work that you plan to reuse on site

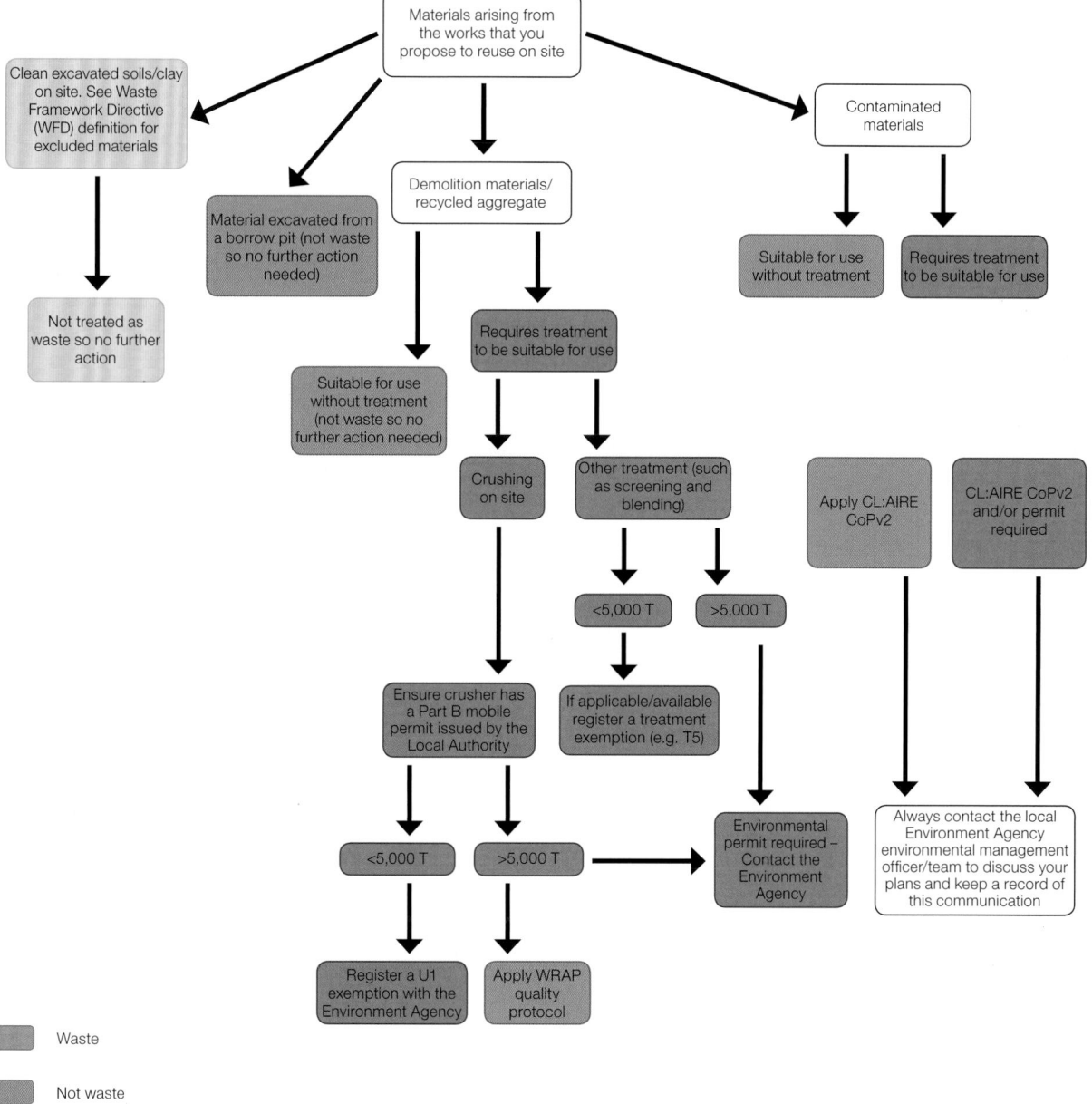

Materials that you propose to bring onto the site

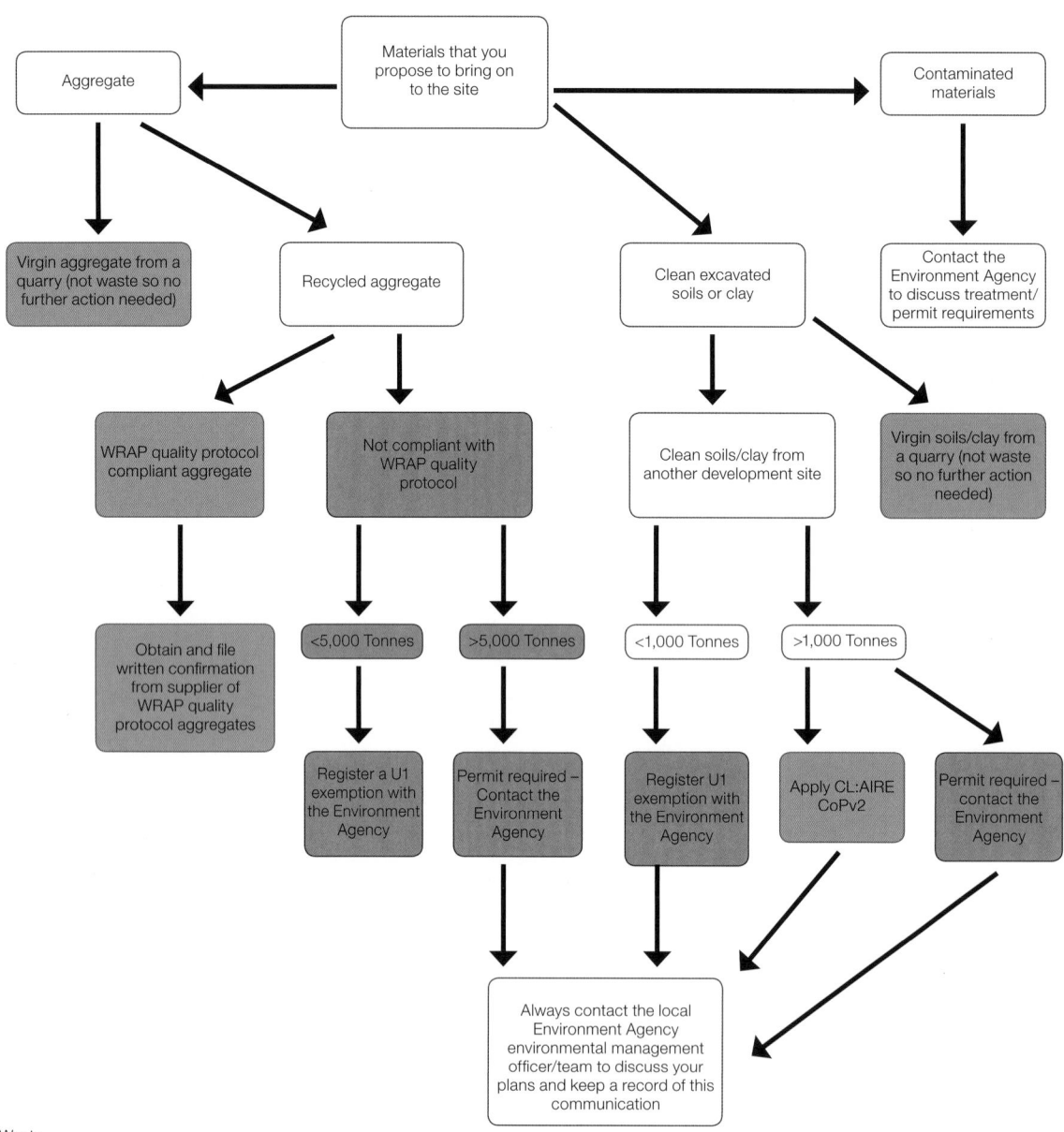

03

Materials that you propose to send off site

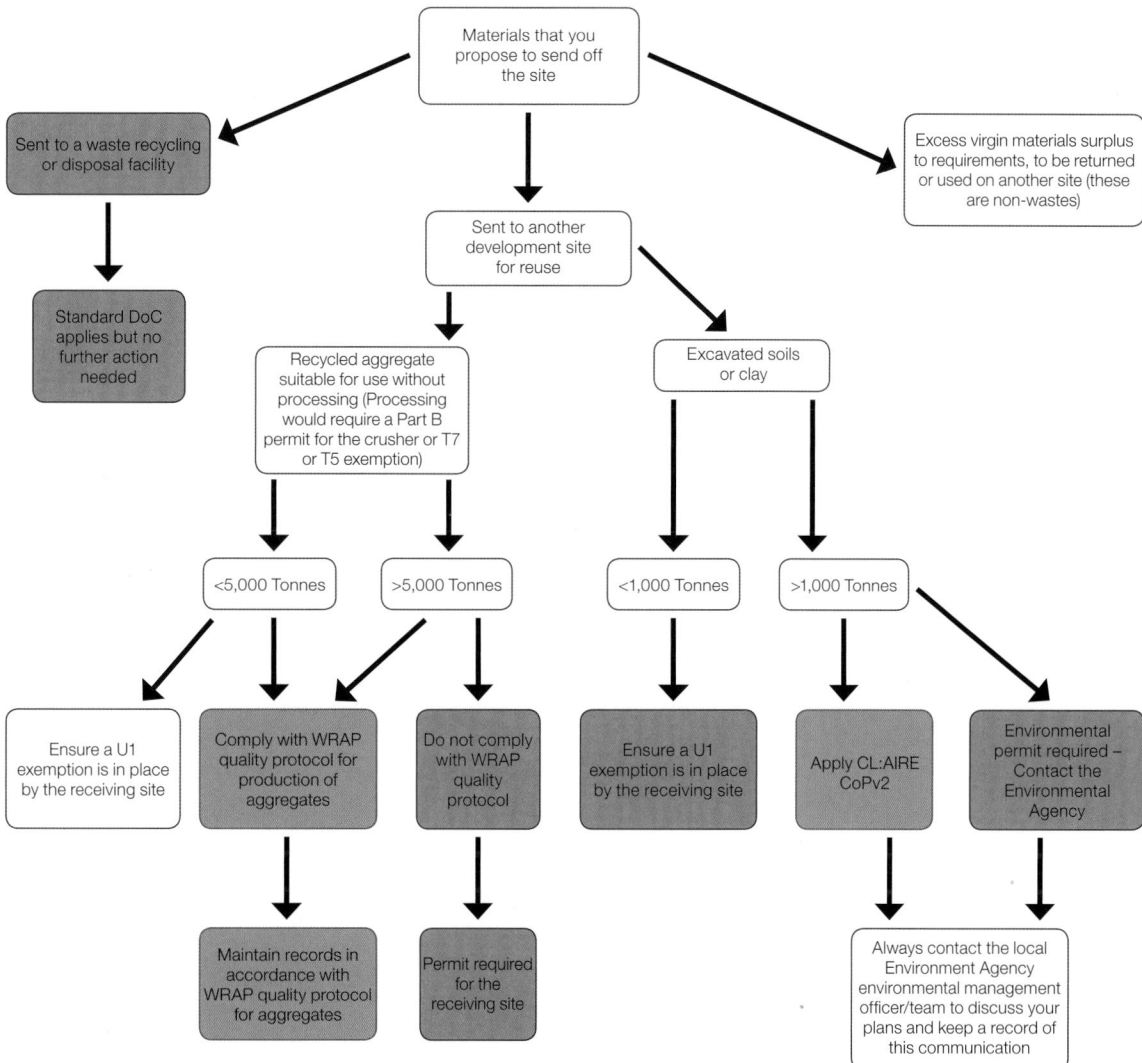

Waste

Not waste

Appendix E – Waste exemption materials and thresholds

Exemption U1 – Use of waste in construction

This exemption allows the use of suitable wastes for small scale construction instead of using virgin raw materials.

Construction for the purposes of this activity means:

> the carrying on of any building or engineering work, which includes the repair, alteration, maintenance or improvement of an existing work and preparatory or landscaping works.

Land reclamation is only permissible under this exemption when it's an integral part of a construction activity.

What types of activities can you do?

Example activities include:

- ☑ using crushed bricks, concrete, rocks and aggregate to create a noise bund around a new development and then using soil to landscape it to enable grass to grow
- ☑ using road planings and rubble to build a track, road or car park
- ☑ using wood chip to construct a track, path or bridleway
- ☑ bringing in some soil from another place for use in landscaping at a housing development.

Where can you carry out this activity?

This can be done at any place that can comply with the environmental controls listed in key limits and conditions.

What can't you do?

You can't:

- ☒ treat waste under this exemption to make it suitable for use
- ☒ dispose of waste under this exemption. You can only use waste types that are suitable for use and you should be able to justify the amount of waste that you use
- ☒ use this exemption for land reclamation or disposal in a landfill. You must read the guidance on disposal vs. recovery RGN13: Defining waste recovery: Permanent deposit of waste on land and make sure that you are using the waste for recovery only
- ☒ register this exemption more than once at any one place during the three-year period from first registration
- ☒ de-register this exemption and then re-register it at the same place within a three-year period.

What are the key limits?

Each table below lists the waste types and quantities that can be used over a three-year period from the date of registering the exemption.

You can use up to:

- ☑ 5,000 tonnes of any single waste stream or any combination of wastes in Table 1
- ☑ 1,000 tonnes of any single waste stream or any combination of wastes in Table 2
- ☑ 50,000 tonnes of any single waste stream or any combination of wastes in Table 3.

What are the key conditions?

You may use a combination of wastes from Tables 1, 2 and 3 provided you do not exceed the limits for each table. Waste can't be stored for longer than 12 months prior to use.

There are three specific conditions to this exemption relating to certain wastes. These are outlined below and also in the relevant section of *What waste can be used under this exemption?* below.

- ☑ Any person or company can use up to 1,000 tonnes of dredging spoil for any construction (within the 1,000 tonnes total for wastes from Table 2). Exception is made for the Environment Agency and other statutory authorities carrying out land drainage functions under the Land Drainage Act, the Water Resources Act or the Environment Act. These organisations may use up to 5,000 tonnes of dredging spoil for drainage work (within the 5,000 tonnes total for wastes from Table 1).
- ☑ You can use 1,000 tonnes of wood chip (or similar waste) or road planings to construct tracks, paths, bridleways or car parks only (within the 1,000 tonnes total for wastes from Table 2). The waste must be processed into chipped form prior to use.
- ☑ If you are constructing a road you can use 50,000 tonnes of road planings and road sub-base. The road should be constructed to a specific engineering standard and have a sealed surface in order to qualify for the higher limit.

What waste can be used under this exemption?

Table 1

You can use up to 5,000 tonnes in total of the wastes below for any construction activity.

Codes	Waste types
010102	Waste from mineral non-metalliferous excavation.
010408	Waste gravel and crushed rock other than those mentioned in 010407*.
010409	Waste sand and clays.
020202	Shellfish shells from which the soft tissue or flesh has been removed only.
101208	Waste ceramics, bricks, tiles and construction products (after thermal processing).
101314	Waste concrete and concrete sludge.
170101	Concrete.
170102	Bricks.
170103	Tiles and ceramics.
170107	Mixtures of concrete, bricks, tiles and ceramics other than those mentioned in 170106*.
170508	Track ballast other than those mentioned in 170507*.
191205	Glass.
191209	Minerals (for example sand and stones).
191212	Aggregates only.

Within the 5,000 tonnes total for use of wastes in Table 1, you can only use the waste below for drainage work carried out for the purposes of the Land Drainage Act 1991(1), the 1991 Act or the 1995 Act.

Codes	Waste types
170506	Dredging spoil other than those mentioned in 170505*.

Table 2

You can use up to 1,000 tonnes in total of the wastes below for construction purposes.

Codes	Waste types
020399, 020401	Soil from cleaning and washing fruit and vegetables only.
170504	Soil and stones other than those mentioned in 170503*.
170506	Dredging spoil other than those mentioned in 170505*.
191302	Solid wastes from soil remediation other than those mentioned in 191301*.
200202	Soil and stones.

Within the 1,000 tonnes total for use of wastes from Table 2, you can only use the waste below for the construction of tracks, paths, bridleways or car parks. The waste must be processed into chipped form prior to use.

Codes	Waste types
170302	Bituminous mixtures other than those mentioned in 170301*.
020103	Plant tissue waste.
030101, 030301	Untreated waste bark, cork and wood only.
030105	Untreated wood including sawdust, shavings and cuttings from untreated wood only.
170201	Untreated wood only.
191207	Untreated wood other than those mentioned in 191206* only.
200138	Untreated wood other than those mentioned in 200137* only.

* For waste codes beginning with 17 refer to Appendix A, for all other codes refer directly to the European waste catalogue.

Table 3

You can use up to 50,000 tonnes in total of the wastes below only for the construction of roads.

Codes	Waste types
170302	Bituminous mixtures other than those mentioned in 170301*.
170504	Road sub-base only.

* Refer to Appendix A.

Exemption T5 – Screening and blending of waste

This exemption allows temporary small-scale treatment of wastes to produce an aggregate or a soil at a place (such as a construction or demolition site).

What types of activities does this cover?

Example activities include:

☑ screening of soils on a demolition site to remove wood and rubble before sending the soils to a construction site for reuse

☑ blending of soils and compost that has been produced under an exemption on a construction site to produce a better soil for landscaping works on that site

☑ crushing wastes (except bricks, tiles and concrete) prior to screening or blending

☑ grading of waste concrete after crushing to produce a required type of aggregate.

Where can this activity be carried out?

You can treat waste on the site where it is:

☑ to be used (for example, on a construction site)

☑ produced (for example, on a demolition site).

What can't you do?

You can't:

☒ import waste, treat it and then export it elsewhere

☒ treat waste where the main purpose is disposal to landfill or incineration

☒ crush waste tiles, bricks or concrete (this comes under a T7 exemption, which must be registered with the Local Authority)

☒ treat hazardous waste.

What are the key limits?

☑ You can store or treat up to 50,000 tonnes of bituminous mixtures for making road stone over a three-year period from the date of registering the exemption.

☑ You can store or treat up to 5,000 tonnes of other wastes listed below over a three-year period from the date of registering the exemption.

☑ Waste can't be stored for longer than 12 months.

What are the key conditions?

Treatment can only be carried out at the place where the waste is to be used or where the waste is produced. This applies even if the resultant material is no longer considered to be waste.

What else do you need to know?

When you have treated the waste the options available are:

☑ if the treated waste meets the requirements of a waste quality protocol (the quality protocols – WRAP) then it will no longer be considered a waste

☑ use the treated waste, subject to the key conditions above, under a use exemption or environmental permit.

What waste can be treated under this exemption?

Codes	Waste types
010408	Waste gravel and crushed rocks other than those mentioned in 010407*.
010409	Waste sand and clays.
020202	Shellfish shells from which the soft tissue or flesh have been removed only.
030101	Untreated waste bark and cork only.
030301	Untreated waste bark and wood.
100101	Bottom ash, slag and boiler dust (excluding boiler dust mentioned in 100104*).
100115	Bottom ash, slag and boiler dust from co-incineration other than those mentioned in 100114*.
170101	Concrete.
170102	Bricks.
170103	Tiles and ceramics.
170107	Mixtures of concrete, bricks, tiles and ceramics other than those mentioned in 170106*.
170201	Untreated wood only.
170302	Bituminous mixtures other than those mentioned in 170301*.
170504	Soil and stones other than those mentioned in 170503*.
170506	Dredging spoil other than those mentioned in 170505*.
170508	Track ballast other than those mentioned in 170507*.
190599	Compost produced pursuant to a treatment described in the paragraphs numbered T23 or T26 of Chapter 2 only.
191205	Glass.
191209	Aggregates only.
191212	Gypsum recovered from construction materials only.
191302	Solid wastes from soil remediation other than those mentioned in 191301*.
191304	Sludges from remediation other than those mentioned in 191303*.
200202	Soil and stones.

* For waste codes beginning with 17 refer to Appendix A, for all other codes refer directly to the European waste catalogue.

04

Energy management

Global warming and climate change have come to the fore as a key sustainable development issue and therefore, how we manage business to minimise CO_2 emissions is a growing concern for clients and the construction industry as a whole.

This chapter gives a general overview of the UK's legally binding energy and carbon reduction targets and what the construction industry is doing in response to them.

This chapter also gives a general overview of the actions that can be taken by construction companies to measure and reduce their energy consumption and associated carbon footprint.

Introduction	50
Energy management issues	50
Carbon footprint	52

4.1   Introduction

Climate change is now seen as the defining challenge of this era. It is recognised that human activity, through the burning of fossil fuels in energy production, manufacturing and use in buildings and transport, together with the generation of waste, create greenhouse gases that contribute to global warming and climate change. Buildings, and the construction activity to produce them, uses a significant proportion of this energy and the industry has a major role to play in improving energy efficiency and reducing greenhouse gases and costs.

Action to address the problem of global warming started in 1988, when the intergovernmental panel on climate change (IPPC) was established. The United Nations Earth Summit at Rio in 1992 was, however, the watershed in the fight against climate change.

In December 1997, in Kyoto Japan, parties to the Climate Treaty (the Kyoto Protocol) agreed to make legally binding cuts in six greenhouse gases, including carbon dioxide. Between 2008 and 2012 developed countries were to reduce their emissions by an average of 5.2% below 1990 levels. Different targets were set for individual countries and the UK's contribution was a 12.5% reduction. As the Kyoto Protocol expired in 2012 negotiations are continuing to form a new agreement.

Meanwhile, the UK has implemented the Climate Change Act, which sets out legally binding targets to reduce greenhouse gas emissions by 34% by 2020 and 80% by 2050 based on 1990 levels. In addition, the UK has a target for 15% of all energy to be provided from renewable sources by 2020 from agreement at a European level.

Many other initiatives, both mandatory and voluntary, have been introduced by the UK and local governments, as well as the European Union, in response to the risk posed by climate change. These include the climate change levy on fossil fuels, the *Code for sustainable homes*, revisions to Part L of the Building Regulations, the Energy Performance of Buildings Directive, the EU emissions trading scheme, the renewable heat initiative, the Carbon Reduction Commitment Energy Efficiency Scheme and the Low Carbon Construction report by the Department of Business Innovation and Skills (BIS) innovation and growth team, to name but a few.

Carbon dioxide accounts for 85% of all emissions from the main six greenhouse gases and was approximately 495 million tonnes in 2010 in the UK. Almost half of these emissions were associated with buildings.

 In 2008, the UK Government and industry published the *Strategy for sustainable construction*, which can be found online.

Included within the strategy is a target set by the construction industry for a 15% reduction in carbon emissions from construction processes and associated transport by 2012 compared to 2008 levels. In addition, all new homes and schools should be zero carbon (based on energy consumption) from 2018.

Work carried out by the Strategic Forum for Construction (SFfC) suggests that the carbon emissions from construction activities and associated transport were around six million tonnes in 2008.

 For further details of the *Strategy for sustainable construction* refer to Chapter E01 Sustainable construction and the environment.

4.2   Energy management issues

Using and conserving energy during site works

In response to the 15% reduction target set out in the *Strategy for sustainable construction*, the SFfC and the Carbon Trust prepared an action plan that identifies what actions can be taken to deliver this target. The key areas for action include:

- ☑ on-site construction (energy use, plant and equipment) and site accommodation
- ☑ transport associated with the delivery of materials and removal of waste
- ☑ business travel
- ☑ corporate offices.

The action plan sets out a number of measures that can be undertaken by companies to help reduce their energy use and carbon emissions, such as:

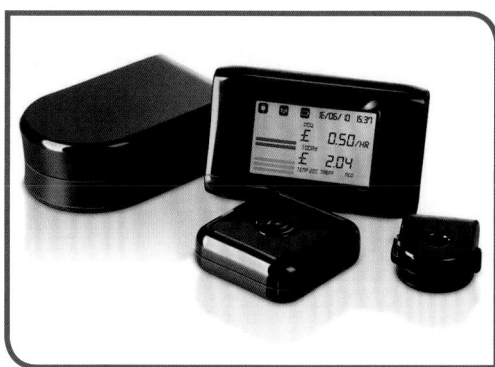

Meter for monitoring electricity use and cost

☑ ensuring sites connect to the electricity supply as early as possible to prevent lots of equipment running on fuel-driven generators

☑ using alternative or recycled products for site set up/logistics and enabling works

☑ installing more energy-efficient site accommodation (for example, environmental cabins containing such items as PIR sensors on lights, double glazing, additional insulation, door closers, waterless urinals and fuel cell and solar panel technology)

☑ efficient use of construction plant through induction and training (such as turning off when not required and keeping them well maintained)

☑ good practice energy management on site (for example, festoon low-energy light bulbs and turning task lighting off when not in use)

04

☑ making use of consolidation centres to reduce transport and handling of materials

☑ fuel efficient driving through driver training

☑ good practice energy management in company offices.

Whilst the action plan focuses on the direct use of energy, significant savings in embodied energy can also be achieved by using low energy products (such as recycled aggregates).

 The Strategic Forum's *Action plan to reduce carbon emissions* (July 2010) is available to view online.

Transport

Vehicle movements and the transport of materials and people represent energy resources being used. It is important that vehicle movements are handled, programmed and managed in an efficient way, as this will lead to greater resource efficiency and reduced costs.

Good logistics, with prompt arrivals and departures and materials being off-loaded in the right locations, will result in multiple positive benefits. Perhaps the key amongst these will be reduced fuel use and therefore less carbon emissions, which brings associated cost savings. Crucially there is also less potential for double handling and wastage of materials.

Efficient vehicle logistics will also lead to reductions in several key negative impacts. Efficient logistics with vehicles arriving promptly, being quickly off-loaded, with less delays and departing quickly, means that several types of potential impact will be reduced.

☑ There will be less time when noise is being generated. Effective vehicle sequencing will also prevent traffic build-up noise being generated from multiple sources.

☑ There will be less time that vehicles are on site, with fewer vehicles sitting with idling engines, resulting in less exhaust emissions. This will reduce the potential adverse impact on air quality.

☑ Vehicle arrivals and departures that are sequenced in the right way will have less of an impact on local traffic flows and reduce local congestion.

☑ Effective traffic management will result in less dust and mud being produced, depending on traffic weather. Road sweeping and dampening down can be incorporated into the traffic management plan.

The flow of vehicles, materials and resources onto a site need to be properly sequenced and planned. This process needs to be undertaken with a proper understanding of local traffic flows and factors that will influence the logistics plan (such as school run times). A lack of understanding will result in congestion, delays in material delivery and a variety of negative impacts occurring.

An effective traffic management plan will lead to improved public relations with the surrounding community and businesses. Traffic to and from a site and flow of materials and people with that traffic are one of the key areas on interaction with a location and it has to be right. The right interface and respect for a location should lead to trust and appreciation in return from the people in that area.

04

 A good traffic management plan will give consideration to the following factors

☑ Local traffic conditions, peak flows and congestion hot spots.

☑ Delivery and departure sequencing and times for all site vehicles.

☑ Off-site delivery and departure routes for all site vehicles.

☑ Signage and directions on site.

☑ Hold areas for vehicles waiting to off-load or depart.

☑ Communication between vehicles and the logistics manager on and off site.

☑ Wheel wash locations, dust suppression and mud sweeping.

☑ Receiving and responding to complaints.

☑ Consultation processes with emergency services, local residents, schools, public facilities and businesses.

☑ Consolidation areas and sharing of transport: the use of off-site consolidation areas and the sharing of transport will reduce the number of vehicle movements to and from site. Vehicle sharing can be planned by site staff. Project suppliers may permit the use of their parking areas as car-pooling points.

☑ Parking and lay down areas:
 – on-site parking for staff, contractors and visitors needs to be clearly identified
 – delivery vehicle and waste removal parking also needs identifying
 – vehicle off-loading and lay down areas should be clearly identified.

☑ Ensure that plant and vehicles are properly maintained to ensure efficiency of operation.

☑ On-site traffic management (safe routes, dust and wheel wash):
 – use wheel washes to prevent mud and any contaminated materials getting onto local roads
 – water bowsers can be used for dust suppression
 – road sweepers can be used to remove any mud accumulations.

4.3   Carbon footprint

Measuring energy and carbon

Measuring overall energy usage and being able to identity where energy is being used and in what form is a prerequisite to starting an energy and carbon management programme. To do so will require the use of meters to measure energy usage, and on large sites this may involve sub-meters. Sites may also be required to measure journeys to and from the project associated with deliveries and business travel, or be required to measure the embodied energy associated for the materials they are using.

Embodied energy is defined as the commercial energy (fossil fuels, nuclear, and so on) that was used in the work to make any product, bring it to market and dispose of it. Embodied energy is an accounting methodology that aims to find the sum total of the energy necessary for an entire product life cycle. This life cycle includes raw material extraction, transport, manufacture, assembly, installation, disassembly, deconstruction and/or decomposition.

To measure the carbon footprint associated with energy use will require the use of conversion factors for each energy type. Different methodologies produce different understandings of the scale and scope of application and the type of energy embodied. Some methodologies account for the energy embodied in terms of the oil that supports economic processes. There are three levels of assessment that are currently being used.

☑ Scope 1 are the emissions from sources under the immediate control of the company.

☑ Scope 2 are the off-site emissions from the purchase of electricity.

☑ Scope 3 are the off-site emissions from the company's supply chain or from products sold by the company.

 The Greenhouse Gas Protocol developed by the World Business Council for Sustainable Development (WBCSD) and the World Resources Institute (WRI) is the global standard for the measurement and reporting of Scope 1, 2 and 3 carbon emissions.

The Environment Agency has a carbon calculator for construction activities. This is an Excel spreadsheet that calculates the embodied carbon dioxide of materials plus carbon dioxide associated with their transportation. It also considers personal travel, site energy use and waste management. The tool has a number of benefits, including:

- ☑ helping to assess and compare the sustainability of different designs, in carbon dioxide (CO_2) terms, and influences option choice at the options appraisal stage

- ☑ helping to highlight where big carbon savings on specific construction projects can be made

- ☑ calculating the total carbon footprint from construction and helping to reduce it.

The tool was developed by the Environment Agency for its own construction activities (predominantly fluvial and coastal construction projects). However, other construction clients, contractors and consultants may find it useful when assessing their own activities.

 The carbon calculator and a number of case studies are available on the Environment Agency's website.

04

Measuring and reporting of site energy use is also a requirement under the management credits of the BRE's environmental assessment method (BREEAM) and the Code for sustainable homes. At present, BREEAM sets no requirement on the use of a particular method or protocol for reporting energy/carbon from construction sites, as there are currently no uniformly accepted protocols for the collection of data and assessment of emissions from construction sites. (*Source: Carbon: Reducing the footprint of the construction process, an action plan to reduce carbon.* Strategic Forum and Carbon Trust, 2010).

The CEEQUAL assessment scheme requires both energy and carbon assessments.

The European Network of Construction Companies for Research and Development (ENCORD) has established a *Carbon measurement protocol*. The document identifies the intended users of the protocol, the main sources of emissions over which a construction company may have some influence, and the method of measuring these emissions. Guidance is also provided on reporting methods at a company and project level, with a view that companies will report their emissions publicly. This is also intended to assist current and future work undertaken to reduce emissions from specific construction-related activities and operations.

As energy supply becomes greener the proportion of energy locked up in building materials increases. The greatest carbon use in the life cycle of a building is during use. Therefore, designers need to think about both embodied and operational energy of the building.

Carbon reduction commitment energy efficiency scheme

The Climate Change Act introduced new regulations from 1 April 2010, through the carbon reduction commitment (CRC) Energy Efficiency Scheme Order 2010, to improve the energy efficiency of larger companies. It applies to England, Wales, Scotland and Northern Ireland. These regulations require companies to measure and report their carbon emissions and to purchases carbon allowances in line with their carbon footprint. Some large construction companies fall under these requirements.

The CRC energy efficiency scheme is being run in phases, with Phase 1 started in April 2010, Phase 2 starting in April 2013 (registration year) and subsequent phases starting in April 2017. The Environment Agency is the administrator for the CRC energy efficiency scheme.

All companies that purchased electricity through mandatory half-hourly meters in 2008, and had a total consumption of more than 6,000 MWh through these meters, are required to participate in Phase 1 of the CRC energy efficiency scheme by doing the following:

- ☑ registering the company by 30 September 2010 for Phase 1 of the scheme by providing details of its structure, meters, relevant contacts and paying the appropriate registration fee

- ☑ from 1 April 2010, recording all details of suppliers and consumption for electricity, gas and other fuels (excluding transport)

- ☑ maintaining a formal evidence pack that includes details of all qualification, supply and consumption data, together with details of company changes, CRC responsibilities, and so on

- ☑ carrying out an internal audit and certifying the evidence pack

- ☑ calculating the carbon footprint of the company from the use of its fuels (excluding transport)

- ☑ purchasing relevant carbon allowances each year (the first purchase of allowances for companies was 2012 for the 2011/12 reporting year)

- ☑ submitting a formal annual report to the regulator in July of each year

- ☑ submitting a footprint to the regulator, one for each phase of the scheme

- ☑ participating in audits by the scheme administrator when requested.

All participants of the scheme are shown in a publicly available league table on an annual basis and a company's position in this league table will be dependent on its performance against various metrics.

The CRC energy efficiency scheme could therefore have an influence on a company's reputation, as clients will look to those that can demonstrate that they are managing their carbon emissions effectively.

There are severe penalties for not complying with the requirements of the CRC energy efficiency scheme (such as £40 per tonne of carbon for inaccurate annual or footprint reports).

 For comprehensive guidance on the CRC energy efficiency scheme refer to the Environment Agency's website.

 The UK Government aims to simplify the CRC scheme and issued a formal consultation in February 2012, which closed in June 2012. At the time of writing the outcome of the consultation had not been published.

Green Deal

The *Energy bill* introduced to Parliament on 8 December 2010 includes provision for the new Green Deal, which is intended to revolutionise the energy efficiency of British properties.

The Government is establishing a framework to enable private firms to offer consumers energy efficiency improvements to their homes, community spaces and businesses at no upfront cost, and to recoup payments through a charge in instalments on the energy bill. The golden rule of the scheme is that the costs to the customer will be no greater than the projected savings, therefore making it cost neutral to the owner or occupier of the building.

Key features of the proposed Green Deal

The following reflect current proposals for operation of the Green Deal scheme.

- ☑ **Property assessment.** One of the main features of the proposed Green Deal is that an energy assessment will be required by an accredited advisor to determine the appropriate energy reduction opportunities that have been approved under the scheme. It is proposed that the criteria that each measure must meet will be defined to be eligible for Green Deal finance.

- ☑ **Green Deal finance.** Following the assessment of the property by the accredited advisor the Green Deal provider would consider the package of measures and make an offer that stipulates the total cost, the charge to be attached to the energy meter, and the length of the repayment period. This should be in line with the objective recommendations provided by the qualified Green Deal adviser, and only approved measures installed by qualified Green Deal installers will be eligible for finance attached to the energy meter in this way. Once agreed, a Green Deal plan would be drafted and signed by the customer to allow the work to proceed.

- ☑ **Installation.** After the customer has signed up to the Green Deal plan, the Green Deal provider will arrange for the work to be carried out by an accredited installer. After the work has been completed the Green Deal provider will notify the energy supplier who will update their register and will add the agreed Green Deal charge to the customer's regular energy bill.

- ☑ **Repayments.** The customer will receive regular energy bills with the Green Deal payment included, which the customer will pay to the energy supplier. The energy supplier will then pass the payments to the Green Deal provider.

As the proposed scheme ties payments into the meter if the customer moves then this information will need to be disclosed and the liability automatically transferred to the new customer.

 For comprehensive guidance on the Green Deal scheme refer to the Department of Energy and Climate Change's website.

Renewable energy

As part of the UK's target to reduce carbon emissions, 15% of all energy must come from renewable sources by 2020. Types of renewable energy include:

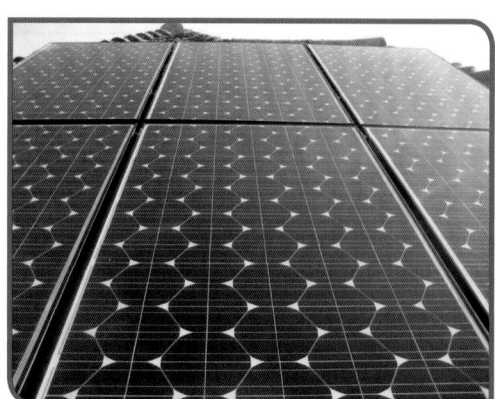

Photovoltaic power

- ☑ **renewable electricity:**
  - solar photovoltaic (PV)
  - wind
  - hydro-electricity
  - electricity generated from anaerobic digestion (AD)
  - electricity generated from combined heat and power

✓ **renewable heat:**

– biomass

– solar thermal

– ground source heat pump

– air source heat pump

– heat generated from combined heat and power

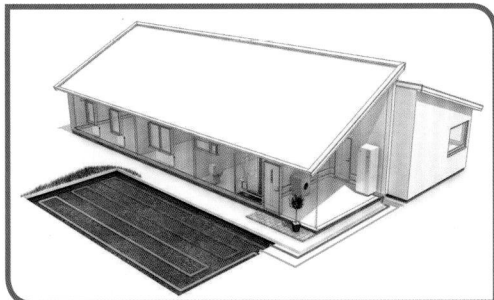

Ground source heat pump

Biomass

The UK Government gives financial support through feed in tariffs (FITs) for renewable electricity technologies, and renewable heat incentive (RHI) for renewable heat technologies. These incentives are primarily designed to stimulate take-up of these technologies until the market is sufficiently developed and prices fall.

Photovoltaic power, for example, has seen a rapid increase in deployment over the last few years because of the generous FITs that have been paid. As the market has been established these tariffs are reducing. In addition, because renewable energy reduces the amount of fossil fuels supplied but not the demand (energy efficiency), it is now a requirement to demonstrate that the building has achieved a certain level of efficiency before full FITs are given. Renewable energy should be a lower priority than facilities management, form and fabric options, in accordance with the energy hierarchy.

Renewable energy will, however, be a key element of achieving zero carbon energy requirements set out in standards such as the *Code for sustainable homes* and BREEAM, together with achieving zero carbon new homes and schools by 2018.

04

05

Water management

Water is one of our most valuable natural resources, vital for our social and economic wellbeing and to maintain precious habitats. Despite the constant renewal of water resources, its supply is not endless. Therefore, we have a duty to ensure that it is protected and managed effectively.

This chapter gives a general overview of the legal framework for the protection of natural water resources, including the permit and licence requirements needed for making discharges to foul and surface water drainage systems.

This chapter also provides practical advice for the prevention of pollution to surface and groundwater and implementing an incident response plan should an accidental spillage occur as a result of construction work.

Introduction	58
Key requirements	58
Water scarcity	59
Groundwater	60
Extraction	61
Disposal	61
Consents	63
Pollution prevention	64
Pollution incident response plans	66
Water efficiency	67
Appendix A – Strategic Forum for Construction – Water toolbox talk example	69

5.1   Introduction

Construction activities can not only cause serious harm to watercourses, plants and wildlife, they can also affect the quality and availability of drinking water resources and can be visually intrusive. Water pollution can contaminate drinking water, suffocate fish, remove essential oxygen from the water and kill plants, animals and insects living in the water. A construction site does not need to be next to a watercourse to cause a problem; any pollutants entering a surface water drain can end up in a watercourse miles away.

Pollution by silt can result in the suffocation of fish, destruction of spawning sites and the blocking of drains, which in turn can lead to flooding. Silt pollution can be caused by dewatering, over-pumping, rainwater run-off from uncovered areas of site (such as stockpiles of material exposed during earthworks), tunnelling operations, cleaning of ditches and drains and processes such as wheel washing.

Oil pollution reduces the levels of oxygen in water and can be toxic to aquatic wildlife. It coats plants, animals and birds. Oil pollution is mainly caused through spillages, often from refuelling, but can also be caused by accidental spills, vandalism and the overfilling of equipment. Oil, for example, spreads rapidly: one gallon of oil can completely cover a lake the size of two football pitches.

Cement and concrete are probably the most common materials used in construction. If cement or concrete is allowed to enter a watercourse it can have a devastating impact on wildlife. Cement is highly alkaline and can alter the pH of the water, which can be toxic to aquatic wildlife and contaminate water supplies. Cement and concrete pollution is mainly caused by the cleaning out of equipment and possible shuttering failure.

Chemical pollution can have a wide range of impacts, including killing fish. Chemical pollution can be caused by spillages, the leaking of containers or incorrectly bunded areas.

Sewage pollution can be unpleasant, unsightly, smell and decrease the amount of oxygen in the water. Sewage pollution often occurs when drains are wrongly connected, blocked or damaged.

The Environmental Protection Act makes reference to controlling the entry of polluting matter and effluents into any place that may ultimately affect a watercourse.

The Water Resources Act makes it an offence to knowingly permit the pollution of controlled waters, such as:

- ☑ rivers, streams, ditches, ponds, swales, underground streams, canals, lakes and reservoirs

- ☑ groundwater, wells, aquifers, boreholes or water in underground strata.

It is also an offence to deliberately or accidentally discharge trade effluents into public sewers without the relevant consent. Trade effluents are any liquids produced as part of a trade or industrial activity, excluding domestic sewage. Trade effluents include the water or slurry from vehicle wheel washers, core drilling, brick/concrete/stone cutting machines, dewatering trenches, pumping out of excavations, concrete washout, pipework cleaning and commissioning and any similar activities.

It is also an offence to contaminate waters in a way which may poison or injure fish, spawn, fish food or spawning grounds.

Monitoring is an essential component of ensuring the protection of water resources, by inspecting to confirm that the correct and necessary preventative measures are in place and working efficiently. Monitoring must be undertaken on a regular basis and in periods of heavy rainfall, on a more frequent basis.

 Just half a teaspoon of soil in a bath full of water would be comparable to water quality that could kill fish and smother plants in a watercourse.

The Strategic Forum for Construction (SFfC) and the Water Working Group have established a 2012 target, for a 20% reduction in water consumption associated with manufacturing and construction activities, based on 2008 levels. Further details can be found later in this chapter (refer to 5.10).

5.2   Key requirements

- ☑ Before any work starts on site it is essential to identify all existing site drainage. Clearly mark these on site plans and distinguish which are surface water and which are foul water systems.

- ☑ Seek to install permanent drainage systems as early as possible, as these can then be used to avoid temporary discharges to surface water.

- ☑ All drains should be covered/protected to prevent accidental ingress from mud and silt.

- ☑ All stockpiled materials should be stored away from drainage systems and watercourses and protected using geotextile silt fencing or cut-off ditches where appropriate.

- ☑ The abstraction of water from surface water or piped mains (using a standpipe) will require consent from the Environment Agency or relevant water authority respectively.

- ☑ All discharges to foul water drainage systems require discharge consent from the local water authority and the consent conditions must be strictly complied with.

- ☑ All discharges to surface water systems will require an environmental permit from the Environment Agency and the permit conditions must be strictly complied with.

☑ In England and Wales, temporary (less than three months) discharges from dewatering excavations can be carried out without the need for an environmental permit but strict conditions have to be complied with.

☑ Where septic tanks are designed to discharge to ground these will require an environmental permit for groundwater activities. Discharges from small domestic septic tanks are exempt but this exemption is required to be registered with the Environment Agency.

☑ Before any discharges are made to surface water systems, the water must be unpolluted and free from silt. Silts can be removed through a variety of techniques:

– settlement tanks

– lagoons

– filtration systems, including the use of gravels, geotextiles or straw bales

– use of flocculants.

☑ All fuels and chemicals should be stored on impervious material away from drains and watercourses. They should be suitably bunded to prevent pollution in the event of leakage or spillage. Refuelling should also be carried out at designated locations away from drains or watercourses.

☑ All water from vehicle and boot washing facilities should be removed to foul water drainage systems (with the consent of the water authority) or taken away by tanker (waste duty of care must be complied with).

☑ Concrete and cement washout should not be allowed to enter surface water systems and should be carried out in designated areas. Washout water must be removed from site by foul sewer or tanker.

☑ Monitoring of all discharges should be made on a regular basis (usually daily) to ensure that consent conditions (quality and quantity) are being complied with. Oil and chemical storage facilities should also be inspected.

☑ Site and public roads should be regularly swept to reduce silt and mud entering surface water drainage systems.

☑ An incident response plan should be implemented identifying the:

– type and location of drainage systems

– type and location of spill kits

– responsibilities for site personnel

– awareness of environmental issues via training and induction

– arrangements for spill kit replenishment

– arrangements for disposal for contaminated materials.

5.3   Water scarcity

Water scarcity is both a natural and a human-made problem. There is enough fresh water on the planet for six billion people but it is distributed unevenly and too much of it is wasted, polluted and unsustainably managed.

Water scarcity is among the main problems to be faced by many societies and the world in the 21st Century. Water use has been growing at more than twice the rate of population increase in the last century, and, although there is no global water scarcity as such, an increasing number of regions are chronically short of water.

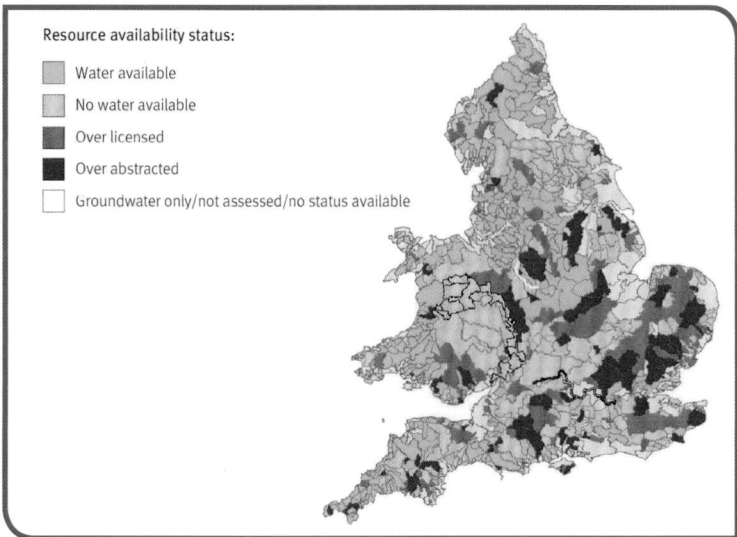

Resource availability status:

▣ Water available

▣ No water available

▣ Over licensed

▣ Over abstracted

☐ Groundwater only/not assessed/no status available

Water available for abstraction (surface water combined with groundwater)

Water scarcity is defined as the point at which the total impact of all users affects the supply or quality of water under existing arrangements to the extent that the demand by all sectors, including the environment, cannot be fully met. It can occur at any level of supply or demand and may be caused by human behaviour or the consequence of altered supply patterns (for example, from climate change).

05

Water management

Scientists typically measure scarcity by looking at the total amount of water available per person. An area is experiencing water stress when annual water supplies drop below 1,700 m³ per person. When annual water supplies drop below 1,000 m³ per person, the population faces water scarcity, and below 500 m³ is absolute scarcity.

Water scarcity already affects every continent. Around 1.2 billion people, or almost one-fifth of the world's population, live in areas of physical scarcity, and 500 million people are approaching this situation. Another 1.6 billion people, or almost one quarter of the world's population, face economic water shortage (where countries lack the necessary infrastructure to take water from rivers and aquifers).

Whilst the UK as a whole does not suffer from water scarcity, areas in the South and East of England regularly suffer from serious levels of water stress. Levels of water stress have been calculated by the Environment Agency based on the following criteria:

- ☑ current per capita demand for water
- ☑ forecast growth in per capita demand for water
- ☑ forecast population growth
- ☑ current water resource availability
- ☑ forecast resource availability.

 For further information on water efficiency and minimisation refer to 5.10.

05

5.4   Groundwater

Groundwater is the largest available reservoir of fresh water and accumulates in gaps in the rocks called aquifers. Groundwater provides a third of our drinking water in England and Wales and also maintains the flow in many of our rivers. In some areas of southern England, groundwater supplies up to 80% of drinking water through the taps.

The Water Resources Act gives the Environment Agency a duty to protect the quality of ground water and to protect it as a valuable water resource. The Environmental Permitting (England and Wales) Regulations replaced the Groundwater Regulations and implemented the requirements of the EU groundwater directives. Similar legislation is in place in Scotland and Northern Ireland.

The Groundwater Directive identifies List I and II substances. Direct discharges of List I substances are prohibited. List II substances will only be authorised with conditions. The existing Groundwater Directive is to be repealed by the Water Framework Directive 2000/60/EC (WFD) in 2013.

As the regulator, the Environment Agency has established groundwater vulnerability maps and source protection zones (SPZs) for 2,000 groundwater sources (such as wells, boreholes and springs) used for public drinking water supply. There are four levels of SPZs (shown below). The shape and size of a zone depends upon conditions of the ground, how the groundwater is removed and other environmental factors.

- ☑ **Zone 1 (inner protection zones)** – an area where any pollution can travel to a borehole within 50 days. Zone 1 protection zones provide a 50 m protection radius of a borehole.

- ☑ **Zone 2 (outer protection zones)** – areas where pollution takes 40 days to reach a borehole, or when 25% of the total catchment area is affected, whichever is the biggest.

- ☑ **Zone 3 (total catchment)** – the total area needed to support the removal of water from a borehole.

- ☑ **Zone 4 or zone of special interest** was previously defined for some sources. Zone 4 (SPZ4) usually represented a surface water catchment that drains into the aquifer feeding the groundwater supply (for example, catchment draining to a disappearing stream). In the future this zone will be incorporated into one of the other zones, SPZ1, 2 or 3, whichever is appropriate in the particular case, or become a safeguard zone.

Groundwater can be polluted by a range of construction materials, including fuels, chemicals, solvents, paints and other liquids. Pollution of groundwater will lead to prosecution. A small quantity of a pollutant has the potential to impact large volumes of groundwater. Remediating large volumes of groundwater is expensive and can take a long time.

Run-off from rainfall has the potential to pick up contaminants as it moves across a construction site. Contaminants may include particulates as well as hydrocarbons and chemicals. Run-off can penetrate permeable surfaces and infiltrate into groundwater.

Every effort must be made to prevent groundwater pollution and this includes:

- ☑ proper materials storage with bunds protecting liquids stores
- ☑ suitable spill kits and competent spill teams with regular drills
- ☑ storing materials on impermeable surfaces
- ☑ use of interceptor drains to catch run-off before it reaches permeable surfaces.

 The unauthorised discharge of chemicals or sewage to groundwater without a permit is an offence and could lead to prosecution.

5.5   Extraction

Water is often taken from natural sources or water mains to reduce dust on haul roads or to reduce dust during cutting operations.

Section 24 of The Water Resources Act states that:

> no person shall abstract water from any source of supply or cause or permit any other person to abstract any water, except in pursuance of a licence granted by the authority.

You should therefore not take water from groundwater, watercourses, lakes, streams or water mains without the permission of the relevant authority. The Environment Agency in England and Wales, and the Scottish Environment Protection Agency (SEPA) in Scotland are responsible for licensing abstractions from groundwater and watercourses. The local water supply company will be responsible for licensing water that is taken from water mains.

In England and Wales abstractions of up to 20 m³ a day can be taken from watercourses and other natural water resources without an abstraction licence from the Environment Agency.

In Scotland, under the Water Environment and Water Services (Scotland) Act and the Water Environment (Controlled Activities) (Scotland) Regulations (as amended), abstractions of up to 10 m³ a day can be taken without registration with SEPA, subject to meeting the relevant general binding rules.

Water volumes abstracted should be monitored on a daily basis to ensure that the conditions of any abstraction licence are complied with. This will also allow you to check whether there are any leaks in the system.

05

Dewatering excavations

If, as part of the works, you are dewatering or pumping water that has gathered in an excavation, it does not require an abstraction licence if the water is to be disposed of solely to prevent interference to building operations.

If, however, you intend to use water from a dewatering operation for dust suppression or pressure testing on site, you may require an abstraction licence if over 20 m³.

Construction dewatering is the temporary lowering of groundwater levels by pumping from wells or sumps to provide stable conditions for excavations below the natural groundwater level. The water being removed may require the appropriate consent for discharge into either the foul water system or controlled waters.

5.6   Disposal

Drains on site should be clearly identifiable as either surface water drains or foul water drains. Surface water drains carry uncontaminated rainwater directly to a stream, river or soakaway. Foul water drains carry foul water directly to a sewage works for treatment before being discharged to a watercourse.

Disposal from dewatering excavations

Water may enter an excavation from either surface water inflows or inflows of groundwater. The inflows may already be polluted or they may pick up pollutants contained within the excavation. The amount of water that is pumped out from an excavation can be reduced by reducing inflows of both surface and groundwater. Edge drains connected to sumps can intercept surface water flows. Cut-off ditches and well dewatering will reduce groundwater inflows.

Any pumping out into a trade effluent system (such as a sewer) will require consent from the water company or an environmental permit from the Environment Agency for a discharge to controlled waters (such as rivers, streams or lakes). However, in England and Wales you do not need an environmental permit for water discharge if the discharge is temporary (for less than three months) and if you can meet the requirements of the Environment Agency's position statement for *Temporary water discharges from excavations*.

If you need a permit to discharge to a watercourse, it can take up to four months to obtain from the Environment Agency. Further details of consent requirements are covered in 5.7.

Treatment of water before discharge will reduce the potential impact that it has. Forms of treatment include:

- ☑ pumping to grassland or other soakaway well away from excavations to avoid recirculation (this option is only suitable for unpolluted water containing only silt)

- ☑ pumping to a settlement tank/lagoon, maximising retention time

- ☑ using a sump at the base of an excavation, wrapping the end of the pump in aggregates and keeping it off the excavation floor

- ☑ passing through a filtration system (such as aggregates, geotextile or straw bales)

- ☑ using flocculants in conjunction with a settlement tank. Consultation with the Environment Agency should take place first as adding chemicals could make things worse.

Water management

Where there is no alternative, water may also be taken and treated off site as waste and will therefore need to be controlled in accordance with the waste duty of care, together with the completion of waste transfer documentation.

Concrete and cement wash out

Concrete and cement wash out is highly alkaline and can cause severe pollution. Effluent produced from washing out any concrete mixing plant or ready-mix concrete lorries mustn't be allowed to flow into any drain, watercourse or to ground (groundwater). Wash out areas should be designated and at least 10 m away from a watercourse and any drains.

A lined skip can be used to place waste concrete and effluent, with the water being pumped to a foul sewer or taken away by tanker. The concrete can also be recycled for reuse into the works.

The Environment Agency has a regulatory position statement (RPS) titled *Managing concrete wash waters on construction sites: Good practice and temporary discharges to ground or to surface waters*. The statement explains what can and cannot be done.

If a company complies with the requirements in the statement, the Environment Agency will allow discharge of concrete wash waters from some construction sites to ground or to surface waters without the need for an environmental permit.

Visit the construction section of the Environment Agency website for the latest version of the statement and for further guidance.

Disposal of sewage

The provision of welfare facilities at fixed and transitional construction sites requires that disposal of sewage must be considered. Where possible, disposal may be made by direct connection to a foul sewer. Direct connection to the foul sewer will require consent from the maintaining authority. On greenfield sites or sites remote from live foul sewers there may be no opportunity to connect to a local foul sewer, in which case a septic tank will be provided that can be regularly pumped out by a liquid waste disposal company. Where sewage waste is taken from site then the waste duty of care must be complied with, and waste transfer documentation completed.

Both the location and design of the septic tank are important considerations to avoid raw sewage from entering groundwater or watercourses. The use of portable toilet facilities should be discouraged wherever possible. Where effluent from septic tanks is designed to be discharged to ground then an environmental permit will be required.

Disposal from vehicle and boot washing

Where wheel-wash facilities are provided on site, the resultant water will be contaminated with silt and possibly oil from vehicle bodies. This effluent must not be discharged to surface water systems and should be removed to foul sewers with the consent of the local water authority. Modern wheel-wash facilities will allow the wash water to be recycled and recovery of the silts to be separately removed as waste. Where the water is contaminated it may be removed by tanker.

Facilities should also be provided to allow site personnel to clean their boots before leaving site or entering site accommodation. The silty water from these facilities should be dealt with in the same way as the vehicle washing effluent.

Sustainable urban drainage system

Sustainable urban drainage systems (SUDs) can be used to manage surface water run-off from large areas (such as part of a housing estate, major roads or business parks). They provide a natural approach to managing drainage in and around developments. SUDs work by slowing down and holding back the run-off from a site, allowing natural processes to break down pollution. They deal with run-off close to the source rather than transporting it elsewhere.

05

They are designed to attenuate surface water from developments in a manner that will provide a more sustainable approach than the previous, conventional practice of routing run-off through a pipe into a watercourse. They are also a tool for preventing flooding.

Facilities for SUDs include:

- ☑ permeable surfaces
- ☑ filter strips
- ☑ filter and infiltration trenches
- ☑ swales

- ☑ detention basins
- ☑ underground storage
- ☑ wetlands
- ☑ ponds.

Other facilities exist (such as hydraulic controls or silt traps).

In England, Northern Ireland and Wales you may have to include plans for SUDs when you apply for planning permission for a development. It is good practice to include the use of SUDs in all development plans.

In Scotland the rules are considerably different and all new developments must use SUDs to control water run-off to the water environment, unless the run-off is from a single dwelling.

You must have a licence from SEPA if you plan to use SUDs for:

- ☑ a development with more than 1,000 houses or more than 1,000 car parking spaces
- ☑ an industrial estate
- ☑ major roads and motorways.

For other developments you may not need to contact SEPA but you must comply with the requirements of the general binding rules (GBRs) 10 and 11 of the Controlled Activities Regulations.

05

5.7 Consents

Discharge consents

Where there is a requirement to discharge effluent from any construction activity to drainage systems, watercourses or rivers and streams, an application for consent to discharge must be made to the relevant authority. The issuing authority will depend on where the discharge is made. For example, discharges to foul sewers are usually regulated by the local water company, whereas any discharges to surface water systems, rivers, lakes or ponds would be regulated by the Environment Agency.

In England and Wales, consents to discharge to surface water systems are regulated under Schedule 21 of the Environmental Permitting (England and Wales) Regulations. The water discharge activities covered by these regulations include the discharge or entry to surface waters that are controlled waters (but not to groundwater) of any poisonous, noxious or polluting matter, waste matter, trade effluent or sewage effluent. The term *water discharge activities* also includes any work that results in deposits that can be carried away in water (such as cleaning the bottom of a river channel).

As highlighted earlier, temporary discharge from dewatering excavations does not require an application for an environmental permit provided that the:

- ☑ discharge is temporary, for an overall period of less than three months
- ☑ discharge is made to a surface water (such as a river, stream or the sea)
- ☑ discharge does not pollute the surface water or adversely affect aquatic life
- ☑ discharge location is not within, or less than 500 m upstream of a river or marine European site or SSSI, or within a site designated for nature conservation (such as NNR, LNR and local wildlife sites)
- ☑ discharge does not cause flooding from the surface water
- ☑ discharge does not cause erosion of the banks or bed of the surface water
- ☑ work on site follows the advice in the Environment Agency's *Working on construction and demolition sites* (Pollution prevention guideline No. 6).

Discharges of uncontaminated surface waters are not classed as a water discharge activity. However, you should discuss any proposed discharge of surface water with the regulator before any work takes place.

Water discharge activities that meet certain conditions are exempt from requiring a permit. These include:

- ☑ a discharge from a small sewage treatment plant discharging 5 m³ or less of effluent per day and subject to meeting other stringent requirements
- ☑ a discharge from a septic tank discharging 2 m³ or less of effluent per day
- ☑ vegetation management activities.

Low risk sewage discharges that meet the relevant conditions can be regulated under an exemption or standard permit.

However, all other applications for a discharge permit will be regulated under a bespoke permit.

An application for a discharge permit must include, but not be limited to, the following information:

- ☑ the place at which the discharge will take place
- ☑ the nature and composition of the material to be discharged
- ☑ the maximum amount of material that is likely to be discharged in any one day
- ☑ the time period over which the discharge will take place
- ☑ details of any monitoring and testing arrangements.

In Scotland, discharge consents to surface and groundwaters are regulated through the Water Environment (Controlled Activities) (Scotland) Regulations (as amended) (CAR) which came into force on 1 April 2006.

The CAR Regulations introduce three levels of authorisations proportionate to the type of risk for the activity:

- ☑ general binding rules
- ☑ registrations
- ☑ licences.

General binding rules (GBRs), set out in Schedule 3 of the CAR, represent the lowest level of control and cover specific low-risk activities. Activities complying with the rules do not require an application to be made to SEPA, as compliance with a GBR is considered to be authorisation. Since the operator is not required to contact SEPA, there are no associated charges. SEPA has prepared a practical guide to implementing the CAR.

Works consents

On 6 April 2012, when a further phase of the Flood and Water Management Act was implemented, responsibility for regulating activities on ordinary watercourses in most areas of England and Wales transferred from the Environment Agency to lead local flood authorities. Lead local flood authorities are unitary authorities where they exist and county councils elsewhere.

In England and Wales a flood defence consent is required from the lead local flood authority before building a flow control structure (such as a culvert or weir) on an ordinary watercourse.

For consent to carry out any works within 10 m of a watercourse, an application must include plans, sections and details including any environmental mitigation measures. Flood defence consent is required from the Environment Agency to carry out any work in, under, over or adjacent (within 10 m) to a statutory main river.

In Scotland, as with discharge consents, if you carry out building and engineering activities that significantly affect the water environment, these are regulated through the Water Environment (Controlled Activities) (Scotland) Regulations (as amended) (CAR) and you must either:

- ☑ comply with certain GBRs that apply to low-risk activities
- ☑ register your activity with SEPA
- ☑ get a licence from SEPA.

Septic tanks

The discharge of any sewage from a septic tank to the ground will require an environmental permit for groundwater activities unless it is a small domestic discharge, then it may be exempt and can be registered under an exemption. Septic tanks with discharges of less than 2 m³ per day are exempt from environmental permitting as highlighted above.

5.8 Pollution prevention

A number of measures may be implemented to prevent spillages and reduce the risk of a pollution incident. The Environment Agency has produced a set of pollution prevention guidelines (PPGs) to assist in the identification and management of issues of pollution risk in construction and other industry areas. PPG01 and PPG06, in particular, provide a general guide to pollution prevention on construction sites.

Site establishment

When planning the site set-up consider:

- ☑ if the site is in a sensitive area (for example, near to a watercourse or in a SSSI). If so, restrictions are likely to be placed on the site (such as limited fuel/oil storage)
- ☑ potential drainage on site (such as land drains, foul sewers, surface water drains and soakaways)
- ☑ the location of plant away from drains and watercourses, especially fuel storage, top soil storage and waste disposal areas
- ☑ that haul roads must be at least 10 m away from a watercourse. Consider construction of gullies/ditches alongside haul roads and around the perimeter of the working area to collect and channel surface water
- ☑ whether the environmental regulator (Environment Agency, SEPA) or relevant body has given permission to any consents/licences required

05

☑ the placing of stockpiles and spoil heaps, which must be away from drains and watercourses (use geotextile silt fencing or cut-off ditches to avoid silt run-off where appropriate).

Cut off ditch

When planning or undertaking construction activities, consideration needs to be given to the history of the site and the surrounding areas.

The site on which construction activities are to be undertaken may be in the path of ground contamination seepage from an adjacent factory, chemical store, buried waste or other process that may result in pollution.

Records of water pollution may exist, which will give an indication of possible health problems for workers. Obtain all available historical records, as any subsequent pollution may be attributed to the construction company and not the originators of the pollution. You should also check if there is any sewage discharge upstream as this may cause issues if you are pumping that water.

Silt management

Silt pollution is easily identified by discolouration/cloudy water. Best practices to avoid problems include:

Silt trap using straw bales and geotextile

☑ only stripping the minimum amount of land required

☑ diverting clean water away from bare ground

☑ not pumping silty water directly into a watercourse

☑ diverting silty water away from drains and watercourses using sand bags, for example

☑ planning for the treatment of silty water when pumping out excavations or managing surface water run-off.

Silt can be removed by using settlement tanks, ponds or lagoons, by allowing silty water to infiltrate through large areas of grassy ground, geotextiles filters or straw bales. *(For further information covering disposal refer to 5.6.)*

Oil and fuel storage

The storage of potentially polluting materials and the refuelling of mobile plant near watercourses/water bodies (within 30 m) should be prohibited as far as practicable.

The storage of all potentially polluting material should be within an impervious bund with a capacity greater than 110% of the total potential stored contents (for multi-tank bunds, the capacity must be 110% of the capacity of the largest tank or 25% of the total tank capacity, whichever is the greater). The maximum holding capacity should be painted on the side. All level gauges, filling valves and vents and filling nozzles (when not in use) should remain within the bund. All valves should be kept locked when not in use and made available to authorised and competent persons only.

The Environment Agency and SEPA have produced a pollution prevention guidance note PPG2 for dealing with above ground oil storage facilities.

The transportation of fuel across the site in drums or other containers should be avoided as far as possible. All mobile plant, including but not limited to cranes, compressors, generators, tanks, and so on, should be maintained and operated such that all leaks and spills of oil are minimised. Oil storage facilities should be regularly inspected for integrity.

Chemical storage

The floor area used for storing or decanting chemicals must not be permeable. Old or corroded drums will cause more problems than those in good condition. Measures that can be taken to minimise the risk of contamination are:

☑ purchase chemicals in the appropriate-sized containers to avoid the need for decanting

☑ where decanting is necessary, have safe procedures that avoid any spillage

☑ provide relevant information, instruction, training and supervision to employees

☑ the proper disposal of all products

☑ provide clear procedures and training for operatives to deal with accidental spillages

05

Water management

☑ make drip-trays available for plant that is known to be leaking environmentally damaging fluids

☑ have set procedures for the refuelling/replenishing of plant so that any spillage cannot permeate into the ground

☑ install bunding around all storage areas, even temporary fuel stores on construction sites

☑ maintain equipment or storage vessels in good condition

☑ get into the habit of only storing or using products that are needed, and only store such products in areas with impermeable floors without drain gullies

☑ maintain good housekeeping procedures and avoid the accumulation of litter or rubbish.

An emergency and incident response plan, appropriate to the size of the site and chemicals being used, should be in place in case of any spillages or pollution alerts (see 5.9 for further details).

Mud

Mud from construction activities has the potential to damage the environment. In wet weather it can enter surface watercourses and drains. In dry weather it can dry out and, as dust, become airborne with the potential to be carried some distance.

Mud can be controlled using road sweepers and by dampening down during dry weather.

5.9   Pollution incident response plans

Incident preparedness and response begins with considering what emergency scenarios and incidents (source) may occur on a construction site, on what pathways the pollution can travel (pathway) and what in the surrounding environment may be impacted by them (receptor).

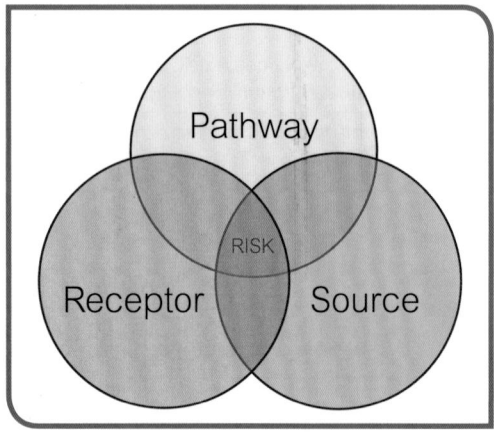

Types of incident include fires, spills and leaks. For each one of these types of incident several different parts of the environment may be affected. For example, a fire will release products of combustion to atmosphere and firewater may enter the surface watercourse, trade effluent sewers and also percolate into the ground.

An effective incident response plan should include:

☑ emergency contact numbers

☑ responsibilities of site personnel

☑ awareness of environmental issues via communication and training

☑ the location of drainage systems/sewers and any arrangements for their stopping up if leakage into them occurs

☑ the use of containment equipment (such as drip trays, bunds and booms) to avoid spillage

☑ the location of spill kits around the site, including designated refuelling areas

☑ arrangements and responsibilities for spill kit replenishment

☑ arrangements for the safe disposal of used spill kit equipment and contaminated materials.

For each type of incident a plan should be put into place setting out the response needed. The basic process of **stop – contain – notify – clean up** must be followed.

In the event of a spillage it is essential that a competent spill response team is deployed with the right spill clean-up materials. The team has to respond sufficiently quickly for the spill to be controlled before it causes any environmental damage.

Booms

If work is to be carried out adjacent to a watercourse or river then arrangements should be put in place to ensure that a boom, which prevents the surface spread of oils and chemicals, can be deployed quickly to contain the spillage. The boom should be long enough to bridge across the river. If the work is carried out on navigable waterways then the appropriate authority should be notified before the boom is installed.

Drip trays

Where drip trays are used they should be in conjunction with absorbent mats so that the contamination can be easily removed. Drip trays should not be left to fill with rainwater as this contaminated water will be more of a problem to dispose of and could cause contamination of drains and watercourses if left to overflow. Plant nappies are also available.

Spill kits

The type and quantity of spill kits deployed around a site will be dictated by the nature of the works and whether they are carried out on land or water. The type of spill kit will also depend on the type and quantity of oils and chemicals that are being used on the site. Typical spill-kit equipment could include, but not be limited to:

- ☑ absorbent booms
- ☑ absorbent granules
- ☑ drain covers
- ☑ heavy-duty plastic bags
- ☑ absorbent pads
- ☑ shovel
- ☑ gloves.

Spill kits should be clearly marked and located at signposted locations around the site. Arrangements for the replenishment of the spill-kit contents should be kept on the inside lid of the spill kit.

Spill-kit equipment contaminated with oils and chemicals is likely to be hazardous waste and should be stored separately and disposed of in accordance with the duty of care and Hazardous Waste Regulations.

Spill kit deployed

05

Spill response tests should be carried out on a regular basis that evaluates the effectiveness of incident response plans. According to the success of the response, improvements may be needed to the system. After any incident, management must conduct a root cause analysis to examine what improvements are needed to prevent the incident from happening again.

5.10   Water efficiency

Water is a precious global resource, critical for life in all its forms. As both the world's population and per capita water use increase there will be ever-rising demands on what is a finite resource. Future climate change and resulting changing patterns of rainfall will make water supply increasingly challenging through the ageing water supply infrastructure.

Water is an expensive item with costs on both the supply side as well as the waste water treatment side. Given these pressures water will become a more expensive resource. What this means within construction is that water efficiency will become a higher priority at all stages in a building's life cycle. Materials with high embodied water content (such as high water usage during manufacture or use) will inevitably increase costs to take account of this priority. The increasing importance of embodied water is recognised in CEEQUAL, for example (physical resources use and management).

Whilst the abstraction of water from site excavations does not require an abstraction licence, abstracting water for other uses (such as dust suppression, washing down, and so on) will require a licence if using more than 20 m^3 per day in England and Wales.

The Government's sustainability strategy for the construction sector identifies reducing water usage in the manufacturing and construction phase by 20% compared to a 2008 baseline (148 m^3 per £m of contractor's output). This target will both reduce pressure on water resources and also save money. There are a variety of techniques that can be used to increase water efficiency. The SFfC has prepared an action plan, measurement protocol, water hierarchy and toolbox talk for managing and reducing water usage on construction sites. Measurement and understanding water performance is important so action can be taken to reduce consumption.

Refer to the SFfC's website for its *Water: An action plan for reducing water usage on construction sites*.

Using and conserving water during site works

On larger construction projects, where high volumes of water are being used, the first action is to establish an approach to measuring and monitoring water usage so that it can be managed. This may involve the use of water meters at appropriate locations and the use of water balances to account for water usage. Water reduction targets can be set based on known volumes of water usage and progress monitored.

Collecting data on water consumption during the construction process will provide the following benefits:

- ☑ understanding and managing costs
- ☑ reducing environmental impact of overuse
- ☑ benchmarking and improving performance
- ☑ obtaining credits under BREEAM, Code for sustainable homes and CEEQUAL
- ☑ demonstrating continual improvement in accordance with ISO 14001/EMAS
- ☑ demonstrating best practice and meeting customer expectations.

Significant savings can be made by using rainwater harvesting systems to collect rainwater from roofs and other flat surfaces. Early installation of suitable collection systems would need to be investigated at the design stage and payback times calculated for the expected volume of water use. Harvested water can be used for dust suppression, avoiding the need to draw water from the mains or abstraction.

During supervisors' site inspections water use can be monitored and any obvious leaks and running hoses identified and dealt with. The use of triggers on hoses will prevent hoses from running whilst unattended.

Vehicle wheel wash equipment is now available with water recycling and recirculation systems fitted. These will reduce the volume of water used and have the potential to save money. These systems work by providing a solids settling area combined with the use of flocculants to further precipitate solids out. The solids collected can be periodically removed.

Site accommodation can be fitted with waterless urinals, push taps and rainwater harvesting for toilet flushes.

Collecting rainwater for reuse

Waterless urinals

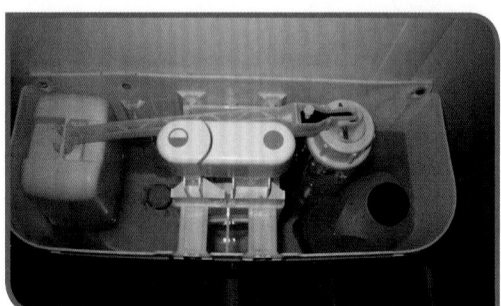

Using a milk bottle to save flush water

Appendix A – Strategic Forum for Construction – Water toolbox talk example

Toolbox Talk: Water

Water use in construction

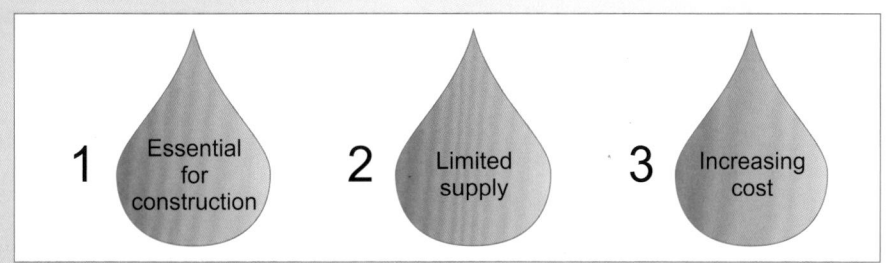

1   Essential for construction   2   Limited supply   3   Increasing cost

Water is integral to the economy, we need it for energy production, industrial processes, to grow food and, of course, for construction. In the coming years, the combined effects of climate change and a growing population are likely to put increasing pressure on our rivers, lakes and aquifers. If we do not act now to manage our demand for water, the security of our water supplies could be compromised.

What is the situation in the UK?

It is a misconception that the UK has plenty of water.
FACT - already, parts of England have less rainfall per person than many Mediterranean countries.
FACT - increasing demand will result in increasing cost both at home and on site as we fund new sources of supply.
FACT - water resources are under pressure and current levels of water abstraction are unsustainable in places.

What does this mean for construction?

- We can ensure no water is wasted.

- By reducing water usage, projects will benefit from cost savings.

- As an industry a commitment has been made to reduce water usage by 20% from a start position of 148m³/£million contractors output. We all have a responsibility to measure progress against this target.

- We will be able to identify if water from other sources might be an appropriate alternative to using water of drinking quality standard.

Toolbox Talk: Water

Water Hierarchy:

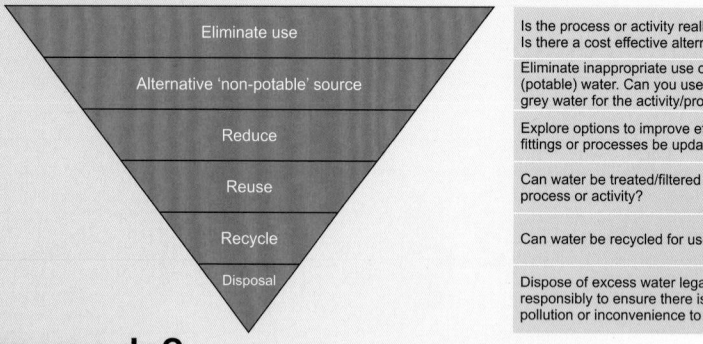

Eliminate use	Is the process or activity really necessary? Is there a cost effective alternative to water?
Alternative 'non-potable' source	Eliminate inappropriate use of drinking (potable) water. Can you use rainwater or grey water for the activity/process?
Reduce	Explore options to improve efficiency. Can fittings or processes be updated?
Reuse	Can water be treated/filtered for reuse in a process or activity?
Recycle	Can water be recycled for use elsewhere?
Disposal	Dispose of excess water legally and responsibly to ensure there is no flooding, pollution or inconvenience to others.

What can you do?

Hold a discussion with your team to identify where you use water on site. Refer to the 'SFfC How to Save Water on Construction Site' guide for the top ten quick reducing water use. Three of the most commonly applicable water saving measures are listed below;

1. Fix Leaks

An unfixed leak can be the most significant water use on site.
Leaks can come from damaged washers in taps, worn valves and corroded or damaged pipework.

2. Fit trigger guns to hoses

Hoses left running when not in use waste a lot of water in a short time.
Fit robust trigger guns to hoses so that flow can be controlled at the point of use.

3. Running taps

Flow from taps is often more than is needed. Consider adapting taps by either fitting a flow restrictor or aerating tap insert. Changing the tap is another option. Turn taps off.

Take away message

- Apply the water hierarchy. Prevent use, improve efficiency, consider alternative sources, reuse and recycle.
- Water is our most precious resource and every one of us has responsibility to conserve it.

06

Statutory nuisance

Construction sites are inherently noisy and can generate dust, exhaust emissions and fumes. Noise is the largest single source of complaint about construction sites.

This chapter identifies the activities defined as statutory nuisance, provides an overview of the legal framework for their control and provides guidance on the minimisation and management of these issues on site.

Introduction	72
Airborne dust, emissions and odours	72
Noise, including consent requirements	74
Vibration	77
Light pollution	78
Community liaison	78

6.1   Introduction

The quality and enjoyment of people's local environment has been recognised in law for many centuries. Construction sites, which generate dust, noise, fumes and artificial light for example, have the potential to cause nuisance to neighbours and must be managed effectively to avoid Local Authority or individual intervention, with the potential of delaying or stopping the works.

There are three types of nuisance: statutory nuisance, where a particular nuisance has been made by statute, and public and private nuisance, which are within common law.

Current legislation for statutory nuisance in England, Wales and Scotland is contained in Part III of the Environmental Protection Act, and is enforced by Local Authorities with controls on various types of noise nuisance regulated under the Control of Pollution Act.

Section 79 of the Environmental Protection Act includes the following statutory nuisances:

- ☑ premises in such a state as to be prejudicial to health
- ☑ smoke emissions that are prejudicial to health or a nuisance
- ☑ fumes or gases emitted from premises so as to be prejudicial to health or a nuisance
- ☑ any dust, steam, odour or other waste that is a nuisance or prejudicial to health
- ☑ any accumulation or deposit that is prejudicial to health or a nuisance
- ☑ any water covering land, or land covered with water, that is in such a state as to be prejudicial to health or a nuisance
- ☑ artificial light emitted from premises so as to be prejudicial to health or a nuisance
- ☑ noise emitted from premises, vehicles, machinery or equipment that may be prejudicial to health or a nuisance.

Local Authorities have a duty to inspect their areas from time to time to detect whether a nuisance exists and investigate all complaints of statutory nuisances. Local Authority lane rental/permit schemes may push work into off-peak times during the night, thus increasing the possibility of creating a nuisance.

Where a Local Authority is satisfied that a statutory nuisance exists or is likely to occur then, under Section 80 of the Environmental Protection Act, the Local Authority can serve an abatement notice on the person responsible for the nuisance. If the person cannot be found then the notice is served on the owner or occupier of the premises.

Failure to comply with the terms of an abatement notice may result in prosecution in a Magistrate's Court. Conviction may result in a fine of up to £5,000 plus a daily fee of £500 for each day the offence continues after conviction. Under Section 82 of the Environmental Protection Act, individuals can also take action through the Magistrate's Court.

All employers should ensure that best practical means have been used to prevent, or to counteract the effects of, the nuisance.

Best practical means is defined as taking into account:

- ☑ current technical knowledge
- ☑ the design, construction and maintenance of buildings and enclosures
- ☑ design, installation, maintenance and periods of operation of plant
- ☑ financial implications
- ☑ local conditions.

6.2   Airborne dust, emissions and odours

A variety of air pollutants have known or suspected harmful effects on human health and the environment and can create a statutory nuisance. The UK Government has made provisions to ensure that air quality standards for certain pollutants are set centrally through the national air quality strategy.

Generally, Local Authorities have control over the management of air quality through the identification of air quality management areas. In addition, Local Authorities regulate the smaller, less polluting, installations and processes (such as batching plants, crushing activities or spray bays). The Environmental Agency, on the other hand, regulates air emissions from the more polluting processes (such as landfill sites and asphalt plants).

Controls under the Clean Air Act

The Clean Air Act provides a comprehensive control mechanism for the protection of the environment from smoke, dust, grit and fumes from all fires and furnaces, with the Local Authority as the relevant environmental regulator who can impose limits on dust, emissions and odours generated from a site.

Under Section 1 of Part 1 of the Clean Air Act, it is an offence to emit dark smoke from the chimney of any building on any day unless these occur within the permitted periods, as specified in the Dark Smoke (Permitted Periods) Regulations.

Under Section 2 of Part I of the Clean Air Act, it is an offence to cause, or permit the emission of, dark smoke from industrial or trade premises (other than chimneys); premises could also include a demolition site. The method for assessing the shade of smoke is based on the Ringlemann chart. This determines the type of smoke depending on its shade. Only when smoke colour reaches the 40% obscuration point is it considered dark.

06

Controls under Environmental Permitting Regulations or Pollution Prevention Control Act

The provisions of the Clean Air Act do not apply to processes that are controlled under the Environmental Permitting Regulations in England and Wales or the Pollution Prevention Control Act in Scotland. From a construction perspective these include, but are not limited to, installations such as batching plants, crushing activities, waste transfer stations and landfill sites.

The standard conditions for a Part B permit for mobile crushing plant requires that no dust must cross the site boundary and the Local Authority must be informed if it does. In addition, visual inspections of dust must be made three times daily.

It is also possible to obtain an environmental permitting D7 exemption from the Environmental Agency for the burning of plant waste on land in the open (this only applies to the burning of waste by an establishment or undertaking where the waste burned is the establishment or undertaking's own waste). This exemption limits the burning of waste of up to 10 tonnes in 24 hours and could include, for example, Japanese knotweed.

Controls under Highway Regulations

The Highways Act, Sections 161 and 161A, forbids the lighting of a fire on or above a highway, within 15.25 metres of the centre of the highway, without authorisation. If a fire is lit on land that is not part of the highway but consists of a carriageway, or a person allows this to happen, and a user of the highway is injured, interrupted or endangered by the fire, smoke or any other fire resulting from the original fire, then those responsible for the fire will be liable to a fine unless reasonable attempts were made to prevent this from occurring.

 Guidance to manage dust and emissions

☑ Identify sensitive receptors and liaise with the Local Authority regarding any likely nuisances that could occur.

☑ Put control measures in place to mitigate any negative dust impacts, including:

– dampening down of haul routes with water

– ensuring public highways are regularly swept

– installing wheel-washing equipment at site exits where appropriate

– ensuring that bulk materials leaving site are covered

– installing dust screens or silt fencing to prevent the horizontal transportation of dust

– using water, where possible, in cutting and grinding activities to suppress dust

– ensuring that bulk materials likely to cause dust are covered where appropriate.

06

Silica dust

Silica is a constituent of sand, and many construction activities produce high concentrations of silica dust.

Activities, including concrete drilling, scabbling, chasing, cutting and sand or grit blasting techniques, can create large volumes of dust.

Clouds of dust do not restrict themselves to the construction site but may migrate and contaminate the environment around the site.

Such pollution may cause problems for people in local food processing companies, restaurants, cafés, schools, hospitals and general living accommodation, and can also contaminate local watercourses or drainage systems and affect wildlife and plants.

 For further information on the health and safety issues associated with silica dust refer to Section B10 Dust and fumes.

Measuring and monitoring dust

There are currently no UK limits for the assessment of deposited dust and its ability to cause a nuisance. Reference is made to an annual deposition of 200 mg/m²/day as a value for the threshold for serious nuisance. In addition, DEFRA's *Process guidance note 3/16*, for crushing activities, for example, does not specify any limits but simply refers to the avoidance of visible emissions crossing the site boundary. Visual assessment of dust is therefore a key indicator as to whether dust may cause a statutory nuisance.

Dust deposit gauge

Care should be exercised when specifying this as a proposed limit because it:

☑ does not consider the nature of the dust

☑ is thought to have essentially been derived using the BS deposit gauge and is not equally acceptable to all types of deposit gauge

☑ is an annual average and is therefore not applicable to shorter measurement periods

☑ has no statutory effect.

Deposit gauges are a simple and accurate method of measuring deposited dust. A dry frisbee dust deposit gauge can be used to determine the amount of dust produced a month at a time. It uses a bowl and bottle to collect large and small dust particles and should be situated 5 m away from any obstruction.

Exhaust emissions

Because of the fuel they burn, motor vehicles or other internal combustion engines, generators and compressors are among the largest sources of airborne pollution. This pollution is increasing steadily as the use of vehicles increases.

Elements from exhaust emissions that pollute the environment include:

☑ carbon dioxide

☑ carbon monoxide

☑ hydrocarbons

☑ lead

☑ nitrogen oxides

☑ particulate matter (smoke).

To minimise the extent of pollution you can:

☑ limit the use of road vehicles or other internal combustion engines

☑ ensure that vehicles are switched off when not required

☑ ensure that haul routes are planned with minimum distances

☑ have a planned and preventative maintenance programme or modify existing engines to produce less pollution

☑ use fuels designed to cause less pollution

☑ consider the use of electrical equipment rather than internal combustion engines

☑ liaise with electricity suppliers early in a project so that equipment can be connected to the grid as early as possible rather than running off generators.

Vapours and fumes

Many materials or products (such as sealants or resins) when used in a work environment may release vapours, fumes or odours. These can damage the environment and be hazardous to the health of workers or other persons.

The likelihood of such hazards must be assessed, and adequate control measures designed and implemented that include appropriate monitoring arrangements. The controls should eliminate the risks, where possible, or otherwise minimise them. The selection of less hazardous products should be considered as this may also avoid the used packaging needing to be disposed of as hazardous waste.

6.3   Noise, including consent requirements

Construction and demolition sites are inherently noisy and often take place in residential areas that are normally quiet. They have the potential to create a statutory nuisance in the form of noise and vibration that disturbs wildlife, causes structural damage to buildings and utilities and can create health risks to site staff and the general public.

Local Authorities may place restrictions on the person responsible for a construction site to observe specified controls designed to minimise noise and vibration nuisance.

The Control of Pollution Act, Section 60, gives Local Authorities the power to serve notices that specify:

- ☑ the maximum levels of noise that may be emitted from any particular point
- ☑ provisions for any change in circumstances
- ☑ the type of plant or machinery that may, or may not, be used
- ☑ the working hours when noise may be made.

BS 5228, which deals with noise and vibration control on construction sites, includes best practice to ensure that a Section 60 notice is avoided. It is in five parts, with Part 1 being a code of practice for basic information and procedures for noise and vibration control.

The Control of Pollution Act or BS 5228 do not specify any limits for construction noise on the basis that a Local Authority knows its area best and should have a better idea on suitable noise limits.

Application for Section 61 noise consent (prior consent)

Where it is possible that a noise or vibration nuisance will be created, the person responsible for the site may make an application to the Local Authority for prior consent to start work. Such consent applications should, where possible, be made at the same time as planning applications, or else as soon as it is known the nuisance cannot be avoided (such as power-floating at night). The Local Authority has 28 days to approve the application.

Applications should contain particulars of the:

- ☑ work to be undertaken
- ☑ location of the works
- ☑ working hours
- ☑ proposed methods, and the plant and machinery to be used
- ☑ proposed steps for minimising the noise and vibration.

The Local Authority, in granting consent for the works to begin, may:

- ☑ attach any conditions they wish to the consent
- ☑ limit or qualify a consent
- ☑ limit the duration of consent for the works to be carried out
- ☑ specify maximum boundary noise level, permitted hours of work, and plant and equipment that may or may not be used.

In the case of works that overrun for sound engineering or health and safety reasons the Local Authority should be advised as soon as is reasonably practicable of the reasons for, and the likely duration of, such works.

Where there are minor variations in the works featured in the consent application, and rescheduling of works are of a critical nature, the applicant may apply for a variation. This procedure may also be used for minor additional activities that were not included in the original application and do not materially affect the predicted noise levels.

Applications for a variation are to be received by the Local Authority, where practicable within seven days, but at least two working days ahead of the start of the works for which the application is made.

Where the proposed works have to be changed from the original program, as given in the application to require operations outside of the terms of the consent, you must apply for a dispensation at least 14 days in advance of the proposed operation, submitting the following:

- ☑ details of the operation in question
- ☑ reasons why the operation cannot be carried out within the terms of the consent
- ☑ proposed working hours
- ☑ predicted noise and vibration levels at relevant locations
- ☑ proposed steps taken to reduce noise and/or vibration to a minimum.

 It is far better to apply for a Section 61 notice and work with the Local Authority to agree how the work will be carried out, than to be stopped following a complaint and have to comply with a Section 60 notice. Once a Section 61 consent has been given, the contractor is protected from action on noise grounds taken by the Local Authority as long as the conditions of the consent are complied with.

Managing noise on site

Before works commence on site the contract documentation should be reviewed to determine whether specific noise limits at various locations from the site boundary have been specified. Where this is the case, it is likely that monitoring of noise levels will be required and may also be a requirement of a Section 61 noise consent, where this has been applied for.

A noise survey will establish the ambient and background noise levels at relevant locations around the site boundary. The purpose of the noise survey will be to establish the best location for noisy operations that could cause a nuisance to neighbours and can also be used to provide supporting evidence for erroneous claims.

06

🔍 How to control noise on site

The control of noise on construction sites can be achieved either by controlling the noise at source or by screening.

Methods for controlling noise at source include:

- ☑ **selection of low noise method**: where possible, methods should be employed to reduce the amount of noise generated in the first place (for example, off-site fabrication of concrete panels would avoid the need for scabbling of concrete and the use of vibrating pokers)

- ☑ **working hours**: adapt working hours to restrict noisy activity to certain periods of the day. Arrange delivery times to suit the area

- ☑ **selection of quiet or low noise equipment**: for some types of noisy operations (such as piling) there are alternative methods available (for example, drop hammer piling could be replaced by hydraulic jack if ground conditions are suitable). Many power tools are now available that can be operated using electricity or compressed air rather than petrol or diesel engines

- ☑ **location of equipment on site**: where possible, noisy stationary equipment should be placed away from sensitive receptors and public areas

- ☑ **provision of acoustic enclosures**: most modern equipment (such as compressors or generators) will come with its own hood or door. These should always be kept closed and in good order. Acoustic enclosures can be purchased that surround equipment to reduce the transport of noise.

Methods for screening noise include the use of:

- ☑ site hoarding
- ☑ purpose-built screens
- ☑ material storage
- ☑ bunding
- ☑ existing structures.

The screen should be placed either close to the source or the receptor.

Other general measures that can be employed to reduce noise levels include:

- ☑ planning site haul routes to avoid vehicles reversing
- ☑ planning delivery times and routes to suit local conditions
- ☑ maintaining haul routes in good order to prevent vehicle noise caused by potholes or uneven surfaces
- ☑ minimising drop heights of materials into lorries and dumpers
- ☑ shutting down plant when not required
- ☑ using only plant conforming with relevant standards and directives on emissions
- ☑ maintaining plant in good order, including compressor air lines
- ☑ placing material handling areas away from sensitive receptors
- ☑ making use of noise-reducing equipment (such as jackets, shrouds, hoods and doors) and ensuring that they remain closed when the equipment is in use
- ☑ ensuring all viewing openings in site hoardings are glazed with Perspex
- ☑ providing good practice guides to all operatives through the provision of toolbox talks.

6.4   Vibration

In simple terms, vibration is caused by sound waves travelling through solid material rather than through air. High levels of vibration can cause damage to buildings, disturb wildlife and disturb neighbours. In the UK, vibration is considered in the same manner as noise as regards statutory nuisance.

The most commonly used standard for environmental vibration assessment for disturbance is BS 6472 *Evaluation of human exposure to vibration in buildings [1 Hz to 80 Hz]*. The British Standard suggests that levels of vibration from 0.1 to 0.2 mm/s (at night) and below in residential buildings would have a very low probability of adverse comment.

BS 7385: Part 2 *Evaluation and measurement for vibration in buildings* gives guidance on the levels of vibration above which building structures could be damaged. The standard states that there is a major difference between the sensitivity of people in feeling vibration and the onset of levels of vibration that damage the structure.

For residential buildings, the standard states that, for cosmetic damage (such as cracking in plaster work) to occur, a peak particle velocity of some 15 mm/s is necessary at a vibration frequency of 4 Hz; this rises to 20 mm/sec at 15 Hz, and thereafter the limit rises to 50 mm/s at 40 Hz and above.

06

Reducing and managing vibration

The potential for vibration is dependent on a number of factors, particularly the distance of the receptor from the source, together with the ground conditions and features within the ground (such as sewers). Piling, vibrating rollers, tunneling and boring are key activities that have the potential to cause vibration. Consideration should be given to the methods used to establish the solution with the least vibration risk. These types of activity should be considered carefully when working near to known archaeological features.

Key questions to be considered when planning the works are listed below.

- ☑ Can the activity be done using a different technique that results in lower vibration levels (for example, hydraulic pressed sheet piling rather than impact piling or vibrating methods)?
- ☑ As high frequency vibration causes less damage than low frequency vibration, can the plant be operated in a way that generates less low frequency vibration?
- ☑ Can the equipment be isolated from the transfer medium (for example, putting generators on timber mats rather than directly on the ground)?

Before starting work, all sensitive structures and buildings should be identified and surveyed. This survey should include photographic and written records of existing:

- ☑ cracks and their width
- ☑ levels and verticality of tilting walls and bulges in walls
- ☑ damage, including broken bricks, tiles, pipework or plaster.

Where some vibration cannot be avoided you should adopt a good neighbour policy and inform local residents and the local environmental health officer.

Vibration levels should be monitored during the works using competent, trained staff with the appropriate equipment. Following the works the same survey should be carried out to confirm that no damage or otherwise has occurred.

6.5 Light pollution

Light pollution is artificial light that illuminates or intrudes upon areas not intended to be lit. There are a variety of sources of light pollution from construction sites, including lighting towers, offices and access/security lighting.

> Check the direction of lighting and reflection off surfaces. Simple adjustments may easily reduce any light pollution affecting neighbours. Where possible lighting should be switched off to avoid disturbance.

In England and Wales light pollution can be a statutory nuisance and Local Authorities have powers to apply an abatement notice. If this is not complied with the matter may then go to a Magistrate's Court. There is no legislation in Scotland or Northern Ireland covering lighting nuisance.

6.6 Community liaison

A good neighbour has consideration for those around them and takes an active interest in their wellbeing. Construction sites can have many different types of neighbour and construction activities will affect neighbours in many ways. Neighbours may include householders, businesses, sports clubs, pubs and shops.

Construction projects need to have a proactive approach to community liaison and ensure that the right processes are in place for engaging with the local community. It is important to inform neighbours of what may affect them before it happens so that people can prepare and also have a chance to have their say. There are a number of different ways in which this can happen, including liaising with neighbours, holding meetings, school visits, site tours or open days, door to door visits and providing regular newsletters.

It is also important that an effective complaints system is in place that provides a rapid and effective response to issues that have been raised. Being a good neighbour will result in a good relationship and will avoid complaints and damage to reputation.

Considerate Constructors' Scheme

Started in 1997, the Considerate Constructors' Scheme (CCS) was set up by the UK construction industry to improve its image. Since then, the scheme has registered and monitored over 40,000 sites and has been instrumental in many of the improvements enjoyed today.

The scheme is recognised by the UK construction industry as a major force in improving its image through the registration and monitoring of UK sites. The scheme is also recognised in, and contributes to, improved performance in certification schemes, including BREEAM, the Code for sustainable homes and CEEQUAL. Some Local Authorities, such as Westminster City Council's Considerate Builders Scheme, have established their own principles.

Any work that could be construed by the general public as construction can be registered as a site, provided it has a duration of six weeks or more. A site registers onto the scheme and agrees to follow the code of considerate practice, which forms the basis of all of the scheme's requirements.

The site is then visited by a monitor, assessed and scored against the code of practice.

The monitor also identifies any measures being taken by a company or its sites that are above and beyond these requirements. Certificates of compliance and certificates of performance beyond compliance are awarded to sites when they meet the codes scoring criteria. There are also national awards for the top performing sites and companies.

>
>
> In January 2013 a new code of considerate practice, new checklists, new report formats and a new scoring system for both site and company registration was launched. For more information visit the website.

07
Ecology

There is a high level of protection given to wildlife through legal controls and contract conditions.

This chapter gives a general overview of the legal framework for the protection of wildlife and their habitats. It highlights endangered and protected species and designated sites for their protection.

This chapter also gives an overview of the legal framework for the regulation of invasive species.

Introduction   80
Key requirements   80
Regulatory bodies for nature conservation   81
Endangered species   81
Protected species and habitats   82
Invasive species   87
Promoting biodiversity   89

Appendix A – Wildlife year planner   90
Appendix B – Dealing with Japanese knotweed   95
Appendix C – Construction activities and their
             potential adverse effects on wildlife   96

7.1   Introduction

The identification and management of wildlife needs to be undertaken early in the planning stage of a project to avoid costly delays to the programme and possible loss of reputation if damage takes place.

Damaging, disturbing or removing protected species can result in prosecution under a range of environmental legislation, and wildlife is also held in high regard by the public.

Construction activities (such as demolition, site clearance and dewatering) potentially impact on plants and wildlife in the form of:

- ☑ disturbance of birds, bats, badgers and other protected species
- ☑ removal and fragmentation of habitats
- ☑ disturbance to aquatic wildlife and water quality
- ☑ disturbance to wildlife from noise and vibration
- ☑ damage to trees and hedgerows
- ☑ changes in lighting conditions.

 Refer to Appendix C for a list of construction activities and their potential adverse effects on wildlife.

Developers must produce an ecological impact assessment when making a planning application identifying intended mitigation measures before, during and after construction activities. The Strategic Forum for Construction (SFfC) set a 2012 target for all construction projects over £1m to have biodiversity surveys carried out and necessary actions instigated.

7.2   Key requirements

 The following practices should be employed to avoid damage to wildlife and their habitats

Before work starts:

- ☑ identify wildlife features and ecologically important areas prior to works commencing and designate protected areas (for example, fence them off). The contract documentation should identify sensitive areas that will require protection and management
- ☑ liaise with statutory bodies and local groups to explain any mitigation measures to be used
- ☑ where there is a need to take, disturb or relocate protected species, consents should be obtained from the relevant regulatory body and competent licensed ecologists used to carry out the work *(refer to 7.3)*
- ☑ plan site clearance/demolition works to avoid any nesting, hibernation or breeding seasons. *(Refer to Appendix A for a yearly ecology planner that identifies the constraints and best times for dealing with the main groups of protected species)*
- ☑ inform and explain to personnel any protected areas and consequences of any damage to these areas.

During construction:

- ☑ regularly check the condition of fencing of any designated protected areas
- ☑ refer to the ecology year planner to be aware of differing seasons and constraints
- ☑ ensure watercourses are free from contaminated run-off or any other forms of pollution
- ☑ confirm compliance against method statements, the construction environmental management plan and any environmental contractual requirements
- ☑ in the event of any unexpected ecological finds, stop work and then consult with the site ecologist (if relevant) and statutory bodies.

7.3   Regulatory bodies for nature conservation

The following organisations have responsibility for nature conservation in each of the devolved administrations:

- ☑ in England – Natural England
- ☑ in Northern Ireland – Northern Ireland Environment Agency
- ☑ in Scotland – Scottish Natural Heritage
- ☑ in Wales – Countryside Council for Wales (Cadw).

 In April 2013 Countryside Council for Wales joins with the Environment Agency Wales and the Forestry Commission Wales to become a single environment body (SEB).

Their remit includes providing ecological advice, consultation during the planning process, promoting biodiversity, and protecting designated ecological sites and protected species.

There are many other bodies involved in the protection and enhancement of plants and wildlife. The Joint Nature and Conservation Committee (JNCC) is the main public body that advises the UK Government and devolved administrations on UK-wide and international nature conservation. Originally established under the Environmental Protection Act, JNCC was reconstituted by the Natural Environment and Rural Communities (NERC) Act.

JNCC is led by the joint committee, which brings together members from the nature conservation bodies for England, Scotland, Wales and Northern Ireland and independent members appointed by the Secretary of State for the Environment, Food and Rural Affairs under an independent chairperson.

7.4   Endangered species

The natural world slowly changes over thousands of years, during which time new species evolve and some species decline and may ultimately become extinct. The impact of human activity, however, can have a dramatic impact on these natural cycles by putting significant pressure on ecosystems through vegetation clearance, deforestation and habitat fragmentation caused by agriculture, development, road building and other infrastructure projects. This can lead to an accelerated decline in species and habitats that support them.

The responsible management of wildlife and their habitats is critical to ensure that it is passed on to future generations, given that they also sustain human life, from the food we eat to the things we manufacture from the earth's renewable resources (such as timber).

At an international level, the International Union for Conservation of Nature (IUCN) is recognised in its work for the publication the *Red list of threatened species*, which is the definitive international standard for species extinction risk. The *Red list* is regularly updated with new information of the status of endangered species.

In the UK, priority species and habitats are those that have been identified as being the most threatened and requiring conservation action under the UK biodiversity action plan (UK BAP). References to priority species and habitats concern those species and habitats identified as being of principal importance in England in Section 41 of the Natural Environment and Rural Communities Act.

The most recent list of UK BAP priority species and habitats represents the most comprehensive analysis of such information ever undertaken in the UK. Following this review, the UK BAP priority list now contains **1,150 species**, and **65 habitats**. Species were assessed according to four criteria:

- ☑ threatened internationally
- ☑ international responsibly and a 25% decline in the UK
- ☑ more than 50% decline in the UK
- ☑ other important factors, where data on decline was lacking but there is other evidence of extreme threat.

Examples of priority species in the UK include:

- ☑ birds:
  - skylark
  - house sparrow
  - lesser spotted woodpecker
- ☑ mammals:
  - dormouse
  - water vole
  - brown, long-eared bat
  - red squirrel

07

Ecology

- ☑ amphibians and reptiles:
  - – common lizard
  - – great crested newt
  - – common toad
  - – adder.

Great crested newt

Lesser spotted woodpecker

Bats roosting

7.5   Protected species and habitats

Several hundred species of birds, wild creatures and plants are protected under The Wildlife and Countryside Act (as amended) and are listed in various schedules to the act, for example:

- ☑ Schedule 1: Birds
- ☑ Schedule 5: Animals
- ☑ Schedule 8: Plants.

The Conservation (Natural Habitats, etc.) Regulations and the Conservation (Natural Habitats, etc.) (Amendment) Regulations cover the protection of European protected species – plants and animals listed in the European Habitats Directive.

The habitat regulations include the:

- ☑ protection of certain species of animals, Schedule 2 (such as great crested newt, dormouse, bats, otter and the large blue butterfly)
- ☑ protection of species of plants, Schedule 4 (such as fen orchid and early gentian)
- ☑ designation of special areas of conservation (SAC) and special protection areas (SPAs), which are intended to protect the habitats of threatened species of wildlife (see below).

Local planning authorities will, in consultation with Natural England, the Countryside Council for Wales or Scottish Natural Heritage, consider SPAs to protect birds from the effects of disturbance, shooting, egg collecting or other activities.

> **!** Disturbing protected species or damaging their habitats could result in prosecution against the above legislation. For example, if species such as badgers, bats or great crested newts are disturbed this may result in a fine of £5,000 per offence, which may include the confiscation of plant, equipment and vehicles.

Designated sites

The UK has a responsibility to ensure the protection of species and their habitats from both a national and international perspective. One approach to achieving this is to establish designated protected sites, as detailed below.

Sites of special scientific interest (SSSI). All sites of national and international importance on land, including national nature reserves (NNRs), nature conservation review (NCR) and geological conservation review (GCR) sites, special protection areas (SPAs), special areas of conservation (SAC) and ramsar sites, are notified as SSSIs.

Owners and occupiers are required to notify the relevant regulatory authority of potentially damaging operations and may not undertake them for four months unless they are in accordance with the terms of a management agreement with consent of the relevant regulatory authority.

As protection, the Secretary of State may make a nature conservation order to protect any sites of national or international importance. SSSIs are classed as such under the Wildlife and Countryside Act.

Local planning authorities are required to consult with the statutory bodies (English Nature, Countryside Council for Wales, Scottish Natural Heritage) prior to allowing any development to proceed that may affect a SSSI. Water, gas and electricity companies must also do the same.

National nature reserve (NNRs) are areas of national, and sometimes international, importance that are owned or leased by the relevant regulatory authority approved by them, or are managed in accordance with nature reserve agreements with landowners and occupiers. The essential characteristic of NNRs is that they are primarily used for nature conservation.

Special protection areas (SPAs) and special areas of conservation (SAC) are intended to protect the habitats of threatened species of wildlife. SACs are strictly protected sites under EC habitats directive. This states the requirement to establish a European network of important, high-quality conservation sites.

SPAs are strictly protected sites classified in accordance with Article 4 of the EC directive on the conservation of wild birds (79/409/EEC), also known as the Birds Directive, which came into force in April 1979. They are classified for rare and vulnerable birds, listed in Annex I to the Birds Directive, and for regularly occurring migratory species.

Ramsar sites. The Ramsar convention requires the protection of wetlands that are of international importance, particularly as waterfowl habitats.

Biogenetic reserve. A number of NNRs and some important SSSIs have been identified as biogenetic reserves under a council of Europe programme for the conservation of heathlands and dry grasslands.

Marine nature reserves (MNRs) are designated under the Wildlife and Countryside Act to conserve marine flora or fauna, geological or physiographical features, or to allow study of such features.

Areas of special protection for birds (AOSPs) are established under the Wildlife and Countryside Act. The purpose of such orders is normally to provide sanctuary to particularly vulnerable groups of birds.

Local nature reserves (LNRs) may be established by Local Authorities under Section 21 of the National Parks and Access to the Countryside Act. These habitats of local significance can make a useful contribution to nature conservation and public amenity.

Badgers

The Protection of Badgers Act is provided to protect badgers from deliberate harm, injury or baiting. It is an offence to:

- ☑ disturb a badger when it is occupying a sett
- ☑ obstruct access to, or entrance to, a sett
- ☑ interfere with, damage or destroy a sett
- ☑ wilfully kill, injure, entrap or ill-treat a badger.

A licence must be obtained from the relevant conservation body when working around or near badger setts. The following are trigger distances for requiring a licence, but the conditions applied may be more stringent, depending upon each situation:

- ☑ the use of heavy machinery within 30 m
- ☑ the use of light machinery within 20 m
- ☑ use of hand tools within 10 m.

If a badger sett is discovered after works have started, it is essential to stop work immediately and seek expert advice.

Badgers

Artificial badger sett being built as part of mitigation

Great crested newts

Great crested newts are fully protected by law and rely on water bodies for breeding but otherwise they spend much of their lives on land. They spend winter on land, normally hibernating underground, and emerge soon after the first frost-free days in January or February to begin the migration to breeding ponds (within 500 m).

Initial surveys for great crested newts (by an ecological consultant) are required by the local planning authority and Natural England where water bodies are within 500 m of any proposed development. Four surveys must be made to determine presence/absence, with three surveys conducted between mid-April and mid-May.

Ideally, it is best if great crested newts and their habitats are protected before planning permission has been given for development of a site. If a known or suspected great crested newt site is threatened by a development, the local planning authority and the local office of the statutory nature conservation organisation (SNCO) should be informed as far in advance as possible and the appropriate mitigation scheme approved as part of the planning permission.

Any mitigation proposals will need the submission of a licence application to Natural England. It requires a report that sets out survey results, impacts and a mitigation scheme. The application will take up to 40 days to determine.

07

> ### e.g. Mitigation for great crested newts could include:
>
> ☑ **minor impact – on site mitigation:**
> - small scale relocation and exclusion
> - fence erecting and traps set up to exclude newts from works (between March and October), survey for 30 days minimum
> - habitat creation (such as creation of refuges and hibernacula – piles of rubble/logs buried beneath surface of ground)
>
> ☑ **major impact – translocation of newts away from site:**
> - fence erecting and traps set up (between March and April), survey for 60 days minimum
> - translocation of newts to area providing equivalent/better habitat (receptor site)
> - habitat creation and restoration prior to translocation (such as areas of coarse grassland, hedgerows and ponds)
> - creation of refuges and hibernaculas (piles of rubble/logs buried beneath surface of ground).

Great crested newt fencing

Great crested newt fencing and mitigation pond

Bats

Bats roost in a number of locations, including:

☑ disused buildings and structures   ☑ roofs and walls of buildings

☑ under bridges   ☑ caves.

☑ holes and cracks in trees

Bats hibernate between October and April and breed between May and September. If it is suspected that bats may be present then a bat survey should be carried out by a suitably qualified specialist to establish the size and location of any roost.

Under the Wildlife and Countryside Act it is illegal to injure, kill, capture or disturb a bat or damage or destroy their roost, even if it is unoccupied at the time. Personnel holding a bat licence are legally allowed to enter a bat roost or to capture, handle or re-locate bats.

Nesting birds

All birds and their nests are protected in Schedule 1 of the Wildlife and Countryside Act. Some species of bird are further protected from disturbance (such as birds of prey and barn owls).

It is an offence intentionally to kill, injure or take any wild bird and this is backed up by offences of taking, damaging or destroying a nest whilst it is in use or being built and taking or destroying eggs. In particular, any vegetation clearance works should be done outside of the nesting period.

As highlighted above, it is essential that construction is carefully planned to avoid any works in areas during the nesting period (March to the end of July). Otherwise, any such areas should be fenced off to avoid damage or disturbance. There is also a risk of finding birds nesting in walling stones or pieces of plant during the construction phase. Good awareness is key and site personnel should be made aware of these risks through induction and toolbox talks.

Tree and hedgerow protection

Under Part 8 of the Town and Country Planning Act and the Town and Country Planning (Trees) Regulations, tree preservation orders (TPOs) can be made by the local planning authority to prohibit the cutting down, uprooting, topping, lopping, wilful damage or destruction of trees without the local planning authority's consent. It is illegal to cut down or alter any tree under a TPO. All trees within a designated conservation are protected.

The Local Authority Planning Department should be contacted before you work on any protected trees. The procedure to gain permission to work on a tree with a TPO is:

☑ obtain the relevant form from the Local Authority

☑ fill out the form outlining the intended work

☑ return the completed form to the Local Authority.

The Local Authority then has up to two months to make a decision.

Under the Hedgerow Regulations, a hedgerow removal notice is required from the Local Authority if it is older than 30 years old or satisfies at least one of the criteria listed in Part 2 of Schedule 1. The removal of a hedge longer than 20 m requires planning permission.

During the planning of a project, you should make contact with the Local Authority to ensure that any trees or hedgerows identified for removal are discussed and, if possible, avoided. Translocation of mature or ancient hedgerows should also be considered. Works on trees and hedgerows are confined to certain time constraints due to nesting birds and bats, which are protected species.

 All trees should be protected in accordance with _Trees in relation to construction_ (BS 5837:2012)

The following practices should be followed.

☑ **Protected zone**: a fenced-off area around the tree to be retained should be established to eliminate tree damage during development. The size of the protected zone is either the distance of the crown spread of the tree (the width of the tree at its widest) or half the height of the tree, whichever is the greater.

Tree and hedgerow protection – good tree protection measures

☑ **Compaction of soil** must be avoided as this destroys the soil's pore structure, which in turn alters the trees' ability for water uptake. Compaction can be caused by the storage of materials, machinery and soil and by the use of an area as a thoroughfare by people and vehicles and for temporary constructions (such as site huts).

☑ **Excavation** for foundations and utilities must be considered in relation to the welfare of root systems. It is a common misconception that the root system of a tree extends in a narrow, deep band directly below the trunk. In reality the roots extend a large distance laterally at a shallow depth, often at approximately 60 cm. Shallow foundations thus impact on the root systems.

The closer the excavation is to the tree the greater the chance of damage. Construction, therefore, should not be within the protected zone of the tree. This also benefits the building as roots can damage foundations. Where foundations are to be located near major roots they should carefully bridge them.

Construction also has an impact on the hydrological cycle with compaction of soils and the laying of tarmac reducing infiltration rates and increasing run-off. This affects water available for tree growth.

☑ **Ground level change** should acknowledge the location of tree roots. Reduction in ground level causes the severance of roots and an alteration of drainage rates that affect water availability. Increases in ground level causes compaction and can suffocate and damage shallow and fragile roots.

☑ **Impact** by machinery can damage trees in an obvious way; torn branches, damaged bark and general trunk wounds allow easier access to disease and parasites that cause decay.

☑ **Contamination of soil** through the leakage of chemicals from construction materials (such as concrete, fuel and oil) should be avoided through secure storage. Storage of these must not occur in the protected zone and should be downhill from the tree, ideally 10 m from the protected zone to allow for leaching of materials through the soil.

☑ **Tree surgery** may require consent if the tree is protected or is within a conservation area. Any surgery or necessary felling should be detailed in the planning application and should be undertaken prior to commencement of construction; it is easier to carry out surgery without unavoidable construction obstacles. It should also be noted that restrictions on felling and surgery could be implemented during bird nesting season.

07

Tree damage caused by inappropriate storage of construction waste within the protection zone

The National Joint Utilities Group (NJUG) has also published *Guidelines for the planning, installation and maintenance of utility apparatus in proximity to trees (Issue 2).* The document provides details for the establishment of a tree protection zone and precautions that should be taken for any works within it.

Tree protection zone

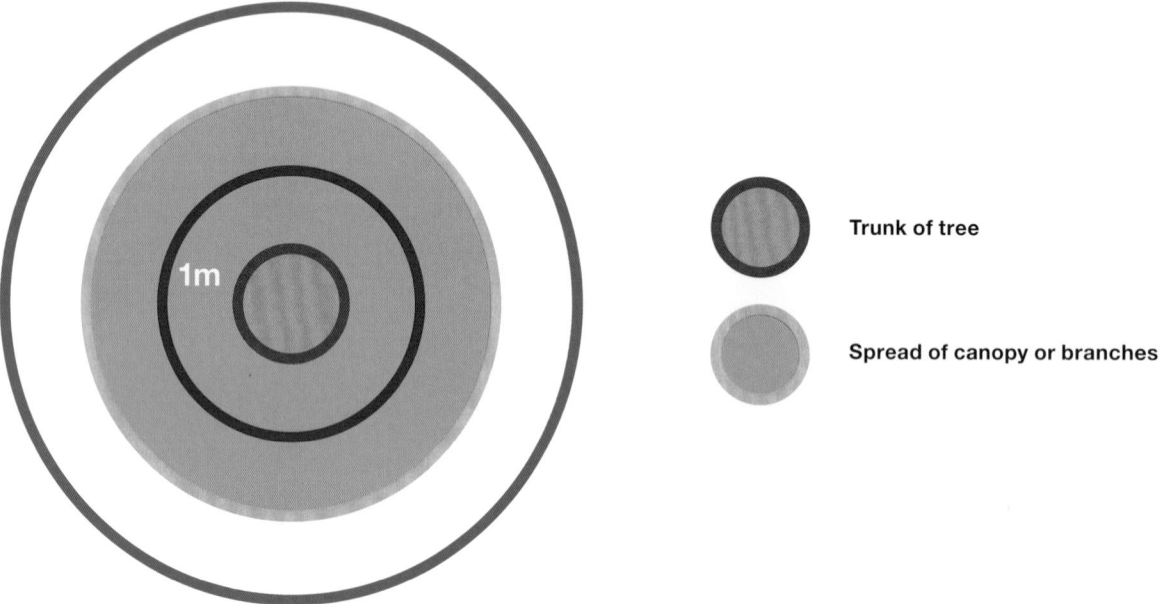

Trunk of tree

Spread of canopy or branches

 **Prohibited zone – one metre from trunk**
Excavations of any kind must not be undertaken within this zone, unless full consideration with the Local Authority tree officer is undertaken. Materials, plant and spoil must not be stored within this zone.

 **Precautionary zone – four times tree circumference**
Where excavations must be undertaken within this zone the use of mechanical excavation plant should be prohibited. Precautions should be undertaken to protect any exposed roots. Materials, plant and spoil should not be stored within this zone. Consult with the Local Authority tree officer if in any doubt.

 Permitted zone – outside of precautionary zone
Excavation works may be undertaken within this zone. However, caution must be applied and the use of mechanical plant limited. Any exposed roots should be protected.

 For further details of these guidelines refer to the NJUG website.

7.6 Invasive species

Species of plants and animals that have been introduced where they do not naturally occur are known as *non-native species*. A number of these species have become invasive, because they are bigger, faster growing and/or more aggressive than native species, which are unable to compete.

The contract documentation or environmental statement for the project, provided by the client, will highlight any non-native species of concern. If these are present then advice should be sought from specialists, who will provide further details on how to best treat and dispose of these in each instance.

Relevant control measures for any invasive species associated with the project should be included within the project construction environmental management plan, together with relevant method statements that may need to be agreed with the relevant agencies before commencement of work.

It is possible that construction activities have an impact on invasive species of animal, most likely caused by accidental dispersal. It is an offence under Section 14 of the Wildlife and Countryside Act to deliberately permit the spread of an invasive species by releasing it into the wild.

One such example species is the American signal crayfish, which is driving the native white-clawed crayfish towards extinction and causing declines in the diversity and richness of aquatic communities. Commercial fisheries have been affected by predation of fish eggs and competition between crayfish and salmon species for refuges. Burrowing by crayfish can cause erosion of riverbanks and destabilise structures built at the edges of rivers.

 Details of invasive species are available on the Environment Agency's website, including a leaflet on how to manage non-native species.

Section 14 of the Wildlife and Countryside Act makes it an offence to plant or otherwise cause to grow in the wild any of the plants listed in Schedule 9, which include:

- ☑ giant hogweed
- ☑ giant kelp
- ☑ Japanese knotweed
- ☑ Japanese seaweed
- ☑ Himalayan balsam
- ☑ rhododendron
- ☑ floating pennywort
- ☑ parrot's feather
- ☑ Australian swamp stonecrop.

The most common of these are giant hogweed, Japanese knotweed and Himalayan balsam.

 Refer to Appendix B for details on how to deal with Japanese knotweed.

Giant hogweed   *Japanese knotweed*   *Himalayan balsam*

There are other pieces of legislation that relate to preventing the spread of invasive species in the UK, which can include both native and non-native species (for example, the native species ragwort is one of the species controlled under the Weeds Act).

07

The following practices should be employed for the effective management of invasive plants

Before work starts:

☑ review the environmental statement and conduct a site survey to identify any non-native species

☑ liaise with landowners and statutory bodies on the appropriate treatment techniques where invasive species have been identified

☑ demarcate and fence off any areas found to contain non-native invasive species.

During construction:

☑ ensure the workforce are made aware of problems with non-native invasive species highlighted at site inductions, using maps of the site, and reinforce through the use of toolbox talks

☑ maintain fenced areas to restrict access and to prevent spread across the site

☑ any use of herbicides near or in watercourses needs to be approved by the Environment Agency. Ensure that treatment companies hold appropriate certificates of competence

☑ ensure that any chemical containers or material contaminated with herbicides are disposed of in accordance with the duty of care and Hazardous Waste Regulations as appropriate

☑ ensure that soils contaminated with invasive plants/roots are removed to an appropriately authorised landfill site.

The management of invasive species will often involve the generation of waste in the form of plant material, soil, water and sediment, or dead animals. This waste needs to be dealt with carefully to ensure that it complies with the relevant waste legislation. For example, when Japanese knotweed is dug up to eradicate it from a site, the soil will contain rhizome (underground root-like stems) from which the plant can regenerate.

This material is likely to be classified as controlled waste under the Environmental Protection Act and can only be transferred by an authorised person (such as a registered waste carrier) and taken to an appropriately authorised landfill site.

 For further information on the management of waste refer to Chapter E03 Waste management.

 In many cases the management of invasive plants will involve the use of herbicides, which are controlled under the Pesticides Act and the Control of Pesticides Regulations. These pieces of legislation place strict controls on the supply, storage and use of all pesticides, including those herbicides used in the control of invasive species. These regulations make it obligatory for those giving advice on the use of these products to hold a certificate of competence recognised by DEFRA. The only qualifications recognised by DEFRA are those issued by the British Agrochemical Supply Industry Scheme (BASIS). Permission is also required from the Environment Agency if spraying in and near watercourses.

7.7 Promoting biodiversity

Working together, planners and developers/clients should, through good design, aim to minimise the ecological impact of the project (such as habitat destruction, fragmentation and species isolation) and, wherever possible, should actively seek to rebuild local ecological networks. This can be achieved through the points set out below.

☑ **Enhance** the overall ecological quality of the site and the surrounding ecological network by creating new habitats, buffer areas and landscape features that are of importance for wildlife. Focus should be made:

– in areas where the most important, fragile and/or threatened habitats and species are known to occur

– where there are species requiring large ranges and/or those with limited powers of dispersal, which have particularly suffered as a result of habitat becoming reduced in size and isolated

– on species with low reproductive capacity (most large mammals) or species highly sensitive to disturbance (most birds of prey) and species subject to recovery programmes (focus for local biodiversity action plan targets).

☑ **Local biodiversity action plans**, species action plans and habitat action plans should be used as a guide to the relevant priorities for such positive measures at the local level. These may include rehabilitation of degraded habitats or the creation of new habitats within and adjacent to development sites.

– Bird boxes, swift bricks, bat boxes, bat bricks, green roofs, green walls and habitat creation are examples where enhancement can be achieved on construction projects.

☑ **Avoid** developing sites, and locations within sites, where existing key habitats, important species, buffer areas and other landscape features of major importance for wildlife would:

– suffer direct impact resulting in the reduction or complete loss of habitat and/or diversity of species present

– suffer an indirect impact from nearby development through increased ecological disturbance and stress, thereby reducing the site's capacity to support the wildlife present

– suffer a reduction in ecological quality so that the site is no longer able to support the migration, dispersal or genetic exchange of wild species

– be further fragmented from other similar features by development that causes a barrier effect in the landscape between fragments.

☑ **Restore** and, where possible, link and connect existing habitats and landscape features, which could potentially be of major importance for wildlife, enhancing their ability to support migration, dispersal and genetic exchange.

☑ **Retain and incorporate** within the development site layout existing habitats, important species, buffer areas and landscape features of major importance for wildlife – making sure that the site retains at least the same capacity to support the diversity, abundance, migration, dispersal and genetic exchange of wildlife as it did prior to development.

☑ **Compensate** for features lost to development through the:

– re-creation, as nearby as possible, of features and landforms capable of maintaining the same quality of habitats and species as would otherwise be lost or displaced through the development

– restoration and enhancement of surrounding/nearby features unaffected by development

– creation of new or additional buffer areas to reduce impacts

– translocation, where possible, of habitats and species that would otherwise be lost.

 For further information on local biodiversity action plans refer to the Business and Biodiversity Resource Centre's website.

 Additional resources can be found at CIRIA in its publication *Working with wildlife*.

07

Appendix A – Wildlife year planner

Guidance on the optimal timing for carrying out specialist ecological surveys and mitigation

		Licence required?	J	F	M	A	M	J	J	A	S	O	N	D
Habitats/ vegetation	Surveys	N	Mosses and lichens. No other detailed plant surveys – Phase 1 only (least suitable time)		Detailed habitat assessment surveys. Surveys for higher plants and ferns. Mosses and lichens in April, May and September only								Mosses and lichens No other detailed plant surveys – Phase 1 only (least suitable time)	
	Mitigation	N	Planting and translocation		No mitigation for majority of species								Planting and translocation	
Badgers	Surveys	N**	Optimal time during spring and autumn when activity levels are high, vegetation levels low and field signs most obvious											
	Mitigation	***	No disturbance of existing setts. Building of artificial setts						Stopping up and excavation of existing setts Licence may be required					See Jan-June
Bats	Surveys	*	Hibernation surveys and inspection of building and tree roosts		Inspection of building and tree roosts	Optimal time for emergence/re-entry surveys from May to August. Other activity surveys may extend from April to October. Inspection of tree and building roosts.							Hibernation surveys & inspection of building and tree roosts	
	Mitigation	***	Works on non-breeding summer and maternity roosts only				Works on hibernation roosts				Works on non-breeding summer and hibernation roosts	Works on non-breeding summer, maternity and hibernation roosts	Works on non-breeding summer and maternity roosts only	
Birds	Surveys	*	Winter birds		Breeding birds and migrant species						Migrant species August through to October		Winter birds	
	Mitigation	N	Clearance works possible but must stop immediately if any nesting birds found		Avoid clearance or construction works in nesting habitat or carry out under Ecological Watching Brief						Clearance works possible but must stop immediately if nesting birds found			
Dormice (n/a in NI)	Surveys	*	Nut searches	Nut searches (sub-optimal time)	Nest tube surveys April–November. Nest searches – any time of year but preferably September to March. Nut searches (September-November)									Nut searches
	Mitigation	***	No clearance works				Clearance works (sub-optimal time)	No clearance works			Clearance works to early October (optimal time)		No clearance works	

Key

Recommended survey period	Recommended timing for mitigation works
No surveys	Mitigation works restricted

07

Guidance on the optimal timing for carrying out specialist ecological surveys and mitigation (continued)

Species	Activity	Licence required?	J	F	M	A	M	J	J	A	S	O	N	D
Fish	Surveys	*	Timing of surveys may be dependent on the migration pattern of the species concerned and the breeding season of individual fish species											
Fish	Mitigation	***	Mitigation for the protection of watercourses is required at all times of year. Mitigation should be timed to avoid fish breeding season which will vary from species to species											
Great crested newts (n/a in NI)	Surveys	*	No surveys – newts in hibernation		Pond surveys for adults: mid-March to mid-June. Surveys must include visits between mid-April and mid-May. Egg searches April to mid-June. Larval surveys from mid-May. Terrestrial habitat surveys				Larval surveys to mid-August. Terrestrial habitat surveys		Terrestrial habitat surveys		No surveys – newts in hibernation	
Great crested newts (n/a in NI)	Mitigation	***	No trapping of newts. Pond management only		Newt trapping programmes in ponds and on land. Note trapping may be limited by cold night temperatures in early months				Newt trapping on land only. Note trapping may be limited by dry nights during July and August				No trapping of newts. Pond management only	
Natterjack toads (n/a in NI)	Surveys	*	No surveys – toads in hibernation			Surveys of breeding ponds for adults April–June. Surveys for tadpoles from May onwards.			Surveys for adults on land				No surveys – toads in hibernation	
Natterjack toads (n/a in NI)	Mitigation	***	Pond management works			Trapping of adults in ponds from April to June. Trapping on adults on land April to September. Trapping of tadpoles from May to early September						Pond management works		
Reptiles: adder, grass snake slow worm and common lizard (n/a in NI except common lizard)	Surveys	N	No surveys – reptiles in hibernation		Activity surveys from March to June and in September/October. Peak survey months are April, May and September. Note surveys are limited by high temperatures during July and August.								No surveys – reptiles in hibernation	
Reptiles: adder, grass snake slow worm and common lizard (n/a in NI except common lizard)	Mitigation	N	Scrub clearance – proceed with caution to avoid disturbance of hibernating reptiles		Capture and translocation programmes can only be conducted while reptiles are active (March–June and September/October). Note trapping is limited by high temperatures during July and August								Scrub clearance – proceed with caution to avoid disturbance of hibernating reptiles	
Common lizard (NI only); sand lizard, smooth snake	Surveys	*	No surveys – reptiles in hibernation		Activity surveys possible from March to June and in September/October but peak survey months are April, May and September. Surveys are limited by high temperatures during July and August.								No surveys – reptiles in hibernation	
Common lizard (NI only); sand lizard, smooth snake	Mitigation	***	Scrub clearance – proceed with caution to avoid disturbance of hibernating reptiles		Capture and translocation programmes can only be conducted while reptiles are active (March–June and September/October). Note trapping is limited by high temperatures during July and August.								No clearance works – proceed with caution to avoid disturbance of hibernating reptiles	
Otters	Surveys	N**	Surveys possible all year round											
Otters	Mitigation	***	Mitigation possible all year round but timing will be restricted where otters are breeding											

07

Guidance on the optimal timing for carrying out specialist ecological surveys and mitigation (continued)

		Licence required?	J	F	M	A	M	J	J	A	S	O	N	D
Pine marten	Surveys	N**	Surveys possible all year round but optimal time is during spring and summer. Breeding den surveys between March and May											
Pine marten	Mitigation	***	Works in pine marten habitat		Avoid works in pine marten habitat								Works in pine marten habitat	
Red squirrel	Surveys	*	Surveys possible all year round but optimal time is during spring and summer. Surveys for breeding females from January to September, with some surveys during peak breeding periods of March–May and/or July–September.											
Red squirrel	Mitigation	***	Avoid all works in red squirrel habitat									Works should be conducted at this time		See Jan-Sept
Smooth newt (NI only)	Surveys	*	No surveys – newts in hibernation		Pond surveys for adults: March to mid-June. Surveys should include visits between mid-April and mid-May. Egg searches April to mid-June. Larval surveys from mid-May. Terrestrial habitat surveys				Larval surveys to mid-August. Terrestrial habitat surveys		Terrestrial habitat surveys		No surveys – newts in hibernation	
Smooth newt (NI only)	Mitigation	***	No trapping of newts. Pond management only		Newt trapping programmes in ponds and on land. Note trapping may be limited by cold night temperatures in early months				Newt trapping on land only. Note trapping may be limited by dry nights during July and August				No trapping of newts. Pond management only	
Water vole (n/a in NI)	Surveys	N**	Reduced activity		Activity and breeding surveys depending on vegetation cover and weather conditions. Optimum survey period March–June								Reduced activity	
Water vole (n/a in NI)	Mitigation	***	Avoid all works in water vole habitat		Works in water vole habitat possible		Avoid all works in water vole habitat			Works in water vole habitat possible		Avoid all works in water vole habitat		
White-clawed crayfish	Surveys	*	Reduced activity			Surveys possible	Avoid surveys (females are releasing young)				Optimum time for surveys		Reduced activity	
White-clawed crayfish	Mitigation	***	Avoid capture programmes (low activity levels may mean animals are missed)			Exclusion from construction areas	Avoid capture programmes – breeding period				Exclusion from construction areas			Avoid capture programmes (low activity levels may mean animals are missed)

*   accepted survey and monitoring techniques may involve the capture, handling or disturbance of these protected species (in the case of birds, those listed on Schedule 1 of the WCA only). Where this is the case, only licensed persons can undertake the surveys. These are obtained from Natural England, Countryside Council for Wales, Northern Ireland Environment Agency or Scottish Natural Heritage

**   accepted survey and monitoring techniques do not typically involve the capture, handling or disturbance of these protected species and so a survey licence is not ordinarily required. However, should further techniques be used that will result in the above, only licensed persons can undertake the survey

***   where mitigation involves the capture, handling or disturbance of a protected species and/or the damage, destruction or obstruction of their habitats, a conservation or mitigation licence must be obtained from Natural England, Countryside Council for Wales, Northern Ireland Environment Agency or Scottish Natural Heritage. Mitigation licence applications take about 30 working days to be processed by government agencies. Where mitigation works need to be conducted under licence before works begin, licence applications need to be submitted considerably earlier.

Traditionally, environmental issues are not considered at an early stage in project planning. The year planners below show the appropriate times of year to deal with specific issues.

Badgers

Task	Jan	Feb	Mar	Apr	May	June	July	Aug	Sept	Oct	Nov	Dec
1	*	*	*	*							*	*
2					*	*	*	*	*	*		
3	*	*										*
4		*	*	*								
5							*	*	*	*	*	

1. **Badger surveys** are best carried out during November to April when the vegetation is low and field signs are easier to identify.

2. **Badger surveys** can continue but become less reliable as the vegetation becomes denser.

3. **Artificial badger sett construction** should be completed at least six months before a sett exclusion. Winter is the time to complete artificial setts to give the badgers time to familiarise themselves before the licensing season.

4. **Badger territorial bait marking surveys.** Territorial marking is at its peak between February and April and the vegetation is low enough to identify latrines. This is the only time of year when bait marking is effective.

5. **Badger licensing season: Between 1 July and 30 November.** Nature conservancy councils will normally only issue disturbance and exclusion licences outside this time period in cases of proven urgency.

Water voles

Task	Jan	Feb	Mar	Apr	May	June	July	Aug	Sept	Oct	Nov	Dec
1			*	*	*	*						
2							*	*	*	*		
3			*	*						*	*	

1. **Water vole surveys** need to be carried out during the summer breeding season. Best carried out between March and June before the vegetation grows too high.

2. **Water vole surveys** can continue for the rest of the breeding season but field signs become harder to identify as the vegetation becomes denser.

3. **Water vole exclusions.** Excluding and trapping are recommended during February and March, before the breeding season, or October and November, after the end of the breeding season.

Otters

Task	Jan	Feb	Mar	Apr	May	June	July	Aug	Sept	Oct	Nov	Dec
1	*	*	*	*	*	*	*	*	*	*	*	*
2	*	*	*	*	*	*	*	*	*	*	*	*

1. **Otter surveys** can be carried out throughout the year, although surveys are easier to carry out during periods of low vegetation.

2. **Otter mitigation** can be carried out throughout the year but may be restricted if evidence of breeding is identified.

Great crested newts

Task	Jan	Feb	Mar	Apr	May	June	July	Aug	Sept	Oct	Nov	Dec
1			*	*	*	*						
2		*	*				*	*	*	*	*	

1. **Great crested newts breeding pond surveys** are the only way to effectively establish presence or absence and to quantify populations. These are best carried out between March and June.

2. **Terrestrial searches** are least effective but can be carried out during early spring and during the autumn, depending upon weather conditions. Surveys should be carried out when night temperatures are above five degrees centigrade and when the ground is moist.

Bats

Task	Jan	Feb	Mar	Apr	May	June	July	Aug	Sept	Oct	Nov	Dec
1			*	*	*	*	*	*	*	*		
2					*	*	*	*	*	*		
3	*	*										*
4				*	*	*	*	*	*	*		

1. **Flight surveys** that involve identification of bats in flight by observation or echolocation can be carried out between March and October, although the optimum time for the surveys is April to September. Surveys of this type can be carried out without a licence as they are non-intrusive.

2. **Dusk emergence and dawn swarming surveys** can be carried out between May and October although the optimum time for the surveys is between May and September.

3. **Hibernation roost surveys** can only be carried out between November and March when the bats are hibernating. These surveys are very difficult to carry out as bats hibernate deep in cracks and crevices and are therefore difficult to identify.

4. **Habitat surveys** can only be effectively carried out between April and October when the bats are active.

Crayfish

Task	Jan	Feb	Mar	Apr	May	June	July	Aug	Sept	Oct	Nov	Dec
1				*			*	*	*	*		
2					*	*						
3	*	*	*								*	*

1. **Crayfish surveys** are best carried out between July and October, although it is possible to carry out surveys during April.

2. **Crayfish releasing young surveys** should not be carried out during May and June because crayfish are releasing their young.

3. **Crayfish reduced activity surveys** should not be carried out during the winter months due to reduced levels of activity.

Nesting birds

Task	Jan	Feb	Mar	Apr	May	June	July	Aug	Sept	Oct	Nov	Dec
1			*	*	*	*	*	*	*			
2	*	*								*	*	*

1. **Nesting bird season.** No vegetation clearance work should be carried out during the nesting bird season unless immediately preceded by a thorough nesting bird survey.

2. **Vegetation clearance work** is best carried out at these times of year when birds are not nesting, although work must stop if nests are found.

Reptiles

Task	Jan	Feb	Mar	Apr	May	June	July	Aug	Sept	Oct	Nov	Dec
1			*	*	*	*	*	*	*	*		
2			*	*	*	*	*	*	*	*		
3	*	*	*	*	*	*	*	*	*	*	*	*

1. **Reptile surveys** can only be carried out between March and October when reptiles are active. During the winter months reptiles are in hibernation, therefore it is not suitable to carry out surveys.

2. **Reptile capture and release programmes** can only be carried out between March and October when reptiles are active.

3. **Scrub clearance** work can be carried out throughout the year.

Appendix B – Dealing with Japanese knotweed

Japanese knotweed can cause structural damage, growing up to 20 mm a day and being strong enough to penetrate foundations. It is an offence under the Wildlife and Countryside Act to encourage the spread of Japanese knotweed. It is often found along railways, riverbanks, roads and derelict sites. Any known areas of Japanese knotweed will be highlighted within the environmental statement for the project. These areas must be cordoned off to prevent inadvertent spread. Extreme care must be taken to ensure that all equipment used on site is free of Japanese knotweed material before leaving the site to avoid contamination.

If works are required in areas of known Japanese knotweed strands, control methods must be applied; the particular method to be employed will be dependent on site conditions. Where possible, excavation should be avoided and the plant should be treated in its original position.

 The Japanese knotweed rhizome system (root zone) may extend to, and beyond, a depth of at least 2 m and extend 7 m laterally from a parent plant.

Chemical control

Chemical control usually takes a minimum of three years to totally eradiate Japanese knotweed. Wherever there is a risk of contamination to a watercourse, choice of herbicide is limited to formulations of Glyphosate and 2, 4-D Amine that are approved for use in or near water. Use of herbicides in or near water requires formal consultation with the Environment Agency. Spraying both the top and underside of leaves improves control. Plants respond best when actively growing. The most effective time to apply herbicide is from July to September.

Non-chemical controls

Cutting – Use a simple scythe method of cutting to prevent stem fragmentation. Continue cutting every 2–4 weeks to reduce both above and below-ground biomass.

Digging – Dig out soil around clump for up to 7 m. Burn or bury rhizome and stem fragments on site, bury 10 m deep or dispose of in landfill (licences are required).

Burning – Controlled burning of stem and crown material may be used as part of the control programme. Such burning must take into account the potential for nuisance or pollution that may occur as a result of the activity. Burning in the open may be undertaken in accordance with a registered exemption in accordance with the Environmental Permitting Regulations.

Burial – Soil containing knotweed material and burnt remains of knotweed may be buried on site of production. On-site burial must be performed to a depth of at least 5 m. Knotweed material should be covered with root barrier membrane consisting of a geotextile layer or a heavy gauge polythene sheet prior to infilling. It is strongly advised to record the burial site location, and that any future owners are advised of its position.

Off-site disposal – Where the option for on-site disposal or treatment is not available, as a last resort in terms of sustainability, material contaminated with Japanese knotweed must be disposed of at an approved disposal facility, having informed the site operator of the presence of viable knotweed within the material.

To ensure compliance with the Wildlife and Countryside Act and to reduce the risk of spreading knotweed, any such on-site burial and any controlled burning must be done in accordance with the Environment Agency's knotweed code of practice *Managing Japanese knotweed on development sites.*

 A copy of the Environment Agency's code of practice for managing Japanese knotweed can be obtained from its website.

 Failure to appropriately dispose of any material containing Japanese knotweed may lead to prosecution under Section 33 and 34 of the Environmental Protection Act and Section 14 of the Wildlife and Countryside Act.

Appendix C – Construction activities and their potential adverse effects on wildlife

Construction activities and their potential adverse effects on wildlife		
Construction activity	**Implication**	**Examples of effect on wildlife**
Site clearance	Removal of trees and shrubs	■ Loss of important species or specimens of tree or shrub that may be protected by a TPO ■ Loss of bird nests or bat roosts ■ Loss of habitat for protected species ■ Loss of important invertebrates, including those that may require deadwood habitat (such as stag beetles)
	Removal of ground vegetation	■ Loss of habitat for protected species ■ Loss of rare plants ■ Loss of bird nests ■ Killing or injury of reptiles or amphibians ■ Killing or injury of small mammals ■ Loss of invertebrates and their breeding habitat
	Removal of soil	■ Loss of habitat for protected species ■ Loss of seed bank ■ Loss of water vole burrows ■ Loss of invertebrates and their breeding habitat ■ Destruction of badger setts
	Demolition of buildings and structures	■ Loss of bird nesting or bat roosting areas
	Removal of rubble and other materials	■ Loss of reptile and amphibian habitat
Site set up	Location of site offices and compounds	■ Disturbance of breeding animals
	Storage areas	■ Potential pollution of important watercourses, wetlands or other water bodies, including coastal waters, through spillage or dust
Establishment of haul roads	Rubble or concrete temporary roads constructed	■ Fragmentation of habitats ■ Road kills ■ Destruction of badger setts ■ Contamination of adjoining habitats by dust ■ Noise or light pollution may disturb nesting birds or other animals ■ Change of pH through leaching
Groundworks	Ground investigations Foundations Excavations and piling Temporary earthworks Tunnelling	■ Impacts on surface and groundwater, which may have secondary impacts on important wetlands both on and off site ■ Noise or light pollution may disturb nesting birds or other animals ■ Destruction of badger setts ■ Run-off and erosion, which may damage important habitats ■ Potential to introduce or spread invasive plants (such as Japanese knotweed)
Construction	Concrete pours and other wet trades	■ Contamination of wetlands ■ Change of soil pH through run-off

08

Contaminated land

This chapter gives a general overview of the legal framework for the definition, regulation and management of contaminated land.

This chapter also identifies the process for assessing and remediating contaminated land, the licences that will be required for its treatment or disposal and guidance for the prevention of pollution. It will also identify the key occupational health considerations when dealing with contaminated land.

Introduction	98
Key requirements	98
Legislative requirements	98
Managing contaminated land	100
Occupational health considerations	104

8.1   Introduction

Building and construction works often involve the redevelopment of land that was used previously for commercial or industrial activities. These sites are often referred to as brownfield sites, and bringing them back into use is considered a more sustainable option than using new or greenfield land. However, the UK's rich industrial past has left the legacy of contamination on many sites, which needs to be dealt with before they can be suitable for their new purpose.

The surface of the ground itself and the ground beneath the surface may be contaminated by materials that have been worked, stored, spilt, buried, dumped or abandoned on the land in previous years. This list will also include the residue, waste or by-products from some industrial processes and the ashes from fires. Both solid and liquid waste may have permeated into the ground to a considerable depth.

Sites that have had previous industrial occupation should be assumed to be polluted, and tests undertaken to ascertain the types of pollutant and their concentration.

Everyone involved in work on such land must make an assessment of potential risks to human health and the environment, and implement any protective measures that need to be taken.

8.2   Key requirements

☑ The contract documentation and planning conditions for a project will identify known contamination of the site and the agreed methods for dealing with it. These should be referred to, and their requirements included, in the construction environmental management plan.

☑ Where a contaminated land assessment needs to be undertaken, this will be carried out in accordance with a systematic process of investigation, testing and appraisal to identify the most appropriate method for its treatment. The agreed method should be approved by the regulators before works commence.

☑ The testing of contaminated land must be carried out by certified, competent staff in accordance with standard field testing and laboratory procedures approved by the regulators.

☑ All contaminated areas of the site should be clearly signed and fenced off to avoid unauthorised access and inadvertent spread across the site.

☑ The use of mobile plant for remediation of contaminated soils will require an environmental permit for the equipment and the need to complete a site deployment form detailing the work and management of the risks at each specific location.

☑ Where, following treatment, materials are still classed as waste, then their use will also require an environmental permit or registered exemption. The Contaminated Land: Applications in Real Environments (CL:AIRE) development industry code of practice can be used to ensure that contaminated materials are treated and managed so that they achieve an end of waste status. This will require the implementation of a materials management plan and a declaration by a qualified person that all requirements have been complied with.

☑ The stockpiling of contaminated soils should be avoided. However, any stockpiled material should be placed on impervious ground and covered to avoid wind-blown contamination or run-off to drainage systems and water courses.

☑ Any removal of waste off site for treatment elsewhere or disposal should comply with the duty of care, including the provision of waste transfer documentation.

☑ All vehicles carrying contaminated materials off site should be appropriately sheeted and should pass through a wheel wash facility to avoid contamination of the public highway.

☑ All personnel involved in the treatment of contaminated land should be aware of the relevant risks associated with the particular contaminants and wear protective clothing, gloves and boots. Depending on the level of risk, a decontamination unit may need to be employed to prevent the spread of contaminants to clean areas of the site.

8.3   Legislative requirements

Regulatory bodies involved in contaminated land

Various organisations will be involved in granting approval for the treatment and the redevelopment of contaminated sites; the:

☑ Local Authority, which has a statutory duty to inspect its land and identify any sites that are formally designated as contaminated

☑ Local Authority, in granting planning permission, will approve the remediation strategy to ensure that the ground is suitable for use of the proposed development

☑ Environment Agency, for issuing an environmental permit for the use of mobile treatment plant to treat contaminated soils or for the reuse of construction and demolition waste

☑ Local Authority for issuing an environmental permit for crushing equipment and for granting an exemption for the crushing and screening of demolition materials

☑ Environment Agency for regulating the disposal of waste under the duty of care

☑ Local Authority environmental health officers for dealing with any complaints regarding dust that crosses the site boundary

☑ water companies and Environment Agency for the disposal of polluted water from contaminated sites.

Effective contact with each of these authorities is essential and must be established at an early point in the project.

Any contaminated site must be totally fenced off and adequate warning notices must be prominently posted, advising all members of the public that the site is dangerous and to refrain from entering.

 For further information on waste management refer to Chapter E03 Waste management.

Contaminated Land Regulation

Part IIA of the Environmental Protection Act (EPA) provides the legal framework for dealing with contaminated land in the UK. It is implemented in each of the devolved administrations through the following regulations.

England:

☑ the Contaminated Land (England) Regulations

☑ the Radioactive Contaminated Land (Modification of Enactments) (England) Regulations, which extends controls on contaminated land to radioactive contaminated land.

Wales:

☑ the Contaminated Land (Wales) Regulations

☑ the Radioactive Contaminated Land (Modification of Enactments) (Wales) Regulations, which extends controls on contaminated land to radioactive contaminated land.

Scotland:

☑ SSI 2007/178 and statutory guidance were brought into force in 2000 and are similar to the regulations that apply in England and Wales

☑ the Contaminated Land (Scotland) Regulations

☑ the Radioactive Contaminated Land (Scotland) Regulations.

08

Under these regulations Local Authorities have a duty to inspect their land, identify whether it is contaminated and decide whether the land should be designated as a special site because of the nature of the contamination. Special sites are regulated by the Environment Agencies. All Local Authorities are required to draw up a contaminated land strategy.

Definition of contaminated land

For the purpose of the above regulations *contaminated land* is defined as any land that:

 appears to be in such a condition, by reason of substances in, on or under the land that:

    ☑ significant harm is being caused or there is a significant possibility of such harm being caused, or

    ☑ significant pollution of controlled waters is being caused or there is a significant possibility of such pollution being caused.

Once a site is identified as contaminated land under the regulations, the Local Authority (or Environment Agency in the case of a special site) has a statutory duty to ensure that remediation takes place by an appropriate person. Following designation of land as being contaminated land the regulatory authority should serve a remediation notice on the appropriate person(s) specifying what needs to be done and by when. The appropriate person(s) will be those who knowingly permitted the pollution or, if these cannot be found, the responsibility will fall to the owner/occupier of the site.

There is a close relationship between the contaminated land regime under EPA Part IIA above and planning controls. Annex 2 to planning policy Statement 23 (PPS23) provides guidance for the development of land affected by contamination.

PPS23 clarifies the relationship between planning and EPA Part IIA and gives more advice on the need to consider possible contamination at all stages of the planning and development process. Planning conditions should ensure appropriate investigation, remediation, monitoring and record keeping. Where contamination is suspected the developer is responsible both for investigating the land to determine what remedial measures are necessary to ensure its safety and suitability and for the actual remediation. There is a significant emphasis on voluntary remediation by the developer to avoid a formal remediation notice being issued where it meets the contaminated land definition.

Where there is a requirement to treat or dispose of contaminated material, then waste controls and the duty of care are likely to apply (discussed later in this chapter).

Brownfield sites

The definition of a brownfield site is very wide but generally relates to land that has had some form of previous development. Planning policy statement 3 (PPS3) defines previously developed land 'which is or was occupied by a permanent structure, including the curtilage of the developed land and any associated fixed surface'.

Many brownfield sites will be land that is affected by contamination but not to an extent that makes it automatically fall within the definition set out in the Contaminated Land Regulations above. Previously published estimates of the extent of land affected by contamination vary widely, from 50,000 to 300,000 hectares, amounting to as many as 100,000 sites. The Environment Agency estimates that, of these, 5,000 to 20,000 may be expected to be problem sites that require action to ensure that unacceptable risks to human health and the environment are minimised.

Some brownfield sites are affected by land contamination because of the previous industrial uses of the site, which has led to the deliberate or accidental release of chemicals onto the land. This will depend on the type of activity previously being carried out. The following are examples of chemicals associated with four industrial processes.

Oil refineries: Fuel oil, lubricants, bitumen, alcohols, organic acids, PCBs, cyanides, sulphur, vanadium.

Lead works: Lead, arsenic, cadmium, sulphides, sulphates, chlorides, sulphuric acid, sodium hydroxide.

Pesticide manufacturing: Dichloromethane, fluorobenzene, acetone, methanol, benzene, arsenic, copper sulphate, thallium.

Textile and dye works: Aluminium, cadmium, mercury, bromides, fluorides, ammonium salts, trichloroethene, polyvinyl chloride.

CLR 8 *Priority contaminants for the assessment of land* published by DEFRA and the Environment Agency identifies contaminants that are likely to be present on many current or former sites affected by industrial or waste management activity in the UK in sufficient concentrations to cause harm. It also indicates which contaminants are likely to be associated with particular industries.

8.4   Managing contaminated land

Managing land affected by contamination involves the identification of risks and then putting in the appropriate control measures to reduce those risks to an acceptable level so that the land is suitable for its intended use.

The process for dealing with contaminated sites should be dealt with in accordance with the following three stages.

Stage 1. Assessment to establish whether there are any unacceptable risks and, if so, what further action needs to be taken.

Stage 2. Reviewing the remediation options and determining the most appropriate remediation strategy.

Stage 3. Implementation of the preferred remediation strategy.

These three steps are based on *Model procedures for the management of land contamination* (Contaminated Land Report 11 (CLR 11)), published by DEFRA and the Environment Agency, and are dealt with in more detail below.

Stage 1 – Assessment of the risks from land contamination

The risks caused by land contamination are based on the concept of pollutant linkage, which is the relationship between the source of the contamination, the pathway that the contaminant could follow and the receptor. Each of these elements can exist independently but they have to be linked in order for there to be a risk.

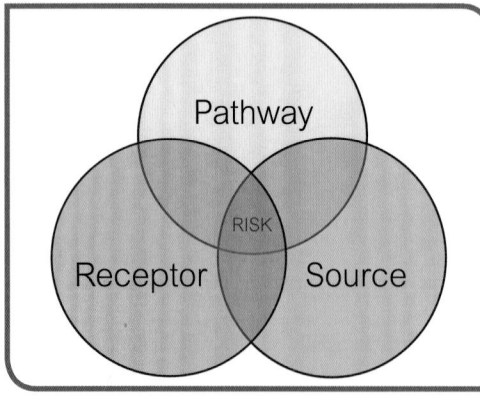

Every site will have different risks due to the type of contamination, geology and receptors, and acceptable levels will be dependant on the proposed end use for the site. The assessment may require a specialist to identify the level of risk.

Receptors can be:

☑ humans – not just risks to site personnel but to end users following development

☑ controlled waters – surface waters and groundwater

☑ existing and potential ecosystems – plants and wildlife living in the site or close by

☑ property – building structures and services.

An example of a source (contaminant), pathway and receptor is:

☑ source – oil

☑ pathway – ground water

☑ receptor – aquifer.

Establishment of the risks associated with the site will be based on information gathered from a preliminary (Phase I) investigation, which may include, but not be limited to:

- ☑ history of the site

- ☑ previous processes, including their location, raw materials, products, waste residues, and methods of disposal

- ☑ layout of the site, above and below ground

- ☑ presence of waste disposal tips, made ground, abandoned pits and quarries with or without standing water

- ☑ mining history

- ☑ information on geology and hydrology

- ☑ potential uses of sites, past or present, in the area adjacent to the site.

This information is derived mainly from a desktop exercise, together with site reconnaissance as appropriate. This will allow a targeted site investigation (Phase II) to be undertaken if this is deemed necessary to determine the type, concentration and extent of any specific contamination.

Refer to BS 10175:2011, *Investigation of potentially contaminated sites – code of practice*. The relevant recommendations and guidance within this standard are intended to ensure that the objectives of an investigation are achieved and that appropriate data for the risk assessment is obtained.

The Environment Agency has established its monitoring certification scheme (MCERTS) performance standard to deliver high quality environmental measurements. For chemical testing of soils where results are to be submitted to the Environment Agency the performance standard is an application of ISO 17025:2000.

Stage 2 – Appraisal of remediation options

The risk assessment described above will identify any unacceptable risks that will need to be reduced through the removal of existing pollutant linkages to make the site suitable for its new intended use. Remediation options will need to consider whether risks can be reduced at the source, pathway or receptor.

Bioremediation

- ☑ Source reduction – reducing, removing or breaking down the contaminant (for example, bioremediation).

- ☑ Pathway management – preventing the migration of contaminants to receptors (for example, installing a physical barrier or encapsulation).

- ☑ Exposure management – protecting the receptor (for example, by limiting the use of the land, such as preventing the growing of vegetables for human consumption).

Contamination identified through site investigation does not necessarily pose a threat if left undisturbed and the construction works should be planned to avoid disturbance if it has been decided to leave the material in situ. The best practical technique for any given site will depend on a number of factors, including:

- ☑ effectiveness – time taken and achievement of the standard of remediation

- ☑ cost of remediation

- ☑ practicality – technical, site, time and regulatory constraints and interaction with other works

- ☑ durability – the period of time that the remediation will need to be maintained.

It is now recognised that the previous practice of digging and dumping contaminated material by disposal to landfill is unsustainable. This is because the cost of landfill tax is rising sharply. Furthermore, tax relief associated with cleaning up contaminated land is being removed. It is also necessary to demonstrate that materials have been subject to treatment before being sent to a landfill site. There are strict limits on the levels of contaminants for material being sent to landfill (waste acceptance criteria). *(Further information on this issue is covered in Chapter E03 Waste management.)*

Treatment of contaminated materials on the site in which they occur is, in many cases, a cheaper option. The recovered materials can also provide a valuable resource, reducing the need to import clean virgin aggregates. There are often opportunities to reuse material after treatment in accordance with the waste hierarchy.

- ☑ Prevent waste (for example, by adjusting site layout to minimise waste quantities).

- ☑ Reuse (for example, on site reuse in an appropriate way).

- ☑ Recycle (for example, treat it to make material suitable for use on or off site).

- ☑ Dispose (for example, landfill or incineration).

Whatever remediation strategy has been identified there are a number of treatment options available. These are identified in *Model procedures for the management of land contamination* (CLR 11) and include the techniques shown in the diagram (contaminated land treatment options). Three main types of remediation are:

- ☑ containment

- ☑ separation

- ☑ destruction.

Contaminated land treatment options

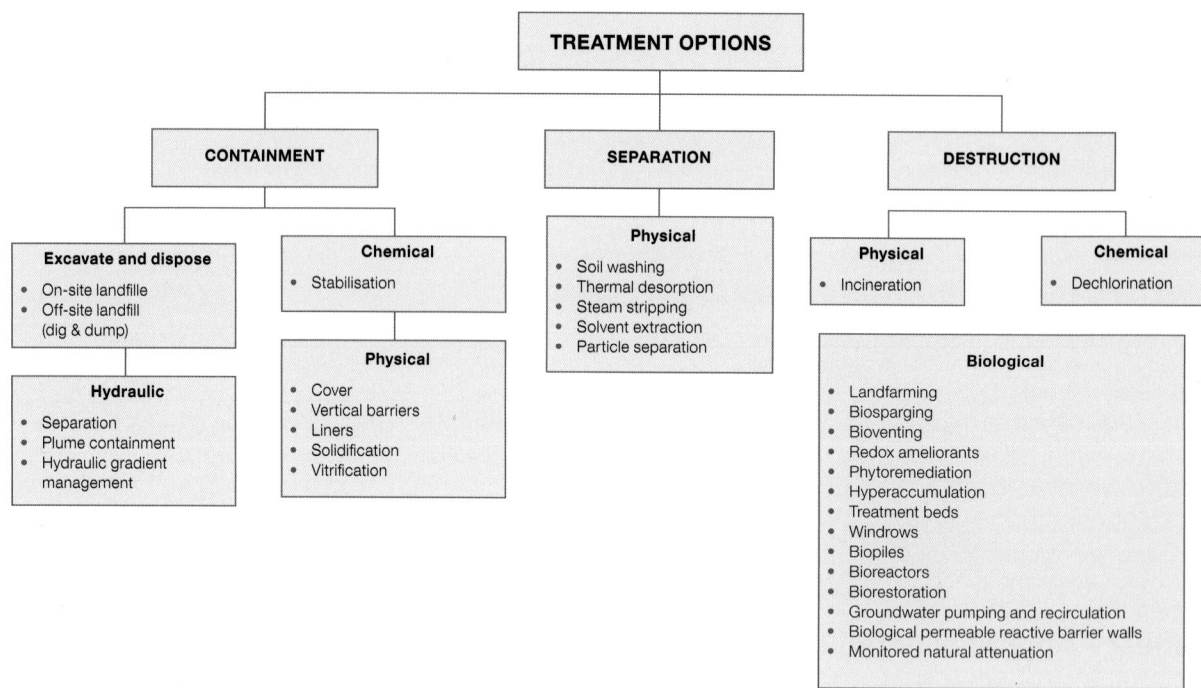

Stage 3 – Implementation of remediation options

The implementation of the preferred remediation option(s) will require consideration of the required permits and licences and discussions with the Environment Agencies and Local Authorities should take place as early as possible.

Waste controls for the treatment of contaminated land

Contaminated material that is excavated, recovered by treatment or disposed of may be classified as waste. Where it is waste then a range of waste regulations will apply.

The treatment of contaminated soil and/or contaminated waters may require a **mobile treatment permit** (England and Wales) or licence (Scotland). These permits are issued by the environment agencies.

A mobile treatment permit is used to regulate mobile plant equipment that involves treatment either in situ or ex situ. The permit sets out the type and extent of activities that can be carried out. A site-based permit has to be used where a mobile plant permit is not applicable. The environmental permit can be either a standard rules permit or a bespoke one, depending upon the type of treatment and site location.

Operators who want to treat contaminated soil and/or contaminated waters using their mobile plant permit at a particular site must also submit a site-specific deployment application (the deployment form and supporting information). The deployment application details site-specific information and potential impacts arising from the proposed use of the mobile plant. The operator must demonstrate that the activity will not cause pollution of the environment, harm to human health or serious detriment to local amenities.

Following treatment under a MTL the material would normally cease to be waste providing it was excavated and treated on the site it was used or is part of a remediation cluster. Where this is not the case then an environmental permit/licence or registered exemption would be required.

The CL:AIRE *Definition of waste: Development industry code of practice* (DiCOP) sets out best practice in England and Wales for dealing with contaminated land and defining when material ceases to be waste. It requires the implementation of a materials management plan (MMP) and a qualified person will declare that the code of practice (CoP) has been complied with.

The MMP can be a sub-tier document of the site waste management plan (SWMP).

A verification report at the end of the development will show that the material has been properly and suitably used and causes no harm to human health and the environment.

Removal of contaminated waste

Where materials cannot be incorporated into the site then the final option is disposal and all duty of care requirements must be met. Before the material can be removed it has to be properly classified to determine whether it is hazardous or non-hazardous waste. It will be necessary to demonstrate that treatment has taken place to reduce the quantity or physical nature of the material, through segregation or sorting.

Where contaminated waste and other materials are to be removed from a site, protective sheeting for skips and lorries will be necessary.

All skips or vehicles must be completely sheeted within the dirty area of a site. Care must be exercised by those carrying out the sheeting operations to ensure that they do not come into contact in any way with contaminated materials.

Vehicle drivers should not sheet their own vehicles, except to finally tighten sheet ropes, which should only be done in the clean area of the site.

Facilities must be available to thoroughly wash all vehicles leaving a contaminated site.

Detailed records must be kept of the disposal of hazardous or contaminated waste. Details should also be recorded within the project SWMP, as appropriate.

For further information relating to waste management refer to Chapter E03 Waste management, in particular, Appendix D, which deals with reuse options for demolition materials and treatment of excavated soils.

Reducing pollution potential

Stockpiling of contaminated material should be avoided. However, where this has to be carried out the following precautions must be taken.

Unexpected discovery of contamination

☑ The contaminated material should be placed on an impermeable surface or sheeting to avoid cross-contamination.

☑ Stockpiles should be covered to avoid dust and wind-blown contaminants.

☑ Access to stockpile areas should be restricted to authorised personnel.

☑ Stockpiles should be placed well away from drainage systems and water courses.

☑ Silt fences may be required to prevent any run-off.

Exposure of contaminated materials in the ground should also be avoided but, where this is not possible, plan management activities in the best season/weather to avoid the spread of contaminated dust or water.

Dewatering from site excavations on contaminated sites should also be considered carefully.

☑ Dewatering from excavations can draw water from contaminated adjacent sources.

☑ Discharges could be contaminated and must be disposed of with the consent of the appropriate authority.

Whilst proper site investigation will significantly reduce the likelihood of discovering contamination, if it is discovered unexpectedly there should be controls in place to deal with it. Obvious signs of contamination could include:

☑ soil discolouration from chemical residues

☑ odours

☑ fibrous materials (such as asbestos)

☑ chemical containers or tanks

☑ previous waste deposits.

Where contamination is suspected:

☑ stop the works immediately

☑ report details of the discovery to site management

☑ prevent access to the area

☑ clear any fuels or substances in the vicinity that could cause fire or explosion

☑ contact the Local Authority or Environment Agency when preliminary details of the contamination is known

☑ test the contamination to determine its exact nature and extent

☑ agree the appropriate remediation strategy with the Local Authority or Environment Agency.

08

8.5   Occupational health considerations

The health of workers on contaminated sites can be affected through one or more of the following ways:

- ☑ asphyxiation
- ☑ gasing
- ☑ ingestion

- ☑ inhalation
- ☑ skin absorption
- ☑ skin penetration.

Personal protective clothing (PPE) and approved respiratory protective equipment (RPE) must be worn at all times when work is carried out on contaminated sites.

Continuous assessments of the risk to health by exposure to any contaminated material or land must be carried out, and the control measures or precautions constantly monitored.

Personal hygiene

The level of risk to health by any contaminants will determine the scale of the need for hygiene facilities, but certain consideration should always be borne in mind when working on a contaminated site.

The diagram below shows a typical layout of a hygiene unit that is divided into three areas, with the dirty entrance remote from the clean exit.

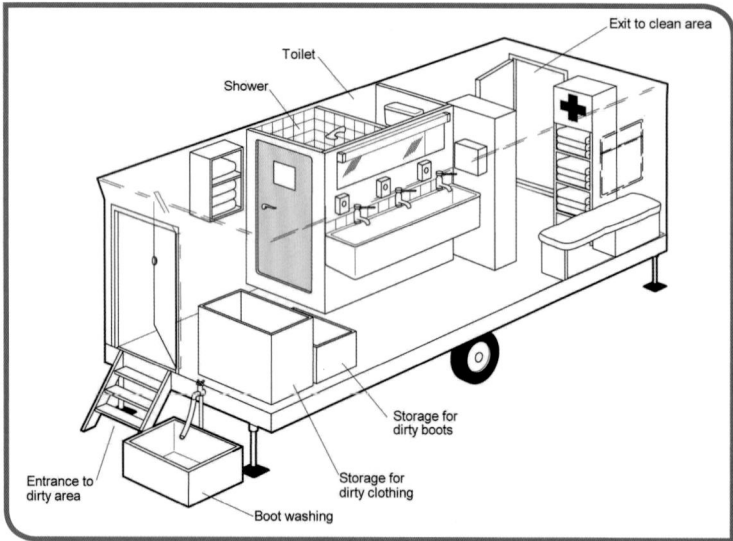

A dirty area is required for workers to discard dirty or contaminated clothing. Such clothing should be bagged and identified within this area before being dispatched to specialist cleaners.

Washing and toilet areas: Toilets, showers and washing facilities should be positioned between the dirty and clean areas, so that workers may wash or shower in order to remove any contaminant from their bodies.

A clean area is required for workers to put on clean and non-contaminated clothing. Access to and exit from this area must only be to the clean part of the site. It is essential that the entry/exit point of the clean area is in the clean part of the site.

Daily cleaning of the toilet facilities and the decontamination of all facilities must be carried out.

Asbestos

Asbestos was widely used in construction and insulation materials and poor management and waste practices has led to its contamination of brownfield sites. In addition, many unprotected sites have suffered from the indiscriminate fly-tipping of asbestos waste.

Asbestos is a highly dangerous material and presents substantial risks to the health of those who work with it and those who may be affected by it. Asbestos is a Category 1 carcinogen, responsible for over 4,000 deaths in the UK every year. Activities dealing with asbestos come within the requirements of the Control of Asbestos Regulations.

Before the commencement of works, the site assessment should identify any risks posed by asbestos and the appropriate controls for dealing with it; which may range from physical containment to disposal.

Any asbestos product or material that is planned for disposal is defined as asbestos waste. Asbestos waste also includes contaminated building materials, tools that cannot be decontaminated, PPE and damp rags used for cleaning. Asbestos waste is classed as hazardous (special waste in Scotland) when it contains more than 0.1% asbestos and will need to be transferred under a hazardous waste consignment note. In England and Wales sites producing over 500 kg of hazardous waste will also need to be registered with the Environment Agency.

Small items of asbestos waste should be double wrapped or double bagged and contain the appropriate labels. Skips should be lockable or, if transported in a vehicle, should be carried in a separate compartment that is lockable and can easily be cleaned.

CL:AIRE is currently developing a CoP on *Asbestos in soils, made ground and construction and demolition waste*, which is planned for publication early in 2014.

Buried explosives

Extreme care must be taken on sites where explosives are known to have been stored or used. This includes old mine workings, coal storage depots, former explosives factories and Ministry of Defence establishments. Disturbing any explosives could have sudden and disastrous consequences, especially if they are old and starting to decay.

Furthermore, unexploded bombs are occasionally unearthed when construction work takes place in areas that were subjected to bombing during World War II.

Once it is agreed that excavation work should proceed, this should be done with utmost caution. Any areas of soil discoloration, unusual objects or unusual cable presence should be taken as an indication that explosives are present. Work should be stopped immediately and the police informed.

Well established procedures already exist for competent military personnel to deal with unexploded devices.

Anthrax

Anthrax spores may lie dormant within soil, or in horse or cow hair binders in old lath and plaster, for many decades.

When such spores are ultimately disturbed, they still have the capacity to cause severe environmental problems. You should regard all premises (such as old tanneries, wool sorting stations and premises used in connection with animal carcasses, hides, bones, offal or for the production of gelatine, or old lath and plaster walls or ceilings) as high risk areas where anthrax spores may be present.

The Department for the Environment, Food and Rural Affairs (DEFRA) will be able to supply advice as to whether contaminated carcasses have been buried on old farm sites.

Where it is suspected that anthrax spores may be present, it is essential for everyone on the site to exercise good personal hygiene and use impervious personal protective clothing, including gloves. Any cuts and scratches that occur before work starts must be adequately covered. As an additional safeguard, advice on immunisation and general health procedures should be sought from a doctor.

Radiation

Before starting work on a site where any work involving radioactive materials has taken place previously, and where radioactive contamination (whether natural or artificial) may be present, consult the Health and Safety Executive (HSE) and the Environment Agencies.

It will be necessary to use specialist contractors for all aspects of both the removal of substances and decontamination where radioactive materials are being dealt with.

08

08

09

Archaeology and heritage

Archaeology is a major factor in construction and development and an estimated £150m is spent by developers on archaeology in the UK each year.

This chapter gives a general overview of the legal framework for the protection and management of archaeological sites and remains. It identifies which types of feature are protected in law and where to obtain consent to carry out works on or near them.

This chapter also gives some guidance on the necessary actions to be taken to protect archaeological features during the works and the necessary action if an unexpected archaeological discovery is made.

Introduction	108
Key requirements	108
Protected monuments, buildings and sites	108
Managing archaeology	110
Unexpected discovery	111

9.1   Introduction

Archaeology is often underestimated as a business or project risk so is often not considered early enough in the feasibility or design stages of projects, leading to unexpected or unplanned consequences.

Archaeological remains and the built environment provide a valuable record of a nation's history and identity and are an irreplaceable part of its national heritage. For these reasons archaeology and built heritage form a key element of planning policy and must be considered early in any construction project. Today, archaeology is a significant element of construction and development, and all parties (developers, archaeologists and the regulatory authorities) should aim to ensure that good practice is applied.

The key reasons why the construction sector should address archaeology are:

☑ **planning law, heritage law and planning policy:** Archaeological remains are an important part of our cultural heritage, and they are a fragile, finite and irreplaceable resource that needs to be protected. This is recognised within the UK planning process and by UK national legislation and guidance. Whilst some archaeological sites are protected by law, all archaeological remains affected by development under planning are treated as material considerations in the planning process

☑ **education and new knowledge:** Archaeology makes a significant contribution to education, social cohesion and the economy and it brings wide public benefits and knowledge gained through archaeological work in schools and universities

☑ **economy and society:** Archaeology underpins the UK tourism and heritage industries and creates jobs. It also plays an important role in regeneration by invoking a sense of place and cultural identity for new developments

☑ **sustainability:** Developers can demonstrate their commitment to sustainability and responsible development through a proactive approach to archaeology, and also a recognition that archaeological remains are a non-renewable resource that need environmental protection and management.

An early, positive and proactive approach to archaeological remains can:

☑ minimise the impacts

☑ provide some research benefits that is mitigation in response to the approved destruction of the resource

☑ ensure an increased sense of place for new developments

☑ provide opportunities for community engagement, leading to positive publicity for the construction project.

9.2   Key requirements

An archaeological statement (as part of an overall environmental statement) may be required to support a planning application and may also require some intrusive works on the site. This is likely to include an archaeological management plan to identify the controls that are required during the works.

A professional archaeologist may be required as a condition of any planning consent to supervise the works as they proceed and to ensure that suitable protection measures are put in place and maintained.

An archaeologist may also be required to excavate and record remains that are due to be removed.

Suitable controls to manage archaeology and heritage should be included in the project as early as possible to:

☑ comply with legal requirements relating to scheduled monuments, listed buildings and protection of the historic environment

☑ ensure buildings are designed to avoid the disturbance of remains and to preserve historic features

☑ enable designers to incorporate historic features of the site in the final development

☑ avoid disturbance during the construction process itself:
   – ensure all archaeological works are segregated from the main works with authorised entry
   – identify existing buried services that might have an impact on archaeology
   – ensure archaeological excavations are suitably protected during the works
   – avoid dewatering activities in the vicinity of archaeological remains.

9.3   Protected monuments, buildings and sites

There are a series of designations and/or statutory protection measures for archaeological and historic remains that have a close link with planning regulations. Planning policy statement 5 (PPS5), together with supporting planning policy guidance are used to regulate planning controls for historic sites.

Certain archaeological sites are protected in law. These are covered on the next page.

Scheduled monuments

The word *monument* covers a whole range of archaeological sites. Scheduled monuments are not always ancient, or visible above ground.

Nationally important sites and monuments are given legal protection by being placed on a schedule for monuments. English Heritage identifies sites in England that should be placed on the schedule by the Secretary of State. The Ancient Monuments and Archaeological Areas Act supports a formal system of scheduled monument consents for any works to a designated monument.

All work to a monument that is scheduled as an ancient monument requires a scheduled monument consent, as do any works to the grounds that surround it.

It is a criminal offence, potentially leading to fines or imprisonment, to:

- ☑ carry out unauthorised works on a scheduled monument without consent
- ☑ cause damage to a scheduled monument
- ☑ fail to adhere to the terms of a consent.

Development or construction works that affect a scheduled monument require formal permission (scheduled monument consent).

The granting of scheduled monument consent does not imply planning permission, or vice versa.

Applications for scheduled monument consent are made:

- ☑ in England, to the Department of Culture Media and Sport
- ☑ in Northern Ireland, to the Northern Ireland Environment Agency
- ☑ in Scotland, to Historic Scotland
- ☑ in Wales, to Cadw.

Listed buildings

A listed building has statutory protection against unauthorised demolition, alteration and extension.

There are three grades of listed buildings:

Grade I – exceptional interest

Grade II – particularly important buildings of more than special interest

Grade III – special interest, warranting every effort to preserve them.

Any works required to be undertaken to a listed building that would affect its character, or the character of any building or structure in its cartilage, requires a listed building consent. It is a criminal offence to demolish, alter or extend a listed building without consent. If this occurs and the character and appearance of the building is affected, a listed building enforcement notice may be served, requiring reinstatement of the building prior to works being carried out. If this is not feasible a fine, sentence of both may be served.

It should be noted that Planning Authorities and National Park Authorities have the power to serve a building preservation notice on the owner of a building that is not listed, but which they consider is of special architectural or historic interest. The building is then protected for six months as per a listed building, in which time the Secretary of State must decide whether to list the building.

09

Conservation areas

A conservation area is an area with a special architectural or historic character, which is desirable to preserve or enhance and are designated as such by the local Planning Authority. It refers to the character of the whole area including open spaces, and not just individual buildings that conservation area designation and policy seek to preserve or enhance.

Conservation areas are given greater protection by the Local Authority as it has extra control over demolition, minor developments and the protection of trees. A conservation area consent from the local Planning Authority must be obtained prior to works being carried out in the designated area. Consultation should be undertaken with the local Planning Authority to determine if works to be carried out require a conservation area consent.

Parks and gardens

Historic parks and gardens can be registered, which means inclusion on the register of park and garden of special historic interest. Alterations to parks and gardens generally do not require statutory consent unless a planning application is required or it affected a tree covered by a tree preservation order. It should be noted that local Planning Authorities are encouraged to include policies in their development plans for the protection of registered historic parks and gardens.

Designated wrecks

Section 1 of the Protection of Wrecks Act provides protection to some 60 wrecks around the UK, designated for their archaeological and historical significance.

Archaeology and heritage

The administration of this Act and the issue of licences allowing diving, survey, collection of objects or excavation on these sites is the responsibility of:

- ☑ in England, English Heritage
- ☑ in Wales, Cadw
- ☑ in Northern Ireland, the Northern Ireland Environment Agency
- ☑ in Scotland, Historic Scotland.

Designated vessels and controlled sites

Certain military aircraft crash sites and military shipwrecks are designated and protected under the Protection of Military Remains Act. These sites are administered by the Ministry of Defence.

Burial grounds and human remains

In England and Wales, authorisation to disturb human remains may be by Act of Parliament, Home Office licence (through the Ministry of Justice), or Church of England Faculty. Under Scottish Law there is no such system of authorisation. In England, disturbance of human remains may be allowed by the Act of Parliament authorising a specific major project, but otherwise the following legislation applies:

- ☑ Town and Country Planning (Churches, Places or Religious Worship and Burial Grounds) Regulations
- ☑ Disused Burial Grounds Act
- ☑ Disused Burial Grounds (amendment) Act
- ☑ Burial Act.

If any form of construction works is to take place on a disused burial ground then the Disused Burial Grounds (Amendment) Act stipulates that the prior removal of human remains should be undertaken. However, if planned works will leave human remains undisturbed then dispensation can be obtained from the Home Office authorising that the burials remain in situ.

Treasure

Under the Treasure Act (England, Wales and Northern Ireland), certain finds are deemed as treasure. All finds must be reported to the nearest local police station/coroner for the district within 14 days who will then advise on the course of action to be taken. Under the above Act, finds classed as treasure include:

- ☑ coins that are least 300 years old (coins are usually only treasure if there are ten or more, or they are with other items meeting the treasure definition)
- ☑ objects containing at least 10% of gold or silver and at least 300 years old
- ☑ any object that is found in the near vicinity of known treasure
- ☑ base metal deposits of prehistoric date.

9.4   Managing archaeology

In risk terms, archaeological remains should be considered as hazards which, if not properly identified and mitigated, may cause an adverse effect on a development. Typical archaeological risks faced by development include:

- ☑ planning constraints and potential for spot listing and scheduling of remains
- ☑ unforeseen or unexpected archaeological remains affecting design, implementation programme and profit margins.

The environmental statement and planning conditions for the project, provided by the client, should identify any obligations for the management of archaeology and heritage. These requirements should be incorporated into the project environmental management plan (EMP). In some cases it will be a condition of the planning consent to prepare an archaeological management plan, which may include the employment of a qualified archaeologist as a watching brief during relevant construction works, to identify:

- ☑ what planning policy and legislation authorities will consider when deciding how to treat any archaeological remains
- ☑ the types of archaeological site and range of features that may occur
- ☑ the range of non-intrusive and intrusive techniques that archaeologists will use to assess and evaluate archaeological remains
- ☑ the key roles of the client, archaeological consultant, contractor and curator.

It is often best to deal with archaeological issues (including excavation) in advance of the main construction phase.

 All field evaluation work should be completed and an agreed mitigation strategy (if required) should be in place before construction/groundwork starts.

It will also be important to agree the appropriate method of working adjacent to sensitive areas as vibration from operations (such as excavation or tunnelling) may cause damage. There may be an obligation to provide vibration monitoring of the works to ensure that vibration levels are not exceeded.

All areas of known archaeological or historic interest should be protected with suitable fencing to prevent damage or encroachment and access to other site traffic and personnel carefully controlled. This is a legal requirement for scheduled sites.

In respect to health and safety, any excavations for archaeological works should be treated as normal and protected to avoid inadvertent access by personnel or site equipment. The location of buried services should also be identified as these could also cross sites where archaeological excavation is planned.

Many archaeological excavations will also take place on brownfield sites that have been contaminated. If from previous uses there is reason to believe that the ground is contaminated, arrangements should be made to undertake sampling and testing before archaeological work starts on site.

Dewatering schemes may also have an impact on archaeological features as this could cause differential settlement or damage to materials that have previously been protected by being waterlogged. Appropriate methods of dewatering should be agreed in advance of the works taking place.

9.5   Unexpected discovery

If suspected archaeological objects or remains are found during the construction works without an archaeologist on site, certain procedures should be followed. Archaeological finds should not be disturbed any further without any specialist investigation and advice. Advice should be sought by contacting the Local Authority archaeological officer on how to proceed.

 In the case of any accidental discovery of archaeological finds or human remains it is good practice to:

- ☑ stop work in the area of the discovery
- ☑ leave the find in situ and undisturbed
- ☑ control access to the area to authorised persons only
- ☑ stop vehicle traffic entering the area
- ☑ report the find to the site manager
- ☑ take specialist advice as appropriate
- ☑ report human remains, treasure and other archaeological finds to the appropriate statutory authority
- ☑ report the find to the appropriate local planning authority or other curator.

Under the Burials Act there is a requirement to report unexpected discoveries of human remains to a coroner. If there is any possibility that the remains are recent (for example, less than 100 years old) the local police should be contacted to determine if the remains are ancient or not.

If human remains are found it will be necessary to report this to the coroner and, for authorisation to continue, approval will need to be given by the Home Office.

09

09

Archaeology and heritage

10

Site environment management systems

This chapter provides a general introduction to environmental management systems and how they can be applied to construction projects.

This chapter also provides guidance on the nature and type of environmental documents and records that should be maintained on a construction site.

Introduction	114
Types of environmental management system	114
Policy, objectives and targets	115
Implementing environmental management on site	115
Environmental documentation	118
Appendix A – Example of environmental objectives and targets	119
Appendix B – Envronmental audit checklist	121

Site environment management systems

10.1 Introduction

An environmental management system (EMS) can help companies reduce their environmental impacts, achieve cost savings, comply with legislation and demonstrate their commitment to securing continual improvement in environmental performance.

Being able to demonstrate that their company understands and is managing its environmental impacts is becoming an important prerequisite for many construction companies when tendering for new business.

It is recognised that adopting standard environmental management policies and practices not only helps in protecting the environment but also brings business benefits in terms of reduction of waste, energy use and improved efficiency. It reduces the risk of causing incidents that may result in enforcement action, which could lead to prosecution.

Managing the environment, or environmental impacts, is not just for one person in an organisation, but is a process of change for all involved.

An EMS can also help all types and sizes of company meet their own environmental and sustainability targets as well as contribute to national targets on climate change, sustainable development, waste, water, emissions, energy, resource efficiency and other environmental issues.

An EMS has a number of key functions:

- [x] **secure positive environmental outcomes:** it should not just document procedures and processes but also focus on improving environmental performance and complying with legal and other client requirements

- [x] **help a company understand its environmental impacts:** it should be a practical tool to identify and describe a company's impact on the environment, manage and reduce these impacts and evaluate and improve performance. An EMS can help with managing risks, liabilities and legal compliance

- [x] **reduce costs and improve efficiency:** they can also help conformity with customer requirements in the supply chain, enable sustainable procurement policies, enhance a company's reputation, secure new markets and help improve communication with employees, regulators, investors and other stakeholders.

To fully contribute to improved environmental performance, a good EMS should:

- [x] be implemented at a senior level and integrated into company plans and policies. Top-level commitment is required so that senior management understand their role in ensuring the success of an EMS

- [x] identify the company's impacts on the environment and set clear objectives and targets to improve its management of these aspects as well as the company's overall environmental performance

- [x] be designed to deliver and manage compliance with environmental laws and regulations on an ongoing basis, and will quickly instigate corrective and preventative action in cases of legal non-compliance

- [x] deliver good resource management and financial benefits

- [x] incorporate performance indicators that demonstrate the above and can be communicated in a transparent way in annual reports.

 Demonstrating to clients that you have policies and arrangements in place to manage and improve environmental performance will enhance your company's reputation and contribute to obtaining future work.

Whilst larger construction companies will want to demonstrate that they have a robust environmental management system through certification to a formal standard (such as ISO 14001 *(refer to 10.2)*), smaller companies should consider implementing an EMS as this will help identify their environmental risks and put in controls to manage them. This will also improve their opportunities in winning future work.

10.2 Types of environmental management system

There are three recognised standards or schemes.

- [x] **ISO 14001** is the international standard for EMS, which specifies the components necessary to help organisations systematically identify, evaluate, manage and improve the environmental impacts of their activities, products and services.

- [x] **EMAS** (the EU Eco-management and Audit scheme) is a voluntary EU-wide environmental registration scheme that requires organisations to produce a public statement about their performance against targets and objectives, and incorporates the international standard ISO 14001.

- [x] **BS 8555** is a British Standard, published in 2003, which breaks down the implementation process for ISO 14001 or EMAS into six stages, making implementation much easier, especially for smaller companies. The Institute of Environmental Management and Assessment (IEMA) has developed the IEMA Acorn scheme, which enables companies to gain UKAS accredited recognition for their achievements at each stage of the standard as they work towards ISO 14001 or EMAS. This process allows early recognition of progress against indicators and can be used very effectively to enhance supply chain management by setting agreed levels of performance, certified to a national standard, and which have been checked by an independent auditor. Organisations who complete each stage of the scheme are entered on a public Acorn register.

10

114

The 14001 standard requires organisations to:

- ☑ establish an environmental policy relevant to the organisation
- ☑ identify the environmental issues associated with the organisation's activities and determine the significant environmental impacts
- ☑ identify applicable legal requirements and other requirements associated with its environmental impacts
- ☑ identify priorities and set appropriate environmental objectives and targets
- ☑ establish a structure and programme(s) to implement the policy, achieve objectives and meet targets
- ☑ implement planning, control, monitoring, preventive and corrective actions, auditing and reviewing procedures to ensure that the policy is complied with and that the environmental management system remains appropriate, and capable of adapting to changing circumstances.

10.3 Policy, objectives and targets

A basic EMS policy should:

- ☑ be appropriate to the organisation, for its size and activities
- ☑ establish a framework for setting and reviewing environmental objectives and targets
- ☑ commit to comply with current legislation and other environmental requirements or obligations
- ☑ commit to pollution prevention and continual improvement
- ☑ be documented, implemented and maintained
- ☑ be readily available for employees, stakeholders and general public.

The policy should be endorsed by someone of authority within the organisation, be it a director or someone of equal seniority.

Setting objectives and targets is key to a successful EMS and demonstrates the commitment of the business to reduce its impacts and set the path for a programme of continual improvement.

An initial baseline assessment of where the organisation is in terms of its current management of the environment will identify areas for improvement.

Areas that could be considered are:

- ☑ measuring and reducing the amount of waste produced
- ☑ improving recycling rates for different waste streams
- ☑ monitoring water use, setting reduction targets and implementing and sharing measures
- ☑ monitoring energy use (electricity and fuel), setting reduction targets and implementing and sharing measures
- ☑ purchasing sustainable services and materials/materials with recycle content
- ☑ assisting and improving supply chain knowledge on environmental matters.

Regular measurement and reporting against company targets will highlight whether they are being met and where future action needs to be focused. This will allow the company to continually improve its environmental performance and demonstrate to clients, its staff and the general public that it is taking its environmental responsibilities seriously.

For typical environmental objectives and targets for a construction project refer to Appendix A.

10.4 Implementing environmental management on site

A company's environmental management system will define what plans and procedures, together with the appropriate forms, will need to be completed at a site level. Whatever documents are used to achieve this, there are some clearly defined steps in order to deliver effective environmental management on site. The following five steps should be followed.

10

Site environment management systems

Step 1 – Identify the project environmental obligations

The first important step in managing the project environmental issues is to identify the environmental obligations. An obligation is a requirement to take some course of action, whether legal or moral. In the case of environmental obligations there a number of potential sources.

☑ The first of these is legal obligations where individuals and organisations have to follow legal requirements or face prosecution (for example, duty of care under waste law or the protection of wildlife).

☑ The next concerns contractual obligations and these might relate to performance requirements that a client specifies (for example, BREEAM or CEEQUAL). Where these are not met a client can resort to a civil action to recover costs for the damages incurred.

☑ Another type of obligation that business have arises from their corporate responsibility and their duty to act in a way that recognises the interests and views of others, sometimes called stakeholders, in relation to the environment. Failure to recognise corporate responsibility can result in damage to corporate reputation.

A review of the project's contractual documentation, including any associated planning conditions, should be undertaken to identify the project-specific environmental obligations. It is essential to identify potential obligations that might arise from different emergency scenarios that could have environmental impacts. Appropriate processes are needed to identify potential emergency scenarios and, if they do occur, have an effective response plan in place that is regularly tested.

Step 2 – Identify the project environmental aspects and risks

Following the identification of the project environmental obligations the next step is to identify the associated environmental aspects and risks. Environmental aspects and risks can be present on a specific project wherever there is an interaction with the environment, arising from either raw material inputs or emissions and other outputs to the environment. The goal of a good environmental management system is to identify what these aspects and risks are and to put in place the necessary controls to manage them to within acceptable limits.

☑ An **aspect** is usually associated with a 'doing word' (such as disposing of waste, discharging of dirty excavation water, storing fuel).

☑ The **risk** (or impact, as defined in ISO 14001) is the consequence of not doing something correctly.

Illegally disposing of waste is the aspect, and the associated risk is it being disposed of incorrectly, such as at an unlicensed tip. Discharging water into a drain is the aspect; the risk is discharging water without consent in place or the discharged water polluting a connected river. Another common aspect is storing fuel; the risk can be that fuel leaks into the ground and pollutes the ground or an underground drinking water aquifer.

The minimum level of performance is compliance with legal and other requirements. Organisations may also decide that they want to work to best practices where risks are minimised as far as reasonably practicable. The best way of managing environmental risks is in a systematic way and ISO 14001:2004 *Environmental management systems* provides an internationally recognised framework for doing this.

The production of a project environmental aspects register, identifying the obligations, together with the associated risks and control measures (including emergency situations or possible worst case scenarios), will be a key tool for communicating these issues to contractors and site personnel.

Environmental risks should be assessed during the pre-construction phase of a project to ensure that environmental management is properly integrated within the project with respect to these risks. Environmental risks are identified in the pre-construction phase in a number of sources, including ecology surveys, desk top studies and ground investigations. These may also be information held by the CDM co-ordinator that contains information about environmental risks.

Step 3 – Identify the environmental responsibilities

Having defined the project environmental obligations and associated risks it will be necessary to identify key responsibilities for their control. An environmental management system can involve every person on a project or within an organisation. Certain people within the management system will have specific responsibilities and it is important that these are clearly defined and set out. Examples of functions and positions with specific responsibilities include:

☑ directors

☑ environmental co-ordinators

☑ noise specialists

☑ waste co-ordinators

☑ sub-contractors

☑ suppliers

☑ community liaison staff.

It is important to ensure that the necessary lines of communication are defined between those individuals that have prepared the project environmental plan and site personnel.

The responsibilities of an environmental manager on a large construction project could include:

☑ implementing the requirements of the company EMS

☑ ensuring that relevant environmental policies are displayed and communicated to all project staff and personnel

☑ ensuring that a project assessment is carried out to identify the key activities and aspects

☑ ensuring that an environmental management plan (EMP) is developed and maintained to identify the specific environmental requirements and responsibilities and includes legal, client and other relevant issues

☑ ensuring that a waste management plan is developed and maintained to manage waste and includes appropriate responsibilities, waste targets and legal compliance information

☑ ensuring that, as well as waste targets, relevant environmental objectives are set, implemented and monitored in line with the project construction programme or establishment requirements

☑ ensuring that the general environmental requirements and objectives are included in inductions, toolbox talks and briefings, and records are maintained

☑ ensuring that specific activity method statements, including those of suppliers, are reviewed to include the relevant project environmental and waste requirements

☑ ensuring that appropriate inspections and monitoring arrangements are put in place to meet the environmental requirements (such as weekly supervisors inspections)

☑ ensuring that appropriate environmental emergency arrangements are identified, implemented and tested, as appropriate

☑ participating in management reviews and audits of the status, adequacy and effectiveness of the project EMP

☑ managing environmental non-conformances and subsequent corrective actions

☑ reviewing advised changes to environmental legislation and other requirements and taking the appropriate action

☑ ensuring that an environmental management file (EMF) is established to contain appropriate records of the above and is sufficient to meet the environmental requirements.

Step 4 – Environmental management plan

A project EMP is a vital tool for setting out what actions are to be taken and who is responsible for them. It will contain information including, for example, method statements, legislation, performance requirements and environmental risks. The project site waste management plan (SWMP) will also be a key document as part of the project EMP. The typical contents of a project EMP may include, but not be limited to, the following:

☑ environmental policies

☑ project environmental objectives and targets

☑ environmental appointments

☑ environmental risk assessments

☑ site waste management plan

☑ environmental emergency response/action plans

☑ consultation

☑ environmental inductions, training and awareness

☑ environmental monitoring, measuring, inspections and audits

☑ environmental incident and investigation reports

☑ project environmental records.

Step 5 – Monitoring and inspection

After implementing a project EMP a robust monitoring and inspection regime should be put in place to ensure that risks are being managed and that compliance with legal and contractual requirements are being met. Examples of monitoring and inspection activities for risk management and compliance include:

☑ noise measurements

☑ water analysis

☑ air quality

☑ dust monitoring

☑ duty of care checks.

Monitoring and inspection can also take place to assess performance delivery and the achievement of performance objectives and targets that have been set by a project. This may include monitoring and inspection of carbon, water, resource and material use efficiency.

10

Site environment management systems

Monitoring and inspection activities can include:

☑ directors' tours

☑ site management tours

☑ supervisors' tours

☑ internal audits

☑ external audits

☑ supplier audits

☑ water monitoring

☑ energy usage

☑ resource use measurement.

Environmental performance improvement

Environmental performance improvement is the key to successful construction projects. Efficient use of carbon, water, raw materials and waste reduction will bring multiple benefits to projects and contribute to cost savings. To achieve performance improvement requires a well-planned and structured management system, the right leadership and a mind-set across the project that results in behaviours that are focused towards resource efficiency.

Regular project reviews involving all site personnel that are identified in the project EMP, including sub-contractors and suppliers, will provide the opportunity to discuss environmental issues and how to improve performance. These reviews need not be separate, formal meetings and could be an agenda item of standard management meetings.

10.5 Environmental documentation

The project environmental requirements will dictate what environmental documentation is required and what records must be kept to demonstrate their compliance. It is likely that a company will have a standard project filing system and it would be good practice to ensure a section of this is reserved for environmental records.

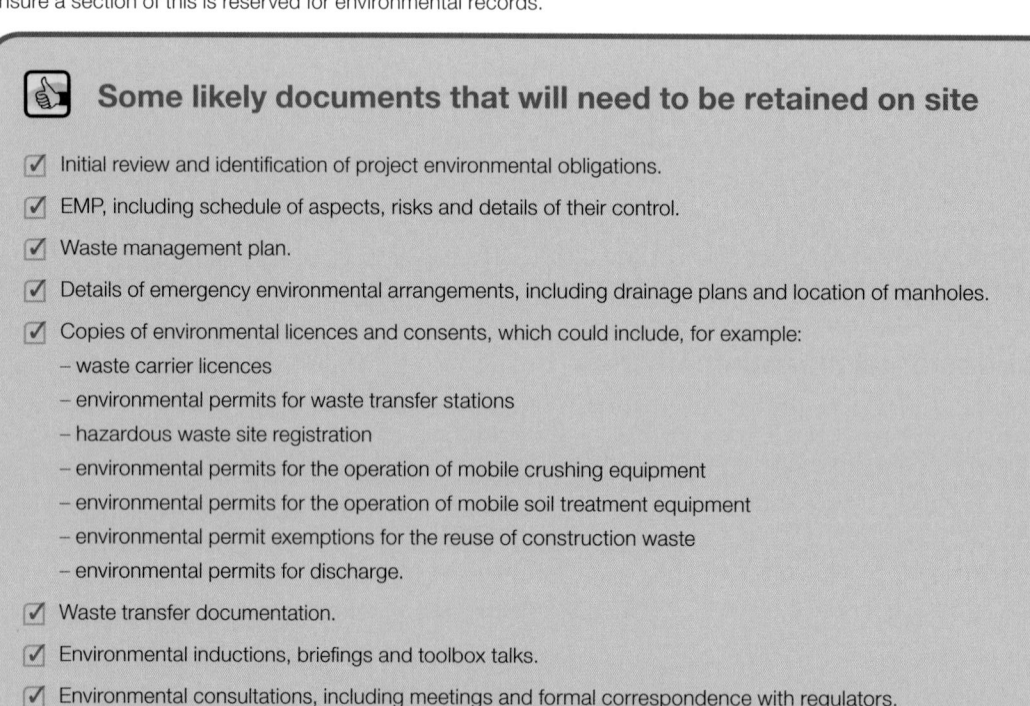

Some likely documents that will need to be retained on site

☑ Initial review and identification of project environmental obligations.

☑ EMP, including schedule of aspects, risks and details of their control.

☑ Waste management plan.

☑ Details of emergency environmental arrangements, including drainage plans and location of manholes.

☑ Copies of environmental licences and consents, which could include, for example:
  – waste carrier licences
  – environmental permits for waste transfer stations
  – hazardous waste site registration
  – environmental permits for the operation of mobile crushing equipment
  – environmental permits for the operation of mobile soil treatment equipment
  – environmental permit exemptions for the reuse of construction waste
  – environmental permits for discharge.

☑ Waste transfer documentation.

☑ Environmental inductions, briefings and toolbox talks.

☑ Environmental consultations, including meetings and formal correspondence with regulators.

☑ Environmental incident reports and non-conformance reports and breaches.

☑ Environmental work instructions and operational procedures.

☑ Environmental monitoring and inspection records, which could include, for example:
  – weekly site inspection records
  – audit reports
  – water sampling records
  – soil and waste sampling records
  – dust and air quality monitoring, including visual inspections
  – visual records of sensitive area protection, including fencing
  – records associated with the achievement of project environmental objectives and key performance indicators.

A number of the above documents will be required to be retained for legal purposes (such as waste transfer documentation, which must be retained for non-hazardous and hazardous waste for two and three years respectively). These requirements must be made clear following completion of the project to ensure all relevant records are archived, together with the project contractual documentation.

Appendix A – Example of environmental objectives and targets

Objective	Action	Key performance indicator/target	Performance*			
			Q1	Q2	Q3	Q4
Water Monitor site water usage and aim for a reduction in usage against previous year baseline. Offices to identify their usage and identify ways to reduce water demand.	▪ Sites to continue measuring and reporting on site water usage. (All sites to fit flow meters or utilise existing meters.) ▪ Projects to identify and implement water saving measures on site. ▪ Advertise and raise awareness of water efficiency through newsletters and communications. ▪ On design and build projects, teams are to identify and communicate stakeholder risks and opportunities presented by water use.	All projects to report on water usage.				
		Projects to identify and implement water saving efficiencies to reduce company usage of water by 5% against previous year's consumption figures/£100k turnover).				
		All offices to identify and install water saving efficiencies.				
		Communicate risks and opportunities presented by water to identified clients.				
Energy and carbon reduction Monitor energy usage on sites and offices to reduce company energy usage by 5% against previous year baseline.	▪ Install sub-meters in all offices to record energy usage. ▪ Promote energy and carbon awareness through training and promotional events. ▪ All offices to prepare a transport and logistics plan. ▪ All offices to create a green travel plan. ▪ Each office to measure the carbon footprint of projects where this has been requested by the client. ▪ Identify suitable sites for carbon footprint assessment.	All new projects and offices to have meters installed (Kwh/100 m²).				
		Each office to create a green travel plan.				
		Each office to receive an energy audit and implement energy saving measures.				
		Measure the carbon footprint of projects where this has been requested by the client.				
Responsible sourcing Monitor the use of responsibly sourced timber.	▪ Projects to procure timber in accordance with Government's CPET requirements where possible. ▪ Projects to identify and implement the use of recycled aggregates/materials, where possible.	All projects to report on the percentage (by value) of all site timber having chain of custody.				
		All projects to report on volume of recycled aggregates.				
Waste Reduce waste production in line with the waste hierarchy and raise waste awareness through training.	▪ Set waste reduction targets based on previous year's data. ▪ Identify and develop best practice for waste reduction. ▪ Undertake supply chain waste reduction workshops. ▪ All sites to appoint a waste champion. ▪ Project staff to receive SWMP refresher training.	Company to divert at least 85% of construction waste from landfill.				
		Sites to reduce waste produced on site by 5% compared to previous year's levels.				

Example of environmental objectives and targets (continued)

Objective	Action	Key performance indicator/target	Performance*			
			Q1	Q2	Q3	Q4
Biodiversity Improve company knowledge on biodiversity issues and benefits whilst improving the biodiversity on our sites.	■ Deliver appropriate biodiversity training to teams. ■ Benchmark and improve the biodiversity on projects where relevant (such as BREEAM, client). ■ Share best practice examples.	Deliver relevant awareness training (identified on a project, risk basis).				
		Projects to identify ways to improve the biodiversity on site.				
Environmental accident rate Ensure all site personnel are aware of environmental incident reporting requirements.	■ Ensure all sites record environmental incidents, near misses and complaints. ■ Encourage dialogue on environmental issues/ situations that are not easy to implement, are misunderstood or ignored. ■ Include environmental incident/near miss reporting within site inductions and toolbox talks.	Target a continued zero incident rate.				
		All risk assessments and method statements to include specific environmental risks.				
		Toolbox talks – environmental topic ratio 1:4.				
Community engagement Increase engagement with local communities and maintain a considerate constructor approach.	■ Capture and collate in an annual report all the community engagement work the company and projects carry out. ■ Create a company community engagement plan. ■ Improve compliance with Considerate Constructors' scheme (CCS) by creating a company minimum standard for sites, share best practice and have a dedicated CCS folder for each registered site.	Record any community engagement work and send to the environmental team/advisor or head office.				
		Each project to have a CCS folder and a target score of 34.				

* Key: **1** Completed/target met   **2** Started/near target   **3** Not started/not on target

Appendix B – Envronmental audit checklist

Resource efficiency and responsible sourcing

		Yes	No	N/A
E2.1	Has the site considered alternative techniques for the efficient use of resources (such as off-site manufacture, design to fit modular sizes, manufacture to fit design)?			
E2.2	Has the design taken into account the reuse of reprocessed demolition materials or the use of recycled aggregate?			
E2.3	Are there procedures in place to identify and order the correct type and quantity of materials?			
E2.4	Are there procedures in place to ensure key materials are sourced responsibly (such as sustainable timber)?			
E2.5	Are deliveries being inspected to avoid damage during unloading, deliveries to wrong area of the site or accepting incorrect specification or quantity?			
E2.6	Are stockpiles and material storage areas away from traffic routes to prevent accidental damage?			
E2.7	Are materials being stored to prevent repetitive handling?			
E2.8	Are materials being stored with the appropriate security to prevent loss, theft or vandalism?			
E2.9	Are stockpiled materials being stored to prevent cross-contamination with other materials or wastes?			
E2.10	Are stockpiled materials being stored away from sensitive areas, drains or watercourses?			
E2.11	Are materials being handled with the correct equipment to prevent accidental damage?			
E2.12	Are hazardous/COSHH materials being stored, issued and disposed of correctly?			

Action points

10

(This checklist is based on the CITB-ConstructionSkills Health, safety and environmental auditing system (SA03 CD).)

Waste management, storage and disposal

		Yes	No	N/A
E3.1	Has a site waste management plan been prepared, identifying waste types and quantities for the project? Is it being maintained/updated?			
E3.2	Has a waste target and any relevant objectives been set for the project?			
E3.3	Have the project waste requirements been included in the contracts with trade contractors and suppliers?			
E3.4	Are the project waste requirements included in the site induction?			
E3.5	Have waste responsibilities been defined to know who is disposing of what and when?			
E3.6	Have designated area(s) been established on site to segregate and reuse waste materials?			
E3.7	Have recycling facilities been established to segregate office/canteen wastes (such as paper, cans, and plastics)?			
E3.8	Has the site been registered for hazardous waste with the Environment Agency?			
E3.9	Are waste management permits, licences or exemptions in place for any processing of waste on site (such as crushing and soil treatment)?			
E3.10	Is the WRAP quality protocol being complied with for the production of aggregates from waste?			
E3.11	Is the CL:AIRE code of practice being complied with for the treatment and use of contaminated soils (such as appointment of qualified person, materials management plan, and so on)?			
E3.12	Are hazardous wastes (oil, fuel, paints, and so on) collected and stored separately from general wastes?			
E3.13	Is the burning of rubbish on site prohibited, unless a permit/licence has been obtained?			
E3.14	Are registered waste carriers used to remove waste from site and are these checked on a regular basis?			
E3.15	Does the tip where the waste is taken have a licence for the type of waste?			
E3.16	Do waste transfer documents include the right information (six-digit waste codes, licence number of carrier, tip location and declaration regarding the waste hierarchy)?			
E3.17	Are waste transfer documents being retained: two years for non-hazardous and three years for hazardous waste?			

Action points

(This checklist is based on the CITB-ConstructionSkills Health, safety and environmental auditing system (SA03 CD).)

Energy and transport

		Yes	No	N/A
E4.1	Have energy objectives and targets been set for the project?			
E4.2	Has an energy monitoring process been implemented to monitor and report energy consumption and carbon emissions, including business travel and transport?			
E4.3	Have discussions with energy supplier(s) been made to ensure electrical supplies are connected at the earliest opportunity to avoid power from generators?			
E4.4	Have site offices been fitted with practical, energy-saving devices, including low energy lighting (LED), passive infrared sensors for lighting, timer switches and thermostats for heating/hot water, and so on?			
E4.5	Does the site induction cover key energy efficiency issues (such as maintaining plant and switching off when not in use)?			
E4.6	Are there signs in place advising site personnel to switch equipment off when not required?			
E4.7	Is site office equipment set up to print efficiently (such as double-sided) and to a central location rather than individual printers?			
E4.8	Has the site considered renewable energy to contribute to powering the site accommodation?			
E4.9	Is there a logistics/transport plan that considers efficient transport arrangements (such as the use of consolidation centres or just-in-time delivery)?			
E4.10	Have local, sensitive areas been identified (such as schools and residents)?			
E4.11	Has the site considered green travel arrangements for reducing staff travel to site?			
E4.12	Has the location of suitable parking arrangements for private cars and plant been defined?			
E4.13	Has permission been obtained from the Local Authority for any road closures or erection of hoarding on the public highway?			
E4.14	Have local pedestrian diversion routes been agreed with the Local Authority?			
E4.15	Have delivery routes for construction traffic been agreed with the Local Authority?			
E4.16	Have suppliers been made aware of any delivery restrictions and routes?			
E4.17	Are entrance and exit gates on main roads rather than side roads?			
E4.18	Are deliveries scheduled to avoid traffic disruption or queuing outside of the site?			
E4.19	Are delivery vehicles switched off when being loaded/unloaded (unless needed to operate a Hiab or similar)?			
E4.20	Have designated vehicle routes on site been defined?			
E4.21	Are deliveries organised to avoid excessive use of reversing sirens?			

Action points

10

(This checklist is based on the CITB-ConstructionSkills Health, safety and environmental auditing system (SA03 CD).)

Water management and pollution prevention

		Yes	No	N/A
E5.1	Have all watercourses and drainage systems been identified on site?			
E5.2	Have all works in, above or near to watercourses been agreed with the local Environment Agency?			
E5.3	Have all discharges to streams, ditches and drainage systems been consented to by the relevant Environment Agency?			
E5.4	Have all water abstractions from rivers, ponds, lakes or water mains been consented to by the relevant Environment Agency?			
E5.5	Are site personnel inducted and suitably trained in dealing with waste water on site?			
E5.6	Have water monitoring procedures been put in place to ensure discharges are the correct quality?			
E5.7	Have water discharges been properly treated (such as using settlement tanks or lagoons)?			
E5.8	Have designated areas been defined to wash out concrete lorries away from watercourses and drains?			
E5.9	Are watercourses and drainage systems protected from run-off and silty water?			
E5.10	Are all fuel tanks effectively bunded to at least 110% of their capacity (or 25% of total capacity for drums)?			
E5.11	Are all oil and diesel tanks and chemicals located as far as possible from drains and watercourses?			
E5.12	Are oil and diesel tanks separated from the ground by an impermeable layer?			
E5.13	Are all oil and diesel tanks and chemicals marked with the type of contents, volume and appropriate hazard warning signs?			
E5.14	Are steps being taken on site to prevent ground contamination or pollution by fuels, oils, chemicals, paint, and so on?			
E5.15	Have site personnel been made aware of the site spillage response procedures through inductions and toolbox talks?			
E5.16	Are appropriate spill kits available and appropriate personnel trained to deal with any accidental spillages to drains or watercourses?			
E5.17	Have proactive measures been taken to reduce water consumption (such as grey water recycling) and water saving devices (such as waterless urinals)?			
E5.18	Is water consumption being monitored and recorded and communicated to site personnel to promote water minimisation?			

Action points

(This checklist is based on the CITB-ConstructionSkills Health, safety and environmental auditing system (SA03 CD).)

Statutory nuisance

		Yes	No	N/A
E6.1	Has the appropriate liaison/communication taken place with local stakeholders that may be affected by nuisance?			
E6.2	Are appropriate dust suppression techniques used to minimise air pollution from timber sawing or planing, stone or block cutting, crushing, and so on?			
E6.3	Is dust on site haul roads and material stockpiles dampened down adequately on dry/windy days?			
E6.4	Are haul roads located away from sensitive areas (such as rivers and ditches)?			
E6.5	Are site vehicle speed limits controlled to reduce dust?			
E6.6	Are public roads regularly cleaned using a road sweeper or vacuum?			
E6.7	Do vehicles that remove granular or dusty materials have sheeted covers?			
E6.8	Are all plant and vehicles in good working order with an up-to-date maintenance or service log?			
E6.9	Are enclosed chutes/covered skips used for lowering dusty demolition or waste materials?			
E6.10	Is cement/concrete being mixed in enclosed areas to prevent dust?			
E6.11	Are material stockpiles or spoil heaps stored away from sensitive areas (such as drains/rivers and ditches)?			
E6.12	Have the works been assessed to identify the noise and vibration impact on local neighbours?			
E6.13	Has the local environmental health officer and neighbours been consulted and forewarned of any out-of-hours or major disruptive activities?			
E6.14	If a Control of Pollution Act Section 61 consent is required, are noise levels being recorded to ensure that levels are kept within limits?			
E6.15	If possible, have working methods been reviewed to use equipment that reduces noise and vibration (such as pile jacking and chemical bursting)?			
E6.16	Have working hours been defined to restrict noisy operations to certain times of day?			
E6.17	Is noisy plant kept as far as possible from sensitive receptors?			
E6.18	Are deliveries planned to suit the local area?			
E6.19	Are haul routes well maintained to prevent vehicle noise and vibration?			
E6.20	Where required, are noise screens being used to reduce noise transmission?			
E6.21	Are noise screens and hoarding well maintained with no holes and gaps?			
E6.22	Has lighting been positioned to avoid a nuisance at night and is non-essential lighting switched off at night?			

Action points

10

(This checklist is based on the CITB-ConstructionSkills Health, safety and environmental auditing system (SA03 CD).)

Ecology

		Yes	No	N/A
E7.1	Has the contractual and client documentation been reviewed to identify all sensitive areas containing wildlife?			
E7.2	Have all relevant ecological risks been included in the construction environmental management plan, together with their mitigation measures?			
E7.3	Have licences been obtained from Natural England or the relevant conservation body to move protected species or disrupt their habitats (such as bats, badgers and lizards)?			
E7.4	Are areas containing wildlife suitably protected from the construction work?			
E7.5	Are trees suitably protected to avoid damage from the works?			
E7.6	Have vegetation removal works been programmed to avoid breeding/nesting periods?			
E7.7	Has permission been given by the Local Authority to remove hedges or trees having a tree preservation order?			
E7.8	Has approval been given by the relevant Environment Agency to deal with invasive plants (such as Japanese knotweed and giant hogweed)?			
E7.9	Has approval been given by the relevant Environment Agency for the treatment/management of plants adjacent to a watercourse?			
E7.10	Do treatment operatives hold the appropriate qualification/certificate of competency for the use of pesticides?			

Action points

10

(This checklist is based on the CITB-ConstructionSkills Health, safety and environmental auditing system (SA03 CD).)

Contaminated land

		Yes	No	N/A
E8.1	Has a preliminary/desktop investigation been carried out of the site and its previous uses to identify the risks from contamination?			
E8.2	Has a site investigation been carried out to identify the type and extent of any suspected contamination?			
E8.3	Are the testing company/laboratory suitably competent to carry out the testing/analysis of any contamination?			
E8.4	Has the proposed remediation strategy been agreed by the local planning authority and Environment Agency, where appropriate?			
E8.5	Does the site induction cover details of contamination and the procedures for working in areas of known contamination?			
E8.6	Are there procedures in place to ensure that work is stopped and appropriate reporting takes place if contamination is accidently discovered or disturbed?			
E8.7	Are areas of contamination fenced off to prevent vehicles and plant spreading the contamination across the site?			
E8.8	Are relevant environmental permits in place for the treatment/remediation of contamination?			
E8.9	Are suitable controls in place for dealing with contaminated water (such as discharge consents to foul sewers or tanker)?			
E8.10	If contaminated materials have to be stockpiled, are they covered to prevent run-off and wind-blown contamination?			
E8.11	Are contaminated materials stored on hard-stand areas to avoid contamination of ground and groundwater below?			
E8.12	Are stockpiles positioned well away from drainage systems or watercourses?			
E8.13	Are there suitable wheel-washing facilities to clean contaminated vehicles before leaving site?			
E8.14	Where vehicles remove contaminated materials, are they covered with sheets before leaving site?			

Action points

10

(This checklist is based on the CITB-ConstructionSkills Health, safety and environmental auditing system (SA03 CD).)

Archaeology and heritage

		Yes	No	N/A
E9.1	Has the contract documentation been reviewed to determine the presence or location of archaeology or protected heritage/buildings?			
E9.2	Have designers been involved to integrate known archaeological features into the project?			
E9.3	Have licences or permissions been obtained to carry out work on or around archaeology or protected heritage/buildings?			
E9.4	Where there are works on or around known archaeology or heritage, has a watching brief or specialist been employed to monitor and record the works?			
E9.5	Have locations containing archaeology or heritage been adequately fenced off or protected?			
E9.6	Have suitable communication arrangements been put in place for unknown finds that may be discovered, and for reporting these to the local archaeological officer or Local Authority and recorded?			

Action points

(This checklist is based on the CITB-ConstructionSkills Health, safety and environmental auditing system (SA03 CD).)

Site environment management systems

		Yes	No	N/A
E10.1	Is the company (or site) environmental policy available and displayed on site, with relevant requirements highlighted at the site induction?			
E10.2	Has the contract and client documentation been reviewed to identify the site-specific environmental requirements, including planning conditions?			
E10.3	Has a construction environmental management plan been prepared identifying the relevant targets, objectives, issues and controls?			
E10.4	Is there a system for ensuring that suitable and sufficient arrangements are in place for the management, storage and disposal of waste through the production of a site waste management plan?			
E10.5	Is there a system for ensuring that all site personnel (including sub-contractors) are made aware of the project environmental issues and standards through site inductions, briefings and toolbox talks?			
E10.6	Have responsibilities for environmental management been defined and communicated through inductions, notice boards, and so on?			
E10.7	Is someone responsible for ensuring that environmentally sensitive areas are identified and protected (such as drains, rivers, streams, groundwater and areas containing protected plants and animals)?			
E10.8	Is there a system for ensuring that the necessary environmental licences have been identified and granted (such as discharges of water and effluent, tree preservation orders, premises producing hazardous waste and waste management licences)?			
E10.9	Is there a system for ensuring that method statements include sufficient control measures for environmental management?			
E10.10	Is there a system for sites to deal with environmental emergencies (such as for spillages and groundwater contamination) and for notifying them to?			
E10.11	Is there a suitable and sufficient monitoring regime in place to ensure that the site environmental requirements are being met (such as relevant environmental inspections for oil and waste storage, protected areas, water quality, noise and dust)?			
E10.12	Are environmental records being maintained (such as waste transfer notes, consignment notes, noise and water monitoring)?			
E10.13	Have adequate arrangements been established for liaison and communication with local stakeholders (residents, shops, businesses, schools, parish council)?			

Action points

10

(This checklist is based on the CITB-ConstructionSkills Health, safety and environmental auditing system (SA03 CD).)

10

Index

Index

abstraction licences 61, 67
acid rain 5
Acorn scheme 114
aggregates 16, 17, 21, 34, 41–43, 101
    see also crushing
air pollution 3, 4, 7, 8, 17, 20, 29, 72–74
    see also emissions
air quality 9, 117
aircraft crash sites 110
anthrax 105
archaeology and heritage 8, 77, 107–111, 128
areas of special protection for birds (AOSPs) 83
asbestos 4, 104–105
audits 15, 53, 121–129
    see also EMAS

badgers 80, 83, 93
banned wastes 23
bats 80, 81, 82, 84, 85, 94
batteries 35–36
BES 6001 15, 16
best practical means 72
biodiversity 3, 4, 9, 80, 89, 120
biogenetic reserves 83
birds 80, 81, 82, 83, 84, 85, 94
booms 67
boot washing 62
BREEAM 3, 9–10, 12, 15, 16, 53, 55, 68, 78
British Waterways 8
brownfield sites see contaminated land
BS 8555 114
building preservation notices 109
burial grounds 110
buried explosives 105

Cadw 8, 81, 109, 110
Canadian Standards Association scheme (CSA) 15
Canal and River Trust 8
CAR Regulations 64
carbon allowances 53
carbon emissions 2, 3, 8, 50, 53, 119
    see also Low Carbon Construction Action Plan
carbon footprints 52–55
carbon negative cement 16
carbon use efficiency 117, 118
CEEQUAL 9, 11–12, 15, 53, 67, 68, 78
cement 16, 58, 59, 62
cemeteries 110
central point of expertise on timber (CPET) 15, 16
chain of custody (COC) 15, 16, 18
chemicals 4, 58, 65–66, 88
    see also contaminated land; contaminated soil;
    dangerous substances; herbicides
CL:AIRE (Contaminated Land: Applications in Real
Environments) 21, 33–34, 102, 105
Clean Air Act 7, 72, 73
climate change 2, 3, 4, 20, 50
    see also greenhouse gases
clothes care and changing facilities 104
Code for sustainable homes 10–11, 15, 16, 50, 53, 55, 68, 78
community liaison 5, 51, 52, 77, 78, 120
competence in herbicide use 88
competence in waste management 30–31, 32
concrete 4, 58, 59, 62
consents see discharge consents; flood defence consents;
noise consents; permits
conservation areas 109
Considerate Constructors' Scheme (CCS) 5, 78
consignment notes 26, 27, 28–29, 40, 104
contaminated land 4, 7, 29, 97–105, 111, 127
    see also CL:AIRE
contaminated soil 21, 22, 23, 30, 33, 85, 88, 98, 101, 102–103
    see also invasive species

contaminated water see discharge consents; water pollution
contractors 5
controlled waste 26–27, 39, 88
Countryside Council for Wales 8, 81
crash sites 110
crayfish 87, 94
CRC energy efficiency scheme 50, 53–54
crushing 14, 24, 30, 31, 46, 73, 98
    see also aggregates; mobile plant

dangerous substances 21, 22
    see also chemicals
deforestation 4
    see also timber
demolition waste 8, 14, 16, 17, 21, 26, 38, 46, 98
    see also aggregates; asbestos; mobile plant
deposit gauges 74
design 3, 14
design for manufacture and assembly (DfMA) 14
designated vessels and controlled sites 110
designated wrecks 109–110
designers 5, 16, 17
dewatering of excavations 61–62, 63, 67, 103, 111
    see also silt
difficult waste 23
discharge consents 8, 29, 58, 60, 61, 62, 63–64, 103, 118
documentation 7, 36, 37, 53, 95, 103, 117, 118
    see also consignment notes; permits; transfer notes;
    waste transfer documentation
drainage 8, 60, 61, 62–63, 64, 118
    see also discharge consents; sewage
drip trays 66, 67
dust 3, 4, 51, 52, 61, 66, 68, 72–74, 99, 103, 117
duty of care 25–26, 35, 36, 62, 67, 88, 98, 99, 103, 117
duty of care regulation 20, 98

eco-reinforcement 16
ecology 8, 79–96, 100, 126
    see also biodiversity; water pollution
effluent 4, 21, 58, 61, 62, 63
EMAS 68, 114
embodied energy 16, 17, 51, 52–53
embodied water 67
emergency procedures 66–67, 116, 117, 118
emissions 10–11, 72–74
    see also air pollution; carbon emissions; exhaust emissions;
    fumes; greenhouse gases
'end-of-waste' status (definition) 17, 21, 30, 34, 102
endangered species 81–82
    see also protected species and habitats
energy conservation 17
energy efficiency 12, 50, 53–54, 55
    see also renewable energy
energy environmental targets 8, 119
energy management 3, 4, 9, 49–55, 115, 123
energy measurement 52–53
English Heritage 8, 109, 110
environment 2, 3–9
environment agencies 7–8
    see also regulation
environmental aspects register 116
environmental impact 2, 3, 15, 114, 115
    see also greenhouse gases
environmental indicators 2
environmental management plans 87, 110, 117
environmental management systems 9, 15, 113–129
environmental performance improvement 114, 118
    see also resource efficiency
environmental permits see permits
Environmental Permitting (England and Wales) Regulations 25,
29, 31, 36, 60, 63, 73, 95
Environmental Protection Act 21, 27, 32, 58, 72, 81, 88, 99
environmental targets 8–9, 115, 117, 119–120

European Waste Catalogue codes 21–22, 27, 28, 38
excavated materials 25, 33
excavations 61–62, 63, 67, 85, 86, 103, 105, 111
exemptions 29, 30, 31, 32, 33, 44–47
exemptions for burning of plant waste 73, 95
exemptions for discharges 59, 61, 63, 64
exemptions for waste treatment 25, 98, 102, 118
exhaust emissions 4, 51, 74
explosives 105

flood defence consents 64
Flood and Water Management Act 8, 64
flooding 4, 34, 63
forest law enforcement, governance and trade (FLEGT) 15
Forest Stewardship Council (FSC) 15
forests *see* deforestation; timber
fuels 4, 58, 65
fumes 8, 72, 74
        see also emissions; toxic gases; vapours

gases 4, 23, 72
        see also emissions; greenhouse gases; vapours
global environmental issues 3, 4–5
        see also climate change; greenhouse gases
great crested newts 82, 83–84, 93
Green Building Council 3, 12, 15
Green Construction Board 6
Green Deal 54
greenhouse gases 2, 4, 16, 20, 50
        see also carbon emissions; climate change
groundwater 29, 58, 60, 100
gypsum and plasterboard wastes 23

habitats *see* biodiversity; ecology
hazardous waste 21–22, 26, 27–29, 30, 31, 32, 38, 74, 103,
105, 118
        see also consignment notes; controlled waste; difficult waste
Hazardous Waste (England and Wales) Regulations 22, 27,
67, 88
hazardous waste separation 25, 27, 67
Health and Safety Executive 8
hedgerows 80, 85–86
herbicides 88, 95
Highways Act 73
historic buildings *see* archaeology and heritage
Historic Scotland 8, 109, 110
human remains 110, 111

IEMA Acorn scheme 114
inert waste 22, 34
Ingsbeck flood alleviation scheme 34
inspection 65, 73, 117–118
Internal Drainage Boards 8
invasive species 23, 73, 87–88, 95
ISO 14001 15, 68, 114, 115, 116

Japanese knotweed 73, 87, 88, 95

landfill 2, 20, 22–23, 25, 29, 30, 44, 46, 73, 88, 101
Landfill (Scotland) Regulations 25
landfill targets 3, 8, 20
lay down areas 52, 65
LEED 12, 15
licences *see* abstraction licences; permits; waste
carrier registration
life cycle assessment 15, 16
        see also embodied energy
light pollution 4, 72, 78, 80
listed buildings 109
Lists of Wastes Regulations 21
lizards *see* reptiles
local authorities 5, 7–8, 20, 30, 31, 46, 109
local authorities and air quality/pollution 7, 8, 20, 29, 72

local authorities and contaminated land 7, 98–99
local authorities and statutory nuisance 8, 72, 73, 74–75, 78
local authorities and wildlife 82, 83, 85, 86
local environmental issues 3–4
local nature reserves (LNRs) 63, 83
Low Carbon Construction Action Plan 6, 50

marine nature reserves (MNRs) 83
materials management plans 33, 102
materials use efficiency 117, 118
mobile plant 29, 30, 31, 65, 73, 98, 102, 118
mobile treatment permits 30, 98, 102, 118
monitoring 58, 59, 61, 68, 73–74, 76, 77, 104, 111, 115, 117–118
monuments 109
mud 51, 52, 66
        see also silt

national community wood recycling project 25
National Nature Reserves (NNRs) 63, 82
Natural England 8, 81, 82, 83
nature conservation bodies 81
nature conservation sites 63, 82–83
noise 3, 4, 51, 72, 74–77, 80, 117
noise consents 75
non-hazardous waste 21, 22, 25, 26, 27, 28, 103, 118
novacem 16
nuisance *see* statutory nuisance

odours *see* fumes
offences/penalties 7, 20, 29, 32, 116
offences/penalties re CRC energy efficiency scheme 54
offences/penalties re scheduled monuments/listed
buildings 109
offences/penalties re statutory nuisance 72–75, 78
offences/penalties re water pollution 58, 60
offences/penalties re wildlife 80, 82, 83, 84, 87, 95
oils and fuels 4, 58, 65
otters 82, 93
ozone 5

parking 52
parks and gardens 109
PAS 2050 16
permits 8, 20, 29–32, 102, 118
        see also exemptions; waste transfer documentation
permits for discharges 8, 29, 58, 60, 61, 62, 63–64, 103, 118
permits for flow control works 64
permits for herbicide use 88
permits for mobile treatment 30, 98, 102, 118
permits for noise or vibration 75, 76
permits for protected sites/buildings 109, 110
permits for recovering aggregates 17
permits for trees and hedgerows 85
permits for waste management 20, 24, 25, 26, 32, 33, 36,
39, 102
permits for waste treatment 25, 30, 73, 98, 102, 118
permits for water abstraction 61, 67
permits for wildlife disturbance 80, 82, 83, 84, 93
permits for work on designated wrecks 110
personal protective equipment 104, 105
planning authorities 5, 8
plasterboard wastes 23
'polluter pays' principle 6
pollution 3, 4, 9, 64–67, 115
        see also air pollution; contaminated land; contaminated
        soil; environmental targets; exemptions; permits; statutory
        nuisance; water pollution
Pollution Prevention Control Act 73
prefabrication 14
principal contractors 36–37
procurement 3, 14, 115, 121
        see also sustainable sourcing
Programme for the Endorsement of Forest Certification (PEFC) 15

protected species and habitats 80, 82–86
see also endangered species

radiation 4, 105
Ramsar sites 82, 83
records see documentation
recycled materials 14, 16–17, 24, 25, 41–43, 51, 62, 68, 101, 115
see also aggregates; 'end-of-waste' status
regulation 3, 5–8, 20, 26, 35, 72, 73, 81, 98–100
see also permits
reinforcement 16
remediation 60, 99, 101–103
renewable energy 4, 8, 50, 54–55
reptiles 82, 94
resource depletion 4
resource efficiency 2, 12, 13–18, 117, 121
see also energy management; recycled materials;
waste management; water efficiency
respiratory protective equipment 104
RICS Ska rating 12
risk assessments 100–101, 104, 116, 117
run-off 4, 10, 60, 62–63, 80, 103
see also silt

scheduled monuments 109
Scottish Canals 8
Scottish Natural Heritage 8, 81, 82
segregation of wastes 23, 25, 27, 35, 103
septic tanks 62, 63, 64
sewage 8, 58, 62, 63, 65
see also drainage
sewage undertakers see water companies
silica dust 73–74
silt 4, 58, 62, 65, 103
see also mud
site waste management plans (SWMPs) 3, 14, 33, 36–37, 102, 103, 117
Sites of Special Scientific Interest (SSSIs) 8, 63, 82, 83
Ska rating 12
skips 20, 25, 62, 103, 104
slurry 4, 58
smoke 4, 7, 72, 73
snakes see reptiles
source protection zones (SPZs) 60
special areas of conservation (SAC) 82, 83
special protection areas (SPAs) 82, 83
Special Waste Regulations 22, 27
spill kits 60, 66, 67
spillages 4, 58, 65–67
stakeholders 5, 116
see also community liaison
statutory nuisance 8, 71–78, 125
see also dust; fumes; noise; pollution; vibration
steel reinforcement 16
sustainability assessment tools 9–12, 53
see also BREEAM; CEEQUAL; Code for sustainable homes;
LEED; Ska rating
sustainable construction 2–3, 9–12, 108
Sustainable Forestry Initiative (SFI) 15
sustainable sourcing 15–16, 18, 114, 119, 121
see also procurement
sustainable urban drainage systems (SUDs) 62–63

technical competence 30–31, 32
timber 9, 15–16, 18, 25, 114, 119
see also deforestation
toilets 104
toxic gases 23
see also fumes
trade effluent 58, 61, 62, 63
traffic 3, 51–52
see also transport; vehicles
transfer notes 26–27, 39

transport 9, 17, 50, 51–52, 65, 123
see also vehicles; waste carriers
treasure 110, 111
trees and hedgerows 80, 85–86, 109

vapours 4, 72, 74
see also emissions; fumes; gases
vehicles 35, 36, 52, 58, 62, 68, 73, 103
see also exhaust emissions; traffic; transport
vibration 77, 80, 111

washing facilities 104
washing of vehicles 52, 58, 62, 68, 73, 103
waste (definition) 21
waste acceptance procedures 22, 23, 101
waste batteries 35–36
waste carrier registration 20, 25–26
waste carriers 8, 26, 27, 35, 36, 88
see also transfer notes
waste description and classification 21–23, 103
waste electrical and electronic equipment 35–36
waste environmental targets 3, 8, 119
waste management 19–47, 88, 95, 98, 99, 102–103, 104–105, 122
see also recycled materials; resource efficiency; sewage
waste management hierarchy 14, 23–25, 26, 27, 28, 30
waste management permits 20, 24, 25, 26, 32, 33, 36, 39, 102
waste management plans see site waste management plans (SWMPs)
waste regulation authorities 8, 20, 26, 35
waste segregation 23, 25, 27, 35, 103
waste transfer documentation 22, 23, 25, 26–29, 36, 62, 118
see also consignment notes; transfer notes; waste
management permits
waste transfer stations 25, 30, 73
waste treatment 24, 25, 31, 35, 62, 101, 103
see also crushing
waste treatment permits 17, 25, 30, 73, 98, 102, 118
water abstraction 61, 67, 68
see also dewatering of excavations
water companies 8
water consents 8
see also abstraction licences; discharge consents;
flood defence consents
water consumption 8, 9, 58, 67–68, 115
water disposal 61–64, 99
see also discharge consents
water efficiency 3, 12, 67–68, 117, 118
water environmental targets 8, 119
Water Industry Act 8
water management 57–70, 124
water pollution 3, 4, 17, 58, 60, 64–67, 124
see also discharge consents; water disposal
water pollution and contaminated land 99, 100, 103
water pollution and wildlife 80, 88
water pollution as statutory nuisance 72
water quality 8, 60, 80, 117
water scarcity 59–60
water toolbox talk 69–70
water treatment 61–62
water voles 81, 93
weather see climate change
welfare facilities 104
wheel washing 52, 58, 62, 68, 73
whole-life costing 16, 17
wildlife see biodiversity; ecology
wildlife year planner 90–94
works consents 64
WRAP (Waste Resources Action Programme) 3, 14, 17, 21, 24, 34
wrecks 109–110
see also designated vessels and controlled sites

Contents

Introduction   iii

How to use GE 700   ix

01 Street works and road works   1

02 Trackside safety   27

03 Demolition   43

04 Shopfitting and interior contracting   61

05 Working over or near to water   71

06 Mobile workforce   83

07 House building   91

Index   **103**

F

Contents

i

Introduction

Construction site safety covers all aspects of current health, safety and environment issues in the building and construction industry. It is designed to help managers, supervisors and small businesses understand how they should comply with, and put into practice, their legal, moral and social responsibilities.

Construction site safety (GE 700)   iv
About the construction industry   iv
Further supporting information from
CITB-ConstructionSkills   vi
Acknowledgements   vii

Construction site safety (GE 700)

Construction site safety is a leading publication within the construction industry, based on current construction health, safety and environment legislation, guidance and best practice. It will assist in the crucial areas of:

☑ accident prevention

☑ the avoidance of occupational ill health

☑ environmental good practice.

The content has been written with the site manager in mind, with a balance between outlining the requirements of relevant legislation and providing practical guidance on how to comply.

It is divided into the standard structure, which is used across all core CITB-ConstructionSkills publications:

Section A	**Legal and management**
Section B	**Health and welfare**
Section C	General safety
Section D	**High risk activities**
Section E	**Environment**
Section F	**Specialist activities**

Each section within *Construction site safety* is contained within a separate book.

There is also a new additional supporting book:

Section G	**Checklists and forms**

Section G is a collection of information (such as forms and checklists) that can be used on a day-to-day basis when running a site.

The content of *Construction site safety*, which is developed with construction industry experts, is revised annually to take into account the latest changes in legislation and new or updated health, safety and environment industry guidance and best practice.

There is a companion website that will keep users informed of legislation changes, content updates and links to further guidance.

Construction site safety is also available to purchase online or on CD-ROM.

Construction site safety is the official supporting publication for the CITB-ConstructionSkills Site Management Safety Training Scheme (SMSTS), a five-day course for construction site managers.

About the construction industry

Approximately 2.1 million people are employed in the UK construction industry. It includes housing, utilities, repair and maintenance, refurbishment, shop fitting, demolition, roofing, mechanical and electrical, plumbing and highways maintenance.

It is made up of 175,000 construction firms and 90% of companies employ less than 10 workers.

Construction workers (just like you) will die due to work-related ill health. Work-related respiratory disease covers a range of illnesses that are caused or made worse by breathing in hazardous substances (such as construction dust) that damage the lungs.

4,000 people die each year from asbestos-related lung diseases.

500 people (and more each year) are dying from silica-related lung diseases (dust from cutting blocks, kerbs, and so on). Many more suffer from occupational asthma or are forced to leave the industry due to work-related ill health.

Each year there are an estimated 36,000 new cases of work-related ill health with rates of musculoskeletal disorder significantly higher than average.

On average 50 workers are killed each year due to accidents. The biggest killer (around half) is due to falls from height.

Each year approximately 2,500 are seriously injured (broken bones, fractured skull, amputations) and 5,700 have reportable injuries.

The most common cause of injuries is due to manual handling and slips, trips and falls. 60% of all work at height injuries are due to falls from below head height.

Why so many accidents?

Many reports of present day construction accidents and ill health make depressing reading because simple actions were not taken to prevent them. In many cases, those planning the jobs totally failed to consider the health or safety of the people carrying out the work (and possibly others who were affected) and to actively manage the situation.

Common examples of such events include:

☑ the increasing number of workers who suffer from cancers and life changing illnesses from breathing and skin complaints. Some of these force the sufferer to give up work, because exposure to dangerous substances such as dust, are not even considered, let alone prevented or controlled

☑ the deaths and serious injuries that occur because people fall from height. Often basic actions (like using temporary work platforms on fragile roofs, installing edge protection or using a safety harness and lanyard clipped to a strong-point) were simply not taken

☑ workers being buried in collapsed excavations because the sides were unstable or not supported

☑ workers being killed or injured by construction plant because pedestrians were not kept out of the plant operating area.

Achieving a reasonable standard of on-site health and safety need not be difficult. Where the work to be carried out is relatively uncomplicated and familiar, the precautions that need to be taken are in many cases simple and common sense or may require just a little investigation or reading. The crucial decision for anyone with responsibility for on-site health and safety is to know when they have reached the limits of their knowledge and capabilities and therefore need the assistance of someone with specialist knowledge.

Caution should also be exercised when a job is not going to plan and there is the temptation to resort to improvised methods of working. If the person in control is not at ease with the way that things are going they should stop the job, step back and think things through carefully before deciding upon a course of action.

Health and Safety Executive (HSE) research has shown that workers are most vulnerable during their first few days on site.

Setting out

Construction is an exciting industry. It is constantly changing as projects move on and jobs get done. As a result of this a building site is one of the most dangerous environments to work in.

But many accidents that occur on sites can be avoided if everyone on site works together. So a free film *Setting out* explains what the site must do and what you must do to stay healthy and safe at work.

 For further information or to view *Setting out* refer to the CITB-ConstructionSkills website.

This film is essential viewing for everyone involved in construction, and should be watched before sitting the CITB-ConstructionSkills' Health, safety and environment test. The content of the film is captured in summary here, and these principles form the basis for the behavioural case study questions, which are a new element of the test from Spring 2012.

Part 1: What you should expect from the construction industry

Your site and your employer should be doing all they can to keep you and their workforce safe.

Before any work begins the site management team will have been planning and preparing the site for your arrival. It is their job to ensure that you can do your job safely and efficiently.

Five things **the site** you are working on **must do**:

☑ know when you are on site (signing in and out)

☑ give you a site induction

☑ give you site-specific information

☑ encourage communication

☑ keep you up-to-date and informed.

Part 2: What the industry expects of you

Once the work begins, it is up to every individual to take responsibility for carrying out the plan safely. This means you should follow the rules and guidelines as well as being alert to the continuing changes on site.

Five things you **must do**:

☑ respect and follow the site rules

☑ safely prepare each task

☑ do each task responsibly

☑ know when to stop (if you think anything is unsafe)

☑ keep learning.

Every day the work we do improves the world around us. It is time for us to work together to build an industry that puts its people first. By working together we can build a better industry that respects those who work in it.

Introduction (vertical text in left margin)

Working Well Together

The Working Well Together (WWT) campaign is an industry-led initiative that helps support micro and small businesses improve their health and safety performance. The campaign undertakes a variety of activities, including health and safety awareness days, designer awareness days, breakfast and evening events, roadshows and regional WWT groups.

 To find out how the WWT campaign can help you and your company refer to its website.

Further supporting information from CITB-ConstructionSkills

CITB-ConstructionSkills has a wide range of products, publications and courses that could help to improve your health, safety and environment knowledge.

 To discover more about CITB-ConstructionSkills and the services, publications and courses offered visit the CITB-ConstructionSkills website.

Health, safety and environment publications

Site managers	GE 700 *Construction site safety* (printed, CD and online)
	RACD *Risk assessment and method statement manager*
	SA 03 CD *Health, safety and environmental auditing system*
	DVDs Range of topics including scaffold inspection, worker engagement and sustainability
Supervisors	GE 706 *Site supervision simplified* (printed, CD, online)
	GT 700 *Toolbox talks* (printed, CD, online)
	GT 701 *Safety critical communication toolbox talks* (printed)
Operatives	GE 707 *Safe start*
Health safety and environment test	GT 100 *Health, safety and environment test for operatives and specialists* (printed, DVD, online)
	GT 200 *Health, safety and environment test for managers and professionals* (printed, DVD, online)

Site Safety Plus courses

Directors	Directors role for health and safety course – one day
Site management	Site Management Safety Training Scheme (SMSTS) – five days
Plant managers	Plant Management Safety Training Scheme (SMSTS) – five days
Supervisors	Site Supervisors' Safety Training Scheme (SSSTS) – two days
Operatives	Health safety and environment awareness – one day
Environment	Site Environmental Awareness Training Scheme (SEATS) – one day
Behavioural safety	Achieving Behavioural Change (ABC) – one day
Shopfitting	Site safety for shopfitters and interior contractors – three days

National Construction College

The National Construction College is focused on creating a highly skilled, safe and professional UK construction workforce. To achieve this, it has more first-class instructors in more locations than any other construction training provider in Europe and offers free professional advice on finding the right training for individuals and companies.

Acknowledgements

CITB-ConstructionSkills wishes to acknowledge the assistance offered by the following organisations in the preparation of this edition of GE 700:

- [x] Access Industry Forum
- [x] Arco
- [x] Balfour Beatty
- [x] Britannia Safety and Training
- [x] Civil Engineering Contractors Association
- [x] Combisafe
- [x] Construction Plant Association
- [x] Drilling and Sawing Association
- [x] eBrit Services Ltd
- [x] Environment Agency
- [x] Environmental and Waste Consulting
- [x] Federation of Master Builders
- [x] Health and Safety Executive
- [x] Henry Boot
- [x] Highways Term Maintenance Association
- [x] Home Builders Federation
- [x] J Breheny Contractors Ltd

- [x] Lead Paint Safety Association
- [x] MJ Fuller and Associates
- [x] Makers Construction Ltd
- [x] May Gurney
- [x] Montpellier International Consulting
- [x] National Access and Scaffolding Confederation
- [x] National Association of Shopfitters
- [x] National Construction College
- [x] National Federation of Demolition Contractors
- [x] Persimmon Homes
- [x] Prospect – The Union for Professionals
- [x] Scafftag
- [x] Temporary Works Forum
- [x] Union of Construction, Allied Trades and Technicians (UCATT)
- [x] Unite
- [x] Wates
- [x] Willmott Dixon

And a special thank you to:

- [x] Carillion
- [x] Costain
- [x] Morgan Sindall
- [x] Skanska

How to use GE 700

The following information sets out how to use *Construction site safety*. Each section is contained within a separate book, which has been designed to provide simple navigation for the end user. It also explains the companion website, which is a significant addition for keeping users informed of legislation changes, content updates and links to further guidance.

Construction site safety structure	x
How to navigate	x
Use of icons	x
Companion website	xi

Construction site safety structure

Construction site safety is divided into the standard structure that is used across all core CITB-ConstructionSkills publications:

Section A	**Legal and management**
Section B	**Health and welfare**
Section C	General safety
Section D	**High risk activities**
Section E	**Environment**
Section F	**Specialist activities**

Within *Construction site safety* each section is contained within a separate book.

There is also a new additional supporting book:

Section G	**Checklists and forms**

This new section is a collection of information that can be used on a day-to-day basis when running a site. The forms, checklists and guidance within Section G follow the same structure as in Sections A to F.

How to navigate

Each section contains a main contents page at the start of the section, followed by the introduction, a detailed chapter contents list at the start of each chapter and an index at the back (but there is no index within Section G).

Chapters have been numbered according to the section you are in. Therefore, chapter one of Section A is numbered 01, chapter two of Section B is numbered 02 and so on. However, references to chapters within other sections will be referred to as A01, B02, and so on.

At the start of each chapter there is a short overview of what the chapter is about.

This is followed by the chapter contents list.

Use of icons

A set of icons emphasises key points within the text and also directs readers to further information. The icons are explained below:

www.	Website/further info	**!**	Important	**"**	Quote
e.g.	Example	👍	Best practice	**Aa**	Definition
?	Question	👎	Poor practice	☑	Checklist
💡	Ideas	✋	Caution	▶	Video
📝	Notes	🗣	Consultation		
★	Favourite	🔍	Guidance/case study		

Companion website

A companion website has been created to support *Construction site safety* and it contains up-to-date information on:

☑ the current edition of each section (book)

☑ news (such as legislation changes, industry guidance and best practice)

☑ any minor amendments or updates to the current editions

☑ web links/phone numbers/addresses

☑ details of CITB-ConstructionSkills' publications and courses.

 This icon indicates that further information (such as useful websites and links) can be found on the companion website at www.citb-constructionskills.co.uk/GE700companion

Rather than printing individual weblinks in each section, which can become out of date, the relevant website will be stated alongside the icon (for example, for more information refer to the CITB-ConstructionSkills website). The actual weblink can then be found on the companion website, referenced to the relevant section and chapter.

The companion website will be regularly updated, to ensure that relevant information (such as weblinks) are current.

 Save the companion website address to your favourites, so it is always available when you need it.

01

Street works and road works

The New Roads and Street Works Act (NRSWA) provides a legislative framework for street works activities (including by public utility companies). In recent years the Health and Safety Executive (HSE) has expressed concern at the number of workers and members of the public killed or seriously injured through accidents related to road works.

The Highways Term Maintenance Association (HTMA) has stated that 'it is not only oncoming vehicles that pose a threat to road workers but the behaviour of drivers in passing vehicles is a growing concern. Road workers have experienced the throwing of missiles (often food and bottles), verbal abuse as well as personal injury caused by road users' vehicles'.

Introduction	2
Key requirements	2
Carrying out road works	2
Safety of gas apparatus	4
Safety of water apparatus	5
Safety of telecommunications apparatus	5
Safety of electrical apparatus	6
Site layout definitions	6
Signage and other site equipment	7
Traffic control	9
Personal protective equipment	12
Training	12
Appendix A – Relevant legislation and guidance	13
Appendix B – Signs and equipment	15
Appendix C – Basic layout of a road works site	17
Appendix D – Basic layout with works vehicle	18
Appendix E – Traffic control by give and take	19
Appendix F – Traffic control by priority signs	20
Appendix G – Traffic control by stop/go boards	21
Appendix H – Traffic control by portable traffic signals	22
Appendix I – Works on footways	23
Appendix J – Temporary footways in the carriageway	24
Appendix K – Sizing and siting distances of signage and cones	25

1.1 Introduction

Road works will almost always bring the workers carrying out construction activities into close proximity with vehicles (both construction plant and passing traffic). The safety of the workers and vehicle drivers/operators will depend upon the works being properly planned, carried out by trained and qualified workers and the behaviour of the passing traffic.

Britain's roads are extremely busy. In terms of overall road safety, current national figures show a decline in road accident casualties over the past 40 years. However, injuries to the 40,000 workers on Britain's roads have risen.

In today's traffic conditions, the live carriageway of any highway is a very dangerous place to work.

Drivers ignoring temporary speed limits is commonplace, leaving road workers even more vulnerable, with very little to protect them from approaching vehicles.

In an attempt to improve the situation, the Highways Agency (HA) introduced a road worker action plan, with the theme of zero harm. The HA's aim is to reduce the risks to the health and safety of road workers by working in partnership with service providers and other stakeholders to improve training and performance, and by changing the way that operations are carried out on the road network, for example by:

- ☑ removing road workers from the live carriageway whenever possible
- ☑ reducing the exposure to risk whenever anyone is working on the road network
- ☑ highlighting the importance of road workers and their safety to road users to influence driver behaviour
- ☑ improving communication methods on road worker safety issues throughout Government and supply chain forums to give a consistent approach to improved performance
- ☑ continually reviewing working practices to reduce the risk to road workers, including the introduction of local targets, investigating layout changes and trialling new technologies
- ☑ reducing speed and improving compliance through road works, including the use of average speed detection.

For its part, the Highways Term Maintenance Association (HTMA), through its members and safety working group, has actively supported the HA in delivering the aims of the road worker action plan.

 A study by Oxford University ranked working on the highway as the sixteenth most hazardous occupation in the United Kingdom.

1.2 Key requirements

- ☑ All work must be carried out in accordance with the Safety at Street Works and Road Works code of practice.
- ☑ Site-specific risk assessments must be carried out.
- ☑ Works include any placement, connection or maintenance of temporary or permanent services, pipes, cables, sewers or drains that are laid or located within the carriageway or footway. This also includes forming new or temporary entrances and roads where they join an existing highway or footpath.
- ☑ Road users, whether in a vehicle or on foot, approaching the works on the road or footway, from any direction, must be able to understand exactly what is happening and what is expected of them.
- ☑ The code of practice (CoP) that supports the above legislation, often referred to as the *Red book*, must be complied with. The CoP specifies minimum safety requirements for:
  - signage and lighting
  - working on different classes of roads
  - methods of traffic control
  - controlling the speed of passing traffic
  - works near to tramways and level crossings.
- ☑ Operatives who carry out work on the highway must be competent to do so, particularly anyone involved in laying out the site, positioning signage or lighting, implementing traffic control measures and undertaking similar jobs.

1.3 Carrying out road works

Code of practice – Safety at Street Works and Road Works

This CoP is a pocket-size reference book intended to be used at the place of work. Its content is aimed at all workers on site but it does not attempt to cover every situation. Whilst it contains authoritative guidance, it does not have the same legal status as a Health and Safety Executive (HSE) approved code of practice (ACoP). However, compliance with the CoP will generally satisfy the requirements of relevant legislation, although Local Authorities have wide powers of discretion with regard to work carried out by them, or on their behalf.

Anyone contemplating work on the highway, particularly anyone new to this type of work, must obtain and refer to it as necessary. It is very easy to use, and given the price it would be difficult to argue that anyone who is managing a project that involves work in the highway should not have a copy. It would normally form part of the safety management system for whoever is doing the traffic management, and checking the site set-up against the layout drawing is a quick and simple way to audit site procedures.

Whilst a supervisor qualified under the New Roads and Street Works Act will know what to do in most situations, it is the employer's responsibility to ensure that:

- ☑ safe procedures are in place and followed

- ☑ proper arrangements for supervision are in place.

 For more detailed advice on subjects not covered in the code of practice (CoP) refer to Chapter 8 of the *Traffic signs manual* and also refer to Appendix A.

 The code of practice can be freely downloaded from the Department for Transport's website, or it can be purchased from TSO. The *Traffic signs manual* can also be freely downloaded.

Before starting work

As for other construction projects, all road works will fall within the requirements of the Construction (Design and Management) Regulations to a greater or lesser degree. Where a project will last over 30 days, it will be notifiable to the HSE, a CDM co-ordinator must be appointed, a health and safety plan must be developed and the principal contractor must actively manage health and safety on site.

Before starting any work on the carriageway or footway, there are specific notice periods for informing the Highway/Streets Authority (or, in Scotland, the Roads Authority) that you intend to start work.

Depending upon where the work is being carried out, the Streets Authority may well be the Local Authority, the County Council, the Department for Transport, or even the County Council on behalf of the Department for Transport, local Government and regions. The principal or main contractor must check to establish to whom they are responsible, and to whom they should give notice.

Co-ordination of road works

When notice is given to the HA that the work is planned, they will inform the other utility undertakers in an attempt to co-ordinate works during a single excavation in order to avoid the same piece of roadway being continually excavated.

Major works

The term *major works* covers works carried out by the Highway Authority, such as:

- ☑ the reconstruction or widening of the highway

- ☑ works on dual carriageways and at roundabouts

- ☑ other similar major works

- ☑ the construction of vehicle crossings over footways and verges.

Diversionary works

The term *diversionary works* covers works to:

- ☑ protect apparatus* on site

- ☑ relocate apparatus elsewhere.

The CoP contains comprehensive information on the responsibilities of the various utility undertakers and highway authorities relating to major road works that may affect the:

- ☑ safety of apparatus

- ☑ need to divert apparatus.

The information includes guiding principles and outlines considerations that should be taken into account and the procedures to be followed.

 * Apparatus is any pipe or ducting buried within the highway or pavement that is owned by one of the utilities. (Examples of apparatus are gas pipes, water mains, sewers, electricity cables, telephone cables and fibre-optic communications cables.)

Unexpected damage to, or disconnection of, any apparatus could have serious implications for many people who are totally unconnected with the work.

Construction activities, which may put apparatus at risk, include:

☑ the removal of the footway or carriageway construction

☑ construction plant crossing or working in the vicinity of apparatus

☑ the undermining or removal of side support to apparatus

☑ any deep construction adjacent to apparatus

☑ piling or ground consolidation operations.

These risks can be minimised by:

☑ providing suitable and safe vehicle crossing and access points (see below)

☑ temporarily moving apparatus to a safe location during the construction work

☑ protecting or temporarily supporting apparatus in situ.

 Methods of supporting apparatus during excavation form part of the assessment process incorporated within the relevant operative and supervisor qualifications.

The correct construction of vehicle crossings is important as otherwise the works could put apparatus at risk in a number of ways, because:

☑ the majority of service apparatus is located in footways

☑ footway construction layers must normally be excavated to accommodate thicker construction layers

☑ the new construction may no longer provide adequate cover to apparatus

☑ the vehicular loading may be greater than the apparatus can withstand

☑ vibrations from vehicles may weaken joints over a period of time.

Excavations

In many cases digging trenches will form a part of road works. It is essential that such excavations are:

☑ only commenced when it has been established that it is safe to do so

☑ adequately guarded where necessary to prevent the public or construction workers being put at risk of falls

☑ supported where the risk assessment shows that it would be unsafe not to do so

☑ fitted with lights at night where otherwise construction workers or the public would be put at risk of falling

☑ equipped with de-watering equipment where necessary

☑ equipped with forced ventilation where otherwise a build-up of hazardous vapour would occur.

There may be occasions where trenchless technology (such as pipe-jacking or thrust-boring) lends itself to the job in hand, although the use of such methods must first be cleared with the client and designers of the scheme.

 For further details on safe working in or near to excavations refer to Chapter D07 Excavations.

1.4 Safety of gas apparatus

Depth of cover

The normal minimum depth of cover for gas mains operating in the low and medium pressure ranges is:

☑ 600 mm in footways or verges

☑ 750 mm in carriageways.

However, in practice these depths may vary, as each area gas board can have its own standards.

In certain circumstances, depending upon the mains material, operating pressure and depth of cover, it may be acceptable for the mains to remain in situ when only subjected to light traffic (for example, a vehicle layby or crossing). It is not generally permissible to allow cast iron mains previously in the footway or verge to be subjected to vehicular traffic.

Risks during construction

Liaison with the gas undertaker during the planning stage is essential because existing mains, specifically older materials (such as cast iron), cannot be raised, lowered or moved laterally even for a few millimetres without risk. Gas apparatus must not be undermined and certain apparatus is particularly vulnerable to deep excavations adjacent to the apparatus.

Any proposals to dig deep trenches may mean that gas apparatus will have to be diverted.

1.5   Safety of water apparatus

Decisions on the protection or diversion of water mains are likely to be influenced by considerations of access to mains for repair purposes.

Depth of cover

The minimum depth of cover for the three types of water mains (trunk mains, distributor mains and service pipes) will vary according to its type.

Further information can be found in the CoP, and by consulting with the water company in whose area you are working.

Risks during construction

Construction plant and lorries travelling over water apparatus with temporarily reduced cover can be an unacceptable risk. Therefore, diversions may be necessary unless protective measures are practicable.

Factors influencing the decision to divert water pipes must include:

- ☑ the maintenance of the continuity of supply and the water quality
- ☑ material types and condition
- ☑ the inability to raise, lower or slew pipes
- ☑ the possible loss of ground support to pipes with the consequential risk of damage.

1.6   Safety of telecommunications apparatus

The need for the rigorous exclusion of moisture from telecommunication cables and joints places constraints on the extent to which older cables can be moved during works.

For maintenance purposes there is the added need for vehicles to have access and be located at or near jointing chambers.

Preferred depth of cover

Varying depths of cover may be found with this type of equipment, depending on the types and design of the cables. As a rough guide, television and telecom cabling can be found at depths varying from 250 mm in the verge or footway, and up to 900 mm in the carriageway.

Risks during construction

According to circumstances, the apparatus may be left in situ if ducts are adequately protected from construction plant and vehicles by the use of metal plates or tracks.

In some cases, it may be possible to accommodate small, temporary or permanent alterations in the line of a duct track by bodily slewing, raising or lowering a nest of ducts with the cables in situ.

Overhead telecommunication lines

Poles must be positioned to:

- ☑ minimise the risk of damage to cables by vehicles
- ☑ give the minimum inconvenience to pedestrians
- ☑ avoid obstructing access to premises.

Road alterations may necessitate the replacement of poles if the clearance under the cables becomes inadequate.

Minimum heights above ground for overhead telecommunication lines are typically:

- ☑ 5.5 metres at any point over a street
- ☑ 6.1 metres on bus routes
- ☑ 6.5 metres on designated roads.

1.7 Safety of electrical apparatus

The following factors should be considered when protecting cables in situ or diverting apparatus.

Underground cables

- ☑ The need to protect and support potentially hazardous equipment from mechanical impact, damage, strain and vibration during and after road works.

- ☑ A requirement to maintain the security of supply if alternative circuits are not available.

- ☑ The operating voltage of the apparatus.

The depth at which electricity cables or ducts are usually laid in the ground is decided by the need to avoid undue interference or damage.

Dependent on the type of cable and the power that it may be carrying, the depth of cover may vary from 450 mm up to 900 mm. It is common to find electrical cables much shallower than these depths, particularly over bridges or culverts, and extreme caution must be exercised.

In all cases, where the depth of cover is likely to increase or decrease, the apparatus owner must be consulted.

Overhead lines

- ☑ The supports and stays of overhead lines may have to be relocated.

- ☑ Ground clearance may be affected.

- ☑ Earth wires from supports may have to be re-sited.

- ☑ Buried pilot wires may be associated with the route of overhead lines.

The minimum height of overhead lines above ground varies according to the voltage of the cable and as directed by the undertaker. They can be as low as 5.2 metres for lines carrying 33 kV, or up to 6.7 metres for lines carrying 132 kV.

 Further information can be obtained from Chapter D08
Underground and overhead services, and in HSE Guidance Note GS6.

Risks during construction

- ☑ Additional protection or temporary diversion may be necessary to prevent damage to any apparatus during the construction stage.

- ☑ The hazards of accidental electrical contact by persons on site must be fully assessed.

- ☑ Damage to underground cables can, in certain circumstances, cause widespread loss of electrical supplies for a long period.

1.8 Site layout definitions

Works area is the excavation, chamber, opening, reinstatement, and so on.

Working space is the space around the works area used to store tools, excavated material, equipment and plant.

It is also the space needed to move around the site without encroaching into live traffic or other hazards. Sufficient working space must be provided to ensure that the movement and operation of the plant (for example, swinging of jibs and excavator arms) is clear of passing traffic and is not encroaching into the safety zone.

Safety zone is the zone provided to protect site personnel from the traffic. No-one must enter the safety zone in the normal course of work. It is only necessary to enter the zone to maintain cones and other road signs. Materials and equipment must not be placed in the zone.

The safety zone comprises of the:

- ☑ **lead-in taper of cones (T)** – The length will vary with the speed limit and the width of the works

- ☑ **longways clearance (L)** – This is the distance between the lead-in taper of cones (T) and the working space. It will vary with the speed limit, as given in the table on the following page

- ☑ **sideways clearance (S)** – This is the width between the working space and moving traffic. It will vary with the speed limit, as given in the table on the following page.

Speed restriction (mph)	Minimum longways clearance (L) (metres)	Minimum sideways clearance (S) (metres)
30 or less	0.5	0.5
40	15	0.5
50	30	1.2
60	60	1.2
70	100	1.2

If an advisory speed limit is in operation the chart above must be used to determine minimum longways and sideways clearances. Wherever traffic speeds are to be reduced, the method must be agreed in advance with the highway authority. For safety reasons, it may be necessary to advise emergency services of the location and duration of the works.

Working spaces and safety zones must be provided when personnel are present. If pedestrians are diverted into the carriageway, a safety zone must be provided between the outer pedestrian barrier and the traffic. (*Refer to Appendix H, and Page 31 of the CoP.*)

Where the highway width is so restricted as to prohibit the provision of the appropriate sideways clearance and diversion of traffic would be impractical, traffic speeds must be reduced to less than 10 mph and a mandatory speed limit imposed. There must also be an agreed safe method of working imposed on the site.

This method of working, which must be decided in advance of the work, should preclude working in the safety zone wherever possible. It is also advisable that it should be recorded in writing.

1.9 Signage and other site equipment

Traffic signs and other apparatus for the control of traffic must comply with the Traffic Signs Regulations and General Directions (amended). Compliance is achieved by the use of equipment conforming to the relevant British Standards. Equipment must also meet any requirements set out in the code as to size or performance.

All street works, irrespective of site and whether taking place on the ground or overhead, require adequate warning and information to be given to pedestrians and drivers.

Crossing high-speed roads on foot

The HSE was so concerned about this aspect of temporary traffic management works that it published specific guidance on it.

The guidance puts the initial onus on the designers of road works to ensure that the risk arising from the installation, alteration and removal of temporary traffic management aspects of their designs are assessed and, where reasonably practicable, eliminated or reduced. Any remaining significant risks should be highlighted and subsequently controlled by the careful planning and management of the works.

Systems of work should not rely on workers crossing the carriageway unless there are:

☑ adequate sight lines

☑ traffic flows in which there are suitable gaps

☑ no more than four continuous lanes to cross (including slip roads)

☑ a central reservation that provides a safe place to work.

Traffic management workers require standards of physical fitness, eyesight and hearing. Their health should be assessed before they are assigned to traffic management work. Health assessment should ensure that workers:

☑ have full use of neck, trunk and legs

☑ have at least 6/12 distance vision when wearing glasses or contact lenses

☑ have good hearing

☑ are suitable for this work if they suffer from specific conditions (such as vertigo, balance disorders, gastrointestinal conditions and sleep disorders)

☑ are not taking inappropriate medication, illegal drugs or excessive amounts of alcohol.

 For further information refer to the HSE publication *Crossing high-speed roads on foot during temporary traffic-management works* (CIS53).

Advance signs

A **'Road works ahead'** sign must be placed in a conspicuous position well before the works.

Its size and minimum distance from the start of the lead-in taper is governed by road type and traffic speed.

 For further information refer to Appendix C and also *Basic site layout, Page 8 of the CoP.*

A **'Road narrows ahead'** sign, indicating which side of the carriageway is obstructed, should be placed between the **'Road works ahead'** sign and commencement of the taper of cones.

Cones and lamps

Traffic cones are placed to guide the traffic past the works.

The length of coned area and size of cones is governed by the speed limit and the type of road. (*Refer to Appendix B.*)

Road danger lamps are added at night, in poor daytime visibility and in bad weather.

 For further information refer to the CoP for *Safety at street works and road works.*

They must not be positioned higher than 1.2 metres above the road surface.

Road danger lamps are used as shown in the table below.

Type of lamp	Conditions of use
Flashing lamp (120 to 150 flashes per minute)	Only to be used when all of the following conditions apply: ■ speed limit is 40 mph or less ■ road danger lamp is within 50 metres of a street lamp ■ street lamp is illuminated.
Steady lamp	On any road with or without street lighting.

Keep left and keep right signs

Place **'Keep left'** or **'Keep right'** signs as appropriate at the beginning and end of the lead-in taper of cones.

Traffic barrier or lane closed sign

A traffic barrier is positioned within the coned-off area facing oncoming traffic to indicate the width of works site.

If a conspicuous vehicle is present, a barrier may not be necessary.

Pedestrian barriers

All sides of an excavation where a pedestrian may gain access must be fenced off.

Information board

All sites must display an information board giving:

☑ the name of the organisation responsible for the road works

☑ a telephone number for emergencies.

It may also include:

☑ the name of the contractor

☑ a description of the works being carried out

☑ a message apologising for any delay or inconvenience.

End sign

An **'End of road works'** sign must be placed beyond the works of a site more than 50 metres long.

An end of road works sign is not necessary where **all** the following conditions exist:

☑ the two-way traffic flow is less than 20 vehicles counted over three minutes (400 vehicles per hour)

☑ fewer than 20 heavy goods vehicles pass the works site per hour

☑ the speed limit is 30 mph or under.

Sign lighting and reflectorisation

Signs and any plates used with them must be directly lit when all of the following conditions apply:

☑ there is a permanent speed limit of 50 mph or above   ☑ the street lighting is on

☑ there is general street lighting   ☑ the sign is within 50 metres of a street light.

All signs, including cones and red and white barrier planks, must be reflectorised to BS 873-6:1983 Class 1 or Class 2. The only exception is the information board and pedestrian signs. (*For further information refer to the CoP.*)

Security and stability of signs

Only use signs that are approved and in accordance with the relevant British Standard, and ensure that they are placed correctly.

Properly secure all signs and guarding equipment so that they cannot be blown over by the wind or dislodged by passing traffic. Use sacks containing sand or other fine granular materials. Do not use kerbstones or similar weights for this purpose as they could be dangerous if hit by moving traffic.

Make sure that the signs are correctly positioned and of adequate size to give early warning of the hazard, in accordance with the table in the CoP.

Check the signs regularly for both position and cleanliness as they may have been moved, damaged or become dirty.

Visibility of signs

All signs must be reflectorised and adequately lit after dark in accordance with the CoP. Signs must be placed so as to give the required forward visibility to approaching vehicles.

Two-way roads

On a two-way road, the signs should be set out for traffic in both directions.

Surplus signs

Any signs or guarding equipment no longer required and left in position, either during or on completion of the work, will be illegal. Remove them immediately.

1.10   Traffic control

Select the method of traffic control from the table within the CoP for *Safety at street works and road works*. The CoP gives precise details of these methods.

You will also need to refer to the table in the inside back cover of the CoP for *Safety at street works and road works*.

Road widths

For two-way traffic, minimum road widths are:

☑ 6.75 metres on bus and HGV routes

☑ 5.5 metres on other roads for cars and light vehicles.

Any width less than 5.5 metres is too narrow for two-way traffic and so the width must be reduced to a maximum of 3.7 metres and a traffic control system introduced.

For one-way traffic, minimum road widths are, for:

☑ **buses and HGV routes:**
   - 3.25 metres desirable minimum width
   - 3 metres absolute minimum width

☑ **cars and light vehicles**
   - 2.75 metres desirable minimum width
   - 2.5 metres absolute minimum width.

Traffic control by give and take system

Only use the give and take system when **all** the following apply:

- ☑ the length of the works from the start of the lead-in taper to the end of the exit taper is 50 metres or less
- ☑ two-way traffic is less than 20 vehicles counted over three minutes (400 vehicles per hour)
- ☑ fewer than 20 heavy goods vehicles pass the site per hour
- ☑ the speed limit is 30 mph or under
- ☑ drivers approaching from either direction can see 50 metres beyond the end of the works.

 For further information refer to the Appendices and the CoP.

Traffic control by priority signs

Only use priority signs when **all** of the following apply:

- ☑ two-way traffic is less than 42 vehicles counted over three minutes (850 vehicles per hour)
- ☑ length of works, including tapers, is no more than 80 metres
- ☑ drivers approaching from either direction can see through the length of works from a specified distance 'D' before the works to a similar distance 'D' beyond the works. Distances vary according to speed restrictions, as follows:
  - 60 metres on 30 mph roads
  - 80 metres on 50 mph roads
  - 70 metres on 40 mph roads
  - 100 metres on 60 mph roads.

 For further information refer to Appendix F and the CoP.

Traffic control by stop/go boards

This system may be used following consideration of the relation of two-way traffic flow to the length of the site. Details of limitations for using stop/go boards can be found in the CoP.

Where the shuttle lane with this type of system is more than 20 metres, or it continues round a bend, stop/go boards will be needed at both ends of that lane.

 For further information refer to Appendix G and the CoP.

Traffic control by portable traffic signals

Portable traffic signals may be used when:

- ☑ the speed limit is a maximum of 60 mph
- ☑ the length of the site is 300 metres or less
- ☑ the site does not straddle a railway level crossing
- ☑ traffic control is at least 50 metres away from a level crossing equipped with twin red light signals
- ☑ the Highway Authority has been informed and, if to be used at a road junction, authorisation has been obtained
- ☑ stop/go boards are available in case the portable traffic signals cease to function correctly.

Traffic control in operation on a private road

 For further information refer to Appendix H and the CoP.

Works on footways

An alternative safe route for pedestrians must:

☑ be provided if a footway or part of a footway is closed, before it is closed

☑ never be less than one metre wide and ideally be 1.5 metres or more in width

☑ be equipped with kerb ramps or a raised footway, as may be necessary, to take account of the needs of children, the elderly, people with disabilities, particularly visual impairment, or those with prams or wheelchairs

☑ be a non-slip surface and free of trip hazards (laps on boarding may trip the elderly or infirm)

☑ provide access to adjacent premises and public areas.

 For further information refer to Appendix I and the CoP.

Barriers

Pedestrian barriers should be used to mark out temporary footways, with a rigid barrier to protect pedestrians from traffic, excavation, plant or materials. Handrails should be between one metre and 1.2 metres above ground level, with tapping rails 150 mm deep, set with the lower edge up to 200 mm above ground level.

Road danger lamps should be placed at the ends of the barriers at night. Barriers may comprise separate portable post and plank systems, gate frames linked together, or semi-permanent constructions built to enclose the site.

There are several different requirements for the barrier planks associated with post and plank systems. The following explains the requirements and how they may be met using barrier planks, which are red and white and manufactured in fully retro-reflective materials.

 Retro-reflective means that at night the material reflects light back to the light source.

Barrier planks are required to carry out three functions, shown in the table below.

1.	As a **traffic barrier**.	When a traffic lane is closed for works to take place, the regulations require this to be done with a retro-reflective red and white barrier plank placed across the lane. This is illustrated on the previous page as a traffic barrier ('Lane closed' sign).
2.	As a **pedestrian barrier**.	Pedestrians must be separated from the works by barriers, which are conspicuous and mounted as part of a portable fencing system. Pedestrian barrier planks may be of several different contrasting colours; yellow, white or orange colours are best detected by partially-sighted people, but red and white is one of the acceptable combinations.
3.	As a **tapping rail** for blind and partially-sighted people.	Tapping rails are placed as the bottom rail in a pedestrian fencing system. A red and white barrier plank may be used.

All barriers facing vehicular traffic should be of the fully retro-reflective red and white form. Red and white barrier planks do not have to be used for pedestrian barriers or tapping rails but, if they are, they must be retro-reflective. Other planks used for these purposes do not need to be retro-reflective.

There are other points to note about the use of barrier planks in portable fencing systems.

☑ The traffic barrier ('Lane closed' sign) is not needed if the works are protected by a conspicuous vehicle.

☑ Pedestrian barrier systems must be rigid enough to guard pedestrians from traffic, excavations, plant or materials. They must be placed with sufficient clearance to prevent pedestrians falling into the excavation and, when placed to create a temporary footway in the carriageway parallel to the traffic stream, must be protected by a row of traffic cones between the barrier and the traffic stream. Consult your supervisor if the excavation is deep, or positioned close to pedestrians, as stronger barriers may be needed and/or other safety measures may be required (such as covering or temporarily refilling the excavation).

☑ Where a work site may be approached by pedestrians crossing the road from the opposite side, you should place barriers, including tapping rails, all around the excavation, even when pedestrians are not diverted into the carriageway.

☑ Where long excavations are sited in situations where pedestrians are not expected to cross from the opposite side, barriers on the traffic stream side of the works area do not need the tapping rail. In these circumstances, on an unrestricted road, the barrier on the traffic stream side can be replaced with an additional row of cones. These cones should be linked with a suitably supported traffic tape to attract attention to the boundary of the safety zone.

Use pedestrian barriers to mark out any temporary footway. You must always use a rigid barrier to protect pedestrians from traffic, excavations, plant or materials. Place road danger lamps at the ends of the barriers at night so that they may be clearly seen by pedestrians.

 For further information refer to the CoP.

1.11 Personal protective equipment

High-visibility clothing

Given the nature of road works and the proximity of moving traffic, the importance of workers being clearly seen by colleagues and the travelling public cannot be overstated. Whether working on site or just visiting, everyone must wear a high-visibility jacket or waistcoat, manufactured to BS EN 471, at all times. Users must ensure that their high-visibility clothing is in good condition, is clean and is properly fastened at the front. There are three classes of high-visibility clothing used for roads and street works, as shown below. Full specifications can be found in BS EN 471.

Class 1	Defines the lowest visibility level.	The colour of the background should normally be fluorescent yellow and the reflective material should comply with Table 5 of BS EN 471.
	Example: high-visibility trousers with two 5 cm reflective bands around each leg. These become Class 3 when worn with a Class 3 jacket.	
Class 2	Defines an intermediary visibility level.	Colour scheme as Class 1.
	Example: vests with two 5 cm bands of reflective tape around body or one 5 cm band around body and braces to both shoulders.	
Class 3	Defines the highest visibility level.	Colour scheme as Class 1.
	Example: jacket with long sleeves, jacket and trouser suit with two 5 cm bands of reflective tape around the body, arms and braces over both shoulders.	Must be worn on dual carriageway roads with a speed limit of 50 mph or above and must comply with the colour scheme to BS EN 471.

Other personal protective equipment

The wearing of other personal protective equipment (PPE) will invariably include safety footwear. Other PPE (such as hearing, eye and skin protection) must be worn when required due to the nature of the work being carried out. Safety footwear must have non-slip soles.

1.12 Training

Although the New Roads and Street Works Act refers to a trained operative, there is no specific requirement in the Act for operatives or supervisors to undergo training or produce evidence of prior training.

However, the Act specifies the requirement for supervisors and operatives to hold suitable qualifications, except in prescribed circumstances. Furthermore, attention should be paid to the employer's duties as regards training as laid down in the Health and Safety at Work Act, the Management of Health and Safety at Work Regulations (as amended) and other relevant legislation.

National Highways Sector Scheme 12

This is a quality management system with qualifications awarded by Lantra Awards. Sector Scheme 12 covers temporary traffic management. There are several parts relating to different road types:

☑ 12A/B – High-speed motorways and dual carriageway roads

☑ 12C – Mobile lane closures on high speed roads

☑ 12D – Works on single carriageway roads

☑ 12D is split into several modules covering different types of traffic control, as defined in Chapter 8 of the *Traffic signs manual*.

Appendix A – Relevant legislation and guidance

There are three pieces of legislation that all have an impact upon the way that road works are carried out. The main relevant requirements are outlined below.

 Copies of all legislation can be found online.

The New Roads and Street Works Act

This legislation:

☑ applies to works carried out in a street by an undertaker exercising a statutory right to inspect, place and maintain pipes, cables, sewers or drains, which are laid in the carriageway or footway. The term *undertaker* also covers holders of street works licences

☑ provides a legislative framework for street works activities by undertakers (including public utilities)

☑ created a number of criminal offences that are triable in Magistrates' Courts (Sheriffs' Courts in Scotland). Amongst the 20 possible offences are:
 – failing to carry out works safely (such as signing, lighting and guarding)
 – not having supervisors and operatives, or either, with the relevant prescribed qualifications
 – failing to complete the contracted works within a reasonable timescale.

When a Local Authority acts as an agent to an undertaker or contractor to carry out work for an undertaker, the execution of the works is governed by the Act.

The efficient co-ordination of street works is one of the most important aspects of street works legislation, benefiting street authorities, undertakers and road users alike. The key objectives of the New Roads and Street Works Act (NRSWA) are to:

☑ ensure safety

☑ minimise inconvenience to people using a street, including a specific reference to people with a disability

☑ protect the structure of the street and the apparatus in it.

The Act comprises:

☑ Part 1 – New Roads in England and Wales

☑ Part 2 – New Roads in Scotland

☑ Part 3 – Street Works in England and Wales

☑ Part 4 – Road Works in Scotland

☑ Part 5 – General

☑ associated schedules.

The Highways Act

This legislation:

☑ was introduced to tackle congestion and disruption on the road network

☑ places a duty on local traffic authorities to ensure the expeditious movement of traffic on their road network and those networks of surrounding authorities

☑ gives authorities additional tools to better manage parking policies, moving traffic enforcement and the co-ordination of street works

☑ empowers the Highway Authorities to impose conditions on those working on the highway. It makes provision for licences for skips and scaffolds and places responsibility for safety with the Highway Authority. Contractors must obtain permission before working on the highway

☑ applies to all work on the highway. The Highway Authority (or Roads Authority in Scotland) must be consulted and grant permission for works to be carried out. This applies to any works for road construction or maintenance purposes.

The Traffic Management Act

This legislation:

☑ places a duty on street authorities (such as County Councils), to secure more efficient use of their networks, to avoid or reduce traffic congestion and disruption and to regulate the use of the network

☑ requires a contractor who will be working on the road to provide notice in advance of all works that directly or indirectly affect the highway network, effectively booking the road space. Minimum notice periods for different categories of work are contained within the NRSWA

☑ empowers Local Authorities to introduce a permitting scheme, which is designed to control the carrying out of specified works, in specified streets, in a specified area. In doing this it replaces the notice system under the NRSWA, whereby utility companies informed Highway Authorities of their intentions to carry out works in their areas.

Non-statutory guidance on safety at street works

Traffic signs manual

Summary

Published by the Department for Transport, the *Traffic signs manual* contents are instructional for roads, Local Authorities, parking, road management and traffic signs.

It gives guidance on the use of traffic signs and road markings prescribed by the Traffic Signs Regulations and covers England, Wales, Scotland and Northern Ireland. Revised editions of the manual will be published here as they are released.

 The chapters may be purchased in hard copy from TSO or freely downloaded from the DTi website.

Chapter 1 – Introduction

Introduction and an outline of the historical, functional and design aspects of signs. The chapter includes sections dealing with the positioning and mounting of signs.

Chapter 2 – Informatory signs

Chapter 2 is currently draft and a work in progress. It will contain advice on the design and use of directional signs, and also other informatory signs (such as 'Home zone' signs). Due to the amount of work required to complete Chapter 2, it is intended that interim advice on individual topics will be made available as and when completed.

The current advice on the design and use of directional informatory signs is published in Local Transport Note (LTN) 1/94. Also available is the latest list of primary destinations in England, which supersedes the information in LTN 1/94, and guidance on the calculation of x-heights, which is site-specific and more accurate than the table in LTN 1/94.

Chapter 3 – Regulatory signs

Gives guidelines on the correct use of regulatory signs prescribed by the Traffic Signs Regulations. These include prohibited turns, waiting and loading restrictions, bus and cycle lanes, and so on. There is also a comprehensive section dealing with the signing of speed limits.

Chapter 4 – Warning signs

Warning signs are used to alert drivers to potential danger ahead. They indicate a need for special caution by road users and may require a reduction in speed or some other manoeuvre. This reprinted edition includes four minor amendments and addition of Appendix A, Note 7.

Chapter 5 – Road markings

Road markings serve a very important function in conveying to road users information and requirements that might not be possible using upright signs. They have the advantage that they can often be seen when a verge-mounted sign is obscured, and, unlike such signs, they can provide a continuing message.

Chapter 7 – The design of traffic signs

How sign faces are designed. This chapter does not include the various methods by which signs are constructed and mounted. It supersedes Local Transport Note *'2/94 Directional informatory signs interim design notes',* which was **withdrawn in 1997**.

Chapter 8 (Part 1) – Road works and temporary situations – design

Guidance for the design of temporary traffic management arrangements, which should be implemented to facilitate maintenance activities, or in response to temporary situations.

Chapter 8 (Part 2) – Road works and temporary situations – operations

Guidance for planning, managing, and participating in operations to implement, maintain and remove temporary traffic management arrangements.

 For enquiries and comments regarding Chapter 8, please email direct.

Appendix B – Signs and equipment

Basic signs and equipment you will need

 Road works ahead

 Road narrows on left-hand side ahead

 Road narrows on right-hand side ahead

 Keep right

 Keep left

 Traffic cone

 Road danger lamp

 Pedestrian barrier

 Traffic barrier ('Lane closed' sign)

 End of road works

 You will also need an information board

 High-visibility clothing

Information about the ownership of traffic signs may be shown as follows:
Traffic cones: embossed on the base in the same colour as the base, in characters not more than 80mm high.
Barrier planks: indicated on the back in characters not exceeding 50mm in height where they are in a contrasting colour, or 80mm in height where they are embossed in the same colour.
Other signs: indicated on the back in characters not exceeding 25mm in height, where they are in a contrasting colour, or 50mm in height where they are embossed in the same colour.

Some other signs you may need for which you should refer to your supervisor

Additional signs may be needed according to the circumstances. Some of the more common situations are dealt with in greater detail in the following pages.

 Road narrows on both sides ahead
 Traffic signals ahead
 Where vehicles should stop at temporary traffic signals
 Traffic control ahead
  Stop/Go boards
 Give way to oncoming vehicles — Priority to vehicles from opposite direction
  Priority over oncoming vehicles — Priority over vehicles from opposite direction

 Other danger ahead (use only with a plate)
 Slippery road
 Traffic cylinder
 High intensity flashing beacon
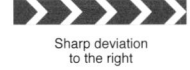 Sharp deviation to the right
 Direction of temporary pedestrian route
 Stop Works
 Traffic signals not in use

Or variations of these signs

 Temporary road surface
 Zebra or signal controlled crossing is not in use
 Loose chippings
 Ramp ahead
 Ramp
 Left-hand lane of a dual two-lane carriageway road closed
 Left-hand lane of a dual three-lane carriageway road closed
 Centre lane of a three-lane two-way road closed

 Cyclists dismount
 Setting out road works ahead
 Single file traffic
 Overhead cable repairs
 Distance over which hazard or prohibition extends
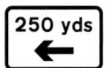 Distance to hazard or obstruction
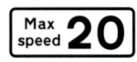 Distance and direction to hazard or obstruction
 Maximum speed advised
 Surveying
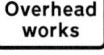 Overhead works

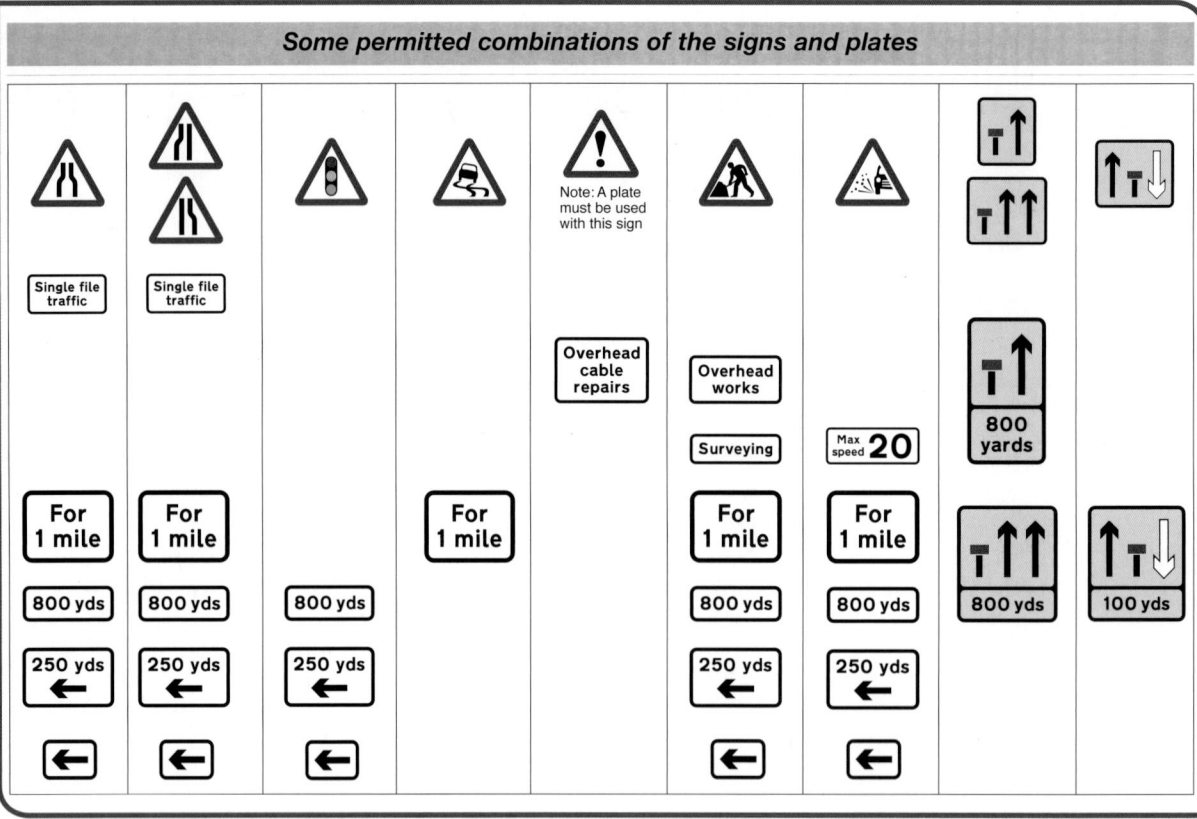

Appendix C – Basic layout of a road works site

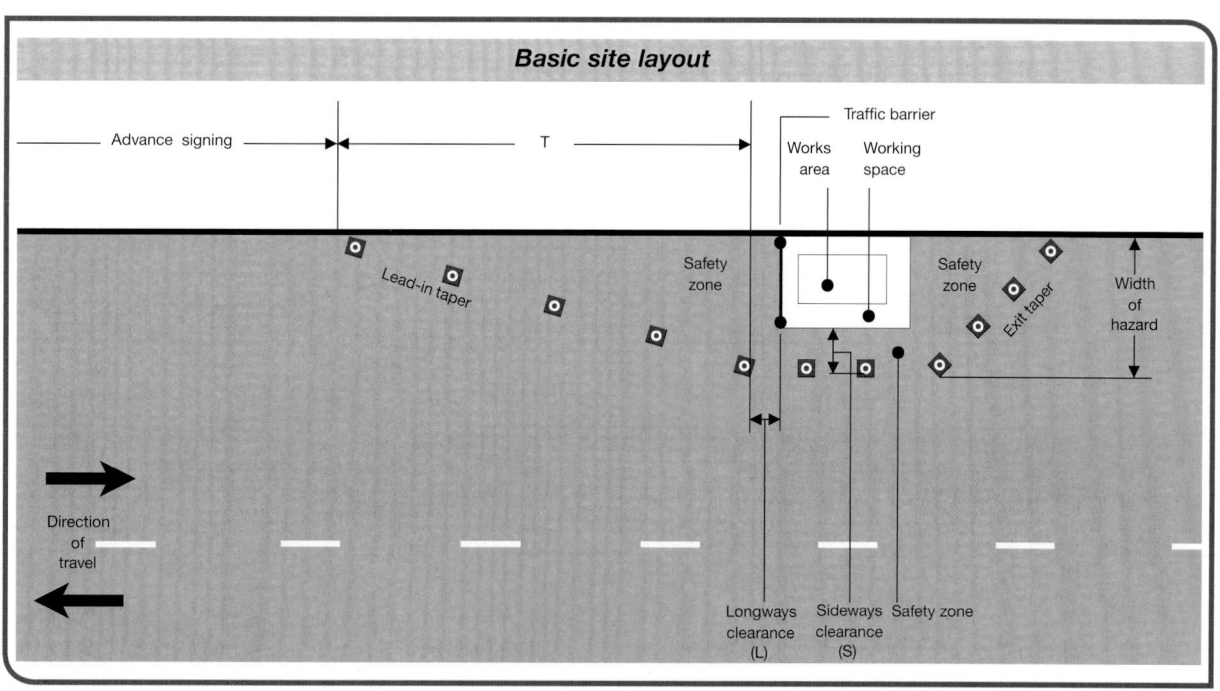

Basic site layout

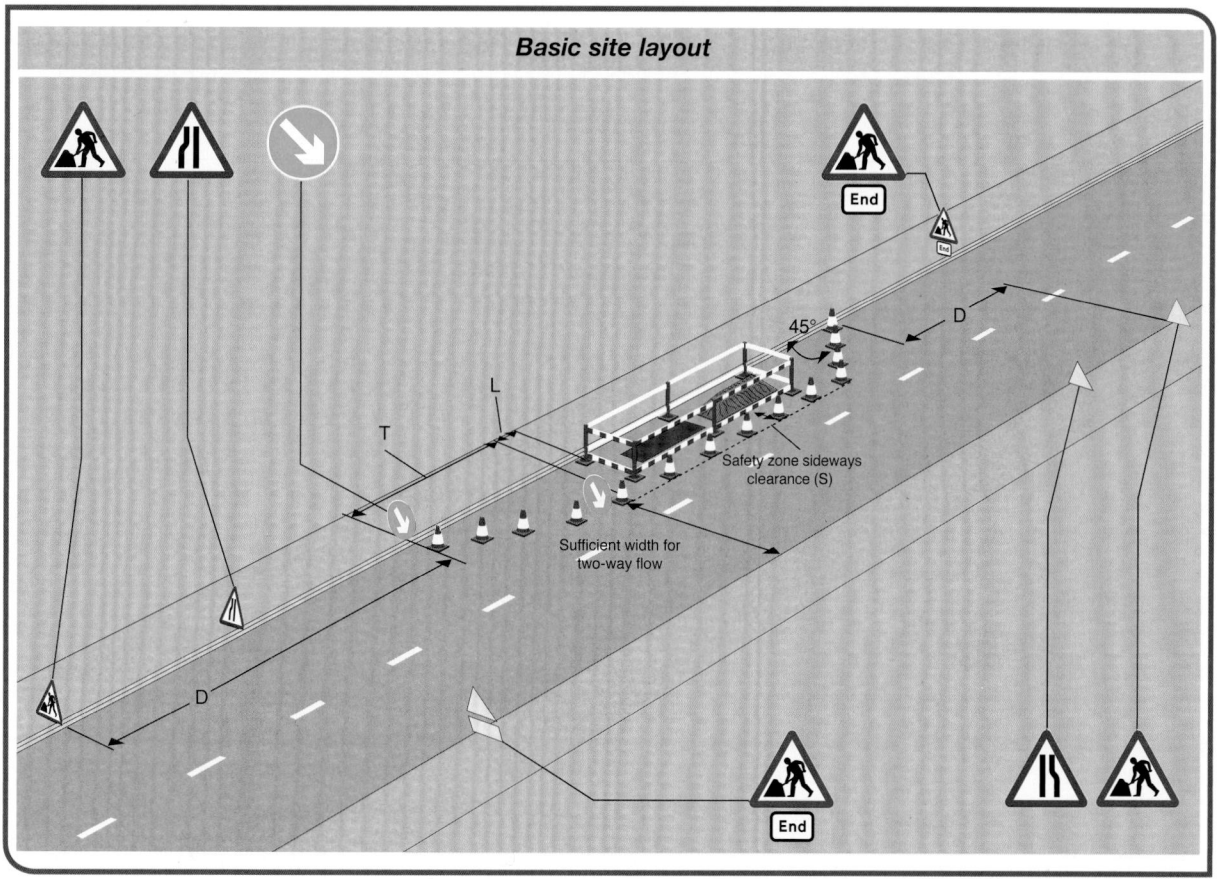

Basic site layout

Appendix D – Basic layout with works vehicle

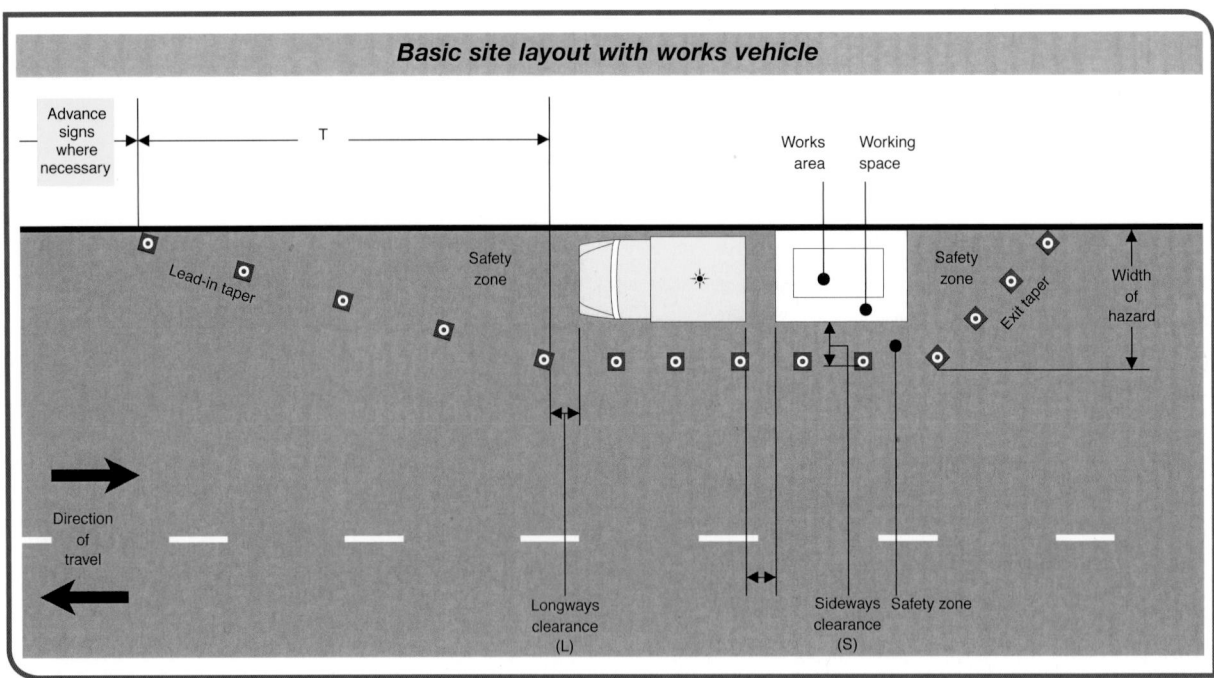

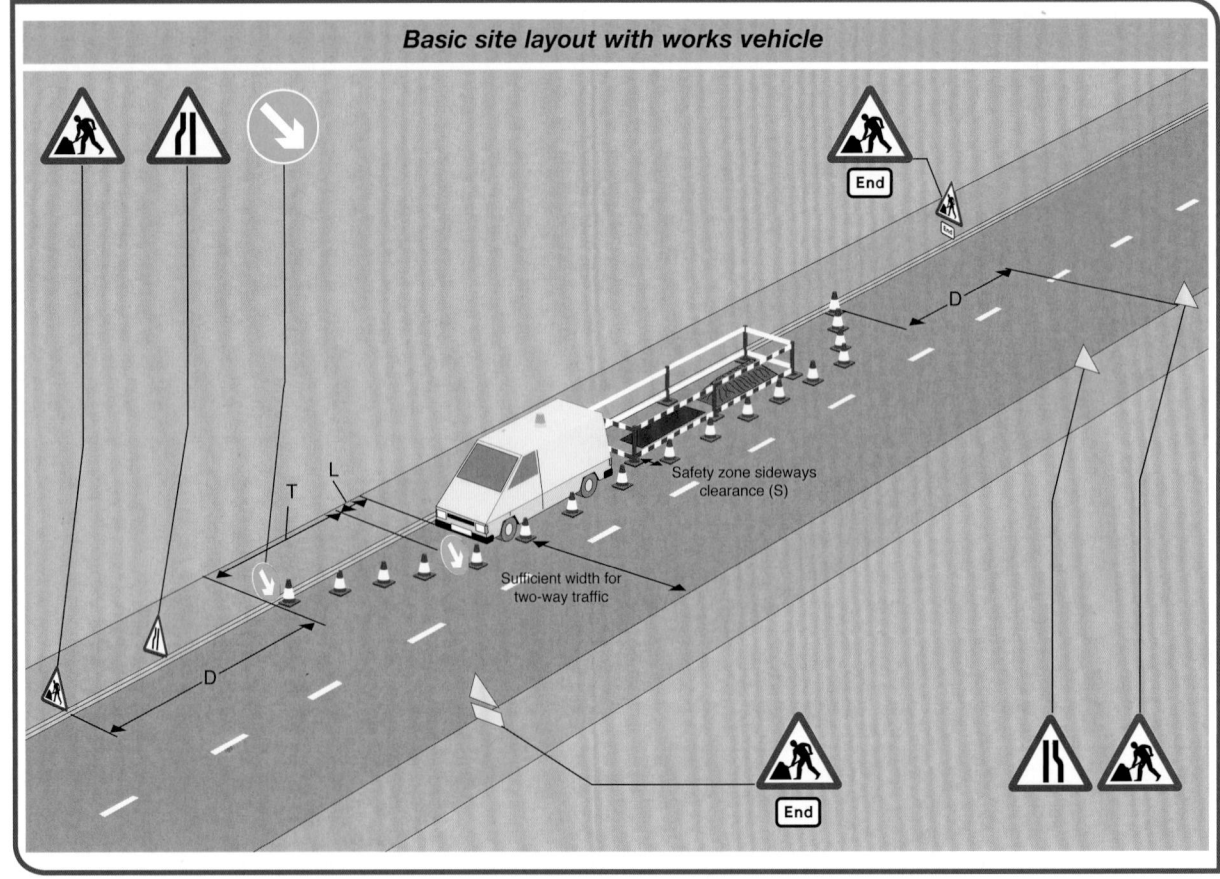

(Based on © Crown copyright diagrams from Safety at street works and road works: A Code of Practice 2001 edition.)

Appendix E – Traffic control by give and take

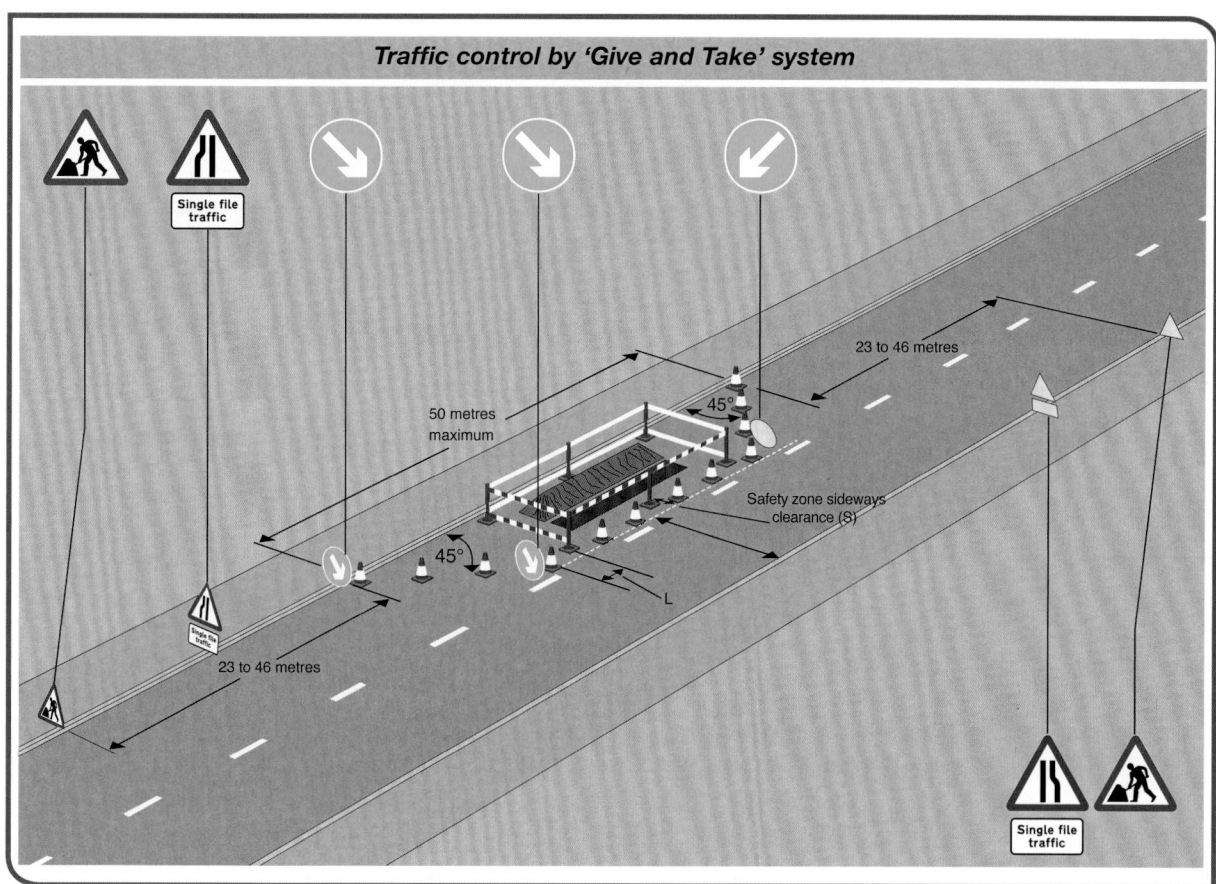

Traffic control by 'Give and Take' system

50 metres maximum

23 to 46 metres

45°

45°

Safety zone sideways clearance (S)

L

23 to 46 metres

Single file traffic

(Based on © Crown copyright diagrams from Safety at street works and road works: A Code of Practice 2001 edition.)

Appendix F – Traffic control by priority signs

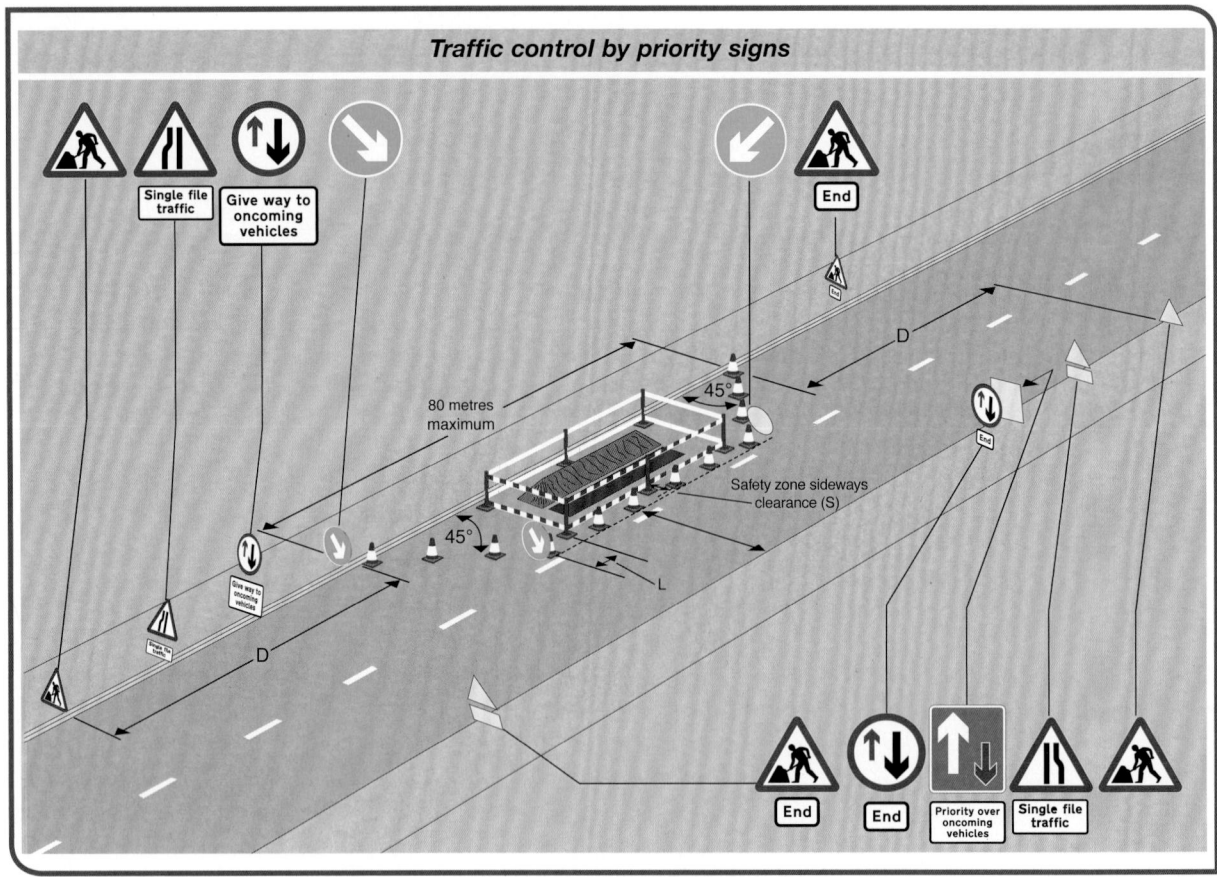

(Based on © Crown copyright diagrams from Safety at street works and road works: A Code of Practice 2001 edition.)

Appendix G – Traffic control by stop/go boards

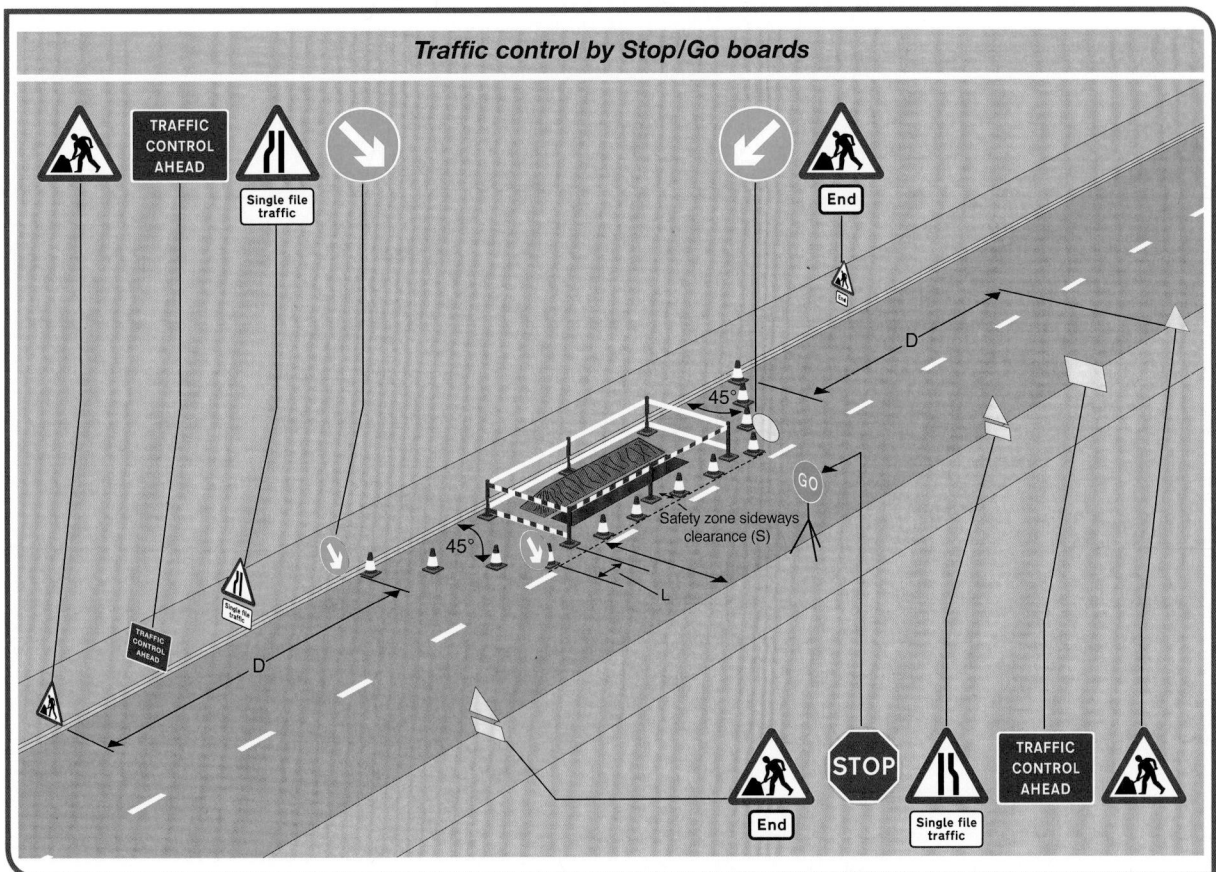

Traffic control by Stop/Go boards

(Based on © Crown copyright diagrams from Safety at street works and road works: A Code of Practice 2001 edition.)

Appendix H – Traffic control by portable traffic signals

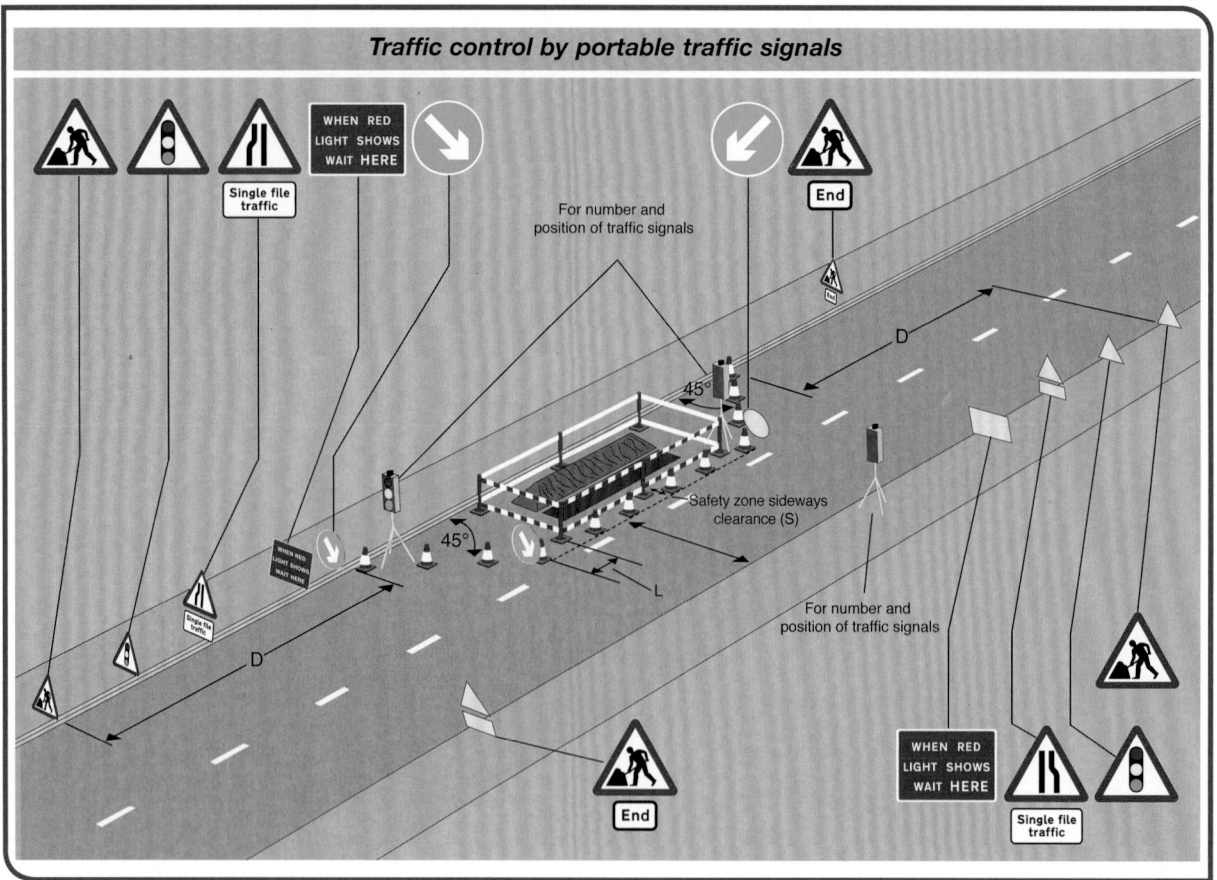

(Based on © Crown copyright diagrams from Safety at street works and road works: A Code of Practice 2001 edition.)

Appendix I – Works on footways

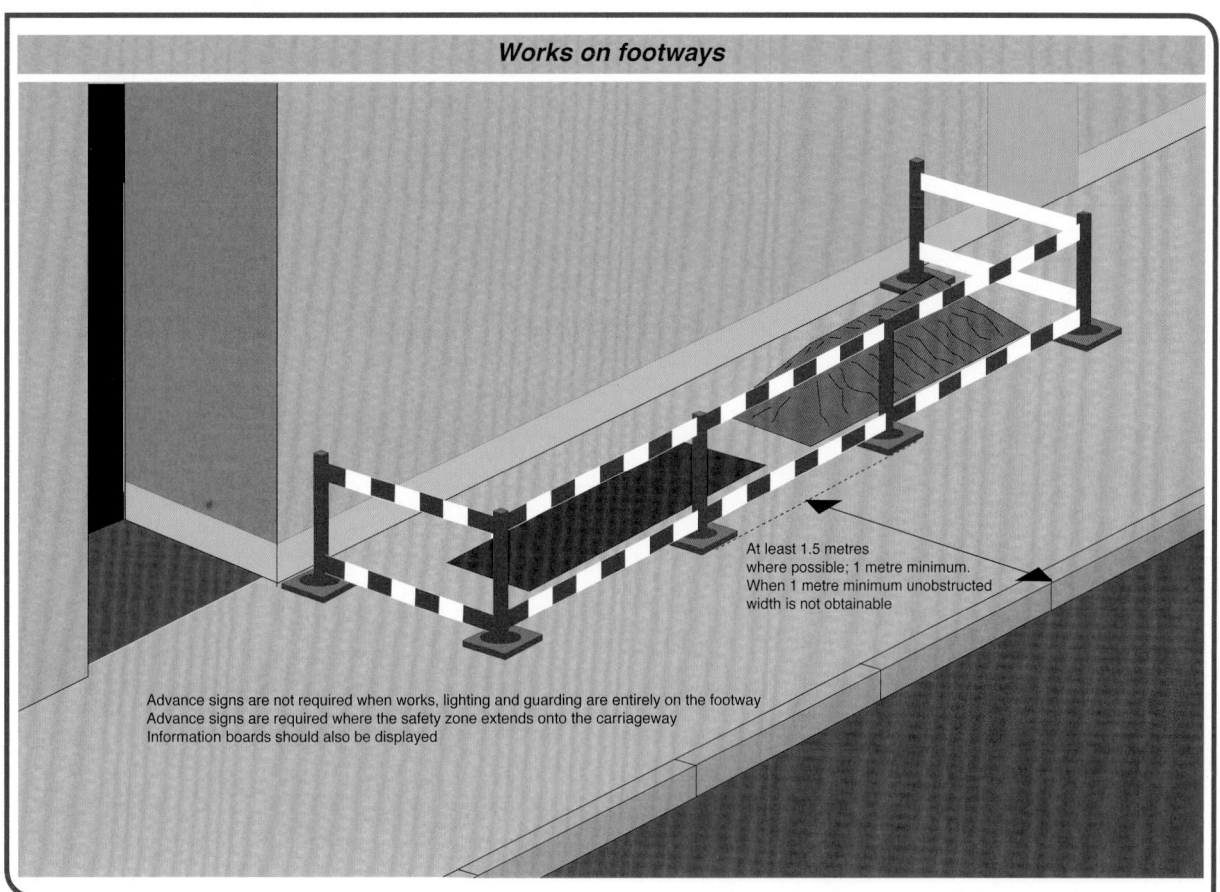

Works on footways

At least 1.5 metres where possible; 1 metre minimum. When 1 metre minimum unobstructed width is not obtainable

Advance signs are not required when works, lighting and guarding are entirely on the footway
Advance signs are required where the safety zone extends onto the carriageway
Information boards should also be displayed

(Based on © Crown copyright diagrams from Safety at street works and road works: A Code of Practice 2001 edition.)

Appendix J – Temporary footways in the carriageway

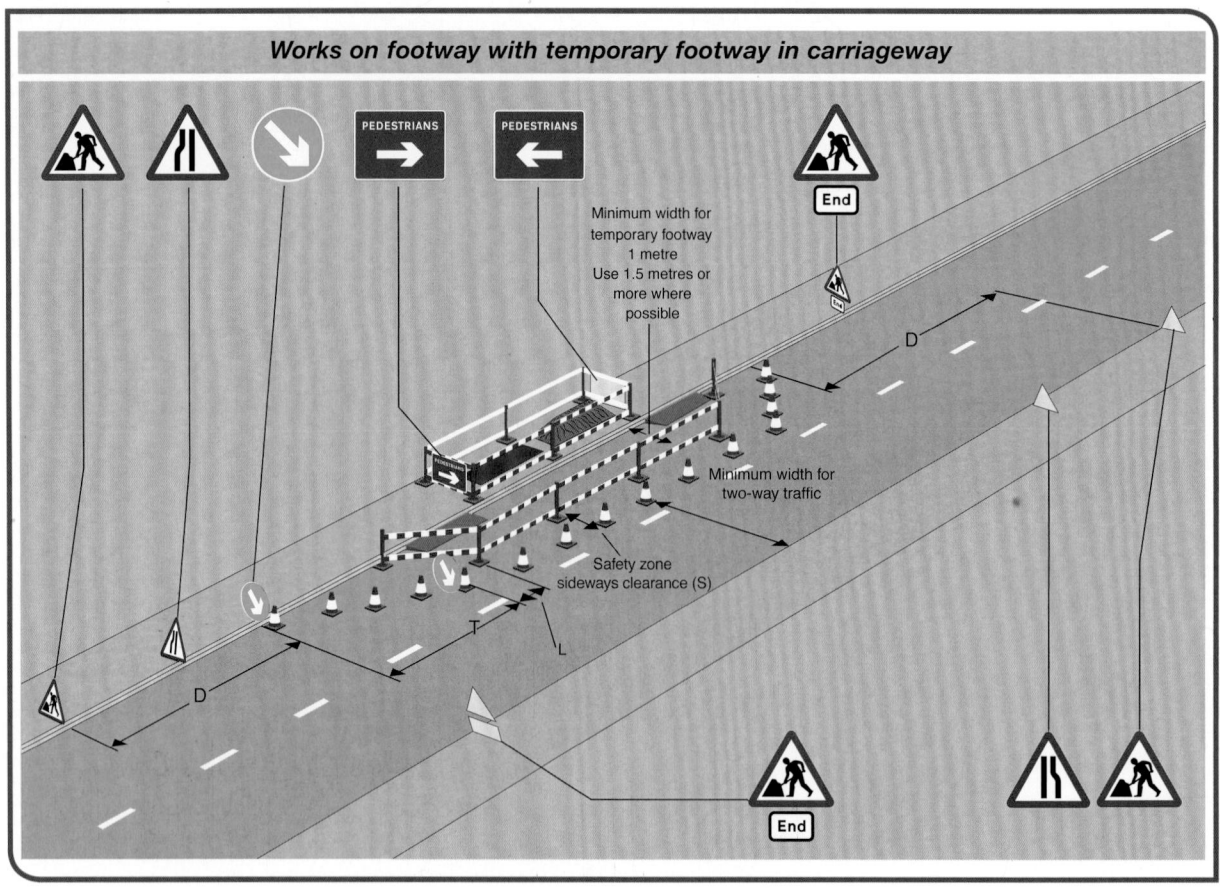

Works on footway with temporary footway in carriageway

Minimum width for
temporary footway
1 metre
Use 1.5 metres or
more where
possible

Minimum width for
two-way traffic

Safety zone
sideways clearance (S)

(Based on © Crown copyright diagrams from Safety at street works and road works: A Code of Practice 2001 edition.)

Appendix K – Size and siting distances of signage and cones

Type of road	Minimum and normal maximum siting distance (D) of first sign in advance of lead-in taper (metres)	Minimum clear visibility to first sign (metres)	Minimum size of signs (mm)	Minimum height of cones (mm)	Sideways safety zone (S)	Details of lead-in cone tapers but see notes (below) Recommended lengths	Width of hazard (metres) including safety zones (S)						
							1	2	3	4	5	6	7
Single carriageway road, restricted to 30 mph or less	20 to 45	60	600	450	0.5 m	Length of taper (T) in metres	13	26	39	52	65	78	91
						Minimum number of cones	4	4	6	7	9	10	12
						Minimum number of lamps at night	3	3	5	5	8	9	11
Single carriageway road, restricted to speeds of 31 to 40 mph inclusive	45 to 110	60	750	450	0.5 m	Length of taper (T) in metres	20	40	60	80	100	120	140
						Minimum number of cones	4	6	8	10	13	15	17
						Minimum number of lamps at night	2	2	7	9	12	14	16
All-purpose dual carriageway road, restricted to 40 mph or less	110 to 275	60	750	450	0.5 m	Length of taper (T) in metres	25	50	75	100	125	150	175
						Minimum number of cones	4	7	10	13	15	18	21
						Minimum number of lamps at night	3	6	9	12	14	17	20
Single carriageway road, with speed limit of 50 mph or more	275 to 45	75	750	450	1.2 m	Length of taper (T) in metres	25	50	75	100	125	150	175
						Minimum number of cones	4	7	10	13	15	18	21
						Minimum number of lamps at night	3	6	9	12	14	17	20
All-purpose dual carriageway road, with speed limit of 50 mph or more	725 to 1,600	150	1,200	750	1.2 m	Length of taper (T) in metres	32	64	96	128	160	192	224
						Minimum number of cones	5	9	12	16	19	23	26
						Minimum number of lamps at night	4	8	11	15	18	22	25

Speed limit (mph)	30 or less	40	50	60	70
Minimum longway clearance (L) metres	1/2	15	30	60	70

Notes:

1. Lead-in tapers used with traffic control, and all exit tapers, shall be at about 45° to the kerb line with cones spaced 1.2 metres apart.

2. The maximum spacing distance of cones in longitudinal lengths of coning shall be nine metres, but no fewer than two cones shall be used in any length between tapers.

3. In certain circumstances on congested roads with speed limits of 30 mph or under, the taper may also be reduced to 45°.

(Based on © Crown copyright diagrams from Safety at street works and road works: A Code of Practice 2001 edition.)

Street works and road works

02

Trackside safety

Working on a railway is a high risk environment. Not only do you have the normal problems of construction work to contend with, you also have the hazard of trains moving in close proximity at speeds of up to 125 mph. There could also be overhead electricity lines at 25,000 volts AC or third and fourth rails carrying up to 750 volts DC.

Despite a gradual reduction in the number of rail accidents per million miles travelled, during recent years several major accidents, which were eventually attributed to defective work practices by contractors, served to bring the focus back to contractor competency.

This is intended as a brief guide for site managers to provide awareness only.

Introduction	28
Key requirements	28
Network Rail licensing	29
Safety management	29
Work sites	33
Safe working practices	34
Personal safety	37
Electrified lines	38
Appendix A – Train sighting chart	41
Appendix B – Fencing and separation	42

02

2.1   Introduction

Competence plays a very important role in controlling health and safety risks when working on an operational railway system. In the context of working on the railway system, controlling the risks to health and safety depends upon managing a complex mix of infrastructure, railway-specific rules, human factors and safety management systems.

Network Rail (which controls the railway infrastructure) has laid down procedures that have to be strictly followed by all people working on railways. While the following information will contribute to working safely on railways, it can only be a summary of this complex subject and it is recommended that readers contact Network Rail directly for more detailed information relating to individual projects.

With the decentralised management of the railways, the fear was that the safety of the railway would be jeopardised by the introduction of independent railway operators. To prevent this happening the Office of Rail Regulation (ORR) took overall responsibility for rail industry health and safety regulation in April 2006. At the same time new regulations were introduced in the form of the Railways and Other Guided Transport Systems (Safety) Regulations (ROGS).

The ROGS Regulations are administered and enforced by Her Majesty's Railway Inspectorate (HMRI) of the ORR.

 An explanation of how ROGS apply to safety critical work is contained within ORR publication *Safety critical tasks – Clarification of ROGS Regulations requirements* (Railways safety publication 4).

The Rail Safety and Standards Board (RSSB) is a not-for-profit company, owned and funded by major stakeholders in the railway industry. A part of RSSB's remit is to publish and update railway group standards, which govern the way that work is carried out on the railways, including the management of health and safety.

Under the leadership of RSSB the industry is embarking on an ambitious project to transform the content and presentation of the rules currently published in the *Rule book* (GE/RT8000). The project is entitled *The new approach*, and the programme to systematically review and revise all modules of the current rule book is scheduled to take four years.

 The onus is on contractors who work on the railways to make sure that they are referring to the most recent edition of any reference material.

The primary purpose is to review and revise the current modular rule book with the aim of significantly rationalising its content and restructuring the document so that it is more accurately targeted at the skill sets of end-users and clearly aligned with operational principles.

The objectives of rationalisation and restructuring are to:

☑ reduce rule-based errors, violations and misapplication

☑ enable end users to exercise greater judgement and discretion in resolving operational issues

☑ reduce the need for and the costs of future rule changes

☑ support industry goals for competence management and performance improvement.

 Contractors who work on the railways must achieve additional competencies when compared to those engaged in conventional construction work.

2.2   Key requirements

☑ Means of access to the work site must be stated in the work package plan/task briefing. The access point may consist of a cabin, which may be staffed for the duration of the work.

☑ In order to ensure that members of the public do not gain access to rail sites, all sites must be secured at the end of each working day and any security or safety-related incident must be reported through the safety management information system (SMIS), as detailed in Railway Group Standard GE/RT8047 – *Reporting of safety related information*.

☑ The site rules must be displayed in the access cabin; each member of staff is required to sign in and out from the site.

☑ The work site must be scanned using a cable avoidance tool (CAT) for buried services by a competent person prior to the work commencing. Any services identified are marked and, if possible, temporarily removed (signalling cables).

☑ The controller of site safety (COSS) must brief the workforce on the site safety rules prior to the work starting, and brief the incoming COSS at the shift changeover.

☑ Following the briefing, each member of staff must sign the COSS briefing form to confirm they have understood the brief.

- [✓] Lighting must be in accordance with the Network Rail Safety 365 document, which details lux levels and permitted lighting systems.

- [✓] Personal protective equipment (PPE) must comply with relevant British Standards and Railway Group Standards; the requirements are different to those for general non-railway construction work.

 Yellow, high-visibility clothing is simply not acceptable when working on the railway network.

2.3   Network Rail licensing

Generally, infrastructure contractors must hold a contractor's licence approved by Network Rail to enable them to work on the railway. The licence encompasses health, safety, the environment and quality.

These rules are applied generally to main or principal contractors, as sub-contractors are allowed to work under the principal contractor's licence. To work directly for Network Rail, contractors must successfully complete their Achilles Link-up accreditation scheme. Once approved the contractor must then obtain a Network Rail principal contractor's licence.

 If making enquiries about becoming a building or civil supplier to Network Rail, a list of key contacts can be found on the Network Rail website or you can email them directly.

When tendering for work on the railways, the contractor has to present a licence and a health and safety plan to Network Rail. These describe how the contractor will manage the safety implications. Subsequently, the performance of the contractor and their workforce is measured against these documents. It is essential therefore that contractor's staff working on a railway project must be made aware of the contents of the two documents, and supervisors must ensure that they adhere to the contents.

A contractor will require sponsorship from Network Rail regions to enable them to enter the licensing system. Applying for a licence is a demanding, time-consuming job and contractors who do not have significant in-house knowledge of work on the railway infrastructure are advised to obtain assistance from someone with experience of this type of work.

However, it is important that everyone involved understands that the main aim is to check the contractor's existing systems, either against the Network Rail procedure or to align the contractor's systems with those of Network Rail (not to invent new ones).

Where a licence has been submitted, but is being reviewed, Network Rail may issue a provisional licence, which will allow the contractor to bid for rail work.

Acceptance of a licence by Network Rail should lead to training for the staff responsible for its implementation. This is important because, whilst the document will contain the company's normal management systems, there will be a number of areas that are specific to rail work (such as drugs and alcohol procedures, competence management, accident reporting and medical requirements). Managers working on rail contracts must understand and implement these requirements.

2.4   Safety management

Safety management systems

Rail operators must obtain a **safety certificate** for operating trains, or a **safety authorisation** for infrastructure managers (which includes station managers).

The status of a safety certificate and a safety authorisation is the same, in that they allow access to the railway; however, their scope will be different. Safety certificates and safety authorisations have a maximum period of validity of five years. There are various exemptions for the requirement to have either a safety certificate or authorisation:

- [✓] those operating only in engineering possessions

- [✓] those operating on non-mainline transport systems where the maximum permitted speed is 40 kph or less

- [✓] tramways

- [✓] railways in factories and most harbours

- [✓] railways within maintenance or goods depots or military establishments.

In order to obtain a safety certificate or safety authorisation the operator must implement a safety management system that includes:

- [✓] a statement of the safety policy

- [✓] targets for the maintenance and enhancement of safety and plans and procedures for reaching those targets

Trackside safety

☑ procedures to meet relevant technical and operational standards or other requirements set out in national safety rules, for example:

  – procedures and methods for carrying out risk assessments and implementing risk control measures

  – provisions for training and maintenance of competency

  – arrangements for the provision of information relevant to safety

  – procedures and formats for the documentation of safety information

  – procedures to control the layout of and changes to vital safety information

  – procedures to ensure that accidents, incidents, near misses and other dangerous occurrences are reported, investigated and analysed and that necessary preventative measures are taken

  – provision of plans for action, alerts and information in the case of an emergency

  – provisions for internal auditing of the safety management system.

In practice, a train operating company, as a vehicle operator, or Network Rail, as an infrastructure manager, will stipulate safety conditions in accordance with their safety management systems that need to be complied with for a particular contract. These will be incorporated into the licensing arrangements (see below) and the health and safety plan for the project. However, if contractors operate trains or carry out infrastructure maintenance outside of possessions then the requirements for the safety certificate, authorisation and safety management system will apply.

Personal track safety scheme

If work on a railway entails working on or near the line, workers must be in possession of a personal track safety (PTS) card. This indicates that they have been trained and are competent to carry out work safely in a railway environment.

Before undergoing training for personal track safety, workers must be certified medically fit for work in a railway environment, and undergo screening for drugs and alcohol. The standards of medical fitness are laid down in Railway Group and Network Rail Standards.

 Workers who successfully undergo PTS training receive a *Keypoints – Personal track safety* (PTS) health and safety booklet outlining safe working procedures and their responsibilities when working on the railways. A PDF copy of the booklet is available online.

Competency and training in track safety supervision

The ORR, having taken over responsibility for health and safety on the railways (from the Health and Safety Executive (HSE) in 2006), introduced a competence management system (CMS), the structure of which is explained in the ORR publication *Developing and maintaining staff competence (Railway safety publication 1)*.

The publication explains how the requirements for competence apply to contractors and their sub-contractors.

All work activities on or near the line must be supervised by a COSS who will set up a safe system of work for the group of workers they are responsible for. The COSS must stay with the group at all times until the work is completed or they have been relieved by another COSS.

The guidelines below outline what competencies are required to allow particular work activities to take place:

☑ controller of site safety (COSS)

☑ individual working alone (IWA)

☑ protection controller (PC).

All the above competencies allow qualified workers to work alone, on or near the line.

Personal track safety

This competency allows qualified workers to:

☑ walk on or near the line alone to access or egress the site only – ensuring they do **not** work

☑ work in a red zone* under the control of a COSS

☑ work in a green zone* under the control of a COSS or PC

☑ work in electrified AC/DC line areas under the control of a COSS, providing the staff show AC/DC as well as PTS on their National Competency Control Agency (NCCA) card.

* The meaning of the terms red zone and green zone are explained later in this chapter.

Lookout/site warden

This competency allows a qualified person to have:

☑ lookout duties in a red zone

☑ site warden duties in a green zone.

Person in charge of possession

This competency enables a person to carry out person in charge of possession (PICOP) duties and take T(iii) possessions.

To be a PICOP (or engineering supervisor), details demonstrating COSS experience within the last 24 months must be held in the employer's competence management system. The PICOP will also be required to meet in full certain experience criteria.

PICOP competence itself does not qualify anyone to do COSS work, which requires a separate COSS qualification.

 Information on developing and maintaining staff competence can be found online.

Safety critical work

The ROGS Regulations lay down a procedure to ensure that those engaged on a transport system in a work situation do so in a manner that will not affect the health and safety of people using that transport system.

All workers must:

☑ be competent and fit to carry out their allotted tasks

☑ carry with them a means of identifying that they are undertaking safety-critical work

☑ work in such a way that the number of hours worked, combined with the rest periods taken between work, does not increase the risk of fatigue to operatives.

It is obvious that any work carried out on the railway – whether to the track, the signalling system or the trains themselves – could have disastrous effects if it is not carried out correctly.

The whole reasoning behind the ROGS Regulations is to ensure that only competent persons carry out work on the railways. These regulations should ensure that the work will be carried out to such a high standard that the risk of disaster will be negligible.

Train movements

 A train travelling at 80 mph will cover nearly 120 feet (36 metres) per second. If it takes 10 seconds to realise that a train is approaching and move off the track to a place of safety, in that time the train will have covered nearly 1,200 feet (360 metres).

When anyone is working on or near a railway line, the driver of an approaching train should blow the train whistle or horn to warn of the train's approach, although this must not be relied upon. The worker, in return, must acknowledge that they have heard the whistle, and have moved to a position of safety, by raising one arm straight in the air above their head.

The time required is decided by the COSS by conducting a risk assessment and will depend on the speed of the approaching train and the length of time necessary to remove staff and place tools away from the running lines to enable the whole group to be standing in a position of safety for at least 10 seconds before the train passes the worksite. The speed of the train is always taken as the maximum permissible speed at that location.

When setting up a safe system of work, a COSS needs to determine the distance at which they must be able to see a train approaching.

 A train sighting chart and an explanation of how it is used is included at Appendix A.

Communications procedure

Communicating clearly

You must make sure you properly understand the meaning of all messages whether they are communicated by phone, radio or face-to-face. You must:

☑ make sure you are talking to the right person

☑ give your location, if using a phone or radio

☑ give your name and the name of your employer

☑ state what task you are performing

☑ if necessary, let the person know how you can be contacted

☑ use the phonetic alphabet to make sure names and locations that are difficult to pronounce are fully understood

☑ never use the words 'not clear' to describe a line that is obstructed; always use 'line blocked'.

Trackside safety

You must say numbers one at a time (for example, you should say 8107 as 'eight, one, zero, seven').

There are exceptions to this (such as when giving the time or when referring to a rule book module or handbook).

If you are receiving a message, make sure you fully understand it. You must repeat the message back so that the other person knows you correctly understand it.

To help make sure your message is fully understood when using a telephone or radio:

- ☑ speak with the mouthpiece close to your mouth and speak directly into the mouthpiece
- ☑ talk slightly slower than normal using a natural rhythm
- ☑ use your normal level of volume when speaking
- ☑ avoid using hesitation sounds (for example 'um' and 'er')
- ☑ use clear sentences
- ☑ get the person to repeat your message back to you.

Lead responsibility

During any conversation, one person must always take lead responsibility.

The person who must take lead responsibility depends on the task being carried out. Examples are shown below.

Lead responsibility	When communicating with
Electrical control operator (ECO)	Anyone.
Signaller	Anyone except the ECO.
PICOP (person in charge of the possession)	Anyone except the ECO or signaller.
Route-setting agent	Points operator.
Protection controller (PC)	Each COSS.
COSS	Members of the work group.
COSS	Each lookout/site warden.

If it is not clear who has lead responsibility, or if two people carrying out the same task are communicating with each other, the person who begins the conversation must always take lead responsibility.

Phrases to use when using a radio or telephone

Phrase	Meaning
This is an emergency call	This message provides information that needs immediate action to prevent death, serious injury or damage.
Repeat back	Repeat all of the message back to me.
Correction	I have made a mistake and will now correct the word or phrase just said.

Other phrases to use when using a radio and only one person can be heard at a time

Phrase	Meaning
Over	I have finished my message and am expecting a reply.
Out	I have finished my message, no reply is expected.

Using the phonetic alphabet

The phonetic alphabet must be used:

- ☑ to identify letters of the alphabet
- ☑ to spell words and place names that are difficult to say, or may be misunderstood
- ☑ if there is interference on the radio or phone
- ☑ when quoting the identity of signals or points
- ☑ when quoting train descriptions.

The phonetic alphabet

A – alpha	**H** – hotel	**O** – oscar	**V** – victor
B – bravo	**I** – india	**P** – papa	**W** – whisky
C – charlie	**J** – juliet	**Q** – quebec	**X** – x-ray
D – delta	**K** – kilo	**R** – romeo	**Y** – yankee
E – echo	**L** – lima	**S** – sierra	**Z** – zulu.
F – foxtrot	**M** – mike	**T** – tango	
G – golf	**N** – november	**U** – uniform	

2.5　Work sites

Work sites are categorised depending upon the degree of danger to the person(s) doing the work.

Red zones

When work must take place on a line of track where trains are still running, this is classed as red zone working. This reflects the danger to work teams posed by train movements on that line.

The COSS must set up a safe system of work at that site. This will allow the workers the required time to get to a position of safety.

The problems associated with this type of working depend on the scale and type of work being carried out.

Work of a light nature should enable people working in a red zone to clear the track easily.

Work of a more complex or heavier type would require more time being required to clear the track of personnel, tools and equipment. Accordingly, the sighting distance required would be much greater. This, in turn, could require more than one lookout in each direction to achieve the sighting distances required.

In some circumstances, all red zone working is banned. Network Rail publishes a hazard directory that gives a comprehensive list of places where red zone working is not allowed.

Network Rail intends to eliminate red zone working and, wherever possible, establish green zone working.

Possession of the line

When major engineering work is to be undertaken, a possession will be required.

This is an agreement with the signaller to give over control of the line, but control must be returned to the signaller when requested.

Possession of the line is taken by the PICOP from the signaller, and the PICOP is the only one who can allow trains in or out of the line(s) under possession. This procedure must be planned well in advance of the possession being required, otherwise it will not be granted.

Extra care is needed if one line is under possession and the line next to it is still open to train movements. Steps have to be taken to prevent people straying from the line under possession onto the open line.

Green zones

These are by far the safest areas of work on a railway, due to the way in which they are set up.

Green zones can be created in a number of different ways. In each situation, it is the responsibility of the COSS to put in place procedures that keep workers within the protection zone.

Blockages of the line

Under this arrangement, trains are not permitted to run. The green zone may be created by various methods, one of which involves hand signallers using red flags to prevent the movement of vehicles past signals.

Extra care is needed if one line is blocked and the line next to it is still open to train movements. Steps have to be taken to prevent people straying from the line that is blocked onto the open line.

Fencing and separation

To prevent people at a work site straying onto lines that are open to train movements, physical reminders can take the form of blue, one metre-high fencing, or black and yellow tape extending beyond the length of the work site. The fencing must be supported to prevent it being dragged under passing trains. An alternative type of fence is a Vortok rigid barrier.

Fencing acts as a continual reminder to people on site that, beyond the fencing, the track is open to movement of trains. Therefore, a safe system of work exists, providing no-one strays beyond the fencing (*refer to Figures 2, 3 and 4 in Appendix B*).

An alternative to fencing is to use site wardens to prevent people straying onto lines that are open to train movements.

The wardens are positioned by the COSS at least two metres away from the nearest rail of any line on which a train may run, to warn anyone who moves beyond that two metre point (*refer to Figure 5 in Appendix B*).

Employing this system as a means of warning depends upon the alertness of the site wardens ensuring their colleagues do not stray beyond the limits set by the COSS, within two metres of the open line.

Prohibition of work

Where it is not possible to set up a green zone and work is not permitted in red zones, work must not be carried out on that site.

Work planning

Whenever possible, work must be planned beforehand and the planning must include the arrangements for protection. The decision on protection arrangements must be written down and given to the COSS.

The protection arrangements chosen must be the best available from the following list.

Best	Safeguarded green zone.
2nd	Fenced green zone.
3rd	Separated green zone.
4th	Red zone with automatic track warning system.
5th	Red zone with train-operated warning system.
6th	Red zone with lookout-operated warning system.
7th	Red zone with lookout and portable warning system.
Last resort	Red zone with lookout(s) only.

Together, the above items form Network Rail's RIMINI (RIsk MINImisation) procedure for working on or near the line. They will lead to work that is better planned and co-ordinated to provide a higher level of safety. They will also help to drive further improvements through the introduction of systems that offer better protection and are simpler to use. These include T-CODs, ATWS and plans for a simplified version of T(ii) protection arrangement to make it easier to obtain green zones.

 In some circumstances, all red zone working is banned or, the use of lookouts is banned. More information can be found in the hazard directory published by Network Rail.

2.6   Safe working practices

Mobile plant

Any mobile plant used on the railways must not create a danger to the passage of trains. This entails the COSS setting up a safe system of work for the use of that plant within the work task to be carried out.

Method statements should identify how plant will be brought to site, used on site and taken off site.

Some mobile plant is capable of being driven on both the road and on rails, as illustrated, and such plant must conform to the appropriate Railway Group Standard. Contractors using plant that can move on rails must have a safety case, not only as a contractor but also as a train operator, because the item of plant is classed as a train.

The method of getting the plant to and from site must be looked at very carefully. Contractors should ensure that the plant does not damage other vital equipment (such as structures, signalling equipment, including cables, and communications equipment).

Ways of protecting the various items of equipment must be clearly outlined in the method statement for the work.

When working on site with mobile plant, various factors have to be taken into consideration, such as:

- ☑ the presence of electrified lines
- ☑ the presence of buried services
- ☑ the presence of signalling equipment
- ☑ working on embankments

- ☑ obstructing the sighting of signals from train drivers
- ☑ the distance from running lines
- ☑ the use of lights on road vehicles.

These are in addition to the normal precautions that have to be taken by plant operators in any working environment.

Where items of plant are used in relation to railway infrastructure, they must be used only by competent persons.

Certificates of competence to operate items of plant must be carried, along with means of identification. These credentials can be asked for at any time. Failure to provide them when requested will result in the person being removed from site.

Scaffolds and mobile towers

Scaffold work in a railway environment is a specialist activity, requiring the scaffolders to be competent not only in scaffolding but also in railway work.

A train requires clearance between itself and any structure that it passes. These clearances vary according to the train speed, the type of rolling stock, the presence or non-presence of curves and the cant of the track.

The required clearances need to be observed when erecting a scaffold or mobile tower to ensure that it cannot be struck by passing trains, and that the movement of air caused by trains passing does not affect the structure.

A thorough survey of the site must be made prior to the erection of any scaffold or mobile tower. The survey must consider the needs of railway personnel who need an unobstructed view of equipment in order to carry out their work safely.

Failure to carry out this survey correctly could have extremely serious effects.

Erection of scaffolds and mobile towers on the railway must be carried out, bearing in mind the:

☑ movement of trains

☑ movement of station staff and passengers

☑ proximity of electrified lines

☑ placing of other equipment used in operations.

It is vital that scaffolds or mobile towers are not erected in positions that will obstruct signals and other equipment that need to be seen by train drivers.

Special regulations exist for the erection and use of scaffolds or mobile towers, adjacent to or over the tracks, and these must be carried out in such a way that train movements are not affected.

When scaffolding has to be erected where electrified lines are situated, the method of erection, working and dismantling must take account of the hazards presented by the presence of the electrified lines.

No erection or dismantling of a scaffold or mobile tower must commence until an isolation permit has been received to indicate that it is now safe to work near the electrified lines. The need for isolation of electrified lines during scaffold erection and dismantling is of paramount importance to avoid contact with live lines when moving scaffold poles around. The stoppage of trains during this process should also be considered because of the possibility of the incomplete scaffold collapsing onto the track.

Even if an electrical isolation permit has been received, it will not prevent the movement of non-electrified trains or runaway, rolling stock.

Signalling systems operate when the wheels and axles of a train running along the rails create an electrical connection of one rail to the other. This allows a small current to flow and operate signal lights, indicating that the train is in that section.

Extreme care must be taken when erecting or dismantling a scaffold or mobile tower over tracks. If scaffold poles fall, or are placed across rails, the signals may change. This will result in false signals being given to train drivers (for example, green lights instead of red or yellow ones), which could have very serious results.

Confined spaces

There are areas on a railway that may be classified as confined spaces. These include box girders, closed arches, culverts, station basements and inspection pits.

Having identified the work station as a confined space, the following questions should be asked.

☑ Is there any way of carrying out the work task without entering that space?

☑ If there is a need to enter that area, how long is it going to take for the work to be completed?

Any entry into a confined space for work purposes must be controlled by means of a permit to work scheme.

For further information on working in a confined space refer to Chapter D09 Confined spaces.

Lineside fencing

The boundary of railway property is protected by the erection of lineside fencing. Any work on this fencing must be carried out in a controlled way to prevent inadvertent or unauthorised access to the railway.

Some sections of fencing, due to the close proximity of electrified lines, should be connected together by bonding to earth. This will avoid the risk of electric shock to people coming into contact with the fence.

Trackside safety

Renewal of fencing should be carried out in such a manner that the access created can be controlled by use of personnel or temporary fencing during periods.

Whenever the site has to be left unattended, the fencing must be left in such a state that access cannot be gained.

Lineside vegetation

Removal of lineside vegetation can be hazardous for those involved. These hazards may be:

- ☑ the close proximity of electrified lines
- ☑ fire
- ☑ the types of tool used
- ☑ discarded rubbish
- ☑ vermin infestation.

Removal of vegetation must be carried out in such a way that it does not come within 2.75 metres of overhead electrified power lines and does not cause an obstruction of the track.

Vegetation must not be burnt, because of the risk of smoke obstructing a train driver's vision.

Tools used for vegetation clearance can present hazards of their own. Safe systems of work should be drawn up when tools such as chainsaws and flails are used.

Rubbish attracts vermin, which in turn can create the hazard of Weil's disease. There is also the hazard of discarded hypodermic syringes. These should be removed while taking every precaution against wounds from contaminated sharps. If you come into contact with an unprotected syringe, you should seek immediate medical advice.

Working on stations and platforms

Although passengers use station platforms regularly and feel safe doing so, when work is being carried out a platform can be just as dangerous as the open track.

Work on platforms and the station infrastructure can be in various guises, such as:

- ☑ painting
- ☑ billboard erection
- ☑ maintenance work
- ☑ installation work.

Whatever the work being carried out, the inherent risks are the same. These are the:

- ☑ passage of trains
- ☑ presence of electrified lines
- ☑ movement of station staff
- ☑ movement of passengers and their luggage
- ☑ risk of fire.

Work on stations and platforms should be planned in the same way as work on any other part of the railway system. This will ensure the health and safety of all concerned.

Consideration must be given to the following points whenever work is undertaken on stations or their platforms.

- ☑ Work must not be allowed to interfere with the normal operation of trains.
- ☑ Work must not be allowed to interfere with the normal operation of the station.
- ☑ Work must be carried out safely, bearing in mind the presence of electrified lines.
- ☑ The use of flammable substances may create additional hazards.
- ☑ The way in which materials to be used on site will be transported and stored.

Over the years, work being carried out on stations and their platforms has resulted in fatal accidents. This has been due to the lack of proper planning, failure to isolate power supplies and lack of proper control.

A safety-conscious approach is now being adopted in the way that contracts are drawn up for tendering. It involves bringing into the contract the requirements of the Construction (Design and Management) Regulations, the Railways and Other Guided Transport Systems (Safety) Regulations and the various Railway Group Standards that govern the way in which people work in a railway environment.

The golden rules to remember when working on station platforms are:

- ☑ beware of passing trains
- ☑ beware of electrified lines
- ☑ do not obstruct a train driver's vision of signalling equipment
- ☑ do not obstruct passenger routes
- ☑ know the fire and other emergency procedures.

Working on platforms within four feet of the platform edge, when carrying out engineering or technical activities, is classed as working on or near the line. People working there are required to hold a valid personal track safety certificate, unless a green zone has been established.

A system of creating a 'high street environment' can be accomplished if the work is not on or near the line.

This can be done by erecting a physical barrier or by appointing a site keeper who is responsible for preventing the work encroaching on the railway infrastructure.

2.7 Personal safety

> ! As far as moving trains are concerned, the best form of personal safety is for every person in the workforce to keep a lookout for themselves and for everyone else.

02

Personal protective equipment

The main priority is that workers are easily seen, particularly by train drivers. Therefore, wearing high-visibility clothing is an important requirement. The clothing must conform to the requirements laid down by Network Rail and must be clean and worn correctly. However, train signals are in three colours: red, yellow and green, and so to reduce confusion to train drivers, there are colour restrictions for items of clothing worn by people working on or near a railway. Anything red or green must **not** be worn in case train drivers mistake them for signals.

The minimum PPE for the work site is:

- ☑ high-visibility upper body clothing with reflective tape, which complies with BS EN 471:2003 Class 2 and Railway Group Standard GO/RT3279

- ☑ high-visibility lower body clothing, which complies with BS EN 471

- ☑ a safety helmet, which complies with BS EN 397:2012

- ☑ safety footwear, which complies with BS EN ISO 20345:2011, provides support to the ankle, includes mid-sole protection and has a protective non-conductive toecap

- ☑ other items of PPE as may be required to safely carry out specific tasks.

Working hours

Lord Justice Hidden at the Clapham Disaster Inquiry made several recommendations regarding the causes of accidents. One of his recommendations was that the hours of work should be controlled so as to prevent excessive times on duty.

As a result of these recommendations, the contractor must now prohibit excessive overtime working and shift lengths. Accordingly, personnel should:

- ☑ not work more than 13 turns of duty within any 14 consecutive days

- ☑ not work more than 72 hours within seven consecutive days

- ☑ have a minimum rest period of 12 hours between consecutive shifts

- ☑ not work more than 12 hours in any one shift.

Where a contractor is engaged to work on signal and control systems or the renewal or maintenance of track, the requirements are enhanced to not more than 13 turns of duty to be worked in any 14-day period, and no more than 23 turns of duty to be worked in any two consecutive 14-day periods.

A contractor is required to keep records of the working hours of all staff working on railways, and these records must be kept available for inspection.

Drugs and alcohol

Any person who carries out work on, or which could affect the operation of, railways must comply with the requirements of the Railway Group Standard relating to drugs and alcohol.

This standard lays down the methods that must be adopted to ensure that anyone working on the railway is not under the influence of drugs or alcohol.

Personnel, both railway staff and contractors, working on a railway will be medically screened prior to employment for the presence of:

- ☑ drugs, other than medication that does not affect their work performance

- ☑ more than 29 milligrams of alcohol in 100 ml of blood

- ☑ more than 13 micrograms of alcohol in 100 ml of breath

- ☑ more than 39 milligrams of alcohol in 100 ml of urine.

Trackside safety

Compare these figures to those laid down for driving a car:

☑ not more than 80 milligrams of alcohol per 100 ml of blood

☑ not more than 35 micrograms of alcohol in 100 ml of breath.

It will be seen that far stricter controls are placed on those working on the railway infrastructure than on the ordinary driver.

There is a 'for cause' screening system for screening after a safety-critical incident has taken place. All personnel working on the railway must comply with screening.

Personnel found to register positive in any screening will be dismissed and could face prosecution under the Transport and Works Act for working under the influence of drugs or alcohol in a safety-critical work post.

2.8 Electrified lines

A large amount of the railway network is electrified, creating a hazard to anyone working in the vicinity of these sections.

There are three different types of electrified line:

☑ alternating current (AC) overhead line systems

☑ direct current (DC) third rail systems

☑ DC fourth rail systems.

AC overhead line system

An example of the typical components incorporated in an overhead line equipment system is shown in the following diagram.

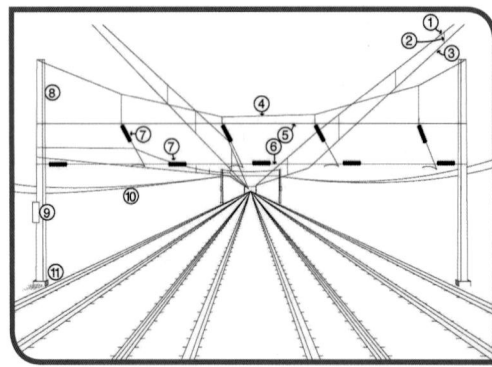

Key

1	Contact wire	7	Insulators
2	Dropper	8	Headspan type structure
3	Contact wire	9	Structure number
4	Headspan wire	10	Return conductors
5	Cross span wires	11	Structure bond
6	Cross span wires		

In addition to the wires shown, bare-feeder wires supply electricity from trackside cabins. The overhead line equipment and attachments are electrified at up to 25,000 volts AC. Current is taken from the suspended contact wire by a pantograph on top of the train and passed through the train equipment to power the motors.

Working on or near overhead line equipment

☑ Assume that the overhead line equipment is live at all times.

☑ Keep people, clothing, tools and equipment at least 2.75 metres from:

– anything attached to, or hanging from, the overhead line equipment

– any broken or displaced wire connected to the overhead line equipment, whether hanging or lying on the ground.

☑ Take extra care not to come within 2.75 metres of overhead line equipment in cuttings, or on embankments, structures or vehicles.

☑ Keep paint, water and other liquids well away from where they could be thrown, splashed or fall onto live overhead line equipment.

☑ Keep tools and equipment or ropes, wires, tapes and surveying equipment clear of live overhead line equipment.

☑ Keep pipes, rods, poles, brooms, mops or ladders horizontal when carried.

☑ Take special care when standing on the floor or load of open wagons if the overhead line equipment is live on the next line.

☑ Make sure there is no possibility of branches or debris coming within 2.75 metres of live overhead line equipment when trimming or felling trees.

☑ Use ladders made of wood or approved non-conducting material. Do not use steel or aluminium ladders, or wooden ladders reinforced by metal attachments.

☑ When cutting water, gas or other metal pipe or metallic cable sheathing you must:

– first connect a temporary electrical continuity jumper cable across the point where you will make the cut

– keep the jumper cable in position until the pipe is again complete.

DC third rail system

Current passes through the third rail, which is raised **slightly above the height** of the running rails and is supported on insulators. The third rail is referred to as the conductor rail and is positively charged at 750 volts DC.

Current is picked up from the conductor rail by a pick-up shoe, situated on the outside of the train and passed through the train equipment down to the motors.

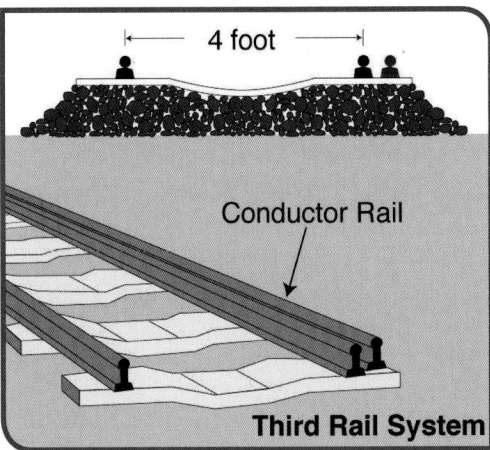

DC fourth rail system

On this system, current is returned to the supply by means of a fourth rail that is situated between the two running rails. The fourth rail, like the third, is mounted upon insulators and is slightly higher than the running rail and positively charged at 750 volts DC.

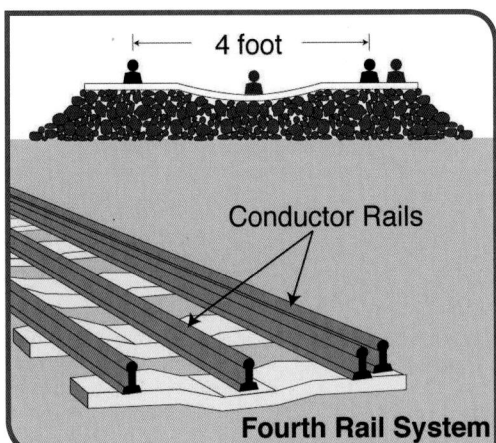

 Even if an electrical isolation permit has been received, it will not prevent the movement of non-electrified trains.

Precautions before working on or near the line

Do not start work on, or close to, the conductor rail (or its connections) until it has been isolated.

The person requiring the isolation will be given a conductor rail permit. However, the issue of this permit does not mean that train movements are stopped on the lines concerned.

Do not work outside the limits shown in the conductor rail permit or those specified by your COSS.

The only exception is when special authority is given for certain types of work to be carried out without isolation. In such instances, precautions are specified that may include the use of approved insulated tools, insulated troughing, approved rubber mats or gloves. These must be in good condition and dry.

Precaution when adjacent to live conductor rails

- ☑ Keep paint, water and other liquids away from where they could be thrown, splashed or fall onto live conductor rails.

- ☑ Keep all tools and equipment or ropes, wires and surveying equipment clear of live conductor rails.

- ☑ Keep pipes, rods, poles, brooms, mops or ladders horizontal when carried, to avoid them accidentally touching the live conductor rails.

02

Precautions when working near DC lines

- ☑ Assume that the conductor rails are live at all times.
- ☑ Avoid crossing the tracks unless it is absolutely necessary, and whenever possible cross at a gap.
- ☑ Do not step on, touch or allow clothing, tools or equipment to come into contact with a conductor rail or any of its connections.
- ☑ Do not step on protection boarding or between a conductor rail and the adjacent running rail but, instead, step over those rails in one movement.
- ☑ Do not touch the collector shoes or their connections on any traction unit, whether or not in contact with the conductor rail.
- ☑ Do not step into flood water, which may be in contact with the conductor rail.
- ☑ If using a track circuit operating clip or device, apply it first to the rail furthest from the conductor rail.

Appendix A – Train sighting chart

Calculating the required sighting distance

 The permissible speed at a location is 75 mph, and the work is of such a nature that the minimum warning time required is 30 seconds. Therefore, the sighting distance required is 1,050 metres.

02

However, not all lengths of track are straight and the view may be obstructed by bends, bridges or other structures. Therefore, it is essential for the COSS to assess these potential hazards as part of the risk assessment and by possibly appointing more than one lookout or alternative mechanical means operated by competent users in order to obtain the necessary sighting distance for an approaching train and to allow time for everyone to get into a position of safety at least 10 seconds before the arrival of the train. There will need to be a warning of the train's approach, which will be given by the site lookout.

Required sighting distances are calculated from the following chart.

Sighting distance chart (metres)

The warning time must be sufficient to enable everyone to be in a position of safety at least 10 seconds before the arrival of a train.

Permissible speed	Sighting distances to provide minimum warning time of:						
(mph)	15 sec	20 sec	25 sec	30 sec	35 sec	40 sec	45 sec
125	900	1,200	1,400	1,700	2,000	2,300	2,600
120	900	1,100	1,400	1,550	1,900	2,200	2,500
115	800	1,100	1,300	1,550	1,800	2,100	2,400
110	800	1,000	1,300	1,500	1,800	2,000	2,300
105	800	1,000	1,200	1,450	1,700	1,900	2,200
100	700	900	1,200	1,350	1,600	1,800	2,050
95	650	850	1,100	1,300	1,500	1,700	1,950
90	650	850	1,050	1,250	1,450	1,700	1,850
85	600	800	950	1,150	1,350	1,600	1,750
80	550	750	900	1,100	1,300	1,500	1,650
75	550	700	850	1,050	1,200	1,400	1,550
70	500	650	800	950	1,100	1,300	1,450
65	450	600	750	900	1,050	1,200	1,350
60	450	550	700	850	950	1,100	1,250
55	400	500	650	750	900	1,000	1,150
50	340	500	600	680	800	900	1,050
45	320	420	520	620	720	820	920
40	280	360	460	540	640	720	820
35	240	320	400	480	560	640	720
30	220	280	340	420	480	540	620
25	180	240	280	340	400	460	520
20	140	180	240	280	320	360	420
15	120	160	180	220	240	280	320
10	80	100	120	140	160	180	220
5	40	60	60	80	80	100	120

If the work involves the use of noisy equipment, the noise produced may prevent the work team from being able to hear any warnings given by lookouts, a problem compounded by the requirement of wearing ear protection.

In such situations, a system of alerting the workers by the use of a touch lookout is implemented. This entails a lookout at the worksite to touch all the members of the work team to warn them of approaching trains.

Appendix B – Fencing and separation

 The green zones are depicted by a hatched area, shown ///

Figure 1

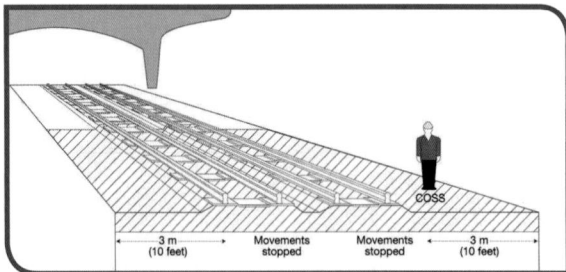

The diagram above shows a **safeguarded** green zone, with movements stopped on all lines.

Figure 2

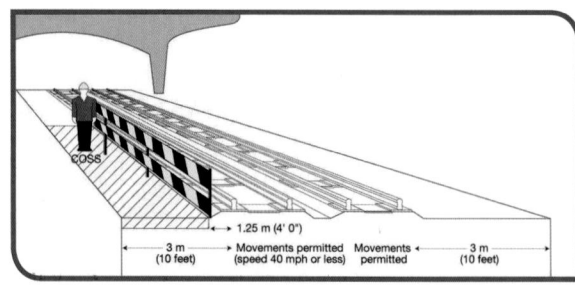

This diagram shows a **fenced** green zone using barricade tape or Netlon, with movements permitted on both lines but at a speed of 40 mph or less on the **adjacent line**.

Figure 3

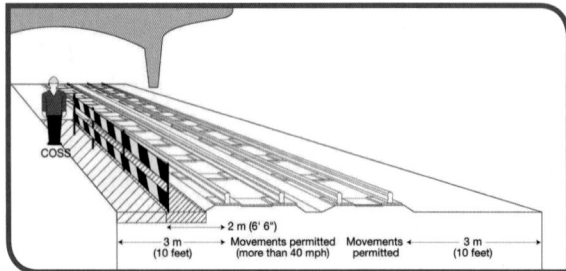

The diagram above shows a **fenced** green zone using barricade tape or Netlon, with movements permitted on both lines and at a speed of over 40 mph on the **adjacent line**.

Figure 4

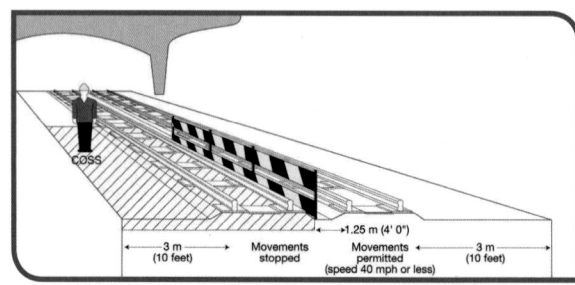

This diagram shows a **fenced** green zone using barricade tape or Netlon, with movements permitted on one line only at a speed of 40 mph or less.

Figure 5

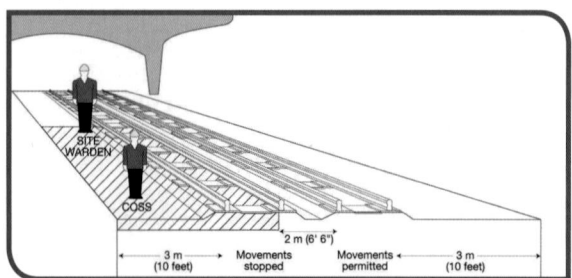

The diagram above shows a **separated** green zone, with movements permitted on one line only and where one or more site warden(s) has been appointed.

Figure 6

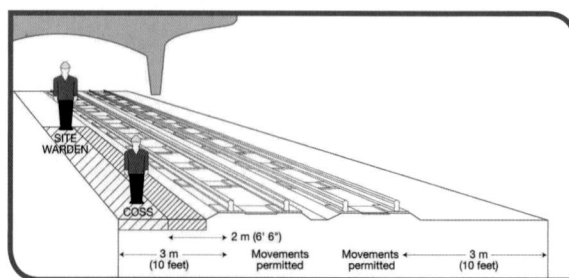

This diagram shows a **separated** green zone, with movements permitted on both lines and where one or more site warden(s) has been appointed.

03

Demolition

Demolition is dangerous, of a technical nature and must be carried out by competent persons only.

This chapter gives an understanding of the problems associated with demolition and the good practices that must be followed to appoint competent demolition contractors.

Introduction	44
Key requirements	44
Legal requirements	45
Project documents	47
The selection and appointment of a demolition contractor	49
Planning for demolition	50
Essential elements of a demolition health and safety plan	51
Methods of demolition	53
Environmental and other considerations	57
Monitoring the work	59
Appendix A – Definitions and terms used by the demolition industry	60

Demolition

3.1 Introduction

Safe demolition is a very complex and technical skill. It is also potentially very dangerous if carried out by contractors who are not fully competent in demolition techniques and planning.

The word *demolition* is often misconstrued to mean large-scale, or to involve the complete removal of a structure or building. However, the removal of a single element or the part-removal of a structure or building also constitutes demolition.

Information, planning, responsible implementation and controls are the essential elements for safe and successful demolition projects.

Whether demolition is required for a small building or structure, or for a complex factory site, you must be aware of the hazards and risks. These need to be identified, assessed and effectively controlled to avoid danger and reduce the potential for injury to persons and damage to property, as far as is reasonably practicable.

A systematic approach to the demolition process starts with responsible clients appointing adequately resourced and competent duty holders, CDM co-ordinators, designers, principal contractors and contractors. Inexperienced clients may well need to seek assistance for guidance in the procurement, appointment and management of demolition.

In general

- ☑ Demolition works should be planned in such a way that it is undertaken using systems of work that take into consideration safety, health, the environment and efficiency.

- ☑ All those involved, from concept, through tender, to contract execution, should ensure effective planning and communication, and the provision of sufficient time to allow the execution of a successful and efficient project.

- ☑ The timescales required for the acquisition of any licences or permits should be allowed for in the programming of works.

- ☑ After the contract has been awarded, and before work commences, the contractor should determine the proposed safe sequence of operations on the basis of an assessment of the comparative risks, related specifically to the site and conditions.

- ☑ This sequence should be used to assess and expand the construction phase plan (CPP) for the tender and proposed programme of works.

- ☑ The expanded plan for the tender should form the basis of the CPP (demolition plan) for the demolition.

- ☑ Management plans for waste may also be considered.

- ☑ The methods of work should allow for demolition activities and site clearance, as stipulated by the contract, taking account of any constraints imposed by the client.

- ☑ Adequate time should be allowed for setting up the site prior to work commencing and for executing the works.

3.2 Key requirements

- ☑ Demolition can be dangerous and should be left to competent persons. Almost all demolition projects will encounter asbestos.

- ☑ Recognise that structural refurbishment may involve demolition activities and plan accordingly.

- ☑ Planning and supervision is vital to ensure a successful project.

- ☑ Demolition should be carried out by following the British Standard.

- ☑ Ensure that prior to all demolition a site-specific refurbishment or demolition asbestos survey, as defined in the HSE publication *Asbestos: The survey guide* (HSG264), has been carried out by a competent person and that the information is available to those who need it.

- ☑ It should be noted that, wherever paintwork/coatings are likely to be damaged or disturbed, the HSE advises lead (paint) surveys are carried out **regardless of the age of the building or the extent of the works**.

- ☑ The Construction (Design and Management) Regulations apply to all demolition and dismantling projects, regardless of size, but not all projects will be notifiable to the HSE.

- ☑ Ensure the works are properly planned with written risk assessments and method statements developed, communicated and understood.

- ☑ Ascertain if the structures are stable before starting, to ensure that instability can be avoided during the works, unless planned.

- ☑ Salvage or soft stripping are particularly hazardous and must be planned and controlled to avoid the risk of uncontrolled release of asbestos, falling objects and/or collapse.

- ☑ Demolition arisings should follow the hierarchy of minimisation: reuse, recycle, with waste being handled, managed and disposed of in accordance with current legislation.

- ☑ If treating demolition arisings/waste (such as screening or crushing) ensure the relevant licences, permits/exemptions are in place.

- ☑ Ensure the waste duty of care documentation is obtained, completed correctly and records kept.

- ☑ A waste management plan must be developed and be kept up-to-date, including records of all demolition waste streams and the quantities.

The *Code of practice for full and partial demolition* (BS 6187:2011) takes the form of guidance and recommendations. The standard has been revised to reflect advances in technology and equipment in the demolition industry, and to give recommendations on the following principal areas:

☑ project development and management, site assessments, risk assessments, decommissioning procedures, environmental provisions and façade retention

☑ deconstruction techniques, including activities for reuse and recycling

☑ exclusion zones and safe working spaces, including their design and application.

Recommendations for methods of, and techniques for, demolition and partial demolition, including for structural refurbishment, have been retained, with consideration of specific types of structure, but the text has been significantly updated to reflect current and developing good practices. By being less prescriptive, this edition also allows for innovative techniques and methods to be employed.

03

3.3   Legal requirements

The Building Act

Section 80 of the Act requires persons intending to carry out the demolition of a structure, or part-structure greater than 1,750 cubic feet (approximately 50 m³), to give six weeks' notice to the Local Authority Building Control Department, which usually incurs an administration fee. A Section 81/82 counter notice is usually issued, providing consent with conditions or a refusal with reasons.

This is normally something that the client should have organised, but it frequently falls to the demolition contractor, as the Local Authority requires timescales with outline detail on the methodology and so on.

The Construction (Design and Management) Regulations

Readers are advised:

☑ **to refer to the Approved Code of Practice (ACoP) that supports the Construction (Design and Management) Regulations (CDM)**

☑ **that under these regulations the definition of construction includes demolition and dismantling, and is to be regarded as such when used in the following text.**

CDM applies to all construction, which includes demolition and dismantling work, as defined in BS 6187, regardless of the project's size or duration. The work will be notifiable to the Health and Safety Executive (HSE) if the thresholds are exceeded requiring the formal appointment of a CDM co-ordinator (CDMC) and principal contractor (PC).

Notifiable CDM project criteria is that it will:

☑ last longer than 30 working days, or

☑ involve more than 500 person-days of demolition and/or construction work.

To ensure site safety during demolition the principal or main contractor must ensure that one or more competent person(s) are appointed to plan and supervise the work. It is a legal requirement under CDM that any duty holder who puts another person to work on a construction site (for example, a principal contractor engaging the services of a demolition contractor) must ensure that the person is competent to do what is required of them.

For non-notifiable projects, the main responsibility for health and safety will normally rest on the contractor doing the work. The client has to ensure that they have supplied adequate information and that there are adequate welfare arrangements in place. The demolition contractor is therefore expected to control and co-ordinate all aspects of health and safety, regardless of the size of the project.

The ACoP gives guidance on competence checks, for example:

☑ for organisations:
   – Stage 1. Knowledge
   – Stage 2. Experience

☑ for individuals:
   – members of institutions (IDE, NFDC and so on)
   – holders of CSCS, CCDO cards.

The National Federation of Demolition Contractors (NFDC) and the Institute of Demolition Engineers (IDE) can provide information regarding the competence required for particular projects.

Demolition

Within CDM, two regulations (summarised below) specifically need to be considered when undertaking demolition activities.

Stability of structures

☑ All practicable steps shall be taken, where necessary, to prevent danger to any persons, to ensure that any new or existing structure or any part of such structure that may become unstable or in a temporary state of weakness or instability, due to carrying out of construction work, does not collapse.

☑ Any buttress, temporary support or temporary structure must be of such design and so installed and maintained as to withstand any foreseeable loads that may be imposed on it, and must only be used for the purposes for which it is so designed, installed and maintained.

☑ No part of a structure shall be so loaded as to render it unsafe to any person.

Demolition or dismantling

The demolition or dismantling of a structure or part of a structure shall be planned and carried out to prevent danger, so far as is reasonably practicable, or reduce the danger to as low a level as is reasonably practicable.

The arrangements for carrying out demolition or dismantling work shall be recorded in writing, prior to the commencement of the work.

CDM duty holders

The **client** is responsible for the provision of information (such as the results of any refurbishment/demolition asbestos survey and the location and status of utility services). The client must also:

☑ appoint various other duty holders where the project is notifiable to the HSE

☑ ensure that adequate welfare facilities are provided

☑ not permit work to start until there is evidence of adequate health and safety management systems and planning.

The client sets the tone for the intended demolition and, as such, care should be taken to ensure sufficient time and resources are made available to properly plan, procure and carry out the works.

The **designer** is responsible for making the client aware of the client's responsibilities under the regulations, as well as the design of the project. Design may include any structural work and temporary works design.

For notifiable works, the **CDM co-ordinator** is responsible for the co-ordination of health and safety design and planning aspects for notifiable projects, including:

☑ advising the client

☑ identifying and collecting pre-construction information

☑ informing the client if there are gaps in the pre-construction information that need to be addressed (for example, additional surveys)

☑ distributing relevant parts of the pre-construction information to contractors to enable them to tender for, or prepare to carry out, the work

☑ generally managing the flow of information between all parties

☑ preparing the health and safety file

☑ ensuring the project is notified to the HSE.

The CDM co-ordinator's role is also to advise the client on the competency and resourcing of contractors and to ensure that the principal contractor's health and safety plan is adequately developed prior to the work starting on site.

The minimum lead times for the project must form part of the information pack. CDM co-ordinators must themselves be competent; demolition and asbestos issues may be too specialist for many who normally perform the co-ordinator's role and they should be prepared to take specialist advice.

For notifiable works, the **principal contractor** must ensure that the client is aware of their duties and is responsible for the overall construction phase, taking into account health and safety issues and the development of the health and safety plan.

Contractors and other workers must all work together as a team to achieve high standards in health, safety and welfare on site. The contractors, which normally include utility companies, must co-operate with the principal contractor by obeying site rules, and so on.

Where the project is too short to be notifiable, the contractor has a responsibility to ensure that the client is aware of their duties and to manage the health and safety of the project. It is foreseeable that a written health and safety plan would be required for all but the very simplest of demolition projects.

The **demolition contractor** may be appointed as the principal contractor for notifiable work subject to having the necessary expertise and understanding to undertake the role.

Irrespective of the size of the project, the demolition contractor must ensure the work is properly planned and carried out safely with the arrangements recorded (risk assessment, method statements, programme and so on). They must also ensure these arrangements are communicated and clearly understood by those carrying out the work.

3.4   Project documents

Demolition plan

All demolition, and partial demolition, activities should be planned and carried out in such a way as to remove or reduce the risks to people to as low as reasonably practicable.

> The arrangements for carrying out such demolition, or partial demolition, should be recorded in writing before the demolition work begins, with a level of detail proportionate to the risks involved. For projects notifiable under CDM the demolition plan should form part of the construction phase plan prepared by the principal contractor.

On individual projects, the demolition plan should be the focus for ensuring adequate co-operation, co-ordination and planning between all members of the project team. Adequate pre-construction information should be provided by the client to allow the contractor to identify the hazards and risks associated with the proposed work.

The construction phase plan

The **construction phase plan** (often referred to as the health and safety plan) provides a focus for the construction phase of a project.

Relevant pre-construction information, relating to the health and safety hazards associated with the work, should be provided by the client regardless of the size of the project. If the project is notifiable, the CDM co-ordinator must carry out the tasks outlined previously, with regard to the collection and distribution of the pre-construction information.

In the context of this chapter, such information is likely to include:

- ☑ the location and physical condition of any asbestos where its presence has been identified by a refurbishment/demolition asbestos survey, as defined in HSG264
- ☑ the results of structural surveys
- ☑ notices, acknowledgements and disconnection certificates received for all services
- ☑ plans identifying the location of underground services
- ☑ the possible presence of contaminants, for example:
  - polychlorinated biphenyls (PCBs) in old electrical transformers
  - the residual contents of tanks and pipelines
  - the location and nature of contaminated ground
- ☑ any other information that is required to ensure that the work can be planned safely and would not reasonably be expected to be known by a competent contractor.

After being appointed by the client, the principal contractor must use the pre-construction information provided by the client to develop the construction phase plan to the satisfaction of the client, as advised by the CDM co-ordinator.

The health and safety plan must be:

- ☑ sufficiently developed prior to any work commencing on site
- ☑ reviewed and amended as often as is necessary for the duration of the project
- ☑ communicated to those on the site insofar as it is necessary for any person to be aware of any part of it.

Risk assessment

The following principles of risk assessment should be followed when determining methods and sequences of work.

☑ Identify the hazards associated with the proposed work.

☑ Consider who might be harmed and how, including workers, site visitors, members of the public and anyone affected by the work.

☑ Evaluate the risks and identify the precautions required by, for example, comparison with good practice and categorisation of risk level (likelihood and severity).

☑ Record the findings and implement the control measures for the residual risks.

☑ Review the risk assessment and update if necessary.

The risk assessment should take into account any constraints that the client has identified, but the contractor should be given the freedom to determine the proposed methods of demolition.

The risk assessment should identify the risks associated with the work and enable the contractor to select appropriate demolition solutions that remove or reduce the risks before the work commences.

The contractor should then select the most suitable methods of demolition, which include measures to properly control any remaining risks.

Method statement

Method statements should address the particular needs of the site and detail the planned sequences and methods of demolition works. The proposed working methods should be assessed to determine whether a number of method statements are required, particularly where the operations are phased.

Method statements should be prepared in such a way that they enable supervisors and managers to ensure that persons on site are made aware of how the work is to be carried out, including the sequence of operations, the plant and types of equipment to be used and the precautions to be taken, as appropriate.

 Methods such as toolbox talks are recommended to help in disseminating the information, especially for those carrying out the work.

Method statements should be regarded as live documents and modified as required to cater for planned changes in systems of work.

The health and safety file

The health and safety file is a record of information for the client or end-user of the premises. Its purpose is to inform anyone who might be responsible for the structure in future, of the risks that will have to be managed during any maintenance, repair or renovation. Generally, for demolition work, the health and safety file will contain information such as details of:

☑ any services that have been capped or discovered and worked around

☑ the presence of any voids and details of any areas that may have been filled

☑ the actions taken to remove or treat contaminated land

☑ asbestos removal, including copies of the four-stage clearance certificate and disposal records.

Such information may be useful to add to the asbestos management plan for a site, or to provide confirmation for future use that contaminants have been removed from the site.

Summary of statutory notifications

The Building Act

Where the volume of demolition exceeds 1,750 cubic feet, six weeks' advance notice must be given to the Local Authority Building Control Office, requesting permission for demolition.

CDM

Notifiable projects are notified to the HSE on Form 10 (revised) by the CDM co-ordinator and follow on when the principal contractor is appointed.

Asbestos Regulations

14 days' notice on form ASB 5 must be given to the HSE or Local Authority where work with licensable asbestos is involved.

Hazardous waste

Regulations require any site generating more than 500 kg of hazardous waste per year (for example, asbestos) to register with the Environment Agency/Scottish Environment Protection Agency. (This can be completed online.)

Advance applications must be made to the Environment Agency or Scottish Environment Protection Agency (SEPA) to carry out a notifiable exempt waste management activity.

3.5   The selection and appointment of a demolition contractor

The client or principal contractor, in selecting a demolition contractor, should satisfy themselves of the contractor's competence, knowledge, ability and resources to carry out the work safely.

Expertise is vital. Under the requirements of CDM, where a project is notifiable, the client has to appoint a competent CDM co-ordinator and principal contractor to co-ordinate and manage the health and safety issues during the demolition works. The principal contractor's role may well be taken by the demolition contractor. References must be sought, and pertinent questions asked, to establish the credibility of the contractor involved.

Assistance may be sought by asking the CDM co-ordinator for their advice and input during the selection and appointment process. Care must be taken to ensure that the CDM co-ordinator has the necessary level of competence in demolition work as it is a very specialist field.

Alternatively, it may be prudent to consider appointing an independent demolition adviser.

 A useful source of information is the Institute of Demolition Engineers.

Pre-qualification

If more than five people are employed, the contractor should have a written health and safety policy, which should be divided into three separate parts.

Part 1	A general statement of health and safety policy.
Part 2	The organisation and structure of that policy with details of people who have responsibilities under this document.
Part 3	Details of the practical arrangements for health and safety.

The health and safety policy should be signed and dated by the director responsible and communicated to employees.

The client should also consider the following.

- ☑ Does the contractor employ a health and safety adviser, or do they utilise the services of a health and safety adviser or consultants?

- ☑ If consultants are used, how often will they visit the site?

- ☑ Are the consultants experienced in the health and safety management requirements of demolition sites?

- ☑ Are the consultants always available for advice, particularly if something goes wrong?

The safety record of the contractor should also be considered.

- ☑ Are safety statistics for injuries, lost time and dangerous occurrences kept and available?

- ☑ Has the HSE issued any improvement or prohibition notices against the contractor? If so, have the causes of the problems been resolved?

- ☑ Are there any pending potential enforcement actions against the contractor?

- ☑ Is it the intention to use contractors? If so, for what elements and how do they select and control contractors?

- ☑ Is the contractor a member of the NFDC?

Membership of this organisation is a useful Stage 1 (knowledge) competence indicator under CDM and will give the client the assurance of a minimum of five years' satisfactory trading experience, and a knowledge that certain recognised minimum standards have been and are being met (for example, insurance, training and supervision).

However, irrespective of membership of the NFDC, checks must be made regarding whether the organisation has the relevant experience (Stage 2) competence under CDM.

- ☑ Does the contractor have adequate public and employer's liability insurance that covers demolition?

Check for any restrictive covenants or other restrictions (for example, for work to be carried out above a height of 30 metres).

- ☑ Are the company's employees on the scheme for the certification of competence for demolition operatives (Levels 1, 2 or 3)?

- ☑ Are references available? It is useful to speak to a client from a similar job as well as from their last project.

Appointing a contractor

A genuine and competent contractor will not object to supplying the name of the client for whom the last contract was carried out. If that client is then contacted, they can be asked whether they were satisfied with the work.

They can be asked for information on the works, type, size, approximate value and so on, and asked the following questions.

☑ Were any problems experienced during the works?

☑ How did the contractor perform overall?

☑ Would they use the contractor again?

These are just examples of the kinds of question that should be asked to ensure satisfaction when considering the appointment of such a contractor.

An interview with the potential contractor should be held to clarify matters. The client can also see if they would be prepared, or if they are qualified and competent, to take on the role of principal contractor.

3.6 Planning for demolition

 It cannot be emphasised too strongly that demolition is dangerous and must be left to the experts (that is, competent persons). Planning and supervision are of paramount importance.

Before any work starts, the implications of the demolition to be carried out must be determined.

☑ What is the age of the building(s) and what was (were) the previous use(s)?

☑ What was the type of construction and what were the materials used?

☑ What is the scope and extent of the works?

☑ How much is to go?

☑ Are floor slabs or piles involved?

☑ Where are the separation points?

☑ Are there any dangerous substances in, around or under the building, which are to be demolished (for example, asbestos, lead paints, flammable liquids, unidentified drums or packages, and so on)?

☑ Is asbestos suspected? If so, a full invasive refurbishment/demolition survey must be carried out to form part of the pre-construction information.

☑ Is the building on contaminated land?

☑ Are there any site restrictions?

☑ Are there people and adjacent properties that may be affected by the proposed working hours?

☑ Will people be affected by noise or vibration emanating from the site? If so, a Section 61 noise notice may be required.

☑ Will there be a need to carry out a dilapidation survey of the adjacent buildings and/or highways?

☑ Will any waste management licences or permits be required to process or reuse the demolished material?

☑ Is the project likely to be notifiable?

☑ Who will notify the Local Authority under the Building Act, Section 80 (>1,750 ft^3)?

The information above would form the basis of the pre-construction information collected by the CDM co-ordinator under CDM.

Once these things have been determined, decisions should be taken as to what are the acceptable or unacceptable methods to carry out the demolition.

Information on contaminated land must include details of the past and current uses of the site. Advice can be sought from the Environment Agency/SEPA and Local Authority Environmental Health Department. This may result in a requirement for a site survey, including the taking, observation and analysis of core samples.

Two important final questions remain.

☑ How should the job and site be left safe?

☑ What is the timescale for the job to be carried out and is it sufficient for the demolition to be carried out safely?

The latter point is particularly relevant as CDM places a duty on the client to indicate the minimum project mobilisation period, with notifiable projects recording this period on the F10.

3.7 Essential elements of a demolition health and safety plan

Some or all of the following points may be covered in the risk assessment and method statement for the proposed job.

Project information

Names, addresses, contacts and telephone numbers should be detailed indicating the client, project managers, quantity surveyors, architects, structural engineers, the CDM co-ordinator and principal contractor.

Scope of work

An explicit and concise opening paragraph should be included, outlining the extent of work, along with any other related activities (such as asbestos removal), items or equipment to be recovered and set aside, façade retention, and so on.

03

Existing environmental information and drawings

Where available, construction drawings should have been supplied to the contractor, along with information on the former use of the site or buildings to be demolished. This information should include the health and safety file, to determine what (if any) physical or chemical hazards are on the site or in the buildings (such as underground tanks and/or potential chemical or biological hazards or contaminated land).

The details of the building or structure should be checked to ensure that it is not a listed building. In addition, the locality of the site in relation to schools, roads, hospitals and so on, which may be affected by the demolition activity, should be taken into account.

Risk assessment and special hazards

Having gathered all available information and visited the site to assess the work involved, along with identifying all known hazards and confined spaces, the contractor's appointed person on site should ensure that risk assessments, and assessments for asbestos, lead, Control of Substances Hazardous to Health (COSHH) or noise are made. Method statements should then be drawn up.

Information from these assessments should be included in the health and safety plan for the project, which must also take into consideration risks to health, and detail any safety precautions that are being taken to control and manage the risks.

Consideration must be given at an early stage to control the access for workers and any visitors, and ensure separate access and egress for vehicles, plant and machinery.

Finally, assess the impact that the site environment will have on any people who might be affected by the activity (such as neighbours or members of the public).

 For further information on method statements and risk assessments, including examples of both, refer to Chapter A05 Risk assessments and method statements.

Personnel and the appointed person

All persons on site are responsible for health and safety. The following have specific responsibility for health and safety and for supervision of the site:

- ☑ all designers
- ☑ the co-ordinator (including changes to the design)
- ☑ the principal contractor (or main contractor on non-notifiable projects)
- ☑ the demolition contractor and specialist sub-contractors (for example, asbestos removal contractors)
- ☑ the director responsible for safety
- ☑ the site safety adviser
- ☑ the contracts manager
- ☑ the appointed person – a competent demolition foreman
- ☑ the person who has first aid or emergency aid training
- ☑ all other contractors on site.

A method of recording who is on site must be rigorously maintained throughout the contract by signing in and out in the (daily) site register.

The principal contractor/contractor, with support from the appointed person and others, must ensure that the relevant sections of the health and safety plan are communicated to all people on site at appropriate intervals (such as site induction, task talks and toolbox talks).

These occasions should be recorded and signed for in order to gain ownership by the recipients.

Demolition

 A card scheme for the certification of competence of demolition operatives is operated by CITB-ConstructionSkills.

- ☑ **Green card** – demolition site operative (little or no experience).

- ☑ **Red card** – labourer/reclamation and salvage operative (one year's experience or more).

- ☑ **White card** – related occupation (with little or no experience).

- ☑ **Blue card** – experienced worker (mattockman or topman) (two years' experience, depending on category).

- ☑ **Blue card** – mattockman (holds an experienced worker card and has achieved NVQ/SVQ Level 2).

- ☑ **Blue card** – topman (holds an experienced worker card and has achieved all eight units of NVQ/SVQ Level 2).

- ☑ **Gold card** – demolition supervisor (holds an experienced worker card and has passed a 12-week distance learning course with minimum five years' experience).

Programme

The programme time allocated must be adequate to allow the demolition work to be carried out safely. This should detail the mobilisation and planning, and correct sequence of the works with any stop and review points.

Where the programme has unavoidable interfaces with other trades or contractors on site, this must be recognised as a potential area of risk. Good communications, planning and management are therefore essential to ensure high standards in health and safety.

The operator of crushing equipment must also give notice to their relevant Local Authority of their intention to carry out crushing activities each time the equipment is moved.

Services

Before any work starts, all utility companies must be contacted by the client or, if agreed, by the CDM co-ordinator, and sent a site plan showing the footprint and extent of the planned demolition, with the proposed commencement date, requesting the disconnection or isolation of the appropriate service (in other words electricity, gas, water, telecommunications or other cables).

These requests should be made in good time and be acknowledged in writing by the relevant utility, with confirmation that the services have or will be isolated or disconnected.

Prior to their arrival on site, utility companies should be sent any relevant sections of the pre-construction information to incorporate within their own safe systems of work (for example, details of ground contamination and/or unsafe conditions or structures prevailing on site).

Where such disconnection is not possible, any pipes or cables should be clearly identified, marked and protected to ensure that they are not disturbed during the works.

Disconnection certificates must be received and be on site before any demolition work commences.

Finally, if in doubt over any services, the contractor should seek further advice from the utility provider.

If overhead power lines are present, care needs to be taken, particularly where machines, cranes or excavators with high reach are to be used. Adequate control measures should be put in place (such as warning goalposts).

 For further information refer to Chapter D08 Underground and overhead services.

Lead

Exposure risks from lead paint, dust and fumes are most likely to occur in pre-1970 buildings, especially during repair, maintenance, refurbishment and demolition, if proper precautions are not followed. It should be noted that, wherever paintwork/coatings are likely to be damaged or disturbed, the HSE advises lead (paint) surveys **regardless of the age of the building or the extent of the works.**

 Information on reducing the health risks in construction work can be found on the HSE's website.

 For further information refer to Chapter B12 Lead.

Asbestos considerations

Under Asbestos Regulations, there is a duty on building owners and/or the tenants 'duty holder(s)' to identify (via asbestos surveys) and manage the presence of asbestos in the non-domestic properties under their control. HSE publication HSG264 provides guidance on:

- ☑ the two types of survey
- ☑ the circumstances in which either type of survey would be required
- ☑ appointing a competent asbestos surveyor
- ☑ the exchange of information that is necessary between all interested parties
- ☑ avoiding caveats whereby some areas would not be surveyed
- ☑ what should be expected by way of a survey report.

The regulations:

- ☑ state that all asbestos-containing materials should be removed prior to demolition, so far as is reasonably practicable
- ☑ require that the necessary planning actions and notifications are carried out.

The management process should be based on the information gained from a refurbishment/demolition asbestos survey, carried out before contractors are invited to tender for the demolition. This should include a drawing of the building footprint (all floors) and a list of the approximate amounts and locations of asbestos-containing materials found. Simply writing 'throughout the building' is not acceptable and the client should be informed that the survey is inadequate. The survey should be checked for any exclusions (caveats) or areas not accessed and for any specific recommendations. However, it should be noted that such clauses are generally unacceptable, as detailed in HSG264.

If the survey identifies high-risk notifiable asbestos materials (typically asbestos insulation, coatings and insulating board), which require a licensed contractor, then 14 days must be allowed for the notification process to the enforcing authority, usually the HSE.

From the survey, an inventory of asbestos-containing materials should be made and ticked off as they are removed. This should prevent creating risk during soft strip and demolition.

There are many occasions when asbestos-containing materials are only revealed during the demolition.

All operatives and machine drivers must receive regular training in basic asbestos recognition (minimum half-day asbestos awareness course) so that they can recognise materials that could be, or contain, asbestos and stop work and take appropriate advice.

3.8   Methods of demolition

This section gives an outline of the types of demolition techniques commonly employed with a view to giving the reader an appreciation of the demolition activity.

Risk assessments, method statements and sequence

The key to a successful demolition is to ensure the appropriate risk assessments and method statements have been developed to identify the correct sequence of carrying out the work. These must be recorded in writing, fit for purpose, clearly communicated and understood by the persons using them.

Partial demolition

Partial demolition is often carried out where refurbishment is being undertaken and can include façade retention. In any demolition, daily or, if required, more frequent checks should be carried out to confirm the stability of the remaining structure.

If at any time during the demolition the structure appears or becomes unsafe, all workers should be withdrawn until actions have been taken to remove any danger.

This may involve the use of mini machines (such as skid steers and/or mini excavators). Therefore, an assessment of the floor-loading capacity should be undertaken by a competent person (such as a structural engineer) to take into account the dead and live loads and so on.

Progressive (top-down) demolition

Progressive demolition is generally carried out in the reverse order to construction, and often follows the soft strip-out phase.

This is the most commonly used method of demolishing structures and should be detailed in the health and safety plan.

In high-rise buildings where a floor-by-floor demolition is being carried out, danger points should be recognised, such as:

- ☑ structural stability
- ☑ on-floor loadings (machinery and arisings)
- ☑ falling debris
- ☑ slips, trips and falls
- ☑ maintaining clear access and egress
- ☑ risk of fire hazards
- ☑ the need for secure edge protection.

03

Demolition by deliberate collapse

Demolition by deliberate collapse can be achieved by pre-weakening the structure, followed by explosives, remote mechanical demolition by an excavator, high-reach or crawler crane or similar, or occasionally by pulling it down, using a wire rope.

When explosives are being considered, only fully qualified explosive engineers should be used (for example, members of the Institute of Explosives Engineers).

Manual demolition techniques

Manual demolition techniques are used when other methods of demolition are not suitable or possible (for example, city centre or confined sites, where there is insufficient space around the structure for remote mechanical demolition).

Some of the types of tools or operations that can be used in manual demolition are:

- ☑ hand tools
- ☑ breakers, compressors or hammers
- ☑ concrete nibblers or hydraulic pulverisers
- ☑ stitch drilling
- ☑ drilling and hydraulic bursting

- ☑ drilling and expansive pastes
- ☑ oxygen and propane cutting equipment
- ☑ diamond cutting and sawing
- ☑ steeplejacking.

General precautions

For brick or concrete structures:

- ☑ identify any pre-stressed or post-tensioned concrete beams that may be present within the structure and determine a safe method of demolition
- ☑ wherever practicable, carry out demolition in the reverse order to construction
- ☑ maintain tools in good condition, and use them safely
- ☑ use compressed air or portable electric power tools, from a 110 volt supply
- ☑ make operatives fully aware of the safe procedures
- ☑ recognise the potential exposure to high levels of noise and vibration levels requiring assessments and the associated control measures
- ☑ in addition to site induction, ensure task and toolbox talks are prepared, delivered and understood at key stages of the work.

As far as is reasonably practicable, employees should not work above each other and care must be taken to ensure that debris does not drop into other working areas.

If lift shafts or other formed openings are used to drop debris down, the lift car and equipment must be removed in advance to remove any snagging points, openings must be adequately protected by either suitable guard-rails and toe-boards (with no gap between guard-rails and toe-boards exceeding 470 mm) or by other substantial, effective barriers. It may not be possible to guard an opening where plant (such as a bob cat) is being used to bulldoze arisings into a shaft or chute. In such cases a safe system of work must be developed, which is sufficiently robust to:

- ☑ stop the item of plant falling into the chute or shaft
- ☑ control when materials will be loaded and unloaded to stop materials being tipped onto someone below
- ☑ protect other workers from falling down the shaft.

It is still acceptable to use window openings as a means of removing debris from upper floors under certain conditions. The opening would have to be protected to prevent operatives falling whilst throwing the debris out. Furthermore, the landing zone (that is, the elevation to receive the arisings) must be clearly identified and completely protected so that materials cannot fall on anyone. Typically the area will be fenced off with mobile fence panels and then the material loaded with an excavator into a hook bin container. If the structure has more than two storeys, consideration should be given to the prevailing wind conditions as well as creating an enclosed drop zone within a scaffold chute.

With regard to falling materials and exposed edges, where necessary danger areas (exclusion zones) must be created in accordance with the requirements of the Work at Height Regulations.

Provision and use of work equipment

The Provision and Use of Work Equipment Regulations (PUWER) cover equipment used in demolition. They require that an employer supplies work equipment that is safe, correct and suitable for the job, and that the equipment is maintained.

Demolition traditionally involves some work being carried out at height, particularly salvage and soft stripping (for example, the recovery of slates), which has in the past been the cause of deaths and injuries to demolition operatives. Due to advances in demolition techniques, and the increasing size and reach of the machines used, there is now a reduced need to work at height. However, the presence of such machines on site brings about responsibilities for servicing, maintenance, thorough inspections, operator competence and so on under these regulations.

Under the regulations, falling object protection is required for machinery. A demolition specification excavator must have a cab guard, as it is foreseeable when working overhead that material could fall onto the cab. The use of reinforcing bars as makeshift retaining pins for attachments would be contrary to these regulations.

It is common to see mobile crushers used in the demolition process to process the demolition arisings for reuse as part of the next use of the site. These machines pose great risks to the untrained. Issues such as machinery guarding and clearing blockages, as well as noise and vibration, must be considered.

Safe working practices dictate that operators must not be standing:

☑ on a crusher whilst it is running (for example, trying to remove foreign objects from the demolition arisings)

☑ near the crushing jaws.

Oxy-propane cutting equipment

The use of oxy-propane cutting equipment requires that:

☑ operatives are trained and competent in the safe use of the equipment

☑ appropriate PPE is used (such as the correct goggles and hand/arm protection)

☑ the equipment is inspected and tested for leaks before use

☑ cylinders are secured in an upright position

☑ hoses are secured with crimped fittings, not jubilee clips

☑ flashback arresters are always fitted between cylinder gauges and hoses

☑ spare cylinder storage areas are separated by a gap of at least three metres between oxygen and propane bottles.

Whenever oxy-propane cutting equipment is used, the correct fire-fighting equipment must always be available. All operatives should be trained in the safe use of fire extinguishers.

Hot work should generally be stopped for an agreed period before leaving site, typically one hour before finishing, to avoid the potential of fire.

 For more information refer to Chapter C02 Fire prevention and control.

Mechanical demolition techniques

Machinery should be fit for purpose, used in safe working spaces, adequately protected (for example, by ROPs and/or FOPs) and operated by authorised competent persons (for example, holding a CPCS card for the appropriate category of machine).

Remote control demolition

This utilises specialised equipment, often in hazardous or aggressive environments (for example, nuclear installations). The use of Brock-type machines is becoming more common and they offer possible solutions to the difficulties of complying with the problems of noise and vibration experienced during hand demolition.

These types of machine are particularly useful where the machine is breaking out the structure of the floor above, and/or when the operating surface is being progressively removed and the operator can stand well clear of the danger.

Using a 360° excavator with multi-functional attachments

This type of demolition is commonly used to demolish low buildings, or is used after other height reduction techniques have been carried out.

To avoid physical injury from movement of the parts of the building being demolished, the machine should work in its own zone and be guided by a signaller. The signaller should always be in visual contact with the machine driver when positioned close to the machine.

Whilst the machine driver is isolated from noise and dust, the signaller is not, and may need to wear PPE depending on the findings of the risk assessments for the work being done (for example, if an impact hammer is being used).

The height of the wall or building to be demolished should not normally be greater than the attack (maximum) reach of the machine; this maintains a safe distance between the machine and the structure being demolished.

In some circumstances, it is possible to create a ramp for the machine to sit on to increase the reach using rubble from previous demolition. Care must be taken to ensure the ramp is properly designed and constructed and that there has been sufficient compaction to avoid the machine sitting on an unstable base.

It is not recommended to construct a ramp within a building, due to potentially overloading the floors or surcharging the outside walls.

It is not recommended to allow undermining or undercutting when the machine cannot reach the top of the building. Any contractor suggesting this method should consider selecting a larger (higher reach) machine to avoid putting the operator at unnecessary risk from falling debris and so on.

03

Super high-reach 360° excavators

Typically these machines have a reach of between 15 and 65+ metres, plus the length of the fitted attachments for crunching concrete or shearing steels. To ensure a safe distance between the machine and the structure, a ratio of 2:1 height to distance must be maintained, which means that the recommended maximum working height for the machine is restricted to 75% of its maximum reach.

A useful visual indicator that the machine is working within safe limits is when the dipper (the last section of the excavator's arm) is horizontal or approximately 90° to the boom.

These sophisticated machines are often fitted with variable width tracks, which usually make them much heavier, giving increased ground-bearing pressure and reduced working envelopes. It is vital that any voids and ducts located where the machine will track are identified, clearly marked (fenced off) and, where possible, adequately filled and compacted. In terms of ground conditions, these machines should be considered more as a crane or piling frame in terms of stability, rather than an excavator.

Operator training is supported by a specialist CPCS category for high-reach machines with various endorsements for different reach machines (for example, up to 15 metres, 30 metres and 30 metres+).

It is essential for operators to understand how to operate the machines safely and also have knowledge of best practice with regard to fitting and changing attachments. The manufacturer or the supplier of the machinery can provide advice on this. There are further CPCS card endorsements for this activity.

 A publication called *High-reach demolition rigs – Guidance notes* is available to members from the National Federation of Demolition Contractors.

Hydraulic pusher arm

Demolition using a hydraulic pusher arm is occasionally used for removing masonry structures. However, with the advent of super high-reach machines with multi-functional attachments, it is almost obsolete now and can only be carried out by experts. It is therefore not covered within the scope of this chapter.

General precautions

Before using the demolition equipment, steps must be taken to ensure that the building is completely empty and that all services are isolated with the appropriate disconnection certificates on site.

Because of the danger of debris falling onto the excavator and its driver, the machine should be a safe distance from the structure and be fitted with a cab guard and, as an added precaution, should be fitted with shatterproof glass.

Demolition ball

Demolition using a ball is extremely rare due to the advent of super high-reach machines. When a ball is used, the crane equipment must be heavy duty and only drop or pendulum (for example, in line with the jib) balling techniques should be employed.

When a ball is employed, regular (for example, hourly) inspections of the equipment must take place, paying particular attention to the attachments and shackles.

Arrangements for safely rectifying the situation should be in place in the event of the demolition ball becoming trapped within the structure.

Further detail is not possible within the scope of this chapter.

Bridges or steel structure demolition

The demolition of bridges, pylons, masts, or similar, requires specialised planning and techniques. The information provided below can be used as a guide, but the detail is not covered within the scope of this chapter.

General precautions

An assessment by a structural engineer should be undertaken to see if the structure could be safely broken down into small component lifts.

A comprehensive safe working plan must be developed providing a safe means of access, using a competent crane hire company and experienced slingers and signallers to ensure compliance with the Lifting Operations and Lifting Equipment Regulations.

For bridges that run over roads, or cross railway lines, liaison must take place with the Highways Department of the Local Authority involved or Network Rail, as appropriate.

 For further information refer to Chapter C07 Lifting operations.

3.9 Environmental and other considerations

Noise, dust, fumes, vibration and fire control need to be properly addressed before and during the demolition operation. Consideration should be given to the following points.

Noise

Where demolition operations are carried out in locations likely to affect the general public, the Local Authority may request the principal contractor to submit an application under Section 61 of the Control of Pollution Act (COPA), specifying working methods, working hours and maximum noise levels (called prior consent). A Local Authority can issue an abatement notice (Section 60 notice) for failure to comply with Section 61 consent conditions, or where noise levels are creating a statutory nuisance.

In accordance with regulations, where noise levels are above (or expected to be above) the lower exposure action value, the demolition contractor must ensure that a noise assessment has been carried out and that, where possible, people are kept out of the danger area.

Any machinery that is to be used in the demolition process should, as far as possible, be fitted and used with soundproofing equipment (such as exhaust silencers).

Where it is necessary for people to work within the area of noisy operations, adequate hearing protection must be provided and used as necessary. If the upper exposure action value is exceeded (85 dBA), or likely to be exceeded, hearing protection must be worn and hearing protection zones clearly indicated.

Where the findings of a risk assessment indicate that the hearing of any employee is at risk due to noise exposure at work, health surveillance, including hearing checks, must be provided.

BS 5228 gives advice on the provisions for noise control on demolition sites.
For further guidance refer to Chapter E06 Statutory nuisance.

Dust

Nearly all demolition activities create dust and many require a COSHH assessment (for example, respirable crystalline silica).

Taking simple precautions (such as the following) ensures the dust nuisance can be reduced to a minimum.

- ☑ Implementing techniques that reduce dust generation.

- ☑ The use of light water sprays both before and during demolition are very effective. However, consideration should be given to any potential run-off contaminants that may be produced and to the proximity of demolition work to electrical services and drains.

- ☑ Where demolition is being carried out inside a building and water sprays are inappropriate, local ventilation, using air movers and filters, can help to alleviate dust levels.

- ☑ Dust masks, as any other PPE, should be used only as a last resort. Where any mask is used, the wearer must be face-fit tested for the mask.

- ☑ Consideration should be given to measuring the actual dust levels to confirm whether or not the anticipated levels are being achieved and thereby whether the measures being taken (for example, personal and perimeter pumps) are effective.

For further guidance refer to Chapter B10 Dust and fumes.

Asbestos

As previously referred to under 'Planning for demolition', where there is a remote risk of asbestos (all buildings constructed before 1999 may contain asbestos) a comprehensive invasive asbestos survey, in accordance with HSG264, must be undertaken prior to contractors being invited to tender for the demolition.

Where asbestos is present, the necessary planning, actions and notifications must be implemented to comply with the Control of Asbestos Regulations. The principles of these regulations are to prevent the exposure to and spread of asbestos by training and adequate control measures.

For further information and guidance refer to Chapter B09 Asbestos.

Fumes

A cutting torch, used on steelwork, may produce toxic gases (such as nitrogen dioxide). If a phosphate coating is present, phosphine may be produced. If a chlorinated solvent has been used, sulphides may be formed, which have no smell until high toxic levels are present. Toxic metal fumes may additionally be given off.

Attention is drawn particularly to lead (lead-painted steelwork), cadmium (cadmium bolt heads) and zinc.

Before any hot work cutting is allowed, available information or paint samples may be required for analysis, a COSHH assessment should be undertaken, and the necessary control measures implemented.

Demolition

Operatives undertaking hot work must be issued with the appropriate PPE, including respiratory protective equipment (RPE), as necessary.

 For further information refer to:
Chapter B07 The Control of Substances Hazardous to Health (COSHH),
Chapter B10 Dust and fumes, and
Chapter B12 Lead.

Vibration transmission

Vibration from demolition operations can cause damage to adjacent property and injury to personnel working on site or, in extreme cases, to members of the public. Exposure to vibration must be controlled in accordance with the requirements of the Control of Vibration at Work Regulations.

☑ Where possible avoid the need to expose persons and/or property to vibration by selecting appropriate demolition techniques.

☑ Attempts should be made to establish the presence of any existing sources of vibration and whether vibration monitors are needed in sensitive locations.

☑ Where buildings adjoining those to be demolished are being retained, separation should be carried out using hand tools rather than machinery.

☑ Necessary precautions should be taken or alternative equipment considered to alleviate the risk of hand-arm vibration syndrome (HAVS) (for example, vibration white finger, from continued use of vibrating tools).

With regard to the last point, the exposure time for most demolition hand tools is extremely short, and the contractor will need a robust policy that includes health surveillance to carry out hand demolition using demolition picks.

 For further information refer to Chapter B14 Vibration.

Fire and explosion risks

Where flammable liquids, gases or vapours have been used, or were released in a building that is under demolition, any equipment, tank or pipes, and so on, which could have contained such substances, must be purged and tested for explosive gases prior to work taking place. Any work should be done under a permit to work system.

General hot work, using oxygen and propane cutting equipment, should be carried out only by operatives trained in its safe and proper use, wearing the appropriate PPE, in other words, goggles, gloves and overalls.

If the occasional burning of debris (such as wood or paper) is allowed on site, the fire must be as small as possible, well away from buildings, roadways, fuel stores, and kept under constant supervision.

Before any burning of debris is undertaken, consideration needs to be given to waste management licensing, or any local by-laws, which may prohibit such actions taking place. Penalties for the contravention of such conditions can be severe in some circumstances.

All fires must be completely extinguished at least one hour before work stops for the day and checked again, to ensure there are no glowing embers before operatives leave the site.

Adequate fire-fighting equipment must be available, with fire points containing extinguishers in prominent and well-marked areas adjacent to the demolition operations.

 For further information refer to Chapter C02 Fire prevention and control.

Recycling

Demolition works should therefore be reviewed carefully to identify what wastes will be produced, what actions will be taken to deal with these wastes and to include the required information in any site waste management plan.

 For further details refer to Chapter E03 Waste management.

In addition to removing recoverable items from demolition operations, it is becoming increasingly common to crush the resultant brick and concrete into a sub-base material for future construction purposes.

☑ Crushing on site should only take place when environmental conditions permit such actions. Environmental emissions (noise, fumes and dust) are required to be recorded at least three times daily on a check sheet. Operations should cease if there are excessive emissions which cross the site boundary.

☑ Crushers must be registered with the supplier's own Local Authority, which must be notified in advance each time the equipment is moved.

☑ All materials to be recycled should be checked for any contaminants and dealt with in the correct manner to the required specification (for example, 6F2). The reuse of construction and demolition waste may require a waste management licence/permit or notified exemption. Advice should be sought from the local waste licensing officer on a case-by-case basis.

☑ Operatives working on the crushers must be properly trained (both general training on the use of crushers and specific training in respect of the equipment being used).

☑ Serious consideration must be given to the need for machinery guarding on crushers. A daily check sheet should be completed by the operator, which confirms that all guards are in place and the emergency stops are working.

☑ Robust safe systems of work are required to deal with blockages. These often happen because the operator loading the crusher simply feeds in lumps that are too big, or because during the demolition process the machine driver did not sort the materials well and large lumps of timber have entered the stockpile.

☑ All crusher operators are likely to require hearing checks and monitoring as the noise levels are normally high.

☑ Even with the dust suppression systems operational, it is unlikely that disposable masks will offer a high enough level of protection. A risk assessment will be required to determine the type of RPE. Face-fit testing may be required following this.

☑ Operators should not be allowed to stand on an operating crusher, particularly near the jaws where the feedstock is being crushed. The risks arising from this practice can be combated at source by effective soft stripping and, if necessary, allowing picking from a product belt (in other words, after it has gone through the crusher).

Removal and disposal of materials

Before any materials are removed from site, both vehicular access to, and egress from, the site must be agreed.

It is prudent, if possible, to leave the floor slabs, roads and hard standings in place until the end of the project to avoid mud and other debris being carried out onto the highway. Where necessary, bog mats and wheel-washing facilities should be provided to ensure that debris is not carried onto the highway.

Depending on the nature of the material, covering lorries to stabilise the load and prevent dust and debris being blown off may be appropriate.

Daily records must be kept of materials taken off site.

It is the responsibility of the demolition contractor to ensure that the carrier they are using is registered with the Environment Agency or SEPA, and that non-hazardous waste is accompanied with a duty of care controlled waste transfer document. These care documents must be kept for a minimum of two years by carriers and producers.

For hazardous waste (such as asbestos) you should use a hazardous waste consignment note. These are available from the Environment Agency or SEPA on request, and you should retain the consignor's original (white copy). All such documentation should be kept for a minimum of three years.

3.10 Monitoring the work

The key to a successful and safe demolition project is to plan, implement, monitor and maintain a safe system of work.

Daily inspection by the site supervisor and/or client

☑ Provide daily briefings to the workforce on complex projects.

☑ Check for continuing safe working practices.

☑ Ensure access and egress routes are properly maintained.

☑ Ensure the site is kept tidy and, as far as possible, free from any piles of combustible rubbish.

☑ Ensure that sufficient signs are available and clearly visible to warn of hazardous areas and activities.

☑ Check the contractor's operatives are continuing to wear suitable protective equipment.

☑ Check the progress and sequence of the job to ensure that it complies with the health and safety plan.

☑ Check that an approved safe system of work is being followed.

Appendix A – Definitions and terms used by the demolition industry

General

CCDO: Certificate of Competence for Demolition Operatives, affiliated to the CSCS scheme (Level 1, 2 and 3 operatives).

Competent person in demolition: someone who has practical and theoretical knowledge, with actual experience, of the type of demolition that is taking place on the site. This person is generally accepted to be on site full time as the person responsible for the demolition activity.

Demolition: the deliberate pulling down, destruction or taking apart of a structure or a substantial part of a structure. It includes dismantling for re-erection or reuse.

Exclusion zone: an area where people are fully (sometimes partially) excluded during a demolition activity. This zone should be determined by a competent person, detailed in the health and safety plan, and may need to be defined by physical barriers on site.

Explosives demolition: this involves the deliberate collapse of a structure using controlled explosives. It is normally preceded by the removal of hazardous materials (for example, asbestos, soft stripping and pre-weakening of the structure).

Façade retention: where the outer wall of a building or structure is retained in its original position during the demolition phase. It is usually supported by a façade retention system, internal or external.

Fan: a protective screen fixed to scaffolding to contain falling debris during demolition. Any fan must be designed to withstand the intended load.

Felling: the deliberate collapse of a structure in such a way that the debris falls in a predetermined area.

Hot work: the application of heat (including the use of tools that can produce an incendiary spark). It generally uses oxygen and propane gas cutting equipment.

Party wall structures: these are as defined under the Party Wall etc. Act and are typically where common structures (horizontal and vertical) exist between two or more parties. There are responsibilities to comply with when work affects a party wall structure.

Propping and shoring: a system of temporary supports to prevent movement.

Remote mechanical demolition: this normally involves the use of excavators, including high-reach machines fitted with attachments (see below) or, occasionally, a crawler crane with a demolition wrecking ball to create progressive controlled collapse of the structure.

Safe working spaces: areas where demolition work is taking place, often protected by physical barriers (for example, machines protected by ROPs, FOPs and MOPs as applicable).

Top-down demolition: this generally involves demolition in a reverse sequence to its construction.

Machine-mounted attachments

Brock: a trade name for a range of remote control excavators, which can carry most demolition attachments.

Combination cutter: a tool that can crush concrete and also cut steel reinforcing bar.

Demolition ball: a cast steel ball (drops or pendulum swings in line with the jib) used to demolish a structure. (Slew balling, although rarely used now, is unacceptable as it places very high stresses on the crane.)

Grapple: a powered claw for handling waste and recycled material.

Impact hammer: a large breaker, mounted on an excavator, and usually powered by hydraulics (occasionally by compressed air).

Pulveriser: hydraulically powered jaws for crushing concrete. It may be hand/machine/crane mounted.

Pusher arm: an extension to an excavator, which enables it to carry out high-reach demolition.

Shear: powered jaws for cutting metal.

Rotator: an attachment fitted between the tool and the end of dipper arm of the excavator, which allows the tool to be turned. Essential for most work in restricted sites.

04

Shopfitting and interior contracting

The nature of shopfitting and interior contracting can give rise to additional challenges, including working in and around live retail environments, tight site logistics, out-of-hours working and congested sites.

This chapter highlights some of the key issues. However most topics encountered on site are common issues and are addressed in other sections of this publication.

Introduction	62
Identifying risk	62
Site-based issues	63
Working at height	65
Fire	66
Other considerations	66
Further information	68

4.1   Introduction

Shopfitting refers to the sector of the construction industry requiring the manufacture and installation of bespoke furniture for interior environments. It should always be remembered that health and safety in all such projects begins the moment the enquiry lands on the estimator's desk.

The term *interior environment* incorporates:

- ☑ retail (shops)
- ☑ non-retail (banks, building societies, museums, offices)
- ☑ leisure (leisure centres, restaurants, pubs, garden centres).

This list is not exhaustive, but it does illustrate the examples of where these activities are conducted.

Essentially anywhere there is an interior environment will be relevant to this chapter.

Shopfitting and interior contracting is fundamentally about developing and generating a strategy of:

'Safe place – Safe person'.

Managing those inherent risks in this sector is therefore the background to this approach.

Following a recent case where a high street retailer was fined £1 million for safety failings and the contractor was also fined for failing to protect the general public, an HSE spokesperson said:

> this outcome should act as a wake-up call that any shopfitting refurbishment programmes involving asbestos-containing materials must be properly resourced, both in terms of time and money – no matter what. Large retailers and other organisations that carry out major refurbishment works must give contractors enough time and space within the store to carry out the works safely. Where this is not done, and construction workers and the public are put at risk, HSE will not hesitate in taking robust enforcement action.

Refurbishing interior environments can and does bring a unique set of hazards, which clearly sets this sector apart from base build construction. These can then be sub-divided into the following categories:

- ☑ sheds (out of town)
- ☑ high street
- ☑ shopping centres
- ☑ existing buildings.

4.2   Identifying risk

The nature of shopfitting and interior contracting can give rise to additional challenges (such as working in and around live retail environments, tight site logistics, out-of-hours working and congested sites).

From a health and safety focus **before the project commences** the fit-out team should give serious consideration to how they intend to manage the following:

- ☑ difference between new build interior and revamp of an existing interior
- ☑ meccano job (removal of some fittings) or full refit (strip back to the original shell)
- ☑ client-appointed contractors – managed by the principal contractor from the commencement of works
- ☑ third-party liability (general public/store staff)
- ☑ merchandisers
- ☑ site logistics
- ☑ project team/retail team
- ☑ asbestos (a survey where appropriate should be provided before works commence)
- ☑ fire safety
- ☑ possible vermin infestation
- ☑ carrying out the work whilst the premises continue to trade, if applicable.

Fatal incident at a retail unit undergoing refurbishment

A recent fatal incident involving a shopfitting contractor has highlighted the need for clients, designers and contractors to be aware of the structural condition of existing works.

If in doubt a structural engineer should be seconded to the project to assist in managing the risk of accidental collapse.

 Everyone controlling site work has health and safety responsibilities.

Checking that working conditions are healthy and safe before work begins, and ensuring that the proposed work is not going to put others at risk, requires planning and organisation.

This applies whatever the size of the site.

04

4.3   Site-based issues

Site-based issues that need to be considered during shopfitting contracts include:

- ☑ **site induction** – ensuring all workers attend a full, site-specific induction, especially during busy weekend and night time working shifts

- ☑ **hoardings** – phasing and safe erection

- ☑ **structural design** and temporary works following design

- ☑ **live services** – identification and isolation, installation of temporary electrics

- ☑ **occupational health** – noise, hand-arm vibration, especially in internal spaces

- ☑ **dust** – breathing in construction dust is a high health risk and must be controlled

- ☑ **welfare** – provision of suitable welfare in restricted spaces to accommodate peak numbers of workers

- ☑ **waste management** – space constraints give rise to challenges of segregation and avoiding build up of wastes, providing chutes

- ☑ **fire** – maintaining integrity of existing fire arrangements, additional risks posed by construction work, avoiding build up of waste

- ☑ **working at height** – prevention of falls, selection and correct use of suitable access equipment

- ☑ **plant and equipment** – use of 110 volts, access for equipment, managing cartridge tools and gas nail guns, selection due to space constraints

- ☑ **logistics** – planning removal of waste, delivery and distribution of materials and large prefabricated items

- ☑ **manual handling** – planning is vital to ensure materials are distributed to minimise manual handling, utilising mechanical means, early/phased deliveries

- ☑ **personal protective equipment** and clothing – ensuring all have correct PPE for risks, enforcing any hearing protection zones

- ☑ **site deliveries** – managing any shared delivery areas, planning phased deliveries, using banksman, consider third parties, light levels.

 For further guidance refer to the corresponding GE 700 chapters, where applicable.

🔍 Large shopfitting contract in a city

Pedestrian and vehicle segregation in front of hoarding to control access and deliveries

Temporary works behind hoarding complete with working platforms

Planned road closures for a crane and lifting in a public space

Pre-planned access removed for steelwork delivery and fall arrest in use for slinger

Moving the steelwork into position

Removing the lifting equipment used to manoeuvre the steel into position

4.4 Working at height

Almost every shopfitting project will involve the shopfitting contractor or their respective trade contractors in working at height. Statistics now clearly illustrate that working at height is a major cause of accidents.

Falls from height lead to serious injuries for all employees, including those in the shopfitting industry. This statement takes into consideration those employers who have manufacturing capability and wish to undertake routine maintenance on their properties, to shopfitting installation on a site owned by a third party.

Full height barriers provide an internal safe zone by segregating the high risk façade replacement works

The Work at Height Regulations encompass all activities where a fall that is likely to cause injury may occur. The scope of the regulations includes all types of access equipment and work platforms, regardless of how long an employee is at height, or of the height at which the activity occurs.

The shopfitting industry, regardless of where the workplace is, includes the use of stepladders as a work platform for maintenance or other tasks, or simply as a means of accessing or leaving work at different levels.

Stepladders are not banned or illegal under the regulations. However, they should only be considered when all other safer alternatives for work at height have been ruled out when following the work at height hierarchy.

Due diligence in the form of a risk assessment must show that the task is of low risk and of short duration, or that there are features in the workplace that mean other equipment is not appropriate. If so, then ladders may be used. It should also be noted that stepladders come in many forms, some of which are safer than others, and include features such as adjustable out-riggers, platforms, handrails, lightweight GRP construction and tool tray attachments.

Lift shafts, new openings, strip out and removal of partitions, windows, façade, handrails, escalators and staircases create open edges that need to be controlled. The method statement must also consider how falls will be prevented while removing or reinstating these features.

Temporary edge protection fixed into position

Edge protection and fall prevention measures must be robust and secured into position, and again the method of installing these must include fall prevention. Plastic or free-standing barriers offer little resistance and a person can easily fall against and through them.

Statistics show that at work some 4,000 major injuries are caused by falls. Over 1,000 of these involve the use of ladders.

The regulations require duty holders to ensure that:

- ☑ all work at height is properly planned and organised
- ☑ those involved in work at height are competent
- ☑ the risks from work at height are assessed and appropriate work equipment is selected and used
- ☑ the risks from fragile surfaces are properly controlled
- ☑ equipment for work at height is properly inspected and maintained.

What constitutes work at height?

Work at height is work in any place, including a place at, above, or below ground level, where a person could be injured if they fell from that place. Access and egress to a place of work can also be deemed to be work at height. Examples in a shopfitter's environment that can be classified as work at height include:

- ☑ working on any type of scaffolding
- ☑ work on a mobile elevating work platform
- ☑ being on the back of a lorry or raised loading bays
- ☑ working close to an excavation or a cellar opening (lift pit)
- ☑ working off steps, hop ups and mobile towers
- ☑ mezzanine floors with no edge protection

- ☑ staircases with no handrails
- ☑ temporary wheelbarrow ramps onto the back of skips
- ☑ creating voids through floors or risers.

Shopfitting and interior contracting

Mobile towers, stepladders and MEWPs providing a typical range of access solutions

 For further information on working at height refer to Chapters D01 to D05.

4.5   Fire

Fire is an ever-present threat throughout the majority of construction and demolition projects. As shopfitting progresses, the nature of the fire risk is likely to change as different work activities start and are completed. Therefore, not only must the risk of fire be managed continuously, but the management process must allow for the changing nature of the risk.

 For further guidance refer to Chapter C02 Fire prevention and control.

Common sources of fire risk

- ☑ Storage and use of flammable materials, including LPG.
- ☑ Hot work.
- ☑ Electrical systems and equipment, including temporary lighting.
- ☑ Arson.
- ☑ Smoking.
- ☑ Operating plant and equipment.
- ☑ Poor housekeeping.

> **!** It is vital that the project fire strategy takes into account all existing third-party fire arrangements.

Specialist advice

The Fire Protection Association (FPA), in conjunction with the Construction Confederation (CC), published the eighth edition of *Fire prevention on construction sites* in July 2012. This joint code of practice (CoP) deals with the protection from fire on construction sites and buildings undergoing renovation.

The CoP does not have any legal status; however, it does outline good practice and many insurance companies now require that the authoritative guidelines (such as those detailed in the CoP) are properly implemented on construction projects before they will give full insurance.

The FPA also publishes *Construction site fire prevention checklist – a guide for insurers, surveyors and construction industry professionals*.

4.6   Other considerations

The following topics must be considered when shopfitting and interior contracting. These are also covered in detail in other chapters.

Construction dust

Many shopfitting activities will give rise to dust, which should be considered as a high health risk.

Typical activities that create harmful levels of dust include:

- ☑ sweeping a dusty floor
- ☑ mechanically cutting, chasing or drilling concrete, bricks and blocks
- ☑ mixing sand and cement to make mortar
- ☑ sanding down MDF or timber
- ☑ rubbing down tape and jointing or plaster.

All dusts are hazardous to health. The creation of dust, regardless of amount, must be controlled – all risk assessments and method statements should state how exposure to dust or fumes will be minimised. It is no longer acceptable to expect workers to work unprotected in dusty conditions.

 Rubbing down tape and jointing

Traditionally rubbing down creates a lot of dust, which is both hazardous to health, has to be cleaned up and is manually intensive. This drywall sander with collection system minimises all these issues to the extent that the operative does not need RPE.

04

 For further guidance on how to manage dust and fumes, and to help check if method statements and risk assessments adequately address respiratory risks, refer to Chapter B10 Dust and fumes.

Asbestos

Asbestos was widely used in the UK until it was banned in 1999; disturbance of the fabric of any building built before this time has the potential to expose asbestos.

The requirements for licensed work remain the same: in the majority of cases, work with asbestos needs to be done by a licensed contractor. This work includes most asbestos removal, all work with sprayed asbestos coatings and asbestos lagging, and most work with asbestos insulation and asbestos insulating board (AIB).

- ☑ All asbestos-containing material (ACM) is hazardous when airborne and dangerous when fibres are inhaled.
- ☑ If you are carrying out non-licensed asbestos work, this still requires effective controls.
- ☑ From 6 April 2012, some non-licensed work needs to be notified to the relevant enforcing authority.
- ☑ From 6 April 2012, brief written records should be kept of non-licensed work, which has to be notified (such as a copy of the notification with a list of workers on the job), plus the level of likely exposure of those workers to asbestos. This does not require air monitoring on every job, if an estimate of degree of exposure can be made based on experience of similar past tasks or published guidance.
- ☑ Before any work that has the potential to expose anyone to asbestos is carried out, a survey must be carried out and a written risk assessment made.
- ☑ The priority for any employer is to prevent exposure to, and spread of, asbestos.
- ☑ A written, site-specific plan (or register) of work must be kept on site and followed.
- ☑ Anyone who does any work with asbestos must be specifically trained to do it, and this training must be repeated at least annually.
- ☑ Contractors producing hazardous asbestos waste must check that the site receiving the asbestos waste is authorised to receive asbestos. They should have an environmental permit.
- ☑ Be aware of other hazards that may arise from working with or managing asbestos (such as working at height, in a confined space or where the presence of live services must be managed).
- ☑ The Health and Safety Executive (HSE) must be notified:
    - of all work involving the disturbance of asbestos, apart from non-licensable work
    - separately, if the project is notifiable under the Construction (Design and Management) Regulations.
- ☑ The regulations require anyone who issues a site-clearance certificate to be accredited by an appropriate accreditation body as competent to carry out such work.

 For further information refer to Chapter B09 Asbestos.

Lead and lead-based paint

Old, lead-based paint is still likely to affect the majority of UK buildings. It was completely removed from general sale by 1992. As a result lead surveys are a mandatory requirement under the Construction (Design and Management) Regulations.

Exposure to lead, lead dust and fumes constitutes a major hazard to the health of those who work with lead, lead products and lead-containing materials (LCMs) (such as lead-based paint).

Lead paint and dust exposure risks are greatest within pre-1970 buildings and structures, especially during repair, maintenance, refurbishment and demolition, if proper precautions are not followed.

 For explanation on the risks and controls that are required when working with lead refer to Chapter B12 Lead.

04

4.7 Further information

 For further guidance, DVDs and copies of the appropriate codes refer to the National Association of Shopfitters.

Guidance

Shopfitter's guide to the Construction (Design and Management) Regulations.

Code of Practice

Code of Practice on the safe erection of hoardings and similar structures.

Code of Practice on manual handling in shopfitting.

Code of Practice on fire safety in the shopfitting industry.

DVDs

Shopfitting safely – a safe pair of hands now and in the future

Who is this DVD for?

This health and safety induction DVD is for those who have entered, or are about to enter, the shopfitting and interior contracting environment as a member of the workforce. It is to help them understand the potential hazards that they are likely to be confronted with on site.

DVD aims and benefits

The DVD aims to give operatives in a shopfitting and interior contracting environment awareness of health and safety and how it affects their daily role. This programme can be used as a presentation or as a refresher for contractor employees. The programme will cover individuals' responsibilities for the safety of themselves and others, typical hazards associated with this sector and how they are controlled, and how everyone can help achieve better practical standards of safety.

Shopfitting safely – Occupational health and safety in a joinery workshop

Who is this DVD for?

This DVD is for all people, in such an environment, to assist them to manage occupational health and safety risks effectively and positively.

DVD aims and benefits

The key elements contained in this DVD, to manage woodworking safely, include:

- ☑ **risk management:** to reduce the chances of an accident occurring, it's best to look at what might cause one and then decide what you need to do to stop it happening

- ☑ **training and supervision:** by law, all workers must receive training and supervision that is appropriate to the equipment they will be using

- ☑ **workplace management:** paying attention to layout, worker movement and keeping workshops and storage areas tidy can help reduce the risks. Workers themselves should also be encouraged to become involved in health and safety as they are often the best people to understand the risks and help find solutions.

Through worker involvement you can act together to reduce accidents and ill health within your manufacturing environment.

04

04

05

Working over or near to water

Where construction or demolition work takes place over or near to water, steps must be taken, primarily to stop anyone from falling into it, but also to ensure that someone who has fallen will not come to harm and can be promptly rescued.

When planning for safe working near to water it may be necessary to take into consideration the safety of the employees of other companies and possibly the public, in areas where they may still have access.

Tidal and fast flowing waters pose additional problems for anyone falling into them and their rescuers.

Whilst the word *water* will be used throughout this chapter, the dangers and precautions apply equally to where work is being carried out near to other liquids (such as slurries and chemicals in vats) and even free-flowing solids (such as foodstuffs in silos).

Introduction	72
Key requirements	72
Areas of risk	73
Risk management	73
Rescue equipment and procedures	74
Rescue techniques	77
Onshore facilities and procedures	77
Training	78
Appendix A – The selection of lifejackets	79
Appendix B – Caring for personal buoyancy equipment	80

5.1 Introduction

Managing and controlling the risks associated with working over or near to water is something that many managers will do on rare occasions. This in itself could be a problem because they could be ill-prepared to do so when the need arises. The dangers in doing such work are significant and must be proactively managed.

The Health and Safety Executive (HSE) state that accidental drowning is often linked to one or more of the following factors:

☑ failure to provide personal buoyancy equipment

☑ failure of personal buoyancy equipment to operate properly

☑ disregard for or misjudging the severity of the risks of getting it wrong

☑ lack of supervision, particularly of the young and inexperienced

☑ inability to cope once a problem arises

☑ the absence of rescuers and rescue equipment

☑ failure to take account of weather forecasts.

Raising the awareness of managers, supervisors and workers to ensure effective control measures are always put in place and followed is fundamental to safe working over and near to water.

 Anyone who may accidentally fall into water will ideally be able to swim or at least feel sufficiently confident in their personal floatation equipment and the effectiveness of the rescue procedures, so that they do not panic.

5.2 Key requirements

☑ Working over water will often, although not always, involve working at height. The potential risks arising from both hazards must be managed.

☑ The risks must be assessed and a written method statement produced.

☑ As with any other work at height, ideally it must be carried out from a stable working platform that will prevent an unplanned fall into the water; only as a last resort should fall-arrest equipment be relied upon.

☑ Where there is a risk of someone accidentally entering the water, appropriate rescue equipment and people who are competent to use it must be available.

☑ Appropriate personal protective equipment (PPE) must be made available.

☑ Instruction and training must be given to the workforce; suddenly falling fully clothed into cold, deep water may induce shock and an increased risk of drowning if appropriate PPE is not worn.

☑ Rescue drills must be planned and practised.

☑ Powered rescue boats must only be operated by someone trained in boat-handling and rescue procedures.

☑ If the use of a rescue boat is not appropriate, an established hierarchy of rescue methods must be followed.

☑ Working near to deep water (for example, adjacent to canal locks) can be as dangerous as working over water if appropriate control measures are not put in place.

☑ Potential health risks must also be managed.

 Would each of your workforce be at ease having fallen into water wearing a lifejacket, providing they were in no immediate danger?

05

5.3   Areas of risk

Hazardous work areas include:

- ☑ docks and wharves
- ☑ locks
- ☑ canals and rivers, including bank-side paths
- ☑ open sea (off-shore construction sites and installations)
- ☑ lakes, reservoirs and ponds (natural and ornamental)

- ☑ sewage and slurry ponds
- ☑ water-filled pits
- ☑ water-holding tanks, including those located underground
- ☑ culverts and other storm-drainage channels.

It is essential that fall prevention measures are taken, as for any other type of construction work

05

5.4   Risk management

Risk assessment

The risk assessment must investigate whether it is possible to eliminate the hazard of working over or near to water by doing the job another way. It is accepted that this will often not be possible. However, it may be possible to reduce the risks of falling and/or drowning by doing at least part of the job elsewhere. An example of this is the complete removal of lock-gates for off-site repair rather than doing the whole job with the gates in situ. The number of people exposed to the hazard, and the length of time they are exposed to it will both be significantly reduced.

As for all work activities, the significant risks arising out of doing the job, and the part they must play in seeing that the job is carried out safely, must be communicated to the workforce.

Where there is a risk of falling from a significant height into water and/or where the water is fast flowing or tidal the employer is advised to consider the selection of workers carefully. The HSE does not make any recommendations regarding whether anyone who runs the risk of falling into water must be able to swim, although it is obviously preferable that they can because they are more likely to be at ease in the water until rescued. A lifejacket will keep a non-swimmer afloat and automatically turn them face up.

Consideration must be given to site access by the emergency services and how an injured person is going to be transferred to an ambulance.

Hierarchy for working at height

As with any other work at height, when working over water the hierarchy of safety will be:

- ☑ avoid working at height (over water) if it is possible to do the job another way
- ☑ prevent falls, if it is necessary to work at height
- ☑ minimise the personal trauma on anyone who does fall.

To avoid duplication, readers are advised to familiarise themselves with the content of other section chapters, some of which are likely to be relevant to working over water, in that they cover:

- ☑ scaffolds and other stable working platforms
- ☑ safe access using ladders
- ☑ the use of mobile elevating platforms

- ☑ fall prevention by harness and restraint lanyard
- ☑ fall arrest by harness and load-absorbing lanyard
- ☑ fall arrest by safety nets and soft-landing systems.

Preventing accidental entry into water

Every effort must be made to eliminate the risk of accidental entry into water. This will involve protecting employees against:

- ☑ falls from heights (including a failure to use the fall prevention or arrest measures provided)
- ☑ trips and slips from low level
- ☑ persons being knocked over by moving objects (for example, crane loads)
- ☑ loss of balance (for example, caused by high winds) particularly when handling sheet materials
- ☑ failure or absence of barriers
- ☑ failure of ropes or lines
- ☑ rising swell or swell from passing waterborne traffic
- ☑ messing around
- ☑ being on-site whilst under the influence of drink or drugs.

Site management must play an active part in ensuring that any of the above points that apply to their project, and others which may not be covered, are effectively managed.

The dangers from falling into water

The most immediate danger of accidental entry into water is drowning. Causes or contributory factors include:

- ☑ shock of sudden immersion in cold water
- ☑ weight of waterlogged clothing
- ☑ incapacity following injury after striking an object during the fall or in the water
- ☑ fatigue or hypothermia where rescue is not immediate.

Other effects of falling, which importantly may render the victim incapable of assisting in their own rescue, include:

- ☑ being knocked unconscious by hitting part of the structure during the fall
- ☑ suffering broken bones by hitting the structure during the fall
- ☑ suffering physical injury by falling into shallow water.

Risks to health include:

- ☑ leptospirosis (Weil's disease) if infected rats are present
- ☑ digestive illnesses from swallowing water contaminated with natural organisms, chemicals used in the work process or other contaminants (such as diesel oil)
- ☑ suffering suspension trauma by being left suspended in a harness for too long.

Immediately it is known that someone has fallen into the water, unless it is obvious that external medical assistance is not required, the emergency services should be called so that they are in transit whilst the rescue is being carried out.

5.5   Rescue equipment and procedures

Although every effort should be made to prevent people falling into the water, the risk of this happening may still remain. In the event of someone falling into water, three things are of paramount importance:

- ☑ the person must be kept afloat
- ☑ their location must be immediately obvious and continuously tracked, if in flowing water
- ☑ rescue must be achieved as quickly as possible.

Personal buoyancy equipment

 Refer to the HSE's information sheet *Personal buoyancy equipment on inland and inshore waters* (AIS1).

Anyone working over or near to water, and at risk of falling in, should wear some form of personal buoyancy equipment; generally a lifejacket or buoyancy aid. Lifejackets and personal buoyancy aids are designed to keep the wearer afloat. There are, however, important differences and it is recommended that lifejackets are used in preference to buoyancy aids for reasons that are explained later in this chapter.

Decisions on the type of equipment best suited to specific types of work should be based on an assessment of the factors involved by the employer, which may have to consult suppliers in some circumstances. These may include, for example, whether a person is a competent swimmer, the length of time a person may be in the water, the risks of injury, water temperature, current and the proximity of assistance.

Lifejackets must be made to the relevant British Standard and must be obtained from a reputable supplier. Their primary aim is to support an unconscious person in the water by turning them face upwards. Inflation of the lifejacket is by means of a CO_2 cartridge, activated manually or automatically, depending upon the item purchased. Lifejackets that inflate automatically are preferable because:

☑ upon contact with the water the lifejacket will inflate within seconds and an unconscious person will be turned face upwards in the water

☑ with manually inflated lifejackets, not only must the wearer be capable of locating and pulling the manual inflation toggle, but the toggle can get caught on obstructions during normal work, inadvertently inflating the lifejacket.

Manually inflated lifejackets, which are inflated by mouth after entry into the water, should not be used.

 For advice on the selection of lifejackets and personal buoyancy aids refer to Appendix A.

Buoyancy aids are intended to provide a conscious person with enough extra buoyancy to stay afloat and achieve a reasonable floating position. A basic buoyancy aid may not turn an unconscious person over from face-down. Buoyancy is achieved by means of closed-cell foam pads sewn into the material of the buoyancy aid.

Buoyancy aids are bulky and, in some people's view, hinder movement and may slow the progress of work, in comparison to lifejackets, which offer greater freedom of movement.

Where a **safety harness** is to be worn in addition to personal buoyancy equipment, it is important to ensure each of these items is compatible, in that each will not interfere with the correct functioning of the other. Safety harness and buoyancy aid combinations are available from some manufacturers, although professional advice should be sought on their suitability for wearing during construction work before committing to them.

The provision of whistles and lights as aids to the location of people in the water may be advisable in some circumstances.

Wearers should be fully trained in the use of safety harnesses, lifejackets and personal buoyancy aids. The functions of the equipment and, where appropriate, its limitations should be clearly understood by users.

 The selection and care of personal buoyancy equipment are covered in Appendices A and B respectively.

Lifebuoys

Lifebuoys should be available wherever people are working on, over or near to water. Standard 760 mm diameter lifebuoys with rope or cord lifelines (usually 30 metres) attached should be placed in conspicuous positions near the water's edge.

A lifebuoy can be thrown only a short distance, perhaps six to eight metres and then with little accuracy.

Handling 30 metres of rope may also present problems to the inexperienced person, although lifebuoys are available with the rope packed into plastic containers, from which it reels out when the lifebuoy is thrown.

Lifebuoys should be suspended from a suitable hook or bracket at a height where they can be clearly seen, with the lifeline coiled ready for use.

Rescue lines

Various types of rescue line (sometimes referred to as throwing lines) are available. Typically they comprise 20 or 30 metres of rescue line enclosed within a canvas bag.

The free end of the line is held, while the bag is thrown underarm towards the casualty. The line can be delivered accurately up to its full length, but underarm throwing may be hindered by guard-rails and other forms of edge protection. Upon completion of the rescue, the line should be left extended to dry and it can then be repacked into the canvas bag when that has also dried.

The photo shows a typical rescue line with a loop tied in the free end to fit over the wrist. The bag, complete with the line is then thrown to the person in the water, trailing the line as it goes. The particular line shown is equipped with a padded handle on the outside of the bag, which the person in the water will hold on to whilst they are pulled ashore.

A typical rescue line

05

Another method of delivering the line is the capsule emergency lifeline. A light but strong line, 40 metres in length, is packed into a small plastic capsule. The free end of the line is secured to a cord grip that is held while the capsule is thrown, the line paying out as it goes.

The capsule may be thrown or flicked to the full distance of 40 metres using an extension rod that fits into the handle. Both line and capsule will float, allowing the casualty to grab the line and be hauled to safety. If the first throw misses, it can be very quickly used again. The ability to deliver the line up to 40 metres may avoid the need to launch a boat or for somebody to enter the water.

The capsules are small enough to be carried in a belt or, alternatively, can be mounted in cabinets (with the extension rod) at convenient locations.

Drownings have occurred close to the bank or water's edge. Safety provision should take account of this, where it is the dominant risk. Lightweight throwing lines or similar equipment should be provided to supplement lifebuoys, especially if workers are moving from place to place, adjacent to the water.

Rescue boats

A rescue boat should be provided whenever work is being undertaken over or near to deep, tidal or fast flowing water; it may also be advisable to provide a boat in some areas of still water, dependent upon the findings of a risk assessment.

The craft may be rigid (wooden or fibreglass) or inflatable. It must have a reliable engine and carry:

☑ a radio if they are being used on site

☑ a first-aid kit

☑ paddles, in case of engine failure

☑ a boat-hook

☑ a throwing line

☑ grab-lines around the hull.

The operator should be experienced and competent at handling small craft on flowing water, particularly in rescue situations that involve special boat-handling skills.

A typical powered rescue boat, equipped with radio, throwing line, paddles, boat-hook and a first-aid box

  Where a powered rescue boat will be used it is strongly recommended that the operator is trained to a minimum standard of Royal Yachting Association (RYA) Power Boat Level 2 and also in rescue techniques. Rescuing a person from the water in a power boat with a rotating propeller demands skill and experience, particularly if there is a current flowing and/or strong winds. Ideally, there will be two people in the boat, the driver and a rescuer.

  The RYA runs courses throughout the United Kingdom. Visit its website for further details.

Whether the rescue boat is to be permanently manned and constantly afloat, or not, will depend on the circumstances, as will its size and the equipment to be carried. If any work is to be done during the hours of darkness, the rescue boat will require high efficiency lighting.

Two-way radio communication between boat and shore may be necessary on large areas of water. Practice rescue drills should be held, so that the best method of rescuing, securing and landing a potential casualty is known in advance.

Stop nets or lines

Given the right circumstances, including still or gently flowing water and no waterborne traffic, nets may be suspended just into the water or lines trailed across or in the water to allow a conscious person to hold on while awaiting rescue, or to pull themselves to the bank. These cannot be totally relied upon, because a casualty may be unconscious or otherwise unable to help themselves.

If there is a weir or sluice, nets should not be relied upon unless they can be positioned well upstream of it.

5.6   Rescue techniques

 Getting an attempted rescue wrong could put the rescuers at risk.

Methods of rescuing a casualty, other than by using a rescue boat, may be summarised as follows:

- ☑ involve the emergency services
- ☑ reach out from the bank or edge
- ☑ throw out a means of personal buoyancy
- ☑ wade out
- ☑ go out.

Emergency services. In many cases, the fire service (or coastguard in appropriate circumstances) will have the expertise and equipment to carry out rescue procedures. A judgement will have to be made as to whether it is advisable or practical to await their arrival. This must be balanced against the risks involved in attempting the following means of rescue.

Reach out. If the casualty is near enough to the bank or edge, it may be possible to grab their hand, or use a sturdy stick, boat-hook, oar, broom handle, or anything they can seize to be pulled in to safety. The rescuer should ensure that they have a secure foothold and sufficient grip and balance to counteract the weight of the casualty in the water.

Throw out. When the casualty is some way out in the water, a lifebuoy and rescue line or any personal buoyancy aid with line attached should be thrown to them. This technique is preferable to entering the water to reach the casualty, especially if the depth of water and state of currents are not known.

Wade out. A shelving bed or shore may enable a rescuer to reach the person in the water while keeping their feet on the bottom. Care is needed, since currents, underwater obstacles and sudden changes in the depth of water may put the rescuer at risk.

Go out. Assistance should be summoned first when possible. Individuals should only act alone if they really have to. A boat should preferably be used to reach the casualty. If not, the rescuer should swim out with a lifeline secured to the shore or edge and a personal buoyancy aid.

 Avoid becoming a casualty. People who cannot swim should not enter the water, but must raise the alarm and wait for assistance.

5.7   Onshore facilities and procedures

First aid. Irrespective of the size of the operation, first-aid facilities must be provided, and trained and qualified first aiders should be present at the site of all work adjacent to water.

Facilities should include provision for transferring casualties from boat to shore and ambulance access.

Alarms. Some effective means of raising an alarm must exist. Gongs, bells, whistles, pressurised canister fog horns, klaxons or similar items of equipment should be provided. All people on site should be instructed in the correct use of the alarm and the actions to be taken when the alarm sounds.

Lighting. Water surfaces should be illuminated at night so that victims of falls can be seen and constantly watched while awaiting rescue.

Communications. The telephone number for the ambulance, coastguard and lifeboat services (999) should be stressed to operatives and adequate provision should be made for effective on-site communications (usually site radios).

Rescue equipment is for use in an emergency. It must be properly maintained, not misused and never relied upon as a primary safeguard against accidents.

Clothing. High-visibility vests or jackets should be worn. These will assist in keeping the casualty in view while the rescue operation is being mounted. High-visibility immersion suits will be appropriate in some circumstances.

Checking personnel. Periodic checks should be made to ensure nobody is missing. Personnel should work in pairs or in sight of each other to enable one person to raise the alarm in the event of an emergency.

Weather and tides. Details of weather and, where appropriate, tides should be obtained before each shift.

Safety ladders. Where there is a quay-heading to the bank, there is likely to be a significant height difference between the water level and the dry land, which can make it difficult or impossible for someone who is fully dressed in wet clothes to clamber out of the water. Safety ladders can be made by cutting good sections out of damaged aluminium ladders, which are then fixed to the quay-heading, using suitable metal brackets, as an easy means of getting back on to the bank.

Recovery of equipment from the water. In the event of tools, equipment or small plant falling into the water, no attempt should be made to recover those using amateur divers or improvised techniques.

Special regulations apply to all diving operations and expert advice should be sought where it is necessary to recover equipment.

5.8　Training

Safe working practices and rescue procedures must be covered during site induction, refresher training and any specialist training.

A clearly defined and documented rescue procedure should be devised. All on site must be familiar with the procedure and understand the actions they must take in an emergency.

The location of emergency equipment should be known and any special training in its use given to the personnel involved. Responsibility for co-ordinating and supervising rescue operations must be allocated to identify individuals, trained and competent to discharge it. Practices in rescue procedures should be held where appropriate.

Locally employed site-based staff and the employees of sub-contractors should receive instruction in emergency procedures and the use of life-preserving equipment, and must be given such information as is necessary to enable them to act effectively in an emergency.

With regard to personal buoyancy equipment, all workers who are likely to use it must be trained to:

- ☑ adjust the securing straps to make sure it will not come off over the head, upon impact with water
- ☑ check that the firing mechanism of a lifejacket has not already been activated
- ☑ carry out pre-use and routine maintenance checks
- ☑ store the equipment when not is use
- ☑ appreciate any limitations in its use or performance
- ☑ report suspected or actual defects and obtain a replacement item if necessary.

Appendix A – The selection of lifejackets

Lifejackets are divided into different categories of buoyancy. The criterion of each class is the support (personal buoyancy) provided by each category, which is expressed in Newtons (N).

The European Union standards that cover lifejackets also require a level of protection for the unconscious person in the water. This means that lifejackets must distribute the weight of the wearer in such a manner that the person is turned face-up. The standards require that automatic lifejackets must self-inflate within 10 seconds of contact with water.

The personal buoyancy level in the standards relate to a person weighing 70 kg, thus the amount of actual personal buoyancy provided by any lifejacket will depend upon the weight of the wearer.

Consider the following situations:

- ☑ wearing a lifejacket with too little personal buoyancy poses obvious problems as there may be too little support for a heavy person to keep their face out of the water or possibly even turn them face-up if unconscious

- ☑ conversely, wearing a lifejacket with too much personal buoyancy could also pose problems; wearers who are not particularly heavy will be more buoyant and, for example, could find it difficult to escape from an air pocket if they have to fully immerse themselves and their lifejacket to duck under an obstruction.

The selection of the most appropriate lifejacket is therefore essential.

50 N personal buoyancy aid

For use by good swimmers in safe water only as long as assistance is at hand. Not safe for unconscious persons.

100 N lifejacket

Suitable for adults who are swimmers and for use in inland waters and safe areas, providing limited protection for unconscious persons depending upon the clothing worn.

150 N lifejacket

Suitable for swimmers and non-swimmers in all waters. Only limited protection for unconscious persons wearing heavy waterproof clothing or in heavy seas.

275 N lifejacket

For offshore use and extreme conditions. Immediate protection for unconscious persons, with turnover guaranteed in five seconds. Adequate personal buoyancy even in heavy clothing.

05

Appendix B – Caring for personal buoyancy equipment

Pre-use checks

These must be carried out each time an item of personal buoyancy equipment is used.

Inspecting personal buoyancy aids is relatively simple with regard to looking for defects in the securing straps, zips, seams and fabric.

---

e.g. Inspecting a life jacket

This is slightly more complex and should be carried out in accordance with the manufacturer's instructions. It will normally include visual checks to ensure:

☑ the firing mechanism has not been activated (this is usually made obvious by the fact that the life jacket is found inflated)

☑ the automatic firing capsule and gas cylinder are correctly screwed in place

☑ there are no signs of corrosion, cracks or dents in the gas cylinder or automatic firing capsule

☑ unwanted movement within the firing mechanism (creepage) has not occurred.

Some automatic inflation mechanisms have colour-coded indicators to show when compression in the spring has been lost. Those that do not have such indicators will require careful inspection to judge whether the spring has lost any compression. Examination of the piston or other visible component may also show whether creepage has happened.

The user must make sure that the:

☑ whistle and light (when fitted) are in position

☑ oral inflation tube is capped

☑ straps and main body of the jacket are not worn or damaged

☑ inflatable bladder of the lifejacket is correctly packed in accordance with the manufacturer's instructions, ensuring that any Velcro is correctly fastened and the manual inflation lanyard is accessible.

Where damage to a personal buoyancy device is discovered, unless it is to be discarded and replaced, it must be returned to the manufacturer or its appointed agent for repair. Local repairs should not be attempted.

Routine maintenance

The routine maintenance of lifejackets must be carried out in accordance with the manufacturer's instructions, in addition to pre-wear checks. As a general guide, where lifejackets are used daily, it is recommended that inspections are carried out at least monthly. However, where lifejackets are used in more harsh conditions, for example off-shore, the periods between inspections may need to be more frequent.

Inspection and testing must be carried out by those competent in recognising defects and the remedial action to be taken. Records must be kept of all inspections and repairs carried out.

Testing the air-tightness of the lifejacket will involve orally inflating the lifejacket and leaving it overnight (or submerging it in water) to check for leaks. The automatic inflation mechanism must be dismantled to make a detailed examination of its condition. Further checks include, as part of the maintenance inspection:

☑ all screw threads must be examined for signs of rust. Rust can lead to problems in locating the cocking cap or keeping the gas cylinder in the correct position

☑ the gas cylinder must be examined for corrosion, cracks, dents and other defects. Particular attention must be paid to the cylinder cap as any indentations found could mean that the automatic firing mechanism has fired but failed to pierce the cylinder. If this is the case, the reason for activation and the cause of failure needs to be identified

☑ the cylinder fitting and groove of the firing pin must be checked to ensure that they are free from dirt

☑ the automatic inflation mechanism must be operated manually (with the gas cylinder removed) to ensure that it operates smoothly, and that there is no obstruction to the movement of the pin that prevents it piercing the cylinder. The firing pin must be checked to ensure that it is sharp

☑ the salt or paper ring must be inspected for any cracking, dissolving or tearing that has taken place since the last inspection

☑ where fitted, the rubber 'O' ring must be inspected for damage and that it is correctly seated

☑ the mechanism must be checked for signs of creepage.

Once the inspection is complete, the lifejacket should be reassembled according to the manufacturer's instructions.

Servicing

The servicing of each lifejacket should be carried out by the manufacturer or their appointed agents, every two years. However, where lifejackets are used regularly and in harsh conditions, an annual or more frequent service may be needed.

Management

A clear policy on the use, inspection and storage of automatically inflated lifejackets must be in place. This policy also addresses the training needs of the lifejacket users.

Lifejackets, if used regularly, should be allocated to individual users. Each individual, having been adequately trained, can then be responsible for carrying out pre-wear checks and inspections, and report defects according to company procedures. This will help ensure correct inflation of the lifejackets is not jeopardised by the carelessness of others.

Management must enforce its policy on lifejackets. This can be achieved by spot checks of both the condition of the lifejackets in use and the records of inspection and servicing.

Storage

Personal floatation equipment must be stored in dry conditions when not in use. Exposure to damp, humid conditions can lead to deterioration in the automatic inflation mechanism, known as creepage. This has the potential to lead to failure of the pin to pierce the carbon dioxide gas cylinder.

Lifejackets must be stored in dry conditions. The following advice should be observed when storing lifejackets.

- ☑ Do not hang lifejackets in contact with wet oilskins or other damp clothing; make sure there is enough space around it to allow the air to circulate.

- ☑ If a lifejacket is wet, unpack it and leave it to dry out on a hanger.

- ☑ Do not store lifejackets close to or directly above heat sources (such as convection heaters).

- ☑ To prevent water getting into the automatic inflation mechanism, do not store wet lifejackets upside down or lying flat.

05

05

06

Mobile workforce

The description of a mobile workforce covers a multitude of trades in many different situations from, for example, a lone worker called out to an emergency with little knowledge and control, to planned work in a strange or hostile environment where customer or client control is minimal.

This chapter provides a general overview of the legal framework and some practical guidance on the management of health and safety at work for mobile, lone and out-of-hours workers; the potential risks they may be exposed to; and practical advice on the management and control of their activities.

Introduction	84
Types of workers	84
Key requirements	84
Overview of legal framework	85
Risk assessment and control	86
Welfare facilities for transient workers	87
Waste storage and disposal	88
Appendix A – Safe driving and work-related road risk	89

6.1 Introduction

This chapter aims to provide employers and managers with general practical guidance on processes and controls that can be put in place to provide their workers with a safe place of work. This ranges from simply saying 'tell us where you are' to planned work that identifies mobile locations where permits may be required.

Management preparation information, pre-job briefing, competence, self-discipline, control, awareness and training are also identified, all of which will form a package of safety for the mobile workforce.

 Employers have responsibility for the health, safety and welfare at work of all of their employees. These **responsibilities cannot be transferred** to any other person, including those people who work alone. It is the **employer's duty** to assess risks to lone workers and take steps to avoid or control risks where necessary.

6.2 Types of workers

The types of workers covered within this chapter are mobile groups of workers (gangs), lone and out-of-hours workers.

Mobile groups of workers

☑ A group of operatives working in a gang away from their home base, undertaking such activities as, for example, domestic and small scale commercial refurbishment. This can include painters and decorators, scaffolders and roof workers.

☑ Gangs of workers undertaking minor road works *(refer to Chapter F01 Street works and road works)* and rail maintenance works *(refer to Chapter F02 Trackside safety)*.

☑ Working in areas accessed by the general public to do work for the utility companies (gas, electric, water and telecommunications).

Lone workers

☑ This group will include maintenance workers (such as plumbers, electricians, lift engineers, water and gas specialists, domestic aerial installers, aerial and mast maintenance personnel, and many others).

Out-of-hours workers

☑ Many of those identified in the lone work group above may, in addition, be required to work out of normal working hours to ensure continuance of 24-hour operations (for example, utility companies – gas, water, electricity and telecommunications).

6.3 Key requirements

Groups of workers

☑ Assess the risks to the mobile workers for that particular environment and the tasks to be undertaken.

☑ Ensure there has been consultation to ensure all relevant hazards have been considered.

☑ Employers with five or more employees have to record significant findings of risk assessments.

☑ Ensure there is a scheme of work in place prior to work commencing.

☑ Provide the supervisor with means to update risk assessment at the scene (such as point of work risk assessment). *(Refer to the example in Appendix A.)*

☑ Verify they have a suitable level of training and competency (such as CSCS, PASMA, trade qualifications).

☑ Decide on equipment needed. Are special transport arrangements required?

☑ Ensure the vehicle is suitable for the number of personnel to be carried.

☑ Ensure the vehicle is appropriate if required to tow equipment (such as mini digger, trailer, welfare unit).

☑ Ensure the vehicle is rated for the safe towing weight limit.

☑ Consider safe access to roof of vehicle (such as mechanised roof access), if it is unavoidable that equipment will need to be carried (such as ladders and pipes).

☑ Avoid climbing on/off flatbed lorries during deliveries, consider use of pallets, loads pre-slung for mechanical means to avoid inertia reels on gallows, and so on.

☑ Does the area need segregation from pedestrians or from other traffic during deliveries?

☑ Is temporary traffic lighting and street signage needed? *(Refer to Chapter F01 Street works and road works.)*

☑ Is a fire emergency plan in place, including details of actions to take, assembly point, audible warning device and fire extinguishers?

☑ Ensure the work area is secure, including storage of materials, suitable waste containers, and so on.

☑ Consider what welfare arrangements are needed for these works, provision of an integral welfare unit that complies with Health and Safety Executive (HSE) requirements (refreshment/seating area, toilet, shower, clothes storage and drying, generator), use of client's facilities (with written agreement) or public facilities within suitable proximity.

☑ Do the works require an emergency rescue plan in situ – are they high risk, confined space, work at height or electrical?

☑ Has a first-aid kit been provided, suitable for the number of persons present?

☑ Is a member of the group trained in basic first aid?

☑ Have suitable receptacles been provided to store waste for removal to suitable disposal facilities?

Lone workers

The following points are additional to the relevant items mentioned above.

☑ Does the lone worker require extra risk control measures?

☑ Ensure training in completion of point of work risk assessment.

☑ Does the workplace present a specific risk to the lone worker?

☑ Is there a safe way in and out of the premises for one person?

☑ Can any necessary temporary access equipment (such as portable ladders or trestles) be safely handled by one person?

☑ Can all the machinery and goods involved in the workplace be safely handled by one person?

☑ Are any chemicals or hazardous substances being used that may pose a risk to the worker?

☑ Does the work involve lifting objects too large for one person?

☑ Is more than one person needed to operate essential controls for the safe running of equipment or workplace transport?

☑ Is there a risk of violence?

☑ Are young, pregnant or disabled workers particularly at risk if they work alone?

☑ Are there any other reasons why the individual (for example, on medication) may be more vulnerable than others?

☑ Are emergency contact arrangements in place in case of an incident (such as regular reporting to supervisor, GPS systems/tracker, regular phone contact, monitoring of staff security systems and so on)?

Out-of-hours workers

Either lone workers or groups of workers may need to work out of hours, frequently at short notice, therefore the following points also apply, in addition to those above.

☑ Are arrangements made for emergency situations (such as who to contact and backup information)?

☑ Has a specific risk assessment been completed? *(Refer to sample point of work risk assessment in Appendix A.)*

☑ Has the operative been provided with method statements for tasks to be undertaken?

☑ Do they have the correct equipment required, and can it be managed by the operative(s)?

6.4 Overview of legal framework

Many pieces of legislation are applicable to these types of workers – some of these are listed below.

☑ **Health and Safety at Work Act** – the umbrella Act under which most health and safety regulations have evolved. For example, it details information regarding an employer's duties in the workplace, about access and egress, provision and suitability of plant provision, information instruction supervision and training of personnel, an employee's duties and much more.

 For further information refer to Chapter A01 Health and safety law.

06

Management of Health and Safety Regulations – risk assessments and controls, monitoring and review.

 For further information refer to Chapter A05
Risk assessments and method statements.

 Provision and Use of Work Equipment Regulations – testing and maintenance information (such as chainsaw, angle grinder, compressor).

 For further information refer to Chapter C05 Plant and work equipment.

 Lifting Operations and Lifting Equipment Regulations – cranes, telehandlers, lorry-loaded cranes and lifting accessories, including testing and maintenance requirements.

 For further information refer to Chapter C07 Lifting operations, and Chapter C08 Lifting equipment.

 Construction (Design and Management) Regulations – Schedule 2 provides guidance for welfare arrangements.

 For further information refer to Chapter A03
Construction (Design and Management) Regulations.

 Work at Height Regulations – provides information on scaffolding, use of ladders and alternative means of working safely at height.

 For further information refer to Chapter D01 The Work at Height Regulations.

 Personal protective equipment – information on legislative requirements, for example types and uses of specific equipment (such as goggles and dust masks) in particular environments and training in the fitting of such items.

 For further information refer to Chapter B06 Personal protective equipment.

6.5   Risk assessment and control

 A risk assessment is an important step in protecting your workers and your business, as well as complying with the law. It helps you focus on the risks that really matter in your workplace – the ones with the potential to cause real harm.

How do we assess and control the risk?

Employers need to investigate the potential hazards faced by workers and assess the risks involved both to these workers and to any person(s) who may be affected by their work. Employers should ensure that measures are in place to control or avoid such risks.

As an employer what should you do?

 Involve staff or their representatives when undertaking the required risk assessment process.

 Take steps to **check control measures** are in place (examples of control measures include instruction, training, supervision and issuing protective equipment).

 Review risk assessments annually or, as few workplaces stay the same, when there has been a significant change in working practice.

 When a risk assessment shows it is not possible for the work to be conducted safely by a lone worker, address that risk by, for example, making arrangements to **provide help or back-up**.

 Where a lone worker is working at another employer's workplace, that employer should **inform the lone worker's employer** of any risks and the required control measures.

 Refer to the HSE's publication *Five steps to risk assessment* (INDG163).

Point of work risk assessment

A risk assessment completed by the employer or supervisor should be provided to the workforce prior to any works commencing on site where practicable. However, there are many occasions when a point of work risk assessment will be required.

- ☑ To update the previously prepared risk assessment.

- ☑ Changes to the working environment.

- ☑ Changes to the works to be undertaken.

- ☑ Out-of-hours working, when each call out will require a specific risk assessment (for example, emergency maintenance (such as a serious water leak/flooding), urgent utilities works (such as a gas leak or explosion)).

- ☑ For a maintenance worker who is undertaking a number of different calls in a day where generic information is available but needs to be tailored to a specific task.

On arrival at site:

- ☑ report to the person on site

- ☑ contact base to confirm arrival (lone worker safety protocol)

- ☑ prepare a point of work risk assessment.

 Employers and supervisors must satisfy themselves that the workforce is competent to carry out a point of work risk assessment. Training should be provided that includes practical, on-site mentoring. If a site activity **cannot** be done safely, the workforce must know when **not to start** and contact the supervisor for further advice.

Examples of an unsafe working area and/or conditions include:

- ☑ an unguarded excavation

- ☑ traffic not segregated

- ☑ permits to work and disconnections and isolations where certificates do not match

- ☑ scaffolding where scaff tags are not present or the date has expired

- ☑ inadequate or wrong equipment and lack of training on the equipment

- ☑ no fire extinguisher

- ☑ incorrect tools

- ☑ inadequate/unsuitable PPE.

Filling in a point of work risk assessment

(Refer to the example in Section G Checklists and forms.)

- ☑ Part 1 – **Stop** and ensure the area is safe with adequate access and egress. Complete items listed under this section. Seek advice from a supervisor if you answer **NO** to any of them.

- ☑ Part 2 – **Think** about what hazards may be present and carry out a safety assessment of those identified. Determine if the existing controls are adequate. Provide brief details of your rescue plan for safe escape in the event of something going wrong. Make a note on the form of any hazards that are significant but without, or with insufficient, controls.

- ☑ Part 3 – **Act.** Detail additional hazards and control measures needed to manage the risk. Is the remaining risk acceptable for work to commence? If no, this needs input from your supervisor.

- ☑ Part 4 – **Review,** and inform your supervisor if the job created any additional hazards, also if there are lessons to be learned.

 This may be on any size of paper, from double-sided A4 to pocket-sized A6.

6.6 Welfare facilities for transient workers

Health and safety legislation requires that welfare arrangements for projects of any size are pre-arranged prior to works commencing on site. For these circumstances there are two types to be considered:

1. Use of client's facilities – pre-arranged and confirmed in writing, or local public convenience.

2. Provision of an integrated hygiene unit, which complies with HSE requirements and includes refreshment area, toilet, drying area and generator.

If local facilities or a portaloo are considered sufficient then van-mounted equipment could be used for washing and preparation of food and refreshment, using a battery-mounted inverter.

Examples of mobile work vans fitted out with welfare facilities

Refer to the *Provision of welfare facilities during construction work* Construction information sheet (CIS) 59.

6.7   Waste storage and disposal

Waste that is created at a site must be disposed of appropriately. Hazardous waste will need to be stored in appropriate containers and removed by licensed contractors using waste transfer notes.

Non-hazardous waste generated during works undertaken by mobile groups of workers or lone workers can be transported to their base for sorting and transferring to suitable recycling facilities or landfill sites.

The following points will need to be considered.

☑ Is the waste suitable for transporting – is it hazardous or non-hazardous, and does it require special handling?

☑ Is the person planning to remove it competent to do so?

☑ Has the waste been segregated (for example, plasterboard separated from electrical)?

☑ Can the waste be segregated in the vehicle, by bagging, being placed in enclosed containers or requiring collection from the location?

☑ Do the mobile workers have suitable materials to package the waste products?

☑ Can the waste be carried without exceeding the safe working load of the vehicle?

If using a company vehicle to carry waste back to a depot or to a licenced waste treatment or disposal facility, then a waste carrier's licence may be required.

For further information refer to Chapter E03 Waste management.

Appendix A – Safe driving and work-related road risk

Prospect guide

(The following guidance has been reproduced with the kind permission of Prospect, the trade union for professionals.)

This guidance is aimed at managers and professionals to give a balanced view of what employers should do, what employees should do and what managers should do as both an employee and representative of the employer.

 Free health and safety guidance can be downloaded from the Prospect website.

Introduction

Fact

 Being killed in a car crash is the greatest risk most Prospect members/managers will ever face.

Risk control

Requires **your employer and you** to share responsibility for:

- ☑ your organisation's driving policy, culture and performance
- ☑ the vehicle you use
- ☑ the journey you make
- ☑ how you drive
- ☑ the ergonomics: your interface with the vehicle.

Aims

This guidance aims to:

- ☑ safeguard you as a road user
- ☑ protect you as a duty holder
- ☑ enable Prospect representatives to measure and promote their employer's compliance.

1.0 Driven to death

It's a tragedy when anyone is killed or maimed on the road. But it's even worse when they were simply trying to do their job, especially if it turns out their workload was overstretching them.

Around 1,000 road deaths and 13,000 serious road injuries every year are work-related.

The facts are that:

- ☑ up to one in three crashes involves a vehicle being driven for work
- ☑ every week, around 200 road deaths and serious injuries involve someone at work
- ☑ research suggests, company car drivers who drive at least once a week are 40-50% more likely to have an incident.

These figures include road users driving for a living (such as road haulage and delivery drivers). However, studies of drivers with **high work-related mileage** (be that for work or long car journeys after work) demonstrate that they tend to have an elevated accident rate and to drive while **fatigued**, under time **pressure** and **distracted** by in-car tasks.

These risk factors are clearly relevant to Prospect members/managers.

2.0 The regulatory framework

The significance of work-related road deaths is rarely highlighted by the Health and Safety Executive, because primary enforcement of road traffic law is the responsibility of the police, not the HSE. But this doesn't eradicate the health and safety requirements on the employer to control and manage work-related road risk, alongside other occupational risks.

 To this end, HSE and the Department for Transport have published *Driving at work: managing work-related road safety* to assist. Details can be found online.

06

In recent years many employers have significantly enhanced their precautions and safety checks. This may have been prompted by the insurance industry telling employers to be more defensive, to address the rise in insurance claims; or it may be because of the introduction of the Corporate Manslaughter and Corporate Homicide Act, when it was widely expected that the police would prosecute companies for work-related road fatalities.

However, many companies still focus on driver-centred interventions (such as selection and training). They pay scant attention to the day-to-day working practices and pressures that mean their staff drive thousands of business miles a year, often at peak times, against deadlines and with the expectation that they will respond to work-related phone calls.

Drivers often feel compelled to divide their attention between driving and an imminent meeting or task. This is dangerous and undermines both employer and driver compliance with the law.

3.0 The law in brief

Work-related road risk is no different from any other work-related risk: the employer has common law duties of care and statutory duties under the Health and Safety at Work Act and its associated regulations.

So health and safety management duties on policy, risk assessment, maintenance, staff training, monitoring and auditing apply equally. This is required by the Management of Health and Safety at Work Regulations and the Provision and Use of Work Equipment Regulations, because a car is included as work equipment.

Typically, success requires commitment from the top, employee consultation and involvement (to ensure shared ownership) and proper policy implementation by line management. It also requires you, as an employee, to adhere to the standards that are agreed and to report any problems that arise in the course of your work.

After all, there may be a flaw or something impractical in the policy or procedure that you are meant to follow which, if left uncorrected, is subsequently held against you as the basis for non-compliance.

So, if you spot a problem, report it!

07

House building

The nature of house building can give rise to additional challenges, such as working in and around live residential environments, tight site logistics, fast-track programmes, changing contractor workforce, finishing trades working in close proximity to each other in small spaces, and security and theft.

This chapter highlights some of the key issues. However, most topics encountered on site are common issues and are addressed in other sections of GE 700.

Introduction	92
Key requirements	92
Planning	93
Environmental considerations	94
Work at height	94
Fire	97
Construction dust	99
Appendix A – Unloading roof trusses	101
Appendix B – Manoeuvring roof trusses	102

7.1　Introduction

House building is a major component of the overall construction industry in Great Britain and, whilst much of the management guidance provided in GE 700 can be applied to the work activities carried on in housing developments, there are some subtle differences.

The Home Builders Federation's (HBF) Health and Safety Forum has developed a charter and action plan for driving continuous improvements in the home building industry. The overall objectives are to agree principles that the industry can work to, and to work collaboratively to learn from each other's experiences and improve health and safety performance. The forum also collects accident and incident statistics from its membership that, year on year, has provided the industry with information on which to respond. For example, a combined campaign with the Health and Safety Executive (HSE) to reduce the number of slips and trips in the industry was a direct result of the findings from these statistics.

In addition to analysing and responding to these statistics, house builders are continually striving to ensure that the requirements of relevant and current health and safety legislation and regulations are interpreted and implemented in a manner that removes and reduces the risk of ill health and injury to its workforce and to those who are affected by its work activities.

In order to achieve this, the likes of the HBF Health and Safety Forum work closely with the HSE and other trade bodies to ensure that they have a positive input into guidance produced by these organisations, which takes into account the needs of house builders.

 Good examples of this can be found when working with the following organisations:

☑ UKTFI (timber frame fire safety)

☑ Strategic Forum for Plant Safety (manoeuvring of roof trusses)

☑ The National Federation of Roofing Contractors (controlling silica when disc cutting roof tiles)

☑ The Building Products Delivery Working Group *(Delivering safely – Guidance for the delivery and receipt of building products).*

7.2　Key requirements

In general the requirements placed on house builders to assess risks in line with the Management Regulations in order to manage work activities that fall under operational regulations (such as Work at Height, PUWER, LOLER, Manual Handling and PPE) are no different to those covered by GE 700.

However, because of the progressive nature of the build programme on housing developments that sees the introduction of customers onto site whilst construction continues, the CDM Regulations become more relevant to house builders.

Many house builders take on the combined role of numerous duty holders detailed in the CDM Regulations (for example, a house builder with technical, commercial and construction departments can very often act as the client, designer, CDM co-ordinator and principal contractor).

Whilst establishing duty holder competency through training and experience is a priority, it is the requirements in Schedule 4 of the regulations that sets house building apart from large-scale one-off projects that can be more easily protected. In particular the proper management of vehicle movement, pedestrian segregation and public protection are of prime consideration.

HBF accident statistics

 The HBF has a comprehensive recording system and produces an annual report on health and safety statistics, provided by a number of its volume house building member organisations, which is available on the HBF website.

The organisations that contribute to these statistics confirm that each year, on average there are:

☑ 70,000 people employed on their sites

☑ over 300 reportable accidents

☑ of which one third are reportable major injuries.

The top four causes are:

☑ slips, trips and falls on the same level (33%)

☑ falls from height (23%)

☑ manual handling (16%)

☑ being hit by an object (13%).

Slips, trips and falls on the same level

Of all the incidents reported to the HSE, 33% were attributable to slips, trips and falls on the same level. Three main areas contributed to over 50% of these, which are:

☑ materials

☑ scaffold use

☑ steps and stairways.

Maintaining good housekeeping, clear access routes and tidy working areas are basic controls that help accident prevention and productivity.

7.3 Planning

The planning of any development, including compound set up, show-house area, car parking welfare, and so on, at the outset is a key factor in the management of health and safety. Often however, as the sales of new homes progress it can dictate and alter the speed and direction of build and ongoing changes to plans require careful management.

Any house building site manager therefore needs to employ sound, ongoing monitoring systems to ensure that neither the workforce nor members of the public are put at risk by the sequence of build.

The major items for ongoing review are shown below.

☑ **Site security (out of hours)** – ensure boundary fences are maintained to prevent access by unauthorised persons to build areas. Children and teenagers are inquisitive and reasonable attempts must be made to keep them out and to protect them from any hazards that are on site (such as securing down manhole covers and blocking off ladders or access towers).

By the very nature of house building, the materials, fixtures and fittings are desirable to thieves and the risk of theft is high, particularly as the build enters the final stages. Measures should reflect the increased risk, especially as fencing and storage areas reduce.

☑ **Site security (during work hours)** – ensure that site entrances and exits clearly indicate that unauthorised access is not permitted. This may, in some circumstances, require the need for a gate person.

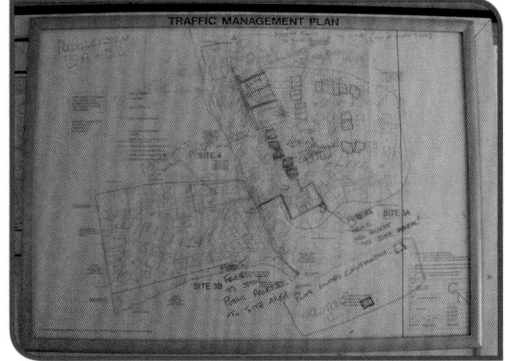

☑ **Traffic management (pedestrian)** – safe pedestrian routes, both within the work area for site operatives and adjacent footpaths used by members of the public. Consideration should be given to how the public used the area before development started, to ensure they do not ignore signage and continue as before. For example, dog walkers may have established routes and may be determined to continue with their route by ignoring signage, only detouring once physical barriers are in place.

☑ **Traffic management (vehicles)** – clear signage and vehicle routes should be established with speed limits and restraints where necessary. One-way systems should, wherever possible, be established and the reversing of vehicles should remain at a minimum.

☑ **Traffic management (deliveries)** – material delivery areas should be established taking into account turning points, use of marshals, and so on. Consideration should be given to routes that pass through residential areas, especially housing developments, taking into account public and home owners' vehicles and peak periods of traffic movement (such as commuting and school runs).

 Consortium agreement pro-formas, for use by house builders developing the same site, are effective tools for identifying agreement on collective controls (such as traffic management and site security). These can be found on the HBF website.

 All the above points will need careful re-evaluation once new homes become occupied and the dynamics of the development change.

Phased construction work and completion of new homes within developments is generally planned at pre-start meetings but progress can be changed dependent on sales, and therefore site planning will be regularly reviewed as part of any house builder's site review process, as plots are released for sale.

07

7.4 Environmental considerations

When planning and monitoring the works, environmental impacts must be assessed. These are covered in Section E *Environment*, together with practical guidance on how to identify and manage key risks.

Consideration should also be given to how activities could impact on the local community, especially nuisance.

Mud

Mud and dust can be difficult to manage, and be made worse by unexpectedly prolonged wet weather or dry spells.

Mud can be carried far along a road, with large lumps being a hazard to cyclists and motorbikes and wet mud making the road slippery, especially in wet, cold and dark weather. Roads must be kept clear, using measures from a spade and broom to hiring a road sweeper.

 Road brush attachments are available, which can be fitted quickly to the forks of a telehandler. Having one on site means roads can be regularly cleaned as and when required.

Dust

Mud can quickly turn to dust, and in dry conditions dust can swirl and carry in the wind, quickly covering neighbouring properties and vehicles. Efforts must be made to dampen down site and road surfaces.

Local community

Proactively keeping local communities and residents informed of what is happening is far more productive than dealing with complaints, which can quickly escalate. Taking the time and effort early on (such as attending parish meetings, knocking on doors and introducing the site manager, or regular letter drops) can pay off in the long term.

Letters can contain information on items such as large deliveries or the increased number of vehicle movements, any weekend work and why the changes have become necessary, together with contact information.

Engaging with the community should also be encouraged (such as carrying out safety talks at local schools or supporting a local community project).

7.5 Work at height

Almost every house building project will involve the main contractor or their respective trade contractors in working at height. Statistics now clearly illustrate that working at height is a major cause of accidents.

The Work at Height Regulations encompasses all activities where 'a fall that is likely to cause injury may occur', including deliveries, roof work and falls into excavations. The scope of the regulations include all types of access equipment and work platforms, regardless of how long an employee is at height, or of the height at which the activity occurs.

Examples in a house building environment that can be classified as working at height include:

- ☑ working on any type of scaffold
- ☑ being on the back of a lorry or raised loading bays
- ☑ working close to an excavation or trench
- ☑ working off steps, hop ups or mobile towers
- ☑ mezzanine floors with no edge protection
- ☑ installing roof trusses or working above open joists
- ☑ stairwells with no stairs or staircases with no handrails
- ☑ temporary wheelbarrow ramps onto the back of skips
- ☑ working off external scaffold, building walls while there is no fall prevention or protection on internal side of the wall or room, and especially across window openings.

House building

F

For further information on working at height refer to Chapter D01 The Work at Height Regulations and Chapter D05 Fall arrest and suspension equipment.

Three issues common to house building are:

☑ deliveries

☑ roof trusses

☑ stairwells and open joists.

Deliveries

The Building Products Delivery Working Group (BPDWG) has produced a leaflet *Delivering safely – Guidance for the delivery and receipt of building products* to help delivery drivers and site managers understand what is required to ensure the safe delivery of building products across the building products delivery industry.

The guidance represents good practice, which may go further than the minimum needed to comply with the law. BPDWG acknowledges the support of the HSE in writing the guidance, which can be downloaded from the BPDWG website.

Roof trusses

Refer to Appendix A which, following the publication of the HSE Information Sheet WPT14, the major suppliers of trusses to the industry now follow, to minimise fall risks during the unloading of roof trusses.

This guidance removes the risk of falls and as such the use of fall prevention measures (such as crash decks) and fall protection measures (such as airbags and safety nets) are kept to a minimum.

For further information on working at height refer to Chapter D01 The Work at Height Regulations and Chapter D05 Fall arrest and suspension equipment.

Refer to the Strategic Forum for Plant Safety website for guidance on manoeuvring roof trusses.

In addition to this guidance the HBF Health and Safety Forum has produced accompanying guidance for the manoeuvring of roof trusses by telehandlers *(refer to Appendix B for extracts)*.

Stairwells and open joists

The risk of falls through open joists, working around open stairwells and fall risks during the installation of staircases and banisters must all be assessed and physically controlled on site. The use of stairwell working platforms and bespoke handrail systems are available for use in these instances.

 Examples of poor work at height practice

Poor use of soft-landing system

Missing midrails, toe-boards and loose boards

Poor stairwell edge protection and working access

Incorrect scaffold access, ramp and edge protection

👍 Examples of good work at height practice

![Good standard of access scaffold] 
Good standard of access scaffold

![Birdcage system]
Birdcage system

![Crash decking system]
Crash decking system

![Soft-landing system] 
Soft-landing system

![Stairwell access platform (viewed from ground floor)]
Stairwell access platform (viewed from ground floor) 

![Stairwell access platform (viewed from first floor)]
Stairwell access platform (viewed from first floor)

07

7.6 Fire

Fire is an ever-present threat throughout the majority of construction and demolition projects. As house building progresses the nature of the fire risk is likely to change as different work activities start and are completed. Therefore, not only must the risk of fire be managed continuously, but the management process must allow for the changing nature of the risk.

 For further guidance refer to Chapter C02 Fire prevention and control.

Common sources of fire risk

☑ Storage and use of flammable materials, including liquefied petroleum gas (LPG).

☑ Hot work.

☑ Electrical systems and equipment, including temporary lighting.

☑ Arson.

☑ Smoking.

☑ Operating plant and equipment.

☑ Poor housekeeping.

 It is vital that the project fire strategy takes into account occupied homes, fire hydrant points and emergency fire and rescue vehicle access.

Specialist advice

The Fire Protection Association (FPA), in conjunction with the Construction Confederation (CC), published the eighth edition of *Fire prevention on construction* sites in July 2012. This joint code of practice (CoP) deals with the protection from fire on construction sites and buildings undergoing renovation.

The CoP does not have any legal status; however, it does outline good practice and many insurance companies now require that the authoritative guidelines (such as those detailed in the CoP) are properly implemented on construction projects before they will give full insurance.

The FPA also publishes *Construction site fire prevention checklist – a guide for insurers, surveyors and construction industry professionals*.

Timber frames

 All timber-framed construction is deemed high risk and additional precautions must be taken. Guidance can be found in the HSE publication *Fire safety in construction* (HSG168), which can be downloaded free from its website.

The UK Timber Frame Association

 The UK Timber Frame Association (UKTFA)'s *Site safe* is the industry leading initiative that allows the construction community to reap all the benefits of timber frame construction in any urban location while mitigating the risk of arson during construction.

The *Site safe* strategy has many component parts. Together these form a comprehensive set of guidelines that are reliant on the collaborative working of the entire construction supply chain to reduce the risk of fire on timber frame construction sites.

Site safe ensures UKTFA manufacturing member companies that are working on large projects give clear, concise information and assistance to the principal contractor regarding fire safety on construction sites.

It also ensures that all contractors involved in timber frame sites are fully briefed on identifying fire risks during the construction phase. While the responsibility for addressing the fire risk lies with the principal contractor, *Site safe* provides a framework through which any risk can be consistently communicated so that appropriate action can be taken.

How does *Site safe* work?

Site safe is formed in three parts:

☑ **design phase** – RIBA plan of works A – E

☑ **project construction/procurement phase** – RIBA plan of works F – H

☑ **on-site phase** – RIBA plan of works J – K.

 UKTFA has also produced guidance called *16 steps to fire safety on timber frame construction sites*. This practical guidance should be read in conjunction with the above FPA publications.

The UKTFA guidance also contains a risk assessment flowchart, which helps identify site security measures required, depending upon the fire-resisting sub-division of the building.

By following the flowchart (which asks such questions about the building as 'Is it more or less than three storeys?' and 'What is the building footprint shape and dimensions?') the outcome is rated A to C and the minimum security arrangements would be as follows:

Security level	Security features
Security package A	Non-climbable perimeter fencing and locked site and building access outside of site hours.
Security package B	Security package A, plus out-of-hours watchman and movement-sensitive security lighting.
Security package C	Security package B, plus CCTV, permanent security lighting and all ground-floor openings secured.

7.7 Construction dust

Many house building activities will give rise to dust, which should be considered a high health risk. Each year thousands of construction workers contract or die from respiratory diseases due to breathing in dust and fumes.

The amount breathed in each day as they work from site to site can seem small or insignificant. In some cases the effects of exposure may be immediate but generally it can take years before the symptoms of ill health become apparent. Because of this, respiratory risks are often overlooked or underplayed.

Typical activities which create harmful levels of dust include:

- ☑ sweeping a dusty floor
- ☑ mechanically cutting, chasing or drilling concrete, bricks and blocks
- ☑ mixing sand and cement to make mortar
- ☑ sanding down MDF or timber
- ☑ rubbing down tape and jointing or plaster.

 All dusts are hazardous to health. The creation of dust, regardless of amount, must be controlled – all risk assessments and method statements should state how exposure to dust or fumes will be minimised. It is no longer acceptable to expect workers to work unprotected in dusty conditions.

 For further information, from an environmental perspective, refer to Section E *Environment* or for the related ill health issues refer to Chapter B10 Dust and fumes.

Cutting roof tiles in valleys has historically created a lot of silica dust, which is hazardous to health. The National Federation of Roofing Contractors has issued recent guidance on this that clearly identifies the controls, including separate cutting areas and suitable dust suppression, which should be in place during this work activity.

 The National Federation of Roofing Contractors (NFRC) guidance sheet *Controlling silica when disc cutting roof tiles* can be downloaded free from its website.

Cutting of other housing development building materials that produce dust (such as using petrol cut-off saws on kerbs and paving slabs) must be done using methods to eliminate or minimise dust (such as using a block splitter, using water suppression or dust extract systems).

 It is recognised good practice to use respiratory protective equipment (RPE) with an FFP3 or P3 rating to protect against all construction dust (such as silica) that is created when mechanically cutting concrete, bricks, slabs, and so on – even when wet cutting (which only removes about 75% of airborne particles). FFP3/P3 offers maximum protection compared to FFP1/P1 or FFP2/P2.

For further guidance on how to manage dust and fumes, and to help check if method statements and risk assessments adequately address respiratory risks refer to Chapter B10 Dust and fumes.

Appendix A – Unloading roof trusses

 The following case study is based upon the HSE Information sheet *Unloading roof trusses* (WPT14), which gives examples of good practice to reduce injuries due to falls from vehicles through sensible management of health and safety risks in the workplace.

The challenge

During a manufacturer's delivery of roof trusses, it was identified that customers had problems when unloading trussed rafters from the lorry by crane.

Slingers were required to climb the trusses on the lorry to cut the securing ropes. They were then required to attach the sling or chains to the truss and connect them to the crane before sliding back down from the truss.

Finding a solution

Introduction of a colour-coded banding system

☑ **Blue bands** are now used to secure the trusses into bundles.

☑ **White bands** secure the trussed rafters to the vehicle frame.

This development eliminated the risk of the wrong band being cut during the unloading process. The drivers, who have been issued with telescopic cutting poles, now have no need to climb onto the lorry.

The next development was the introduction of **sacrificial slings** attached at the factory. As these are accessible from the ground by the slingers there is again no need to climb onto the vehicle.

Results

07

☑ The introduction of these measures has eliminated the risk of falls from vehicles.

☑ In addition, as there is now no requirement for the use of fall arrest systems, there have been savings in time and money.

☑ Customers are now able to unload vehicles more quickly and safely.

 Further information can be found on the workplace transport and falls sections of the HSE's website.

Appendix B - Manoeuvring roof trusses

 The information below is based on manoeuvring of roof trusses guidance developed by members of the Home Builders Health and Safety Forum, which is available to download from the HBF website.

Transporting or manoeuvring trusses

The following options can be applied to the transport, manoeuvring and placement of trusses on site.

All roof trusses should be delivered on vehicles in such a manner that operatives do not need to access the rear of vehicles to remove straps or attach lifting strops.

Where practicable, trusses should be lifted directly from the delivery vehicle onto the roof (such as just-in-time delivery); this will require planning of both the site and delivery of trusses and should be the primary method of delivery and lifting.

Where just-in-time deliveries cannot be achieved (for example, if the plot is not ready) trusses should be lifted from the delivery vehicle via the telehandler onto truss racks designed on loading bays or gable end scaffolds. The delivery vehicle should be positioned as close as possible to the plot under construction and the distance to be travelled by the telehandler limited. The storage of trusses must not impede the safe operation of the telehandler or access to the loading bays.

If the above is not practicable and/or access to the construction area is restricted for the delivery vehicle, the trusses can be lifted from the vehicle onto an appropriately designed, freestanding storage rack. The rack should be positioned close to the plots under construction to limit the distance the trusses need to be moved when required. The truss rack should be continually re-sited as close to the work area, where possible, and be fully accessible by delivery vehicles.

Lifting of trusses onto the wall plate

In the majority of circumstances, lifting of roof trusses should be undertaken by a mobile crane where a full pack can be lifted directly onto the wall plate. A lifting plan completed by an appropriately trained appointed person would be required for the lift.

If an alternative method is utilised to lift roof trusses onto a roof, then this will need to be justified by the completion of a lifting plan for each plot, by an appropriately trained appointed person, which will take into consideration:

☑ the capabilities of the lifting appliance

☑ any restrictions to the lifting operation (such as scaffolding or other obstructions)

☑ height of the structure

☑ handling the trusses by workers on the scaffold working platform

☑ method of lifting the trusses safely, including consideration of the pitch, size and weight of the truss.

Transporting of trusses via a telehandler

The following conditions apply if trusses are to be suspended via the forks of a telehandler and transported on a development.

☑ The route from the truss rack or delivery vehicle to the plot should not be through occupied areas of the development where practicable. If this is necessary a traffic marshal(s) will be required to ensure occupants or others are not put at risk from the movement of the trusses.

☑ The route should be reviewed prior to transporting the trusses and an assessment made if any obstacles (such as lamp posts or scaffold) will affect the ability of the operator to manoeuvre the telehandler and load safely.

☑ The maximum load of trusses that can be transported via a telehandler from a truss rack or delivery vehicle to a plot is 600 kg. The weight of all trusses installed on site should be known by site management and detailed in the lifting plan. This is the maximum load, but this may need to be reduced depending on the span/pitch of the trusses, potential obstructions, gradients/cross slopes and capabilities of the machine.

☑ The tyre pressures should be within +/- 5% of the maximum stated by the manufacturers and be checked prior to moving the load.

☑ The telehandler should be driven at no more than 7 mph with no sharp turns or manoeuvres.

☑ The operator should have full vision from the driving position and the trusses suspended from the forks so that the lowest point of truss (top chord overhang) is within 500 mm (+/- 150 mm) of the ground. A banksman should be available, where there are obstacles to full visibility, to provide appropriate signals to the operator and ensure no other persons are affected by the movement of the trusses.

Trusses should not be moved when wind speeds at ground level are forecast to be or exceed 7 m/s or 16 mph. This should be assessed by the use of an anemometer and/or weather reports for the area.

Index

360° excavators 55–56

AC overhead line systems 30, 38
access 51, 53, 56, 59, 65
access equipment 65, 85
    see also ladders
access prevention see barriers; fencing; security
accident reporting and investigation 30
Achilles Link-up accreditation 29
advance signs for road works 8
alcohol 7, 30, 37–38, 74
apparatus 3–6, 34, 47, 48, 52, 56, 57, 84
appointed persons 51–52
asbestos 46, 47, 48, 50, 51, 53, 57, 62, 67
audits 30

barriers 7, 8, 11–12, 33, 36, 54, 74
    see also fencing; traffic cones
blockages of the line 33
boats 76, 77
bonfires 36, 58
bridge demolition 56
BS 6187 45
Building Act 45, 48
buoyancy equipment 73, 74–75, 77, 78, 79–81
buried services see apparatus

CDM co-ordinators for demolition work 44–52
CDM co-ordinators for road works 3
CDM Regulations and demolition work 45–46, 48, 49, 50
CDM Regulations and mobile workforce 86
CDM Regulations and road works 3
CDM Regulations and shopfitting/interior contracting 67, 68
CDM Regulations and trackside work 36
CDM Regulations duty holders 44, 45, 46–47, 51, 53, 65, 92
    see also CDM co-ordinators; demolition clients; designers;
    principal contractors
CDM Regulations notifiable projects 3, 45–50, 53, 67
clearances for overhead lines 5, 6, 38
clearances for pedestrian barriers 11
clearances for road works 6–7
clearances for trains 35
    see also separation for trackside safety
clients see demolition clients
co-ordination of road works 3, 13
Code of practice – Safety at Street Works and Road Works 2–3
colours of high-visibility clothing 37
communication in demolition work 47, 48, 51, 52, 54
communication in rescue work 76, 77
communication in trackside work 31–33
communication with lone workers 85
community liaison 93, 94
competency in asbestos work 67
competency in demolition work 45, 46, 49, 52, 55, 56
competency in mobile plant use 35
competency in trackside safety 30–31, 35, 36
conductor rail permits see isolation permits
conductor rails see DC third/fourth rail systems
cones see traffic cones
confined spaces 35, 51
    see also excavations
Construction (Design and Management) Regulations see
CDM Regulations
construction phase plans 3, 29, 30, 44, 47, 51–53
    see also demolition plans
contamination see pollution
contractors 51, 52, 62, 67
    see also demolition contractors; principal contractors
contractors for trackside work 28, 29, 30, 34, 37
controllers of site safety (COSSs) 28, 30, 31, 32, 33, 34, 41
COSHH assessments 51, 57
crossing high-speed roads on foot 7
crushing 52, 55, 58–59

cutting 38, 54, 55, 57–58, 99
    see also dust; fumes

danger areas see exclusion zones
dangerous occurrences 30
DC third/fourth rail systems 30, 39–40
deliberate collapse 54
deliveries 63, 84, 85, 93, 95, 102
demolition 43–60
demolition balls 56, 60
demolition clients 44, 45, 46, 47, 49–50, 52, 53
demolition contractors 44, 45, 46, 47, 48, 49–50, 51, 59
demolition plans 44, 46, 47, 50–53
depth of cover 4, 5, 6
designers 7, 44, 46, 51
disconnection certificates 47, 52, 56
    see also isolation permits
diversionary works 3–4
diving 77
documentation for asbestos removal 67
documentation for demolition 46, 47–48, 51, 52, 53, 59
    see also demolition plans; health and safety files; method
    statements for demolition; permits for demolition; site waste
    management plans
documentation for trackside work 30, 37
    see also licences for trackside work; method statements for
    trackside work
driving 89–90
drugs 7, 30, 37–38, 74
dust in demolition work 50, 52, 57, 58, 59
dust in house building 94, 99–100
dust in shopfitting/interior contracting 63, 66–67, 68
duty holders 44, 45, 46–47, 51, 53, 65, 92
    see also CDM co-ordinators; demolition clients; designers;
    principal contractors

earthing of lineside fencing 35
electrical apparatus 6, 57
electrified railway lines 30, 34, 35, 36, 38–40
emergency procedures 30, 56, 58, 85, 87
    see also rescue equipment and procedures
emergency services 7, 73, 77
emissions 58
    see also dust; fumes
'end of road works' signs 9
environmental issues 57, 58, 94
    see also dust; fumes; noise; pollution; vibration
excavations 4, 5, 8, 11, 12, 65, 94
    see also confined spaces
excavators 54, 55–56
exclusion zones 45, 54, 60
    see also barriers; safety zones; security
explosion hazards 58
explosives 54, 60
eye protection 12

fall prevention 54, 65, 73–74, 94–95
    see also work at height
falling object protection 54, 56
falls 65, 74, 92–93
fencing 33–34, 35–36, 42, 93
    see also barriers
fire 36, 55, 58, 62, 63, 66, 97–99
first aid 51, 77
fitness 7, 30
floor-by-floor demolition 53
footways 4, 11, 12, 23–24, 93
fumes 52, 57–58, 68

gas apparatus 4–5
give and take traffic control 10, 19
green zones 30, 33, 34, 36, 42
guard-rails 54

guarding excavations 4

hazardous substances 85
    see also asbestos; COSHH assessments; dust; lead
hazardous waste 48, 59, 88
    see also asbestos
Health and Safety at Work Act 12, 85
health and safety files 46, 48, 51
health and safety plans see construction phase plans;
demolition plans
health surveillance 57, 58, 59
hearing protection 12, 41, 57, 59
high-rise building demolition 53, 54
'high street environment' 36
high-visibility clothing 12, 37, 77
Highway Authority 3, 7, 10, 13
Highways Act 13
hot work 55, 57–58, 60
house building 91–102
hydraulic pusher arms 56, 60

individuals working alone (IWAs) 30
    see also lone workers
information boards 8, 9
information provision 30, 45–48, 51, 52
    see also communication; community liaison
inspection of crushing equipment 59
inspection of demolition work 56, 59
inspection of oxy-propane cutting equipment 55
inspection of traffic signs 9
isolation permits 35, 39
    see also disconnection certificates

joists 96

'keep left'/'keep right' signs 8

ladders 38, 39, 65, 77
lamps 8, 11, 12
'lane closed' signs 8, 11
lead 51, 52, 57, 68
lead-in taper of cones 6, 8
lead responsibility 32
licences for asbestos work 67
licences for trackside work 29, 30
lifebuoys 75, 76, 77
lifejackets 73, 74, 75, 79–81
lifelines 75–76, 77
lift shafts 54, 65
Lifting Operations and Lifting Equipment Regulations 56, 86
lighting for work over water 76
lighting of excavations 4, 11
lighting of road works 8, 11, 12
lighting of signs 9
line blockages 33
lineside fencing 35–36
lineside vegetation 36, 38
lone workers 30, 84, 85, 89
longways clearance 6, 7
lookouts 30, 33, 34, 41

major works 3
Management of Health and Safety Regulations 12, 86, 92
manual demolition techniques 54
manual handling 63, 85
mechanical demolition techniques 55
medical fitness 7, 30
method statements for demolition 46, 48, 51, 53
method statements for out-of-hours workers 85
method statements for shopfitting and interior contracting
65, 67
method statements for trackside work 34
mobile plant 34–35, 55, 58–59, 65

mobile towers 35
mobile workforce 83–90
monitoring of demolition work 57, 58, 59
mud 94

National Highways Sector Scheme 12
near misses 30
needlestick injuries 36
Network Rail 28, 29, 30, 33, 34, 37, 56
New Roads and Street Works Act 3, 12, 13
noise 41, 50, 54, 55, 57, 58, 59, 63
notifiable work 3, 45–50, 53, 67

offences and penalties 13, 38, 58
on or near the line 30, 36, 39
open joists 96
openings 54, 65
out-of-hours workers 84, 85, 87
overhead lines 5, 6, 36, 38, 52
oxy-propane cutting equipment 55, 57–58

partial demolition 45, 53
pavements see footways
pedestrian barriers 7, 8, 11, 12
pedestrian routes 7, 11
    see also footways
pedestrians 7, 92, 93
permits for confined spaces work 35
permits for demolition 50, 58
permits for trackside work 35, 39
permits for waste management 50, 58, 59, 67
person in charge of possession (PICOP) 31, 32, 33
personal protective equipment see PPE
personal track safety (PTS) 30, 36
phonetic alphabet 31, 32–33
plant and equipment 63, 85
    see also mobile plant; noise; vibration; work equipment
platforms 36
point of work risk assessments 85, 87
pollution 47, 48, 50, 51, 57, 59, 74
    see also asbestos; environmental issues
portable traffic signals 10, 22
possession of the line 33
PPE for demolition work 55, 57, 58, 59
PPE for mobile workforce 86
PPE for oxy-propane cutting equipment 55, 58
PPE for shopfitting and interior contracting 63
PPE for street works and road works 12
PPE for trackside work 37, 39, 41
PPE for work over water 74–75, 77, 79–81
principal contractors for demolition work 44–51, 57
principal contractors for road works 3
principal contractors for shopfitting/interior contracting 62
principal contractors for timber frame construction 98
principal contractors for trackside work 29
priority signs 10, 20
progressive demolition 53, 60
protection controllers (PCs) 30, 32
protective footwear 12, 37
Provision and Use of Work Equipment Regulations (PUWER)
54–55, 86
pusher arms 56, 60

radio communications 31, 32, 76, 77
railway stations and platforms 35, 36
railways 27–42, 56
Railways and Other Guided Transport Systems (Safety)
Regulations see ROGS
recycling 45, 58–59
    see also crushing; waste management
red zones 30, 33, 34
reflectorisation 9
remote control demolition 55

rescue boats 76, 77
rescue equipment and procedures 74–81
    see also emergency procedures
rescue lines 75–76, 77
respiratory protective equipment 57, 58, 59, 99
rest periods 31, 37
RIMINI (RIsk MINImisation) procedure 34
risk assessments for demolition work 44, 45, 48, 51, 53, 54, 55, 56, 59
risk assessments for lone/out-of-hours workers 84, 85, 86–87, 89
risk assessments for noise 57
risk assessments for road works 7
risk assessments for shopfitting/interior contracting 62–63, 65, 67
risk assessments for timber frame construction 99
risk assessments for trackside work 30, 31, 41
risk assessments for work over water 73, 76
road danger lamps 8, 11, 12
'road narrows ahead' signs 8
road widths 9
road works 1–25, 84
'road works ahead' signs 8
Roads Authority 3, 13
    see also Highway Authority
ROGS 28, 31, 36
roof trusses 95–96, 101–102

safe systems of work for demolition 44, 54, 55, 56, 59
safe systems of work for road works 3, 7
safe systems of work for tracksides 30, 31, 33, 34–36
safe working spaces 45, 55, 60
safety authorisations 29–30
safety certificates 29–30
safety critical work 28, 31
safety footwear 12, 37
safety harnesses 75
safety helmets 37
safety management for trackside work 29–33
safety zones 6–7
    see also barriers; exclusion zones; traffic cones
scaffolds 35, 65, 93, 94
security 93
    see also fencing
security of signs 9
separation for trackside safety 33–34, 42
    see also barriers; clearances; lineside fencing
services *see* apparatus
shifts *see* working hours
shopfitting and interior contracting 61–69
sideways clearance 6, 7
signallers 33, 55, 56
signals and signalling for trackside work 33, 35
signs *see* traffic signs
silica dust 92, 99
site keepers 36
site layout for road works 6–7, 17–18
site wardens 30, 33–34, 42
site waste management plans 58
skin protection 12
speed limits *see* traffic speeds
stability of signs 9
stability of structures 46, 53, 63
stairwells 96
stations 35, 36
statutory nuisances *see* dust; fumes; noise; pollution; vibration
steel structure demolition 56
stepladders 65
    see also ladders
stop/go boards 10, 21
stop nets/lines 76
street works 1–25
Streets Authorities 3

super high-reach 360° excavators 56
supervision 3, 29, 30, 50
    see also controllers of site safety (COSSs)
surplus signs 9
suspension trauma 74

tapping rails 11
telecommunications apparatus 5
telephone communications 31, 32
timber frame construction 98–99
toe-boards 54
top-down demolition 53, 60
touch lookouts 41
trackside safety 27–42
traffic barriers 8, 11–12
traffic cones 6, 8, 11, 25
traffic control 9–12, 19–22
traffic management 7–12, 93
Traffic Management Act 13
traffic signals 10, 22, 93
traffic signs 7–9, 14, 15–16, 25
Traffic signs manual 3, 14
traffic speeds 7
train clearances 35
    see also separation for trackside safety
train movements 31, 33, 35
train sighting distances 31, 33, 41
training for asbestos work 53, 67
training for lone workers 85
training for rescue work 76, 78
training for street works and road works 12
training for trackside work 29, 30
training for work over water 75, 76, 78
training in crushing equipment operation 59
training in fire extinguisher use 55
training in oxy-propane cutting equipment use 55
training in point of work risk assessment 85, 87
training in power boat use 76
training in safety harness and buoyancy aid use 75, 78
trenches *see* excavations
trenchless techniques 4
two-way road signage 9

underground cables 6
underground services *see* apparatus
utilities 3, 52
    see also apparatus

vegetation 36, 38
vehicle crossings 4
vehicles 59, 65, 88, 92, 94
    see also driving; mobile plant; road works; traffic management
ventilation of excavations 4
vibration 50, 54, 55, 58, 63
visibility of signs 9
    see also lighting

waste management 36, 44, 48, 50, 58–59, 63, 67, 88
    see also asbestos; crushing; recycling
water apparatus 5
Weil's disease (leptospirosis) 36, 74
welfare facilities 45, 46, 63, 87–88
work at height 54, 63, 65–66, 73, 94–97
    see also fall prevention; work over water
Work at Height Regulations 54, 65, 86, 94
work equipment 54–55, 65, 85
    see also mobile plant; noise; vibration
work over water 71–81
    see also work at height
work sites 33–34
working hours 31, 37
    see also out-of-hours workers

working on or near the line 30, 36, 39
working space 6, 7
works areas 6

Index

Contents

Introduction iii

GA Legal and management – GA 01 to GA 20 1

GB Health and welfare – GB 01 to GB 13 41

GC General safety – GC 01 to GC 16 65

GD High risk activities – GD 01 to GD 29 91

GE Environment – GE 01 to GE 14 135

GF Specialist activities – GF 01 to GF 04 151

Introduction

This section should be read and used in conjunction with guidance contained within each of the corresponding sections (A to F) of *Construction site safety* (GE 700).

It contains a selection of checklists, forms, aide memoires and useful information to help manage a site on a day-to-day basis. These either appear as appendices, in Sections A to F, or have been included here as they are useful in their own right.

Construction site safety (GE 700) structure   iv

Further supporting information from
CITB-ConstructionSkills   iv

Acknowledgements   v

Use of icons   v

Companion website   vi

Construction site safety (GE 700) structure

Construction site safety is divided into the standard structure that is used across all core CITB-ConstructionSkills publications:

Section A	**Legal and management**
Section B	**Health and welfare**
Section C	General safety
Section D	**High risk activities**
Section E	**Environment**
Section F	**Specialist activities**

Each section within *Construction site safety* is contained within a separate book.

There is also a new additional supporting book:

Section G	**Checklists and forms**

Section G is a collection of information (such as forms and checklists) that can be used on a day-to-day basis when running a site.

The content of *Construction site safety*, which is developed with construction industry experts, is revised annually to take into account the latest changes in legislation and new or updated health, safety and environment industry guidance and best practice.

There is a companion website that will keep users informed of legislation changes, content updates and links to further guidance.

Construction site safety is also available to purchase online or on CD-ROM.

Construction site safety is the official supporting publication for the CITB-ConstructionSkills Site Management Safety Training Scheme (SMSTS), a five-day course for construction site managers.

Further supporting information from CITB-ConstructionSkills

CITB-ConstructionSkills has a wide range of products, publications and courses that could help to improve your health, safety and environment knowledge.

 To discover more about CITB-ConstructionSkills and the services, publications and courses offered visit the CITB-ConstructionSkills website.

Health, safety and environment publications

Site managers	GE 700 *Construction site safety* (printed, CD and online)
	RACD *Risk assessment and method statement manager*
	SA 03 CD *Health, safety and environmental auditing system*
	DVDs Range of topics including scaffold inspection, worker engagement and sustainability
Supervisors	GE 706 *Site supervision simplified* (printed, CD, online)
	GT 700 *Toolbox talks* (printed, CD, online)
	GT 701 *Safety critical communication toolbox talks* (printed)
Operatives	GE 707 *Safe start*
Health safety and environment test	GT 100 *Health, safety and environment test for operatives and specialists* (printed, DVD, online)
	GT 200 *Health, safety and environment test for managers and professionals* (printed, DVD, online)

Site Safety Plus courses

Directors	Directors role for health and safety course – one day
Site management	Site Management Safety Training Scheme (SMSTS) – five days
Plant managers	Plant Management Safety Training Scheme (SMSTS) – five days
Supervisors	Site Supervisors' Safety Training Scheme (SSSTS) – two days
Operatives	Health safety and environment awareness – one day
Environment	Site Environmental Awareness Training Scheme (SEATS) – one day
Behavioural safety	Achieving Behavioural Change (ABC) – one day
Shopfitting	Site safety for shopfitters and interior contractors – three days

National Construction College

The National Construction College is focused on creating a highly skilled, safe and professional UK construction workforce.
To achieve this, it has more first-class instructors in more locations than any other construction training provider in Europe and offers free professional advice on finding the right training for individuals and companies.

Acknowledgements

CITB-ConstructionSkills wishes to acknowledge the assistance offered by the following organisations in the preparation of this edition of GE 700:

☑ Access Industry Forum
☑ Arco
☑ Balfour Beatty
☑ Britannia Safety and Training
☑ Civil Engineering Contractors Association
☑ Combisafe
☑ Construction Plant Association
☑ Drilling and Sawing Association
☑ eBrit Services Ltd
☑ Environment Agency
☑ Environmental and Waste Consulting
☑ Federation of Master Builders
☑ Health and Safety Executive
☑ Henry Boot
☑ Highways Term Maintenance Association
☑ Home Builders Federation
☑ J Breheny Contractors Ltd

☑ Lead Paint Safety Association
☑ MJ Fuller and Associates
☑ Makers Construction Ltd
☑ May Gurney
☑ Montpellier International Consulting
☑ National Access and Scaffolding Confederation
☑ National Association of Shopfitters
☑ National Construction College
☑ National Federation of Demolition Contractors
☑ Persimmon Homes
☑ Prospect – The Union for Professionals
☑ Scafftag
☑ Temporary Works Forum
☑ Union of Construction, Allied Trades and Technicians (UCATT)
☑ Unite
☑ Wates
☑ Willmott Dixon

And a special thank you to:
☑ Carillion
☑ Costain
☑ Morgan Sindall
☑ Skanska

Use of icons

A set of icons emphasises key points within the text and also directs readers to further information. The icons are explained below:

 Website/further info
 Important
 Quote
 Example
Best practice
 Definition
Question
 Poor practice
Checklist
Ideas
 Caution
Video
 Notes
 Consultation
 Favourite
 Guidance/case study

Companion website

A companion website has been created to support *Construction site safety* and it contains up-to-date information on:

- ☑ the current edition of each section (book)
- ☑ news (such as legislation changes, industry guidance and best practice)
- ☑ any minor amendments or updates to the current editions
- ☑ weblinks, phone numbers and addresses
- ☑ details of CITB-ConstructionSkills' publications and courses.

 This icon appears within each section and indicates that further information (such as useful websites and links) can be found on the companion website at **www.citb-constructionskills.co.uk/GE700companion**.

Rather than printing individual weblinks in each section, which can become out of date, the relevant website will be stated alongside the icon (for example, for more information refer to the CITB-ConstructionSkills website). The actual weblink can then be found on the companion website, referenced to the relevant section and chapter.

The companion website will be regularly updated, to ensure that relevant information is current.

G A

Legal and management

The contents of this chapter should be read and used in conjunction with guidance contained within Section A.

GA 01 Requirements for welfare facilities on all
       construction sites   2
GA 02 Health, safety and environment risk assessment   4
GA 03 Risk assessment   6
GA 04 Risk assessment – return to work   8
GA 05 Risk assessment – expectant mothers   9
GA 06 Risk assessment – young person   10
GA 07 Risk assessment – post-completion defect work   11
GA 08 Method statement   12
GA 09 Risk assessment and method statement review
       (Example 1)   17
GA 10 Risk assessment and method statement review
       (Example 2)   20
GA 11 Briefing sheet   22
GA 12 Induction training checklist   23
GA 13 Site induction register   24
GA 14 Health, safety and environment inspection report   25
GA 15 Near miss or learning event report (Part 1)   27
GA 16 Near miss or learning event report (Part 2)   28
GA 17 Accident/incident report   30
GA 18 Accident/incident investigation report (Part 1)   34
GA 19 Accident/incident investigation report (Part 2)   36
GA 20 Statement of witness   39
GA 21 Report of enforcement authority visit   40

A

GA 01 Requirements for welfare facilities on all construction sites

The table summarises the requirement for the client and contractors (or the principal contractor on notifiable projects) to ensure that adequate welfare facilities are provided as required by the CDM Regulations.

Sanitary conveniences

Suitable and sufficient sanitary conveniences must be provided or made available at readily accessible places. *So far as is reasonably practicable*, the rooms containing sanitary conveniences must be:

- adequately ventilated and lit

- kept in a clean and orderly condition.

Separate rooms containing sanitary conveniences must be provided for men and women except where each convenience is in a separate room, the door of which can be locked from the inside.

Welfare facilities

Suitable and sufficient washing facilities including showers, if required by the nature of the work or for health reasons, must, so far as is reasonably practicable, be provided or made available at readily accessible places.

Washing facilities must be provided adjacent to:

- sanitary conveniences, whether or not provided elsewhere

- changing rooms, where provided, whether or not provided elsewhere.

Washing facilities must include:

- a supply of clean, hot (or warm) and cold water that, so far as is reasonably practicable, shall be running water

- soap or other suitable skin cleansers

- towels or other suitable means of drying.

Rooms containing washing facilities must be lit and sufficiently ventilated.

Washing facilities and the rooms containing them must be kept in a clean and orderly condition.

Except for washing facilities that are intended for the washing of hands and forearms only, separate rooms must be provided for men and women except where:

- they are in a room, the door of which can be locked from the inside

- the room is intended to be used by one person at a time.

Drinking water

An adequate supply of wholesome drinking water, conspicuously marked with the appropriate sign, should be provided or made available at readily accessible places.

Sufficient cups or other drinking vessels must be provided, unless the water supply is in the form of a jet (drinking fountain) from which a person can easily drink.

Changing rooms and lockers

Suitable facilities must be provided or made available at readily accessible places if:

- the worker has to wear special clothing for the purposes of work

- for reasons of health or personal privacy, changing cannot be carried out elsewhere.

Where necessary, in the interests of personal privacy, separate changing rooms for men and women must be provided.

Changing rooms must:

- be provided with seating
- include, where necessary, facilities to dry clothing and personal effects
- include, where necessary, facilities for locking away:
  - special clothing that is not taken home
  - a person's own clothing that is not worn at work
  - personal effects (property).

GA 01 *continued*

Facilities for rest

Suitable and sufficient facilities for rest must be provided at readily accessible places. They must:

- include suitable arrangements to protect non-smokers from the discomfort caused by tobacco smoke
  (this requirement has largely been overtaken by the legal ban on smoking in enclosed and substantially enclosed workplaces)
- be equipped with an adequate number of tables and adequate seating with backs (not benches)
- where necessary, include facilities for any pregnant woman and nursing mother to rest, lying down
- where necessary, include a means of boiling water and suitable arrangements to ensure that meals can be prepared and eaten
- be maintained at an appropriate temperature
- if gas heaters and/or a gas cooker are used, be equipped with a permanent supply of fresh air (such as a vent or louvre) **that cannot be closed**, to ensure that the heater or cooker can function properly without producing excessive amounts of carbon monoxide
- if electric heating is used, be equipped with a high temperature cut-out and not be draped with wet clothes: many fires have occurred through this practice.

For further guidance refer to Chapter A03
Construction (Design and Management) Regulations.

GA 02 Health, safety and environment risk assessment

Project title and contract no.		Risk assessment no.	
Activity		Location	
Person conducting assessment		Date	
Person supervising work		Date	

Persons exposed (tick below)

Employees		Other workers		Public/visitors		Young persons	
New/expectant mothers		Disabled		Others			

Estimated total number of persons at risk

Hazards. (What might cause harm?)

No.	Hazard	S	H	E		No.	Hazard	S	H	E
1	Adverse weather conditions					17	Loading/unloading			
2	Cold					18	Materials			
3	Electricity					19	Moving parts of machinery			
4	Excavation					20	Proximity to water			
5	Fire/flammable atmosphere					21	Scaffold			
6	Floor/ground conditions					22	Sharp objects			
7	Flying particles/dust					23	Stairs/steps			
8	Hand or power tool					24	Static equipment/machinery			
9	Hazardous substance					25	Structure			
10	Heat/hot work					26	Temporary works			
11	Lack of experience					27	Vehicle/mobile equipment			
12	Lack of training					28	Working hours/fatigue			
13	Lack of/too much oxygen					29	Workstation design			
14	Access					30	Work at height			
15	Lifting equipment appliances					31	Third parties			
16	Lighting					32	Other			

Risk factor

Risk quantity

	No injury, damage or environment impact	Minor injury, damage or environment impact	Major injury, damage or environment impact	Fatality, building loss or catastrophic environment impact
Almost no probability	A	A	A	A
A small probability	A	A	A	U
A high probability	A	A	U	U
Almost certain	A	U	U	U

Acceptable — Unacceptable

Risk level	Action
Insignificant	No action required and no documentary records need to be kept.
Acceptable	No further preventative action. Consideration shall be given to more cost effective solutions or improvements that impose no additional cost burden. Monitoring required to ensure that controls in place are properly maintained.
Unacceptable	Work shall not be started or continued until the risk level has been reduced to an acceptable level. While the control measures selected shall be cost-effective, legally there is an absolute duty to reduce the risk. This means that if it is not possible to reduce the risk, even with unlimited resources, then the work shall not be started or shall remain prohibited.

Notes:

1. Physical hazards are the nature of issues that may cause harm. Tick box for hazard.
2. Preventative/control measures are the actions that will stop it going wrong.
3. Control measures are to ensure that residual risks are reduced to a minimum. Where controls fail to reduce the risk to an acceptable level then refer assessment to your line manager.
4. If the operations are likely to affect the public or the safe operation of a public infrastructure or transport system, the control measures must reduce the likelihood of significant harm to the level that existed before our work commenced.
5. Where young persons or expectant mothers are involved in the activity, ensure that any additional controls are put in place in accordance with local procedures.
6. In addition to the above, consideration must be given to other individuals' susceptibility due to pre-existing health conditions (such as a bad back or poor hearing). Additional human factors (such as ergonomics and workplace design) should also be considered.
7. Where a hazard is identified that is not listed in the physical hazards list, enter the hazard description followed by 'other' in brackets, for example (Other).

GA 02 *continued*

Hazard number *(from previous page)*	Nature of risk (What might go wrong?)	Risk before controls U/A	Control measures (How do you stop it going wrong?)	Control measures implemented by *(name)*	Risk after controls U/A

Method statement required?	Yes	No	Method statement number

Additional risk assessment (Tick box as required)

Noise		Handling		Helmet		Respiratory		Boots		Hi-vis	
COSHH		Radiation		Hearing		Eye		Harness		Others	
Asbestos		Lead									

PPE (Tick box as required)

	Name	Signature	Date
Person completing the assessment			
Person reviewing the assessment			
Date to be reviewed			

A

GA 03 Risk assessment

Site:		Activity:		Persons conducting assessment:		
Risk assessment no:		Review date:		Revision no:		
				Name:	Signature:	Date:
Person supervising work:			Employer:	Name:	Signature:	Date:
Persons exposed:	Employees:		Other workers:	Public/visitors:	Vulnerable persons:	Total at risk:

Likelihood

Rating 1 = Very unlikely
Rating 2 = Unlikely
Rating 3 = Likely
Rating 4 = Very likely
Rating 5 = Almost certain

Severity

Rating 1 = No injury
Rating 2 = Minor injury or illness
Rating 3 = 7-day injury or illness
Rating 4 = Major injury or illness
Rating 5 = Fatality, disabling injury, and so on

Risk = Likelihood x Severity

Severity \ Likelihood	1	2	3	4	5
5	5	10	15	20	25
4	4	8	12	16	20
3	3	6	9	12	15
2	2	4	6	8	10
1	1	2	3	4	5

Acceptable   Further review   Unacceptable

Hazard	1 Factors of harm Likelihood	2 Factors of harm Severity	3 Risk (Multiple of columns 1 × 2)	4 Control measures	5 Factors of harm Likelihood	6 Factors of harm Severity	7 Residual risk (Multiple of columns 5 × 6)	8 Control measures implemented by (name)	9 Control frequency check rate

GA 03 *continued*

Hazard	1 Factors of harm — Likelihood	2 Factors of harm — Severity	3 Risk (Multiple of columns 1 × 2)	4 Control measures	5 Factors of harm — Likelihood	6 Factors of harm — Severity	7 Residual risk (Multiple of columns 5 × 6)	8 Control measures implemented by *(name)*	9 Control frequency check rate

GA 04 Risk assessment – return to work

Name of person returning to work:	Date of birth:

Nature of injury, illness or condition that rendered the person unfit for work:	Department/site:

Obtain a copy of the doctor's note confirming the person is fit to return to work: | Occupational health contacted for advice by:

Proposed working hours (using 24-hour clock): | Safety induction carried out by:

Nature of work to be undertaken:	Specific activities that **must not** be undertaken by the employee:

Specific hazards/risk identified:	Control measures required:

Safety briefing carried out by:

Date:

Note: the health and safety briefing must include the:

- risks identified by the assessment
- preventative/protective measures required to ensure the employee's health and safety
- duties/tasks that are forbidden
- emergency procedures and how they will be implemented
- first-aid arrangements.

Signed: .... Department manager: ....

Date: ....

GA 05 Risk assessment – expectant mothers

Name:	Employee number:
Position:	Operating unit:
Line manager:	Date of notification:
Date risk assessment period commenced: Duration: Proposed/agreed working hours (using 24-hour clock):	Department/site/location: The expectant mother shall be supervised by:
Nature of work to be undertaken:	Specific activities that **must not** be undertaken by the expectant mother (see guidance notes):

Specific hazards/risk identified:
Control measures to be employed, emergency procedures and first aid/welfare arrangements:
Any additional training requirements:

Note: *the briefing shall include the:*

- *risks identified*
- *preventative/protective/control measures required, ensuring the expectant mother's health and safety*
- *emergency procedures and how they will be implemented*
- *first aid/welfare arrangements.*

Risk assessment prepared and briefed by:	I have been briefed on this risk assessment:
Name: .... (Department manager)	Name: .... (Expectant mother)
Signed:	Signed: ....
Date:	Date: ....

A

GA 06 Risk assessment – young person

Name of young person:	Date of birth:
Date of employment/work experience commenced: Proposed/agreed working hours (using 24-hour clock):	Department/site: Young person supervised by: Safety induction carried out by:
Nature of work to be undertaken:	Specific activities that **must not** be undertaken by the young person:
Specific hazards/risk identified:	Control measures required:
Safety briefing carried out by: Date:	Specific training required by the young person:

Note: the briefing shall include the:

  ■ the risks identified by the assessment
  ■ the preventative/protective/control measures required, ensuring the young person's health and safety
  ■ the emergency procedures and how they will be implemented
  ■ the first aid/welfare arrangements
  ■ a warning against horseplay.

Risk assessment prepared and briefed by: Name: .... (Department manager) Signed: .... Date:	I have been briefed on this risk assessment: Name: .... (Young person) Signed: .... Date: ....

A

GA 07 Risk assessment – post-completion defect work

Contract/site/building				Contract no.	
Address					
Reason for assessment	Six month defects		12 month defects		*Other (state)*	
Sub-contractor(s)					
Brief description of work/defects/call out.					

Have details of defects/reason for call out been passed onto those carrying out the work?	Yes	No
Is work to be carried out in live/occupied premises?	Yes	No
If 'yes' are there any client requirements, access restrictions or site rules (*state below*)?	Yes	No

Tick PPE required						Other (*state*)	

Will work require lone working? If 'yes' state precautions/checks (raising alarm, first aid, etc.)	Yes	No

Is work deemed high risk? If 'yes' a separate risk assessment is required	Yes	No

If 'no' state control measures required, including task PPE, access, manual handling, COSHH, and so on

What working at height/access is required? (*tick ✓*)

	Existing (such as 'safe' type system)	⚠	**Must be trained in the use of, prior to starting work.**
	Scissor lift/cherry picker/MEWP	⚠	**Must be trained** operator (e.g. IPAF) plus risk assessment.
	Mobile tower	⚠	**Must be trained** to erect and use (e.g. PASMA).
	Podium steps/room mate	⚠	**Erect correctly, lock wheels** – no over reaching.
	Stepladder	⚠	Short duration work only **plus complete ladder permit.**
	Ladder	⚠	**Access only – else complete ladder permit.**
	Other	⚠	Include any training or special requirements.

State plant, equipment and materials (including disposal measures) to be used

State any other issues/comments

Assessment completed by					
Name (*print*)		Signature		Date	

This assessment and safe system of work has been explained to me and I understand and will follow the controls					
Name (*print*)		Signature		Date	

The works have been completed, as detailed above, and the area left safe and clean					
Name (*print*)		Signature		Date	

A

GA 08 Method statement

Contract title	
Contractor	
Method statement no.	

This method statement (MS) has been developed further to the completion of the following references' risk assessments.	
Risk assessment number	Title

Section 1 – General details

Scope of works

Location of the works *(use sketch boxes if required)*

Prepared by			
Position held			
Signed		Date	
Review date			
Work supervisor(s)			
Refer to method statement tracking and content sheet			

GA 08 *continued*

Section 2 – Programme of operations

Start date/time	
Preceding works to be completed	
Duration	
Permit required *(tick below)*	

☐ **Permit to work** *(general)*	☐ **Permit to enter** *(confined spaces)*	☐ **Permit to dig**
☐ **Hot-work permit**	☐ **Out-of-hours work permit**	☐ **Other** *(specify below)*

Section 3 – Personnel

Include details of all personnel involved in the task and any special training, skills or qualifications required.

Name	Role	Competence details

Section 4 – Safe system of work to be adopted

(Use sketches if necessary)

GA 08 *continued*

Safe system of work *continued* *(or use as sketch box)*

Sketch box

Safe system of work *continued* *(or use as sketch box)*

GA 08 *continued*

Section 5 – Plant and equipment

Match plant and equipment to qualified personnel and include any specific PPE details.

Equipment description	Test certificates in date *(matched to equipment)*	Operator details

Personal protective equipment (PPE)

Equipment description	Specification *(for example, type or grade)*	Training required

Receipt acknowledgements

Supervisor in charge of the work

I confirm that I have read and understand the requirements of this method statement and associated risk assessments and will ensure their communication to operatives under my control and to those who may be affected by its requirements.

Signed		Date	
Print name		Supervisor	

GA 08 *continued*

Communication

Communicate the contents of the method statement to all those involved or affected by the works and record their details below. It is important you test understanding and do not rely purely upon them just reading this method statement.

Name	Signature

*Note: If you have any doubt about any information given or contained in this method statement – **ask for clarification**.*

GA 09 Risk assessment and method statement review (Example 1)

Risk assessment/method statement – content review and tracking sheet

Project		Contractor	
Method statement title			
Date issued to site management			

Proposed date of work to start on site						
Project/site manager	1st review date	Status*	Name *(Print)*	2nd review date	Status*	Name *(Print)*
Temporary works co-ordinator *(as required)*	1st review date	Status*	Name *(Print)*	2nd review date	Status*	Name *(Print)*
Technical advisor *(as required)*	1st review date	Status*	Name *(Print)*	2nd review date	Status*	Name *(Print)*
H,S&E function *(as required)*	1st review date	Status*	Name *(Print)*	2nd review date	Status*	Name *(Print)*

(Method statement content is to be reviewed in accordance with the prompt list overleaf).

Comments/observations *(if appropriate)*

* Status user notes

Complete 1st review using prompt list overleaf. Once complete, make an assessment on status (see below). If status is A then no further action is required. If B or C, return the method statement with the prompt list and comments/ observations. Re-assess amended method statement (2nd review) following the same process until status A is achieved.

Status: *A – Work can proceed as described*
B – Work can proceed when comments are incorporated
C – Re-submit and review before work can proceed

Signed off by activity supervisor	Name *(Print)*		Signature	
			Date	
Signed off by site management as current working document	Name *(Print)*		Signature	
			Date	

Note: *clearance to proceed with this method statement does not relieve the sub-contractor of their contractual obligations, including safety, structural integrity or any implications to permanent works arising from these proposals.*

A

GA 09 *continued*

Safe system of work – prompt list

Note: *this list should also be used when preparing method statements.*

Safe system of work – prompt list

1 – Description	Yes	No	In part	N/A
Fully describes the work, tasks, sequence, method and process for change?				
Programme of works and working hours identified?				
2 – Resources	**Yes**	**No**	**In part**	**N/A**
Names and titles of key personnel/supervisors responsible?				
Details of resources required (such as equipment, plant, workers and materials)?				
Certificates of competence or qualification of operatives provided?				
Certificates for plant/equipment inspection/examination provided?				
Crane/lifting equipment – certificates/checklist/lifting plan in place?				
Sub-contracted work element/personnel.				
3 – Hazard identification	**Yes**	**No**	**In part**	**N/A**
Specific risk assessment attached and satisfactory? Have all the risks been evaluated? Are there arrangements in place for reviewing control measures due to changing circumstances?				
Approval of sub-contractor's risk assessment and method statement?				
Access/scaffolding (including ancillary arrangements, such as anchor points) fully detailed and described?				
COSHH, noise and manual-handling issues dealt with?				
Workplace environment, design, layout, limitations identified and human factors taken into consideration (such as experience, fatigue, and so on)?				
4 – Control measures	**Yes**	**No**	**In part**	**N/A**
Supervision?				
High risk or safety critical activities identified and controls specified?				
Permit requirements identified?				
Monitoring (checks and inspections) identified?				
Environmental controls/waste disposal identified?				
Details of toolbox talks to be provided?				
Personal protective equipment specified?				
5 – Emergency arrangement	**Yes**	**No**	**In part**	**N/A**
Rescue – how – by whom?				
First aid requirements?				
Spillage containment?				
Special welfare?				
6 – Temporary works	**Yes**	**No**	**In part**	**N/A**
Details of temporary works schemes identified, including all documents?				
Temporary protection/support identified (such as fire, traffic and services)?				

GA 09 *continued*

Safe system of work – prompt list *(continued)*

7 – Interfaces	Yes	No	In part	N/A
Interfaces/security of the client/public/other contractors identified?				
Any builder's work in connection identified/adequate notice given?				
Security?				
Traffic routes, emergency arrangements, services and existing method statements?				
8 – Training and information	Yes	No	In part	N/A
Conformation of briefing of method statement to operatives?				
Special training (confined space, tower erection, use of plant, and so on)?				
9 – Environmental issues	Yes	No	In part	N/A
Environmental risks?				
Statutory permit and licence conditions?				
Pollution prevention?				
10 – Monitoring and compliance	Yes	No	In part	N/A
Monitoring – by whom?				
Enforcement – how – by whom – equipment, sampling?				
Testing and commissioning?				
Checking, review and update?				
Change requirements?				
Confirmation of operative's briefing?				
Any other (specify)?				

GA 10 Risk assessment and method statement review (Example 2)

Contract no.		Contract name	

Risk assessment and method statement for activity: ....

Preparing company: .... **Prepared by (name):** ....

Document reference no. (if any): .... **Revision:** ....

Record of principal contractor's review. (Results of review to be formally communicated to preparing company.)

Check	Guidance on aspects that should be covered	Adequate? (See comments overleaf)
Scope of work	Brief description of work with scope defined by area, floor or structure (where specified conditions dictate). Should also define any limitations of use and **must be site specific**.	Yes/No*
Organisation	Key staff involved in managing and supervising the work and the anticipated type of labour required, including any required induction, training and proof of competence.	Yes/No*
Materials	Materials required, including storage location, any identifying marks and any special safety measures to be taken during storage, handling, use and protection. COSHH details as required.	Yes/No*
Plant/equipment	Major plant and equipment required, including any lifting equipment and any plant or equipment calibration/certification/12-monthly or 6-monthly for chains/weekly inspections.	Yes/No*
Preparation	Details of any permit approvals, notices or completion of other work needed prior to starting work (such as permit to dig, work or load), electrical isolations, mechanical isolations, commissioning, access proposals, restrictions and requirements.	Yes/No*
Safety and health	Safety and health of all who may be affected (employees/third parties), including anticipated hazards and required precautions (included or by reference to risk assessment). PPE, access, egress, control of work at height, husbandry, first aider, barriers, training, planning, inspections, communication, etc.	Yes/No*
Environment	Anticipated hazards or special conditions requiring precautions (such as traffic conditions, waste management/disposal, dust or noise, ground conditions, watercourses, environmentally sensitive areas and wildlife protected) and appropriate mitigation measures.	Yes/No*
Emergency procedures	Procedures and arrangements for dealing with health, safety or environmental incidents and accidents (overarching is company/site management incident investigation process).	Yes/No*
Method and sequence	Definition of how the work is to be carried out, including the proposed sequence and any temporary works. (Required for complex operations only.)	Yes/No*
Protection	Protection of partly and fully completed work against damage, deterioration, third parties and/or the public.	Yes/No*
Inspections/checks/ tests	Required prior to, during and on completion of work. Any hold points where approval to continue is required and who can release them.	Yes/No*
Records	To be obtained or produced during and on completion of the work.	Yes/No*

This document is/is not* considered suitable and sufficient to allow the work outlined above to commence.

	Name	Signed	Date
Checked by			

All site supervisors and operatives undertaking the activity must be aware of and understand the risk assessment and method statement. It is important that the risks and controls are explained and understanding tested.

(* Delete as applicable.)

GA 10 *continued*

A

Contract no.		Contract name	
Comments			
1.			
2.			
3.			
4.			
5.			
6.			
7.			
8.			
9.			
10.			
11.			
12.			

GA 11 Briefing sheet

Briefing for *(tick below)*					
Risk assessment		Method statement		Toolbox talk	
Pre-task briefing		Permit briefing		Worker engagement	
Other *(state)*					

Activity/subject	
Project/location	

Briefing delivered by		Signature	
Company		Date and time	

List of persons attending briefing (obtain signatures at end of briefing as a record of attendance).

Name	Company	Signature

Workforce feedback and comments

GA 12 Induction training checklist

Access		Dangerous occurrences		Fall prevention		Medication	
Accident reporting		Dermatitis		Fire		Method statements	
Alcohol and drugs		Discipline		First aid		Mobile elevating work platforms	
Asbestos		Dress code		Flammable liquids		Near-miss incidents	
Assembly points		Dust and fumes		Health and safety committee		Needles and syringes	
Boundaries		Drying rooms		Hearing protection zones		Noise	
Buried services		Edge protection		High-visibility clothing		Occupational health	
CDM Regulations		Electricity		Hoists		Overhead electricity cables	
Competence		Emergency evacuation		Ladders/stepladders		Permits to work	
Confidential issues		Emergency procedure		Lasers		Personal protective equipment	
Confined spaces		Environment		Legal issues		Plant and equipment	
Consultation with employees		Escape routes		Lifting equipment		Powers of inspectors	
Contamination		Excavations		Lighting		Registration schemes	
COSHH		Eye protection		Liquefied petroleum gas		Reporting defects	
CSCS cards		Fall arrest		Manual handling		Restricted or prohibited areas	
Risk assessments		Site layout		Traffic routes		Waste minimisation	
Safe systems of work		Site security		Training		Welfare facilities	
Safety harnesses		Skin protection		Types of injury		Working at height	
Safety policy		Smoking		Vehicles and deliveries		Working near, on or over water	
Safety signs and notices		Tidiness (housekeeping)		Vibration			
Scaffolding (incl. mobile scaffolds)		Toilets		Waste disposal			

A

GA 13 Site induction register

Ref no.	Date	Name (capitals)	Signature*	Employed by	Occupation	Approved competency card/ certificate held (i.e. CSCS/CPCS)	Type of card held (plus any relevant categories)	Person giving induction
						Yes ☐ No ☐		
						Yes ☐ No ☐		
						Yes ☐ No ☐		
						Yes ☐ No ☐		
						Yes ☐ No ☐		
						Yes ☐ No ☐		
						Yes ☐ No ☐		
						Yes ☐ No ☐		
						Yes ☐ No ☐		
						Yes ☐ No ☐		
						Yes ☐ No ☐		
						Yes ☐ No ☐		
						Yes ☐ No ☐		
						Yes ☐ No ☐		
						Yes ☐ No ☐		
						Yes ☐ No ☐		

Site induction register   Project/site   Contract ref.

*I confirm that I have attended the site induction, understand the site rules and that I am not taking medication or drugs that could affect my concentration or safety on site.

GA 14 Health, safety and environment inspection report

Site/project/contract		Reference no.	
Supervisor/manager		Date	
Person completing inspection		Signed	

Key	✓ (tick) = No action. X = Action required. **blank** = Not seen or applicable.						
1	Health and safety plan		**2**	Registers and records		**3**	Notices and signage	
4	Inductions		**5**	Consultation/toolbox talks		**6**	Competence/training	
7	Risk assessments		**8**	Method statements		**9**	Permits	
10	COSHH		**11**	HFL/fuel storage		**12**	Fire and first aid	
13	Site establishment		**14**	Security/public protection		**15**	Welfare facilities	
16	Traffic management		**17**	Material delivery/storage		**18**	Vehicle unloading	
19	Health risks		**20**	Respiratory risks		**21**	Noise and vibration	
22	Manual handling		**23**	Hand-held tools/equipment		**24**	PPE	
25	Safe access/egress		**26**	Housekeeping		**27**	Lighting/temp electrics	
28	Demolition/asbestos		**29**	Excavations/earthworks		**30**	Live services	
31	Temporary works		**32**	Scaffolding		**33**	Work at height	
34	Access equipment		**35**	Ladders/steps/podiums		**36**	Edge protection/barriers	
37	MEWPs, etc.		**38**	Lifting operations		**39**	Mobile plant	
40	Energy/resource use		**41**	Waste management		**42**	Consents/permits, etc.	
43	Pollution prevention		**44**	Ecology		**45**	Community engagement	
46	Accidents/near misses		**47**	Previous report closed out		**48**	Other	

Item no.	Areas for improvement/advice/positive observations	Action by	Action date

Report received by		Signed		
Distribution				

A

GA 14 *continued*

Site/project/contract				Reference no.	
Sheet		of		Date	

Item no.	Areas for improvement/advice/positive observations	Action by	Action date

Report received by		Signed			
Distribution					

GA 15 Near miss or learning event report (Part 1)

To be completed and handed to site management

Name (optional)		Company (optional)	
Date		Time	
Project		Location on site	

Classification (tick)

☐ Health   ☐ Safety   ☐ Environment

Details of the learning event (include all relevant information)

Please report anything that is unsafe or a near miss

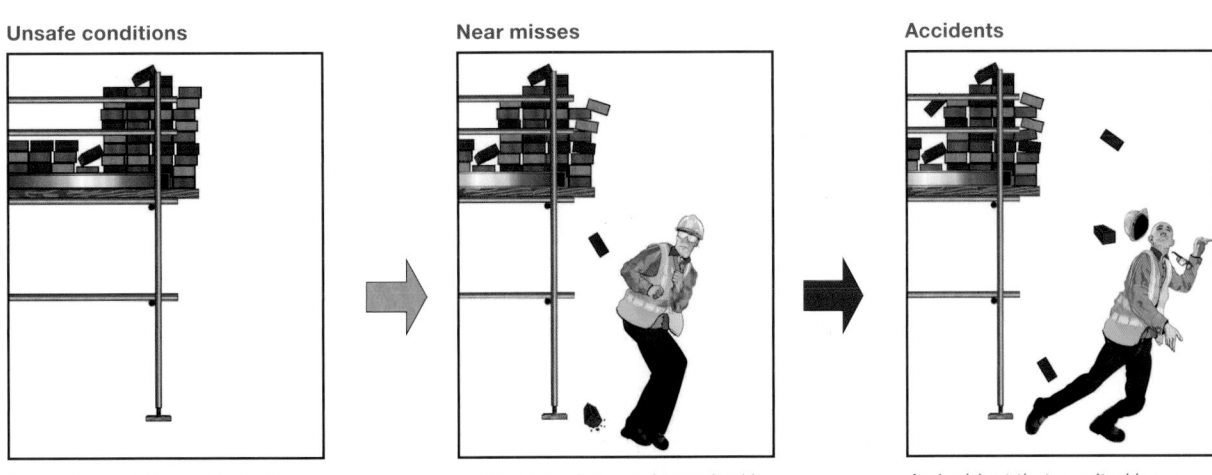

Unsafe conditions

Something with the potential to cause harm

Near misses

An incident that nearly resulted in an injury or damage

Accidents

An incident that resulted in an injury or damage

It really does help to prevent accidents

A

GA 16 Near miss or learning event report (Part 2)

To be completed by site management

Project		Contact no.	
Date		Location on site	
Reported by		Part 1 – date received	

Classification *(tick)*

☐ Health	☐ Safety	☐ Environment
☐ Main contractor	☐ Sub-contractor	☐ Third party/public

Details of the learning event *(include all relevant information)*

Potential outcome *(please tick)*	Potential severity *(please tick)*
☐ Personal injury	☐ Negligible
☐ Property or equipment damage	☐ Slight
☐ Environmental issue	☐ Moderate
☐ Other (please state below)	☐ High
	☐ Very high

Lessons learned (consider immediate and root causes) *(please tick)*

Work environment

☐ Defective workplace	☐ Design/layout
☐ Housekeeping	☐ Lack of room
☐ Lighting	☐ Noise/distraction
☐ Weather	☐ Access/egress

Management

☐ System of work	☐ Supervision
☐ Training	☐ Communication
☐ Management of change	

GA 16 *continued*

Plant/equipment

☐ Construction/design	☐ Installation
☐ Safety device	☐ Operation/use
☐ Mechanical failure	☐ Maintenance

Human factors

☐ Failure to follow rules	☐ Instructions misunderstood
☐ Error of judgement	☐ Lack of experience
☐ Unsafe attitude	☐ Undue haste
☐ Horseplay	☐ Lapse of concentration
☐ Fatigue	☐ Working without authorisation

PPE

☐ Design	☐ Wrong type used
☐ Maintenance	☐ Not provided/unavailable
☐ Not used	

Other

☐ Third party	☐ Under investigation
☐ Other (please state)	

Follow up

Actions required	Responsible	Completed

Name		Signed		Date	

A

GA 17 Accident/incident report

Instructions for use
1. To be completed and returned as soon as possible after any incident/accident (*please* **print** *clearly*).
2. To be used for all incidents (minor and reportable), dangerous occurrences, near misses, environmental incidents, complaints, thefts and incidents involving material damage, including cable strikes.
3. Send completed form to the Health and Safety Department after the incident. Keep site copy in a secure place (Data Protection Act).

Workplace name			This form consists of		pages
Telephone no.		Comments			
Incident date		Incident time (24-hour clock)			

Incident type (*Please tick all that apply and then complete further parts of this form as indicated*)

☐ Fatality*	**Parts A, B (i and ii) and F**	☐ Minor incident/injury (no first aid)	**Parts A, B (i and ii) and F**	
☐ Major injury*	**Parts A, B (i and ii) and F**	☐ Dangerous occurrence* (RIDDOR reportable)	**Parts A ,B (ii) and F**	
☐ Over seven-day injury*	**Parts A, B (i and ii) and F**	☐ Environmental Incident	**Parts A, C and F**	
☐ Reportable disease*	**Parts A, B (i and ii) and F**	☐ Near miss/dangerous occurrence (Not RIDDOR reportable)	**Parts A and F**	
☐ Ill health	**Parts A, B (i and ii) and F**	☐ Utility damage	**Parts A, D and F**	
☐ First aid (on site)	**Parts A, B (i and ii) and F**	☐ Theft/vandalism/violence	**Parts A, E and F (also B (i) for violence)**	
☐ Medical treatment (off site)	**Parts A, B (i and ii) and F**	☐ Complaint	**Parts A and F**	
*HSE incident notification number		Date reported		

Part A – Description of incident

Where on site did the incident occur?					
Were photographs taken?	Yes/No	(Please include a copy with this form)	Were samples taken?		Yes/No

Describe what happened and how. In the case of an injury, state what the injured person was doing at the time and side of body (left or right). (Where possible, take photographs of the general area but not of injured persons.) In the case of an environmental incident, state the events that caused the incident (details of plant involved, photographs, wherever practicable, must be taken). In the case of damage, indicate if damage is to permanent works, temporary works, plant, temporary buildings/contents, employees permanent effects. (Photographs must be taken.)

Please sketch the general area of the incident (include any relevant measurements)
(If more space is required, please attach additional sheets and include references to them in this box)

Name		Occupation		Employer	
Can it be established what company caused the incident?	Yes/No	Give details (company's name and individual's name)			

GA 17 *continued*

Part B – Health and safety

Part B(i) – Details of injured person

Surname		Forename(s)		Date of birth		Signature *(if possible)*	
Address							
Postcode		Contact telephone no			Occupation		

Was any time lost?	Yes/No	Date finished work		Time finished work		Date restarted work		Time restarted work	

Name and telephone no. of hospital *(where applicable)*	
Detail **all** PPE required by the risk assessment for the operation		Detail **all** PPE worn at time of incident	
Details of person's employer (name, address and telephone). If member of the public then write 'public'	

Location of injury *(please tick as many as appropriate)*

☐ Head	☐ Chest	☐ Arm/shoulder	☐ Finger	☐ Foot	☐ Other (state below)
☐ Face/neck	☐ Abdomen	☐ Wrist	☐ Leg/hip	☐ Respiratory system	
☐ Eye	☐ Back	☐ Hand	☐ Ankle	☐ Digestive system	

Type of injury *(please tick as many as appropriate)*

☐ Amputation	☐ Strain/sprain	☐ Foreign body	☐ Multiple	☐ Crush
☐ Bruising/swelling	☐ Asphyxiation/gassing	☐ Fracture	☐ Shock/concussion	☐ Ingestion
☐ Dislocation	☐ Loss of consciousness	☐ Burn/scald	☐ Puncture	☐ Internal
☐ Electric shock	☐ Cut/laceration/abrasion	☐ Whiplash	☐ Ill health	☐ Other (state below)

Was the injured person advised to see their doctor or visit a hospital?	Yes/No	
Is drug or alcohol testing required?	Yes/No	Details of result	Positive/negative

Part B(ii) – Details of incident

Basic cause of incident *(please tick **one** box only)*

☐ Fall from height	☐ Manual handling	☐ Repetitive motion/action
☐ Fall on same level	☐ Contact with tool/equipment/machinery	☐ Collision
☐ Fall down stairs/steps	☐ Contact with flying particle	☐ Fire
☐ Struck by moving object	☐ Contact with electricity	☐ Explosion
☐ Struck by falling object	☐ Contact with/exposed to heat/acid	☐ Drowning
☐ Struck/trapped by something collapsed/overturning	☐ Contact with/exposed to air/water pressure	☐ Loss of containment/unintentional release
☐ Trapped between objects	☐ Contact with/exposed to hazardous substance	☐ Asphyxiation
☐ Step on/struck against stationary object	☐ Exposure to noise/vibration	☐ Other (state below)

Source of hazard *(please tick **one** box only)*

☐ Lifting equipment	☐ Scaffold	☐ Temporary works	☐ Flying particle
☐ Vehicle/mobile equipment	☐ Excavation	☐ Materials	☐ Dust
☐ Static equipment/machinery	☐ Stairs/steps	☐ Floor/ground condition	☐ Proximity to water
☐ Moving parts of machinery	☐ Working surface	☐ Lack of oxygen	☐ Workstation layout
☐ Power tool	☐ Structure	☐ Heat/hot work	☐ Hazardous substance
☐ Hand tool	☐ Ladder	☐ Cold	☐ Other (state below)

A

GA 17 *continued*

Part C – Environmental incident

Type of incident *(please tick as many as appropriate)*

| ☐ Air pollution | ☐ Noise or vibration | ☐ Plants or wildlife | ☐ Fly tipping |
| ☐ Water contamination | ☐ Ground contamination | ☐ Waste disposal | ☐ Other (state below) |

Severity of incident *(please tick **one** box only)*

| ☐ Minor | ☐ Significant | ☐ Major |

| Has incident been reported to the environment agency/SEPA? | Yes/No | Contact details/reference | |

Part D – Utility damage

Description of service		Owner of service	

Cause of damage *(please tick as appropriate)*

| ☐ Mechanical plant | ☐ Hand-operated plant | ☐ Hand tools | Plant owner's name/plant hire company's name | |

If the plant was on hire, state who to	

Who undertook the repair of the service?		Date and time repair undertaken	
Was the service **clearly** shown on permit to dig?	Yes/No	If 'no' state why	

In your opinion, state company responsible for the damage		Will they be invoiced direct by utility company?	Yes/No	If 'no' state why	

Details of communications with company responsible for damage

Date on correspondence		Reference of correspondence *(such as unique letter reference)*	

Part E – Theft/vandalism/violence

List affected items/works involved (including serial numbers/plant numbers and value if known), if applicable

Details of owner (name and address), if applicable

Crime number/police log reference		Date and time reported		Name of person who reported the incident	

GA 17 *continued*

Part F – Root cause and prevention *(please tick as many as appropriate)*			
Work environment	**Human factors**	**PPE**	**Plant/equipment**
☐ Defective workplace	☐ Failure to follow rules	☐ Design	☐ Construction/design
☐ Housekeeping	☐ Instructions misunderstood	☐ Wrong type used	☐ Installation
☐ Lighting	☐ Error of judgement	☐ Maintenance/defective	☐ Safety device
☐ Weather	☐ Lack of experience	☐ Not provided/unavailable	☐ Operation/use
☐ Design/layout	☐ Unsafe attitude	☐ Not used	☐ Mechanical failure
☐ Lack of room	☐ Undue haste	**Management**	☐ Maintenance
☐ Noise/distraction	☐ Failure to adhere to risk assessment, and so on	☐ Non-communication of risk	**Other**
☐ Access/egress	☐ Horseplay	☐ Supervision	☐ Third party
	☐ Lapse of concentration	☐ Training	☐ Under investigation
	☐ Fatigue	☐ System failure	☐ Other (state below)
	☐ Working without authorisation		

Details of actions taken immediately following the incident to recover the situation

Action taken (or suggested) to prevent reoccurrence and to communicate lessons learnt from the incident

Name of person completing form		Person with overall workplace responsibility	
Signature		**Date**	
Signature		**Date**	

GA 18 Accident/incident investigation report (Part 1)

Date		Reference no.	
Business division, sector or unit			
Contract		**Contract no.**	

General location of accident/incident

☐ Access route	☐ Car park
☐ At task location whilst undertaking activity	☐ Delivery/storage area
☐ Loading/unloading area	☐ Office/site offices
☐ Public highway	☐ Residential dwelling
☐ Site perimeter/off site	☐ Vehicle
☐ Welfare site	☐ Other

Date of accident		**Time**	
Injured person's name		**Occupation**	
Address			
Employer		**Supervisor**	
Site manager		**First aider**	

Injury	**Treatment administered (on or off site)**

1. Witness		Employer	
2. Witness		Employer	
3. Witness		Employer	

Incident classification (indicate appropriate category)

☐ RIDDOR – Fatal	☐ RIDDOR – Disease	☐ Process interruption
☐ RIDDOR – Major injury	☐ Lost time 1 – 7 days	☐ Environmental incident
☐ RIDDOR – Over seven-day injury	☐ Minor	☐ Environmental near miss
☐ RIDDOR – Dangerous occurrence	☐ Member of public injury	☐ Significant learning event
☐ RIDDOR – Injury to member of public	☐ Service strike	☐ Reportable ill health

Previous experience/training of IP

Relevant training details	
Other (specify)	
Date of induction		**Date of last relevant awareness talk(s)**	

GA 18 *continued*

Supporting information available
* Digital photographs must have the correct level of validation (date, independent witness, etc.)

1 ☐ Risk assessment		7 ☐ Witness statement		– ☐ **Other** *(please specify below)*	
2 ☐ Method statement		8 ☐ Site sketch		13 ☐	
3 ☐ Competency checks/card		9 ☐ Photographs		14 ☐	
4 ☐ Induction log		10 ☐ Construction drawings		15 ☐	
5 ☐ Toolbox talk attendance		11 ☐ Maintenance checks (PPM)		16 ☐	
6 ☐ Injured person's statement		12 ☐ F2508/A		17 ☐	

Date/time	**Background information:** in date/time order (to include – start dates, previous works, contract progress, work group personnel, adjacent trades, nature of work being undertaken, etc.)

Date/time	**Summary of accident:** in date/time order (concise description of the incident including location, personnel involved, activity being carried out, tools/equipment/substances involved, permits to work, site drawings and working conditions. Record timeline of events.)

Immediate action taken: emergency plan, first aid, securing site, hospital, contacts made, prevention of further loss.

Investigation team

Name	Position	Signed

Investigation approval

Name		Position		Signed	

Distribution

Name	Position	Telephone	Email	Dist. (✓)

GA 19 Accident/incident investigation report (Part 2)

Report title	

Report date		Accident date		Accident reference no.	

Initial/final report *(delete as appropriate)*		Business unit	

Contract		Contract no.	

Immediate cause of accident *(consider all factors, including temperature, weather, system failure, design failure, equipment failure, poor housekeeping and the influence of alcohol or drugs)*

Root cause of accident *(consider issues, such as lack of training and awareness, time constraints, communication and external influences)*

Remedial action *(use continuation sheet if necessary)*

Conclusion and recommendations *(analysis of evidence, comparison with standards, highlight the main issues, who is responsible, and so on)*

A

GA 19 *continued*

Recommendations				
Immediate				
Interim				
Long term				

Learning opportunities and responsibilities				
Person responsible	**Action**	**Target date**	**Close out date**	**Signature**

Communication of learning (tick all that apply)		
☐ Safety alert	☐ Safety bulletin	☐ Safety briefing
☐ Toolbox talks	☐ Review of RA/MS	☐ Review of procedures or standards
☐ Review of training requirements	☐ Other (please specify)	

GA 19 *continued*

Investigation team		
Name	**Position**	**Signed**

Investigation approval and distribution			
Position	**Name**	**Signature**	**Date**
HS&E Department			
Project manager			
Project director			
Managing director			

Appendices

Supporting information *(tick those appended)*

Other report forms

☐ RIDDOR F2508/A form

☐ Contractors completed accident book entry form (where applicable)

☐ Contractors completed incident/accident investigation report (where applicable)

☐ Client incident/accident investigation report (where applicable)

Witness statements

☐ Name

☐ Title/occupation

☐ Employer

Photographs

☐ Photograph index sheet and photographs

Drawings

☐ Scale drawing/plans

☐ Incident site sketch

Training/control

☐ Copy of signed method statement/risk assessment

☐ Copy of any relevant permits or other work instructions

☐ Copy of signed induction log

☐ Last completed toolbox talk or relevant safety briefing

☐ Copy of relevant skills card (CPCS, CSCS, etc.)

GA 20 Statement of witness

Name of witness	
Address	
Company	Occupation

Statement	Page	of

This statement (consisting of   pages, each signed by me) is true to the best of my knowledge and belief and I make it knowing that, if it is tendered in evidence, I shall be liable to prosecution if I have wilfully stated in it anything that I know to be false or do not believe to be true.

Signed		Date	
Signature witnessed by		Signed	

GA 21 Report of enforcement authority visit

Site/project/contract			
Project no.		Site manager	
Person completing report		Date	
Enforcing authority			
Name of inspector(s)			
Office or address			
Contact information			
Reason for visit		Was enforcement action taken?	

Summary of any enforcement action	Actions taken or to be taken

Summary of inspector's observations	Actions taken or to be taken

Other	

This notification must be issued as soon as practicable after the visit

GB

Health and welfare

The contents of this chapter should be read and used in conjunction with guidance contained within Section B.

GB 01	Welfare requirements	42
GB 02	Eye protection selection	43
GB 03	Respiratory protective equipment selection	46
GB 04	Hearing protection selection	47
GB 05	Skin protection selection	48
GB 06	Identifying hazardous substances	50
GB 07	Places and materials that can contain asbestos	51
GB 08	Lead hazards checklist	52
GB 09	Specimen lead-based paint risk assessment	53
GB 10	Vibration – actions by employers	56
GB 11	Manual handling checklist	57
GB 12	Manual handling assessment	58
GB 13	Controlling construction dust	62

GB 01 Welfare requirements

The table summarises the requirement for the client and contractors (or the principal contractor on notifiable projects) to ensure that adequate welfare facilities are provided, as required by the CDM Regulations.

Sanitary conveniences	Suitable and sufficient sanitary conveniences must be provided or made available at readily accessible places. So far as is reasonably practicable, the rooms containing sanitary conveniences must be:
	■ adequately ventilated and lit
	■ kept in a clean and orderly condition.
	Separate rooms containing sanitary conveniences must be provided for men and women except where each convenience is in a separate room, the door of which can be locked from the inside.
Welfare facilities	Suitable and sufficient washing facilities, including showers, if required by the nature of the work or for health reasons, must, so far as is reasonably practicable, be provided or made available at readily accessible places.
	Washing facilities must be provided adjacent to:
	■ sanitary conveniences, whether or not provided elsewhere
	■ changing rooms, where provided, whether or not provided elsewhere.
	Washing facilities must include:
	■ a supply of clean cold and hot (or warm) water that, so far as is reasonably practicable shall be running water
	■ soap or other suitable skin cleansers
	■ towels or other suitable means of drying.
	Rooms containing washing facilities must be lit and sufficiently ventilated.
	Washing facilities and the rooms containing them must be kept in a clean and orderly condition.
	Except for washing facilities that are intended for the washing of hands and forearms only, separate rooms must be provided for men and women except where:
	■ they are in a room, the door of which can be locked from the inside
	■ the room is intended to be used by one person at a time.
Drinking water	An adequate supply of wholesome drinking water, conspicuously marked with the appropriate sign, should be provided or made available at readily accessible places.
	Sufficient cups or other drinking vessels must be provided, unless the water supply is in the form of a jet (drinking fountain) from which a person can easily drink.
Changing rooms and lockers	Suitable facilities must be provided or made available at readily accessible places if:
	■ the worker has to wear special clothing for the purposes of work
	■ for reasons of health or personal privacy, changing cannot be carried out elsewhere.
	Where necessary, in the interests of personal privacy, separate changing rooms for men and women must be provided. Changing rooms must:
	■ contain seating
	■ include, where necessary, facilities to dry clothing and personal effects
	■ include, where necessary, facilities for locking away:
	– special clothing that is not taken home
	– a person's own clothing that is not worn at work
	– personal effects (property).
Facilities for rest	Suitable and sufficient facilities for rest must be provided at readily accessible places. They must:
	■ include suitable arrangements to protect non-smokers from the discomfort caused by tobacco smoke (this requirement has largely been overtaken by the legal ban on smoking in 'enclosed' and 'substantially enclosed' workplaces)
	■ be equipped with an adequate number of tables and adequate seating with backs (not benches)
	■ where necessary, include facilities for any pregnant woman and nursing mother to rest, lying down
	■ where necessary, include a means of boiling water and suitable arrangements to ensure that meals can be prepared and eaten
	■ be maintained at an appropriate temperature
	■ if gas heaters and/or a gas cooker is used, be equipped with a permanent supply of fresh air (such as a vent or louvre) **that cannot be closed,** to ensure that the heater or cooker can function properly without producing excessive amounts of carbon monoxide
	■ if electric heating is used, be equipped with a high temperature cut-out and not be draped with wet clothes: many fires have occurred through this practice.

GB 02 Eye protection selection

The standards of eye protection

Hazard description	Marking
Increased robustness.	BS EN 166 (1 or 2).S.
Low energy impact (45 m/sec).	BS EN 166 (1 or 2).F.
Medium energy impact (120 m/sec).	BS EN 166 (1 or 2).B.
High energy impact (190 m/sec).	BS EN 166 (1 or 2).A.
Droplets and splashes of liquid.	BS EN 166 (1 or 2).3.
Large dust particles.	BS EN 166 (1 or 2).4.
Gas and fine dust particles.	BS EN 166 (1 or 2).5.
Short-circuit electric arc.	BS EN 166 (1 or 2).8.
Molten metal and hot solids.	BS EN 166 (1 or 2).9.
Hard coat (resistance to fine particles).	BS EN 166 (1 or 2).K.
Non-mist (resistance to fogging).	BS EN 166 (1 or 2).N.
Face shields (welding).	BS EN 175.

1. The 1 or 2 in the BS EN numbers refer to the optical characteristics of the PPE.

2. Eye protectors manufactured to the British and European Standard are subjected to a number of tests (including temperature, robustness and optical quality) before approval.

3. In the test of robustness, for example, general purpose goggles to EN 166.1.S must withstand the impact of a 6 mm steel ball travelling at 12 m/sec (27 mph). Impact goggles to EN 166.1.F must withstand the impact at 45 m/sec (100 mph) and for EN 166.1.B they must withstand an impact at 120 m/sec (270 mph).

4. Eye protection to BS EN 166 A is for specialist applications and is only available in the form of a face shield.

5. Safety goggles are marked with a combination of letters and numbers to indicate the standard of protection provided, for example:

    – BS EN 166.1.F is impact-resistant to a low energy projectile

    – BS EN 166.1.B.3.4 is impact-resistant to medium energy projectiles, droplets, splashes of liquid and large dust particles

    – BS EN 166.1.A.9 is impact-resistant to high energy projectiles, molten metal and hot solids.

 Safety glasses, commonly referred to as light eye protection, are either low or medium energy impact rated. They are not **high** energy rated and must never be used as a substitute for safety goggles during high impact activities (such as using grinders, petrol cut-off saws, cartridge guns, gas-powered nail guns and breaking out).

B

GB 02 *continued*

Selection

The following hazards are those most likely to be encountered in construction operations. Approved eye protection is required and must be provided for all persons engaged in any of the processes specified below.

The protection listed below is recommended as containing good practical value, but should be regarded as the **minimum** standard required.

Eye protection must be selected in the light of the work activity to be undertaken and the assessed level of risk. A suitable and sufficient risk assessment will identify hazards and indicate the control measures required to minimise the likelihood and severity of potential risks.

Process to be considered	Hazard	Recommended protection	BS specification
Part I: Processes in which approved eye protectors are required			
Use of compressed air with shot or other abrasives for blasting or cleaning.	High speed flying fragments or particles.	Goggles and/or face shield.	BS EN 166.B.
Cleaning by means of high pressure water jets.	Flying fragments or particles.	Goggles, spectacles and/or face shield.	BS EN 166.S.
Use of hand or power tools to strike masonry nails.	Flying fragments or particles.	Goggles, spectacles and/or face shield.	BS EN 166.F.
Handling and use of cartridge-operated tools.	High speed flying fragments or particles.	Goggles and/or face shield.	BS EN 166.B.
Chipping of metal, chipping; knocking out or cutting of cold rivets, bolts, nuts, lugs, pins, collars and so on using hand or power tools.	Flying fragments or particles.	Goggles, spectacles and/or face shield.	BS EN 166.F.
Chipping or scuffing of paint, scale, slag, rust and so on from metal and other hard materials using hand or power tools.	Flying particles or dust.	Goggles.	BS EN 166.4.
Use of power-driven, high-speed, metal cutting saw, or abrasive cutting-off wheel or disc.	High speed flying fragments or particles.	Goggles and/or face shield.	BS EN 166.B.
Operation, maintenance, dismantling or demolition of plant that contains or has contained acids, alkalis, corrosive materials, or other dangerous substances, whether liquid or solid.	Flying particles, chemical splash or injurious dust.	Goggles.	BS EN 166.3 and 4.
Handling in open vessels or manipulation of the substances described above.	Flying particles, chemical splash or injurious dust.	Goggles.	BS EN 166.3 and 4.
Pressure injection of liquids or solutions into buildings or structures.	Chemical splashes.	Goggles.	BS EN 166.3.
Use of hand or power tools to drive in bolts, pins, collars and so on.	Flying fragments or particles.	Goggles, spectacles and/or face shield.	BS EN 166.F.
Breaking up of metal by use of a hammer (whether power-driven or not).	Flying fragments or particles	Goggles, spectacles and/or face shield.	BS EN 166.F.
Use of compressed air to remove swarf, dust, dirt and so on.	Flying fragments or particles.	Goggles, spectacles and/or face shield.	BS EN 166.S.
Pouring or skimming molten metal.	Molten metal, splashes and sparks.	Goggles and/or face shield.	BS EN 166.9.

GB 02 *continued*

Process to be considered	Hazard	Recommended protection	BS specification
Part I: Processes in which approved eye protectors are required *(continued)*			
Breaking, cutting, dressing, carving or drilling with hand or power tools the following materials: ■ glass, hard plastics, concrete, fired clay, plaster, slag, natural or artificial stone, and any similar materials. Also any articles consisting wholly or partly of these materials ■ stonework, brickwork, or blockwork ■ bricks, tiles, or blocks.	Flying fragments or particles.	Goggles, spectacles and/or face shield.	BS EN 166.F.
Cutting of wire and related operations.	Flying fragments or particles.	Goggles, spectacles and/or face shield.	BS EN 166.S.
Cutting of wire or metal strapping under tension.	High speed flying fragments or particles.	Goggles, spectacles and/or face shield.	BS EN 166.B.
Processing and handling of glass or cullet.	Flying fragments or particles.	Goggles, spectacles and/or face shield.	BS EN 166.S.
Part II: Processes in which approved shields or fixed shields are required			
Electric arc welding.	Glare, radiation, heat or spatter.	Fixed shield and/or welding helmet or band screen.	Housing BS EN 175. Filters BS EN 169.
Part III: Processes in which approved eye protectors, shields or fixed shields are required			
Gas welding.	Glare, radiation, heat or spatter.	Goggles.	Housing BS EN 175. Filters BS EN 169.
Cutting, boring, cleaning, surface-conditioning or spraying of material using apparatus supplied with oxygen or flammable gas under pressure.	Flying fragments or particles.	Goggles.	Housing BS EN 175. Filters BS EN 169.
Processes involving the use of lasers.	Radiation and burning.	Fixed shield and/or goggles.	BS EN 60825.
Part IV: Process in which approved eye protectors, shields or fixed shields are required			
Truing or dressing of abrasive wheels.	High speed particles or fragments.	Fixed shield and/or goggles.	BS EN 166 B.
Dry grinding of materials or articles using a power-driven wheel, disc or band, or a portable tool.	Flying particles or hot sparks.	Goggles, spectacles and/or face shield.	BS EN 166 F.
Machining of metals including any dry grinding process not elsewhere specified.	Flying particles.	Goggles and/or spectacles.	BS EN 166 S.
Welding of metals by an electric resistance process or a submerged electric arc.	Flying particles or spatter.	Goggles, spectacles and/or face shield.	BS EN 166 S.
Cases in which protection is required for persons at risk from, but not employed in, the process			
Chipping of metal, knocking out or cutting of cold rivets, bolts, nuts, lugs, pins, collars, and so on using hand or power tools.	Flying fragments or particles.	Goggles, spectacles, face shield and/or fixed shield.	BS EN 166 F.
Electric arc welding.	Glare, radiation or spatter.	Cover, goggles and/or spectacles.	BS EN 166 S. Filters BS EN 169.
Process involving lasers.	Radiation and burning.	Goggles and/or spectacles.	BS EN 60825.

GB 03 Respiratory protective equipment selection

All RPE should conform to European Standard BS EN 529.

Each type of RPE is assigned a filter protection factor, which gives the user some idea of the level of protection that the device will provide. For example, a filtering half-mask marked:

FFP1 or P1 is a low efficiency device offering a **protection factor of four**

FFP2 or P2 is a medium efficiency device offering a **protection factor of 10**

FFP3 or P3 is a high efficiency device offering a **protection factor of 20**.

A protection factor of 10 means that, in controlled conditions, for every 10 units of contaminant outside the mask, only one unit will get inside the mask, or for every 20 units outside the mask there will be two units inside, and so on. It is important, therefore, that the correct filter is selected for the type and level of contaminant in the air.

 Use RPE with an FFP3 or P3 rating to protect against dust (such as silica) that is created when mechanically cutting concrete, bricks, slabs and so on – even when wet cutting, which only removes about 80% of airborne particles.

There are many types of RPE, including:

- ☑ disposable face mask respirators
- ☑ half-mask dust respirators
- ☑ high-efficiency dust respirators
- ☑ self-contained breathing apparatus
- ☑ positive, pressure-powered respirators
- ☑ ventilator visor or helmet respirators
- ☑ compressed, air-line breathing apparatus.

 It should be noted that cheap nuisance masks (cup-shaped filters often held in place by a single strap with no BS EN 529 markings) are not classed as PPE or RPE. They do not meet any current standards or legislative requirements and offer very little or no protection to the wearer.

 Common failings

- ☒ There is an assumption that workers know how to put on and use RPE.
- ☒ RPE misuse is common – but it is generally blamed on the workers.
- ☒ There is limited management input or involvement when it comes to RPE.
- ☒ There is little information provided to the worker wearing the RPE.
- ☒ There are poor standards of training, hazard awareness and RPE use.
- ☒ There is little supervision and enforcement of correct RPE use.

 For further information on respiratory protective equipment (RPE) and selection refer to Chapter B06 Personal protective equipment.

B

GB 04 Hearing protection selection

Types of personal hearing protectors

Disposable earplugs and reusable earplugs are made of rubber or plastic and need regular, careful washing.

Ear defenders (or muffs) completely cover the ear and are sealed to the head with a foam or liquid-filled seal. Badly designed, badly produced or poor fitting defenders may give little or no protection against noise.

Standards for hearing protection

Personal hearing protection must be CE-marked showing it meets the relevant European Standard BS EN 352.

EN 352-1 – Hearing protectors – earmuffs
In addition to the Standard number, maker and model identification: ■ indication of orientation of the earmuff, where required, e.g. 'TOP' and/or 'LEFT' and 'RIGHT'.
EN 352-2 – Hearing protectors – earplugs
Markings may only appear on the packaging. In addition to the Standard number, maker and model identification: ■ whether disposable or re-useable ■ fitting instructions ■ nominal size of formable plugs, in range 5 to 14 mm ■ left-right differentiation for custom moulded plugs.
EN 352-3 – Hearing protectors – earmuffs attached to a safety helmet
In addition to the Standard number, maker and model identification: ■ indication of orientation of the earmuff, where required, e.g. 'TOP' and/or 'LEFT' and 'RIGHT'.
EN 352-4 – Hearing protectors – earmuffs attached to a safety helmet
■ As for EN 352-1.
EN 352-5 – Hearing protectors – active noise reduction earmuffs
■ As for EN 352-1.
EN 352-6 – Hearing protectors – earmuffs with electrical audio input
■ As for EN 352-1.
EN 352-7 – Hearing protectors – level dependent earplugs
■ As for EN 352-2.
EN 352-8 – Hearing protectors – entertainment audio earmuffs
■ As for EN 352-2.

 Selection of hearing protection

In order to select the correct type of hearing protection you need to know the noise level on site and be able to select the right type of hearing protection required to reduce the noise exposure to a safe level (which is below 80 dB).

For example, 100 dB would need to be reduced by 20 dB to bring it to 80 dB. This reduction is known as attenuation or single noise reduction (SNR) and this value is shown on manufacturers' products.

The HSE recommends providing hearing protectors that perform 4 dB better than the required minimum, in order to take into account real world factors (such as poor fitting). This means that to protect the worker against 100 dB of noise, you need to select hearing protection with attenuation or SNR of 24 dB.

Personal hearing protectors should not over-protect, whereby users can become isolated from their work environment and be unable to hear warnings, reversing vehicles, and so on.

The optimum value with hearing protection is between 70 dB and 80 dB. Thus, in this example, select hearing protection with an attenuation or SNR of between 24 dB and 34 dB.

 For further information and guidance refer to Chapter B13 Noise.

GB 05 Skin protection selection

Protection of the skin

		Yes	No
1.	Have the materials or substances in use been correctly identified?		
2.	Is up-to-date manufacturers' information available on the safe use of the substances?		
3.	Have the hazardous substances that will be produced by a work process been identified?		
4.	Have the necessary risk assessments been carried out?		
5.	Has an attempt been made to control the hazard at source (for example, by using a less hazardous substance)?		
6.	Has a COSHH risk assessment been carried out for the substances in use?		
7.	Have the significant findings of the risk assessment been communicated to those who will be using or otherwise affected by the substance?		
8.	Are the correct warning and cautionary notices displayed?		
9.	Are the methods of handling, transport and storage correct for the substances being used?		
10.	Are there adequate selection and training procedures available for operatives using harmful substances?		
11.	Is it necessary for workers to have wet hands for long periods or repeatedly get their hands wet?		
12.	Have operatives been properly trained in the necessary precautions and protective measures required for safe working?		
13.	Are safe working procedures and methods being properly implemented?		
14.	Is the correct handling equipment available and in use?		
15.	Is there adequate ventilation where toxic materials are in use?		
16.	Are there adequate washing facilities, barrier creams and cleansing agents of the correct type available and in regular use?		
17.	Are there gloves and protective clothing of the correct type and specification available and in use?		
18.	Have they been selected by a competent person, who can be the supplier?		
19.	Is there provision for cleaning protective clothing?		
20.	Is protective clothing regularly changed?		
21.	Are there adequate supervision and inspection procedures in place?		
22.	Is medical surveillance available for operatives, when applicable?		
23.	Have appropriate welfare and first-aid facilities been provided?		
24.	Other.		

BS EN 420 – General requirements for gloves

- Mark identifying the manufacturer.
- Product identifying mark.
- Size designation (normally in range **6** to **11**).
- Date of obsolescence (if appropriate).
- Dexterity performance in range **1** (lowest) to **5** (highest), if required.
- Markings specific to individual risks, including pictograms where appropriate.

GB 05 *continued*

Choosing the right glove for the right job

Mechanical hazard

Mechanical hazards are associated with the handling of rough or sharp objects that could abrade, cut or pierce the skin (such as glass, thin metal sheet and masonry blocks). A mechanical hazard is not associated with moving machinery, in fact it can be extremely dangerous to wear gloves that could catch in moving parts or serrated blades.

 Gloves should not be used when working with serrated blades – ***use guards***.

4. 1. 4. 1. **BS EN 388**	■ 4 = Abrasion. Performance index 1 to 4. ■ 1 = Blade Cut. Performance index 1 to 5. ■ 4 = Tear. Performance index 1 to 4. ■ 1 = Puncture. Performance index 1 to 4.

Chemical hazard

Whether total immersion or merely splash is involved, any substance that would irritate, inflame or burn the skin is classed as a chemical hazard. In order that a more informed and relevant glove selection can be made, there is a list of 12 chemicals, identified by the letters A to L. Refer to the manufacturer for details of the specific chemicals.

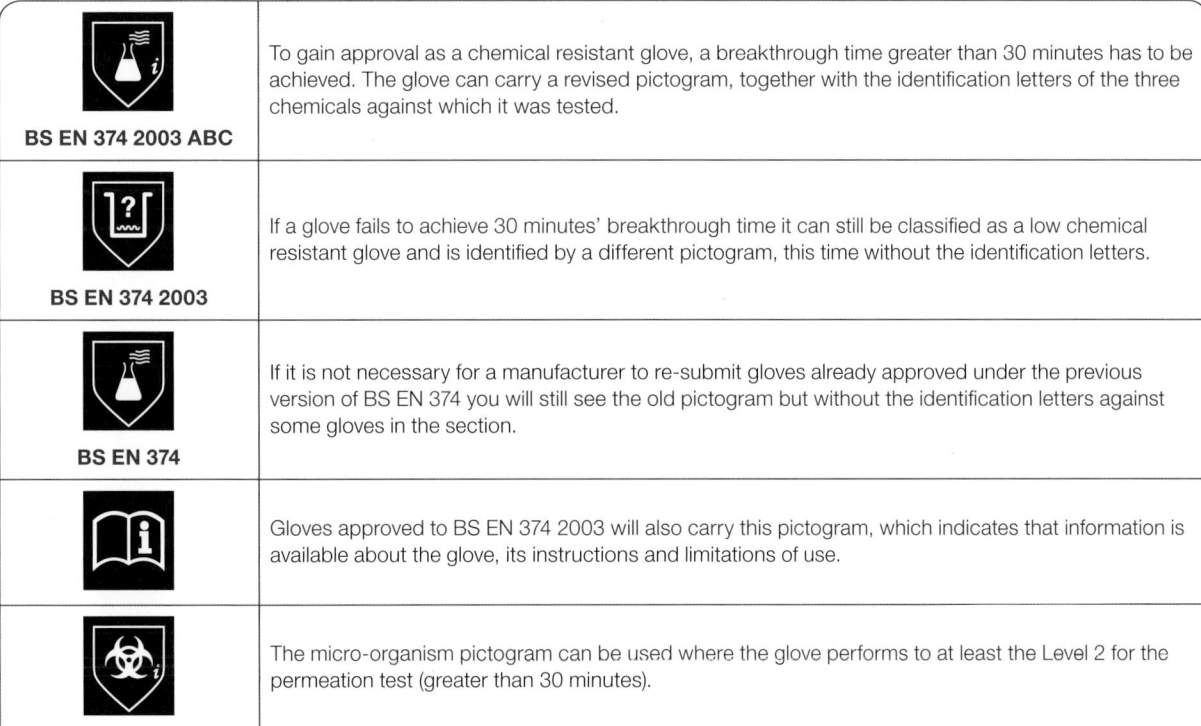

BS EN 374 2003 ABC	To gain approval as a chemical resistant glove, a breakthrough time greater than 30 minutes has to be achieved. The glove can carry a revised pictogram, together with the identification letters of the three chemicals against which it was tested.
BS EN 374 2003	If a glove fails to achieve 30 minutes' breakthrough time it can still be classified as a low chemical resistant glove and is identified by a different pictogram, this time without the identification letters.
BS EN 374	If it is not necessary for a manufacturer to re-submit gloves already approved under the previous version of BS EN 374 you will still see the old pictogram but without the identification letters against some gloves in the section.
	Gloves approved to BS EN 374 2003 will also carry this pictogram, which indicates that information is available about the glove, its instructions and limitations of use.
	The micro-organism pictogram can be used where the glove performs to at least the Level 2 for the permeation test (greater than 30 minutes).

Thermal hazards hot and cold

BS EN 407	Thermal hazards come in many forms. Heat can be radiated and conducted, or it may be actual flames.
BS EN 511	Cold can be anything from cold water to frozen gases. It is important to know the type of hazard and the temperature involved in order to recommend suitable protection.

(Table reproduced with the kind permission of Arco Ltd.)

GB 06 Identifying hazardous substances

Packaging or labels

New globally harmonised symbols	Existing European hazard (CHIP) symbols
Fatal if inhaled, swallowed or in contact with skin.	**Very toxic or toxic** Substances that, in very low quantities or low quantities, cause death or acute or chronic damage to health when inhaled, swallowed or absorbed via the skin.
Warning – harmful if inhaled, swallowed or in contact with skin. Can also cause serious eye irritation.	**Harmful** Substances that may cause death or acute or chronic damage to health when inhaled, swallowed or absorbed via the skin.
Warning – harmful if inhaled, swallowed or in contact with skin. Can also cause serious eye irritation.	**Irritant** Non-corrosive substances that may cause inflammation through immediate, prolonged or repeated contact with the skin or mucous membrane.
Danger – causes severe skin burns and eye damage.	**Corrosive** Substances that may, on contact with living tissues, destroy them.
Danger (Category 1) – may cause allergy or asthma symptoms or breathing difficulties if inhaled. Danger (Category 1a and 1b) – may cause cancer.	None

GB 07 Places and materials that can contain asbestos

> **e.g.** **Building fabric**
>
> ☑ Corrugated roofing, tiles, slates, soffits, gutters, downpipes, walls and panels.
>
> ☑ Insulation under the roof, on beams and stanchions.
>
> ☑ Boards and panels, and any insulation between these.
>
> ☑ Insulation around pipes, on a heater, boiler, calorifier, in storage heaters.
>
> ☑ Decorative coatings on walls or ceilings.
>
> ☑ Insulation around windows.
>
> ☑ Water cistern.
>
> ☑ Flues, waste water pipes.
>
> ☑ Plastic floor tiles.
>
> Also check **outbuildings**.

> **e.g.** **Equipment**
>
> ☑ Oven, brakes, soundproofing, ironing surfaces and insulating mat.
>
> ☑ Fire blanket, fire insulation in or on doors and insulating gloves.
>
> Note down the **condition** and **amount** of materials that might contain asbestos.
>
> **Where you can't get access (for example, roof void, undercroft, wall cavities) presume that these contain asbestos.**
>
> The following materials **do not** contain asbestos:
>
> ☑ stone
>
> ☑ brick or breeze-block and mortar
>
> ☑ concrete
>
> ☑ metal
>
> ☑ glass
>
> ☑ wood
>
> ☑ most furnishings and fabrics (but see 'Equipment' above).
>
> But they **may conceal asbestos**.

 Steel frames that were clad in asbestos for fire protection may have underlying lead paint coatings and thus a lead paint survey will also be required.

> **www.** **The HSE's website contains further guidance on asbestos**
>
> It covers:
>
> ☑ identifying asbestos risk
> ☑ licensed work with asbestos
> ☑ other work with asbestos
> ☑ waste
> ☑ instruction and training.

 For further information refer to Chapter B09 Asbestos.

GB 08 Lead hazards checklist

Lead hazards

	Yes	No
1. Have you been provided with a copy of the lead survey report and/or lead register?		
2. Has a suitable and sufficient risk assessment been carried out?		
3. Have all persons who have to work with lead received adequate information, instruction and training?		
4. Has the HSE publication *Lead and you* been issued to all employees?		
5. Has the nature and extent of any exposure to lead been assessed?		
6. Has the monitoring of lead in air levels been carried out?		
7. Is medical surveillance of individuals (which includes checking blood-lead levels before the works) necessary and, if so, undertaken?		
8. Should blood-lead levels be determined from a blood sample or a saliva check?		
9. If medical surveillance is necessary, are medical records kept as required?		
10. Are measures in place to control levels of exposure to lead?		
11. Is protective equipment and clothing in use, as necessary and required?		
12. Is the correct type of respiratory equipment being used for the hazard being encountered?		
13. Are measures being taken to control the spread of any lead contamination and how is this being checked (for example, dust-wipe sampling)?		
14. Is there adequate provision of washing and changing facilities?		
15. Are separate areas provided for eating and drinking?		
16. Are all operatives adequately trained in safe working procedures?		
17. Are operatives aware of the risks to health that can arise from not working safely?		
18. Are records being kept as required by the relevant regulations?		
19. Are arrangements in place to deal with accidents, incidents and emergency?		

Comments

GB 09 Specimen lead-based paint risk assessment

This document does not relate to any non-paint sources of lead exposure, for which a separate risk assessment should be completed.

1. Lead-based paint risk assessment details

Project		Location	
Document ref no.		Assessment date	
Issue date		Originator	
Review date		Responsibility	

Lead-based paint hazard *(Hazard location – room reference)*	Who may be harmed? *(List those at risk)*	Is risk adequately controlled? *(List existing controls)*	Further action required to control risk *(List further action to be taken and cross-reference to manager's action plan)*	Review dates

Comments/sketch

GB 09 *continued*

2. Lead-based paint risk assessment record

This document is an easy-to use checklist to allow a **suitable and sufficient assessment of the risk to health and safety** arising from the proposed works likely to involve the disturbance or removal of lead-based paint.

Full completion of this sheet is not a legal requirement.

Hazard location		Room reference			
Description	Reference	Lead check? Yes/No	Lead hazard? Yes/No	Lab check?	Lead amount
Floors					
Floor voids					
Walls					
Skirtings					
Panelling					
Dado rails					
Picture rails					
Windows					
Cills					
Sub-cills					
Windowboards					
Pelmets					
Curtain rails					
Shutters					
Fanlights					
Doors					
Frames					
Linings					
Stops					
Architraves					
Stairs					
Stair treads					
Newel posts					
Spindles					
Stringers					
Spandrel panels					
Miscellaneous					
Access hatches					
Meter cupboards					
Roof access/ceiling voids					
Floor access/floor voids					
Cellar access					
Boxed-in pipework/services					
Beams/columns					
Beneath asbestos fireproofing					
Fascias/soffits					
Fitted components					
Cupboards					
Fireplace surrounds					
Tank/boiler housings					
Architectural details					
Behind dry lining and false or suspended ceilings					
Other					

GB 09 *continued*

3. Lead-based paint risk assessment record (manager's action plan)

Manager's name	
Department/location	

Further action identified from risk assessment	No action to be taken/risk accepted *(Yes/No)*	Person responsible to carry out action	Date by which action is to be completed	Review date of action *(Comments)*	Date of action completed, signature of manager
1.					
2.					
3.					
4.					
5.					
6.					

Additional notes

 For further information and guidance refer to Chapter B12 Lead.

GB 10 Vibration – actions by employers

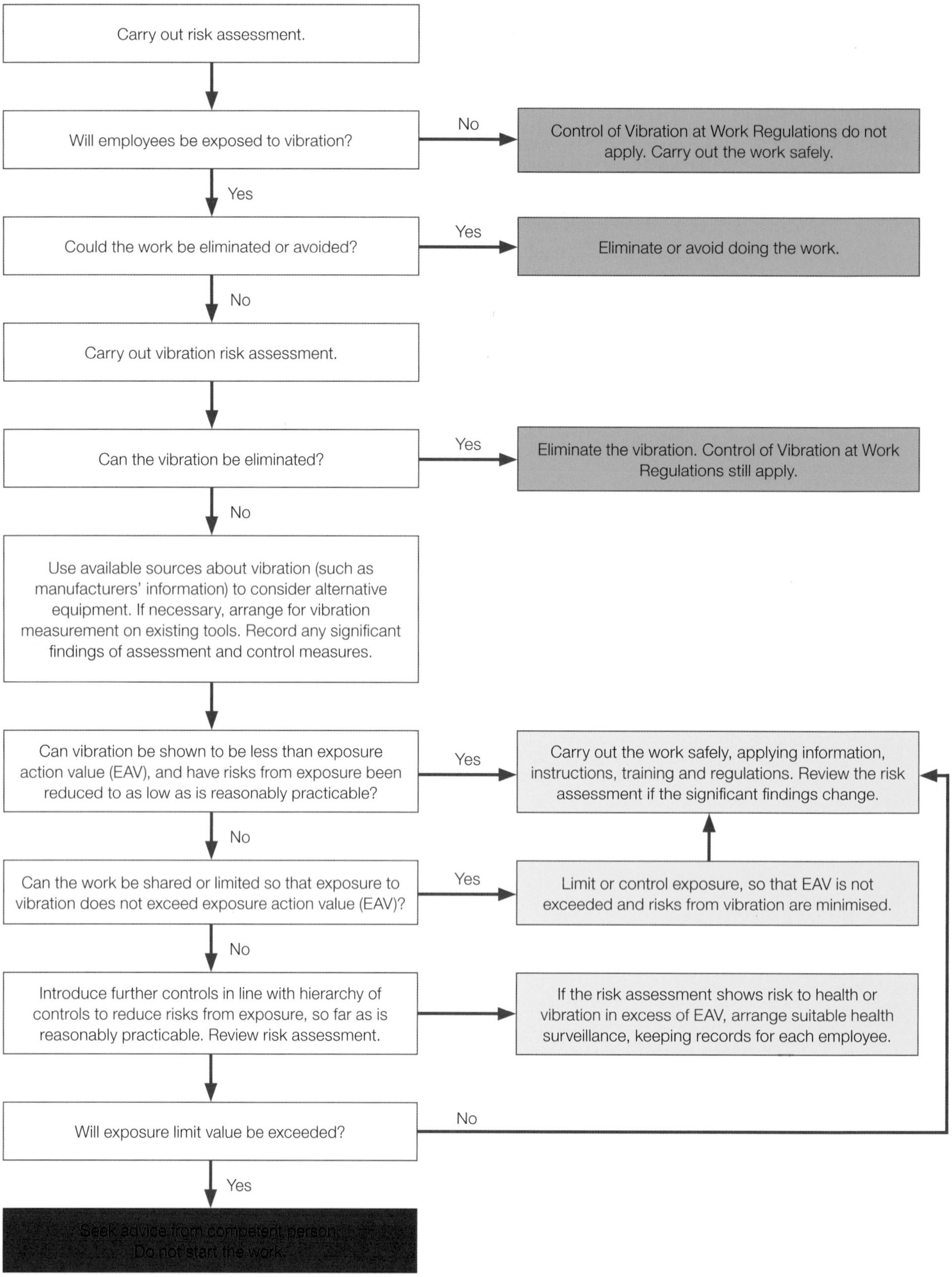

Carry out risk assessment.

↓

Will employees be exposed to vibration? —No→ Control of Vibration at Work Regulations do not apply. Carry out the work safely.

↓ Yes

Could the work be eliminated or avoided? —Yes→ Eliminate or avoid doing the work.

↓ No

Carry out vibration risk assessment.

↓

Can the vibration be eliminated? —Yes→ Eliminate the vibration. Control of Vibration at Work Regulations still apply.

↓ No

Use available sources about vibration (such as manufacturers' information) to consider alternative equipment. If necessary, arrange for vibration measurement on existing tools. Record any significant findings of assessment and control measures.

↓

Can vibration be shown to be less than exposure action value (EAV), and have risks from exposure been reduced to as low as is reasonably practicable? —Yes→ Carry out the work safely, applying information, instructions, training and regulations. Review the risk assessment if the significant findings change.

↓ No

Can the work be shared or limited so that exposure to vibration does not exceed exposure action value (EAV)? —Yes→ Limit or control exposure, so that EAV is not exceeded and risks from vibration are minimised.

↓ No

Introduce further controls in line with hierarchy of controls to reduce risks from exposure, so far as is reasonably practicable. Review risk assessment. → If the risk assessment shows risk to health or vibration in excess of EAV, arrange suitable health surveillance, keeping records for each employee.

↓

Will exposure limit value be exceeded? —No→

↓ Yes

Seek advice from competent person. Do not start the work.

	HAV	WBV
Exposure action value (EAV) =	2.5 m/s²	0.5 m/s²
Exposure limit value (ELV) =	5.0 m/s²	1.15 m/s²

 For further information and guidance refer to Chapter B14 Vibration.

GB 11 Manual handling checklist

The following can be used as a checklist when developing safe systems of work.

Manual handling

Preparation	Notes
▪ What is being lifted?	
▪ Where to and how far?	
▪ Has a manual handling risk assessment been carried out?	
▪ Would mechanical means be more practical or appropriate?	
▪ Is the operation part of a routine? If so, could it be more effectively planned and executed?	
▪ How many people will be needed to move the load safely?	
▪ Are they all trained in kinetic lifting and handling?	
▪ Are proper (kinetic) lifting methods being employed?	
▪ What methods and equipment will be required?	
▪ Is the required equipment available?	
▪ Is the lifting and handling area clear of hazards?	

Lifting and handling	Notes
▪ Is the proper personal protective clothing in use?	
▪ Is co-ordination satisfactory in dual and team lifting with one person taking charge of the lift?	
▪ Is the necessary equipment in use or to hand?	
▪ Are excessively heavy weights being lifted?	
▪ Are loads being deposited or stacked safely and securely?	
▪ Is adequate supervision employed where necessary?	

After lifting and handling	Notes
▪ Has there been any past incidents or accidents?	
▪ Is there anything to be learnt from them to avoid similar incidents happening again?	
▪ Did anyone receive an injury and does this need to be taken into account for future tasks?	
▪ Has any damage or loss of equipment been recorded and repaired/replaced?	

 For further information and guidance refer to Chapter B15 Manual handling.

GB 12 Manual handling assessment

(Reproduced from Guidance on The Manual Handling Operations Regulations under licence from Her Majesty's Stationery Office.)

Section A – Preliminary

Task name					
Task description					
Load weight					
Frequency of lift					
Carry distances (if applicable)					
Are other manual handling tasks carried out by these operators?					
Assessment discussed with employees/safety representatives					
Is an assessment needed? (Tick)	**Yes***			**No**	

* An assessment will be needed if there is a potential risk of injury (such as if the task falls outside the guidelines)
   If 'Yes' continue. If 'No' the assessment need go no further.

Operations covered by this assessment (detailed description)					
Locations					
Personnel involved					
Date of assessment					
Diagrams (other information, including existing control measures)					
Overall assessment of the risk of injury*?	**Low**		**Medium**		**High**	

* *Make your overall assessment **after** you have completed Section B.*

GB 12 *continued*

B

Section B – Lifting and carrying – more detailed assessment, where necessary

Questions to consider	If yes, tick appropriate level of risk			Problems occurring from the task	Possible remedial action *(such as changes to be made to the task, load, working environment, etc.)*
	Low	Med	High		
Do **the tasks** involve:					
▪ holding loads away from trunk?					
▪ twisting?					
▪ stooping?					
▪ reaching upwards?					
▪ large vertical movement?					
▪ long carrying distances?					
▪ strenuous pushing or pulling?					
▪ unpredictable movement of loads?					
▪ repetitive handling?					
▪ insufficient rest or recovery?					
▪ a work rate imposed by a process?					
Are **the loads**:					
▪ heavy?					
▪ bulky/unwieldy?					
▪ difficult to grasp?					
▪ unstable/unpredictable?					
▪ intrinsically harmful (for example, sharp/hot)?					
Consider **the working environment – are there:**					
▪ constraints on posture?					
▪ poor floors?					
▪ variations in levels?					
▪ hot/cold/humid conditions?					
▪ strong air movements?					
▪ poor lighting conditions?					
Consider **individual capability** – does the job:					
▪ require unusual capability?					
▪ pose a risk to those with a health problem or a physical or learning difficulty?					
▪ pose a risk to those who are pregnant?					
▪ call for special information/training?					

GB 12 *continued*

Questions to consider	Yes/No	Problems occurring from the task	Possible remedial action *(such as changes to be made to the task, load, working environment, etc.)*
Other factors to consider			
Protective clothing			
■ Is movement or posture hindered by clothing or personal protective equipment (PPE)?			
■ Is there an absence of the correct/suitable PPE being worn?			
Work organisation (psychosocial factors)			
■ Do workers feel that there has been a lack of consideration given to the planning and scheduling of tasks/ rest breaks?			
■ Do workers feel that there is poor communication between managers and employees (not involved in risk assessments or decisions on changes in workstation design)?			
■ Are there sudden changes in workload, or seasonal changes in volume without mechanisms for dealing with the change?			
■ Do workers feel they have not been given enough training and information to carry out the task successfully?			

GB 12 *continued*

Section C – Remedial action to be taken

Remedial steps that should be taken, in order of priority	Person responsible for implementing controls	Target implementation date	Completed (Yes/No)
1.			
2.			
3.			
4.			
5.			
6.			
7.			
8.			
9.			
Date by which actions should be completed			
Date for review of assessment			
Assessor's name		Signature	

 Take action… and check that it has the desired effect.

 For further information and guidance refer to Chapter B15 Manual handling.

GB 13 Controlling construction dust

Respiratory risks are often misunderstood and overlooked, under played or just ignored. Each year 1,000s of construction workers contract or die from respiratory diseases due to breathing in dust and fumes.

The amount breathed in each day as they work from site to site can seem small or insignificant. In some cases the effects of exposure may be immediate but generally it can take years before the symptoms of ill health become apparent.

 For further information and guidance refer to Chapter B10 Dust and fumes.

Avoiding dust – examples of good practice

  **Rubbing down tape and jointing.** Traditionally, rubbing down creates a lot of dust, which is hazardous to health, has to be cleaned up and is manually intensive. This drywall sander with collection system minimises all these issues to the extent that the operative does not need respiratory protective equipment (RPE).

  **Cement boarding** used as part of a vertical cladding system had to be cut to size on site. A circular saw, complete with vacuum collection, was used in a designated cutting area and the operator also wore FFP3-rated RPE.

  **Cutting concrete, slabs, blocks and kerbs.** It is now unacceptable to dry cut these products. Where possible purchase pre-sized or cut materials. For some products eliminate dust by using a block splitter. When using a petrol or compressed air cut-off saw it must be wet cut with a constant water feed. RPE must still be worn.

 It is recognised good practice to use RPE with an FFP3 or P3 rating to protect against all construction dust (such as silica), which is created when mechanically cutting concrete, bricks, slabs, and so on – even when wet cutting (which only removes about 75% of airborne particles). FFP3/P3 offers maximum protection compared to FFP1/P1 or FFP2/P2.

GB 13 *continued*

Silica dust

The health hazards of silica come from breathing in the dust produced when materials such as brick, concrete, block, mortar and screed are cut, sanded, grit-blasted, chased, drilled and broken out.

Examples of typical levels of silica exposure in some common construction activities

Activity	Control measures	Exposure	Improvements required*
Drilling in poorly ventilated undercroft	■ No dust suppression ■ No extraction ■ No forced ventilation ■ Inadequate respiratory protective equipment (RPE)	**HIGH – 300 times the MEL**	■ Fit water suppression or dust extraction to drilling equipment ■ Provide appropriate RPE ■ Ensure correct use of RPE
Drilling into brickwork under arch blocked at one end	■ Primitive extraction by fan and airbag ■ Disposable face masks worn	**HIGH – 5 times the MEL**	■ Fit water suppression or dust extraction to drilling equipment ■ Provide appropriate RPE ■ Ensure correct use of RPE
Using jackhammers to break out concrete in large open indoor area	■ Limited ventilation ■ No dust suppression ■ No local exhaust ventilation ■ No RPE in use	**MEDIUM – within the MEL but double the level regarded as reasonably practicable**	■ Wet down concrete and rubble
Chasing out cracks in screeded cement floor in large open indoor area	■ RPE provided but not worn properly ■ Breathing zone of worker crouching over grinder very close to source of dust	**HIGH – 6 times the MEL**	■ Attach dust extraction to grinder ■ Wet down ahead of the chasing ■ Provide appropriate RPE ■ Ensure correct use of RPE
Chasing out mortar between bricks prior to re-pointing	■ Ineffective extraction fitted to hand-held electric grinder ■ RPE correctly worn but not to correct standard	**HIGH – 21 times the MEL**	■ Attach dust extraction to grinder ■ Provide appropriate RPE ■ Ensure correct use of RPE
Cutting paving kerb (33% silica) in open area	■ Petrol driven saw not fitted with water spray or local exhaust ventilation	**HIGH – 12 times the MEL**	■ Provide effective water suppression system to saw
Cutting blue brick (32% silica) in open area	■ Petrol driven saw not fitted with water spray or local exhaust ventilation	**HIGH – 5 times the MEL**	■ Provide effective water suppression system to saw
Cutting breeze block (3% silica) in open area	■ Petrol driven saw not fitted with water spray or local exhaust ventilation	**HIGH – twice the MEL**	■ Provide effective water suppression to saw
Cutting window openings in concrete wall with wall saw/ Cutting concrete with floor saw	■ Water suppression on saw used	**LOW – well below the MEL and also below the level regarded as significant**	
General clearing and removing rubble	■ Hand sweeping with brush	**HIGH – twice the MEL**	■ Damp down rubble before clearing ■ Use mechanical means to sweep up ■ Provide appropriate RPE ■ Ensure correct use of RPE
General clearing and removing rubble	■ Use of mechanical sweeper with rotating brushes and vacuum extraction	**MEDIUM – within the MEL but double the level regarded as significant**	■ Provide appropriate RPE ■ Ensure correct use of RPE
Concrete crushing from demolition job for use as hard core	■ Machine with enclosed cab ■ Water jets fitted	**LOW – well below the MEL and also below the level regarded as significant**	

* To reduce exposure to below the maximum exposure limit (MEL) and so far as is reasonably practicable.

(Table reproduced from the HSE's Construction Information Sheet no. 36 Silica.)

GC

General safety

The contents of this chapter should be read and used in conjunction with guidance contained within Section C.

GC 01 Site organisation   66
GC 02 Fire prevention and control – risk management   68
GC 03 Fire prevention and control – evacuation and escape   69
GC 04 Fire prevention and control – managing hot work   71
GC 05 Fire prevention and control – hot-work permit   72
GC 06 Electrical safety – safe isolation   73
GC 07 PUWER inspection report   74
GC 08 Periodic inspection and checks – examination
       carried out for mobile plant   75
GC 09 Construction plant reception and inspection report   76
GC 10 MEWP reception and inspection report   78
GC 11 Lift plan   80
GC 12 Lift schedule   85
GC 13 Site crane permit to lift (Part 1)   86
GC 14 Site crane permit to lift (Part 2)   87
GC 15 LOLER inspection report   88
GC 16 Lifting equipment and accessories inspection report   90

GC 01 Site organisation

Overview

What you need to know

In order that a construction site can be set up correctly to meet the requirements of the size and complexity of the project, there are many factors to be taken into consideration. The checklists below identify some of the significant hazards and risks to be considered.

What you need to do

Use the information detailed in the health and safety plan to tailor the site set up to meet the needs of the construction project (for example, existing building(s), contamination and demolition).

Significant hazards and risks

Safety	Yes	No	N/A
1. Can a safe working area be provided, with pedestrians and vehicles segregated?			
2. Is there a secure working area, areas for storage of materials and for waste skips with suitable access for deliveries and removals?			
3. Are there adequate emergency escape routes from all areas of the site?			
4. Is there a suitable fire plan, sounder, fire extinguishers and communication?			
5. Are there rescue plans for high risk activities (such as excavations and work at height)?			

Health	Yes	No	N/A
1. Has an adequate risk assessment been prepared for the tasks to be undertaken?			
2. Have welfare facilities been arranged for the site – suitable for tasks/number of workers anticipated and available from day one?			
3. Are there any hazardous substances being used – COSHH?			
4. What measures will be put in place to prevent or minimise all work activities which create dust?			

Environment	Yes	No	N/A
1. Are there any watercourses or other potential pollution receptors nearby?			
2. Does any wildlife need to be considered?			
3. Is there potential for contaminated land?			
4. Is there potential for pollution by the work activity (such as spills, noise, dust and light, provision of spill kits)?			

Managerial/supervisory tasks (including pre-planning)	Yes	No	N/A
1. Has the construction phase plan been prepared and approved for work to begin?			
2. Have the risk assessments been reviewed and found to be task/site specific?			
3. Has a traffic management plan been prepared, with pedestrian segregation?			
4. Has a suitable site waste management plan been developed for the site?			
5. Is the level of supervision and monitoring of work activities sufficient?			

GC 01 *continued*

Significant hazards and risks *(continued)*

Training/competency requirements	Yes	No	N/A
1. Have competency assessments been undertaken for contractors being used?			
2. Do the supervisors and workers have the requisite skills and training records for the tasks to be undertaken?			
3. Do supervisors and workers hold any required competency card (such as CPCS, CSCS and/or alternative schemes)?			

Safe systems of work/basic control measures	Yes	No	N/A
1. Have high risk activities been identified, and risk controls minimised to an acceptable level? Do they include risks to those putting in control measures (such as those erecting edge protection)?			
2. Have the method statements and risk assessments been approved prior to contractors commencing on site?			
3. Is there a procedure to update documentation during the works, which should be detailed as part of a competency check?			
4. Are employees empowered to take action if they feel additional control measures are needed and are there measures in place for effective worker engagement?			

Specific regulatory or special requirements	Yes	No	N/A
1. Are there registers on site for statutory inspections (such as scaffolding or excavations)?			
2. Are there any high risk activities that may require rescue plans (such as work at height)?			
3. Have electrical installations been completed by competent contractors and tested?			

C

GC 02 Fire prevention and control – risk management

Overview

What you need to know

You must be aware of the fire risk arising out of the materials and substances that are stored and used on site, should they come into contact with a source of ignition.

What you need to do

- ☑ Assess the fire risks and update them periodically as the project progresses and on-site conditions change.
- ☑ Take into account any existing third-party arrangements and others who may be put at risk by fire. Put in place control measures that eliminate the risk of fire or reduce it to an acceptable level.
- ☑ Communicate the significant fire risks and the preventative measures to all on site.

Significant hazards and risks

Safety	Yes	No	N/A
1. Burns from coming into contact with fire.			
2. Slips, trips and falls during rapid site evacuation.			
3. Spread of fire to third-party buildings or areas.			
Health	**Yes**	**No**	**N/A**
1. Inhalation of smoke and toxic fumes (both on and off site).			
Environment	**Yes**	**No**	**N/A**
1. Fire-fighting water run-off entering watercourses.			
2. Emission of noxious and toxic fumes.			
3. Ground contamination from products of combustion.			
Managerial/supervisory tasks (including pre-planning)	**Yes**	**No**	**N/A**
1. Assess the fire risks and put effective control measures in place.			
2. Compile a fire action plan where necessary.			
3. Liaise as necessary with the Fire and Rescue Service.			
4. Prevent unauthorised access to site.			
Training/competency requirements	**Yes**	**No**	**N/A**
1. Include fire safety as part of induction and refresher training.			
2. Provide training for anyone with specific fire safety duties.			
3. Provide training on the selection and use of fire extinguishers for some staff.			
Safe systems of work/basic control measures	**Yes**	**No**	**N/A**
1. Ensure the safe storage of flammable materials.			
2. Pay particular attention to the safe storage and use of flammable and explosive gases.			
3. Implement hot-work permits for higher risk activities.			
Specific regulatory or special requirements	**Yes**	**No**	**N/A**
1. Ensure everyone is competent to do what is asked of them with regard to fire safety.			
2. Establish who is the responsible person with regard to fire safety.			
Further information/references/links	**Yes**	**No**	**N/A**
This checklist has been produced as an aide memoire for those with on-site responsibility for fire safety. Additional guidance is available from the Health and Safety Executive (HSE) and the Fire Protection Association.			

GC 03 Fire prevention and control – evacuation and escape

Overview

What you need to know

☑ The danger to people on site from not being able to escape to a place of safety within a reasonable time.

☑ Where, when, what type and in what quantities flammable and highly flammable materials will be stored and used on site – the 'high risk periods'.

☑ How many people would have to evacuate the site at any one time and from which locations?

What you need to do

As part of the fire action plan, develop an emergency evacuation plan and keep it up-to-date, which should include:

☑ identification of one or more assembly points

☑ an effective method of detecting fires and raising the alarm

☑ an effective method of accounting for all who are on site, and instructing them what to do next, when they get to the assembly point

☑ providing appropriate and adequate fire-fighting equipment, at suitable locations, and training sufficient people to use it

☑ making a commitment to use site inductions to promote the plan and to communicate changes to it to those on-site at the time

☑ deciding how to co-ordinate an evacuation where only part of the site has to be evacuated or, where the site is in premises, parts of which are occupied by others

☑ periodically practising the emergency evacuation of the site to confirm the adequacy of the plan and highlight shortcomings

☑ liaising with the local Fire and Rescue Service as necessary

☑ compartmentalising the partially finished structure to prevent or slow the spread of fire

☑ nominating fire wardens whose job would be to ensure and confirm that their area of responsibility is clear of people when an evacuation takes place

☑ paying due regard to the adequacy of fire escape routes.

Escape routes must be:

☑ adequate in number and size for the number of people likely to use them (specialist advice might be needed)

☑ clearly designated by signage complying with the Health and Safety (Safety Signs and Signals Regulations), particularly at changes of direction and level

☑ lit (including standby emergency lighting) if it is possible that they could be used when there is insufficient natural light

☑ not obstructed; if work is necessary that unavoidably blocks an escape route, an alternative route must be designated throughout the duration of the work, adjusted if necessary as construction progresses and inspected at least once a week.

Significant hazards and risks

Safety	Yes	No	N/A
1. Danger of fatalities if people are unable to escape in time to a place of safety.			
2. Risk of slips, trip and falls possibly resulting in crush injuries in the rush to escape.			

Health	Yes	No	N/A
1. Risk of burns and other heat-related injuries resulting from contact with fire or hot surfaces/ atmospheres.			
2. Risk of respiratory problems resulting from inhalation of smoke and other toxic gases.			

Environment	Yes	No	N/A
1. No issues directly related to emergency evacuation.			

Significant hazards and risks *(continued)*

Managerial/supervisory tasks (including pre-planning)	Yes	No	N/A
1. Develop an effective emergency evacuation plan that identifies emergency escape routes and any changes to them.			
2. Identify one or more assembly points.			
3. Publicise the escape routes and assembly points through induction and refresher training.			
4. Indicate the escape routes and assembly points with signs (illuminated if necessary).			
5. Hold practice evacuations. (Even a pre-notified practice evacuation is better than none.)			

Training/competency requirements	Yes	No	N/A
1. The person managing fire risks must be aware of the location and type of hazards at all times and be competent to develop an effective emergency escape plan.			
2. Through site induction and refresher training, each individual must be aware of the risk of fire and what to do should one break out.			
3. Provide specific training for those with specific duties (such as fire marshals).			

Safe systems of work/basic control measures	Yes	No	N/A
1. Ensure that escape routes are adequate for the maximum number of people, well signed, lit where necessary and their location publicised during induction and refresher training.			
2. Establish one or more assembly points, publish their locations and ensure people know what to do when they get there.			
3. Practise evacuations.			
4. Monitor behaviour and evacuation times.			
5. Establish effectiveness and accuracy of roll calls.			

Specific regulatory or special requirements	Yes	No	N/A
1. A responsible person, who carries the burden of ensuring that fire risks are adequately managed, must be appointed in accordance with fire safety law.			
2. The responsible person is likely to be someone senior within the company and may delegate the day-to-day responsibility for fire safety to a site manager.			

Further information/references/links	Yes	No	N/A
1. HSE publication *Fire safety in construction* (HSG 168).			
2. Fire Protection Association publication *Fire prevention on construction sites, Code of Practice and Checklist* (8th edition).			

GC 04 Fire prevention and control – managing hot work

Overview

What you need to know

You must determine if any particular tasks represent an enhanced risk of fire breaking out due to the use of a source of heat.

What you need to do

- ☑ Establish a hot-work permit system and ensure that it is complied with.
- ☑ Put in place additional controls for higher-risk work activities.

C

Significant hazards and risks

Safety	Yes	No	N/A
1. Risk of burns from coming into contact with fire.			
2. Risk of injuries to others who are off-site and not prepared, if the fire spreads.			

Health	Yes	No	N/A
1. Risk of burns from coming into contact with fire.			
2. Risk of inhalation of smoke and other toxic fumes.			

Environment	Yes	No	N/A
1. Risk of fire-fighting water run-off entering watercourses.			
2. Risk of emission of noxious and toxic fumes.			
3. Risk of ground contamination from products of combustion			

Managerial/supervisory tasks (including pre-planning)	Yes	No	N/A
1. Determine which tasks warrant being carried out under a hot-work permit.			
2. Physically monitor compliance with the hot-work permit system.			
3. Ensure activities cease at least one hour before the end of the working day.			
4. High risk activities (such as timber frames) may require additional time (two hours).			
5. Co-ordinate hot-work activities when more than one are taking place at the same time.			

Training/competency requirements	Yes	No	N/A
1. Train those who have to carry out hot work on how to use the permit system.			
2. Tell others, who are not involved, to keep clear of the area.			

Safe systems of work/basic control measures	Yes	No	N/A
1. Hot work carried out in accordance with the conditions stipulated in the hot-work permit.			
2. Anyone not involved to be kept out of the area (use physical barriers if required).			
3. Appropriate fire extinguisher to hand.			
4. Liaise with third parties if hot works could interfere with existing fire detection systems.			

Specific regulatory or special requirements	Yes	No	N/A
1. Ensure everyone is competent to do what is asked of them with regard to fire safety.			
2. Establish who is the responsible person with regard to fire safety.			

Further information/references/links	Yes	No	N/A
This checklist has been produced as an aide memoire for those with on-site responsibility for fire safety. Additional guidance is available from HSE and the Fire Protection Association.			

GC 05 Fire prevention and control – hot-work permit

Hot-work permits are required for any operation involving open flames or producing heat and/or sparks and must be prepared by a competent person. Hot works include brazing, torch cutting, grinding, soldering and welding.

Hot-work permit		Permit no.		
Contractor		Supervisor		
Location of work				
Description of work				
Equipment used				
Date of works	Between	hrs	and	hrs

Precautions to be taken	Yes	No
Hot work must **cease** two hours before end of shift.		
Services affected must be **isolated** before work commences.		
Isolate smoke detectors in vicinity of hot works.		
A suitable fire extinguisher must be available and be kept close at hand, at all times.		
Supervisor must ensure suitable personal protective equipment is provided and **worn** by operative.		
All cylinders must be transported and secured **upright**.		
Valves and hoses **must** be in good condition.		
All cylinders must have **flash back** arrestors fitted.		
When not in use cylinders must be **shut off** and returned to store.		
LPG cylinders must **not** be **left in the building** overnight without formal approval.		
Arc welding equipment will comply with current standards.		
Spent welding rods **must be** immersed in a bucket of water.		
Minimum radius of hot work to be two metres from other persons working. Screens should be erected if needed.		
Work areas to be kept **tidy** and free from combustible materials before and during the hot works. Check both sides of partition walls in case heat can be transferred by conduction.		
When working in **riser shafts** or on staging cylinders, work will be secured and openings to other levels covered with a fire blanket or other non-combustible materials.		
Operatives must remain in the area for 15 minutes **following completion** of work to ensure there is no hot spot residue.		

Operatives carrying out hot work	Yes	No
Must understand the permit conditions and the fire and safety precautions.		
Must be in possession of a permit at all times.		
Must stop work if required to do so by an authorised person.		
Must report immediately any hazard likely to affect the fire and safety precautions.		
Must ensure a satisfactory access/egress from the work area.		

Confirmation by contractor's supervisor: I confirm that the precautions specified above will be complied with and I will ensure that the persons carrying out the work, described above, are fully briefed on the safe method of work.

Signed: .... Print: .... Date: ....

Confirmation by operator: I understand the precautions to be taken in carrying out the hot works.

Signed: .... Print: .... Date: ....

Site management authorisation: I certify that the above work can commence with the precautions listed above.

Signed: .... Print: .... Date: ....

Cancellation by operator: *(Note: hot works must cease two hours before end of shift.)* I confirm that the work has been completed and the area has been checked and is safe.

Signed: .... Print: .... Date: ....

Cancellation by site management.

Signed: .... Print: .... Date: ....

Inspection of area covered by hot-work permit after cancellation	Inspection is required after two time elapse periods			
Fire warden/site management: Signed: .... Print:........................	**1 hr**		**2 hrs**	

GC 06 Electrical safety – safe isolation

Overview

What you need to know

☑ Electricians and possibly some other trades will at times need to isolate electrical supplies so that electrical wiring systems and equipment can be installed, removed or otherwise worked upon.

☑ Not only the trades directly involved but others working nearby could be injured, burnt or killed if the isolation procedures go wrong.

What you need to do

☑ Make sure that an effective isolation procedure is in place and it is followed by the trades concerned.

☑ Make sure that the details of the isolation procedure have been communicated to all persons involved in operating it.

Significant hazards and risks

Safety	Yes	No	N/A
1. Risk of electrocution and death.			
2. Risk of impact injuries arising out of recoiling from contact with live electrical parts.			

Health	Yes	No	N/A
1. Risk of electrical burns.			
2. Risk of inhalation of smoke and other toxic fumes.			

Environment	Yes	No	N/A
1. Risk of noxious fumes from the ignition of combustible materials.			

Managerial/supervisory tasks (including pre-planning)	Yes	No	N/A
1. Make sure contractors have a safe isolation procedure in place.			
2. Ask the contractors to explain it to you.			
3. Request that you are informed each time prior to the safe isolation procedure being used.			
4. As far as possible, periodically check that the procedure is being used properly.			
5. Liaise with other trades as necessary, when isolated circuits or equipment could adversely affect their safety.			

Training/competency requirements	Yes	No	N/A
1. Inspect training records to confirm that those engaged in operating the safe isolation procedure are competent to do so.			

Safe systems of work/basic control measures	Yes	No	N/A
1. The safe isolation procedure is itself at the heart of a safe system of work.			
2. The safe isolation procedure should be backed up with a permit to work system.			

Specific regulatory or special requirements	Yes	No	N/A
1. Management of Health and Safety at Work Regulations.			
2. Electricity at Work Regulations.			

Further information/references/links	Yes	No	N/A
1. SELECT/HSE publication *Guidance on safe isolation procedures*.			
2. HSE publication *Electrical safety and you, a brief guide* (INDG 231).			
3. HSE publication *Electricity at work: Safe working practices* (HSG 85).			

GC 07   PUWER inspection report

Provision and Use of Work Equipment Regulations (PUWER) inspection report

Inspection carried out for *(Company)*

Project/site/depot

Date of inspection	Description of plant or equipment	ID no.	Details of inspection *(Defects identified and actions taken)*	Date of next inspection	Inspected by

GC 08 Periodic inspection and checks – examination carried out for mobile plant

Plant checked by operator/user. If defective, then quarantine and complete a plant defect report.

Date of inspection	Plant/equipment description and reference, including safe working load	Outcome of inspection (If defective then remove from service and complete plant defect report)	Name (print) and signature of person inspecting plant	Defect reported	Plant quarantined
				☐	☐
				☐	☐
				☐	☐
				☐	☐
				☐	☐
				☐	☐
				☐	☐
				☐	☐
				☐	☐
				☐	☐
				☐	☐
				☐	☐
				☐	☐
				☐	☐
				☐	☐
				☐	☐
				☐	☐
				☐	☐
				☐	☐
				☐	☐

C

GC 09 Construction plant reception and inspection report

Guidance notes

These guidance notes are provided to assist the persons appointed by the site manager to complete reports.

Mobile plant is defined as mechanical or electrical plant that is self-propelled. The types of plant typically covered by the mobile plant reception report are as follows:

☑ all types of excavator

☑ all forward or rearward tipping dumpers/trucks

☑ all types of cranes

☑ all types of compacting rollers

☑ rough terrain forklift trucks

☑ tractors and their trailer units.

In the case of plant provided by a plant hirer, then, at the site manager's discretion, a competent person appointed by the plant hirer may conduct the inspection and complete the report.

In the case of plant owned or hired by a contractor, then a competent person employed by the contractor may conduct the inspection and complete the report.

All completed mobile plant reception reports shall be retained for inspection on site.

The report is produced in a checklist format for ease of use and is intended to provide a means by which the condition of all plant delivered to site can be checked by the appointed person. All questions shall record an answer, with a suitable comment or action included when necessary.

The appointed person is also required to confirm the validity of relevant statutory documentation (such as test certificates) thorough examination and inspection reports.

An aide memoir is provided below to assist the appointed person on statutory requirements that apply to certain items of plant.

Plant	Thorough examination	Comments	Documentation
All types of cranes used for lifting people and mobile elevating work platforms (MEWPS).	Current six-monthly thorough examination report.	■ Fitted with suitable devices to prevent persons being crushed, trapped, struck or falling when riding or working from carrier. ■ Provision of suitable devices to prevent risk of a carrier failing. ■ Safe means of escape for persons trapped in a carrier.	Evidence of daily or weekly inspection and six-monthly thorough examination, including certification of a SWL.
Excavators used as cranes without any restriction and a fixed or variable SWL greater than one tonne.	Current 12-monthly thorough examination report.	■ Fitted with controlled lowering devices (check valves). ■ Provided with a properly fitted hook or lifting shackle marked with SWL. ■ Supplied with a register for the weekly inspections of the excavator and, where fitted, safe load indicator. ■ Have the SWL clearly marked on the machine or displayed in the cab.	Evidence of daily or weekly inspection and 12-monthly thorough examination, including certification of a SWL.
All types of cranes and excavators used as cranes without restrictions and a fixed SWL of one tonne or less.	Current 12-monthly thorough examination report.	■ Provided with properly fitted hook or lifting shackle marked with SWL. ■ Supplied with a register for weekly inspections of the machine and where fitted, a safe load indicator. ■ Have the SWL clearly marked on the machine or displayed in the cab.	Evidence of daily or weekly inspection and 12-monthly thorough examination, including certification of a SWL.

GC 09 *continued*

Project/location:		
Equipment type and model:	**Unique identification no:**	
Plant owner's name:	**Plant user's name:**	

1.0	**General**	**Comments/actions**
1.01	Is there any obvious visual damage (distressed welds) or missing parts?	
1.02	Is the operator's manual provided securely with the item of plant?	
1.03	Are items such as linkages, props, struts, cables and hoses in good order?	
1.04	Does the plant clearly display all appropriate SWL, pressures or speeds?	
1.05	Are all moving parts protected by fully operating and suitable guards?	
1.06	Are suitable warning notices fitted where necessary?	
1.07	Are all controls, including emergency stops, clearly identified and marked?	
1.08	Is the plant generating excessive noise, fumes or other exhaust gases?	
1.09	Are edge protection and handrails suitable and secure?	
1.10	Are the brakes and steering fully functional?	
1.11	Is the plant fitted with headlights, indicators, number plates and a horn?	
1.12	Are the wheels/nuts, tyres or tracks intact and securely in place?	
1.13	Is the plant fitted with working driver/passenger seating and restraints?	
1.14	Is a falling object protective structure (FOPS) fitted where necessary?	
1.15	Is a roll-over protective structure (ROPS) fitted?	
1.16	Check fuel, engine/hydraulic oils and coolant levels, including leakage.	
1.17	Is the item provided with secured special gas cylinders if LPG powered?	
1.18	Is the item provided with the correct drawbar or tow hitch?	
1.19	Other –	

2.0	**Lifting equipment**	**Comments/actions**
2.01	Is the plant fitted with hydraulic check valves where necessary?	
2.02	Are slewing or elevation restrictors fitted and working as necessary?	
2.03	Are ancillary items (such as the chains, rope, hook and block) in good order?	
2.04	Is the plant provided with sufficient working outriggers?	
2.05	Is certificate of thorough examination in date (six or 12 months as appropriate)?	
2.06	Is the automatic safe load indicator (ASLI) fitted and operational?	
2.07	Other –	

3.0	**Safety critical items**	**Comments/actions**
3.01	Does the operator have 360° visibility at a height and distance of one metre all around (this can be achieved by items immediately below)?	
3.02	Is plant fitted with working reversing cameras or convex mirrors?	
3.03	Is plant fitted with working reversing alarm, clearly audible at 10 metres?	
3.04	Is the maximum gradient displayed or inclinometer provided where required?	
3.05	Is plant fitted with a quick hitch/coupler?	
3.06	Is plant fitted with amber beacon or light bar as necessary?	
3.07	Has the plant a suitable fire extinguisher in a convenient location?	
3.08	Is plant fitted with fire or exhaust suppression systems for work in tunnels, etc?	
3.09	Other –	

I have carried out the above checks where appropriate and have established to the best of my ability that this item is/is not* in safe working order (* delete as applicable).

Name: Signature:

Position: Date:

 Following completion of the report at receipt of the plant on site, formal inspection/examination must be repeated at least at the intervals specified by legislation or policy.

GC 10 MEWP reception and inspection report

Guidance notes

These guidance notes are provided to assist the persons appointed by the site manager to complete reports.

The term MEWP covers pedestrian-controlled, self-propelled and power-operated mobile elevating work and access platforms. The types of plant typically covered by the MEWP reception report are as follows:

- ☑ scissor lifts
- ☑ telescopic boom or jibs
- ☑ articulating and telescopic booms

- ☑ towable units
- ☑ vehicle mounted
- ☑ self-propelled, or pedestrian controlled.

In the case of plant provided by a plant hirer, at the site manager's discretion, a competent person appointed by the plant hirer may conduct the inspection and complete the report. In all other cases the inspection must be carried out by the main contractor's appointed person.

In the case of plant owned or hired by a contractor, then a competent person employed by the contractor may conduct the inspection and complete the report.

All completed MEWP reception reports shall be retained for inspection on site.

The report is produced in a checklist format for ease of use and is intended to provide a means by which the condition of all plant delivered to site can be checked by the appointed person. All questions shall record an answer, with a suitable comment or action included when necessary.

The appointed person is also required to confirm the validity of relevant statutory documentation (such as test certificates) and thorough examination and inspection reports.

An aide memoir is provided below to assist the appointed person on statutory requirements that apply to certain items of plant.

MEWP	Regime	Comments	Documentation
All types of mobile elevating work platform (MEWPS).	Thorough examination: ■ current six monthly (LOLER) ■ after 1,000 operational hours ■ after major repair or modification ■ following an incident. **Note:** *conducted by a competent engineering surveyor/fitter with reports kept for two years.*	■ Fitted with suitable devices to prevent persons being crushed, trapped, struck or falling when riding or working from carrier. ■ Provision of suitable devices to prevent risk of a carrier failing. ■ Safe means of escape for persons trapped in a carrier.	Evidence of six-monthly thorough examination, including certification of a SWL.
	Weekly maintenance inspection conducted by a competent operator or fitter.		Evidence of weekly inspection.
	Daily (pre-use) visual inspection conducted by a competent operator.		Evidence of daily inspection.

GC 10 *continued*

Project/location:		
Equipment type and model:	**Unique identification no:**	
Plant owner's name:	**Plant user's name:**	

1.0	**General**	**Comments/actions**
1.01	Condition of the boom/scissor structure including pins, etc?	
1.02	Is the operator's manual provided securely with the MEWP?	
1.03	Are all boom operations fully functional?	
1.04	Does the plant clearly display all appropriate SWL, etc?	
1.05	Are all moving parts protected by fully operating and suitable guards?	
1.06	Is the ground/basket switching of controls operating correctly?	
1.07	Are all controls, including emergency stops, clearly identified and marked?	
1.08	Is the plant generating excessive noise, fumes or other exhaust gases?	
1.09	Are edge protection and handrails suitable and secure?	
1.10	Are the brakes and steering fully functional?	
1.11	Is the horn operating clearly?	
1.12	Are the wheels/nuts, tyres or tracks intact and securely in place?	
1.13	Are the directional travel instructions (decals) clearly identified on the body?	
1.14	Is there a hand tool storage facility?	
1.15	Condition of extending axles or outriggers, where fitted?	
1.16	Check fuel, engine/hydraulic oils and coolant levels, including leakage.	
1.17	Is the item provided with secured special gas cylinders if LPG powered?	
1.18	Battery condition, including leads and where accessible water levels.	
1.19	Are running and working lights functioning?	
1.20	Hours run on receipt?	
1.21	Other –	
2.0	**Lifting equipment**	**Comments/actions**
2.01	Is certificate of thorough examination in date (six months)?	
2.02	Are ancillary items (such as the chains, rope, and so on) in good order?	
2.03	Other –	
3.0	**Safety critical items**	**Comments/actions**
3.01	Does the plant have suitable attachment points for safety harnesses?	
3.02	Is the dead-man's pedal working correctly?	
3.03	Is plant fitted with working travelling and tilt alarms, clearly audible at 10 metres?	
3.04	Is maximum gradient displayed or inclinometer provided where required?	
3.05	Is emergency lowering function enacted and operational?	
3.06	Can a portable drain earth be attached when working in substations?	
3.07	Maximum gradient for safe operation and is it displayed?	
3.08	Maximum wind speed for safe operation and is it displayed?	
3.09	Has the plant a suitable fire extinguisher in a convenient location?	
3.10	Is plant fitted with fire or exhaust suppression systems for work in tunnels, etc?	
3.11	Other –	

I have carried out the above checks where appropriate and have established to the best of my ability that this item is/is not* in safe working order (* delete as applicable).

Name: Signature:

Position: Date:

 Following completion of the report at receipt of the MEWP on site, formal inspection/examination must be recorded weekly in normal operating conditions, or under higher risk conditions, daily.

GC 11 Lift plan

This lift plan is specific to the lifting operations described in the scope of works. It is not and should never be considered generic.

Contract	
Date of lifting operation	
Lift plan reference or activity	

Appointed person preparing this lift plan		
Date		Signed
Lift supervisor		

Purpose

The purpose of this lifting plan is to identify the control measures necessary to negate the primary hazards of the:

- crane overturning
- load falling from the crane
- load or machine striking someone or any other identified hazard.

Scope of works

Details of crane provider

Company name		
Address		
Contact name		Telephone

Details of crane operator(s)

CPCS card no. and operating history	

Load details *(also refer to lift schedule at end)*

Maximum weight		Maximum size of load	

Other details *(centre of gravity, lifting points, packaging, pallets and so on)*

GC 11 *continued*

Details of crane	
Capacity and type	
Height (ground – jib head)	
Radius	
Main jib length	
Fly jib length	
Total jib length	
Safe working load	
Actual working load	
Outrigger spread	
Counterbalance weight	
Ground conditions (CBR/Strata), temporary works design in place and checked off (where appropriate)	
Outrigger loadings	
Spread mat requirements	

Note: where operating (jib) height equals or exceeds 10 m at any time, the appointed person must advise and consult with the manager from any airport/airfield within 6 km of the site.

Airport/airfield requirements	

Lifting accessories and configuration	
Equipment details	
Type *(for example spreader beam)*	
Safe working load	*(**Note:** will configuration affect SWL?)*

Sketch of slinging method

Site conditions and hazards

The following non-exhaustive list should be considered during the lift plan along with any other factors that could affect any aspect of the lift:

- excavations
- embankments
- overhead and underground services or obstructions
- culverts
- drainage
- manhole/inspection chambers
- buildings, stationary objects
- scaffolding

- plant and equipment
- roads
- rivers
- railways
- personnel and public
- other cranes
- environmental considerations.

Hazard	Control

Strength and stability

Ground conditions must be suitable and sufficient and remain so during crane lifts to take the anticipated loads. Include details of the ground conditions and any additional works required to the ground, including spreader mats specification and any testing regime required (for example, CBR tests).

A temporary works design must be in place and checked off before any lifting operation or crane set up takes place.

Weather/environmental considerations

Indicate in this section detail of wind speeds/environmental conditions that have been referenced/anticipated for the duration of the lifting operations.

Access

Include any special travelling routes, road closures/highways notifications, access problems.

Third party considerations

Over-sailing, works adjacent to railways, noise and restriction of view.

GC 11 *continued*

Emergency/breakdown procedures

Signalling

Indicate whether hand signals or radios are to be used. Also indicate signalling source and radio frequency/channel. This section can also include any unique slinger/signaller identification (that is, different colour helmet/hi-vis) if required.

Site and crane layout plan

Include crane position, lay-down/rigging area, position of delivery vehicles, landing points, banksman positions, ground and overhead hazards and exclusion zones. If required use elevation drawings.

C

C

Safe system of work – methodology

Include pre-lift, lift and post-lift.

Lift team

The details of this lift plan, along with any other associated risk assessment, method statement or safe system of work, have been brought to the attention of, and explained to, the persons listed below, who have acknowledged that they understand the contents, hazards and associated control measures.

Other relevant documentation (list and attach)

Position	Name	Signature	Date
Site/project manager			
Lift supervisor			
Crane operator			
Slinger/signaller			
Others			

This plan is specific to the lift as detailed in the scope of works.

In the event of any changes to circumstances, personnel or equipment, the plan should be reviewed and revised by the appointed person and any changes recommunicated to the lift team.

GC 12 Lift schedule

Schedule of lifts (common lifts)

Item to be lifted	Maximum weight	Crane used	Lifted from	Lifted to	Lifting accessories used	SWL	Comments

GC 13 Site crane permit to lift (Part 1)

Contract

Location | Task/method statement no. (If applicable)

| Appointed person | Date and time of visit |
| Employed by | |

Standard lift ☐ | Contract lift ☐ | Complex lift ☐

Single crane position ☐ *(Complete Part 1 only)* | Multiple crane positions ☐ *(Complete Parts 1 and 2)*

Description of works

Load details

Maximum weight	Maximum size of load
Maximum radius	Maximum lift height
Other (e.g. unusual centre of gravity, lifting points, etc.)	

Crane details

Capacity and type	
Maximum available boom length	Maximum boom length to be used for lift
Counterweight req.	Hook block reeving (no. of falls)
Outrigger spread (centre to centre) m. x m.	Outrigger pad size (without mats)
Maximum outrigger load	

Site surface conditions

Access for crane	Access for transport
Lifting position	Laydown area
Safe ground bearing capacity under outrigger	Assessed by

Proximity hazards. *(Provide details and attach sketch (overhead lines, public roads, drains, ground conditions, etc.)* A temporary works design for the lifting platform must be in place and signed off prior to setting up/commencing lifting operations. *(Permit Part 2 shall be completed for all crane positions/repositions of the crane.)*

Crane accessories required *(state type and safe working load)*

Wire ropes	Chains
Web slings	Shackles
Beams	Outrigger mats *(state size)*
Others (including specialist equipment)	
Operational requirements (such as road closures/possessions/site clearance)	

Permit valid from   to

Crane team

	Name	CPCS card	Signature	Date
Appointed person		No.		
		Expires		
Crane supervisors		No.		
		Expires		
Crane operator		No.		
		Expires		
Signaller/slinger		No.		
		Expires		

Where contractors are required to complete this form, assistance shall be given by the site management authorised person who shall agree the details entered on the form and sign below.

Lifting operations must not commence until this form has been signed by the site management authorised person.

Distribution: Site file ☐   Appointed person ☐   Crane supervisor ☐
                       Crane operator ☐

Details agreed on behalf of site management

....
Signature   Date

If for any reason the details contained within this permit cannot be adhered to, the lifting operation must not continue and the appointed person must be notified immediately.

GC 14 Site crane permit to lift (Part 2)

Arrangements for multiple crane positions

I agree that the crane described in Part 1 may be re-positioned within the constraints defined within the lift plan, provided that each time it is set up in a new position the items in the list below are checked and signed for by the crane supervisor. When the crane is being operated by a contractor, each entry shall be countersigned by a site management person authorised by the project manager. The signature(s) shall be entered on this form prior to allowing the crane to operate in the new position.

....

Appointed person   **Date**

This form shall remain in the crane cab during lifting operations and be returned to the site management project manager on completion of the lifting operations, as described in Part 1.

Position ref. as lift plan	Time	Date	Outriggers extended to spread stated in lift plan	All outriggers on crane platform and within designated lifting area defined in lift plan	Mats as defined in lift plan correctly placed under each outrigger	Additional items to be inserted by AP, if required		Crane lift supervisor's signature	Site management authorised signature

C

GC 15 LOLER inspection report

C

The Lifting Operations and Lifting Equipment Regulations (LOLER) – Inspection report (Part 1)

Company/person on whose behalf the inspection was carried out					
Location of the place of work inspected (site address)					
Lifting appliance and ID no.	SWL	Date and time of inspection	Details identified that could give rise to a risk to the health or safety of any person	Can work be carried out safely?	If not, name of person informed

GC 15 *continued*

The Lifting Operations and Lifting Equipment Regulations (LOLER) – Inspection report (Part 2)

Company/person on whose behalf the inspection was carried out			
Location of the place of work inspected *(site address)*			
Details of any action taken as a result of any matter identified in Part 1 *(details identified)*	Details of any further action considered necessary	Name and particulars of the person making this report	Date of report

GC 16 Lifting equipment and accessories inspection report

Project				Contract no.							
Description of item	Date on site	ID no.	SWL	Owner	Date of last thorough examination	Date of next thorough exam	Date of last service	Date of next service	Date off site		

GD

High risk activities

The contents of this chapter should be read and used in conjunction with guidance contained within Section D.

GD 01 Work at height flowchart   92

GD 02 Common access equipment checklist   93

GD 03 Checklist for planning scaffolding and related
       work at height activities   95

GD 04 Scaffold checklists   100

GD 05 Putlog scaffold checklist   102

GD 06 Independent tied scaffold checklist   103

GD 07 Birdcage scaffold checklist   104

GD 08 Inspection checklist guide   105

GD 09 Specimen handover certificate   106

GD 10 Scaffold inspection report sheet   107

GD 11 Unauthorised modifications to scaffolds   108

GD 12 Boatswain's chair (bosun's chair) safety checklist   111

GD 13 Cradles checklist   112

GD 14 Safety belts, harnesses and lanyards
       safety checklist   114

GD 15 Inspection of webbing harnesses and lanyards   115

GD 16 FASET top ten dos and don'ts for safety net use   116

GD 17 Safety nets – Safety checklist   117

GD 18 Steelwork safety checklist   118

GD 19 Excavations checklist   119

GD 20 Safety awareness around excavators   121

GD 21 Permit to dig   123

GD 22 Excavation inspection report   125

GD 23 Underground and overhead services checklist   126

GD 24 Confined space checklists   128

GD 25 Confined spaces permit   130

GD 26 Confined space entry RAMS checklist   131

GD 27 Entry/access permit (limitation of access)   132

GD 28 LPG storage checklist   134

GD 01 Work at height flowchart

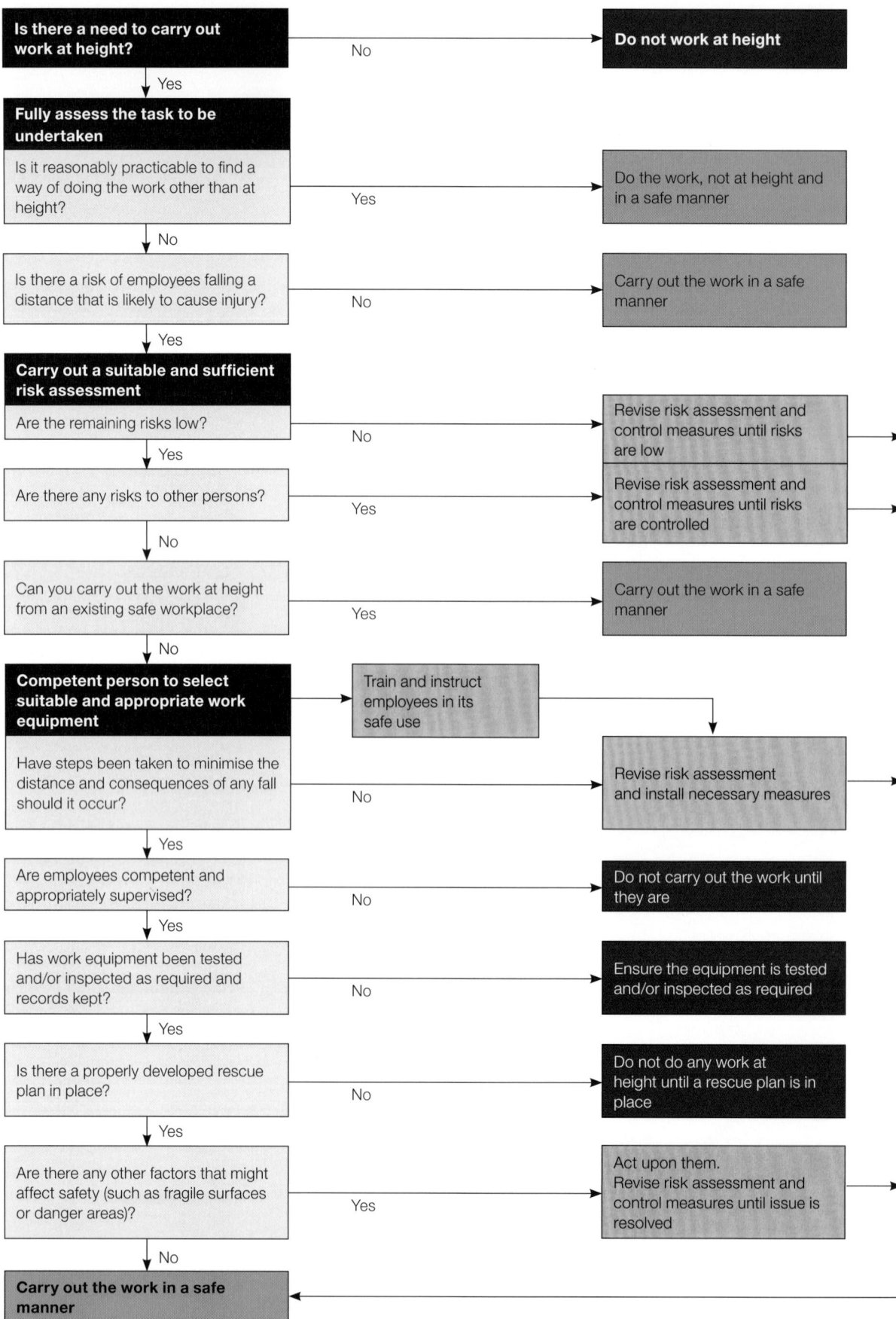

GD 02 Common access equipment checklist

Common access equipment

Ladders		Yes	No	N/A
1.	Is a ladder the right piece of access equipment to be using?			
2.	Has the person received training in the correct use of the equipment?			
3.	Are ladders only used for very light work of short duration or access?			
4.	Are all ladders properly stored and inspected regularly?			
5.	Are the ladders that are being used suited to the purpose or use to which they are being put?			
6.	Are there any damaged, loose or missing parts?			
7.	Are the rungs of ladders clean and free of mud or grease?			
8.	Are sufficient persons available to handle and place ladders properly and safely?			
9.	Are ladders set on firm and level ground?			
10.	Are ladders properly erected and secured?			
11.	If there is not an alternative suitable handhold, does the ladder project sufficiently above the landing place?			
12.	Is the overlap correct on extension ladders?			
13.	Are the methods for raising tools or materials safe?			
14.	Are ladders placed so that the work does not involve overreaching?			
15.	Is suitable footwear that will give a satisfactory grip and prevent slipping being worn?			
16.	Are ladders set at the correct angle of 75°?			
17.	Are ladders clear of excavations or other potential hazards?			
18.	Are ladders being leant against or secured to any fragile material?			
19.	Are all lashings used of sound material and made properly secure?			

Stepladders		Yes	No	N/A
1.	Has the person received training in the correct use of the equipment?			
2.	Is the stepladder level and stable?			
3.	Is it open to the full extent of the retaining cords or hinges?			
4.	Are steps set at right angles to the workface wherever possible?			
5.	Are the user's knees below the top step?			
6.	Could the person using the stepladder fall a distance that would cause an injury?			
7.	Is the person using the ladder not using the top third?			

Trestles		Yes	No	N/A
1.	Are trestles, and any boards that are being used with the trestles, safe, undamaged and of adequate strength?			
2.	Has the person received training in the correct use of the equipment?			
3.	Are the trestles set on a firm and level base?			
4.	Is the working platform of a sufficient width for the job in hand?			
5.	Are guard-rails and toe-boards fitted to trestle platforms, if indicated as being necessary by a risk assessment?			
6.	Where indicated as necessary by a risk assessment, is the trestle tied to the adjacent structure?			
7.	Is a safe ladder access provided?			
8.	Is the maximum permitted distributed load indicated and complied with?			

D

GD 02 *continued*

Common access equipment *(continued)*

Podium steps	Yes	No	N/A
1. Are the podium steps of sufficient size and the correct type for the task?			
2. Has the person received training in the correct use of the equipment?			
3. Have the operators been supplied with and fully understood the supplier's instructions for use?			
4. Are all of the components available and in good condition?			
5. Is the floor surface sound and of a level construction?			
6. Are brakes provided, in working order and used?			
7. Do all podium steps carry unique identifying marks and are they subjected to frequent inspection?			

Management responsibilities	Yes	No	N/A
1. Are the regulations and guidance on work at height that is appropriate to ladders, stepladders, podium steps, trestles and other access equipment known and have management received training in the correct application of the equipment?			
2. Has any safer system of work or access been considered?			
3. Do management know how and where access equipment is being used by employees?			
4. Have permanently fixed ladders been installed wherever possible?			
5. Has any necessary safety equipment been provided?			
6. Has adequate storage for ladders and access equipment been provided?			
7. Has a system of proper inspection and the keeping of records for all ladders and access equipment been implemented?			
8. Are all ladders, stepladders, podium steps, trestles and boards of sound design and manufacture, and kept in good condition?			
9. Have all users have been properly instructed and trained, and are competent to use the equipment safely and without risk to themselves or others?			
10. Is proper supervision of **all** employees who are using any form of access equipment provided?			

GD 03 Checklist for planning scaffolding and related work at height activities

Design stage

Element	Information/notes	Response
Considerations at design stage		
Have discussions taken place with scaffold designers?		
Has the building design considered work at height issues?		
How will the building be maintained? Are the high-level services (such as lighting) accessible?		
Will ground conditions be suitable for the scaffold and supporting elements?		
Will steel sections allow fixing of load-bearing scaffold components?		
Will site access suit heavy vehicle deliveries?		
If a high-rise project, have climbing screens been considered in the floor slab designs?		
If a fully-glazed building, is an external scaffold required and can it be fixed to the façade?		
What scaffold standard will be required?	TG20, BS EN 12811.	

Tender stage

Element	Information/notes	Response
Provisional design		
Procedure for ensuring only final design used.		
Quotations – scaffolding tender stage		
Criteria required from sub-contractors to be invited to tender.	See scaffold specification template.	
	Membership of key trade association:	
	NASC	
	FASET.	
	Industry standard safety record.	
	Previous experience of this application.	
	Resources (no. employees/assets).	
	Qualifications of workforce.	
	Good safety management system.	
	Financial stability.	
	Access to designers.	

D

GD 03 *continued*

Scaffold design

Element	Information/notes	Response
Is a scaffold design needed?		
Is it a standard configuration? *(Refer to Work at Height Regulations.)*		
Is it designed to TG20 or equivalent?		
Is it a basic scaffold, to TG20?		
Does BS EN 12811 apply instead?		
Is it a system scaffold?		
Does it meet the manufacturer's data sheets standard configuration?		
Have you seen the manufacturer's data sheets?		
Has the latest wind code been applied?		
Eurocode 1 (BS EN 1991-1-4:2005).	BS 6399-2:1997 (replaced).	
Third party/in house temporary works checking scaffold design?		
Means of access?		
What type of access to working levels? *(See NASC hierarchy.)*	NASC *Access and egress from scaffolds* (SG25).	
What is the height to top working area?		
What is the duration of project requiring access?		
How many people using it?		
Preference: staircase.		
Otherwise: internal or external ladders.		
Any edge protection details where BS EN 13374 applies?		
Has scaffold design drawing been received?		
Are tie loadings and positions shown?		
Is rating for scaffold load class shown?		
Are loading bays designed?		
Are loading bay gates included?		

Anchorage systems/scaffold ties

Element	Information/notes	Response
Method anchoring/securing	NASC Anchorage systems for scaffolding (TG4)	
Types of ties to be used:	Ring (Hilti). Concrete, not brickwork.	
	Screwplug. Concrete and suitable brickwork.	
	Chemical anchors. Concrete and suitable brickwork.	
	Self-tapping (excalibur). Concrete and suitable brickwork.	
	Through ties.	
	Reveal ties. Max 50%.	
	Rakers and butt ties.	
	If buttress to be used....design requested.	
Tie testing		
Confirm requirements for testing reports.		
Minimum of 5% to be tested (see TG4 11).	NASC TG4.	
Regular calibration of tie test equipment.		
*Timber frame construction.	*Special case.	

GD 03 *continued*

Contract awarded

Element	Information/notes	Response
Scaffold sub-contractor appointed – Scaffold details		
Procedure to ensure final drawing is issued to replace provisional		
Review scaffold design.	Confirm to TG20 or manufacturer's design data.	
If system scaffold, check manufacture source.	NASC *System scaffold Code of Practice*.	
Internal edge protection details.	NASC SG29.	
Need for securing of scaffold boards? Criteria stated?	*Tying down of scaffold boards* (TG12).	
Specify permitted gaps.		
	Internal service gap.	mm
	Between main and inside platform.	mm
	Between boards/decking.	mm
	Gaps in guard-rail/edge protection.	mm
Confirm start date and programme timings		

Delivery of scaffold materials

Element	Information/notes	Response
How will it be delivered and unloaded?		
Unloading	**Working from vehicles (SG30).**	
Banksman.	Check qualification.	
Unloading safety work at height methods:	Site gantry/alsipercha.	
	Entirely crane/forklift handled.	
	Truck with edge protection/netting.	
	Personal fall arrest.	
Lifting	NASC *Use, inspection and maintenance of lifting equipment and accessories for lifting in scaffolding* (SG9).	

Erection process

Element	Information/notes	Response
Who will build it?		
Qualifications of scaffolders		
Confirm requirement of qualifications of scaffolders.	Ratio of advanced/scaffolder/trainee.	
Traditional scaffolding qualification.	CISRS Part 1 Scaffolder.	
System scaffold (should be type specific).	CISRS System scaffold training.	
Mobile aluminium/GRP towers.	PASMA.	
Erectors and installers competency	**Scaffolder CISRS card qualifications**	
Cards seen?	Labourer.	
	Trainee.	
	Scaffolder.	
	Advanced scaffolder.	
Alternatives		
MEWPs.	IPAF.	
Mobile towers.	PASMA.	
How will it be built?		
Erection system of work.	CISRS Scaffolder (SG4).	

D

GD 03 *continued*

Erection process *(continued)*

Element	Information/notes	Response
Erection system of work.	PASMA Mobile towers. 3T/Advanced guard-rail system.	
SG4 *Toolbox talk training confirmation.*		
Inspection of fall protection/fall arrest equipment.	NASC SG16 and SG17 *Management of fall protection equipment.*	
Evidence of working to SG4?	Single guard-rail clearly visible on scaffolds.	
Safe system of work	NASC *Guide to risk assessments* (SG27).	
Site specific risk assessment.		
Method statements.		
Pre-start risk assessment.		
Rescue plan.		
Method statement.		
Rescue plan	NASC *Guide to formulating a rescue plan* (SG19).	
Evidence of training.		
Confirm plan not reliant on emergency services.		

Inspection regime

Element	Information/notes	Response
Who is inspecting? **Who signs the register?** **What qualification?**		
Sub-contractor.	Advanced scaffolder or CISRS Two-day scaffold inspection certificate?	
Independent safety consultant.		
Own staff.	CISRS Two-day scaffold inspection certificate?	
More complex designed structures.	CISRS Advanced scaffold inspection course?	
Retain record for three months.		
Inspection of safety nets		
Who is inspecting nets?	FASET management/inspection course.	
Scafftag system to be used?		
Pasma tag system for mobile towers?		
Completion of scaffold		
Scaffold handover certificate.	NASC *Handover of scaffold structures* (SG35).	

GD 03 *continued*

Other matters		
Element	**Information/notes**	**Response**
Ongoing work at height control		
Scaffolders wearing harnesses?		
Regularly clipping on when required?		
Is scaffold being altered by non-scaffolders?	NASC *Unauthorised modification of scaffolds* (SG36).	
Safety nets	**Safety nets (SG14)**	
Installed by FASET qualified persons?		
Specification of netting?	BS EN 1263-2.	
Storage on site arrangements made?		
Requirements for particular structures		
Steelwork		
Scaffolders accessing steelwork?	NASC 27 *Temporary edge protection on open steelwork.*	
Timber frame	NASC *Safe system of work for scaffolding associated with timber frame building construction* (SG28).	
House building	NASC *Requirements for use of brickguards* (SG10).	
Temporary roofs	NASC *Guide to the design and construction of temporary roofs and buildings* (TG9).	
Traditional tube and fittings temporary roof.		
System-type temporary roof.		
Materials compliance	NASC *Guide to risk assessments* (SG27).	
Equipment		
Tube.	BS EN 39:2001.	
Fittings.	BS EN 74 and TG17 Identification of EN 74 fittings.	
Scaffold boards.	BS 2482 1.2 m span.	
	BS 2482 1.5 m span.	
System scaffold.	BS EN 12810.	
MEWPs.		
Mobile towers.	BS EN 1004.	
Podium steps.	Draft PASMA document.	
Edge protection (system or tube and fittings).	BS EN 13374.	
Ground conditions preparation		
Has the ground been prepared?		
Any heavy imposed loads?		
Scaffold.	Soft and medium hard ground.	
Mobile elevating platform.	Hard surface (such as concrete, tarmac).	
Mobile access tower.	Hard surface (such as concrete, tarmac).	

(Thanks to National Access and Scaffolding Confederation and AIF for their help in producing this checklist.)

GD 04 Scaffold checklists

(Reproduced with the kind permission of National Access and Scaffolding Confederation.)

Widths of access scaffold platforms

Table 7 from TG20

Purpose [1]	Minimum clear width [2] mm	Minimum number of 225 mm nominal width boards	Effective width of boarded platform for loading calculations [3] mm
Working platforms for persons without materials or only for the passage of materials	500	3 boards	705
For persons and materials provided there is 430 mm left clear for the passage of persons or 600 mm if barrows are used	800	4 boards 4+1 boards 4+2 boards	930 1,205 1,430
For carrying trestles or other similar higher platforms	1,050	5 boards 5+1 boards 5+2 boards	1,155 1,435 1,655
For use in dressing or roughly shaping stone[4]	1,300	6 boards 7 boards	1,350 1,605

Notes
1. *Where internal ladders are incorporated the minimum width may be 430 mm, i.e. two boards.*
2. *For hop up platforms, a minimum width of 450 mm is required.*
3. *Effective width as defined in BS EN 12811-1 includes a 30 mm allowance for toe-board.*
4. *These scaffolds should be specially designed.*

Maximum and target span of scaffold boards

Table 8 from TG20

Board specification	Thickness		Transom spacing (span of board)			Board overhang	
			Target span		Maximum span		
	Nominal	Tolerance	Span	Tolerance		Minimum	Maximum
	mm	mm	mm	mm	mm	mm	mm
BS 2482-1 38-1.2 m 38-1.5 m [1]	38 38	± 2 ± 2	1,200 1,500	+100 +100	ns ns	50 50	150 150
BS 2482-2	50 63	± 3 ± 3	ns ns	ns ns	2,600 3,250	50 50	200 250

Notes
1. *Board properties verified by machine stress grading.*
ns *Means 'not stated' as calculation indicates the stress exceeds the allowable limit on the scaffold.*

GD 04 *continued*

Load classes (for access and working scaffolds made from tube and fittings)

Table 1 from TG20 (Extract)

Load class	Duty	Likely use of platform	Max. bay length m	Max. spacing board transoms mm	Max. number of boards
1	Inspection and very light duty	Inspection, painting, stone cleaning, light cleaning and access	2.7	1,200	3
2	Light duty	Plastering, painting, stone cleaning, glazing and pointing	2.4	1,200	4
3	General purpose	General building work including brickwork, window and mullion fixing, rendering and plastering	2.1	1,200	5 4+1 4+2 5+1 5+2
4	Heavy duty	Masonry work, concrete block work, and very heavy cladding	1.8	900	54+1 4+2 5+1 5+2

(The above table is an extract of Table 1 from NASC Guidance Notes TG20. It is reproduced only for the purpose of highlighting to readers the different load classes to which scaffolds may be erected and examples of work activities for which each class might be used.)

GD 05 Putlog scaffold checklist

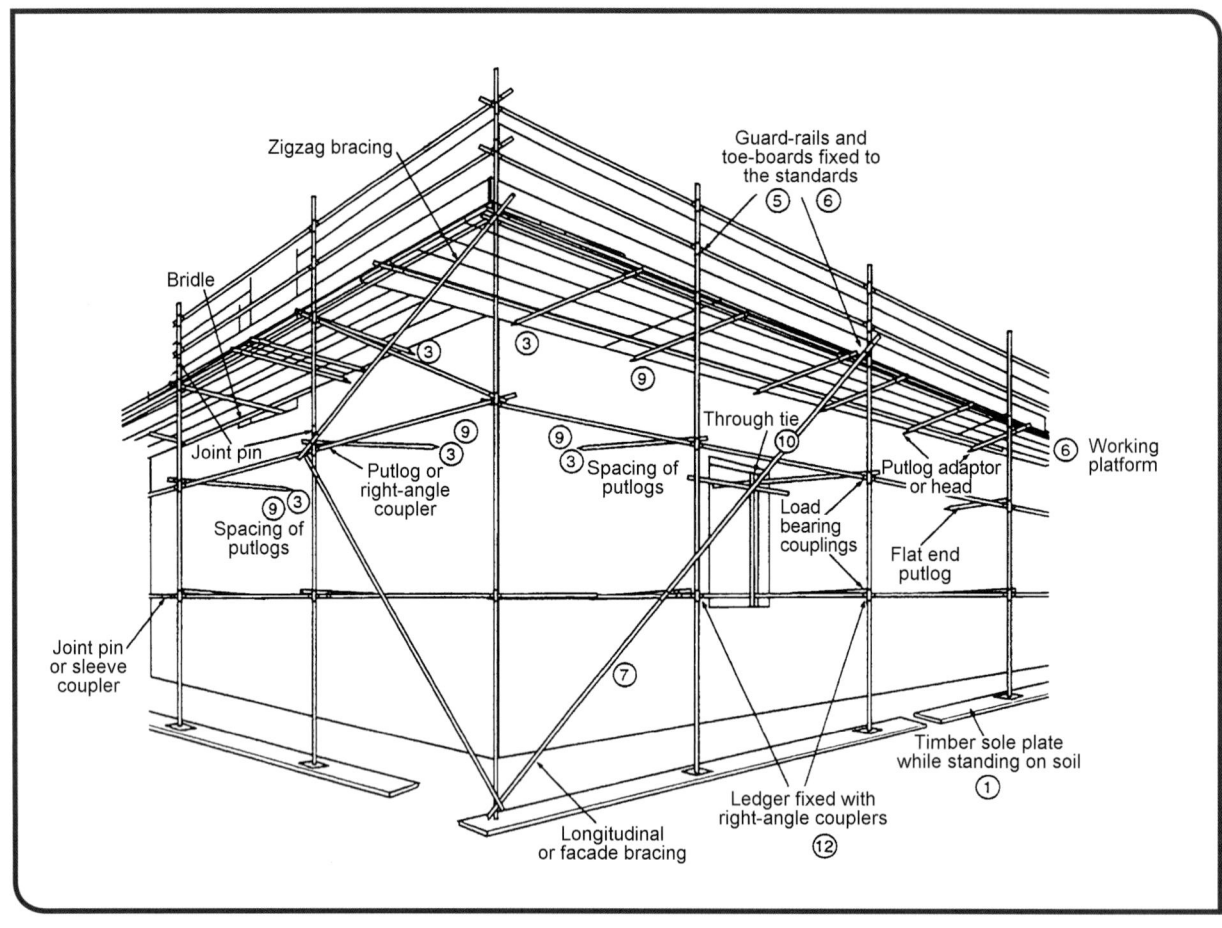

Components fitted during the erection of the scaffold to comply with the guidance given in NASC publication SG4 have been omitted for clarity.

Safety checklist	
Check from the ground	Check from inside building or on the scaffold
1. Base soundness; adequate spread of load; particularly as there is only one line of standards, avoidance of pavement lights, manhole covers, and so on; no nearby excavation	9. Spade end of putlog laid horizontally where possible, fully home (75 mm) in brickwork (bed joint)
2. Line of standards and ledgers. Standards vertical	10. Ties, particularly on lift below working platform or, in early stages, rakers on alternate standards. Special attention to 'through' ties on large flank ends without windows. Load-bearing couplers to be used
3. Spacing of putlogs	11. Platform loading (not overloaded)
4. Working platform. Check line and even support of boards; overhang; lapped boards and fillets	12. Security and correct use of all fittings (couplers), particularly on transoms and bracing
5. Guard-rails and toe-boards	13. Condition of tubes and fittings
6. Security of boards, toe-boards and guard-rails	14. Damage from falling material
7. Longitudinal bracing	15. Security of stacked materials
8. Means of access	

GD 06 Independent tied scaffold checklist

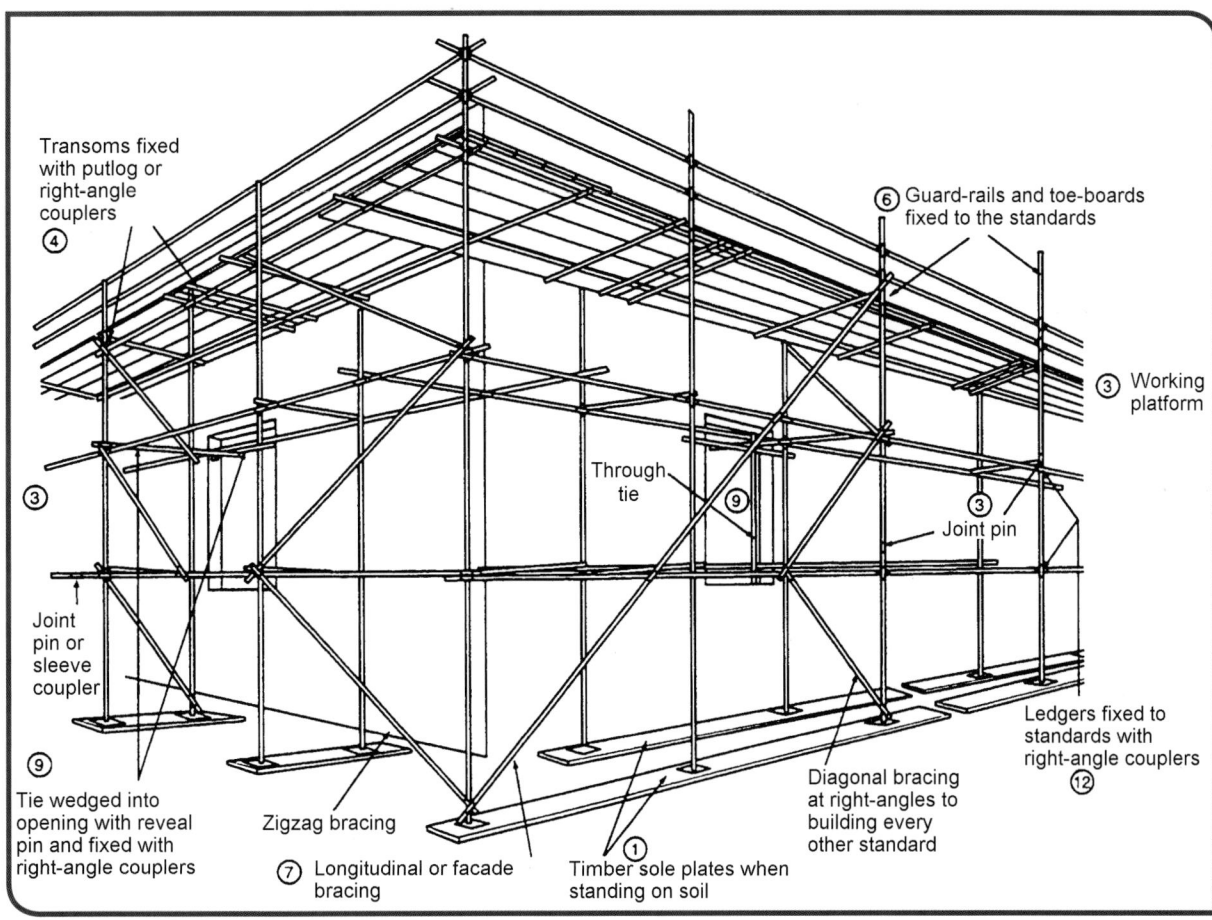

Transsoms fixed with putlog or right-angle couplers ④

⑥ Guard-rails and toe-boards fixed to the standards

③ Working platform

Through tie

⑨

D

③

③

Joint pin

Joint pin or sleeve coupler

⑨

Tie wedged into opening with reveal pin and fixed with right-angle couplers

Zigzag bracing

⑦ Longitudinal or facade bracing

① Timber sole plates when standing on soil

Diagonal bracing at right-angles to building every other standard

Ledgers fixed to standards with right-angle couplers ⑫

Components fitted during the erection of the scaffold to comply with the guidance given in NASC publication SG4 (latest version) have been omitted for clarity.

Safety checklist	
Check from the ground	Check from the scaffold
1. Base soundness; adequate spread of load; avoidance of pavement lights, manhole covers, and so on; no nearby excavation	9. Ties, particularly on lift below working platform or, in early stages, rakers on alternate standards. Special attention to 'through' ties on large flank ends without windows. Load-bearing couplers to be used
2. Line of standards and ledgers; standards vertical	10. Special loadings by protective fans, wind sails, and so on; anchorage and spread of load
3. Staggering of joints (vertical and horizontal)	11. Security of boards, toe-boards and guard-rails
4. Spacing of transoms	12. Security and correct use of all fittings (couplers), particularly on transoms and bracing
5. Working platform. Check line and even support of boards; overhang; lapped boards and fillets	13. Condition of tubes and fittings
6. Security of guard-rails and toe-boards	14. Damage by loads swinging from cranes or by falling material
7. Longitudinal, ledger and plan bracing	15. Overloading
8. Means of access	16. Security of stacked materials

GD 07 Birdcage scaffold checklist

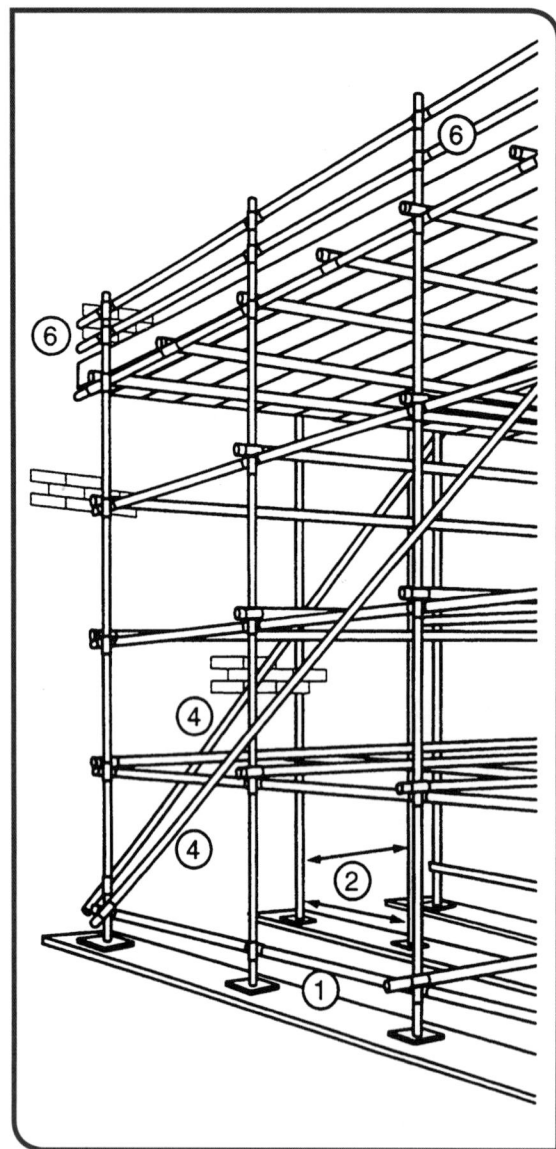

D

Safety checklist
1. Base
2. Line of standards and ledgers
3. Line and spacing of transoms
4. Diagonal bracing (in both directions)
5. Plan bracing
6. Security of boards, toe-boards and guard-rails. Maximum gap at wall
7. Security and correct use of couplers and fittings
8. Condition of tube and fittings
9. Even spread of load on platform
10 Means of access
11. Overloading
12. Security of stacked materials

With birdcage scaffolds, the floor of the building has to carry the full weight of the scaffold and its load. Sole plates are therefore necessary to help distribute the load as widely as possible – and they should always be set at right angles to the underlying floor beams or joists.

Components fitted during the erection of the scaffold to comply with the guidance given in NASC publication SG4 (latest version) have been omitted for clarity.

GD 08 Inspection checklist guide

Check at each inspection that the scaffold does not have these faults.

Footings	1	2	3	4
Soft and uneven				
No base plates				
No sole boards				
Undermined				

Bracing (facade and ledger)	1	2	3	4
Some missing				
Loose				
Wrong fittings				

Ties	1	2	3	4
Some missing				
Loose				

Standards	1	2	3	4
Not plumb				
Jointed at same height				
Wrong spacing				
Damaged				

Putlogs and transoms	1	2	3	4
Loose				
Wrongly spaced				
Wrongly supported				

Boarding	1	2	3	4
Bad boards				
Trap boards				
Incomplete boarding				
Insufficient supports				

Ledgers	1	2	3	4
Loose				
Not level				
Joint in same bays				
Damaged				

Couplings	1	2	3	4
Wrong fitting				
No check couplers				
Loose				
Damaged				

Guard-rails and toe-boards	1	2	3	4
Loose				
Wrong height				
Some missing				

Bridles	1	2	3	4
Weak support				
Wrong spacing				
Wrong couplings				

Ladders	1	2	3	4
Not tied				
Damaged				
Insufficient length				

Key: 1 = good, 2 = average, 3 = poor, 4 = N/A

D

GD 09 Specimen handover certificate

This is a type of handover certificate that could be used. Employers could also consider a form of handover certificate that meets the requirements of the Work at Height Regulations schedule for the inspection requirement before first use.

Scaffolding – handing over certificate

To (*contractor*): .... Date: ....

Site: .... Time: ....

Description of scaffold or section of scaffold handed over: ....

....

....

Drawing no: ....

(where applicable)

Scaffolding as described above has now been completed and complies with the Work at Height Regulations and current standards. It is structurally sound and should only be used and loaded in accordance with our quotation number:

(...)

a)   Use only for: ....

b)   Loading to be: .... working lifts with distributed

Load of: ....(kN/M² lbs/ft² per lift)

The detailed requirements of the regulations with regard to guard-rails – working platforms – toe-boards – bracing and ties have been complied with.

In order to comply with the regulations, this scaffold must be inspected before being taken into use for the first time, at regular intervals not exceeding seven days since the last inspection, after any event likely to have jeopardised the safety of the scaffold and after any substantial addition, dismantling or other alteration. Particulars of each inspection must be recorded in a report of inspection.

This scaffold has/has not (*delete as appropriate*) been designed to take tarpaulin sheets (or other windsails).

Scaffold contractor: ....

Depot: ....

Certificate received on behalf of the contractor: ....

GD 10 Scaffold inspection report sheet

Scaffold inspection report (in line with the Work at Height Regulations)

Company name and address					
Site address		Sheet			
No.	Location and description of workplace inspected	Date and time of inspection	Matters observed that give rise to any health and safety risks	Details of action taken at time of inspection	Details of any further action considered necessary	Name, signature and position of inspector

GD 11 Unauthorised modifications to scaffolds

Introduction of safe structures

The consequences of any unauthorised alterations/modifications to scaffolds could result in a fatality or serious injury to contractors, the general public or yourself and may result in damage to adjacent property.

The practice of interfering or modifying of scaffolds by non-qualified scaffolding operatives is unacceptable under any circumstances and may lead to prosecution by the enforcing authorities. Scaffolds should only be modified by competent scaffolders who have been authorised to do so by the scaffold contractor. It is also unacceptable for the client/user to authorise alterations without prior consent from the scaffold contractor as it may invalidate their insurance cover and could be an offence under Section 7 of the Health and Safety at Work Act. Most principal contractors now enforce a zero tolerance policy in regards to unauthorised scaffold interference by their contractors, and work closely with the scaffolding contractor to ensure it is applied.

The most common types of scaffold interference are the removal of scaffold structural ties by other trades, the removal of handrails and toe-boards to allow materials to be loaded directly onto the working platforms and the undermining of the scaffold foundations by utility contractors.

Good planning and communication with all contractors will help prevent unauthorised scaffold modifications.

The guidance below will help the user in assuring that scaffold structures are, and remain, fit for purpose.

All scaffolds shall be erected in accordance with statutory requirements and in accordance with the manufacturer's instructions when using system scaffolds. Wherever possible NASC-approved companies should be utilised.

All tube and fitting and system scaffolding of any height shall be erected, modified and dismantled by a Construction Industry Scaffolders' Records Scheme (CISRS) qualified scaffolder or trainee under the supervision of a CISRS qualified scaffolder.

All mobile tower scaffolds shall be erected by a competent person who is in the possession of a PASMA qualification or other recognised qualifications.

All structures must be handed over by a competent person to the customer, in some cases a 'tag' type system is used at the ladder access points which clearly shows the validity/suitability of the structure. It is a legal requirement within the Work at Height Regulations that all scaffolds must be inspected:

- ☑ before it is put into use
- ☑ at seven-day intervals until it is dismantled
- ☑ after bad or excessively wet weather or high winds or another event likely to have affected its strength or stability
- ☑ after any substantial additions or other alterations
- ☑ after unauthorised interference.

A written report must be prepared by the competent person. A copy of the report should be kept on site and a further copy be retained for a period of three months from the completion of the work with the person on whose behalf the inspection was carried out. If a scaffold fails inspection this must be reported by the person carrying out the inspection, to the person responsible for the scaffolding, as soon as possible.

How to identify unauthorised modifications

The following information is not an exhaustive list but should assist you to recognise good practice before and whilst using scaffold structures.

Ground works around scaffold foundations

(Photographs courtesy of Safety & Access Ltd.)

Removal of inside boards by other trades

Removal of guard-rails by other trades

GD 11 *continued*

☑ Check that the foundations have not been disturbed or undermined and the standards are on base plates and sole boards (as necessary).

☑ Check that guard-rails are not missing and they are installed on every lift.

☑ Check that toe-boards have not been removed, or displaced.

☑ Check that any scaffold boards have not been removed, displaced or damaged (such as disc-cutter marks).

☑ Check that transoms are suitably placed to support the boards and that the maximum support span identified on the board end plate has not been exceeded.

☑ Check that scaffold ties have not been removed.

☑ Check that any bracing is not missing.

☑ Check that any brickguards and/or netting, where fitted, are still in place.

☑ Check that the structure is not being overloaded.

☑ Check for any other signs of unauthorised interference. If found, report them to the scaffold contractor immediately.

Bricklayer tampering with the structure

Stop-end removed by other trades

Ladder removed by other trades

(Photographs courtesy of GKR Scaffolding Ltd.)

Action to be taken if concerned

If for any reason you identify that the structure has been interfered with, the first priority will be to ensure the safety of any contractors who may be working, or intending to work, on the structure. All users must vacate the structure by a safe means and access to the scaffold should be restricted until such time that it has been inspected and, if required, the components replaced by competent scaffolding operatives.

Case studies of when interference has taken place

 Case study 1

On Tuesday 11 April 2006, just after noon, an independent tied perimeter scaffold collapsed at a construction site in Milton Keynes. The collapse started on the west elevation, with a partial collapse of the north elevation. The scaffold collapse was contained within the site boundary. Three workers who were on the scaffold sustained multiple injuries. Sadly, one worker died three days later in hospital.

The Health and Safety Executive (HSE) issued a safety alert to the construction industry following this incident. The warning aimed to alert those working on similar projects to the importance of their arrangements to provide and maintain stable scaffolds. HSE recommended that those arrangements are reviewed regularly.

HSE principal inspector Stephen Hartley said:

 It is totally unacceptable for companies to disregard the safety of their workers. If the scaffolding had been designed, erected and managed properly, this incident would never have happened.

GD 11 *continued*

 Case study 2

A Tyneside construction company was fined after a worker suffered serious injuries following a fall from unsafe scaffolding. The company was prosecuted by the Health and Safety Executive (HSE) following the incident in the grounds of an old vicarage in County Durham on 1 May 2009.

The Magistrates' Court heard a worker was working on the windows of a new building when the scaffolding platform he was standing on became dislodged, causing him to fall more than four metres to the ground. The worker suffered several crushed vertebrae in his spine and a fractured left foot and was in hospital for two weeks following the incident.

The HSE investigation revealed that the company had failed to control alterations to the scaffolding, failed to conduct inspections of the scaffold at least every seven days, failed to identify and correct unsafe alterations and allowed workers to use unsafe scaffolding. The company pleaded guilty to breaching Section 2(1) of the Health and Safety at Work Act 1974.

After sentencing, the injured person said:

 I took it for granted the scaffolding I was working on was safe. If it had been checked properly the incident never would have happened and I wouldn't be left with the injuries I have to live with now.

I've had steel rods put in my spine, I'm in constant pain and it restricts my movement and makes walking really difficult. I'll probably never be able to do the job I did again.

I hope this prosecution helps make other employers realise the importance of ensuring scaffolding is safe so other workers don't have to suffer as I have.

After the case, a HSE construction inspector said:

This incident could and should have been prevented. The company failed in its legal duty to ensure the safety of its employees by failing to manage the scaffolding on site adequately.

As a result of these failures, the injured person has suffered serious injuries and is still living with the effects of those injuries more than a year and a half later.

Scaffolding is widely used as a temporary working platform or means of access and this incident clearly illustrates the absolute need to ensure that it is safe.

I'd like to stress to all companies and employees who use scaffolding that it should always be constructed to a recognised standard, any alterations should only be made by a competent person and it should be inspected by a competent person on handover and at least every seven days as work progresses.

Note: whilst every effort has been made to provide reliable and accurate information, we would welcome any corrections to information provided by the writer which may not be entirely accurate, therefore and for this reason, the NASC or indeed the writer, cannot accept responsibility for any misinformation posted.

(The information within GD 11 has been reproduced with kind permission from NASC, publication SG36:13.)

GD 12 Boatswain's chair (bosun's chair) safety checklist

Boatswain's chair (bosun's chair)

Before use	Yes	No	N/A
1. Has a risk assessment been carried out?			
2. Have emergency rescue procedures been established?			
3. Has a separately anchored safety line been installed?			
4. Is the installation and use of a boatswain's chair supervised by trained, experienced and competent personnel?			
5. Is the chair and associated equipment carefully examined for defects prior to use?			
6. Is confirmation at hand that test and examination certificates are valid?			
7. Has the safe working load been established?			
8. Have checks been carried out to ensure that the user is both trained and competent in the use of the chair?			
9. Are warning notices displayed and has notification of intention to carry out work been given?			

During use	Yes	No	N/A
1. Is the chair free of materials or articles that could interfere with the user's control of the chair?			
2. Has the fall rope been properly tied off whilst the chair is in use and always under or around a cleat to act as a brake?			
3. Has a safe area been created below the work area or protection installed?			
4. Is the safety line being properly used?			

After use	Yes	No	N/A
1. Is the chair inspected for defects following its use?			
2. Are chairs and ropes left in a safe condition, in other words:			
– is the chair raised to the first floor level if possible, and the top rope secured?			
– have the chair and rope been secured to prevent swing?			
– have the ropes (and chair, if timber) been dried before storage?			

GD 13 Cradles checklist

Cradles

Before use		Yes	No	N/A
1.	Has a risk assessment been carried out?			
2.	Have emergency rescue procedures been established?			
3.	Are cradles installed and supervised by a competent person?			
4.	Are cradles inspected and appropriate reports made?			
5.	Are current test certificates available for winches, wire ropes, blocks and so on?			
6.	Have users been properly trained?			
7.	Has adequate protection been installed and proper warning given to members of the public and other people who might be affected?			
8.	Have occupiers of the building been warned not to open windows?			
9.	Have steps been taken to erect the correct warning signs?			
10.	Have secondary safety ropes and harnesses been provided as necessary?			
11.	Is the safe working load of the cradle marked?			
12.	Has a check been carried out for obstructions on the face of the structure?			
13.	Have effective fall arrest measures been installed?			

During use		Yes	No	N/A
1.	Is a competent person in charge of all operations when cradles are being used?			
2.	Are operations being carried out with authorised operatives only?			
3.	Are inspections carried out weekly?			
4.	Have checks been made to ensure that there are no knots or kinks in the ropes?			
5.	Are ropes correctly reeved on the drum with at least two turns left when the cradle has reached its maximum operating distance? (Power-operated cradles only.)			
6.	Have both power supplies and cables been checked before operating?			
7.	Have checks been carried out to the controls for correct function and to ensure that pendant controls are secured to the cradle?			
8.	Have all ropes been securely anchored?			
9.	Are the stops and over-runs operational?			
10.	Are secondary safety devices properly secured and anchored?			
11.	Has the cradle been tied-off to the building to prevent sway?			
12.	Have checks been made to ensure that the safe working load is not being exceeded?			
13.	Is the cradle kept clean and clear of rubbish?			
14.	Have all necessary precautions been taken to ensure that the platform is not slippery?			
15.	Are all tools carried in the cradle secured?			
16.	Is there adequate protection from above to stop any falling materials?			
17.	Are all necessary steps being taken to ensure that the proper access is being used?			
18.	Is the practice of climbing down ropes strictly prohibited?			
19.	Are all personnel aware that there must be no transferring between adjacent cradles?			
20.	Have all possible steps been taken to ensure that personnel do not allow ropes and cradles or connections to lie in gutters?			
21.	Are all operatives aware that use in high winds or adverse weather conditions is not safe and is prohibited?			

GD 13 *continued*

Cradles *(continued)*

After use	Yes	No	N/A
1. Are the cradle and all ropes in a secure position to prevent unauthorised access or usage?			
2. Are checks carried out to ensure that power supplies are isolated and control equipment is removed and secured?			
3. Are defects and breakdowns reported promptly and correctly?			
4. Are all warning signs removed after the completion of work?			

Management information	Yes	No	N/A
1. Has it been established that the supplier is reputable and experienced?			
2. Has the necessary communication taken place between the user and supplier?			
3. Do both parties have the necessary competence?			
4. Have other parties been consulted as may be necessary?			

D

GD 14 Safety belts, harnesses and lanyards safety checklist

Safety belts, harnesses and lanyards

Before use	Yes	No	N/A
1. Has a risk assessment been carried out?			
2. Have emergency rescue procedures been established?			
3. Has the most suitable harness or belt been selected for the type of operation and hazard?			
4. Are the operatives who are to use the equipment adequately trained in its inspection and use?			
5. Is it all in good order and fit for purpose?			
6. Is a secure and appropriately positioned anchorage point available?			
7. Have checks been made to ensure that the weather conditions are such that an operative can work safely in the prevailing conditions?			
8. Is there a schedule of detailed examination of the equipment?			
9. Are records of the examinations kept?			
10. Have steps been taken to see that adequate warning notices are displayed?			

During use	Yes	No	N/A
1. Have safety lines been set by a competent person?			
2. Are only authorised, trained and competent personnel allowed to use the equipment?			
3. Is all equipment inspected before the start of work each day, following an established routine, particularly for damage to webbing lanyards?			
4. Have set procedures been established and implemented?			
5. Is messing about strictly prohibited?			

After use	Yes	No	N/A
1. Is the equipment inspected for damage?			
2. Are defects reported promptly and correctly?			
3. Is defective equipment quarantined (if it can be repaired) or discarded?			
4. Is the equipment cleaned and stored correctly?			

GD 15 Inspection of webbing harnesses and lanyards

The Health and Safety Executive recommends that a three-tier inspection regime is implemented where webbing harnesses and lanyards are in use. The regime should be drawn up by a competent person.

The regime should include:

☑ the identity of each piece of equipment to be inspected, and the frequency and type of inspections necessary

☑ who should carry out each tier of inspections (competence at all levels) and the way in which inspections should be recorded

☑ the training of users of the equipment

☑ a verification process to ensure that inspections are carried out as required.

All persons who carry out any tier of inspection must have the independence and impartiality to make objective decisions, and sufficient authority to discard defective equipment.

> In the unlikely event of a fall, a webbing harness and lanyard that are worn or damaged may not take the impact and stress of a person arresting, and fail. A harness, lanyard and secure anchor point are the last resort to a person falling – their sole purpose is to save lives.
>
> The importance of pre-use checks and regular inspections cannot be overemphasised.

D

Introduction inspection regime

Lanyards should be subjected to the following checks and inspections.

Pre-use checks

These are visual and tactile inspections, carried out by slowly passing the lanyard through the hands to detect small cuts in the edges, softening or hardening of the fibres and traces of contaminants. The inspection should only take a few minutes.

Detailed inspections

These are more formal and in-depth inspections carried out at least every six months and three months for frequently used lanyards, particularly where these are used in demanding conditions (such as demolition scaffolding and steel erection).

Interim inspections

These are in-depth, formal inspections, carried out when it is suspected that a lanyard has deteriorated and an inspection is needed before the next scheduled detailed inspection.

All inspections should be carried out in good daylight with the results of detailed and interim inspections recorded.

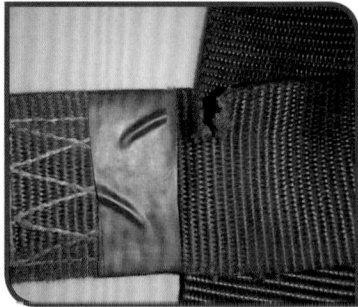

Check for signs of tears, damage and wear

GD 16 FASET top ten dos and don'ts for safety net use

FASET Top ten dos and don'ts for safety net use

Dos

☑ Ensure you use competent safety net rigging companies with relevant experience (such as FASET member companies).

☑ Ensure you use competent safety net riggers (CSCS FASET trained).

☑ Ensure that methods of access for work at height have been properly assessed, and the safest method that is reasonably practicable has been chosen.

☑ Carry out a formal inspection if nets are in place for more than seven days, or subjected to extreme weather conditions. A visual user inspection should be carried out prior to working above the safety nets.

☑ Ensure that all materials are secure before lifting/craning above a safety net.

☑ Ensure that a handover certificate is completed prior to allowing works above a safety net.

☑ Ensure that nets are struck prior to any hot works being carried out above.

☑ Report any damage to a safety net.

☑ Ensure all falls into a safety net are reported to site management and call FASET. Ensure the supervision of the loaded nets removal from service.

☑ Ensure that the safety nets used conform to BS EN 1263 1:2002 and are rigged in accordance with BS EN 1263 2:2002.

Don'ts

☒ Allow the use of nets unless there is evidence of an appropriate inspection and maintenance regime and UV testing within the last 12 months.

☒ Allow the use of nets unless a competent person has verified there is sufficient clearance distance (rule of thumb: no less than three metres).

☒ Allow work above nets without evidence that any repairs have been carried out by a competent person authorised by the manufacturer.

☒ Allow work above nets which don't have serial numbers or labels.

☒ Allow workers to use the nets as a means of access or working platform.

☒ Attach nets to any structure without first confirming it has the capacity to deal with a minimum 6 kN loading at a 45° angle.

☒ Allow gaps >100 mm unless exceptional circumstances dictate otherwise (in these cases not >225 mm).

☒ Tamper with or adjust any nets and attachment points.

☒ Allow work above net systems which have been damaged or loaded.

☒ Allow work above the net if it is positioned >2 metres from the working level.

GD 17 Safety nets – Safety checklist

Safety nets

Before use		Yes	No	N/A
1.	Has a risk assessment been carried out?			
2.	Are the safety nets rigged to minimise the height of any fall such that an uninjured person can simply climb out?			
3.	If not, have emergency rescue procedures been established?			
4.	Have checks been made to ensure that freefall distances are not more than specified?			
5.	Have the safety nets been rigged by trained and competent persons?			
6.	Is the use of safety nets to be supervised by competent persons?			
7.	Have safety nets been inspected prior to current use?			
8.	Are complete and proper records kept of all inspections and examinations?			
9.	Has the safety net system been inspected within the previous week?			
10.	Are all anchors and supports secure?			
11.	Is the safety net clear of all debris?			
12.	Have checks been made to ensure that nothing is positioned under the net to reduce the minimum clearance distance required?			
During use		**Yes**	**No**	**N/A**
1.	Is the net being kept clear of debris?			
2.	Are the safety nets inspected: – after a fall – for the effects of contamination – every seven days during use to ensure that the safety net is not damaged and that the anchorage points and ties are sound?			
After use		**Yes**	**No**	**N/A**
1.	Are safety nets inspected for any damage following use and before being stowed away?			
2.	Are any defects reported promptly and correctly?			
3.	Are repairs only carried out by a competent person?			
4.	Are adequate records maintained as to the use and condition of safety nets?			
5.	Are safety nets dried and stored correctly?			
6.	Are the annual condition tests being undertaken?			

D

GD 18 Steelwork safety checklist

Steelwork safety

		Yes	No	N/A
1.	Is the contractor responsible for erection competent?			
2.	Has a risk assessment been undertaken for the project?			
3.	Does the contractor have a method statement?			
4.	Does it specify the sequence of erection and how the structure will be kept stable at all times?			
5.	Does everyone know what types of temporary support will be used?			
6.	Does everyone know the requirements for safe erection?			
7.	Does everyone know how the structure components will be erected and connected safely?			
8.	Will as many connections as possible be done at ground level?			
9.	Where work must be done at height, have safe means of access and safe places of work been planned?			
10.	Has the site been surveyed for hazardous features (such as overhead power lines)?			
11.	Is there sufficient access for off-loading lorries?			
12.	Is there a planned delivery sequence of components?			
13.	Are there plans to deal with lorries that have to reverse?			
14.	How will components be off-loaded, stacked and de-stacked safely?			
15.	Are the weights of individual components known?			
16.	Does all lifting gear that is to be used have adequate safe working loads?			
17.	Have crane capacities been calculated?			
18.	Have steps been taken to eliminate the need for manual handling?			
19.	Are the steel erectors competent? Have they been adequately trained?			
20.	Will all lifts be supervised by a competent person?			
21.	If MEWPs are to be used, are all the operators trained and competent?			
22.	Is it necessary to survey and prepare the ground so that MEWPs can operate safely?			
23.	Will work at height be carried out other than from a MEWP?			
24.	Does everyone know what measures will be taken to prevent or arrest falls?			
25.	Are emergency rescue procedures in place?			
26.	Have any special risks been identified (for example, work in confined spaces)?			
27.	Is there a plan to monitor the weather?			
28.	Is there a contingency plan?			

GD 19 Excavations checklist

Excavations (bulk, trenches, pits, utility trenches and trenchless technology)

Overview

What you need to know

When preparing for an excavation there are many factors to take into consideration. The checklist below will identify the significant hazards and risks to be considered. These will include soil composition, depth, support structures and emergency evacuation.

What you need to do

Refer to information detailed in the health and safety plan, which should identify hazards that may impact on your excavation (such as buried services and adjacent buildings). Ensure the design takes account of traffic routes, material storage and lay-down areas, proximity of external factors (such as neighbouring businesses, public roads and spaces).

D

Significant hazards and risks

Safety	Yes	No	N/A
1. Is there a design for the excavation and have identified hazards been taken into account (such as traffic routes and location within the site)?			
2. Is temporary lighting provided for periods of darkness or foggy conditions?			
3. Has a risk assessment of the task been prepared, covering risks from hazards identified and showing control measures to be implemented?			
4. Has an emergency plan been provided showing how workers will be removed from the excavation (such as during a medical emergency or accident)?			

Health	Yes	No	N/A
1. Have the workers been issued with additional appropriate PPE and RPE?			
2. Has the excavation been purged of any gases prior to being entered by workers?			
3. Are there any hazardous substances being used – COSHH?			
4. Has soil sampling been carried out to check for contaminants?			

Environment	Yes	No	N/A
1. Has the site been designed so that the excavation is not at risk from vehicle and plant movement around the site (such as surcharging the walls of the trench)?			
2. Have surveys been undertaken to check for buried services that could be affected or damaged by the excavation (such as cable exposed by installation of a trench box)?			
3. Are there neighbouring structures/features that would affect the integrity of the excavation (such as watercourses, roads and railway lines)? Archaeology also needs to be considered.			

Managerial/supervisory tasks (including pre-planning)	Yes	No	N/A
1. Have the risk assessments been prepared and approved for excavation work to commence and include emergency rescue information, and access and egress?			
2. Has a traffic management plan been prepared showing site(s) for excavation(s)?			
3. Have welfare facilities been arranged for the site – suitable for tasks/number of workers anticipated (showers, drying facilities, lockers for storage of clothing)?			
4. Have the workers got adequate PPE and any additional equipment made available (such as overalls, RPE and goggles)?			
5. Have arrangements been made for inspections of the excavation as required by legislation?			

GD 19 *continued*

Significant hazards and risks *(continued)*

Training/competency requirements		Yes	No	N/A
1.	Do the workers have the requisite skills for the tasks to be undertaken (are they competent, do they have confined space training)?			
2.	Are CPCS/CSCS and/or alternative qualification cards required for the project?			
3.	How frequently will safety inspections take place?			
4.	Have the operatives been trained in the use of RPE that may be required (such as face fitting of the mask)?			

Safe systems of work/basic control measures		Yes	No	N/A
1.	Have method statements and risk assessments been approved prior to contractors commencing on site?			
2.	Have workers been briefed on the methodology, hazards and risks and do they understand the control measures required?			
3.	Have checks been carried out to prove any unsupported ground is safe?			
4.	Do excavations have adequate support/shoring or are they benched/battered to prevent possible collapse?			
5.	Where risk of flooding exists, have cofferdams/caissons been installed with pumps?			
6.	Have suitable barriers been erected around excavations to prevent materials, plant, people or excavation operatives falling in (such as fencing, guard-rails and toe-boards)?			
7.	Are poorly ventilated areas continually monitored for the presence of gas?			
8.	Have stop barriers been used to prevent vehicle entry?			
9.	Are spoil and materials stacked at least 1.5 metres from the edge of the excavation?			
10.	Are ladders provided for safe access/egress?			
11.	Have cable location devices (CAT and Genny) and utility drawings been used to trace buried services prior to commencement of work?			
12.	Have suitable signs and barriers been provided to warn of the work?			
13.	Have water discharges off-site been approved by the Environmental Agency/Local Authority?			
14.	Where possible, has permission and discharge to the foul sewer been gained?			
15.	If discharging into watercourses or soakaways, an advanced discharge licence and suitable treatment will be required that could involve the use of a settlement lagoon, tank or grassed area. Has this been gained?			
16.	Has site run-off been prevented from entering watercourses or surface water drainage and, where possible, water prevented from entering excavations?			

Specific regulatory or special requirements		Yes	No	N/A
1.	Are there registers on site for statutory excavation inspection?			
2.	Has an emergency plan for evacuation from the excavation been prepared and communicated to the workers on site and in the excavation?			
3.	Does the excavation need a permit to work (such as confined space or buried services)?			

Further information/references/links		Yes	No	N/A
1.	HSE publication – CDM 2007, Approved Code of Practice (L144), includes: – excavations, cofferdams and reports of inspection.			
2.	HSE publication Avoiding danger from underground services (HSG47).			
3.	HSE publication The safe use of vehicles on construction sites (HSG144).			
4.	HSE publication *The Confined Spaces Regulations, Approved Code of Practice, regulations and guidance* (L101).			

GD 20 Safety awareness around excavators

This information covers basic safety rules that should be followed by the operator, banksperson, vehicle marshal and others working around both tracked and wheeled excavators to reduce the risk of injury and allow everyone to go home safely. Plant and plant movements are a significant risk for everyone on site, not just those working directly around the excavator.

 Plant movements on site are a significant risk for everyone, and on average 10 people are seriously injured or killed working around plant each year.

People working around excavators are at high risk of sustaining serious injuries, possibly leading to major injuries or death, and some less serious injuries (such as crushing of feet), if the work is not managed safely. In confined work areas or where more than one piece of plant is in use, near misses involving collisions and plant damage are also highly likely.

Technical advances in machinery (such as remote operated cut-off switch) and familiarisation periods for new machines coming on to site, help to reduce incidents and accidents.

Communication and risk assessment

 Before beginning any activity, a pre-task briefing should be carried out to ensure everyone involved is familiar with the task, is aware of any risks and the control measures required. Any interface between different tasks can also be discussed to co-ordinate activities.

A risk assessment of the task should reflect the hierarchy of risk control to eliminate, reduce, isolate, control and provide PPE in order to manage the risks associated with working near to an excavator.

☑ Does the workforce need to be working around the excavator?

☑ Where personnel are close to plant, are exclusion zones in place and are the required safety critical items fitted to the excavator fully functional?

☑ Are adequate vehicle plant marshals (VPM) required for a safe system of work?

☑ Is everyone wearing appropriate high-visibility clothing, which is in good order?

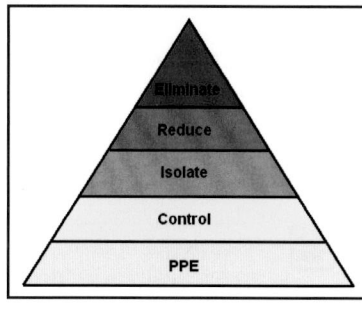

Safety zones

 When working around an excavator it is important to be aware of the operator's limited all-round vision and the safety zones for the machine. Where a risk assessment has identified the need for a competent VPM to manage the excavator movements then all instructions by the VPM must be followed. A VPM is responsible for managing the movement of people and vehicles safely around the excavator.

A banksperson carries out a separate role and supervises the specific activity that the excavator is carrying out (for example, excavating a trench).

Before entering the radius of the excavator, wait in an area of safety and acknowledge the machine operator, or where provided VPM. The VPM will then instruct the excavator to stop and, when this has been done, the operator to power down the engine, apply the dead man's lever and turn the engine off. Once the operator has acknowledged you, if you wish to approach, it is then safe to approach the excavator.

 Approach the excavator cabin in the operator's clear line of sight.

Safety zones of an excavator

You should only approach the excavator cabin in the operator's clear line of sight. Approaching the excavator from any other angle should be avoided (Zone 1 in the illustration on the following page). Where this is not possible (such as when an excavator is working near to a pedestrian route) the machine operator or VPM must acknowledge your need to approach and the correct shut-off procedure followed, as described above, before personnel enter the exclusion zone.

GD 20 *continued*

The machine operator should only restart the machine once the VPM has confirmed that it is safe to do so.

Pedestrians often still approach an excavator from the operator's blind side, assuming the operator is unlikely to move or that they can be seen by the operator. It is important that all personnel on-site are aware of the visibility available in excavators. This can be done by allowing non-excavator operators to sit in the cab in controlled conditions. Stickers on the machine can be used as a reminder.

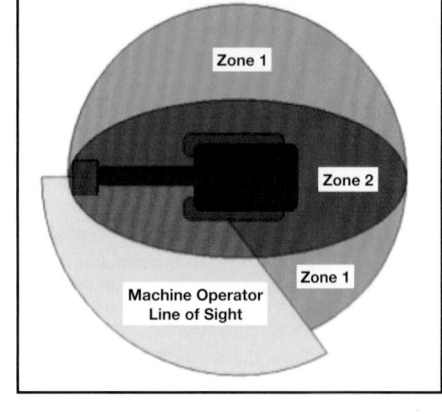

e.g. Danger! You are approaching on my blind side. I cannot see you.

It should not be necessary to enter the area directly around the machine or underneath the boom (Zone 2 in the illustration). Any tasks where this is unavoidable should be individually considered and have a site and task specific safe system of work put in place. These activities may include:

- ☑ drainage
- ☑ archaeology
- ☑ piling
- ☑ earth moving
- ☑ bearing tests
- ☑ lifting operations
- ☑ plant maintenance.

 Always gain permission from the VPM or banksperson before entering an excavator's working area.

 Case study

Using the safety zones guidance spot, what is wrong in the example below?

- ☒ Supervisor and workforce are on the blind side of the plant operator.
- ☒ No exclusion zone visible if operatives are to be excluded from works area.
- ☒ No visible control of excavator. No eye contact with operator, no VPM present.
- ☒ No-one taking the decision to work safely or not at all.

GD 21 Permit to dig

Work must not start until Sections A, B and C of this permit have been completed and signed by authorised persons.

Section A. Project details
To be completed by project/package manager

Company: ....Job/contract reference: ....

Contractor: ....Location of works: ....

Start date: ....Completion date: ....

Brief description of works

Section B. Preliminary work
To be completed by the supervisor in change of the works

Essential procedures	Yes	No	Comments
1. Have contract drawings and details been issued by the client or otherwise obtained?			
2. Do drawings show the location, type and status of buried services?			
3. Have live services been made dead as far as it is possible or necessary to do so?			
4. Has the work area been surveyed by a competent person, using appropriate detection equipment to confirm the exact location of buried services?			
5. Has a method statement been written and submitted for comment and approval?			
6. Has the method statement been explained to the operatives carrying out the work?			
7. Is the person in charge of the excavation fully conversant with the principles of safe digging and/or avoidance of buried services?			
8. Are all operatives familiar with safe excavation practices?			
9. If plant is being used, is the operator competent and familiar with safe digging practices?			

I declare that the above safety precautions will be put into place before work commences or that an explanation is given as to why some or all are not necessary.

Name: ....Signature: .... Date: ....Time: ....

GD 21 *continued*

Section C. Certification
To be completed by the supervisor in charge of the works

I am satisfied that the precautions identified on the previous page are satisfactory to enable the excavation to be undertaken safely*

I am **not** satisfied that the precautions identified on the previous page are satisfactory to enable the excavation to be undertaken safely and require the additional precautions/work outlined below to be undertaken before excavation work commences*

* Delete as appropriate

Name: ....Signature: .... Date: ....Time: ....

Additional precautions/work necessary prior to commencement

Section D. Completion of work
To be completed by the supervisor in charge of the works

I am satisfied that:
- the excavation has been backfilled and the surface reinstated*
- the work is completed and the area has been left in a safe condition*
- the work area is clear of operatives and all equipment*
- utility company(ies) have been informed that services made dead may now be reactivated*

I am **not** satisfied that the work has been completed satisfactorily and the additional work described below must be completed before this permit may be cancelled*

* Delete as appropriate

Name: ....Signature: .... Date: ....Time: ....

Additional work that is necessary to enable this permit to be cancelled

Section E. Cancellation of permit
To be completed by the supervisor in charge of the works

I am satisfied that all work has been completed and this permit is now cancelled

Name: ....Signature: .... Date: ....Time: ....

GD 22 Excavation inspection report

Report of inspection on *excavations, *cofferdams and caissons

* Delete as appropriate

The Construction (Design and Management) Regulations, Regulation 31 and Schedule 3

Inspection carried out on behalf of..

Inspection carried out by (name)... (position) ....

Address of site ....

Date and time of inspection	Location inspected	Description of place of work, or part inspected	Details of any matter identified giving rise to a risk to the health and safety of any person	Details of any action taken as a result of any matter identified	Details of any further action considered necessary

GD 23 Underground and overhead services checklist

Overview

What you need to know

When you plan to undertake works that may cross above underground services or below overhead services there are many hazards that need to be taken into consideration. With both types of services the risks are potentially fatal and can also have large scale serious consequences and costs (such as power outage to an area, including hospitals and businesses).

What you need to do

Plans and drawings provided with the health and safety construction phase plan should detail existing buried and overhead services to provide a starting point. These can never be guaranteed to be accurate, so you will need to make contact with all local utility companies and then carry out appropriate investigations. Following that, a safe system of work can be devised, in conjunction with all relevant parties.

Significant hazards and risks

Safety	Yes	No	N/A
1. Have all previous plans and drawings been obtained for the site?			
2. Have all the utility companies been contacted for information, including any private ones, before any work commences on site (such as telecommunications)?			
3. Have risk assessments and method statements been reviewed prior to any investigations being done?			
4. Ensure that all necessary investigations are undertaken before any works are commenced, including site set up and any ground works (such as CAT and Genny).			

Health	Yes	No	N/A
1. Prior to works starting near overhead services, have suitable barriers and goal posts been erected, and signage put in place indicating safe passage, where necessary?			
2. Have all workers been informed of the dangers of working with either underground or overhead services (such as injuries from electrical contact or fire/explosion from gas mains)?			
3. Have suitable welfare facilities been provided – as in CDM Schedule 2?			
4. Have an adequate number of suitably trained first aiders been provided, given the increased severity of risk from this type of work?			

Environment	Yes	No	N/A
1. Has the site been designed to either eliminate or reduce risks from overhead services (such as when preparing the traffic management plan)?			
2. Have surveys been undertaken to check for buried services that could be affected or damaged by excavation, by vehicles/plant crossing them, and so on?			

Managerial/supervisory tasks (including pre-planning)	Yes	No	N/A
1. Has the construction phase health and safety plan been approved and does it include information on overhead and underground services?			
2. Have you or the project manager set up communication links with the utility services?			
3. Have the necessary inspections and/or investigations been completed and their reports made available to all who need them (such as architects and the principal contractor)?			
4. Have any specialist contractors you want to use been checked for their competency, as required under CDM?			
5. Have you, as a site manager, been involved in the design for the site set up and therefore instrumental in ensuring overhead and underground services are kept as clear as possible (such as traffic routing around the site and material storage areas)?			

GD 23 *continued*

Significant hazards and risks *(continued)*

Training/competency requirements	Yes	No	N/A
1. Do the workers have the requisite skills for the tasks to be undertaken (are they competent to work at height, have they been briefed on working near overhead services)?			
2. Are CSCS and/or alternative qualification cards required for the project?			
3. Will the barriers and goal posts around the overhead services be checked, ensuring this is done by a competent person?			
4. Have arrangements been made for toolbox talks as required (to update on procedures or to highlight an issue that has arisen on site)?			

Safe systems of work/basic control measures	Yes	No	N/A
1. Have the method statements and risk assessments been submitted and approved prior to contractors commencing on site; are they compatible with the safe system of work contained with the construction phase health and safety plan?			
2. Have the workers read and signed the risk assessments and method statements, thereby ensuring they work according to the site's safe system of work?			
3. Is there a feedback system so workers can comment when they feel control measures are unsuitable or inadequate? (This could be an anonymous system.)			

Specific regulatory or special requirements	Yes	No	N/A
1. Are there registers on site for statutory inspections?			
2. Has an emergency plan been prepared (for example, in the case of a contact with an overhead services or a gas main breached, such as fire and/or explosion, serious injuries)?			
3. Has a system been set up for permits to dig and/or permits to work (such as buried services or working in close proximity to overhead services)?			

Further information/references/links	Yes	No	N/A
1. HSE publication *Avoidance of danger from overhead electric power lines* (Guidance Note 6).			
2. National Joint Utilities Group (NJUG) *Guidelines on the positioning and colour-coding of underground utilities' apparatus* (latest issue).			

D

GD 24 Confined space checklists

Work in a confined space without entry of persons

Checklist 1	Yes	No	N/A
1. Ensure that entry into the space is totally prohibited.			
2. Ensure that the isolation of services and processes is carried out as necessary.			
3. Wash, clean and purge the workplace, as appropriate, for work to be done.			
4. Ensure that there is a safe system of work for the people concerned.			
5. Ensure that other people know that work is going on.			
6. Authorise work to start only on the issue of a permit to work.			

Entry into a confined space without breathing apparatus

Checklist 2	Yes	No	N/A
1. Follow a safe system of work.			
2. Put in place adequate emergency arrangements before work starts, which will also safeguard rescuers.			
3. Initiate a permit to work that includes the requirements of a permit to enter, unless separate permits are raised.			
4. Withdraw the space from service.			
5. Isolate the workplace from electrical, mechanical, chemical, heat and all other sources.			
6. Check that no inward leakage of gas, fumes, steam or liquids is possible.			
7. Clean, drain and purge the workplace as necessary for the type of work to be carried out and entry to be made.			
8. Test the atmosphere for oxygen, flammable gas, toxic gas, and so on.			
9. Carefully check any sludge or deposit that may harbour gas, fumes or liquids.			
10. Carry out a COSHH assessment, if necessary.			
11. Arrange for any checking to be carried out remotely.			
12. If necessary, clean, purge and ventilate the workplace again until the atmosphere is safe to enter.			
13. Ensure that all tools and equipment are safe to use in the area.			
14. Check the provision of protective clothing, harnesses, lifelines, rescue equipment and rescue personnel.			
15. Ensure that rescue personnel are trained in the use of the equipment and capable of using it.			
16. Ensure rescue equipment is available and easily accessible.			
17. Ensure that the fire and rescue service is informed of the location and nature of the work, where appropriate.			
18. If appropriate, ensure that the external emergency rescue services are informed of the location and type of work being carried out.			
19. Brief all personnel on what is to be done and arrange communications.			
20. Issue the permit to work, which authorises entry and fixes a timescale within which the work must be completed.			
21. Constantly monitor the workspace and communications.			
22. If the task is completed within the timescale, advise all concerned, cancel the permit to work and return the space to service.			
23. If the work is not completed in time, withdraw all staff, cancel the permit to work and consider how best to proceed.			

GD 24 *continued*

Entry into a confined space with breathing apparatus

Checklist 3	Yes	No	N/A
1. Follow a safe system of work.			
2. Put in place adequate emergency arrangements before work starts, which will also safeguard rescuers.			
3. Initiate a permit to work.			
4. Withdraw the space from service.			
5. Isolate the workplace from electrical, mechanical, chemical, heat and all other sources.			
6. Check that no inward leakage of gas, steam or liquids is possible.			
7. Clean, drain and purge the workplace as necessary for the type of work and entry.			
8. Test the atmosphere for flammable gas, toxic gas, oxygen, and so on.			
9. Decide which type of breathing apparatus is to be used.			
10. Ensure that the personnel involved have a current, valid certificate for the type and use of breathing apparatus.			
11. Ensure that all tools and equipment are safe for use in the work area.			
12. Check the provision of protective clothing, harnesses, lifelines, rescue equipment and rescue personnel.			
13. Ensure that rescue personnel are adequately trained in the use of rescue equipment and are capable of using it correctly.			
14. Ensure rescue equipment is available and easily accessible.			
15. Ensure that the fire and rescue service is informed of the location and nature of the work, where appropriate.			
16. If appropriate, ensure that the external emergency rescue services are informed of the location and type of work being carried out.			
17. Brief personnel on what is to be done and arrange communications.			
18. Issue the permit to work, which authorises entry and fixes a timescale within which the work must be completed.			
19. Constantly monitor the workspace and communications.			
20. If the task is completed within the timescale, advise all concerned, cancel the permit to work and return the space to service.			
21. If the work is not completed in time, withdraw all staff, cancel the permit to work and consider how best to proceed.			

D

GD 25 Confined spaces permit

Serial no. CS.........

Part 1 – Authorisation by permit co-ordinator

Project name/no:	Permit date:
Contractor:	Permit start time:
Contractor's supervisor:	Permit finish time:

Confined space location and description, including any plant or processes:

Hazards

The following processes within the confined space have been **withdrawn** from service:

- electrical power	Yes/No	- pressure systems	Yes/No
- mechanical power	Yes/No	- liquids/flowing substances	Yes/No

Relevant isolation permit no.

There exists the potential for the following hazards to be present:

- flammable substances	Yes/No	- ingress/presence of liquids	Yes/No
- oxygen enrichment/deficiency*	Yes/No	- solids that can flow	Yes/No
- toxic gases, fumes or vapours	Yes/No	- excessive heat or cold*	Yes/No

Activities within confined space:

Safe systems

A suitable and sufficient written safe system of work must be produced for this activity.

Risk assessment document no.		Author:
Method statement document no.		Author:

The risk assessment/method statement* is enclosed with the original permit.	Yes/No

The confined space has been assessed and the following control measures, identified within the written safe system of work, are to be implemented (✓ in box).

Removal of residues.	Full breathing apparatus (BA).	
Use of intrinsically safe tools.	Escape BA only.	
Purge atmosphere before entry.	First aid/emergency procedures.	
Forced ventilation/extraction.*	Tools and equipment checked for safe use.	
Weil's disease cards issued.	System of communication in place (e.g. radios/mobiles).	
Team leader only/rescue team.*	Warning signs/barriers in place.	
Safety harnesses/lifelines.*	Competency of work team checked.	

Continued atmospheric testing – record unit type/serial no.

Permission is granted to work within the confined space according to the safe systems.

Name:	Position:
Signature:	Date and time:

Part 2 – Receipt by supervisor

As the supervisor, I am familiar with the scope of work and safe systems to be implemented.

A recorded briefing has been delivered to the workforce on this safe system of work.	Yes/No

Name:	Position:
Signature:	Date and time:

Part 3 – Completion by supervisor

The activities authorised by this permit have finished and the confined space fully vacated.

Name:	Position:
Signature:	Date and time:

Part 4 – Cancellation by permit co-ordinator

The activities authorised by this permit have now ceased. The cancellation of this permit now precludes any further work taking place in this confined space.

The confined space and any plant within it, have been **returned** to service.	Yes/No

Name:	Position:
Signature:	Date and time:

* Delete as applicable

GD 26 Confined space entry RAMS checklist

This risk assessment and method statement (RAMS) checklist must be completed by the competent, nominated person and reviewed by the appointed person before a confined space entry permit can be issued. A copy of the checklist must also be attached to the permit and its findings briefed to all operatives entering the confined space.

Confined space entry RAMS

		Yes	N/A	Comments
1.	Has a risk assessment and method statement been approved?			
2.	Are all those entering the confined space trained and competent?			
3.	Is the correct personal protective equipment (PPE) identified on the risk assessment, readily available and fit for use?			
4.	Is there adequate access and egress?			
5.	Is an emergency and rescue plan in place and approved?			
6.	Is adequate emergency and rescue equipment in place?			
7.	Has the rescue team been trained in its use?			
7.1	Rescue services informed? Telephone no.			
8.	Has a system of communication been established and are emergency contact numbers available?			
8.1	Confined space supervisor's contact details. Telephone no.			
9.	Is there a requirement for forced ventilation to be in place? If so, what type?			
10.	Has the atmosphere been monitored prior to entry and the results recorded?			
11.	Has the monitoring equipment been calibrated?			
12.	Is the monitoring equipment correct (is it capable of detecting gases, lack of oxygen or flammable atmospheres, etc.)?			
13.	Have all those entering the space been briefed on the monitoring equipment and what to do in the event of an emergency?			
14.	Have all possible harmful substances been removed from the space?			
15.	Have all services to the space been isolated or disconnected? If so, who is responsible for continued isolation?			
16.	Is breathing apparatus required? If so, what type and is it HSE approved?			
17.	If breathing apparatus is required, are all persons competent in its use?			
18.	If breathing apparatus is to be used have those entering been face-fit tested?			
19.	Are all the necessary signs and barriers available?			
20.	Is intrinsically safe task lighting available?			
21.	Are any other permits required (such as hot works)?			

Name:	Position:
Signed:	Date:

D

GD 27 Entry/access permit (limitation of access)

Ref no.	

Part 1

Contract no. and site			
Contractor			
Description of work			
Team completing work	Name:		Signature:
Competent person supervising the work			
Other members of the team			
Location			
Location entrance(s) must be signed with the notice of access control			

Part 2 – Attachments

Risk assessment and method statement	Y/N	Approved risk assessment and method statement no.	
Checklists	Y	*(Permit will not be approved if checklists not attached)*	

Part 3 – Authorisation

Any special precautions required	

The persons designated above (and only those persons) are hereby granted permission to enter and work in the controlled location in accordance with the approved risk assessment and method statement.

Permit to commence	Date		Time	
Permit to expire	Date		Time	

This permit cannot cover more than one shift and can only be issued for the maximum of a 12-hour period

Date		Position	
Name		Signature	

Part 4 – Acceptance of permit

I hereby confirm that all persons working within the scope of this permit will be adequately briefed on its content and will abide by the conditions of the permit

Date		Position	
Name		Signature	

Part 5 – Completion of work

The work for which this permit was issued is complete and all persons, materials and equipment under my supervision have been withdrawn

Date		Time	
Name		Signature	

Part 6 – Works complete

I certify that I personally examined the work area detailed above and that the work specified has been satisfactorily completed

Date		Time	
Name		Signature	
Comments			

The permit is now cancelled – a new permit will be required if work is to continue.

GD 27 *continued*

This checklist must be completed by the trade contractor's competent, nominated person and reviewed by the appointed person before a limitation of access permit can be issued. A copy of the checklist must also be attached to the permit.

Note: only questions 3, 4, 6, 7, 8, 11, 14 and 15 can be answered N/A.

Entry/access permit (limitation of access)

		Yes	N/A	Comments
1.	Is there adequate access and egress?			
2.	Has a risk assessment and method statement been approved?			
3.	Is monitoring equipment required (and if so has it been calibrated)?			
4.	Have all harmful substances been removed from the space?			
5.	Are all those entering the area trained and competent?			
6.	Is a rescue plan in place and approved?			
7.	Is adequate rescue equipment in place?			
8.	Has the rescue team been trained in its use?			
9.	Has a system of communication been established and are emergency contact numbers available?			
10.	Have all services to the area been isolated or disconnected?			
11.	Is the correct personal protective equipment (PPE) readily available and fit for use?			
12.	Are all the necessary signs and barriers available?			
13.	Is intrinsically safe task lighting available?			
14.	Is there a risk of spark or fire? (If 'Yes' a hot-works permit is required.)			
15.	If working in riser shafts, lift shafts, roof areas etc:			
	- is adequate fall prevention in place			
	- have precautions been taken to avoid falling materials/tools			
	- has the area been checked for potential fragile surfaces?			

Name: **Position:**

Signed: **Date:**

D

GD 28 LPG storage checklist

This questionnaire has been worded so that the correct answers are all **yes**. If you answer **no** to any question you may need to give the matter further attention.

LPG storage

		Yes	No	N/A
1.	Has a risk assessment been carried out?			
2.	Has specialist advice been sought prior to the location of fixed or moveable storage tanks?			
3.	Is there the required separation distance between the storage tanks and adjacent buildings or boundaries?			
4.	Is the base supporting the tanks level?			
5.	Is the base paved or concrete?			
6.	Is there a chain-link fence surrounding the tank?			
7.	Are there barriers to prevent collision?			
8.	Are the correct warning signs displayed?			
9.	Are there outward opening exits from the cylinder storage compound?			
10.	Are the exits non-self locking?			
11.	Is the area kept weed free?			
12.	Are all access areas being kept clear?			
13.	Are the correct types of fire extinguishers provided?			
14.	Are all cylinders stored upright?			
15.	Are the LPG cylinders three metres from cylinders containing any other products?			
16.	Are cylinders being handled safely?			
17.	Is the LPG being grouped in not more than 1,000 kg?			
18.	Are there 1.5 metre wide gangways?			
19.	Is lighting provided?			
20.	Is lighting at least two metres above the tallest stack?			

Fire precautions		Yes	No	N/A
1.	Are emergency procedures provided and displayed prominently?			
2.	Are the correct types of fire extinguishers provided?			
3.	Are staff trained in the use of fire extinguishers?			
4.	Are staff and visitors aware of the site emergency evacuation alarm and procedure?			

GE

Environment

The contents of this chapter should be read and used in conjunction with guidance contained within Section E.

GE 01 Wildlife year planner   136

GE 02 Resource efficiency and responsible sourcing
       checklist   138

GE 03 Waste management, storage and disposal
       checklist   139

GE 04 Energy and transport checklist   140

GE 05 Water management and pollution prevention
       checklist   141

GE 06 Statutory nuisance checklist   142

GE 07 Ecology checklist   143

GE 08 Contaminated land checklist   144

GE 09 Archaeology and heritage checklist   145

GE 10 Site environment management systems checklist   146

GE 11 Six-digit European waste catalogue codes   147

GE 12 Materials arising from work that you plan to
       reuse on site   148

GE 13 Materials that you propose to bring onto the site   149

GE 14 Materials that you propose to send off site   150

GE 01 Wildlife year planner

Traditionally, environmental issues are not considered at an early stage in project planning. The year planners below show the appropriate times of year to deal with specific issues.

Badgers

Task	Jan	Feb	Mar	Apr	May	June	July	Aug	Sept	Oct	Nov	Dec
1	*	*	*	*							*	*
2					*	*	*	*	*	*		
3	*	*										*
4		*	*	*								
5							*	*	*	*	*	

1. **Badger surveys** are best carried out during November to April when the vegetation is low and field signs are easier to identify.

2. **Badger surveys** can continue but become less reliable as the vegetation becomes denser.

3. **Artificial badger sett construction** should be completed at least six months before a sett exclusion. Winter is the time to complete artificial setts to give the badgers time to familiarise themselves before the licensing season.

4. **Badger territorial bait marking surveys.** Territorial marking is at its peak between February and April and the vegetation is low enough to identify latrines. This is the only time of year when bait marking is effective.

5. **Badger licensing season: Between 1 July and 30 November.** Nature conservancy councils will normally only issue disturbance and exclusion licences outside this time period in cases of proven urgency.

Water voles

Task	Jan	Feb	Mar	Apr	May	June	July	Aug	Sept	Oct	Nov	Dec
1			*	*	*	*						
2							*	*	*	*		
3			*	*						*	*	

1. **Water vole surveys** need to be carried out during the summer breeding season. Best carried out between March and June before the vegetation grows too high.

2. **Water vole surveys** can continue for the rest of the breeding season but field signs become harder to identify as the vegetation becomes denser.

3. **Water vole exclusions.** Excluding and trapping are recommended during February and March, before the breeding season, or October and November, after the end of the breeding season.

Otters

Task	Jan	Feb	Mar	Apr	May	June	July	Aug	Sept	Oct	Nov	Dec
1	*	*	*	*	*	*	*	*	*	*	*	*
2	*	*	*	*	*	*	*	*	*	*	*	*

1. **Otter surveys** can be carried out throughout the year, although surveys are easier to carry out during periods of low vegetation.

2. **Otter mitigation** can be carried out throughout the year but may be restricted if evidence of breeding is identified.

Great crested newts

Task	Jan	Feb	Mar	Apr	May	June	July	Aug	Sept	Oct	Nov	Dec
1			*	*	*	*						
2		*	*				*	*	*	*	*	

1. **Great crested newts breeding pond surveys** are the only way to effectively establish presence or absence and to quantify populations. These are best carried out between March and June.

2. **Terrestrial searches** are least effective but can be carried out during early spring and during the autumn, depending upon weather conditions. Surveys should be carried out when night temperatures are above five degrees centigrade and when the ground is moist.

GE 01 *continued*

Bats

Task	Jan	Feb	Mar	Apr	May	June	July	Aug	Sept	Oct	Nov	Dec
1			*	*	*	*	*	*	*	*		
2					*	*	*	*	*	*		
3	*	*										*
4				*	*	*	*	*	*	*		

1. **Flight surveys** that involve identification of bats in flight by observation or echolocation can be carried out between March and October, although the optimum time for the surveys is April to September. Surveys of this type can be carried out without a licence as they are non-intrusive.

2. **Dusk emergence and dawn swarming surveys** can be carried out between May and October although the optimum time for the surveys is between May and September.

3. **Hibernation roost surveys** can only be carried out between November and March when the bats are hibernating. These surveys are very difficult to carry out as bats hibernate deep in cracks and crevices and are therefore difficult to identify.

4. **Habitat surveys** can only be effectively carried out between April and October when the bats are active.

Crayfish

Task	Jan	Feb	Mar	Apr	May	June	July	Aug	Sept	Oct	Nov	Dec
1				*			*	*	*	*		
2					*	*						
3	*	*	*								*	*

1. **Crayfish surveys** are best carried out between July and October, although it is possible to carry out surveys during April.

2. **Crayfish releasing young surveys** should not be carried out during May and June because crayfish are releasing their young.

3. **Crayfish reduced activity surveys** should not be carried out during the winter months due to reduced levels of activity.

Nesting birds

Task	Jan	Feb	Mar	Apr	May	June	July	Aug	Sept	Oct	Nov	Dec
1			*	*	*	*	*	*	*			
2	*	*								*	*	*

1. **Nesting bird season.** No vegetation clearance work should be carried out during the nesting bird season unless immediately preceded by a thorough nesting bird survey.

2. **Vegetation clearance work** is best carried out at these times of year when birds are not nesting, although work must stop if nests are found.

Reptiles

Task	Jan	Feb	Mar	Apr	May	June	July	Aug	Sept	Oct	Nov	Dec
1			*	*	*	*	*	*	*	*		
2			*	*	*	*	*	*	*	*		
3	*	*	*	*	*	*	*	*	*	*	*	*

1. **Reptile surveys** can only be carried out between March and October when reptiles are active. During the winter months reptiles are in hibernation, therefore it is not suitable to carry out surveys.

2. **Reptile capture and release programmes** can only be carried out between March and October when reptiles are active.

3. **Scrub clearance** work can be carried out throughout the year. GE 02 – Resource efficiency and responsible sourcing

GE 02 Resource efficiency and responsible sourcing checklist

Resource efficiency and responsible sourcing

		Yes	No	N/A
E2.1	Has the site considered alternative techniques for the efficient use of resources (such as off-site manufacture, design to fit modular sizes, manufacture to fit design)?			
E2.2	Has the design taken into account the reuse of reprocessed demolition materials or the use of recycled aggregate?			
E2.3	Are there procedures in place to identify and order the correct type and quantity of materials?			
E2.4	Are there procedures in place to ensure key materials are sourced responsibly (such as sustainable timber)?			
E2.5	Are deliveries being inspected to avoid damage during unloading, deliveries to wrong area of the site or accepting incorrect specification or quantity?			
E2.6	Are stockpiles and material storage areas away from traffic routes to prevent accidental damage?			
E2.7	Are materials being stored to prevent repetitive handling?			
E2.8	Are materials being stored with the appropriate security to prevent loss, theft or vandalism?			
E2.9	Are stockpiled materials being stored to prevent cross-contamination with other materials or wastes?			
E2.10	Are stockpiled materials being stored away from sensitive areas, drains or watercourses?			
E2.11	Are materials being handled with the correct equipment to prevent accidental damage?			
E2.12	Are hazardous/COSHH materials being stored, issued and disposed of correctly?			

Action points

GE 03 Waste management, storage and disposal checklist

Waste management, storage and disposal

		Yes	No	N/A
E3.1	Has a site waste management plan been prepared, identifying waste types and quantities for the project? Is it being maintained/updated?			
E3.2	Has a waste target and any relevant objectives been set for the project?			
E3.3	Have the project waste requirements been included in the contracts with trade contractors and suppliers?			
E3.4	Are the project waste requirements included in the site induction?			
E3.5	Have waste responsibilities been defined to know who is disposing of what and when?			
E3.6	Have designated area(s) been established on site to segregate and reuse waste materials?			
E3.7	Have recycling facilities been established to segregate office/canteen wastes (such as paper, cans, and plastics)?			
E3.8	Has the site been registered for hazardous waste with the Environment Agency?			
E3.9	Are waste management permits, licences or exemptions in place for any processing of waste on site (such as crushing and soil treatment)?			
E3.10	Is the WRAP quality protocol being complied with for the production of aggregates from waste?			
E3.11	Is the CL:AIRE code of practice being complied with for the treatment and use of contaminated soils (such as appointment of qualified person, materials management plan, and so on)?			
E3.12	Are hazardous wastes (oil, fuel, paints, and so on) collected and stored separately from general wastes?			
E3.13	Is the burning of rubbish on site prohibited, unless a permit/licence has been obtained?			
E3.14	Are registered waste carriers used to remove waste from site and are these checked on a regular basis?			
E3.15	Does the tip where the waste is taken have a licence for the type of waste?			
E3.16	Do waste transfer documents include the right information (six-digit waste codes, licence number of carrier, tip location and declaration regarding the waste hierarchy)?			
E3.17	Are waste transfer documents being retained: two years for non-hazardous and three years for hazardous waste?			

Action points

E

GE 04 Energy and transport checklist

Energy and transport

		Yes	No	N/A
E4.1	Have energy objectives and targets been set for the project?			
E4.2	Has an energy monitoring process been implemented to monitor and report energy consumption and carbon emissions, including business travel and transport?			
E4.3	Have discussions with energy supplier(s) been made to ensure electrical supplies are connected at the earliest opportunity to avoid power from generators?			
E4.4	Have site offices been fitted with practical, energy-saving devices, including low energy lighting (LED), passive infrared sensors for lighting, timer switches and thermostats for heating/hot water, and so on?			
E4.5	Does the site induction cover key energy efficiency issues (such as maintaining plant and switching off when not in use)?			
E4.6	Are there signs in place advising site personnel to switch equipment off when not required?			
E4.7	Is site office equipment set up to print efficiently (such as double-sided) and to a central location rather than individual printers?			
E4.8	Has the site considered renewable energy to contribute to powering the site accommodation?			
E4.9	Is there a logistics/transport plan that considers efficient transport arrangements (such as the use of consolidation centres or just-in-time delivery)?			
E4.10	Have local, sensitive areas been identified (such as schools and residents)?			
E4.11	Has the site considered green travel arrangements for reducing staff travel to site?			
E4.12	Has the location of suitable parking arrangements for private cars and plant been defined?			
E4.13	Has permission been obtained from the Local Authority for any road closures or erection of hoarding on the public highway?			
E4.14	Have local pedestrian diversion routes been agreed with the Local Authority?			
E4.15	Have delivery routes for construction traffic been agreed with the Local Authority?			
E4.16	Have suppliers been made aware of any delivery restrictions and routes?			
E4.17	Are entrance and exit gates on main roads rather than side roads?			
E4.18	Are deliveries scheduled to avoid traffic disruption or queuing outside of the site?			
E4.19	Are delivery vehicles switched off when being loaded/unloaded (unless needed to operate a Hiab or similar)?			
E4.20	Have designated vehicle routes on site been defined?			
E4.21	Are deliveries organised to avoid excessive use of reversing sirens?			

Action points

GE 05 Water management and pollution prevention checklist

Water management and pollution prevention

		Yes	No	N/A
E5.1	Have all watercourses and drainage systems been identified on site?			
E5.2	Have all works in, above or near to watercourses been agreed with the local Environment Agency?			
E5.3	Have all discharges to streams, ditches and drainage systems been consented to by the relevant Environment Agency?			
E5.4	Have all water abstractions from rivers, ponds, lakes or water mains been consented to by the relevant Environment Agency?			
E5.5	Are site personnel inducted and suitably trained in dealing with waste water on site?			
E5.6	Have water monitoring procedures been put in place to ensure discharges are the correct quality?			
E5.7	Have water discharges been properly treated (such as using settlement tanks or lagoons)?			
E5.8	Have designated areas been defined to wash out concrete lorries away from watercourses and drains?			
E5.9	Are watercourses and drainage systems protected from run-off and silty water?			
E5.10	Are all fuel tanks effectively bunded to at least 110% of their capacity (or 25% of total capacity for drums)?			
E5.11	Are all oil and diesel tanks and chemicals located as far as possible from drains and watercourses?			
E5.12	Are oil and diesel tanks separated from the ground by an impermeable layer?			
E5.13	Are all oil and diesel tanks and chemicals marked with the type of contents, volume and appropriate hazard warning signs?			
E5.14	Are steps being taken on site to prevent ground contamination or pollution by fuels, oils, chemicals, paint, and so on?			
E5.15	Have site personnel been made aware of the site spillage response procedures through inductions and toolbox talks?			
E5.16	Are appropriate spill kits available and appropriate personnel trained to deal with any accidental spillages to drains or watercourses?			
E5.17	Have proactive measures been taken to reduce water consumption (such as grey water recycling) and water saving devices (such as waterless urinals)?			
E5.18	Is water consumption being monitored and recorded and communicated to site personnel to promote water minimisation?			

Action points

GE 06 Statutory nuisance checklist

Statutory nuisance

		Yes	No	N/A
E6.1	Has the appropriate liaison/communication taken place with local stakeholders that may be affected by nuisance?			
E6.2	Are appropriate dust suppression techniques used to minimise air pollution from timber sawing or planing, stone or block cutting, crushing, and so on?			
E6.3	Is dust on site haul roads and material stockpiles dampened down adequately on dry/windy days?			
E6.4	Are haul roads located away from sensitive areas (such as rivers and ditches)?			
E6.5	Are site vehicle speed limits controlled to reduce dust?			
E6.6	Are public roads regularly cleaned using a road sweeper or vacuum?			
E6.7	Do vehicles that remove granular or dusty materials have sheeted covers?			
E6.8	Are all plant and vehicles in good working order with an up-to-date maintenance or service log?			
E6.9	Are enclosed chutes/covered skips used for lowering dusty demolition or waste materials?			
E6.10	Is cement/concrete being mixed in enclosed areas to prevent dust?			
E6.11	Are material stockpiles or spoil heaps stored away from sensitive areas (such as drains/rivers and ditches)?			
E6.12	Have the works been assessed to identify the noise and vibration impact on local neighbours?			
E6.13	Has the local environmental health officer and neighbours been consulted and forewarned of any out-of-hours or major disruptive activities?			
E6.14	If a Control of Pollution Act Section 61 consent is required, are noise levels being recorded to ensure that levels are kept within limits?			
E6.15	If possible, have working methods been reviewed to use equipment that reduces noise and vibration (such as pile jacking and chemical bursting)?			
E6.16	Have working hours been defined to restrict noisy operations to certain times of day?			
E6.17	Is noisy plant kept as far as possible from sensitive receptors?			
E6.18	Are deliveries planned to suit the local area?			
E6.19	Are haul routes well maintained to prevent vehicle noise and vibration?			
E6.20	Where required, are noise screens being used to reduce noise transmission?			
E6.21	Are noise screens and hoarding well maintained with no holes and gaps?			
E6.22	Has lighting been positioned to avoid a nuisance at night and is non-essential lighting switched off at night?			

Action points

GE 07 Ecology checklist

Ecology

		Yes	No	N/A
E7.1	Has the contractual and client documentation been reviewed to identify all sensitive areas containing wildlife?			
E7.2	Have all relevant ecological risks been included in the construction environmental management plan, together with their mitigation measures?			
E7.3	Have licences been obtained from Natural England or the relevant conservation body to move protected species or disrupt their habitats (such as bats, badgers and lizards)?			
E7.4	Are areas containing wildlife suitably protected from the construction work?			
E7.5	Are trees suitably protected to avoid damage from the works?			
E7.6	Have vegetation removal works been programmed to avoid breeding/nesting periods?			
E7.7	Has permission been given by the Local Authority to remove hedges or trees having a tree preservation order?			
E7.8	Has approval been given by the relevant Environment Agency to deal with invasive plants (such as Japanese knotweed and giant hogweed)?			
E7.9	Has approval been given by the relevant Environment Agency for the treatment/management of plants adjacent to a watercourse?			
E7.10	Do treatment operatives hold the appropriate qualification/certificate of competency for the use of pesticides?			

Action points

GE 08 Contaminated land checklist

Contaminated land

		Yes	No	N/A
E8.1	Has a preliminary/desktop investigation been carried out of the site and its previous uses to identify the risks from contamination?			
E8.2	Has a site investigation been carried out to identify the type and extent of any suspected contamination?			
E8.3	Are the testing company/laboratory suitably competent to carry out the testing/analysis of any contamination?			
E8.4	Has the proposed remediation strategy been agreed by the local planning authority and Environment Agency, where appropriate?			
E8.5	Does the site induction cover details of contamination and the procedures for working in areas of known contamination?			
E8.6	Are there procedures in place to ensure that work is stopped and appropriate reporting takes place if contamination is accidently discovered or disturbed?			
E8.7	Are areas of contamination fenced off to prevent vehicles and plant spreading the contamination across the site?			
E8.8	Are relevant environmental permits in place for the treatment/remediation of contamination?			
E8.9	Are suitable controls in place for dealing with contaminated water (such as discharge consents to foul sewers or tanker)?			
E8.10	If contaminated materials have to be stockpiled, are they covered to prevent run-off and wind-blown contamination?			
E8.11	Are contaminated materials stored on hard-stand areas to avoid contamination of ground and groundwater below?			
E8.12	Are stockpiles positioned well away from drainage systems or watercourses?			
E8.13	Are there suitable wheel-washing facilities to clean contaminated vehicles before leaving site?			
E8.14	Where vehicles remove contaminated materials, are they covered with sheets before leaving site?			

Action points

GE 09 Archaeology and heritage checklist

Archaeology and heritage

		Yes	No	N/A
E9.1	Has the contract documentation been reviewed to determine the presence or location of archaeology or protected heritage/buildings?			
E9.2	Have designers been involved to integrate known archaeological features into the project?			
E9.3	Have licences or permissions been obtained to carry out work on or around archaeology or protected heritage/buildings?			
E9.4	Where there are works on or around known archaeology or heritage, has a watching brief or specialist been employed to monitor and record the works?			
E9.5	Have locations containing archaeology or heritage been adequately fenced off or protected?			
E9.6	Have suitable communication arrangements been put in place for unknown finds that may be discovered, and for reporting these to the local archaeological officer or Local Authority and recorded?			

Action points

E

GE 10 Site environment management systems checklist

Site environment management systems

		Yes	No	N/A
E10.1	Is the company (or site) environmental policy available and displayed on site, with relevant requirements highlighted at the site induction?			
E10.2	Has the contract and client documentation been reviewed to identify the site-specific environmental requirements, including planning conditions?			
E10.3	Has a construction environmental management plan been prepared identifying the relevant targets, objectives, issues and controls?			
E10.4	Is there a system for ensuring that suitable and sufficient arrangements are in place for the management, storage and disposal of waste through the production of a site waste management plan?			
E10.5	Is there a system for ensuring that all site personnel (including sub-contractors) are made aware of the project environmental issues and standards through site inductions, briefings and toolbox talks?			
E10.6	Have responsibilities for environmental management been defined and communicated through inductions, notice boards, and so on?			
E10.7	Is someone responsible for ensuring that environmentally sensitive areas are identified and protected (such as drains, rivers, streams, groundwater and areas containing protected plants and animals)?			
E10.8	Is there a system for ensuring that the necessary environmental licences have been identified and granted (such as discharges of water and effluent, tree preservation orders, premises producing hazardous waste and waste management licences)?			
E10.9	Is there a system for ensuring that method statements include sufficient control measures for environmental management?			
E10.10	Is there a system for sites to deal with environmental emergencies (such as for spillages and groundwater contamination) and for notifying them to?			
E10.11	Is there a suitable and sufficient monitoring regime in place to ensure that the site environmental requirements are being met (such as relevant environmental inspections for oil and waste storage, protected areas, water quality, noise and dust)?			
E10.12	Are environmental records being maintained (such as waste transfer notes, consignment notes, noise and water monitoring)?			
E10.13	Have adequate arrangements been established for liaison and communication with local stakeholders (residents, shops, businesses, schools, parish council)?			

Action points

GE 11 Six-digit European waste catalogue codes

Section 17 – Construction and demolition waste

A six figure EWC code for the type of waste being removed MUST be written on every waste transfer note (for example, skip/muck away tickets).

17 01 Concrete, bricks, tiles and ceramics

17 01 01	Concrete.
17 01 02	Bricks.
17 01 03	Tiles and ceramics.
17 01 06*	Mixtures of, or separate fractions of concrete, bricks, tiles and ceramics containing dangerous substances.
17 01 07	Mixtures of concrete, bricks, tiles and ceramics other than those mentioned in 17 01 06.

17 02 Wood, glass and plastic

17 02 01	Wood.
17 02 02	Glass.
17 02 03	Plastic.
17 02 04*	Glass, plastic and wood containing or contaminated with dangerous substances.

17 03 Bituminous mixtures, coal tar and tarred products

17 03 01*	Bituminous mixtures containing coal tar.
17 03 02	Bituminous mixtures other than those mentioned in 17 03 01.
17 03 03*	Coal tar and tarred products.

17 04 Metals (including their alloys)

17 04 01	Copper, bronze, brass.
17 04 02	Aluminium.
17 04 03	Lead.
17 04 04	Zinc.
17 04 05	Iron and steel.
17 04 06	Tin.
17 04 07	Mixed metals.
17 04 09*	Metal waste contaminated with dangerous substances.
17 04 10*	Cables containing oil, coal tar and other dangerous substances.
17 04 11	Cables other than those mentioned in 17 04 10.

17 05 Soil (including excavated soil from contaminated sites), stones and dredging spoil

17 05 03*	Soil and stones containing dangerous substances.
17 05 04	Soil and stones other than those mentioned in 17 05 03.
17 05 05*	Dredging spoil containing dangerous substances.
17 05 06	Dredging spoil other than those mentioned in 17 05 05.
17 05 07*	Track ballast containing dangerous substances.
17 05 08	Track ballast other than those mentioned in 17 05 07.

17 06 Insulation materials and asbestos-containing construction materials

17 06 01*	Insulation materials containing asbestos.
17 06 03*	Other insulation materials consisting of or containing dangerous substances.
17 06 04	Insulation materials other than those mentioned in 17 06 01 and 17 06 03.
17 06 05*	Construction materials containing asbestos (7).

17 08 Gypsum-based construction material

17 08 01*	Gypsum-based construction materials contaminated with dangerous substances.
17 08 02	Gypsum-based construction materials other than those mentioned in 17 08 01.

17 09 Other construction and demolition wastes

17 09 01*	Construction and demolition wastes containing mercury.
17 09 02*	Construction and demolition wastes containing PCB (for example, PCB containing sealants, PCB-containing resin-based floorings, PCB-containing sealed glazing units).
17 09 03*	Other construction and demolition wastes (including mixed wastes) containing dangerous substances.
17 09 04	Mixed construction and demolition wastes other than those mentioned in 17 09 01.

 Entries marked with * are either potentially hazardous (mirror entry) and will require testing to determine if hazardous properties are present or definitely hazardous (absolute) and must be disposed of as hazardous waste.

GE 12 Materials arising from work that you plan to reuse on site

This flowchart helps you decide whether use and reuse of soil and aggregate materials in construction works is a waste activity or not and what you need to do to ensure legal compliance whilst minimising the regulatory burden.

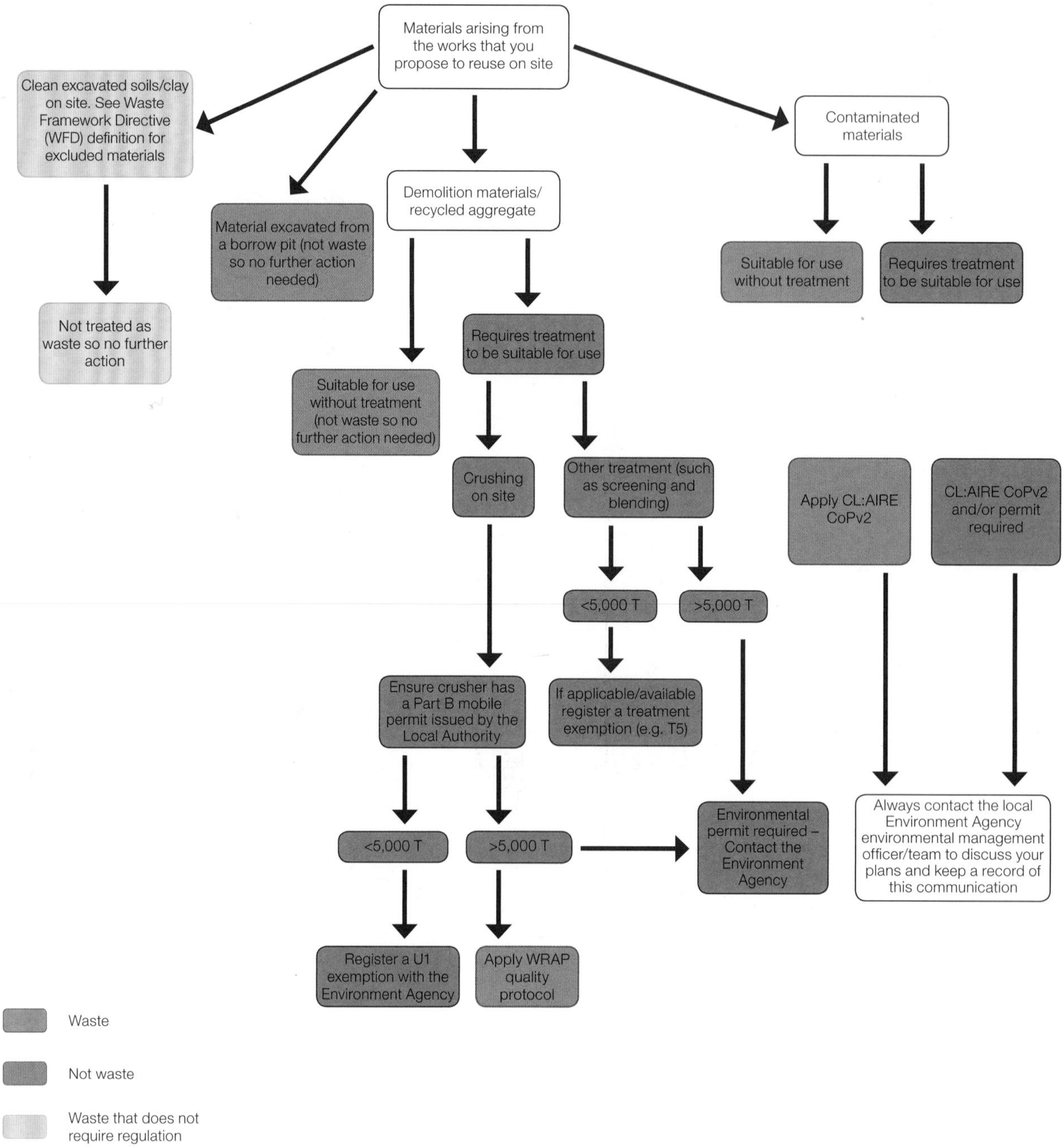

E

Materials arising from the works that you propose to reuse on site

Clean excavated soils/clay on site. See Waste Framework Directive (WFD) definition for excluded materials
↓
Not treated as waste so no further action

Material excavated from a borrow pit (not waste so no further action needed)

Demolition materials/ recycled aggregate
↓
Suitable for use without treatment (not waste so no further action needed)

Requires treatment to be suitable for use
↓
Crushing on site
Other treatment (such as screening and blending)

Contaminated materials
↓
Suitable for use without treatment
Requires treatment to be suitable for use

Apply CL:AIRE CoPv2

CL:AIRE CoPv2 and/or permit required

<5,000 T **>5,000 T**

Ensure crusher has a Part B mobile permit issued by the Local Authority

If applicable/available register a treatment exemption (e.g. T5)

<5,000 T **>5,000 T**

Environmental permit required – Contact the Environment Agency

Always contact the local Environment Agency environmental management officer/team to discuss your plans and keep a record of this communication

Register a U1 exemption with the Environment Agency

Apply WRAP quality protocol

▮	Waste
▮	Not waste
▮	Waste that does not require regulation

 For further guidance refer to Section E, Chapter E03.

GE 13 Materials that you propose to bring onto the site

This flowchart helps you decide whether use and reuse of soil and aggregate materials in construction works is a waste activity or not and what you need to do to ensure legal compliance whilst minimising the regulatory burden.

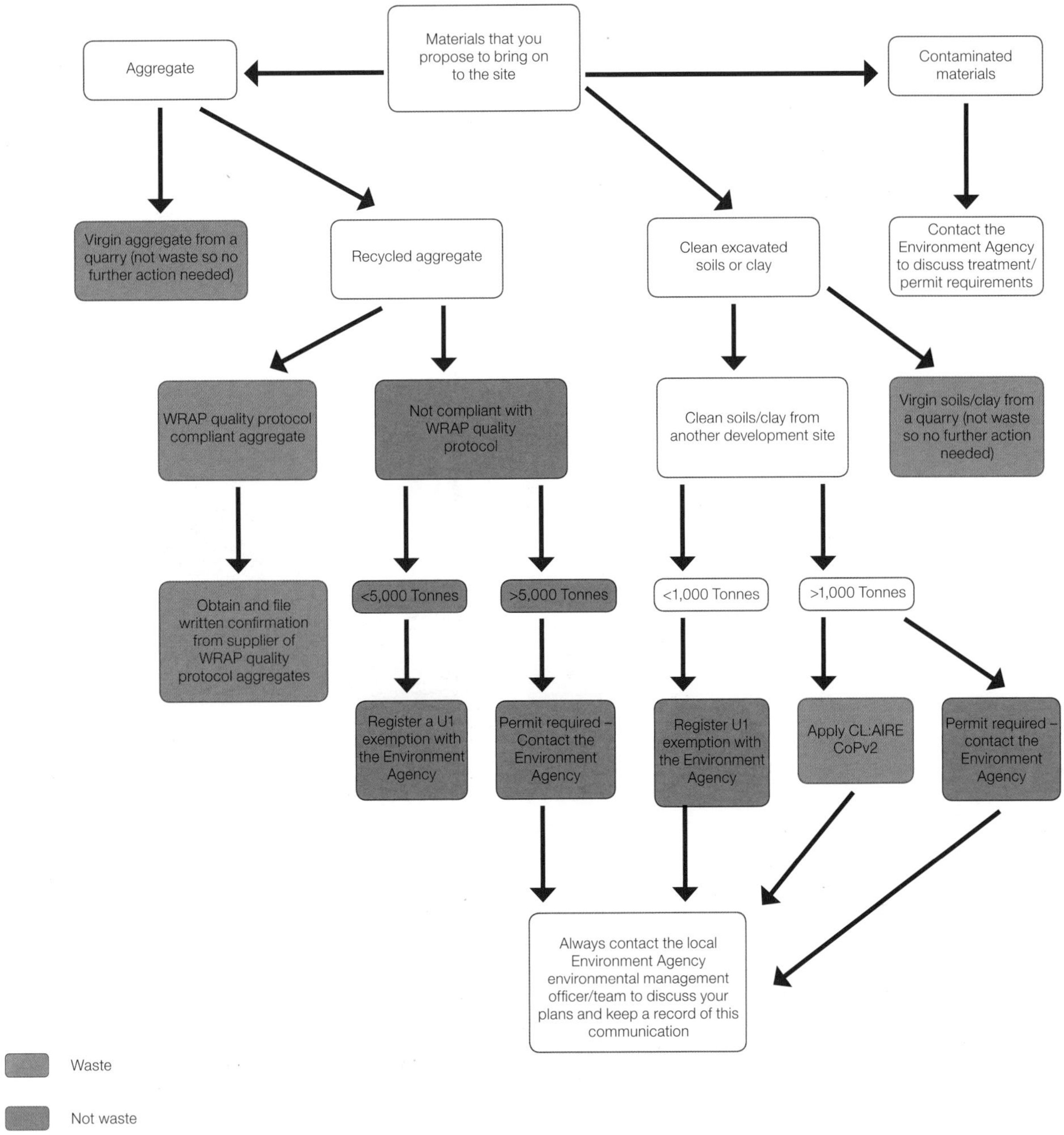

```
                              Materials that you
      Aggregate  ◄──────────  propose to bring on  ──────────►  Contaminated
                              to the site                       materials
```

- **Aggregate**
  - Virgin aggregate from a quarry (not waste so no further action needed)
  - Recycled aggregate
    - WRAP quality protocol compliant aggregate
      - Obtain and file written confirmation from supplier of WRAP quality protocol aggregates
    - Not compliant with WRAP quality protocol
      - <5,000 Tonnes → Register a U1 exemption with the Environment Agency
      - >5,000 Tonnes → Permit required – Contact the Environment Agency

- **Clean excavated soils or clay**
  - Clean soils/clay from another development site
    - <1,000 Tonnes → Register U1 exemption with the Environment Agency
    - >1,000 Tonnes → Apply CL:AIRE CoPv2
  - Virgin soils/clay from a quarry (not waste so no further action needed)
    - Permit required – contact the Environment Agency

- **Contaminated materials**
  - Contact the Environment Agency to discuss treatment/permit requirements

Always contact the local Environment Agency environmental management officer/team to discuss your plans and keep a record of this communication

- ◼ Waste
- ◼ Not waste

 For further guidance refer to Section E, Chapter E03.

E

GE 14 Materials that you propose to send off site

This flowchart helps you decide whether use and reuse of soil and aggregate materials in construction works is a waste activity or not and what you need to do to ensure legal compliance whilst minimising the regulatory burden.

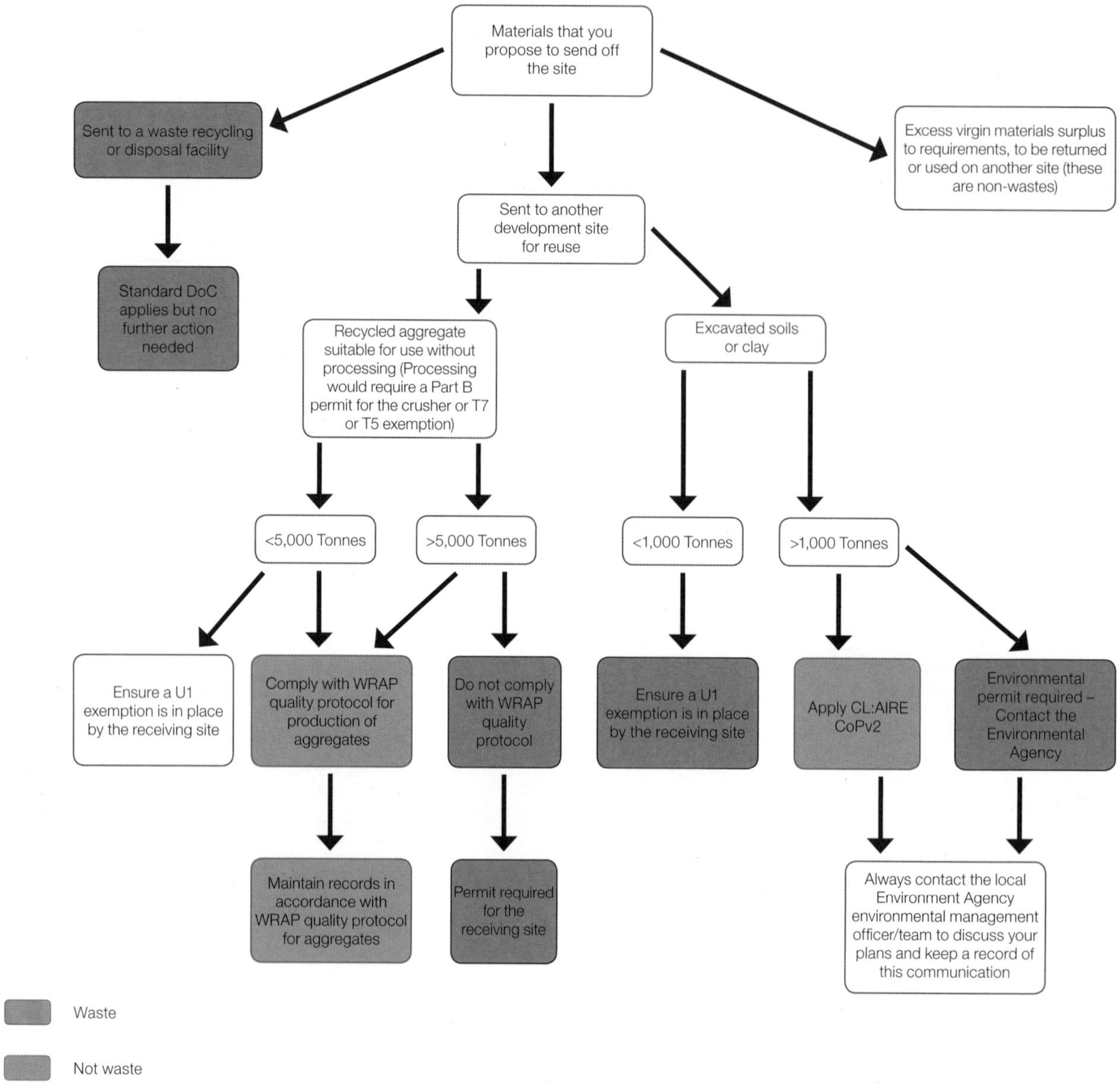

Materials that you propose to send off the site

Sent to a waste recycling or disposal facility

Excess virgin materials surplus to requirements, to be returned or used on another site (these are non-wastes)

Standard DoC applies but no further action needed

Sent to another development site for reuse

Recycled aggregate suitable for use without processing (Processing would require a Part B permit for the crusher or T7 or T5 exemption)

Excavated soils or clay

<5,000 Tonnes

>5,000 Tonnes

<1,000 Tonnes

>1,000 Tonnes

Ensure a U1 exemption is in place by the receiving site

Comply with WRAP quality protocol for production of aggregates

Do not comply with WRAP quality protocol

Ensure a U1 exemption is in place by the receiving site

Apply CL:AIRE CoPv2

Environmental permit required – Contact the Environmental Agency

Maintain records in accordance with WRAP quality protocol for aggregates

Permit required for the receiving site

Always contact the local Environment Agency environmental management officer/team to discuss your plans and keep a record of this communication

Waste

Not waste

For further guidance refer to Section E, Chapter E03.

GF

Specialist activities

The contents of this chapter should be read and used in conjunction with guidance contained within Section F.

GF 01 Street work and road works checklist   152
GF 02 Mobile workforce – point of work risk assessment 153
GF 03 Mobile workforce checklist   155
GF 04 Working over or near to water   157

GF 01 Street work and road works checklist

Competence for working on the highway

Overview

What you need to know

Due to the proximity of the travelling public, and to a lesser degree construction plant, carrying out construction at road works can be disproportionately hazardous, as reflected in the rising number of accidents at road works. The Highways Agency and the Highways Term Maintenance Association are working together to improve the situation.

What you need to do

If you do not already carry out work on the highway but intend to do so, you must ensure that your workers gain the appropriate qualifications and competencies before you bid for work.

You must familiarise yourself with the:

- ☑ hazards and significant risks arising out of working on the highway so that you can compile meaningful risk assessments and method statements

- ☑ requirements for signage and other traffic management equipment

- ☑ different standards of high-visibility clothing required.

Significant hazards and risks

Safety	Yes	No	N/A
1. The proximity of moving road traffic and construction plant.			
2. General safety hazards (such as excavations, manual handling, working at height, and so on).			

Health	Yes	No	N/A
1. Noise and vibration from adjacent traffic and construction plant.			
2. Skin contact with hazardous substances.			

Environment	Yes	No	N/A
1. Multiple risks of land contamination through use of substances and disposal of waste.			
2. Dust created by ground works, plus cutting and drilling activities.			

Managerial/supervisory tasks (including pre-planning)	Yes	No	N/A
1. Identify specific hazards and eliminate or reduce the risks.			
2. Communicate the significant findings of the risk assessment and the method statement to the workforce – review and update both as necessary and communicate any changes.			

Training/competency requirements	Yes	No	N/A
1. Site manager/supervisor – New Roads and Street Work Act (NRSWA) qualified.			
2. Plant movements signaller – refer to Construction Plant-hire Association guidance.			

Safe systems of work/basic control measures	Yes	No	N/A
1. In accordance with the requirements of the Code of Practice to the NRSWA.			
2. In accordance with further Highways Agency guidance.			

Specific regulatory or special requirements	Yes	No	N/A
1. Ensuring the safety of road users, including pedestrians, through effective signage.			
2. Ensuring the health and safety of all workers through thorough planning and strong management.			

Further information/references/links	Yes	No	N/A
The Code of Practice to the New Roads and Street Works Act (often referred to as the *Red book*).			

GF 02 Mobile workforce – point of work risk assessment

Point of work risk assessment				

Part 1: Stop

Task	Site/plant location	Date		
		Job no.		

Before you start *(tick appropriate box)*	Yes	No	N/A
Are you at the correct site/item of plant/location?			
Do you have the right documentation for the job?			
Do you have the right PPE for the job?			
Are power tools and leads and plant tested?			
Are scaffolds and ladders inspected (access safe)?			
Is lifting equipment inspected?			

If you have answered no to any of the above, take required action or report to your supervisor. If in doubt always ask!

F

Part 2: Think

Safety and health assessment *(If the hazard is present tick the box)*

Slips, trips or falls on the same level.		Entry into a confined space.		Poor lighting.	
Falls from height.		Dust.		Temperature (high/low).	
Falling/flying objects.		Fumes.		Adverse weather.	
Chemicals/harmful substances.		Noise.		Uncertified equipment.	
Heat/fire/explosion.		Vibration.		Risk to you from your work.	
Asphyxiation/drowning.		Electricity.		Risk to others from your work.	
Risk to plant.		Residues.		Stored energy or insecure load.	
Contact with stationary object.		Underground services.		Traffic/moving vehicles.	
Object overturning/collapsing.		Manual handling.		Other *(Specify)*.	

You must have a rescue plan in place**. Provide brief details.**
(You must always be able to provide a way of safe escape in the event of something going wrong.)

Circle any ticks for hazards (above) that are significant and for which there are no (adequate) controls.

If you have circled any ticks for hazards, Part 3 (overleaf) needs to be completed and appropriate control measures put in place before work commences.

GF 02 *continued*

Point of work risk assessment

Part 3: Act

Additional safety assessment

Hazard (circled from overleaf)	Control measures/precautions	Remaining risk (high, medium or low)

End of job review	Yes	No
Are there any lessons for next time?		
Has the work created any new hazards?		

If you have answered Yes to either of these questions, make a brief note below and tell your supervisor.

Signature	
Date	

Lessons learnt and future site/location visit advice

List here any information that would make the next visit safer and include contact details if appropriate.

GF 03 Mobile workforce checklist

Overview

What you need to know

In order to provide mobile workers, including lone and out-of-hours workers, with a safe working environment, means of getting to and from it, suitable welfare facilities and the appropriate tools and materials for the job, planning and a risk assessment must be undertaken before work begins.

What you need to do

Prepare a risk assessment whilst considering what resources are needed to complete the job safely. Liaise with workers and others involved, ensuring all hazards are identified and suitable controls implemented to eliminate or reduce the risks.

Significant hazards and risks

Safety	Yes	No	N/A
1. Can it be a safe working area with pedestrians and vehicles segregated?			
2. Is temporary traffic lighting and street signage needed?			
3. Is there a secure working area with material storage and waste area?			
4. Is there adequate access/egress from the area in the event of an emergency?			
5. Is there a suitable fire emergency plan, sounder, fire extinguishers, communications?			
6. If a lone worker, is the work suitable for one person alone (such as manual handling)?			

Health	Yes	No	N/A
1. Has an adequate risk assessment been prepared for the tasks to be undertaken?			
2. Have welfare facilities been provided or arranged with the client?			
3. Are there any hazardous substances being used – COSHH?			
4. Has a member of the group received first-aid training?			
5. Has a suitable first-aid kit been provided and information on reporting of accidents?			

Environment	Yes	No	N/A
1. Are there any watercourses nearby?			
2. Does any wildlife need to be considered?			
3. Is there potentially contaminated land?			
4. Is there a potential for contamination by the work activity (such as provision of spill kits)?			

Managerial/supervisory tasks (including pre-planning)	Yes	No	N/A
1. Is there a suitable and sufficient planned scheme of work for what is proposed?			
2. Have the risk assessments been reviewed and found to be task/site specific?			
3. Has the correct transport and equipment been provided?			
4. Have welfare facilities been arranged for the site or arranged with the client?			
5. Have the workers got adequate PPE and any additional equipment (such as goggles or dust masks)?			

F

GF 03 *continued*

Significant hazards and risks *(continued)*

Training/competency requirements	Yes	No	N/A
1. Do the workers have the requisite skills for the tasks to be undertaken (are they competent)?			
2. Are CSCS or similar qualification cards required for the project?			
3. Who is available to give toolbox talks?			
4. Will the works undergo a safety inspection during their operation?			
Safe systems of work/basic control measures	**Yes**	**No**	**N/A**
1. Has a point of work risk assessment been completed?			
2. Is there a procedure to update documentation during the works?			
3. Are employees empowered to take action if additional control measures are needed?			
Specific regulatory or special requirements	**Yes**	**No**	**N/A**
1. Are contact information and safeguards in place for lone workers?			
2. If necessary, is a rescue plan in place (such as for rescue from a trench)?			
Further information/references/links	**Yes**	**No**	**N/A**
1. HSE publication *Provision of welfare facilities during construction work* (CIS59).			
2. HSE publication *Working alone, health and safety guidance on the risks of lone working* (INDG73).			

GF 04 Working over or near to water

Ready for a rescue?

Overview

What you need to know

The skills and equipment that will be necessary for rescuing someone from the water, with regard to the prevailing circumstances on site.

What you need to do

Put a rescue management plan in place and ensure it is communicated to, and understood by, anyone who is at risk of accidental entry into the water.

Provide the equipment and training necessary.

Significant hazards and risks

Safety	Yes	No	N/A
1. Drowning due to any one or more of many factors.			
2. Serious injuries resulting from impact with the structure during the fall.			

Health	Yes	No	N/A
1. Leptospirosis (Weil's disease) from ingesting contaminated water.			
2. The ingestion of other contaminants in the water.			
3. Hypothermia from being in cold water for too long.			
4. Suspension trauma from being left suspended in a harness for too long.			

Environment	Yes	No	N/A
1. None directly associated with rescuing a person from the water.			
2. Close control of petrol or diesel when refuelling rescue craft.			

Managerial/supervisory tasks (including pre-planning)	Yes	No	N/A
1. Provide measures to prevent falls.			
2. Where falls are possible provide life jackets, training and monitor correct use.			
3. Select the appropriate rescue equipment and maintain it as necessary.			
4. Train the people at risk how to avoid falling into the water and what to do if they do.			

Training/competency requirements	Yes	No	N/A
1. General safe working at height guidance.			
2. Additional training for safety boat operators and crew (RYA trained).			
3. Qualified first aiders (HSE-accredited training)			

Safe systems of work/basic control measures	Yes	No	N/A
1. Safe working practices at height to avoid a rescue being necessary.			
2. The prompt location and rescue of anyone who is in the water.			
3. Immediately summon the emergency services if it is obvious that expert medical assistance is needed.			

Specific regulatory or special requirements	Yes	No	N/A
1. Management and workers to comply with the Work at Height Regulations.			
2. Provision of personal flotation equipment and other PPE as may be necessary.			

Further information/references/links	Yes	No	N/A
HSE information sheet *Personal buoyancy equipment on inland and inshore waters* (AIS1).			